nature

The Living Record of Science

《自然》百年科学经典

英汉对照版　套装共十卷

第三卷

1934-1945

总顾问：李政道（Tsung-Dao Lee）

英方主编：Sir John Maddox
Sir Philip Campbell

中方主编：路甬祥

外语教学与研究出版社　·　麦克米伦教育　·　自然科研

FOREIGN LANGUAGE TEACHING AND RESEARCH PRESS　·　MACMILLAN EDUCATION　·　NATURE RESEARCH

北京 BEIJING

图书在版编目 (CIP) 数据

《自然》百年科学经典：套装共十卷. 第三卷：英汉对照／（英）约翰·马多克斯（John Maddox），（英）菲利普·坎贝尔（Philip Campbell），路甬祥主编. —— 北京：外语教学与研究出版社，2020.9

ISBN 978-7-5213-2021-3

Ⅰ. ①自… Ⅱ. ①约… ②菲… ③路… Ⅲ. ①自然科学－文集－英、汉 Ⅳ. ①N53

中国版本图书馆 CIP 数据核字 (2020) 第 155154 号

地图审图号：GS (2020) 5244 号

出 版 人　徐建忠
项目统筹　章思英
项目负责　刘晓楠　黄小斌
责任编辑　王丽霞
责任校对　黄小斌
封面设计　高　蕾
版式设计　孙莉明
插图设计　麦克米伦提供原图扫描版
出版发行　外语教学与研究出版社
社　　址　北京市西三环北路 19 号（100089）
网　　址　http://www.fltrp.com
印　　刷　北京华联印刷有限公司
开　　本　787×1092　1/16
印　　张　67
版　　次　2021 年 1 月第 1 版　2021 年 1 月第 1 次印刷
书　　号　ISBN 978-7-5213-2021-3
定　　价　8000.00 元

购书咨询：（010）88819926　电子邮箱：club@fltrp.com
外研书店：https://waiyants.tmall.com
凡印刷、装订质量问题，请联系我社印制部
联系电话：（010）61207896　电子邮箱：zhijian@fltrp.com
凡侵权、盗版书籍线索，请联系我社法律事务部
举报电话：（010）88817519　电子邮箱：banquan@fltrp.com
物料号：320210001

记载人类文明
沟通世界文化
www.fltrp.com

《自然》百年科学经典（英汉对照版）

总顾问：李政道（Tsung-Dao Lee）

英方主编：Sir John Maddox　　　　　　中方主编：路甬祥

Sir Philip Campbell

编审委员会

英方编委：　　　　　　　　中方编委（以姓氏笔画为序）：

Philip Ball　　　　　　　　许智宏

Vikram Savkar　　　　　　赵忠贤

David Swinbanks　　　　　滕吉文

本卷审稿专家（以姓氏笔画为序）

于　禄	马宇蒨	王乃彦	王晓晨	王鹏云	邓祖淦	厉光烈
田伟生	冯兴无	朱永生	刘　纯	刘　武	刘京国	李　淼
李三忠	李芝芬	李军刚	杨　志	吴庆举	何香涛	汪长征
张元仲	张焕乔	陈平富	昌增益	金　侠	周筠梅	郑东宁
孟庆任	赵见高	赵凌霞	郝　项	秦志海	莫　辐	栗付平
夏海鸿	顾孝诚	陶宏杰	葛墨林	蒋世仰	鲍重光	

编译委员会

本卷翻译工作组稿人 （以姓氏笔画为序）

王耀杨　　刘　明　　关秀清　　李　琦　　沈乃澂　　张　健　　郭红锋
黄小斌　　蔡则怡

本卷翻译人员 （以姓氏笔画为序）

王　静	王耀杨	毛晨晖	田晓阳	史春晖	刘　霞	刘东亮
刘振明	刘皓芳	齐红艳	孙惠南	李世媛	李忠伟	吴　彦
沈乃澂	张玉光	张效良	张锦彬	金世超	周　杰	赵凤轩
胡雪兰	钱　磊	韩玲俐	蔡则怡			

本卷校对人员 （以姓氏笔画为序）

王帅帅	王阳兰	王丽霞	王晓萌	王晓蕾	王赛儿	王德孚
甘秋玲	丛　岚	冯　翀	乔萌萌	刘　明	孙　娟	孙　琳
苏　慧	杜赛赛	李红菊	吴　茜	何　铭	何思源	张世馥
张竞凤	张媛媛	陈学雷	周少贞	周玉凤	郑期彤	顾海成
徐秋燕	黄小斌	崔天明	梁　瑜	韩少卿	曾红芳	蔡　迪
管　冰	潘承志					

Contents
目录

Volume III

(1934-1945)

Planetary Photography[*]

V. M. Slipher

Editor's Note

Vesto Slipher was director of the Lowell Observatory in Flagstaff, Arizona, when he wrote this review of planetary imaging carried out there. The observatory was founded by American astronomer Percival Lowell in 1894, and in subsequent decades it offered some of the clearest direct views of the planets. Slipher's description of Mars, thought to have a substantial atmosphere of oxygen and water vapour, makes it clear why many regarded the seasonal colour changes as being due to vegetation. Lowell himself believed there were even signs of intelligent life. Slipher has been under-rated as an astronomer, having understood the recession-induced redshift of galaxies before Edwin Hubble, and overseeing the observations that led to the discovery of Pluto in 1930.

THE Lowell Observatory was founded in 1894, by the late Percival Lowell, who maintained and directed it during his lifetime and endowed it by his will, that it might permanently continue astronomical research and in particular that of the planets. For nearly four decades now, it has been occupied with planetary investigations. It is situated at Flagstaff, Arizona, because, of the numerous places he had tested, it was here that Lowell found the conditions best for planetary studies. The major instruments of the Observatory are: (1) 24-inch aperture Clark refractor of 32 feet focus, (2) 42-inch Clark reflecting telescope, (3) a new 13-inch photographic telescope, (4) 15-inch Petitdidier reflector, and in addition several smaller instruments, together with a number of spectrographs, special cameras for photographing the planets, radiometric apparatus for use with the 42-inch reflector, for measuring the heat of the planets, and such laboratory equipment as is needed in the work carried on.

During the first decade, the work at the Observatory was mainly visual observations of the planets, then it was extended to include their spectrographic study, and during the second decade direct photography of the planets was added and has been continued since, giving a permanent record of them to the present time. During the past decade, their heat measurement has also been made a regular part of the observational programme. In short, whenever it has been possible to apply new means, they have been made use of in order that the planets be studied from every possible point of view.

During the early years of the Observatory, Lowell was able to observe Mercury and to confirm Schiaparelli's conclusion that the planet constantly keeps its same face to the

---

[*] From a discourse entitled "Planet Studies at the Lowell observatory", delivered at the Royal Institution on Friday, May 19.

行星的照相分析[*]

斯里弗

编者按

当维斯托·斯里弗写下这篇关于洛威尔天文台行星照相的综述时，他正是这个天文台的台长。该天文台位于亚利桑那州弗拉格斯塔夫市，于 1894 年由美国天文学家珀西瓦尔·洛威尔创建，并在之后的几十年中提供了一些对于行星最清晰的直接观测结果。斯里弗认为火星的大气中含有氧气和水蒸气，他对于火星的描述明确地解释了火星上为何会有如植被存在而出现的季节性颜色变化。洛威尔本人甚至认为那里有智慧生物存在的迹象。作为一个天文学家，斯里弗是超前的，因为他先于埃德温·哈勃理解了退行运动导致的星系光谱红移，并指导了促使 1930 年发现冥王星的那些观测。

洛威尔天文台由已故的珀西瓦尔·洛威尔于 1894 年创建，洛威尔先生生前一直领导并维护该天文台，后来根据他的遗嘱该天文台被捐赠出来以用于永久性地开展天文学特别是行星方面的研究。在过去将近四十年间，该天文台一直致力于行星方面的研究。它位于亚利桑那州的弗拉格斯塔夫市，因为在洛威尔先生曾经勘查过的众多地方中，该地是最适于进行行星研究的。该天文台的主要设备包括：(1) 24 英寸口径、32 英尺焦距的克拉克折射式望远镜，(2) 42 英寸口径克拉克反射式望远镜，(3) 一架新型的 13 英寸照相望远镜，(4) 15 英寸珀蒂迪迪埃反射式望远镜，此外还包括一些小型仪器，如摄谱仪、用于拍摄行星的特殊相机、用于测量恒星热量的辐射测量仪（与 42 英寸折射式望远镜一起使用），以及其他一些工作所需的实验室设备。

在最初的十年间，洛威尔天文台的主要工作是目视观测行星，后来扩展到光谱研究。在第二个十年间，开始对行星进行直接照相并且一直持续到现在，对这些年的行星活动进行了持续的记录。在最近的十年间，热辐射测量也已成为该天文台进行观测的例行程序之一。简而言之，无论何时只要有可能使用新方法，这里的天文学家就会加以利用，以便从每个可能的角度去研究行星。

在该天文台成立初期，洛威尔对水星进行了观测，并证实了斯基亚帕雷利的结论，即水星总是保持同一个面朝向太阳，如同月亮总是同一个面朝向地球一样。因此，

---

[*] 基于 5 月 19 日星期五在英国皇家科学研究院发表的一篇演讲，题为"在洛威尔天文台的行星研究"。

Sun, as our Moon does to the Earth. Thus its small mass and the intense heating by the Sun long since dissipated its atmosphere. Venus proved more difficult, and with very faint surface markings, its length of day was left somewhat uncertain, while from all considerations it appeared that this planet also keeps the same face constantly toward the Sun, for even the spectrograph showed no evidence of a day shorter than a few weeks. Spectral studies of Venus have failed to give any evidence of an Earth-like atmosphere, no bands of oxygen or water being found, although it might have been expected that Venus would be the planet most like the Earth.

From this non-committal and veiled planet we pass to the best observed of all, Mars, which has long attracted wide interest. Martian seasonal change shows itself clearly in the polar caps, which alternately increase and decrease, and in the blue-green markings which darken in the growing season and pale again as winter approaches, the great ochreish expanses, changing little from winter to summer, except as influenced by light spots and clouds. The shrinking of the polar cap with summer's coming is to be seen in Fig. 1, where are shown five photographs of the same face of the planet showing particularly the upper hemisphere, but made at Martian seasonal dates. With the contraction of the cap the shaded areas darken and enlarge, as may readily be seen in the photographs.

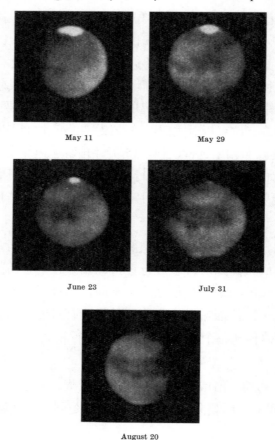

May 11   May 29

June 23   July 31

August 20

Fig. 1. Photographs of Mars showing the shrinking of the polar cap and the growth of dark areas.

由于水星自身较小的质量以及太阳长期对其强烈的加热，其大气已经消失殆尽。由于表面特征模糊，金星上每日的长度存在某种程度的不确定性。要证明金星始终是同一个面朝向地球是很困难的。但是综合各方面来看，金星还是很可能保持同一个面朝向太阳的，因为光谱研究也没有证据表明金星上的一天会短于地球上数周。尽管人们曾认为金星是最接近地球的行星，但在金星的光谱研究中，我们并没有发现其大气与地球大气类似的证据，它的大气光谱中并不含有氧或水的谱带。

让我们把目光从这个不合作且隐藏起来的星球上移开，下面看一下目前为止获得了最好的观测的行星——火星，天文学家一直对火星观测有着浓厚的兴趣。火星的季节性变化可以清楚地反映在极冠的交替消长变化中；也会反映在蓝绿斑的变化中，当生长季节到来时，火星上的蓝绿斑会变深，而当冬季到来时其又会变淡；而火星上赭红色的宽阔区域除非受到光线和云层的影响，否则从冬季到夏季几乎没有什么变化。夏季来临时极冠收缩的情况如图 1 所示，图中五幅照片显示的是火星的同一个面，以上半球为主，其中标出的时间为火星日期。随着极冠的收缩，阴暗区域变暗并且面积扩大，这点在图中非常明显。

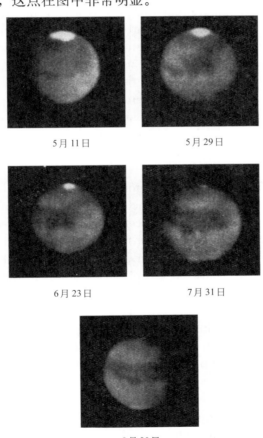

5月11日　　　　　　　5月29日

6月23日　　　　　　　7月31日

8月20日

图 1. 火星表面的照片显示了极冠的收缩和阴暗区域的增加

Dark rifts appear in the melting caps, always at precisely the same time and the same places each Martian year, which clearly prove the caps to be deposits on the planet's surface. Irregularities of the surface must cause this patchy melting of the caps to be repeated always with most punctual harmony to the Martian calendar. Such features of the melting caps are to be seen in Fig. 1. The melting cap is bordered by a dark collar, and is more disposed to be regular in outline than the forming cap, which is irregular in outline and indefinite, and to begin with is erratic storm clouds only. An autumn cap appears at the opposite side of the planet to the polar cap.

The behaviour of the caps means that Mars has an atmosphere, for that is the only vehicle which does such transportation of substance. Occasionally, when Mars is so placed that we look a little into its night sky, we see on it a bright streak of light due to a cloud high in its atmosphere, catching the sunlight, while the surface is dark beneath it. Such allow us to measure their height above the Martian surface, and a fine one in 1903 was fully 15 miles high, whereas clouds are rarely more than 5 miles above the Earth. Hence Mars must have quite a considerable atmosphere, and the spectrograph at Flagstaff showed it to contain water and oxygen, but no strange substances. Thus it closely resembles that of the Earth, but is less dense, because the Martian surface gravity is only three-eighths of ours. There is, therefore, good proof that the polar caps of Mars are snow. Long ago someone suggested they might be frozen carbonic acid gas, but Faraday himself showed experimentally the conditions of pressure and temperature required to solidify this gas; conditions which we are sure cannot prevail on Mars.

Lowell, some years ago, deduced the temperature of Mars from a full evaluation of the factors involved, such as albedo, the behaviour of the caps, etc., and arrived at a value of 48 °F. This has recently been confirmed by the radiometric measurements made at Lowell Observatory by Coblentz and Lampland.

While there is room for difference of opinion as to the interpretation of the canals of Mars, their existence as true markings on the planet has been clearly established, for they have been photographed and have been seen by nearly all skilled observers who have observed the planet carefully with powerful instruments. The Lick astronomers Schaeberle, Campbell and Hussey of the early observers, and Trumpler more recently, all drew the canals. Because changes take place in the planet's features in quite short time intervals sometimes, observers may seem to disagree and yet both be right.

Lowell regarded the canals as strips of vegetation along artificially produced water courses, for they, like the larger blue-green areas, darken when the time comes for seasonal growth in vegetation; and this led to the belief that vegetable life, and hence also probably animal life of some degree of intelligence, exist on Mars.

Jupiter has received much study at the Lowell Observatory. What we see on Jupiter are mostly atmospheric features, apparently nothing of a solid surface appearing. Usually

在每个火星年中，火星上极冠融化时出现的黑色裂缝总是准确出现在相同的时间和相同的地方，这就明确地证明了极冠的确是存在于火星表面的。火星表面的不规则必然引起极冠不均匀的融化，并且按照火星日历每年准时地重复。这些极冠融化的特征可以参见图1。消融中的极冠边界上嵌有黑边，并且相对于形成中的极冠它的轮廓要更规则，而形成中的极冠轮廓既不规则也不清楚，且总是起源于无规律的风暴云。秋季的极冠出现在与这个极冠位置相对的火星的另一端。

极冠的变化特征表明火星存在着一种大气，因为大气是物质输运的唯一途径。偶尔，当火星的位置合适到我们可以看到一点火星上的夜空时，我们可以发现一条明亮的光带，这是由于火星高层大气中的云受太阳光照射形成的，而云层下面的火星表面则是暗黑的。我们可以据此测量出火星云距离火星表面的高度，1903年的一个测量结果显示这些云的高度有15英里，而地球上云的高度很少超过5英里。因此，火星的大气应该是相当可观的，同时在弗拉格斯塔夫进行的光谱观测表明火星大气中含有水和氧气，但没有什么特别的物质。因此，火星的大气与地球大气非常的相似，但后者较为稠密，因为火星表面的引力只是地球的八分之三。也有很好的证据表明，火星极冠是由雪构成的。很久以前，有人认为极冠可能是冰冻的碳酸气体，但是法拉第用实验给出了这种气体固化时所需的温度和压力条件，而我们确信这种条件在火星上并不普遍存在。

若干年前，洛威尔通过全面测定星体反照率以及极冠的变化特征等各种影响因素，从而对火星的温度进行了推算，得出的温度数值为48°F。最近洛威尔天文台的科布伦茨和兰普朗德通过辐射测量确认了这一温度值。

尽管对于火星运河的解释存在着不同的见解，但作为火星的特征，它们的存在已得到确认，因为这些运河已经被拍成照片而且几乎所有曾经通过强大的仪器对火星进行过仔细观察的训练有素的天文观测者都曾经看到过它们。利克天文台早期的观测者舍贝勒、坎贝尔、赫西，以及最近的特朗普勒，都曾绘制过这些运河。但是由于这些火星的特征有时可能会在很短的时间内发生变化，所以不同天文学家的观测结果看起来不太一致，但他们都是正确的。

洛威尔认为这些运河是沿人工开凿的水渠生长的植被带，因为当植物生长季节来临时它们会变深，这和火星上较大片的蓝绿色区域的变化一致。这就使人相信，火星上存在着植物，同时也很可能存在具有某种程度智慧的动物。

洛威尔天文台对木星也进行了大量的研究。我们所看到的木星主要是其大气的特征，几乎看不到其固态表面上的任何特征。由于木星的转动速度很快，在观测条

so much detail is present that the visual observer, owing to the planet's rapid rotation, has difficulty in recording properly in drawings and notes all he is able to see under good observing conditions. In these circumstances the aid of photography has been very important, and a photographic record of the planet, as complete as possible, has been kept at Flagstaff since 1905. Fig. 2 indicates the nature of the Jupiter markings and gives some idea of their rapid and sometimes extensive changes, which give some hint of the very great activity present on the planet.

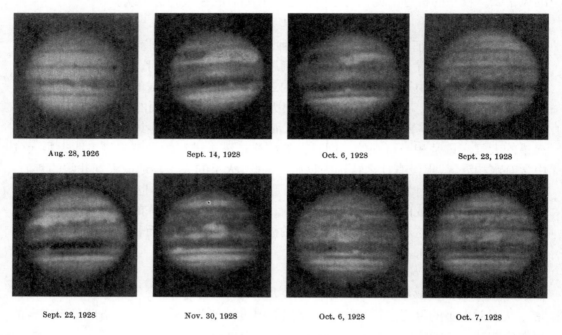

| Aug. 28, 1926 | Sept. 14, 1928 | Oct. 6, 1928 | Sept. 23, 1928 |

| Sept. 22, 1928 | Nov. 30, 1928 | Oct. 6, 1928 | Oct. 7, 1928 |

Fig. 2. Photographs of Jupiter.

Spectrum analysis of the light of Jupiter has revealed a great number of dark bands in the red and infra-red, due to the selective absorption of its atmosphere. Most of these are yet unidentified, but ammonia is present, and possibly also methane gas. The most remarkable quality of the planet's atmosphere is its rapidly increasing absorption into the longest wave-lengths, which must affect the radiation in a decided manner.

Saturn has been regularly observed at Flagstaff, visually, photographically, and spectrographically. Lowell studied theoretically the planet's law of mass distribution, the polar flattening and relation of satellites to divisions in the ring system, leading to new results. Photographs of the planet and rings in light of different colours show some surprising changes, sometimes from year to year. It was found in 1921, when the Earth and Sun were very near the plane of Saturn's rings, that, contrary to previous belief, the rings could always be seen, and that the rings caused two dark lines across Saturn's ball, one the shadow of the rings and the other the rings themselves as seen dark against Saturn (Fig. 3).

件较好时，会有太多的细节呈现于眼前以至于目视天文观测者难以绘制和记录下他的所见。在这种情况下，我们借助于照相技术就显得非常重要了；弗拉格斯塔夫天文台保存了自 1905 年以来几乎最为齐全的图像资料。图 2 显示了木星斑纹的特征，可以使我们对于木星急剧的、有时大范围的变化有一些了解，这些变化表明木星表面是非常活跃的。

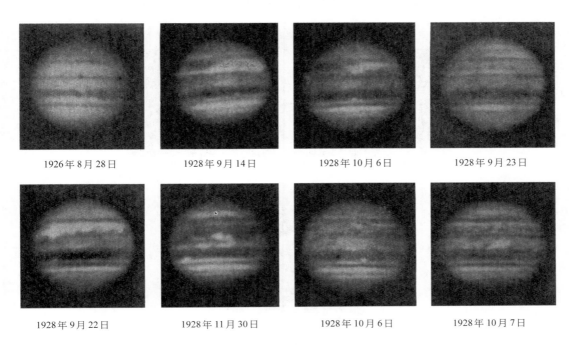

| 1926 年 8 月 28 日 | 1928 年 9 月 14 日 | 1928 年 10 月 6 日 | 1928 年 9 月 23 日 |

| 1928 年 9 月 22 日 | 1928 年 11 月 30 日 | 1928 年 10 月 6 日 | 1928 年 10 月 7 日 |

图 2. 木星的照片

对来自木星的光进行的光谱分析显示，在光谱红端和红外端存在着大量的吸收带，这是由于木星大气的选择性吸收造成的。这些吸收带中的大多数还未确认，但可以确定有氨气存在，可能还存在甲烷。木星大气最显著的特征就是，在波长最长处吸收量迅速增加，这对于木星的辐射有着决定性的影响。

在弗拉格斯塔夫，也采用目视、照相以及光谱的方式对土星进行了常规观测。洛威尔从理论上研究了土星质量分布规律、两极扁平化以及卫星与土星环中缝隙的关系，并给出了一些新的结果。土星及土星环的不同颜色的照片会显示出一些奇异的变化，有时不同年份也会有所不同。1921 年，观测发现当地球和太阳非常靠近土星环平面时，仍然可以看到这些土星环，这与先前的观点是相反的；这时，这些土星环在土星的球体上呈现为两道黑线，其中一道是环的阴影，另一道是环自身，这是因为环的颜色比土星深（图 3）。

Nov. 4, 1911   Feb. 11, 1916

April 22, 1921   May 15, 1922

Sept. 2, 1929

Fig. 3. Photographs of Saturn.

Spectrum analysis of Saturn's light shows much the same absorption bands as were found for Jupiter (except that those of ammonia are weaker in Saturn), so their atmospheres are much alike. The rings show no atmosphere, but are meteoric. The fact that the cloud belts of Saturn are so much weaker than those of Jupiter is doubtless due to the former having a very great seasonal disturbance owing to its highly tipped axis. This factor is practically absent from Jupiter, and so allows its clouds to form and continue strongly belted parallel to the equator, whereas for Saturn the seasonal disturbance tends to destroy such belts.

While Uranus and Neptune are each more than sixty times the volume of the Earth, their great distances, nineteen and thirty times our distance from the Sun, give them only tiny discs even in the largest telescopes, and markings on them are very difficult of observation. Hence to get the rotation of Uranus the spectrograph was employed; it showed the planet's day to be 10.7 hours, and the rotation to be in the direction in which the satellites revolve.

1911 年 11 月 4 日　　　　1916 年 2 月 11 日

1921 年 4 月 22 日　　　　1922 年 5 月 15 日

1929 年 9 月 2 日

图 3. 土星的照片

　　对来自土星的光进行的光谱分析表明，它的吸收带几乎与木星完全相同（只不过土星中的氨气吸收带比较弱），由此可见这两颗行星的大气非常相似。土星环没有大气而仅仅是流星体。土星的云带比木星的云带弱得多，这肯定是由于前者高度倾斜的自转轴会导致非常大的季节性扰动。对木星而言这个影响因素是不存在的，这就允许了木星中云的形成，并且持续的呈带状平行分布于赤道附近。在土星上，季节性的扰动往往会破坏这样的云带。

　　天王星和海王星的体积均大于地球的 60 倍，但由于它们与地球的距离分别是日地距离的 19 倍和 30 倍，因此，即使我们借助于最大的望远镜，它们看起来仍只是很小的圆盘，因而难以观测其表面细节特征。因此引进了摄谱仪对天王星的自转进行研究；结果显示天王星上的一天时间是 10.7 个小时，它的自转方向与其卫星的转动方向一致。

The spectrum analysis of these two planets has also taught us much as to their atmospheres. They bear resemblance to those of Jupiter and Saturn, but show much more intense and numerous absorption bands, the strongest of which are present in the two latter planets. This atmospheric band system is much more intense in Neptune than in Uranus; in short, the bands increase from Jupiter to Uranus and again from the latter to Neptune, somewhat with the distance of the planet from the Sun.

Fig. 4 shows the spectra of these four planets compared with that of the Moon, and gives a good idea of the manner in which the absorption bands increase from Jupiter to Neptune. It is of interest to note that the ammonia band clearly evident in Jupiter, a little way to the left of C, is weak in Saturn, Uranus and also in Neptune.

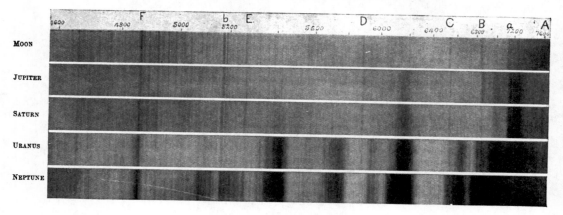

Fig. 4. Spectra of planets and the Moon.

This study of the planets at the Lowell Observatory, in addition to many results not given here relative to the several planets, has much emphasised the differences of the two main groups of planets: Earth, Venus, Mercury and Mars, and the giant group—Jupiter, Saturn, Uranus and Neptune. The first group are comparable with the Earth in size, in density, in energy they receive from the Sun and in atmospheres, so far as they show any at all. The other group are much larger bodies, but of much lower densities, and have a very different type of atmosphere, while the solar energy they receive is much less than the Earth's share—ranging from 1/26 for Jupiter to 1/900 for Neptune. But these studies indicate that these planets may be much more effectively utilising this small energy gift from the Sun than does the nearer group of planets, for their atmospheres, as their spectra show, are as blankets retaining energy of the longer heat-waves, and may let little or none pass out in the heat spectrum available to observers on the Earth.

These studies further direct attention to that important break between the two groups of planets between Mars and Jupiter, and emphasise the need of its further study, and perhaps from theoretical grounds as well, for when we know what has happened to produce the asteroids and cause this vast change in the planetary bodies, we shall better understand the past of the solar system.

(**133**, 10-13; 1934)

对这两颗行星的光谱分析可以使我们了解到很多关于它们大气的信息。它们的光谱与木星和土星相似，但是却拥有更加密集且数目更多的吸收带，其中最强的吸收带就出现在了天王星和海王星的光谱中。相比而言，海王星大气吸收带比天王星更加密集；简言之，吸收带从木星到天王星再到海王星逐渐增加，这在一定程度上与行星距离太阳的远近有关。

将上述四颗行星的光谱与月球的光谱进行比较，如图 4 所示，从中可以清楚地看到吸收带数目从木星到海王星递增的特点。值得注意的是，木星光谱中氨气的吸收带非常明显，其位于 C 波段的左侧附近，但是在土星、天王星和海王星中氨气的光谱则较弱。

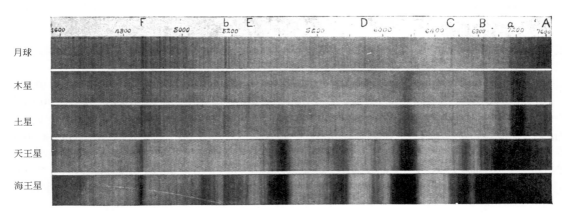

图 4. 行星与月球的光谱图

洛威尔天文台根据以上研究，以及这里未给出的其他一些相关观测结果，从而清楚地表明了两组行星的差别：一组是地球、金星、水星和火星，另一组是木星、土星、天王星和海王星。第一组行星在尺寸、密度、大气以及吸收的太阳能量方面均与地球相近，而后一组天体具有非常大的体积，但是密度较低，其大气构成与前一组显著不同，吸收的太阳能量比地球少得多——其中木星最多，其吸收的能量是地球的 1/26，海王星最少，其吸收的能量是地球的 1/900。研究表明，这些巨行星可能会比第一组距离太阳更近的行星更加有效地利用所获得的有限的太阳能，因为它们的大气可能只让很少一部分或者不让具有热效应的光谱波段透出，因而地球上的观测者很难观察到它们，正如光谱所显示的，在热长波长段显示的能量基本为空白。

这些研究使我们的注意力进一步集中到以火星和木星为界的两组行星的巨大差别上；同时也强调了要对此进行深入研究的必要，也许还要进行基础理论方面的研究，因为只有当我们最终弄清楚小行星是如何产生的，以及行星之间为什么存在这样巨大的差异，我们才有可能对整个太阳系的形成有更好的理解。

（金世超 翻译；蒋世仰 审稿）

Experiments in the Stratosphere

Editor's Note

Until the 1930s, what was known about the structure of the stratosphere had been derived largely from the reflection of radio waves by the layers of ionisation present there. Both in France and in the Soviet Union, however, there was great interest in the direct exploration of the stratosphere by means of balloons. This news report in *Nature* describes Russian plans for launching manned balloons in which people would be protected from the external environment by means of tightly fitting suits.

IT has recently been reported in the daily Press that an attempt is shortly to be made by balloon ascent to reach higher altitudes than 61,000 ft. (pressure 50 mm.) claimed to have been reached by Prokofiev and his companions in the U.S.S.R. balloon. It is to be recalled that observations were made by Regener in 1932 using self-registering apparatus attached to rubber balloons up to a pressure of 22 mm. It was reported that the American balloonists Settle and Fordney reached a pressure last autumn of about 64 mm., whilst the minimum pressure from the records of the Belgian flights of Cosyns, Kipfer and Piccard was 73 mm.

The new attempt represents a departure from the previous methods in that the observers are to travel in an open basket but will themselves be completely sealed in flexible rubber suits. To prevent these from ballooning at low external pressure the suits, adequately supported, will be exhausted down to the minimum that a man can withstand with comfort if he be supplied with sufficient oxygen. The advantages claimed are that the great saving in weight by the absence of the heavy gondola of the previous flights will enable the observers to reach greater heights. The apparatus has already been tested with safety up to an external pressure supposed to correspond to a height of 90,000 ft.— roughly that attained by Regener's balloons. These preparatory ground experiments are being conducted by an American, Mr. M. E. Ridge, with the advice of Dr. J. S. Haldane, at the works of Messrs. Siebe, Gorman and Co. Ltd. at Lambeth, London. It is assumed that the ballooning of the suit at the greatest height attainable will not incommode the occupant even though he himself is under a very much reduced pressure. The observer will be enabled to move about freely and make meteorological and other observations with instruments in contact with the atmosphere.

It is true that from the point of view of record breaking, this saving in weight is an important feature, for it was made clear by Dr. M. Cosyns, when lecturing in England a short time ago, that the only practical limits imposed turned on the very awkward elongated cigar shape of an extremely large envelope when filled with hydrogen only to

平流层中的实验

编者按

在 20 世纪 30 年代之前，对平流层结构的认识主要来源于平流层内电离层对无线电波的反射情况。不过，在法国以及苏联，人们热衷于利用气球直接探索平流层。本篇刊于《自然》上的报道讲述的是关于苏联发射载人气球的一项计划，在这个气球上，飞行员身着紧身保护服以抵御恶劣的外界环境。

近期的日报上报道，科学家们即将进行一项尝试，让气球上升的高度超过普罗科菲耶夫与其同伴利用苏联气球创造的 61,000 英尺（气压 50 mm）的记录。这让我们回想起 1932 年雷格纳利用绑定在橡胶气球上的自动记录仪所作的观测，当时气球上升到了气压为 22 mm 的高空。据报道，美国的气球驾驶员塞特尔和福德尼也曾于去年秋天飞到了气压为 64 mm 的高度，而比利时飞行员科桑、基普弗以及皮卡德的最低气压记录则为 73 mm。

与以往的方式不同，在这次新尝试中，观测者置身于一个敞开式的吊篮中进行飞行，但观测者自身将会穿着完全封闭的、有弹性的橡胶制服。为了防止这些制服在外部压力较低的情况下膨胀，会在保证有充足氧气供应并且人能够轻松承受的前提下把内部空气排到最少。据称这样做的优点是去掉了以前飞行时所采用的笨重的吊篮，使重量大大降低，因而观测者能够飞得更高。经测试，该设备在外部气压达到相当于 90,000 英尺的高空（大致相当于雷格纳的气球所到达的高度）时仍能保持安全可靠。相关的地面预备实验是由美国人里奇先生领导完成的，同时采纳了霍尔丹博士的建议，该实验是在位于伦敦兰贝斯区的西贝与戈尔曼先生的工厂里进行的。尽管在预计所能达到的最大高度处气压已经大大降低，制服的膨胀也不会使观测者感到不便。观测者可以自由走动，并可以利用仪器在大气中进行气象学以及其他方面的观测。

从打破纪录的角度看，减少重量确实是一种重要的方式，因为不久前科桑博士在英国的演讲中说得很清楚：在飞行中唯一的限制就是那个当在地面上充入占其容量一小部分（1/5 或 1/10）的氢气时就已经很狭长笨重的雪茄形大封袋。全部风

a small fraction—one fifth or one tenth—of its capacity on the ground. The whole risk lies with the possible entangling of the practically parallel ropes supporting the gondola. When once off the ground the mishap cannot be rectified. So great was the risk that, in the last Belgian ascent, the balloon was purposely filled with twice as much hydrogen as was required in order to keep the ropes apart, the surplus being discharged en route.

Turning now to the instrumental observations, it must be remarked at the outset that the values of J, the rate of production of ions per cubic centimetre by the cosmic rays, obtained by the Belgian observers, lie within the limits of those of Regener and agree well with them. Those of the stratostat *USSR* are said to agree slightly better with the Belgian than with Regener's results. Other interesting experimental results from the Russian source are that the composition of the air is the same at the lowest pressure reached as on the ground, the relative humidity fell from 92 percent on the ground to 42 percent on the borders of the stratosphere and that, contrary to expectations, gradients of temperature over a few degrees were experienced within the stratosphere. It is noticeable, however, that previous observers have attempted rather too much on each flight, but commenting on the new departure and its relation to previous methods, the barothermograph looks after itself, as does the recording electrometer for obtaining the potential gradient. Perhaps a small advantage would be obtained here in manipulating the leads strung out from the car. The Kolhörster ionisation chamber failed to work on the Belgian flight due to the deposition of body moisture on the insulations, but the advantages of exposing the battery, insulators, electrometers, etc., to the rigorous conditions of the stratosphere are doubtful. Spectrometers for recording the Sun and sky light, pyrheliometer for determining the solar constant, air samplers and camera can all be worked in the open. Eyes and ears must unfortunately always be enclosed. The deep purple of the sky noticed by both the Belgian and the Russian observers must always be seen through glass.

Of all the observations likely to be made, the greatest promise comes from the projected Wilson chamber experiments by Dr. Cosyns that were mentioned in *Nature* of November 25, p. 812. The need for a further examination of cosmic rays is urgent, for their origin remains unknown. The interesting effect accentuated in the Belgian flights was the difference in the behaviour of the ionisation chamber and the Geiger counter as standardised on the ground with γ-rays from radium and used in the upper atmosphere. The relative indications of the counter increase at a greater rate than those of the ionisation chamber, and in the highest altitudes reached, the activity of one has become thrice that of the other. The greater attenuation of the ions along the track of the cosmic ray than along that of the standardising β-ray accounts for the comparative falling off of the indications of the ionisation chamber, whilst the counter goes on no matter how small the disturbance. This result, however, is deceptive, for as the ground experiments of Blackett and Occhialini have abundantly shown, only a very inadequate part of the life-history of a cosmic ray may be obtained from the study of a localised portion of the track of one of the secondary particles. The intrinsic ionisation per centimetre along the track with its secondaries and tertiaries may be just as high as along that of a β-ray. It is well known that, of all the instruments, the Wilson chamber set for photographing β-rays

险就在于本应平行的吊篮绳可能会相互缠绕在一起。一旦脱离地面，任何事故都将不可挽回。由于有这么大的风险，所以之前比利时的气球升空时，特意给气球充了两倍于所需量的氢气以保证绳子处于分开状态，多余的氢气则在途中放掉。

现在来看一下仪器的观测结果，首先需要说明的是，比利时观测者所获得的 J 值，即每立方厘米体积中由宇宙射线诱发的离子的产生速率，均在雷格纳所得结果的范围之内，并与雷格纳的结果吻合得很好。据说苏联的平流层气球的测量数据与比利时的吻合程度略好于与雷格纳所获结果的吻合程度。俄罗斯的气球实验还得到了其他一些有趣的结果：在所到达的气压最低的高度上，大气的组成与地面上是相同的，相对湿度在地面为 92%，到平流层边界处则降为 42%，并且平流层内也存在着与预期结果相反的若干度的温度梯度。然而，值得注意的是，之前的观测者在每次飞行时都要完成大量的任务，而与以前方法相比，在这次新尝试中，气压温度计可以自动工作，静电记录计也可以自动测量电位梯度。在操纵从气球座舱延伸出去的引线时可能也会有一些优势。在比利时人的飞行中，绝缘材料受潮使科尔赫斯特电离室无法工作，不过，把电池、绝缘体以及静电计等暴露在平流层的恶劣环境中是否有好处也值得怀疑。记录太阳和天光的分光计、用于测定太阳常数的日温计、大气采样器以及照相机等，都可以在开放的条件下工作。遗憾的是，人的眼睛和耳朵却不能暴露在外面，比利时和俄罗斯的观测者们只能透过玻璃欣赏天空的深紫色。

在所有可能进行的观测中，前景最被看好的是科桑博士设计的威尔逊云室实验，11 月 25 日出版的《自然》第 812 页提到了这项计划。由于对宇宙射线的起源依旧未知，所以迫切需要对其进行更多的实验。在比利时人的多次飞行中所强调的一个有趣的现象是电离室与盖革计数器在计数上的差异，其中盖革计数器是在地面用镭的放射性 γ 射线校准之后才应用于上层大气的。盖革计数器的相对示数以一个比电离室更大的速率增加，并且在气球到达最大高度时，其中一个的活性是另一个的三倍。离子沿宇宙射线径迹的衰减程度大于沿标准 β 射线的衰减程度是造成电离室示数相对下降的主要原因，但不管如何，盖革计数器受到的扰动始终很小。不过这一结果会造成误导，因为布莱克特和奥恰利尼的地面实验已经充分证明，研究一个次级粒子的局部径迹所能得到的仅仅是宇宙射线在整个生命周期中很短暂的一段。沿它的二次粒子和三次粒子轨迹的每厘米长度上的本征电离可能仅仅与沿一束 β 射线所得到的强度是一样的。大家都知道，在所有的仪器中，威尔逊云室拍摄 β 射

and cosmic rays is most delicately poised. Small variations in temperature conditions and expansion ratio with water or alcohol vapour as indicator upset the observations. Such an instrument, if it is ever constructed for the purpose, must be used in a closed gondola, on account of its heavy coils for obtaining the requisite magnetic field and extra large chamber for taking in as much as possible of these simultaneous happenings, the non-ionising links, the tracks radiating forwards from diffuse centres consisting of neutral particles and positive and negative electrons and the localised heavy bursts of ionisation supposed to be associated with the complete destruction of a chance heavy molecule.

Apart from the investigations in pure science for which such heroic efforts have recently been made and are likely to be made in the future, the reported change in tactics has reopened the question of the feasibility of employing such a flying suit in an open aeroplane flying the stratosphere. It is claimed that the control will be easier than from a completely sealed cockpit.

(**133**, 15-16; 1934)

线和宇宙射线是最灵敏的。温度条件以及作为示踪剂的水或酒精蒸气在膨胀比率上的微小变化都会干扰观测结果。如果以气球测量为目的而建造这样的云室，就必须把它放在一个封闭的吊篮中，因为为了获得所需的磁场要用笨重的线圈，为了接收尽可能多的同时发生的粒子现象需要超大的云室空间，这些现象包括：无电离的连接、来自包括中性粒子和正负电子在内的扩散中心的辐射前锋的径迹，以及可能与恰好被彻底摧毁的重分子相关的本地重电离爆发等等。

对于纯粹的科学研究，目前已做出并将继续做出巨大的努力。除此之外，在战略角度提出了一个新的问题，即是否有可能穿着这样的飞行服乘坐敞式飞机在平流层中飞行。据称这样的操作要比在完全封闭的机舱里更容易。

（蔡则怡 齐红艳 翻译；王鹏云 马宇蒨 审稿）

Reaction Rates of the Hydrogen Isotopes

M. Polanyi

Editor's Note

Physicists studying the difference between deuterium (or in Britain, "diplogen") and ordinary hydrogen in chemical reactions had concluded that the heavier isotope should react more slowly. Here the influential physical chemist Michael Polanyi admits that his earlier work may have been in part responsible for this belief, but he now wishes to correct it. Two effects may cause differences in the reaction rates, the first being the quantum leakage of particles across energy barriers, and the second being the minimal zero-point energy permitted by quantum theory. The former should indeed always favour hydrogen, but not the latter. Polanyi was among the pioneers who were then using the new quantum theory to build up the theoretical foundations of chemistry.

IT seems to be generally assumed that diplogen will always react more slowly than hydrogen. As I may partly be responsible for this view[1], I should like to point out that this is not always correct. Lower reactivity of diplogen compared with hydrogen results mainly from two causes: (1) the existence of zero point energy; and (2) the quantum mechanical leakage of particles through energy barriers. Whilst the leakage through the barrier is always greater for the hydrogen than for the diplogen atoms, the effect of the zero point energy may occasionally favour the reverse ratio. I will confine myself to one special case, as the general treatment will be published shortly by C. E. H. Bawn and G. Ogden. Compare the reaction of a free hydrogen and a diplogen atom; in the initial state the atoms possess no zero point energy and their energies will be equal. However, at the top of the barrier there will be a zero point energy present[2], and this will be greater for the complex reacting with the hydrogen atom than for that reacting with the diplogen atom. The effect of the zero point energy at the top of the barrier is, therefore, to increase the activation energy of the hydrogen atoms to a greater extent than that of the diplogen atoms.

(**133**, 26-27; 1934)

M. Polanyi: Victoria University, Manchester, Dec. 18.

References:
1. Cremer and Polanyi, *Z. phys. Chem.*, **19** B, 443; 1932. See also Eyring, *Proc. Nat. Acad. Sci.*, **19**, 78; 1933.
2. Eyring and Polanyi, *Z. phys. Chem.*, **12** B, 279; 1931.

氢同位素的反应速率

波拉尼

编者按

在对氘（在英国称之为"diplogen"）和普通氢在化学反应中的差别进行了研究之后，物理学家们得出结论认为较重的氢同位素应该反应得更慢一些。具有影响力的物理化学家迈克尔·波拉尼在这篇文章中承认他早期的工作可能在某种程度上促成了这种想法，但是现在他希望对此进行纠正。有两种效应可能会导致反应速率的差别，一种是粒子穿过能量势垒的量子隧穿效应，另一种是量子理论所允许的最小的零点能。实际上前者总是氢原子占优，但对后者却并非如此。波拉尼是当时使用新的量子理论构建化学理论基础的先驱者之一。

人们似乎普遍认为氘总会比氢反应得更慢。由于我可能要为这一观点承担一部分责任[1]，所以我愿意指出这种观点并不是完全正确的。氘相对于氢而言较低的反应性主要来自于两个原因：(1)零点能的存在；(2)粒子穿过能量势垒的量子力学隧穿。氢原子对势垒的隧穿总是比氘原子强，而零点能的效应则偶尔会倾向于相反的状况。由于鲍尔和奥格登很快会发表一般性的处理方法，因此这里我仅就一种特殊情况进行说明。对一个自由的氢原子和氘原子的反应进行比较；在初始状态时由于原子不具有零点能，因此它们的能量是相等的。但是，在反应势垒的顶部将会出现零点能[2]，而有氢原子参与的络合反应的零点能将会大于有氘原子参与的反应。因而，势垒顶部的零点能效应会使氢原子的反应活化能增大并且大于氘原子。

（王耀杨 翻译；郝项 审稿）

21

Recent Discoveries at Choukoutien[*]

D. Black

Editor's Note

Davidson Black and his team discovered the remains of a new kind of fossil man, *Sinanthropus* ("Peking Man", later assigned to *Homo erectus*) at the cave site of Choukoutien (now Zhoukoudian) in China. Here Black presents a brief report on excavations in younger strata at the same site, producing a rich fauna including *Homo sapiens*. This evidence, said Black, showed that Choukoutien had been occupied over a long period, successively by *Sinanthropus* and *Homo sapiens*.

Upper Palaeolithic Culture in "Upper Cave" Sediments

A detailed account of the results of the Choukoutien excavations up to May 1933 has already been presented in our memoir "Fossil Man in China" (*Mem. Geol. Surv. China*, Series A, No. 11). In that report it was noted that above the *Sinanthropus* deposits there occurred towards the top of the hill a pocket of grey sediments of apparently modern facies, the site being described as the "Upper Cave". During the past season, Mr. W. C. Pei has systematically investigated the deposits of the latter site, ably assisted by Mr. M. N. Pien. Their efforts have been rewarded by the discovery of much additional material of unexpected archaeological significance.

(1) *Sedimentary and lithological characters of Upper Cave deposits*. The "Upper Cave" was a true cave but became completely filled with a mixture of grey cave loam and angular flat limestone fragments, the latter being derived from the collapsed portion of its roof. The roof is preserved over a quite large recess of the cave which extends to a smaller lower chamber not yet completely excavated. Where exposed, the cave walls are covered with stalactites and stalagmites. The grey Upper Cave sediments are largely unconsolidated and are in contact only over a few square metres with the hard red beds and stalagmitic floors capping the *Sinanthropus* strata of Locality 1. Elsewhere the Upper Cave appears to be developed as an independent system.

(2) *Fauna of the Upper Cave*. Though not very abundant, the Upper Cave fauna is remarkably rich in types and includes a puzzlingly large number of almost complete skeletons, the bones of which lie in correct association and are but slightly fossilised. The most interesting forms are as follows:—*Hyaena* (an extinct species very different from that found in the *Sinanthropus* beds but similar to that of Sjara-osso-Gol); *Felis tigris* (entire

---

[*] Report of excavations during the field season 1933, presented at the annual meeting of the Geological Society of China on November 11.

周口店的最新发现[*]

戴维森·布莱克（步达生）和他的研究小组曾在中国周口店的岩洞里发现了一种新的化石人类，即"中国猿人"（"北京人"，后来被归为"直立人"）。在这里步达生简略地报告了同一地点更新层位的挖掘工作，这次发掘获得了丰富的动物群，其中包括智人。步达生认为这个证据表明很长一段时期内在周口店先后生活着中国猿人和智人。

"山顶洞"堆积中的旧石器晚期文化

在我们的研究报告《中国的化石人类》中已经详细记述了 1933 年 5 月前在周口店的挖掘工作结果（《中国地质专报》，A 辑，第 11 期）。这份报告指出了在中国猿人沉积物之上，靠近山顶的位置出现了一个明显具有现代特征的灰色堆积，这个地点被描述为"山顶洞"。在过去的一段时间内，裴文中先生在卞美年先生的得力帮助下，对后一遗址的堆积物进行了系统的研究。他们的努力换来了大量具有考古价值的意外发现。

（1）**山顶洞堆积物的沉积特点和岩石学特征。**山顶洞是一个真正的山洞，但是已完全被灰色坺姆土和扁状石灰岩碎片填满，后者来自洞顶塌落部分。洞内有一处洞壁向内形成一个较大的凹陷，其上方的洞顶保存了下来，而这个凹陷一直延伸至一个较小较低的尚未完全被挖掘的小室。露出的洞壁上覆盖着钟乳石和石笋。灰色的山顶洞堆积物大部分没有胶结，只有几平方米的面积与胶结坚硬的红色基底和石笋层接触，而这一层正是 1 号地点中国猿人地层的封顶。山顶洞的其他部分看起来是独立形成的一个系统。

（2）**山顶洞的动物群。**尽管山顶洞的动物群数量不是很大，但是种类丰富，令人费解的是，这其中包括大量近乎完整的骨架，这些骨架的骨骼正常关联，只是轻微石化。其中最令人感兴趣的种类如下：鬣狗（该物种现已灭绝，它与在中国猿人地层发现的物种存在很大差异，但与在萨拉乌苏发现的物种很相似）；虎（完整骨架）；

---

[*] 这是一篇 1933 年田野考古工作季关于发掘现场的报告，发表于 11 月 11 日中国地质学会的年会上。

skeleton); *Cynailurus*, which is now restricted to India (an entire skeleton); *Viverra* (no longer found in North China); the wild ass; *Equus hemionus;* and the deer, *Cervus elaphus* (an entire skeleton), having antlers curiously similar to the special form from Sjara-osso-Gol.

(3) *Human and cultural remains*. In association with this fauna there occur both human skeletal remains and traces of industry. The skeletal remains are of modern type (*Homo sapiens*) and so far comprise two almost complete but somewhat crushed skulls, other skull fragments and teeth, fragmentary lower jaws, bones of the upper extremity (including one clavicle displaying a healed fracture), vertebrae, leg and foot bones. Traces of fire (charcoal and ash) are abundant.

There are three stone implements in a beautiful black chert, a well-made scratcher in vein quartz and several flakes and nuclei in vein quartz, and also a needle (eye broken), a deer canon bone worked at both ends, some thirty or more fox canine teeth perforated for necklace, an ornamental cylindrical piece made from a long bone of a bird, and a considerable quantity of oolitic haematite probably imported from a considerable distance. So far, no trace of pottery, polished stone or microlithic industry has been encountered.

Conclusions. The material recovered will shortly be made the subject of a full report and the conclusions here offered are wholly tentative. (*a*) The Upper Cave deposits appear to be decidedly younger than the *Sinanthropus* layers of Locality 1, from which they are separated by stratigraphic and lithological disconformity and by a faunistic interval (absence of thick-jawed deer, occurrence of a special *Hyaena*, presence of *C. elaphus*, *E. hemionus*, etc.). (*b*) The Upper Cave deposit is, however, probably also Pleistocene in age (collapsed cave, loess-like sediments, presence of Hyaena; cf. *speloea*, *Cynailurus*, *Viverra*, *E. hemionus*, special deer, etc.). (*c*) In these circumstances, we are inclined provisionally to attribute the associated human remains to a Late Pleistocene, Palaeolithic culture. The latter would seem to correspond approximately to the same stage as the Upper Palaeolithic of Siberia and Europe. It appears, however, to be somewhat more advanced than the Ordos industries (Shui-tung-ko and Sjara-osso-Gol) in which no typically worked bones have thus far been found in certain association.

Cynocephalus Remains

In a cylindrical solution cavity about a metre in diameter in the limestone to the south of Locality 1, Mr. M. N. Pien discovered this season a considerable number of fossil bones imbedded in a peculiar red deposit containing a large proportion of small well-rounded pebbles. These bones are remarkably fossilised and heavy, many of them being water-worn and rounded. A few, however, are well preserved, among the latter being several teeth and limb bones of a large baboon, probably *Cynocephalus wimani*, Schlosser. Strikingly similar deposits containing the same type of heavy rolled bone fossils have already been encountered at the very base of the *Sinanthropus* deposits of Locality 1 (Lower Cave). At the present stage of excavation it remains an open question whether or not these beds represent a pre-Choukoutien stage or merely correspond to an early phase in the last filling of the clefts.

猎豹，现在只在印度有发现（一具完整骨架）；灵猫（在中国北方再也没发现过）；野驴；马鹿(一具完整骨架)，令人奇怪的是，该鹿的鹿角与萨拉乌苏发现的那具鹿角形状非常相似。

（3）**人类和文化遗迹**。与动物群同时发现的既有人骨残骸，也有文化遗迹。人骨属于现代类型（智人），到目前为止发现的人骨残骸包括两个近乎完整但稍微有点被压破的头骨，此外还有一些头骨碎片和牙齿、下颌骨碎块、上肢骨（包括一块显示有一处骨折愈合迹象的锁骨）、椎骨、腿和趾骨。用火遗迹（木炭和灰）很丰富。

发掘物中包括三个用漂亮的黑燧石制成的石器，一个制作精良的脉石英刮削器，几个脉石英石片和脉石英石核，一枚骨针（针眼破损），一个两端都进行了加工的鹿胫骨，约三十个或者更多被钻孔用于制造项链的狐狸尖牙，一个由鸟的长管骨制成的装饰性圆柱状物件，还有很多可能是从相当远的地方带来的鲕状赤铁矿。到目前为止，尚未发现陶器、磨制石器或者细石器文化的任何痕迹。

结论。不久将会以修复的材料为主题完成一份详尽的报告，此处提供的结论都只是暂定的。(*a*)毫无疑问，山顶洞的堆积层看起来比1号地点的中国猿人地层更晚，地层学和岩石学的假整合性以及动物群的间隔（没有出现厚颌骨的鹿，出现了一种特别的鬣狗，还出现了马鹿、野驴等）使其与1号地点的中国猿人地层区别开来。(*b*)然而，山顶洞的堆积层可能在年代上也属于更新世（坍塌的洞穴，黄土样沉积物，存在鬣狗；同样也可以见到猎豹、灵猫、野驴、特殊的鹿等）。(*c*)在此情况下，我们暂时倾向于将相关的人类遗迹归属于一种更新世晚期旧石器文化。后者好像与西伯利亚和欧洲的旧石器时代后期的相同阶段基本对应。不过，它好像比鄂尔多斯文化（水洞沟和萨拉乌苏）更先进一些，鄂尔多斯文化中至今还没有发现类似的经过特别加工的骨头。

狒狒的遗迹

在1号地点以南有一个直径约1米的圆柱形石灰岩溶洞，卞美年先生于本季在该洞穴中发现了大量骨头化石，它们嵌于一块很特别的红色堆积物中，其中还含有大量磨圆的小鹅卵石。这些骨头石化很深且很重，其中许多受到了水磨作用变得光滑而没有棱角。但是，有几个保存得很好，其中有几颗大狒狒的牙齿和肢骨，可能就是施洛瑟命名的维氏狒狒。曾在1号地点（下洞）的中国猿人沉积层的基底处发现过与此惊人相似的、含有经过强烈滚动的同类骨头化石的沉积物。根据现阶段的挖掘进展，这些层位是代表一个前周口店时期还是只相当于裂隙最后填充的早期阶段仍是一个未解决的问题。

In any case it would seem that one must conclude from this latest discovery that the Choukoutien fissures have been successively inhabited by baboons, by *Sinanthropus* and by a modern type of *Homo*. However, such a coincidence appears less extraordinary when it is recalled that though Ordovician limestone is widely distributed along the Western Hills, at Choukoutien, on account of its low anticlinal structure at the borders of the plain, it is exceptionally well situated for dissection into fissures and caves.

(**133**, 89-90; 1934)

Davidson Black: F.R.S., Honorary Director, Genozoic Research Laboratory, Geological Survey of China.

　　不管怎样，根据这一最新发现似乎必然能够得出一条结论，即周口店裂隙先后被狒狒、中国猿人和一种现代类型的人属居住过。然而这种巧合似乎不足为奇，要知道，尽管奥陶纪石灰岩沿西山广泛分布，但周口店的平原边界处属于低背斜构造，因此正好有利于裂隙和洞穴的形成。

（刘皓芳 翻译；赵凌霞 审稿）

The Ether-Drift Experiment and the Determination of the Absolute Motion of the Earth[*]

D. C. Miller

Editor's Note

The ether-drift experiment was that in which Michelson and Morley in 1892, using an optical interferometer they had constructed in Ohio in the United States, demonstrated that the supposed ether filling all of space did not exist. This paper uses similar equipment to work out what is called the "absolute" movement of the Solar System through space. The use of the term "absolute" pays scant attention to the theory of relativity, but the result does suggest how the Solar System is moving with respect to the surrounding galaxies.

THE ether-drift experiment first suggested by Maxwell in 1878 and made possible by Michelson's invention of the interferometer in 1881, though suitable for the detection of the general absolute motion of the Earth, was actually applied for detecting only the known orbital component of the Earth's motion. For the first time, in 1925 and 1926, I made observations at Mount Wilson of such extent and completeness that they were sufficient for the determination of the absolute motion of the Earth. These observations involved the making of about 200,000 single readings of the position of the interference fringes.

The ether-drift observable in the interferometer, as is well known, is a second order effect; and the observations correctly define the line in which the absolute motion takes place, but they do not determine whether the motion in this line is positive or negative in direction.

At the Kansas City meeting of the American Association for the Advancement of Science, in December, 1925, before the completion of the Mount Wilson observations, a report was made showing that the experiment gives evidence of a cosmic motion of the solar system, directed towards a northern apex; but the effects of the orbital motion were not found, though it seemed that the observations should have been quite sufficient for this purpose[1].

The studies of the proper motions and of the motions in the line of sight of the stars in our galaxy have shown that the solar system is moving, *with respect to our own cluster*, in the general direction of a northern apex in the constellation Hercules. This apex is near that

---

[*] Paper read before Section A (Mathematical and Physical Sciences) of the British Association meeting at Leicester on September 13, 1933.

以太漂移实验和地球绝对运动的确定[*]

米勒

编者按

迈克尔逊和莫雷于 1892 年用他们在美国俄亥俄州建造的光学干涉仪进行了以太漂移实验，实验表明原先假设充满整个宇宙的以太其实并不存在。这篇文章利用相似的仪器测量了太阳系在宇宙中的"绝对"运动。使用"绝对"这个术语表明作者没有考虑到相对论，但是实验结果的确表明了太阳系是如何相对于周围星系运动的。

1878 年麦克斯韦首次提出了以太漂移实验，1881 年迈克尔逊发明的干涉仪使该实验成为可能。虽然这个实验可以适用于探测地球总体的绝对运动，但实际上它仅在探测人们所熟知的地球运动的轨道分量时被应用过。1925～1926 年，我在威尔逊山上进行了首次观测，这次观测无论从范围上还是完备性上都足以用来确定地球的绝对运动。这些观测数据包含大约 200,000 个单独的干涉条纹位置的读数。

众所周知，干涉仪中可观察到的以太漂移是一个二阶效应；通过观测可以准确地确定绝对运动的路线，但无法确定沿该路线运动的方向。

1925 年 12 月，即威尔逊山的观测完成之前，美国科学促进会在堪萨斯城召开了一个会议，会议上的一个报告指出，实验证明，太阳系在宇宙中是朝着一个北向点运动的；尽管这个实验似乎应当足以观测到轨道运动的效应[1]，但是这一目的并未达到。

对银河系中恒星的自行和视向运动的研究表明，**相对于我们本星系团**，太阳系是大致朝着武仙座北向点的方向运动的。这个向点和前述报告中的以太漂移观测所示出的方向接近，这似乎是证明其正确性的有力证据。也许，这正是导致接下来的

---

[*] 本论文发表于1933年9月13日在莱切斯特举行的英国科学促进会会议A分会场（数学与物理科学）。

indicated by the ether-drift observations as just reported, and seemed to be confirmatory evidence of its correctness. Probably it was this that caused the continuation of the analysis of the problem, on the supposition that the absolute motion was to the northward in the indicated line. All possible combinations and adjustments failed to reconcile the computed effects of combined orbital and cosmic motions with the observed facts.

In the autumn of 1932, a re-analysis of the problem was made, based upon the alternative possibility that the motion of the solar system is in the cosmic line previously determined, but is in the opposite direction, being directed southward. This gives wholly consistent results, leading for the first time to a definite quantitative determination of the absolute motion of the solar system, and also to a positive detection of the effect of the motion of the Earth in its orbit.

The absolute motion of the Earth may be presumed to be the resultant of two independent component motions. One of these is the orbital motion around the Sun, which is known both as to magnitude and direction. For the purposes of this study, the velocity of the orbital motion is taken as 30 kilometres per second, and the direction changes continuously through the year, at all times being tangential to the orbit. The second component is the cosmical motion of the Sun and the solar system. Presumably this is constant in both direction and magnitude, but neither the direction nor magnitude is known; the determination of these quantities is the particular object of this experiment. The rotation of the Earth on its axis produces a velocity of less than four tenths of a kilometre per second in the latitude of observation and is negligible so far as the velocity of absolute motion is concerned; but this rotation has an important effect upon the apparent direction of the motion and is an essential factor in the solution of the problem. Since the orbital component is continually changing in direction, the general solution is difficult; but by observing the resultant motion when the Earth is in different parts of its orbit, a solution by trial is practicable. For this purpose it is necessary to determine the *variations* in the magnitude and in the direction of the ether-drift effect throughout a period of twenty-four hours and at three or more epochs of the year. The observations made at Mount Wilson correspond to the epochs April 1, August 1 and September 15, 1925, and February 8, 1926.

The point on the celestial sphere towards which the Earth is moving because of its absolute motion is called the apex of its motion. This point is defined by its right ascension and declination, as is a star, and the formulae of practical astronomy are directly applicable to its determination from the interferometer observations. The theoretical consideration of the determination of the apex of the motion of the Earth has been given in a paper by Prof. J. J. Nassau and Prof. P. M. Morse[2].

Table I gives the right ascensions and declinations of the apexes of the Earth's cosmical motion as obtained from the interferometer observations for the four epochs on the presumption of a southward motion, together with the right ascensions and declinations calculated upon the theory of an ether-drift.

研究都假设绝对运动是沿着所示路线向北的原因。然而在这种假定下，所有可能的组合和调整都不能使计算得到的轨道和宇宙运动的联合效应与实际的观测结果相符。

　　1932 年秋，人们基于另外一种可能性重新对这个问题进行了分析，即太阳系沿着之前确定的宇宙轨道运动，但方向相反，也就是向南运动。这一次得到了完全一致的结果，从而第一次定量地确定了太阳系的绝对运动，同时也首次明确地探测到了地球在其轨道内的运动效应。

　　地球的绝对运动可以被看成是两个独立运动分量的和。其中一个是绕太阳的轨道运动，其大小和方向都是已知的。在此项研究中，地球轨道运动的速度取为 30 千米／秒，其方向在一年中连续变化，并总是沿着轨道切线的方向。第二个分量是太阳和太阳系在宇宙中的运动。假设该运动的大小和方向都是恒定的，但均属未知；确定这些量正是这项实验的目的。在进行观测的纬度处，地球绕轴的自转将产生一个小于 0.4 千米／秒的速度，这相对于地球绝对运动速度而言可以忽略不计；但是地球自转对运动的视方向有着重要的影响，这也是求解此问题时的一个重要因素。由于轨道运动分量在方向上持续变化，所以要得到通解很困难；但是通过观测地球在轨道不同位置的合运动，从而得到实验解还是可行的。为此，必须在一年中选择三个或者更多个不同的时期，确定以太漂移效应的大小和方向在 24 小时内的**变化**。这项观测在威尔逊山上进行，其观测的时期分别是：1925 年 4 月 1 日、8 月 1 日、9 月 15 日以及 1926 年 2 月 8 日。

　　地球绝对运动所指向的天球上的那个点被称为地球运动的向点。天球就如同一颗恒星，这个点可由天球上的赤经和赤纬确定，通过干涉仪的观察结果，利用实测天文学的公式可以直接确定这个点的位置。纳索教授和莫尔斯教授的文章已经对确定地球运动的向点给出了理论思考 [2]。

　　表 1 给出了假定太阳系是在向南运动的情况下，利用干涉仪的观测结果得到的四个时期地球在宇宙中运动相应向点的赤经和赤纬，以及用以太漂移理论计算得到的相应值。

Table I. Location of resultant apexes

Epoch	α(Obs.)		α(Calc.)		δ(Obs.)		δ(Calc.)	
Feb. 8	6^h	0^m	5^h	40^m	−77°	27′	−78°	25′
April 1	3	42	4	0	76	48	77	50
Aug. 1	3	57	4	10	64	47	63	30
Sept. 15	5	5	5	0	62	4	62	15

Apex of cosmic component α= 4^h 56^m, δ= −70° 33′

From these resultant apexes are determined four values for the apex of the cosmic component, which is the apex of the motion of the solar system as a whole. This apex has the right ascension 4^h 56^m and the declination 70° 33′ south.

Continuing the astronomical description, having found the elements of the "aberration orbit", these are used to compute the apparent places of the resultant apexes for the four epochs of observation. On the accompanying chart of the south circumpolar region of the celestial sphere (Fig. 1), the large star indicates the apex of the cosmic motion, and the four circles show the locations of the calculated apexes. These apexes necessarily lie on the closed curve representing the calculated aberration orbit, the centre of which is the apex of the cosmic component of the Earth's motion. This aberration orbit is the projection of the Earth's orbit on the celestial sphere, which in this case is approximately a circle. The observed apexes for the four epochs are represented by the small stars. The locations of the pole of the ecliptic and of the star Canopus are also shown. The close agreement between the calculated and observed apparent apexes would seem to be conclusive evidence of the validity of the solution of the ether-drift observations for the absolute motion of the Earth and also for the effect of the orbital motion of the Earth, which hitherto has not been demonstrated.

It may seem surprising that such close agreement between observed and calculated places can be obtained from observations of such minute effects, and effects which are reputed to be of such difficulty and uncertainty. Perhaps an explanation is the fact that the star representing the final result for the February epoch is, in effect,

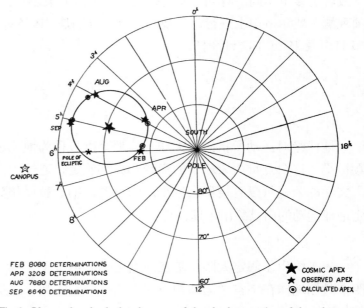

Fig. 1. Observed and calculated apexes of the absolute motion of the solar system.

FEB 8080 DETERMINATIONS
APR 3208 DETERMINATIONS
AUG 7680 DETERMINATIONS
SEP 6640 DETERMINATIONS

★ COSMIC APEX
★ OBSERVED APEX
⊙ CALCULATED APEX

表 1. 地球在宇宙中合运动的向点位置

时期	赤经（观测值）	赤经（计算值）	赤纬（观测值）	赤纬（计算值）
2 月 8 日	6 小时 0 分	5 小时 40 分	−77° 27′	−78° 25′
4 月 1 日	3 42	4 0	76 48	77 50
8 月 1 日	3 57	4 10	64 47	63 30
9 月 15 日	5 5	5 0	62 4	62 15

宇宙分量的向点 赤经 = 4 小时 56 分，赤纬 = −70° 33′

由上表中四个合运动的向点可以确定宇宙分量的向点，它也是太阳系作为一个整体运动的向点。这个向点的位置是赤经 4 小时 56 分，赤纬 −70° 33′。

让我们继续天文学的描述，在得出"光行差轨道"的根素后，即可以用其计算出四个观测时期合运动的向点的视位置。附图是天球南拱极区（图 1），图中大星号表示宇宙运动的向点，四个圆圈表示计算得到的向点位置。这些向点必须落在计算得到的光行差轨道的闭合曲线上，光行差轨道的中心即为地球运动宇宙分量的向点。此光行差轨道是地球轨道在天球上的投影，在这种情况下近似为圆。在四个时期观测到的向点在图中以小星号表示。图中还标出了黄极和老人星的位置。计算和观察得到的视向点的高度吻合似乎有力地证明了用以太漂移观测来求解地球绝对运动以及地球轨道运动效应的正确性，而对于后者迄今为止尚未得到实验证明。

令人惊奇的是，虽然以太漂移这种微弱的效应被公认为是难于观测且其结果会有很高的不确定性，但最后却得到了计算值和观察值如此高度一致的结果。也许，我们可以这样解释：这些观察结果实际上是由大量独立的位置测量平均得出的，二月

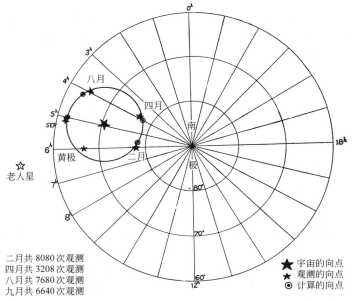

二月共 8080 次观测
四月共 3208 次观测
八月共 7680 次观测
九月共 6640 次观测

★ 宇宙的向点
☆ 观测的向点
◉ 计算的向点

图 1. 太阳系绝对运动顶点的观测位置和计算位置

the average of 8,080 single determinations of its location; the star for the August epoch represents 7,680 single determinations, that for September, 6,640, and that for April, 3,208 determinations.

The location of the apex of the solar motion is in the southern constellation Dorado, the Sword-Fish, and is about 20° south of the star Canopus, the second brightest star in the heavens. It is in the midst of the famous Great Magellanic Cloud of stars. The apex is about 7° from the pole of the ecliptic and only 6° from the pole of the invariable plane of the solar system; thus the indicated motion of the solar system is almost perpendicular to the invariable plane. This suggests that the solar system might be thought of as a dynamic disc which is being pulled through a resisting medium and therefore sets itself perpendicular to the line of motion.

It is presumed that the Earth's motion in space is projected on to the plane of the interferometer, and the *direction* of this motion is determined by observing the variations produced in the projected component by the rotation of the Earth on its axis and by the revolution around the Sun. Both the magnitude and the direction of the observed effect vary in the manner and in the proportion required by an ether-drift, on the assumption of a stagnant ether which is undisturbed by the motion of the Earth through it. But the observed *magnitude* of the effect has always been less than was to be expected, indicating a reduced velocity of relative motion, as though the ether through which the interferometer is being carried by the Earth's motion were not absolutely at rest. The orbital velocity of the Earth being known, 30 kilometres per second, the cosmical velocity of the solar system, determined from the proportional variations in the observed effects, is found to be 208 kilometres per second.

Table II gives the observed periodic displacement of the fringe system as the interferometer rotates on its axis, and the corresponding velocity of relative motion of the Earth and ether.

Table II. Displacements and velocities

Epoch	Fringe Shift	Velocity (Obs.)	Velocity (Calc.)
Feb. 8	0.104 l	9.3 km./sec.	195.2 km./sec.
April 1	0.123	10.1	198.2
Aug. 1	0.152	11.2	211.5
Sept. 15	0.110	9.6	207.5

The last column gives the velocity to be expected in the stagnant ether theory on the presumption that the cosmic component and the orbital component are both reduced in the same proportion in the interferometer. The mean factor of reduction is $k = 0.0514$. The azimuth of the observed effect is subject to a diurnal variation, produced by the rotation of the Earth on its axis. The observed oscillations of the azimuth are in accordance with theory as to magnitude and time of occurrence, but for some unexplained reason, the

有 8,080 次单次测定，八月有 7,680 次，九月有 6,640 次，而四月有 3,208 次。

太阳运动的向点位于南天的剑鱼座内，处在天空中第二亮的老人星以南约 20° 处，著名的大麦哲伦星云的中间。该向点偏离黄极 7° 左右，而仅偏离太阳系的不变平面的 6°，因此太阳系的运动几乎是垂直于其不变平面的。这表明，太阳系可以被看作是一个动力盘，这个圆盘被牵引着穿过某种阻尼介质，从而使其与运动路线垂直。

我们通常假设地球在宇宙中的运动被投影到干涉仪的平面上，通过观测由于地球的自转和绕太阳的公转所引起的这一投影分量的变化可以确定该运动的**方向**。观测到的效应的大小和方向均和假设以太静止时，即以太不被运动的地球所扰动时所预期的变化方式和比例相符。但是，观测到的效应的**值**总比预期的小，这表明相对运动速度的减小，这似乎表明载着干涉仪的地球所穿过的以太并不是绝对静止的。已知地球的轨道速度为 30 千米 / 秒，而根据观测到的效应成比例变化而确定的太阳系的宇宙速度为 208 千米 / 秒。

表 2 给出了干涉仪绕其轴旋转时观测到的条纹系统的周期性位移，以及相应的地球和以太的相对运动速度。

表 2. 位移和速度

时期	条纹位移	速度（观测值）	速度（计算值）
2 月 8 日	0.104 l	9.3 千米 / 秒	195.2 千米 / 秒
4 月 1 日	0.123	10.1	198.2
8 月 1 日	0.152	11.2	211.5
9 月 15 日	0.110	9.6	207.5

假设干涉仪所测得的宇宙分量和轨道分量都以相同的比例减小，最后一列给出的是在静止以太理论下的预期速度。平均减缩因子 $k=0.0514$。观测到的效应的方位角由于地球的绕轴自转存在周日变化。观测到的方位角振荡在大小和时间上与理论结果一致，但是由于一些未知原因，振荡轴偏离了子午线。为了解释这里给出的结果，

axis of the oscillations is displaced from the meridian. In order to account for the results here presented, it seems necessary to accept the reality of a modified Lorentz-FitzGerald contraction, or to postulate a viscous or dragged ether as proposed by Stokes.

The results here reported are, notwithstanding a common belief to the contrary, fully in accordance with the original observations of Michelson and Morley of 1887, and with those of Morley and Miller of 1904-5. The history of the ether-drift experiment and a description of the method of using the interferometer, together with a full account of the observations and their reduction, has been published elsewhere[3].

(133, 162-164; 1934)

Dayton C. Miller: Case School of Applied Science, Cleveland, Ohio.

References:
1. *Science*, **63**, 433; 1926. *Nature*, **116**, 49; 1925.
2. *Astrophys. J.*, March, 1927.
3. *Rev. Mod. Phys.*, **5**, 203, July, 1933.

似乎必须要接受修正后的洛伦兹－斐兹杰惹收缩理论，或者像斯托克斯所提出的那样，假设以太有黏性或具有拖曳效应。

尽管这里给出的结果与普遍的观念相反，但却与 1887 年迈克尔逊、莫雷所进行的原始观测以及 1904~1905 年莫雷、米勒所进行的实验观测完全一致。另外，我们已经在其他刊物 [3] 上发表了相关的内容，包括以太漂移实验的发展、利用干涉仪进行实验的相关方法，以及进行观测及其归算过程的完整说明等。

（王静 孙惠南 翻译；邓祖淦 审稿）

Heavy Hydrogen and Heavy Water

Editor's Note

In a recent lecture, *Nature* reports, Harold Urey had given further details of the heavy isotope of hydrogen he had discovered with Ferdinand Brickwedde. This was deuterium, in which the hydrogen nucleus has a neutron as well as a single proton. Efforts to purify liquid "heavy hydrogen" through distillation had failed, due to the low surface tension of liquid hydrogen. But methods based on electrolysis proved more successful. Urey reported distinct physical properties for heavy water as compared with ordinary water, including significant differences in density, refractive index, viscosity and magnetic susceptibility. The behavior of bacteria and other organisms were also altered when living in heavy water solutions. Urey won the Nobel Prize for Chemistry in 1934 for his discovery.

IN a lecture delivered before the New York Section of the American Chemical Society on December 8, Prof. H. C. Urey gave some further information as to the properties of the heavy hydrogen isotope of mass 2.01356, that of light hydrogen being 1.00778 (both on the $O^{16} = 16$ scale).

Attempts had been made to separate the hydrogen by fractional distillation of the liquid, calculation showing that the vapour pressures should be different, but the method was not successful because the low surface tension of liquid hydrogen makes it difficult to prevent its escape as mist in the fractionating column. A method depending on diffusion into flowing mercury vapour was no more effective. Some details of the actual method of separation, depending on electrolysis with water-cooled nickel electrodes in cells each containing 300 c.c. of potash solution in water from commercial cells enriched to 0.5-1 percent of "deuterium oxide", are given. The current is 25 amp., and 30 cells are placed in series across 110 volts. Electrolysis is carried on until the volume is reduced to one third, when the residual electrolyte is removed, two thirds distilled from the potash, and combined with the undistilled liquid. Electrolysis to one third is again carried out, and beginning with the second stage, the hydrogen and oxygen gases are recombined to give a liquid containing 0.3-0.4 percent of "deuterium oxide". The progress of the fractionation is followed by observation of the refractive index.

Investigations on the equilibrium

$$2H^2I \leftrightharpoons H_2^2 + I_2$$

gave results agreeing with calculations which show, for example, that the ratio of the equilibrium constants with light and heavy hydrogen should be 1.222 at 700° abs. The equilibrium constants for the reaction

重氢和重水

编者按

《自然》杂志报道，哈罗德·尤里在最近的一次报告中给出了他和费迪南德·布里克韦德共同发现的氢的重同位素的进一步的细节。那是氘原子，它的原子核含有一个质子和一个中子。由于液态氢的表面张力较低，通过蒸馏纯化液体"重氢"的努力宣告失败。但是基于电解的方法被证明是比较成功的。尤里报道了重水相对于普通水而言所具有的独特物理性质，包括密度、折射率、黏度和磁化率的显著区别。当生活在重水溶液中时，细菌和其他有机体的行为也会发生变化。尤里因为发现了重氢而获得了1934年的诺贝尔化学奖。

12月8日，尤里教授在美国化学学会纽约分会作了一次报告，报告中他对于质量为2.01356的氢的重同位素的性质给出了进一步的资料，而氢的轻同位素质量为1.00778（都是以$O^{16} = 16$为质量标准）。

由于计算结果显示两种液态氢应该有不同的蒸气压，所以人们尝试了用液体分馏法来分离它们，但是这个方法没有成功，因为液态氢的表面张力较低，这就很难阻止它以雾态形式从分馏柱中逃逸。另一种扩散到流动的汞蒸气中的方法也没有取得很好的效果。使用水冷式镍电极在电解池中（含有300立方厘米来自商业电解池的苛性钾水溶液）进行电解，即可使水溶液中的"氧化氘"富集到$0.5\% \sim 1\%$，据此，人们已获得了实际分离方法的某些具体条件。将30个电解池串联于电压为110 V、电流为25 A的电路中进行电解。当苛性钾溶液体积减少到1/3时停止电解，倒出残余电解液；取蒸馏出来的2/3的液体，将其与未蒸馏的液体合并，而后再次电解，至液体体积减少到1/3，从第二步开始，氢气与氧气结合形成一种含有$0.3\% \sim 0.4\%$"氧化氘"的液体。进行分馏之后，观测折射率。

通过研究平衡过程

$$2H^2I \rightleftharpoons H_2^2 + I_2$$

人们所得到的结果与计算结果相吻合，例如，在绝对温度700 K时轻氢和重氢平衡常数的比值为1.222。反应

$$H_2^1 + H_2^2 \rightleftharpoons 2H^1H^2$$

gave 3.28 (3.27), 3.73 (3.77) and 3.75 (3.82) at 298.1°, 671° and 741°, abs., the calculated values being in brackets[1]. Experiments by Crist and Dalin showed that no interaction between heavy hydrogen and the light hydrogen of water over which the gas was confined had occurred in a few weeks; the different result reported by Oliphant[2] may have been due to the presence of a catalyst.

Experiments by Rittenberg and Urey on the electrolytic separation of hydrogen isotopes pointed to a kinetic explanation of the phenomenon; unless the differences in electrode potentials are much greater than those indicated by calculations, it does not seem possible that the separation is due to this cause[3]. The physiological properties of heavy water are supposed to depend on possible differences in ionisation constant and in reaction velocities as compared with ordinary water.

A design of electrolytic cell for concentrating heavy water has been described by Harkins and Doede[4] but no details of performance are given. The specific rates of discharge of light and heavy hydrogen atoms on various metal cathodes have been measured by Topley and Eyring[5] and the results considered with reference to the theory of over-voltage: they are not inconsistent with the view that the separation is almost entirely due to the zero-point energy difference. The slow process at the cathode does not appear to be combination of atoms to molecules.

A method for determining the concentration of the heavy oxygen isotope O^{18} in water during treatment[6] depends on decomposing the heavy water with heated iron and combining the liberated hydrogen with ordinary oxygen from hot copper oxide and condensing the water (X) so formed. The iron oxide is then decomposed by heating in ordinary hydrogen and the water formed (Y) condensed. The water X was found to be identical with the initial heavy water, whereas Y was identical with ordinary water. Hence there is no appreciable concentration of O^{18} in the electrolytic process.

Several investigations of the properties of heavy water, in addition to those already reported in these columns[7], have been published. The solubilities of one or two salts in heavy water are distinctly lower than in ordinary distilled water[8]: 1.000 gm. of ordinary water dissolves 0.359 gm. of sodium chloride at 25° and 1 gm. of water containing 92 percent of hydrogen as H^2 dissolves 0.305 gm., a difference of 15 percent, whilst the corresponding figures for barium chloride show a difference of 19 percent.

The densities, refractive indices (n^d_{20} and n^c_{20}), molar refraction for D line, viscosity (η), surface tension (γ), dielectric constant (D), magnetic susceptibility (χ) and molar susceptibility of water containing 31, 63.5 and 92 percent hydrogen as H^2 (assuming the density 1.1056 for pure H_2^2O) have been measured, and the values extrapolated to pure H_2^2O. Selwood and Frost's values[9] are (the values for ordinary water in brackets): n^d_{20}, 1.3281

$$H_2^1 + H_2^2 \rightleftharpoons 2H^1H^2$$

的平衡常数，在绝对温度 298.1 K、671 K 和 741 K 时分别为 3.28（3.27）、3.73（3.77）和 3.75（3.82），其中括弧中显示的是计算值 [1]。由克里斯特和达林所做的实验表明，密封保存的气态水分子中的重氢与轻氢原子在几周内没有发生相互作用，奥利芬特 [2] 所报告的不同结果可能是由于某种催化剂的存在而造成的。

里滕伯格和尤里用电解法分离氢同位素的实验指出了对这一现象的动力学解释；然而，除非电极电势差比计算结果大很多，否则，分离似乎不太可能是由这个原因造成的 [3]。与普通水相比，重水的生理性质应该取决于它在电离常数和反应速度等方面可能体现出来的差异。

哈金斯和多伊德 [4] 曾描述过一种用来浓缩重水的电解池的设计方案，但并未给出具体的操作细节。托普利和艾林 [5] 测定了轻氢、重氢原子在各种金属阴极表面放电的比速率，考虑到过电位理论，这些结果与认为分离几乎完全是由于零点能差异的观点毫无冲突之处。阴极表面的缓慢过程看来并不是原子结合成分子的过程。

测定实验所用水中的重氧同位素 O^{18} 浓度的方法 [6] 如下：用加热的铁将重水分解，令释放出来的氢气与加热氧化铜所产生的普通氧气相结合，再将所形成的水（X）冷凝。接着将氧化铁在普通氢气中加热使其分解，并使形成的水（Y）冷凝。这样，水 X 的组成就与最初的重水一样，而水 Y 则与普通水一样。因此，在电解过程中 O^{18} 不会有很明显的浓缩。

除了那些已见诸报道的文章 [7] 之外，还有一些关于重水性质的研究论文也已发表。有一两种盐在重水中的溶解度明显比在普通蒸馏水中低 [8]：在 25℃时 1 克的普通水可溶解 0.359 克氯化钠，而 1 克含有 92% 重氢 H^2 的水则可溶解 0.305 克氯化钠，二者相差 15%；用氯化钡进行的相应实验显示的差异为 19%。

人们已分别测定了含有 31%、63.5% 和 92% 重氢 H^2 的水（假定纯 H_2^2O 的密度为 1.1056）的密度、折射率（n^d_{20} 和 n^c_{20}）、D 线的摩尔折射率、黏度（η）、表面张力（γ）、介电常数（D）、磁化率（χ）和摩尔磁化率，并根据它们来外推纯 H_2^2O 的性质。塞尔伍德和弗罗斯特得到的纯 H_2^2O 的性质是 [9]（括弧中显示的是普通水的数值）：n^d_{20}，1.3281（1.3329）；n^c_{20}，1.3265（1.3309）；η_{20}，14.2 mp（10.87 mp）；γ，67.8（72.75）；

(1.3329); n^c_{20}, 1.3265 (1.3309); η_{20}, 14.2 mp (10.87 mp); γ, 67.8 (72.75); $\chi \times 10^6/$gm. (92 percent water), -0.65 (-0.72); molar susceptibility $\times 10^6$, -13 (-13).

Lewis and Macdonald found the viscosity at several temperatures (5°-35°) higher than that of ordinary water, but their value at 20°, 12.60, is not in agreement with Selwood and Frost's. The dielectric constant is lower than that of ordinary water: $D^2/D^1 = 0.982$ at 10°, 0.990 at 25°. The abnormality as compared with ordinary water decreases with rise in temperature for all properties investigated.

The refractive index[10] affords a convenient method of determining the proportions of H^1_2O and H^2_2O[10] : the effect of the O^{18} isotope is opposite in sign from that of H^2, and the measurement of the density and refractivity gives the complete isotopic composition (H^1, H^2, O^{16}, O^{18}) of a sample of water. The mutarotation of α-d-glucose in heavy water shows that the displaceable hydrogen atom of the sugar is immediately replaced by H^2 from the water, and the mutarotation is due to a change in which the double bond in a carbonyl group, $=C=O$, is replaced by a ring formed by the migration of a hydrogen atom[11].

By the interaction of heavy water with magnesium nitride, ammonias in which the hydrogen atoms are predominatingly H^2 (deutero-ammonias) are produced, which have higher melting points, boiling points and latent heats than ordinary ammonia[12].

Further experiments on the physiological effects of heavy water[13] show that the filaments of *Spirogyra* in water of specific gravity 1.000061 are characterised by lack of movement, absence of abscission or cell disjunction, and greater longevity. The usual effect with ice and steam water was confirmed[14]. The results suggest a stabilising action of water containing H^2, perhaps an effect on the colloids in the organism, the water bound in such colloids being known to be denser than free water. A slightly higher pH (as determined with bromthymol blue) for this sample of water was found. In other experiments[15], decreased enzyme activity and fermentation in isotope water, a more extensive spread of *Oscillatoria* (perhaps due to a pH of 6.77 as determined by the glass electrode), and the following results with *Spirogyra nitida* were found: a representative filament of 31 cells in isotope water had 43 cells after 6 days, of which 3 were dead; a filament of 37 cells in ordinary water showed no cell division at the end of 6 days and 20 cells died; in ice water renewed twice daily, a filament of 50 cells showed 15 abnormal at the end of five days, whilst the filament in freshly condensed water renewed twice daily showed all its 50 cells dead or shrunken in the same period; the control filament (pond water) had 47 cells initially and 64 normal cells after six days.

(**133**, 197-198; 1934)

References:
1. Cf. A. and L. Farkas, *Nature*, **132**, 894, Dec. 9,1933.

$\chi \times 10^6/g$（92%的水），－0.65（－0.72）；摩尔磁化率$\times 10^6$，－13（－13）。

刘易斯和麦克唐纳发现，重水的黏度在一些温度（5℃~35℃）下比普通水的高，不过在 20℃时他们得到的重水的黏度为 12.60，与塞尔伍德和弗罗斯特得到的数值不一致。重水的介电常数比普通水的低：10℃时，$D^2/D^1 = 0.982$，25℃时则为 0.990。对于所研究的各项性质而言，重水与普通水的差异随着温度升高而逐渐减小。

折射率为测定 H_2^1O 与 H_2^2O 的比例提供了一个便捷的方法 [10]：由于 O^{18} 同位素产生的影响与 H^2 的影响正好相反，所以对密度和折射性的测量可以给出一份水样完整的同位素组成信息（H^1，H^2，O^{16}，O^{18}）。α–d–葡萄糖在重水中的变旋现象表明，糖分子中可替代的氢原子能够快速地被水中的 H^2 置换，而变旋过程是由于一个羰基 =C=O 中的双键被一个由氢原子迁移所形成的环替代 [11]。

通过重水与氮化镁的相互作用可以产生所含氢原子主要为 H^2 的氨（氘氨），它具有比普通氨更高的熔点、沸点和潜热 [12]。

关于重水的生理学效应的进一步实验 [13] 表明，水绵的丝状体在比重为 1.000061 的水中具有下列特征：很少运动，不发生脱落或细胞分离，寿命更长。冰和水蒸气的普通效应也得到了证实 [14]。结果表明含 H^2 的水具有稳定的作用，这种作用可能是对生物体内的胶体的影响，我们都知道在这些胶体中结合水比自由水更稠密。另外还发现该水样具有略高的 pH 值（利用溴百里酚蓝测定）。在其他实验中人们发现 [15]，酶活性和发酵作用在同位素水中有所下降，颤藻扩散得更为广阔（可能是由于 6.77 的 pH 值，这个结果是用玻璃电极测定的），还发现了光洁水绵的如下现象：一个典型的有 31 个细胞的丝状体放在同位素水中，6 天后变成了 43 个细胞，其中有 3 个死亡；而在普通水中，一个有 37 个细胞的丝状体在 6 天内没有出现细胞分裂的现象，并有 20 个细胞死亡；在每天更新两次的冰水中，一个有 50 个细胞的丝状体在 5 天后有 15 个细胞异常，而在每天更新两次的新鲜冷凝水中，这种丝状体中的 50 个细胞在同一时期内全部死亡或皱缩；开始时具有 47 个细胞的对照丝状体（处于池塘水中）在 6 天后有 64 个正常细胞。

（王耀杨 翻译；李芝芬 审稿）

2. *Nature*, **132**, 675, Oct. 28, 1933; cf. Polanyi and Horiuti, *ibid.*, 819, Nov. 25.

3. cf. Collie, *Nature*, **132**, 568, Oct. 7, 1933.

4. *J. Amer. Chem. Soc.*, **55**, 4330; 1933.

5. *J. Amer. Chem. Soc.*, **55**, 5058; 1933.

6. Selwood and Frost, *J. Amer. Chem. Soc.*, **55**, 4335; 1933.

7. *Nature*, **132**, 536, Oct. 7, 1933.

8. Taylor, Caley and Eyring, *J. Amer. Chem. Soc.*, **55**, 4334; 1933.

9. Selwood and Frost, *J. Amer. Chem. Soc.*, **55**, 4335; 1933. Lewis and Macdonald, *ibid.*, 4730. Lewis, Olson and Maroney, *ibid.*, 4731; Lewis and Luten, *ibid.*, 5062.

10. Crist, Murphy and Urey, *J. Amer. Chem. Soc.*, **55**, 5060; 1933. Lewis and Luten, *ibid.*, 5061.

11. Pascu, *J. Amer. Chem. Soc.*, **55**, 5056; 1933.

12. Taylor and Jungers, *J. Amer. Chem. Soc.*, **55**, 5057; 1933.

13. Barnes, *J. Amer. Chem. Soc.*, **55**, 4332; 1933.

14. *Nature*, **132**, 536, Oct. 7, 1933.

15. Barnes and Larson, *J. Amer. Chem. Soc.*, **55**, 5059; 1933.

Ernst Haeckel

Editor's Notes

Professor Ernst Haeckel was an enthusiastic supporter of Darwin's theory of evolution and, from his base, at the University of Jena in Germany, did much to ensure the spread of this area of natural selection on the European mainland. This article was published on the centenary of Haeckel's birth. Before his attention was diverted by Darwin's thesis, Haeckel was best known as an embryologist: he is the originator of the notion, widely accepted in the nineteenth century, that the developing embryo recapitulates the evolutionary track of animals. W. H. Brindley added the following information about Haeckel's relationship with the University of Jena.

THE career of Prof. Ernst Heinrich Haeckel, the centenary of whose birth falls on February 16, belongs to the heroic stage of the history of the theory of evolution. In 1862, at the early age of twenty-eight, he was appointed to the chair of zoology in the University of Jena, a post which he held until his death in 1914.

Haeckel's life bears a strong resemblance to that of Huxley, for like Huxley his life's task was propaganda in favour of the theory of evolution against the then prevalent theory of the origin of species by a series of supernatural interpositions of the Divine Being. Like Huxley too, he was an ardent advocate of the animal origin of the human race. But there were marked differences between the two men; Haeckel was a harder hitter than Huxley, and withal a much more reckless one, since he was apt to make wild statements on the basis of insufficient data, as, for example, when he stated that if there were a line to be drawn between animals and men, the lower races must be included amongst the apes. The most recent anthropological studies seem to indicate that in the essential make-up of their minds the most primitive men are very like ourselves: the data and presuppositions from which they start are different and so are their customs and traditions, but granted these postulates the conclusions at which they arrive are natural enough. But on the whole, Haeckel was a sounder biologist than Huxley: whilst he embraced with enthusiasm Darwin's arguments about natural selection, he was never deceived into thinking that the mere survival of some and the death of others could account for progressive evolution: he saw quite clearly that the vital question was the origin of the "variations" which distinguished the survivor from his less fortunate brother, and in this matter he followed Lamarck. When he popularised his views in his famous "History of Creation" he dedicated the work to "Jean Lamarck and Charles Darwin".

Haeckel excelled Huxley also in the amount of actual zoological work which he accomplished. Thus he wrote a descriptive monograph of the Radiolaria collected by H. M. S. *Challenger*, giving the characters of no less than 3,600 new species. This work

恩斯特·海克尔

编者按

恩斯特·海克尔教授是达尔文进化理论的坚决支持者，他在其所任职的德国耶拿大学做了大量工作以确保自然选择理论在欧洲大陆的传播。本文发表于海克尔百年诞辰之际。在海克尔将兴趣转向达尔文学说之前，他是一位著名的胚胎学家，他最先提出了胚胎的发育过程会重现种系进化历程这一观点，这在19世纪被广泛接受。威廉·哈里森·布林德利在文后补充了一些关于海克尔与耶拿大学关系的信息。

恩斯特·海因里希·海克尔教授出生于一百年前的 2 月 16 日，他所生活的年代正好处于进化理论创建历史上的英雄时期。1862 年，海克尔刚满 28 岁就被任命为耶拿大学的动物学教授，并一直担任此职直到 1914 年去世（译者注：根据《不列颠百科全书》，海克尔逝于 1919 年）。

海克尔的一生与赫胥黎极为相似，像赫胥黎一样，他一生都以宣传支持进化论为己任，反对当时盛行的认为生物物种起源于某些神圣存在的超自然力量的学说；他也像赫胥黎一样热忱拥护人类起源于动物的学说。但是他们彼此之间也有明显的不同之处。同赫胥黎相比，海克尔更具攻击性，更加鲁莽，因为他动辄就在没有充分数据的情况下急于作出很不成熟的论断。例如，当他说如果在人和动物之间划一条界线的话，那么类人猿一定是与猿类划到一起的。最近的人类学研究似乎表明最原始的人类在思想的本质构成上与我们是非常相像的，尽管由研究结论得出的这些推测是非常自然的，但是最原始的人类的思想开始形成时所基于的信息和前提与我们不同。但是总的来说，与赫胥黎相比，海克尔可以称得上是更理性的生物学家。当他满腔热情地拥护达尔文的自然选择论断时，从来没有盲目地认为某些生物的生存和另一些生物的死亡可以解释为渐进性演化，他很清楚问题的关键在于"变异"的起源，正是这些变异将幸存者与被淘汰者区别开来，对待这一问题，他的观点与拉马克一致。当他在他著名的《自然创造史》一书中推广自己的观点时，他把这些工作献给了"让·拉马克和查尔斯·达尔文"。

在实际完成的动物学工作量方面，海克尔也胜过赫胥黎。他根据英国皇家海军舰艇"挑战者号"采集的资料撰写了一本描述放射虫的专著，介绍了不少于 3,600

occupied him for ten years. He also monographed the calcareous sponges, but the greatest task which he attempted was to sketch, assuming the truth of the evolution theory, the actual course which evolution had pursued in producing modern plants and animals. His conclusions were embodied in his "Allgemeine Morphologie", of which the "History of Creation" may be regarded as a popular edition. Of course, the state of zoological and botanical knowledge at the time that these books were written was far too incomplete to permit of any but the vaguest sketches of the course of evolution, but there can be nothing but admiration for Haeckel's bold adventure. In the circumstances, It was the right course to pursue: it summarised pre-existing knowledge and provided both a foundation and a framework for future work, and some of the most important and fundamental of Haeckel's ideas have stood the test of time. Thus he divided living beings into Animals, Plants and Protista; regarding the last group, which included the simple unicellular organisms, as the common seed-bed from which both animals and plants have sprung. The discovery of green ciliates like some species of *Stentor* and *Vorticella*, and of colourless carnivorous Dinoflagellates which devour young oysters, in addition to the ordinary brown species which live like brown seaweeds, has more than justified Haeckel's classification.

Haeckel's most far-reaching hypothesis was, however, his famous "biogenetic law". He invented the terms phylogeny and ontogeny—the first, according to him, designated the palaeontological history of the race, the second the history of the development of the individual from the egg to the adult condition. The law connecting these two was the "Biogenetic fundamental principle": stated in his own words, it ran thus: "Ontogeny is a short and quick repetition, or recapitulation of Phylogeny determined by the laws of inheritance and adaptation". Haeckel pointed out that if this principle be admitted, there is some hope of tracing, in outline at least, the actual course of evolution; whereas if we were to confine ourselves to palaeontological evidence, we should only see glimpses of evolution in special cases. The past history of the Vertebrata may be traced from fossils with considerable exactitude since vertebrates possess an internal skeleton which is often preserved and which gives in its scars and processes, evidence of the muscles which once accompanied it and consequently of the actions and habits of the animal which possessed the skeleton. The external skeleton of extinct Crustacea which clings tightly to every protuberance of the body, also reveals a good deal about the activities of its former possessor. But what scanty light do the shells of extinct Mollusca and the tests (testas) of ancient Echinoderms throw on the internal structure of their owners! Who would dream from their evidence that radiate Echinoderms were derived from bilateral ancestors?

In our judgment the formulation of this biogenetic law was the greatest service which Haeckel did to the science of zoology, and the more we reflect on it the greater the service will appear. Haeckel was, of course, aware that these reminiscences of ancestral life could be modified, blurred or occasionally completely obscured. He knew that for the elucidation of life-histories only the comparative method would avail; and just as in the comparison of two ancient documents the truth will shine through the errors peculiar to each one, so with life-histories.

个新种的特点。这一工作花费了他整整 10 年时间。他还写了一部关于钙质海绵类的专著，但是他试图完成的最伟大的工作是在假定进化论正确的前提下勾勒出进化在产生现代动植物的过程中所经过的真实路径。他的结论收录在他的《普通形态学》一书中，《自然创造史》可以被视为该书的科普版。当然，写这本书时动物学和植物学知识的发展程度还远不完善，这种状况决定了他能得到的只是进化过程的最模糊的轮廓，但是海克尔这种勇敢的冒险精神让我们非常钦佩。其实在这种情况下，概括已经存在的知识从而为今后的工作提供基础和框架，这是一条探寻真理的正确路线。海克尔的观点中最重要和最基本的部分已经经受住了时间的考验。例如他将生物划分成动物、植物和原生生物三大类，原生生物包括简单的单细胞生物，他认为动物与植物皆起源于这一类群。后来发现了绿色纤毛虫（如喇叭虫和钟形虫）、以幼牡蛎为食的无色肉食性沟鞭藻类、像褐海藻一样生存的普通棕色沟鞭藻类，这些发现已经证明了海克尔的分类方法是合理的。

然而，海克尔的假说中意义最深远的是著名的"生物发生律"。他发明了系统发育和个体发育这两个术语——根据他的说明，系统发育是指种系的古生物学历史，个体发育则指个体从卵子到成年的发育史。联系二者的法则就是"生物发生的基本原理"，用他自己的话说就是"系统发育由遗传定律和适应性法则共同决定，而个体发育是系统发育史的简短而迅速的重复或重演"。海克尔指出，如果这一原理成立，那么就有希望探索到真实的进化过程，至少也可以得到大致的轮廓。反之，如果我们把自己局限于古生物学证据的范围内，那么我们只能在特殊的例子中才能看到进化的发生。脊椎动物的内骨骼通常会以化石的形式保存下来，通过内骨骼上留下的疤痕和突起可以得到曾经与其结合在一起的肌肉的情况，进而获得具有这种内骨骼的动物的行为和习惯方面的信息，因此可以依据化石较为准确地追溯脊椎动物过去的历史。已灭绝的甲壳纲动物的外骨骼紧紧贴附在身体的各处结节上，这些外骨骼也揭示了关于其从前的主人活动的大量信息。但是，已灭绝的软体动物类的贝壳和远古棘皮动物的甲壳所揭示的关于其生物体内部结构的信息却少得可怜！谁能从这些外壳联想到辐射对称的棘皮动物是从两侧对称的祖先进化而来的呢？

依我们看来，生物发生律的提出是海克尔对动物科学最伟大的贡献，而且我们对其思考得越多，就越觉得其意义重大。当然，海克尔意识到了对于远古生命的这些追忆可能会被修改、可能会变得模糊，也可能会在不经意间就完全湮没。他知道只有比较法才有助于阐明生命史，正如比较两份古老的的档案，真相将通过它们各自特有的错误表现出来，生命史亦是如此。

The acceptance of this law as giving a picture of evolution drew with it certain conclusions as to the causes of evolution. Haeckel described variations as "adaptations". There were, he said, two classes of these, namely, (1) small ones which were the result of habits and which were *transmitted to posterity with greater certainty the longer they had lasted* (this is pure Lamarckian doctrine), and (2) great adaptations which appeared suddenly and the causes of which were unknown to us, though in some cases they appeared to have originated with intra-uterine influences. These latter are now, of course, called mutations, and it was the first category alone which Haeckel believed to be significant for evolution, for the growth of the individual suggests that evolutionary growth was slow, functional and continuous.

The biogenetic law proved a tremendous stimulus to zoological research. Of course, it encountered opposition; its enthusiastic votaries desired, like all enthusiasts, to reach the "promised land" at once: they failed to realise that ancestral history could only be elucidated by prolonged, careful and comparative research. They could not deny themselves the pleasure of making wild guesses as to ancestry based on the study of some one life-history and in time "Haeckelismus" became a term of reproach. But the principle was essentially sound; from all opposition it emerged triumphant: it has been transferred to ever wider fields and has been found to throw light even on the development of the mental life of man. A certain school of biologists at the present day affects to denigrate it and that for obvious reasons, for if it is sound then one thing is certain, mutations have played no part in evolution. But ancestral history stands out so clearly in some life-histories that none but the wilfully blind can deny its presence. Amongst the Ctenophora, for example, there are two aberrant forms, *Tjafiella* and *Coeloplana*. The first resembles a sponge, the second a flat-worm; yet both begin their free existence as typical little Ctenophores, globular in form with 8 meridional bands of cilia radiating from the upper pole. But if ancestral history is the foundation of some life-histories is it not reasonable to assume that it lies at the base of all?

The real originator of the theory that evolution proceeded by jumps and that "Discontinuity in variation was the cause of discontinuity in species" was the late Dr. Bateson. In his first and best work on the development of *Balanoglossus* he found himself driven to the conclusion that Echinoderms and Vertebrates had radiated from a common stock and his faith in "recapitulation" failed him, although it is interesting to record that this conclusion has been sustained by recent research and that from the most unlikely quarter, namely, biochemistry. He then made "*il gran rifiuto*" and fell back on sports and monstrosities as the material of evolution. At the meeting of the Zoological Congress in Cambridge in 1898, Bateson put forward his views. Haeckel was present at the meeting and some sentences of his still linger in our memory. He said that if views like these are to be accepted, "Kehren wir lieber zu Moses zurück".

E. W. MacBride

(**133**, 198-199; 1934)

认可生物发生律可以描绘进化的图景便可得出一些关于进化起因的结论。海克尔将变异描述为"适应性"。他说这种适应性包括两类：（1）小的适应性，这是习性的结果，**它们由父辈传给后代，这些习性持续的时间越久，传递给后代的可能性越大**（这属于纯粹的拉马克学说）；（2）大的适应性，这是突然出现的，尽管在有些例子中它们似乎是由母体内的某些影响引发的，但是其具体原因还不清楚。这些大的适应性现在被称为突变，而海克尔认为对于进化有意义的只有第一种适应性，因为个体生长表明进化的过程是缓慢的、功能性的和连续的。

生物发生律极大地刺激了动物学研究的发展。当然，也有人表示反对。像所有狂热者一样，该学说的忠实信徒们渴望能立刻"修成正果"，但却没有意识到祖先们的历史只能通过长久的、仔细的比较研究才能得以阐明。他们基于某一生命史的研究便对祖先展开漫无边际的遐想并沉浸在这样的乐趣中，最终，"海克尔主义"沦为耻辱的代名词。但是该学说的原理本质上是合理的，因而它以胜利者的姿态屹立于所有反对呼声之上，于是它被应用到了更加广阔的领域，人们甚至发现它对理解人类精神生活的发展也有帮助。现代生物学家中有一流派意在贬低海克尔的这一学说，他们指出如果这一学说是合理的，那么很显然可以确定突变对进化没有任何影响。但是祖先的历史在某些生命史中表现得如此明显清晰，除非故意对其视而不见否则就无法否认它的存在。例如，栉水母动物门存在 *Tjafiella* 和 *Coeloplana* 两种迥异的生命形式。第一种类似海绵，第二种则像扁形虫，而二者在生命开始时的状态与典型的小栉水母是一样的，即呈球形，具有自上端辐射发出的八行纤毛子午带。如果祖先历史确实是某些生命史的基础，那么假定在所有生命史中都存在祖先历史难道是不合理的吗？

进化是跳跃式进行的并且"变异的不连续性造成了物种的不连续性"，这一理论的真正创始人是已故的贝特森博士。其第一部也是最好的一部作品是关于柱头虫属发育史的研究，在这本著作中，他得到了如下结论：棘皮动物和脊椎动物从共同的祖先进化而来，他对"重演"学说的信仰导致了他的失败，然而有趣的是最近的研究以及从最不可能的生物化学角度得到的结果均支持了这一结论。后来他又来了个"大转折"，转而以突变体和畸变材料为研究进化的素材。在 1898 年召开的剑桥动物学大会上，贝特森提出了他的观点。海克尔也出席了那次会议，至今他的许多话我们仍记忆犹新。他说如果这样的观点都被认可的话，"那么我们宁愿相信摩西的存在"。

麦克布赖德

*   *   *

Many scientists will have read with keen interest Prof. MacBride's delightful sketch of Haeckel's work in *Nature* of February 10. As he points out, Haeckel's career belongs to the heroic stage of the history of the theory of evolution; certainly few men have been subjected to greater obloquy for promulgating that or any other doctrine. When his "General Morphology" appeared, it was met with "icy silence"—a reception which the impetuous and combative Haeckel could not tolerate. He would have preferred hostile criticism, rather than indifference; and to this indifference on the part of his fellow-scientists can be traced the commencement of that series of popular works on evolution which were met, not with "icy silence", but with fiery blasts from scientists and laymen alike.

At one period of the controversy, Haeckel felt that his presence at Jena was jeopardising the good name of his beloved university, so he offered to resign his chair; but the head of the governing body replied: "My dear Haeckel, you are still young, and you will yet come to have more mature views of life. After all, you will do less harm here than elsewhere, so you had better stop here." In point of fact, Jena never forsook Haeckel and Haeckel never forsook Jena, despite the flattering offers he received from the Universities of Vienna, Würzburg, Bonn and Strasbourg; and he died there, not in 1914 as mentioned by Prof. MacBride, but on August 8, 1919. An obituary notice appeared in *Nature* of August 21, 1919.

W. H. Brindley

(**133**, 331; 1934)

W. H. Brindley: 11, Millmoor Terrace, Glossop, Derbyshire, Feb. 9.

* * *

许多科学家都将怀着极大的兴趣拜读将发表于 2 月 10 日的《自然》上、由麦克布赖德教授执笔的对海克尔工作的精彩介绍。正如他所指出的，海克尔生活的年代正好处于进化理论创建历史上的英雄时期，的确很少有人因为发表了某一学说而招致比海克尔所受到的更多的责难。他的《普通形态学》问世时遭遇了"冰冷的沉默"——这是冲动好胜的海克尔最不能容忍的。他宁可受到怀有敌意的批评，而不愿别人对他毫不在意。其同行的科学家们对他的这种漠视一直持续到他出版了一系列关于进化方面的科普作品，与之前受到的"冰冷的沉默"相反，这些作品发表之初，就引发了来自科学家和外行们的猛烈抨击。

在争议四起的一段时间里，海克尔觉得自己的存在已经使他所深爱的耶拿大学的声誉受损，所以他提出辞去教授一职，但是管理机构的负责人回复道："亲爱的海克尔，你还年轻，你终会获得更加成熟的关于生命的观点。其实你不会对这里造成任何损害，所以希望你继续留在这里。"事实上，耶拿大学从未抛弃海克尔，而海克尔尽管收到过来自维也纳大学、维尔茨堡大学、波恩大学和斯特拉斯堡大学等众多大学的盛情邀请，但他也从未抛弃耶拿大学，直至 1919 年 8 月 8 日海克尔在此辞世（并非如麦克布赖德教授所言的 1914 年）。1919 年 8 月 21 日的《自然》刊登了一则他的讣告。

布林德利

（刘皓芳 翻译；陈平富 审稿）

Artificial Production of a New Kind of Radio-Element

F. Joliot and I. Curie

Editor's Note

Scientists were still exploring the kinds of nuclear transmutations that could be induced by bombarding stable elements with particles such as alpha particles. Here Irène Curie and Frédéric Joliot report the formation of new, unstable isotopes of nitrogen, silicon and phosphorus made by alpha-irradiation of aluminium, boron and magnesium. The new "radio-elements" are evident from their decay over periods of several minutes, with emission of positrons. Uniquely, the two French scientists use chemical methods to separate the new isotopes and thereby identify their chemical nature. Short-lived positron-emitting isotopes, including the nitrogen-13 reported here, are now used in the medical imaging technique of positron emission tomography. (Note that the third paragraph seems to mistakenly mention "beryllium" in place of "boron".)

SOME months ago we discovered that certain light elements emit positrons under the action of α-particles[1]. Our latest experiments have shown a very striking fact: when an aluminium foil is irradiated on a polonium preparation, the emission of positrons does not cease immediately, when the active preparation is removed. The foil remains radioactive and the emission of radiation decays exponentially as for an ordinary radio-element. We observed the same phenomenon with boron and magnesium[2]. The half life period of the activity is 14 min. for boron, 2 min. 30 sec. for magnesium, 3 min. 15 sec. for aluminium.

We have observed no similar effect with hydrogen, lithium, beryllium, carbon, nitrogen, oxygen, fluorine, sodium, silicon, or phosphorus. Perhaps in some cases the life period is too short for easy observation.

The transmutation of beryllium, magnesium, and aluminium α-particles has given birth to new radio-elements emitting positrons. These radio-elements may be regarded as a known nucleus formed in a particular state of excitation; but it is much more probable that they are unknown isotopes which are always unstable.

For example, we propose for boron the following nuclear reaction:

$$_5B^{10} + _2He^4 = _7N^{13} + _0n^1$$

$_7N^{13}$ being the radioactive nucleus that disintegrates with emission of positrons, giving a stable nucleus $_6C^{13}$. In the case of aluminium and magnesium, the radioactive nuclei would be $_{15}P^{30}$ and $_{14}Si^{27}$ respectively.

一种新放射性元素的人工制造

约里奥，居里

编者按

科学家们仍旧在探寻粒子（比如 α 粒子）轰击稳定元素所导致的核嬗变的种类。这篇文章中伊雷娜·居里和弗雷德里克·约里奥报道了有关通过 α 粒子照射铝、硼和镁分别产生了氮、硅和磷的新的不稳定同位素的信息。从它们在数分钟内放出正电子的衰变来看，新"放射性元素"的存在是证据确凿的。特别的是，这两位法国科学家使用化学方法分离出了这些新的同位素，从而鉴定了它们的化学性质。短寿命的放射正电子的同位素，包括本文中所报道的氮-13，现在被用在正电子发射层析的医学成像技术中。（注意文中第三段似乎将"硼"错写成了"铍"。）

几个月之前，我们发现某些轻元素在 α 粒子的作用下会放出正电子[1]。我们最近的实验得到了一个令人十分惊喜的结果：以钋样品所产生的辐射照射铝箔，当移开放射性的钋样品时，正电子的发射不会立即停止。铝箔仍然保持着放射性，辐射就像普通的放射性元素一样以指数形式衰减。对于硼和镁，我们也观察到了同样的现象[2]。放射性活度的半衰期分别是：硼 14 分钟、镁 2 分 30 秒、铝 3 分 15 秒。

我们在氢、锂、铍、碳、氮、氧、氟、钠、硅和磷等元素中都没有观测到类似的效应。也许在某些情况下由于这一效应寿命过短，所以通过简易的观测无法观测到。

在 α 粒子作用下，铍、镁和铝元素嬗变产生了新的发射正电子的放射性元素。这些放射性元素可以视为是处于特定的激发态上的一个已知的核，不过它们是未知同位素的可能性更大，而通常这些同位素都是不稳定的。

例如，我们认为硼发生了下面的核反应：

$$^{10}_{5}B + ^{4}_{2}He = ^{13}_{7}N + ^{1}_{0}n$$

其中 $^{13}_{7}N$ 是一个放射性核，蜕变时放出正电子，最终得到一个稳定的核 $^{13}_{6}C$。对于铝和镁来说，所得到的放射性核分别是 $^{30}_{15}P$ 和 $^{27}_{14}Si$。

The positrons of aluminium seem to form a continuous spectrum similar to the β-ray spectrum. The maximum energy is about 3×10^6 e.v. As in the case of the continuous spectrum of β-rays, it will be perhaps necessary to admit the simultaneous emission of a neutrino (or of an antineutrino of Louis de Broglie) in order to satisfy the principle of the conservation of energy and of the conservation of the spin in the transmutation.

The transmutations that give birth to the new radio-elements are produced in the proportion of 10^{-7} or 10^{-6} of the number of α-particles, as for other transmutations. With a strong polonium preparation of 100 millicuries, one gets only about 100,000 atoms of the radioactive elements. Yet it is possible to determine their chemical properties, detecting their radiation with a counter or an ionisation chamber. Of course, the chemical reactions must be completed in a few minutes, before the activity has disappeared.

We have irradiated the compound boron nitride (BN). By heating boron nitride with caustic soda, gaseous ammonia is produced. The activity separates from the boron and is carried away with the ammonia. This agrees very well with the hypothesis that the radioactive nucleus is in this case an isotope of nitrogen.

When irradiated aluminium is dissolved in hydrochloric acid, the activity is carried away with the hydrogen in the gaseous state, and can be collected in a tube. The chemical reaction must be the formation of phosphine (PH_3) or silicon hydride (SiH_4). The precipitation of the activity with zirconium phosphate in acid solution seems to indicate that the radio-element is an isotope of phosphorus.

These experiments give the first chemical proof of artificial transmutation, and also the proof of the capture of the α-particle in these reactions[3].

We propose for the new radio-elements formed by transmutation of boron, magnesium and aluminium, the names *radionitrogen, radiosilicon, radiophsphorus*.

These elements and similar ones may possibly be formed in different nuclear reactions with other bombarding particles: protons, deutrons, neutrons. For example, $_7N^{13}$ could perhaps be formed by the capture of a deutron in $_6C^{12}$, followed by the emission of a neutron.

(133, 201-202; 1934)

F. Joliot and I. Curie: Institut du Radium, Paris.

References:

1. Irène Curie and F. Joliot, *J. Phys. et. Rad.*, 4, 494; 1933.

2. Irène Curie and F. Joliot, *C.R.*, **198**; 1934.

3. Irène Curie et F. Joliot, *C.R.*, meeting of Feb. 29, 1934.

铝放出的正电子似乎构成一个类似于 β 射线谱的连续谱，其最大能量约为 3×10^6 eV。就 β 射线的连续谱来说，为了在嬗变中满足能量守恒与自旋守恒的原则，允许同时放出一个中微子（或者一个路易斯·德布罗意的反中微子）似乎是必要的。

至于其他的嬗变情况，产生新放射性元素的嬗变正比于 α 粒子数的 10^{-7} 或 10^{-6}。使用放射性强度达 100 毫居的钋样品，我们也只能得到大约 100,000 个放射性元素的原子。不过，使用计数器或者电离室来探测它们的辐射，就可以确定它们的化学性质。当然，前提是它们在放射性活度消失之前的几分钟内完成化学反应。

我们已经照射了化合物氮化硼（BN）。使用苛性钠溶液来加热氮化硼，可以产生气态的氨。实验结果表明，放射活性与硼元素分离并转移到氨中了。这个结果与此种情况中放射性核是氮的一个同位素这一假设吻合得很好。

将被照射的铝溶解于盐酸中，放射活性会被氢转移到气态，且可以被收集在试管中。该化学反应必定形成了磷化氢（PH_3）或者四氢化硅（SiH_4）。而在酸性溶液中，放射活性与磷酸锆一起沉淀下来，这似乎意味着放射性元素是磷的一个同位素。

这些实验给出了人工嬗变的第一个化学证据，同时也给出了在上述的反应中 α 粒子被俘获的证据 [3]。

我们提议将以硼、镁和铝嬗变形成的新的放射性元素命名为**放射性氮、放射性硅**和**放射性磷**。

在使用其他轰击粒子，如质子、氘、中子引起的一些核反应中，也有可能生成这些元素或者类似的其他元素。例如，$^{12}_{6}C$ 俘获一个氘后，释放出一个中子，就有可能会形成 $^{13}_{7}N$。

（王耀杨 翻译；张焕乔 审稿）

The Indian Earthquake (1934) Area

J. de Graaff Hunter

Editor's Note

The earthquake in Bihar, northeastern India, in January 1934 was one of the worst the subcontinent has ever experienced, killing about 30,000 people. Here James de Graaff Hunter, recently retired director of the Geodetic Branch of the Survey of India, explains how the event was thought to have happened. The earthquake risk in this region had been long recognized, primarily because the crust bore significantly different loads—in some places underloaded, elsewhere overloaded—which created stresses that could not be accommodated by purely elastic deformation. In other words, fracturing seemed likely. This analysis offers an early example of attempts to forecast earthquake hazard from geological conditions. The greater challenge of forecasting earthquake occurrence remains beyond reach, and may be practically impossible.

MUCH attention has been recently focused on Bihar and Orissa Province as a result of the disastrous earthquake of January 15, and some facts about the condition of the Earth's crust in that region have an enhanced interest. It is, of course, no consolation to those who have suffered by the earthquake to be told that there were good reasons for it. These reasons have been in existence for a long time and yet, so far as I am aware, no earthquake of any magnitude has occurred there during the previous century.

The area roughly bounded on the north by the Himalayan foothills, on the south by the Ganges River and stretching from Meerut to beyond Darjeeling, between longitudes 78° and 89° is one of excessive underloading in the Earth's crust (Fig. 1). The average underloading of this area of about 100,000 square miles is on the average equivalent to a thickness of rock of more than 3,000 ft.; or, put otherwise, the deficiency of pressure in the crust is above 200 tons per square foot. This underloading arises from abnormally low densities in the crust. It is in part accounted for by the low density of the alluvium of the Ganges valley; but unless this alluvium extends to a greater depth than most geologists would believe, the explanation is not wholly there.

The presence of this region of underloading is revealed by measurements of the shape of the Earth which have been accumulated during the past century by the Survey of India. The area of underload is flanked both on the north and on the south by regions of overload; and the total overloading of the two outer regions is roughly equal to the underloading of the Ganges valley. Both the underload and overloads are reckoned from a state of isostatic compensation; so the northerly area of overload is not to be thought of as the weight of the Himalaya but something much smaller, as a considerable degree of compensation of the Himalaya is existent.

1934年印度地震的区域

德格拉夫·亨特

编者按

1934 年 1 月发生在印度东北部比哈尔邦的地震是印度次大陆上发生过的最严重的地震之一，共造成 3 万人死亡。在这篇文章中，刚刚从印度测量局大地测量部负责人的职位上退下来的詹姆斯·德格拉夫·亨特解释了诱发该地震的可能机制。他们早已意识到这一区域存在的地震风险，主要是因为这一地区的地壳承受了差异巨大的载荷，即一些地方欠载，一些地方过载，因而产生了通过纯粹的弹性形变无法调节的应力。或者说，断裂是很有可能的。该分析提供了早期人们试图通过地质状况来预测地震灾害的例子。现在对地震的预测仍旧无法做到，也许根本就不能做到。

最近印度比哈尔邦和奥里萨邦引起了人们的极大关注，这是因为 1934 年 1 月 15 日这里发生了一场灾难性地震，有关该地区地壳情况的现状引起了人们浓厚的兴趣。现在告知那些地震的受害者说，地震的发生是有充分原因的，这当然算不上什么安慰。诱发地震的机制已经存在了很长的时间。但是据我所知，上个世纪那里没有发生过任何震级的地震。

该区域大致上北起喜马拉雅山麓，南至恒河，东起密拉特，向西延伸到大吉岭以外，位于东经 78° 到 89° 之间，是地壳欠载过度的地区之一（图 1）。该地区面积约为 10 万平方英里，平均欠载量相当于 3,000 多英尺厚的岩石。换句话说，每平方英尺的地壳缺失 200 吨以上的应力载荷。这种欠载是由于地壳密度的异常低值造成的。其中部分原因是恒河流域冲积层的密度较低；但是除非这些冲积层的深度远超出大多数地质学家们所相信的值，否则这种解释不能完全成立。

印度测量局在上个世纪连续进行的地形测量中，发现了这个地壳欠载区域。该区域南北两侧与地壳过载区域相连接，并且这两侧过载区域的总过载量与恒河流域的欠载量大致相等。这里的欠载和过载都是根据地壳均衡补偿状态推算出来的；所以并不能认为北侧过载区的过载量就是喜马拉雅山的重量，而是应该小得多，因为喜马拉雅山存在很大程度上的补偿。

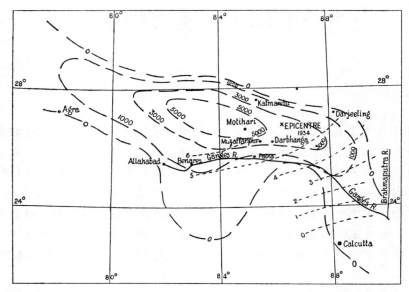

Fig. 1. Sketch map showing main region of underload in Bengal, Bihar, etc. and secular changes of level in Bengal.
— — — —, contours of underload in feet of equivalent thickness of rock, density 2.67.
- - - - - - -, generalised contours of secular change of crustal level in feet per century.

These regions of great loading anomaly must cause very great stress-differences in the Earth's crust which supports them. The region of underload and the amount of underloading are very much of the order which has been estimated by Dr. H. Jeffreys to be sufficient to cause fracture in the lithosphere. Now these stresses have no doubt been in existence for a long time. In so far as the land level has been rising from sedimentation, known to have been in progress, some measure of relief has been afforded; but this has not been more than a small palliative. Meanwhile, evidence of another kind has recently come to light—again from the measurements of the Survey of India.

In 1858, spirit-levelling operations on a comprehensive scale were begun in India by General Walker. In 1862 work was carried out in Bengal, and since then measurements of this kind have accumulated. This accumulation gave rise to some embarrassment a few years ago, in that the newer lines of levelling gave results at variance with those of the older lines. After the whole system of lines had been carefully scrutinised, it was found that the apparent discrepancies would all be accounted for on the hypothesis that the land level had been rising so much each year, the rate of rise varying from place to place in a nearly uniform manner. Thus along a line passing a little north of Benares and directed towards east-north-east an annual increase of elevation of 0.06 ft. was found; and other lines, approximately evenly spaced and roughly parallel to the first, showed rates of increase of 0.05, 0.04, 0.03, 0.02, 0.01, 0.00, the last being some fifty miles from Calcutta.

It will be seen that this rising of the land is occurring in the south-east quadrant of this area of excessive underloading in the Earth's crust. It is not necessarily confined to that

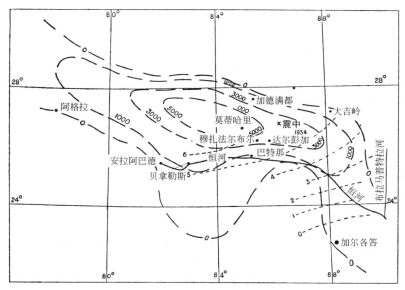

图 1. 孟加拉地区和比哈尔邦地壳欠载区域和孟加拉地区高程的长期变化示意图。
————，地壳欠载等值线，相当于密度为 2.67 的等厚度岩石载荷，单位：英尺。
- - - - -，地壳长期变化等值线概图，单位：英尺 / 百年。

地壳要承受这些地区的巨大异常载荷，必然会产生巨大的应力差。据杰弗里斯博士估算，欠载的地区和欠载量都达到了足以引起岩石圈断裂的程度。毫无疑问，这些应力已存在了很久。到目前为止，一些地形测量表明，地面高程已经从沉降转向持续的隆升；然而，这只是一个权宜的解释。与此同时，另一种证据最近被曝光——同样是来自于印度测量局的测量结果。

早在 1858 年，沃克将军在印度就开展了大规模的水准测量。1862 年，测量工作推进到孟加拉地区，从那时起水准测量资料便积累了下来。几年前，这些资料引发了人们的一些困惑，原因是新测线的水准测量结果与旧测线得到的水准测量结果存在差异。仔细检查整个测线系统后，发现以下假说可以解释二者的明显差异，该假说认为地面高程每年都上升很多，并且同一位置的上升速率几乎是恒定的，但不同位置的上升速率会有所不同。例如，经过贝拿勒斯北边一点，沿东 – 北 – 东走向的一条测线，其地面高程每年升高 0.06 英尺，取与该测线大体平行、近乎等间距分布的一组测线，其地面升高速率为每年 0.05、0.04、0.03、0.02、0.01、0.00 英尺，其中最后一条测线距加尔各答大约 50 英里。

可以看到，在这一地壳过度欠载地区的东南部，地面正在升高，当然并不一定局限于东南部。因为，其他地区水准测量所得的地面海拔变化的结果不够完整，尚

quadrant. Evidence of change of level from spirit levelling results elsewhere has not yet been so carefully analysed, being not sufficiently complete. None the less, revision levelling in the present century shows a persistent rise from Dhulia (lat. 20.9°, long. 74.7°) to Cawnpore (which also shows a small rise from Benares); and this, so far as it goes, confirms the Bengal results, which in turn are closely in sympathy with the underloading of which they are a natural consequence.

Before the earthquake occurred, the relevant facts accordingly were (a) that there was a large area of serious underloading, flanked by areas of overloading; (b) that in the part of this region where spirit levelled heights had been determined in sufficient detail at sufficient time intervals, the results indicated that the land has been rising steadily where the underload occurs, the rate of rise increasing as the centre of that region is approached.

A slow but continuous yielding of the crust has been in progress. When a material is stressed beyond its elastic limit, it yields in a non-elastic way and eventually fractures. In the present case, the earthquake gives evidence of fracture having occurred; and the floods which have followed the earthquake indicate the resulting rising of some portions of the area.

In the case of such a large area, fracture is not likely to extend throughout the entire region of stress, but it occurs at the position where the relation of stress to strength is most severe, and leads to a modification of the general stress distribution. There is no question of one earthquake of the magnitude of that which has recently occurred entirely relieving the stress differences. To do that an uplift amounting to thousands of feet would be necessary. I have little doubt that spirit levelling will show that there has been some sudden rising of the land. Were this of the order of tens of feet, it would immediately be made apparent by a wholesale change in the courses of the local rivers; and indeed, a recent report in the Press states that one of the most impressive features of the disaster has been such changes in river courses.

As stated earlier, the area from Meerut to Darjeeling is one of excessive underloading. A smaller amount of underload exists over a much larger area—a strip skirting the Himalaya from the Punjab to Bengal of width varying from 150 miles to twice that amount. We have so far discussed the eastern portion which provides the area of most acute underloading; but there is another region, roughly centred on Lahore (31.6°, 74.3°) where underloading of very considerable amount—about 2,000 ft. of rock-equivalent—exists. This region is not completely defined, as in the north-west it passes out of the area for which the necessary geodetic observations have been made. It is just in this neighbourhood that the last serious Indian earthquake—Kangra (32°, 77°)—occurred in 1905. Eight years previously, in 1897, there was the Shillong earthquake, with epicentre at 26°, 91°. Unfortunately, this is outside the area of full geodetic survey, and spirit levelling was not commenced in that region until 1900, so as yet we have no knowledge of what anomalies of loading exist there or of the secular changes of ground height.

(**133**, 236-237; 1934)

未进行仔细分析。尽管如此，本世纪的重复测量显示，从杜利亚（北纬20.9°，东经74.7°）到坎普尔，地面仍然在持续上升（从贝拿勒斯到坎普尔也有较小的上升）；这就进一步证实了孟加拉地区的测量结果，即地面上升与地壳欠载有密切关联，它们是自然的因果关系。

在地震发生前，相关的事实有：(a) 与过载区相毗邻的区域存在大面积的地壳严重欠载区；(b) 开展过详细水准重复测量地区的结果显示，在地壳欠载的地方，地面正持续稳定地上升，并且越靠近区域的中心，地面高程上升的速率越大。

地壳一直经受着缓慢而连续的变形，当物质受压超过其弹性限度时，它就会产生非弹性形变，即最终的断裂。当前的地震就是地壳发生断裂的证据，而地震之后发生的洪水，正是该地区某些区域上升的结果。

就范围如此之大的该地区而言，断裂不可能遍及整个应力区，但是断裂会发生在应力和地壳强度失配最大的地方，并导致应力整体重新分布。毫无疑问，最近发生的这次大地震已经完全消除了应力的差异。要做到这一点，地壳必须抬升数千英尺。水准测量将会显示地面有突然的升高，对此我毫不怀疑。如果地面升高的量级达到几十英尺，就会立即大规模改变当地河流的走向；事实上，最近的一个新闻就已报道说，这次地震灾害最显著的特征之一便是河流的改道。

如前所述，从密拉特到大吉岭是一个地壳过度欠载的区域。在沿喜马拉雅山边缘，从旁遮普到孟加拉宽度从150英里到300英里的一条更大的带状区域内，有较小的欠载量。迄今为止我们一直在讨论地壳欠载最严重的东部地区；其实，还有一个大致以拉合尔（北纬31.6°，东经74.3°）为中心的西部地区，其地壳欠载也相当可观，与约2,000英尺厚的岩石相当。这一地区还未完全确定，因为其西北部不在已经开展了大地测量的区域之内。它又正好邻近坎格拉（北纬32°，东经77°），上一次印度最严重的地震就于1905年发生在那里。在此八年前，即1897年，发生了西隆地震，震中在北纬26°、东经91°。遗憾的是那里不在现有的完整的大地测量区域之内，而且在1900年以前，那里还没有进行过水准测量。因此到目前为止，我们还不了解那里存在何种地壳负载异常，也不知道地面高程的长期变化。

（张效良 翻译；吴庆举 审稿）

Recent Developments of Sterol Chemistry in Relation to Biological Problems

J. Pryde

Editor's Note

Organic chemistry became an important economic activity in the nineteenth century with the development of the dyestuffs industry in Germany and later in Britain and the United States. In the twentieth century, organic chemists turned their attention to the chemicals produced by living things (some of which were also dyestuffs). This brief paper summarises what had been learned by the 1930s from the investigation of steroids and carcinogens (some of which are also steroids).

ONCE again there has been demonstrated in striking fashion the impetus which organic chemistry gains from biology, and how a field of organic research, formerly of purely academic interest, enters on a fresh phase of development in virtue of a new correlation with biological problems. The field in question is that of the sterols and the polycyclic aromatic hydrocarbons.

It is well known that the fundamental researches of Wieland, Windaus, Mauthner, Borsche, Diels and others on the sterols and bile acids received a new interest on the isolation of calciferol (vitamin D) from the products of irradiation of ergosterol, $C_{28}H_{44}O$, with which the vitamin is isomeric, and that our conceptions of the structure of these, and of other members of the cholane series to which they belong, have been re-oriented by the new formulae advanced by Rosenheim and King[1]. The structures below show the old (I) and the now accepted representation (II) of the cholane nucleus. The new, and at the time somewhat revolutionary, formulae conferred a great stimulus on the investigation of the whole series of compounds. They are based upon evidence which cannot be detailed here, but some of the more salient of the recent observations can be summarised.

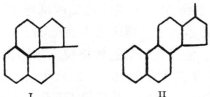

I   II

Thus, on drastic dehydrogenation with palladium-charcoal or zinc, cholesterol and cholic acid yield the fully aromatic hydrocarbon chrysene (III)[2], whilst less drastic dehydrogenation of these compounds and of ergosterol using selenium yields an interesting hydrocarbon of the composition $C_{18}H_{16}$, first obtained by Diels and his associates[3]. For this latter the constitution IV was suggested by Rosenheim and King[4].

与生物学问题相关的甾体化学的最新进展

普赖德

编者按

在 19 世纪，随着染料工业在德国以及而后在英国和美国的发展，有机化学研究成为一种重要的经济活动。到了 20 世纪，有机化学家将他们的注意力转向生命体产生的化学物质（其中一些也是染料）。这篇短文总结了 20 世纪 30 年代之前人们对甾体化合物和致癌物（其中一些也属于甾体化合物）研究所取得的成果。

有机化学可以从生物学获得发展的动力再次得到了证实：由于与生物学问题发生新的联系，之前仅具有纯粹学术意义的有机化学领域进入了崭新的发展阶段。本文要讨论的这个领域是有关甾醇和多环芳香烃的。

众所周知，由维兰德、温道斯、莫特纳、博尔舍、迪尔斯以及其他一些学者对甾醇和胆汁酸所作的基础研究，已引起了人们从麦角固醇 $C_{28}H_{44}O$（维生素 D 的同分异构体）的辐照产物中分离钙化醇（即维生素 D）的兴趣。此外，基于罗森海姆和金提出的分子式 [1]，人们对这些物质以及它们所属的胆烷系列的其他成员的结构也有了新的认识。下图所示为胆烷母核的旧结构式（I）和目前公认的新结构式（II）。这个新的、在当时带有几分革命性的结构式促进了人们对整个胆烷系列化合物的研究。在此我们要总结一下最近研究中的一些较为突出的成果，对于它们所依据的证据就不详细叙述了。

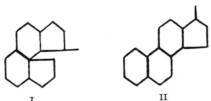

I   II

首先，在用钯－炭或锌进行剧烈脱氢反应时，胆固醇和胆汁酸会产生"菧"（III）这种完全芳香化的烃 [2]。当用硒进行不太强烈的脱氢反应时，上述化合物和麦角固醇都会产生一种令人感兴趣的、化学组成为 $C_{18}H_{16}$ 的烃，这种烃最早是由迪尔斯及其同事获得 [3]。罗森海姆和金提出这种烃具有图 IV 所示的结构 [4]。最近，科恩 [5] 通

Kon[5] has very recently proved the correctness of this suggestion by a synthesis yielding the desired 3-methyl*cyclo*pen-tenophenanthrene. It is therefore clear that the formation of chrysene in the more drastic process is due to ring enlargement associated with the migration of a methyl group, and the revised cholane formula of Rosenheim and King becomes firmly established upon fact.

III   IV

Secondly, the recent isolation and investigation of the female sex (oestrous-producing) hormone, mainly due to the efforts of Doisy in the United States, Marrian in Great Britain, and Butenandt in Germany, show that the hormone occurs in two forms— oestriol (V) and oestrone (VI), to adopt the nomenclature recently advanced in *Nature* by workers in this field[6]. Evidence is available which amply establishes the close relationship of the oestrane and cholane series, which may be inferred from the isolation of the same 1:2-dimethyl-phenanthrene from oestriol and from aetiobilianic acid of the cholane series[7]. Mention may also be made of the isolation from oestrone, after dehydrogenation in the presence of zinc, of a hydrocarbon of the same C_{18} series as that obtained from the cholane compounds. To this hydrocarbon Butenandt has ascribed the composition $C_{18}H_{14}$, but in all probability the compound is impure chrysene $C_{18}H_{12}$.

V   VI

Thirdly, it has been known for many years that the tars and pitches resulting from the pyrogenic decomposition of coal and other organic products frequently possess carcinogenic properties. Much patient work in Great Britain, with which the names of Kennaway and Cook and their collaborators are associated, has culminated in the isolation[8] from a soft coal-tar pitch of a pure actively carcinogenic hydrocarbon, namely, 1:2-benzpyrene (VII). This together with certain other but somewhat less active carcinogenic hydrocarbons [for example, 1:2:5:6-dibenzanthracene (VIII) and 5:6-*cyclo*penteno-1:2-benzanthracene(IX)][9] has been synthesised and the peculiar biological properties of these compounds have been amply proved.

过合成预期产物 3– 甲基环戊烯并菲证实了这种假设的正确性。由此可见，在较为强烈的反应中䓛的生成显然是由于发生了与甲基迁移有关的扩环反应，这为罗森海姆和金修正的胆烷分子结构提供了坚实的事实基础。

III

IV

其次，最近人们对雌激素（有引起发情的作用）进行分离和研究的结果表明，该激素以两种形式出现——用该领域研究人员最近在《自然》上提出的命名法 [6] 来表示，就是雌三醇（V）和雌酮（VI）。这主要归功于美国的多伊西、英国的马里安以及德国的布特南特等人的努力。有充分的证据证明雌烷和胆烷系列之间存在密切的联系，这一点可以从雌三醇和胆烷系列的原胆汁烷酸中都能分离出同样的 1,2– 二甲基菲 [7] 推断出来。此外，雌酮在锌的催化下发生脱氢反应后，可以分离出一种 C_{18} 系列的烃类物质，这与从胆烷系列的化合物中分离得到的 C_{18} 系列烃类完全相同。布特南特曾认为这种烃的组成是 $C_{18}H_{14}$，不过它很可能是不纯的"䓛" $C_{18}H_{12}$。

V

VI

第三，多年前人们就知道，由煤和其他有机物热分解产生的煤焦油和沥青往往具有致癌性。在英国，肯纳韦、库克以及他们的合作者们通过大量耐心细致的工作最终从软煤焦油沥青中分离出了一种纯的有致癌活性的烃类物质 [8]，即 1,2– 苯并芘（VII）。现在，人们已经合成了这种物质以及其他一些致癌活性较小的烃类物质，例如 1,2,5,6– 二苯并蒽（VIII）和 5,6– 环戊烯并 –1,2– 苯并蒽（IX）[9]。这些化合物特有的生物学性质也已经得到了充分的研究。

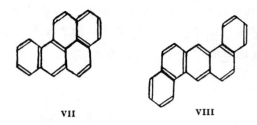

VII   VIII

It will therefore be realised that calciferol, oestrous-producing hormones, and carcinogenic hydro-carbons, all correlated with some phase of growth, all have the phenanthrene nucleus (X) in common. Lastly, the group of the cardiac-stimulating glucosides—strophanthin, digitoxin—yields aglucones in which the phenanthrene nucleus again occurs[10]. It may also be significant that some of the most powerful alkaloids, such as morphine, codeine, etc., of the opium group, the corydalis alkaloids and colchicine (meadow saffron) contain a phenanthrene nucleus. To this nucleus are added various cyclic and straight-chain substituents which confer on each group its characteristic biological activity.

H_2C
H_2C CH_2

IX   X

That these groups of compounds, of such apparently diversified physiological activities, should exhibit such fundamental constitutional similarities is sufficiently striking, but the story does not end here and indeed it would be bold to attempt to predict where it will end. Mention has already been made in these columns[11] of the oestrogenic action of certain synthetic hydrocarbons and their derivatives—either themselves carcinogenic or closely related to carcinogenic compounds—and of the similar activity of some of the sterols and calciferol. Amongst the former are 1-keto-1:2:3:4-tetrahydrophenanthrene (XI) and 1:2:5:6-dibenz-9:10-di-*n*-propylanthraquinol (XII). In reference to the activity of the latter compound, it is of interest to note that a series of diols derived from 1:2:5:6-dibenzanthracene was investigated[12]. Of these the dimethyl, di-*n*-amyl, and di-*n*-hexyl compounds are inactive, whilst the intermediate diethyl, di-*n*-propyl and di-*n*-butyl compounds are all highly active, the propyl derivative showing the maximum activity. The compounds mentioned above are the most active of those so far investigated; then follow in order of activity neoergosterol, 5:6-cyclopenteno-1:2-benzanthracene, 1:2-benzpyrene, calciferol and ergosterol. That behaviour characteristic of a specific hormone should be shared by other compounds of related structure, some possessed of physiological activities of their own, provides a remarkable extension of our conceptions of biological specificity. It suggests future developments of great interest in the chemistry and biology of the sterols and the polycyclic hydrocarbons.

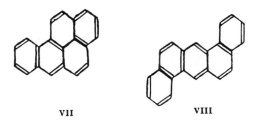

VII   VIII

由此我们会发现，钙化醇、能引起发情作用的激素以及具有致癌作用的烃类物质都与生长发育的某些阶段有关，并且它们都具有菲母核结构（X）。毒毛旋花子苷和洋地黄毒苷等具有强心作用的糖苷类物质的苷元也都含有菲母核结构[10]。某些非常强效的阿片生物碱如吗啡和可待因等、延胡索素类生物碱和秋水仙碱（藏红花）中都含有一个菲母核结构，这也是很值得注意的。与菲母核结构相连接的是各种不同的环状取代基和直链取代基，这些取代基赋予了每类化合物特有的生物学活性。

IX   X

这些生理活性明显不同的各类化合物却具有如此相似的基本结构，这是十分令人惊奇的。然而，故事远不止于此，现在就企图预言最终会如何恐怕还为时尚早。一些专栏文章[11]曾经提到过，某些合成的烃类物质及其衍生物具有雌激素的作用（这些烃类及其衍生物要么本身就是致癌物要么就是与致癌物有密切的关系），一些甾醇和钙化醇也具有类似的活性。属于第一类化合物的有 1- 酮基 –1,2,3,4– 四氢化菲（XI）和 1,2,5,6– 二苯 –9,10– 二正丙基蒽二酚（XII）。关于后一种化合物的活性，值得注意的是，人们已经对一系列由 1,2,5,6– 二苯并蒽衍生出来的二醇类物质进行了研究[12]。其中，二甲基、二正戊基和二正己基化合物是无活性的，而中间的二乙基、二正丙基和二正丁基化合物则具有很强的活性，丙基衍生物的活性最强。以上提及的化合物是目前研究过的化合物中活性最强的。按照活性大小排序，依次是新麦角固醇、5,6–环戊烯并 –1,2– 苯并蒽、1,2– 苯并芘、钙化醇和麦角固醇。一种特定激素的特征性功能也会被其他具有相关结构的化合物所共有，某些化合物还具有自身特有的生理活性。这极大地拓展了我们对生物学特异性的认识。这也预示着未来关于甾醇和多环烃类物质的化学和生物学将有非常引人注目的发展。

XI   XII

(**133**, 237-239; 1934)

References:

1. *J. Soc. Chem. Ind.*, **51**, 464, 954; 1932.

2. Diels and Gädke, *Ber.*, **60**, (B), 140; 1927.

3. *Annalen*, **459**, 1, 1927; **478**, 129; 1930.

4. *J. Soc. Chem. Ind.*, **52**, 299; 1933.

5. *ibid.*, 950.

6. *Nature*, **132**, 205, Aug. 5, 1933.

7. Butenandt, *J. Soc. Chem. Ind.*, **52**, 268, 287; 1933.

8. Cook, Hewett and Hieger, *J. Chem. Soc.*, 395; 1933.

9. *Proc. Roy. Soc.*, B, **111**, 455, 485; 1932.

10. Jacobs and Fleck, *J. Biol. Chem.*, **97**, 57; 1932.

11. *Nature*. 132. 1933.

12. Discussed at a meeting of the Royal Society on Nov. 16, 1933.

XI

XII

（王耀杨 翻译；田伟生 审稿）

Evolution of the Mind*

G. Elliot Smith

Editor's Note

In this transcript of a discourse at London's Royal Institution, Australian-born anatomist Grafton Elliot Smith reveals how neuroanatomy can help researchers understand the evolution of the mind. He highlights the importance of the neopallium (neocortex), which evolved in higher mammals to give them the ability to consciously direct movement. The structure interacts with other interconnected regions, including the cortex, thalamus and hypothalamus. In turn, the cortex influences muscular activity, shaping our experience of the world through motor control. "It is largely by doing things that experience is built up," says Elliot Smith, who sees other senses, such as vision and taste, as being equally important in the evolution of the mind.

IT may be asked by what right an anatomist, whose proper business is concerned with very concrete subjects, presumes to discuss so elusive and immaterial a subject as the evolution of the mind, even if it be admitted that the evolution of the chief organ of the mind comes within the proper scope of his field of work. I am encouraged, however, to embark on this hazardous attempt by the considered judgment of Prof. S. Alexander, who once expressed the opinion "that we are forced to go beyond the mere correlation of the mental with [the] neural processes and to identify them".

The great physiologist who is most competent to express an opinion on this issue has recently impressed upon us the need for caution in touching it. In the closing passage of his Rede Lecture on "The Brain and Its Mechanism", delivered in Cambridge on December 5, 1933, Sir Charles Sherrington used these words: "I reflect with apprehension that a great subject can revenge itself shrewdly for being too hastily touched. To the question of the relation between brain and mind the answer given by a physiologist sixty years ago was 'ignorabimus'. But today less than yesterday do we think the definite limits of exploration yet attained. The problem I have so grossly touched has one virtue at least, it will long offer to those who pursue it the comfort that to journey is better than to arrive, but that comfort assumes arrival. Some of us—perhaps because we are too old—or is it too young?—think there may be arrival at last." These opinions are even more appropriate to those who lack Sir Charles Sherrington's immense competence.

Hence I seize upon a confession made by Sir Charles elsewhere in his Rede Lecture:

"What right have we to conjoin mental experience with physiological? No scientific right;

---

* Friday evening discourse delivered at the Royal Institution on Jan. 19.

思维的进化[*]

埃利奥特·史密斯

编者按

在这份伦敦皇家研究院的演讲记录中，出生于澳大利亚的解剖学家格拉夫顿·埃利奥特·史密斯展示了神经解剖学如何帮助研究者理解思维的进化过程。他强调了新大脑皮质（新皮层）的重要性，高等哺乳动物新大脑皮层的进化使得它们能够有意识地指导运动。新大脑皮层与其他互相连接的区域（包括皮层和丘脑以及下丘脑）互相作用。然后，皮层影响肌肉的行为，通过对运动的控制来塑造我们对世界的体验。埃利奥特·史密斯说，"经验在很大程度上是通过做事建立起来的。"他认为，其他感觉，例如视觉和味觉，在思维的进化中具有同等的重要性。

即便承认思维主要器官的进化属于解剖学家正常的研究范围，我们仍可以追问，一个本职工作在于研究非常具体的事物的解剖学家有什么权力来探讨诸如思维的进化这样一个难以捉摸而又非物质性的课题呢。亚历山大教授曾表达过如下观点，"我们必须突破精神与神经过程之间简单的联系，必须要透彻地认识它们"。正是这一深思熟虑的论断使我受到鼓舞而从事这次有风险的尝试。

最近，在这个问题上最有发言权的一位卓越的生理学家提醒我们，在尝试研究思维的进化时需要保持谨慎。1933年12月5日，在剑桥里德讲坛，查尔斯·谢灵顿爵士在"脑及其机制"的演讲的结束语中说道："我所忧虑的是，如果过于草率地行事，那么这个重要的课题就会巧妙地报复我们。对于脑与思维的关联这个问题，60年前一位生理学家所给出的答案是'一无所知'。不过，我们认为现今探索这个问题遭遇的明确局限比过去少。这个我只是非常粗略地涉及过的问题至少具有这样一个优点，它将长期为那些致力于此的人们提供一种安慰，即，旅行的过程比到达终点更美好，但是这种安慰预设了到达的终点。我们中的一些人——或许是因为我们已经太老了——或者是这个问题太年轻？——认为终点最终是有可能到达的。"对于那些并不具备查尔斯·谢灵顿爵士那样卓越才能的人来说，上述观点就显得更恰如其分了。

因此，我要引用查尔斯爵士在里德演讲中所作的一则声明：

"我们有什么权利将精神体验与生理学实验结合起来呢？没有科学意义上的权

---

*1月19日在英国皇家研究院周五晚上的演讲。

only the right of what Keats, with that superlative Shakespearian gift of his, dubbed 'busy common sense'. The right which practical life, naïve and shrewd, often exercises."

If scientific proof, however, is demanded, surely Sir Henry Head's investigation of sensation and the cerebral cortex supplies it by demonstrating in wounded soldiers the concern of the cortex with psychical functions—the dependence of mind on brain ("Studies in Neurology", 1920). Prof. Shaw Bolton, by comparative and clinico-pathological researches, has demonstrated the dependence of mind on the supragranular layer of the cerebral cortex.

With these assurances the mere biologist, while discussing strictly biological issues, can direct attention to certain psychological implications of anatomical facts and comment also on their neurological aspects for the interpretation of the mind and its working. In previous lectures at the Royal Institution I have discussed the significance of the heightened powers of vision in man's ancestors, which conferred upon them the ability to see the world in which they were living and appreciate something of what was happening in it, as well as to guide their hands to acquire skill, by the practice of which fresh knowledge and understanding were obtained.

Significance of Visual Guidance

We know enough of the comparative anatomy and palaeontology of the Primates to select a series of animals that can be taken to represent approximately the stages through which man's ancestors passed in their evolution towards man's estate, and by examining the connexions of the optic tracts in the brain, arrive at an understanding of what is involved in the acquisition of higher powers of visual discrimination (Fig. 1).

In this series of diagrams, it will be observed that at first the areas for touch, vision and hearing come into contact with one another but that eventually an area marked P (parietal association area) develops between them to provide a more efficient place of blending of the impulses from these three senses. At the same time there emerges from the front end of the brain a prefrontal area (F) which is essentially an outgrowth of the motor territory and an instrument whereby the activities of the whole cortex can in some way be concentrated on the process of learning to give motor expression to the total activities of the hemisphere. Certain poisons which exert a destructive influence on the supragranular layer of this part of the cortex lead to very significant mental results, such as are displayed in general paralysis of the insane, characterised at first by grandiose delusions and afterwards by a failure of the mental process altogether, profound dementia. The discussion of this evidence by Dr. J. Shaw Bolton ("The Brain in Health and Disease", 1914) affords another precise demonstration of the dependence of the mind upon particular parts of the brain.

利，而只是被具有超凡的莎士比亚式天赋的济慈称为'闲不下来的常识'的权利。这是一种现实生活（无论是幼稚还是精明）经常会使用的权利。"

然而，如果需要科学性的证据，那么毫无疑问，亨利·黑德爵士关于感觉与大脑皮层的研究已经提供了。亨利·黑德爵士的研究表明，受伤士兵的脑皮层状况与精神功能之间具有相关性——即思维对于脑的依赖性（《神经学研究》，1920 年）。肖·博尔顿教授则通过比较研究和临床病理学研究，阐明了思维对大脑皮层的上颗粒层的依赖性。

因为有了这些论断，所以在严格讨论生物学问题时，纯粹的生物学家才能将注意力放在解剖学事实的明确心理学含义上，并且从神经学方面评论对于思维及其作用机制的解释。在英国皇家研究院此前的演讲中，我已经讨论了人类祖先视觉能力提升的意义，这一提升赋予了他们看清自身所处世界并评估发生于其中的某些事情的能力，同时也赋予了他们在实践过程中（新的知识和理解都藉此而得）通过自己的双手掌握各种技能的能力。

视觉引导的意义

我们所掌握的关于灵长类的比较解剖学知识和古生物学知识，已经足以使我们选出一系列动物来近似代表人类祖先在其向人类阶段进化的过程中曾经历过的各个阶段，并且通过检查大脑中视觉神经束的连接，我们也可以理解与较高视觉辨别能力的获得有关的因素（图 1）。

在这组图中，我们首先会观察到负责触觉、视觉和听觉的区域相互之间逐渐接触，但是最终一块标记为 P 的区域（顶部联系区）在它们之间发展起来，为来自上述三种感觉的冲动的混合提供了更为高效的场所。与此同时，在大脑的前端出现了一个前额区（F），它在本质上是运动区域的扩张，也是一种工具，整个皮层的活动能借此而以某种方式集中于学习过程，从而对大脑半球的全部活动给出运动表达。某些能对皮层此部分的上颗粒层施加破坏性作用的有毒物质能导致非常严重的精神后果，例如，精神全面麻痹所表现出来的症状，其特征最初为夸大妄想症，随后精神过程完全紊乱而发展为严重痴呆。肖·博尔顿博士对这一证据的讨论（《健康的大脑和患病的大脑》，1914 年）给思维对于大脑特定部分的依赖性提供了另一番精确的论证。

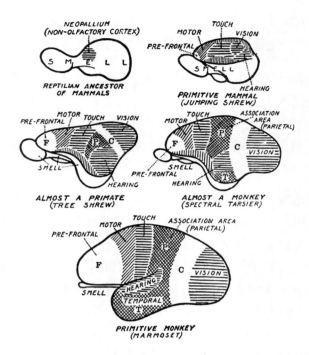

Fig. 1. A series of diagrams to suggest the origin of the neopallium in the ancestor of mammals; the rapid development of this cortical area in mammals, as touch, vision, hearing, as well as control of skilled movements, attain an increasing significance, the growing cultivation of vision which leads to the emergence of the Primates, the increased reliance on vision brings about an enhancement of skill in movement (and a marked expansion of the motor territory) and of tactile and auditory discrimination. (Based in part on the work of Profs. W. E. Le Gros Clark and H. H. Woollard.) From "Human History" (1930).

This is an example of the means whereby comparative anatomy can throw light upon the process of mental evolution, the structural changes in the eyes and brain which make possible not only the refinement of visual discrimination, but also the increasing participation of visual perception in the conscious life and in the guidance of the instruments (such as the hands) of muscular skill. The latter consideration is one of fundamental importance. For the study of the evolution of the nervous system impresses upon us the fact that one of its essential purposes is to make possible quicker, more complex and more purposive responses to changes in the animal's environment or the conditions in its own body.

It is a matter of real importance, therefore, that every advance in the powers of sensory perception and discrimination should be brought into relationship with this essential biological need of finding expression in action. Each of the major advances in vertebrate evolution is obviously correlated with differences in locomotion and muscular aptitude. When an amphibian emerged from a fish-like ancestor, the most obtrusive change was the substitution for swimming as a means of locomotion, the use of the newly-created "gadgets" which are represented by the limbs of a tetrapod land-living animal. The attainment of greater competence and agility in the control of the amphibian's four legs led to the

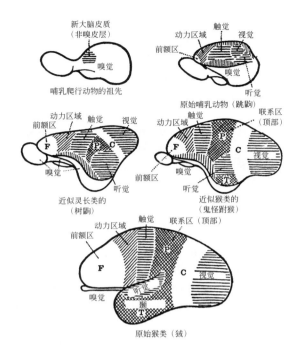

图 1. 暗示出哺乳动物祖先的新大脑皮质起源的一组图片；就像触觉、视觉、听觉以及对熟练动作的控制一样，哺乳动物这一皮层区域的快速发展获得了越来越显著的重要性。视觉能力的不断发展导致了灵长类动物的出现，对视觉不断增加的依赖性带来了运动能力的增强（以及运动区域的显著扩张）以及触觉与听觉分辨能力的增强。（部分依据勒格罗·克拉克和乌拉德两位教授的工作。）引自《人类的历史》（1930 年）。

　　这是比较解剖学能够以某种方式有助于阐明思维进化过程、眼睛和大脑的结构改变的一个实例，其中眼睛和大脑的结构改变不仅使视觉分辨能力的提高成为可能，还使视觉感知在意识支配的生活中以及在对肌肉技能部件（例如双手）的指挥中的参与程度逐渐增加。对于眼睛和大脑的结构改变的考虑具有根本的重要性。因为，对于神经系统的进化的研究使我们深切地感受到这样的事实：进化的本质目的之一就是对动物所处环境的变化或者其自身内部条件的变化的反应尽可能变得更快、更复杂、更果决。

　　因此，尤为重要的是，感官感知能力与分辨能力的每一次进步都应该与寻找有效表达这一生物学本质需求建立关联。脊椎动物进化过程中的每一个重要进展都与移动力和肌肉能力的差异有很明显的关系。当两栖动物从与鱼类相似的祖先中演变而来时，最突出的改变就是不再将游泳作为主要的移动方式，而是使用新生的"结构"——这可以被看作四足陆生动物肢体的原型。两栖动物在四肢的控制方面获得了更强的能力和灵敏性，这导致了爬行动物的出现，随着时间的推移，鸟类和哺乳

emergence of reptiles, from which in course of time birds and mammals were evolved; the former by high specialisation of the forelimbs by flight, and the latter by the acquisition of a cerebral instrument, the neopallium, which conferred the ability to attain unlimited powers of acquiring skill and to profit from experience. The highest powers of skill were made possible by the evolution of greater powers of visual guidance.

It is an obvious truism that man's mental superiority is largely the outcome of the perfection of the co-operation of hand and eye in the attainment of manipulative skill and dexterity. In the use of the hands for the expression of skill, the skin of the fingers acquires heightened powers of tactile discrimination, and thus becomes the special organ of the sense of touch and an instrument of perceptual knowledge second only to the eyes in significance.

The researches of Sir Henry Head and his collaborators have given us a new understanding of what is involved in tactile discrimination. The great sensory pathways in the spinal cord and brain-stem lead up to the thalamus in the forebrain, where they end in its ventral nucleus, the nerve cells of which transmit impulses in two directions—one to the cerebral cortex and the other to what Sir Henry Head calls the essential organ of the thalamus. The former is regarded by him as the mechanism for sensory discrimination, and the latter as the instrument for awareness to sensation and the appreciation of its affective qualities, its pleasantness or unpleasantness.

Hypothesis of a Thalamo-Cortical Circulation

In the *British Journal of Medical Psychology* in 1932, Mr. George G. Campion discussed the psychological implications of Head's clinical results. Emphasising the impossibility of separating from perception the affective factor, which is continually at work in our thought-processes, Mr. Campion gave expression to the view that the biological purpose of giving a meaning to experience is the essence of the comprehension of the nature of sensation. Mr. Campion has emphasised the further fact that the concept—the ultimate constituent element of what are called our cognitive dispositions—is not fixed and unchangeable, but is "a living plastic mental symbol subject to a process of organic growth, and that its growth is due to an affective factor which is constantly at work determining the selection of new sense data from the perpetual flux, interpenetrating the conceptual contents of our minds, and integrating all these various and varying constituents into the slowly maturing dispositions which constitute organised knowledge. The affective factor involved in this process has been variously called 'libido', 'love', 'interest', 'feeling', 'desire', 'liking', etc."

Mr. Campion further maintains that there is a continuous stream of neural impulses from the thalamus to the cortex and from the cortex to the thalamus, which keeps alive this living process of mental growth—the enrichment of the concept as the result of personal experience, the success or failure of the attempts to do things.

动物又从爬行动物进化而来；前者是通过飞行引起的前肢的高度特化，后者则是通过一种大脑结构——新大脑皮质获得的，新大脑皮质不但使生物能够通过学习技能而获得无限的能力，也赋予了他们从经验中受益的能力。更强的视觉指导能力的进化使生物具有最高能力的技能成为可能。

人类的精神优越性在很大程度上是手与眼在获得操作技能和灵活性的合作中完善的结果，这明显是真实的。在用手来表达技能的过程中，手指的皮肤获得了增强的触觉分辨能力，从而变成了触觉专用器官和在重要性上仅次于眼睛的知觉认识的结构。

亨利·黑德爵士及其同事的研究已经为我们提供了关于触觉分辨力的新理解。脊髓和脑干中的主要感觉通路导向前脑部分的丘脑并终结于其腹侧核，腹侧核的神经细胞沿两个方向传导脉冲——一个传向大脑皮层，另一个传向亨利·黑德爵士所称的丘脑核心结构。亨利·黑德爵士认为，前一个方向的传导是感觉辨别的机制，而后一个方向的传导则是作为认识感觉以及对其诸如喜悦或不快等情感属性进行评价的工具。

丘脑 - 皮质循环的假说

在 1932 年的《英国医学心理学期刊》中，乔治·坎皮恩先生讨论了黑德的临床研究结果的心理学含义。通过强调将情感因素——它一直作用于我们的思维过程——从感知中分离的不可能性，坎皮恩先生表达了以下观点：给经验赋予意义的生物学目的是对感觉本质的基本理解。坎皮恩先生还强调了更进一步的事实，即概念——我们通常所说的认知倾向的最终组成要素——并不是固定不变的，而是"一种受机体成长过程影响的、鲜活的、可塑的精神象征，它的发展可归因于情感因素，情感因素始终有效地决定着从连续的数据流中选取新的有意义的数据的过程，贯穿我们思维的概念性内容，并且将所有这些不同的变化的组分整合成缓慢成熟的倾向，它们构成了有组织的知识。这个过程中涉及的情感因素一直以来被冠以不同的名称：'感情冲动'、'爱'、'兴趣'、'情感'、'欲望'、'嗜好'等等。"

坎皮恩进一步认为：从丘脑到皮质以及从皮质到丘脑之间都存在持续的神经脉冲流，这可以保持思维成长过程的活性——由个人经历造成的概念的丰富，尝试去做某些事情的成功或失败的结果。

Developing this idea, Mr. Campion directs attention to the various parts of the cortex linked in an incredibly complicated way by association fibres and cortical association areas. The necessary implication of his hypothesis of the thalamo-cortical circulation of neural impulses (by means of the various thalamo-cortical and cortico-thalamic tracts of fibres), involves functional connexions of the various parts of the thalamus with one another by intercommunicating fibres. He predicts that as "the cortical association areas may be assumed to have a counterpart also in the thalami, it will be for neurologists to say whether these hypothetical association areas lie in and constitute a chief part of what Head has called the essential thalamic organs."

Since this prediction was made, Prof. Le Gros Clark, in the course of studies (*Brain*, vol. 55) in the comparative anatomy and physiology of the thalamus, has directed attention to the fact that such elements are actually found in the thalamus of the higher mammalia. There are cell masses (lateral nucleus (Fig. 3)) deriving their impulses from the main sensory part (ventral nucleus) of the thalamus, which merge sensory impulses of different kinds and establish direct connexions with those association areas of the cortex which link together the cortical sensory areas. This remarkable confirmation of Mr. Campion's hypothesis adds force to the argument that the mechanism of correlation in the thalamus is far more complicated than has hitherto been supposed, and represents what, following the lead of Sir Henry Head, one may suppose to be a mechanism for the integration of affective processes in the same way as the cortex effects the integration of the discriminative or cognitive aspects of experience.

In the process of acquiring knowledge and building up these vital mental elements, the concepts, to which reference has already been made, it is obvious that there must be a circulation of nervous impulses such as Mr. Campion assumes to maintain the cohesion and the integrity of the vital processes of thought. This circulation of impulses must be even more complicated than he has assumed, because the hypothalamus undoubtedly enters into the process and influences the activities both of the thalamus and the cortex, adding as its quota the visceral element which confers upon experience an emotional factor which is something more than the affective interest the thalamus is able to provide. Intimately intertwined with the whole of this complicated system—hypothalamus, thalamus and the sensory and association areas of the cortex—we have the complex mechanism for giving expression to their combined activities in actions which represent the biological purpose of the whole process. The powerful instrument of thought represented by speech affords an admirable illustration of the intimate correlation of muscular skill with cognitive aptitude to provide the essential currency of mind.

Almost every part of the cerebral cortex is intimately connected directly and indirectly with mechanisms in the central nervous system which are concerned with muscular activities, either those which directly effect movements, or on a vastly greater scale those which prepare and co-ordinate the state of the muscles of the whole body in readiness for prompt and efficient action. More than two-thirds of the fibres that leave the hemisphere have as their immediate purpose the establishment of connexions with the cerebellum,

通过发展这一观念，坎皮恩先生将注意力转向脑皮层的各个部分，它们是由联合纤维和皮层联系区以一种令人难以置信的复杂方式连接在一起的。他这种神经脉冲的丘脑－皮质循环（借助于各种丘脑－皮质和皮质－丘脑纤维束）假说的必然推论，就是丘脑各个部分彼此之间借助互相连接的纤维实现功能性联系。他预言，由于"可以假定丘脑中存在皮质联系区的一种匹配物，神经学家会疑问：这种假说性的联系区是否确实存在，这些联系区是否构成了黑德所称的丘脑核心结构的主要部分。"

上述预言出现之后，勒格罗·克拉克教授在对丘脑进行比较解剖学研究和生理学研究时（《脑》，第55卷）将注意力转向以下事实：在高等哺乳动物的丘脑中确实发现了上述要素。细胞团块（外侧核，图3）从丘脑的主要感觉部位（腹侧核）获得脉冲，这些部位将不同类型的感觉脉冲综合起来并与连接皮层感觉区的各皮层联系区之间建立直接联系。这一引人关注的对坎皮恩先生假说的确证推动了以下观点的产生，即丘脑中相关性的机制远比此前所假定的要复杂得多，而且还指出，追随着亨利·黑德爵士的指引，也许可以假设这样一种机制：情感过程的整合与皮层达成经验的识别方面或认知方面的整合是以相同的方式进行的。

在获得知识和构建这些至关重要的思维基础即概念的过程中（我们已经谈论过它），很明显，必定存在一个像坎皮恩先生假定的那样的神经脉冲循环，以保持思维重要过程的内聚性和完整性。这种脉冲循环甚至必然要比他所假定的更为复杂，因为下丘脑无疑要参与到该过程之中，并且影响丘脑和皮质的活动，依其作用增加本能要素，这种要素给经验赋予了一个情感因素——后者超过了丘脑所能提供的情感兴趣。考虑到与整个复杂系统——下丘脑、丘脑以及皮质中的感觉区与联系区——的密切交缠，我们用一种复杂的机制来解释它们在体现着整个过程的生物学效果的活动中的协同行为。以语言为代表的强大的思想工具提供了一个极好的例证：肌肉技能与认知能力密切相关而保证思维的实质性流通。

几乎大脑皮层的每个部位都直接或间接地与中枢神经系统中控制肌肉活动的机构有密切的关联，这些肌肉活动要么直接影响运动，要么在更大的尺度上预备和协调全身肌肉的状态从而为发出迅速而有效的动作做好准备。在离开大脑半球的纤维中，有2/3以上是以与小脑建立联系为直接目的，而其功能则是为诸如躺倒等灵巧

and as their function, the rapid distribution of the muscular tone of the body in readiness for such skilled action as lies at the root of the brain's efficiency. The circulation of the thalamic and cortical currents maintains this constant state of readiness and is a vital and essential part of consciousness and mind.

The building up in the brain of concepts is dependent not merely on affective and cognitive experience based upon afferent impulses from the sense organs, but is also brought about as the result of muscular activity, the doing things with the hands, the gradual perfecting of the movements, the results of the success or failure of such efforts, and the afferent impulses which pour into the brain from the joints, the muscles and the skin areas to record the success or failure of particular muscular activities. It is largely by doing things that experience is built up. It is important therefore to recognise the very large part which such conative activities play in the building up of concepts. They are due not merely to the interaction of the affective and cognitive dispositions, but also to the dynamic factor which is conferred upon these processes by attempting to express in action the result of the discriminative activities of the cortex.

The Neopallium as the Essential Mental Instrument

More than thirty years ago, I directed attention to the fact (*J. Anat. and Physiol.*, p. 431; 1901) that with the evolution of mammals a new cortical instrument, which I called the neopallium, came into existence, and with its expansion provoked the vastest revolution that ever occurred in the cerebral structure. It came into being to form a receptive organ for fibres coming from the thalamus, whereby touch, vision, hearing and taste—in fact all the non-olfactory senses—secured representation in the cerebral cortex. To express this fact, Prof. Winkler, of Utrecht, calls the neopallium the thalamocortex.

In its earliest form the neopallium consists of a tiny area far forward in the hemisphere, where tactile impulses from the lips and tongue are brought into relationship with olfactory and gustatory impulses, and this area afterwards acquires the ability to control the movements of the lips and tongue. As the neopallium grows it establishes similar relations to the rest of the body and increases the range of its receptive powers not merely to the skin of the whole body, but also to the eyes and ears, and it establishes direct connexions with all the motor nuclei in the central nervous system. The neopallium not only gives the senses other than smell representation in the dominant part of the brain and a part in the control of behaviour, but it also provides a continuous territory in which co-operation between these various sensory influences can be established and their conjoint effects be brought to bear upon the mechanisms that control motor activities.

It is often supposed that there are in the cerebral cortex long association bundles to establish connexions between distant parts of the cerebral cortex. There has recently been published an important memoir by Dr. Stephan Poljak, a Jugoslav neurologist who began the research in question in my laboratory eight years ago, which disproves the existence of such long connexions. An impulse from one cortical area can only reach and influence

动作做准备时对机体中肌肉紧张的快速传送，这是脑效率的根本。丘脑与皮质的脉冲流的循环维持着这种准备式的恒定状态，而且这种循环是意识与思维的一个至关重要和本质的部分。

概念在脑中的建立不仅仅依靠于由来自感觉器官的传入脉冲产生的情感和认知体验，而且还取决于肌肉活动的结果，用双手所做之事，对运动的逐渐熟练，这些努力的成功或失败的结果，以及从记录特定肌肉活动的成功或失败的各关节、肌肉和皮肤区域注入脑的传入脉冲。经验在很大程度上是通过做事建立起来的。因此下面的认识是重要的，即这种意动活动在概念建立的过程中起了非常大的作用。它们不仅仅归因于情感和认知倾向的相互作用，还源于通过试图有效地表达皮质识别活动的结果而赋予这些过程的动力学因素。

作为基本精神结构的新皮层

三十多年以前，我曾关注过如下事实（《解剖学与生理学期刊》，第 431 页；1901 年）：随着哺乳动物的进化，一种新的皮质结构出现了，我称其为新皮层，它的扩张激发了在脑结构中曾经发生的最深远的一次变革。它逐渐形成了一个汇聚来自丘脑的纤维的接受器官，借助这些纤维，触觉、视觉、听觉和味觉——事实上是嗅觉以外的所有感觉——在大脑皮层中得到了固定表征。为了表现这一事实，乌得勒支的温克勒教授称新皮层为丘脑皮层。

在最早的形式中，新皮层由脑半球远前端的一小块区域构成，来自唇和舌的触觉脉冲与嗅觉和味觉脉冲在该区域产生了联系，后来这片区域获得了控制唇和舌运动的能力。随着新皮层的生长，它与机体其他部分建立了类似的联系，并且将接受能力的范围提升到不仅包括整个机体的皮肤还包括两眼和双耳，它还与中枢神经系统中的所有运动核建立了直接的联系。新皮层不仅在大脑主要区域和行为控制的一部分区域中对除嗅觉以外的其他感觉给予表征，而且还提供了一个连续区域，使上述各种感觉影响可以在这里建立协作，并且它们的协同效应可以影响控制肌肉运动行为的机制。

人们经常认为在大脑皮层中存在长的联系束，以便在大脑皮层中相距较远的部分之间建立关联。斯蒂芬·波利亚克博士最近发表了一份重要的论文集，这位南斯拉夫神经学家 8 年前就在我的实验室开始研究这个问题，他的研究证明这种长距离的联系并不存在。从一个皮层区域发出的脉冲只能通过在皮层自身中传输而到达

distant areas by travelling through the cortex itself. The act of correlation involves the whole cortex. Even in the simplest act of thought or skill, the whole neopallium participates. The manifold currents which circulate throughout the brain in the process of regulating muscular activities represent the means of integrating the cognitive, affective and curative activities in thought.

Not only the neopallium but also the brain as a whole adds its quota to the action—in particular the great mass of nervous matter at the threshold of the cerebral hemisphere known as the thalamus. It contributes the affective element, which is the interest, the stimulative of the whole complex process, to which it gives coherence. The cortex not only preserves the records of previous experience which provide the means for comparing present experiences with past happenings, but it also adds the spatial quality to sensation and the means of judging degrees of stimulation, and the afferent impulses which pour into the brain from the joints, the muscles and the skin areas, to record the success or failure of particular muscular activities. It is by doing things that experience is built up. It is important therefore to recognise the very large part which such conative activities play in the building up of concepts. They are due not merely to the interaction of the affective and cognitive dispositions, but also to the dynamic factor which is conferred upon these processes by attempting to express in action the result of the discriminative activities of the cortex.

For some years I have been attempting to demonstrate how vast a part the cultivation of visual discrimination has played, not simply in making it possible for human beings to see the world in which they live and appreciate some of the activities which are revealed to them by their eyes, but even more in contributing to conscious control of behaviour.

The earliest type of cerebral cortex necessarily has to perform both affective and cognitive functions. It enables its possessor to appreciate the attractiveness or unattractiveness of a particular scent, and to experience an interest in addition to the cognitive recognition of it.

The cortex, at first, however, exercises no immediate direction over the motor activities of the animal beyond provoking them and providing the initiative to action. This it accomplishes by transmitting to a mass of grey matter in its base (the corpus striatum) impulses which indirectly throw other parts of the brain and spinal cord into action to direct the movements that it starts. It is the impulses from the eyes, skin and "ears" (as yet organs not of hearing, but of recording movements in the water) which consciously direct the animal's movements, while its posture and equilibrium are being maintained by the automatic mechanism of the membranous labyrinth.

The tracts in the brain which convey the impulses from skin, eyes and ears are mainly concerned with transmitting to the various motor nuclei impulses that unconsciously influence and direct reflex movements, but they all send some of their impulses to a mass of grey matter in the forebrain, which lies immediately behind the striatum, to which it is intimately linked by many nerve fibres. This is the thalamus (Fig. 2). It confers upon all the

和影响远距离区域。关联过程涉及到整个皮层。即使是在最简单的思考或技能过程中，也要全部新皮层参与。在调控肌肉活动的过程中，循环于大脑中的各种脉冲流表现了对思维中的认知、情感和治疗活动进行整合的方式。

不仅新皮层，脑作为一个整体也对该过程作出了自己的贡献——尤其是位于脑半球开端处的大量神经物质，通常称之为丘脑。它促成情感要素——这是关键所在，是整个复杂过程的刺激因素——它在这里提供了一致性。皮层不仅保留了先前体验的记录，从而为将当前体验与过去经历相比较提供了途径，它还给感觉增加了空间属性，增加了判断刺激强度的方式，增加了从关节、肌肉以及皮肤区域传入大脑的输入性脉冲，以记录特定肌肉活动的成功或失败。经验是通过做事建立起来的。因此，认识到这种意动活动在概念建立过程中所起的极大作用是很重要的。它们不仅仅归因于情感和认知倾向的相互作用，还源于通过试图有效地表达皮质识别活动的结果而赋予这些过程的动力学因素。

若干年来，我一直致力于阐释视觉辨别力的培养曾经起到的非常重要的作用，它绝不仅仅是使人类得以看到自身生活的世界以及认识一些通过自己的眼睛看到的某些活动，而更多的是有助于对行为进行有意识的控制。

大脑皮层的最初形态不可避免地要同时履行情感和认知的功能。它使得自己的拥有者能够评价一种特定气味的诱人之处或者不吸引人之处，并且除了对它的感知识别之外还体验到一种兴趣。

不过，皮层最初并不承担对于动物肌肉运动行为的直接指导，而只是激发它们和启发动作。这个功能的实现是通过将脉冲传输到位于基部的大量灰质（纹状体），间接地引发脑的其他部分和脊髓发挥作用以指导它所开始的运动。来自于双眼、皮肤和"两耳"（那时还不是听觉器官，而是在水中记录运动的器官）的脉冲有意识地指导动物的运动，而它的姿势与平衡则通过膜迷路的自动机制得以保持。

脑中负责传输来自皮肤、双眼和两耳的脉冲的纤维束，主要负责将无意识地影响和指导反射运动的脉冲传输到各种运动核，但是它们都将自己的一些脉冲发送给前脑中的大量灰质——它紧挨于纹状体之后，二者通过很多神经纤维紧密相连。这就是丘脑（图 2）。它给所有非嗅觉的感觉脉冲赋予了一种情感属性，这使它们获得

non-olefactory sensory impulses an affective quality which gives them a meaning and an influence in modifying behaviour. In other words, the effects of this sensory experience, when transmitted to the striatum, are to alter the animal's reactions to smell.

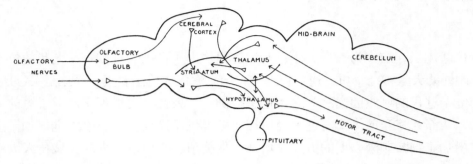

Fig. 2. Diagram of the primitive vertebrate brain to suggest the hypothalamic, thalamic, striatal and cortical connexions.

Emotional Factor in Mind

The activities of the striatum, when stimulated by the cerebral hemispheres and the thalamus, are expressed in impulses which proceed from it to the hypothalamus, a mass of grey matter lying beneath the thalamus. This surprising arrangement seems to confer upon the hypothalamus the decisive influence in translating into behaviour the initiative to action which lies in the cerebral cortex. The hypothalamus is the part of the brain which controls, by means of the sympathetic and parasympathetic systems, the most vital activities of the body itself, its visceral functions, its growth and metabolism, and even such appetites as those of sex. It is the essential instrument of emotional expression.

As the springs of action are profoundly influenced by hunger, thirst, sexual desire and other appetites and cravings, it is perhaps not surprising that in the most primitive vertebrates the instrument of the animal's vegetative needs should play a crucial part in shaping its conduct. To this part of the brain, impulses proceed from the olfactory tracts so as directly to control the activities of the alimentary and genital systems in anticipation of the realisation of the satisfaction of the respective appetites.

The study of the primitive brain impresses upon us the intimacy of the integration of the functions concerned with affective and discriminative knowledge and the translation of such information into appropriate action.

The higher type of brain distinctive of mammals, which opens up the possibility of the attainment of real conceptual knowledge and its biological application in increasingly complex acts of skill and thought, is distinguished by the growth of the thalamus and the transmission from it to the cerebral cortex of fibres in increasing numbers (Fig. 3).

了一种意义和对于行为进行调整的影响力。换言之，这种感觉经验的效应一旦传输到纹状体，就会改变动物对于气味的反应。

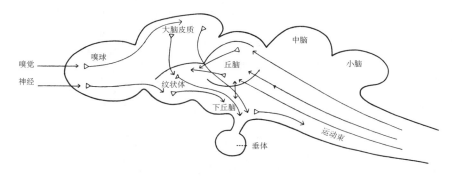

图 2. 原始脊椎动物脑的示意图，揭示了下丘脑、丘脑、纹状体和皮层的联系。

思维中的情绪因素

在受到大脑半球和丘脑的刺激时，纹状体的活动就会表现为脉冲，并且从这里传输到下丘脑——位于丘脑之下的大量灰质。这种令人惊奇的排布方式似乎使下丘脑在将位于大脑皮层之中的动作发端转变为行动时具有决定性的影响。下丘脑是脑的一部分，它通过交感神经系统和副交感神经系统控制机体自身最重要的活动，包括它的内脏功能、生长与新陈代谢乃至像性欲这样的各种欲望。它是情感表达的基本结构。

由于行动的发生受到饥饿、口渴、性欲以及其他种种欲望与渴求的深刻影响，可能以下也不足以为奇了，在大多数原始脊椎动物体内，负责动物的植物性需求的结构应该在塑造其行为方面具有至关重要的作用。对脑的这部分来说，脉冲从嗅觉纤维束直行而来，以便直接地控制消化系统和生殖系统的活动，使种种欲望的满足得以实现。

通过对原始大脑的研究，我们对情感和分辨性知识相关功能的整合与将这些信息转化为适当的行动之间的密切关系留下了深刻的印象。

哺乳动物所特有的高级类型的脑，开启了获得真正概念性知识和这些知识在越来越复杂的技能与思考过程中的生物学应用的可能性，其不同之处在于丘脑的发育，以及有更多数量的纤维从这里传向大脑皮层（图3）。

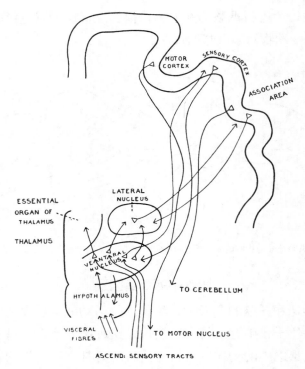

Fig. 3. Diagram of the thalamic, hypothalamic and cortical connexions of the human brain.

The recent progress in our knowledge of the structure and connexions of the thalamus and hypothalamus with the cerebral cortex, the hypothalamus and the sympathetic and visceral tracts of the organism had made it possible to carry Mr. Campion's suggestions a stage further than he himself has done. That this is possible is in large measure due to the illuminating researches of Prof. W. E. Le Gros Clark. The intensive studies which have recently been made by scores of investigators on the structure and connexions of the hypothalamus enable us to broaden the issues and consider the part played by these portions of the brain, which control the growth and metabolism of the body, and in particular visceral function, and how they are related to the thalamus and the cerebral cortex and provide the instrument for determining the emotional colour of experience and of regulating the manifestations of the appetites.

If Mr. Campion's views are correct, that the study of this neural machinery is essential for the understanding and interpretation of thought and behaviour, its structure and functions might be expected to be of great complexity. Hence it becomes essential to look at the whole issue from a much broader point of view than the mere connexions of thalamus and cerebral cortex.

Importance of Smell in the Primitive Vertebrate

In the brain of the most primitive vertebrate, the structural pattern is determined by

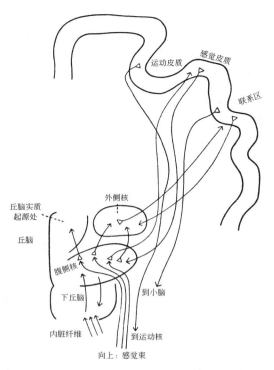

图 3. 人脑中丘脑、下丘脑和皮层的联系。

关于丘脑、下丘脑与大脑皮层之间、下丘脑与交感神经和有机体内脏纤维束之间的结构和联系方面的认识的近期进展使我们有可能将坎皮恩先生的建议推进到比他本人所做的更进一步的阶段。这一可能性在很大程度上归功于勒格罗·克拉克教授很有启发性的研究。最近很多研究者对下丘脑的结构和联系进行的深入研究使我们得以拓宽这一论题，进而考虑脑中各部分——它们控制着机体发育和新陈代谢，特别是内脏功能——所具有的地位，以及它们如何与丘脑及大脑皮层相关联，如何促成经验的感情色彩的确定和如何促成调控欲望的表现形式。

如果坎皮恩先生的观点正确，即研究这一神经系统对于理解和解释思想与行为来说是不可缺少的，那么可以预期它的结构和功能具有很高的复杂性。因此，从一个更广阔的视角看待整个论题而不是仅仅考虑丘脑与大脑皮层的联系就显得十分必要了。

嗅觉对于原始脊椎动物的重要性

在大多数原始脊椎动物的脑中，其结构模式是由下列事实所决定的：嗅觉是主

the fact that smell is the dominant sense. The cerebral cortex is essentially a receptive instrument for impressions of smell, and the mechanism whereby consciousness of smell can influence the behaviour of the animal. When a primitive vertebrate such as a dogfish scents attractive food and pursues it, the culmination of the pursuit is represented by the seizure of the food and the appreciation of its taste. This is nearly akin to the initial olfactory experience which started the pursuit and dominated it, so that all the incidents of the pursuit become integrated into one experience, which is thus given coherence and meaning. Thus is initiated the ability to anticipate the result of a given course of action, and to recall in memory the connexion between the various incidents.

One must assume, therefore, that the primitive cortex is concerned not merely with the awareness of smell and the ability to discriminate between different kinds of smells, but also that it is concerned with the affective side of olfactory experience, with the attractiveness or repulsiveness of any scent and the influence of such affective experience in determining the nature of the response an individual odour can evoke. The cerebral cortex in such a primitive animal is incapable of directing movements, seeing that the sense of smell is utterly devoid of any spatial quality. When an animal scents an attractive food, it acquires from the sense of smell no idea as to the position in space of the object which provides the stimulus. It is merely stirred into action, and other neural mechanisms are responsible for controlling and directing the resulting activities. The cerebral cortex, so to speak, is the mere trigger which releases the activity of the brain and provokes and directs the movements.

The part of the cerebral hemisphere which translates these stimuli into action is the corpus striatum, and the striatum is connected with the thalamus, which receives from the body, that is through the skin, the eyes and the ears as well as the muscles and joints, impulses which modify and direct movements which result when the animal is thrown into action. The thalamus transmits the effects of these stimuli to the striatum and so modifies the motor activities. In the case of organs such as the eyes, the primary functions were concerned not merely with the awareness of illumination, but also of movements in the outside world, or rather movements of objects in the outside world in reference in its own body. The eyes have associated with them, in the brain, a complicated mechanism which enables them automatically to direct the movements of the body in relationship to events in the outside world. But quite apart from this, the eyes transmit to a part of the thalamus (the lateral geniculate body) impulses which are concerned with the awareness of the stimulus of light, and which influence these bodies and through them the thalamus as a whole, which in turn affects the functions of the striatum and the movements of the animal.

In the primitive vertebrate one must assume that the thalamus acts as an affective organ of all senses other than smell, and represents the instrument whereby the organism is pleasantly or unpleasantly affected by sensory experience, and that the cerebral cortex performs the analogous but more dominating aspect of the same function in relationship with smell. The dominant part of the cerebral cortex in the most primitive vertebrate is the hippocampal formation, and if one assumes the supreme function of the cortex

导性的感觉。大脑皮层在本质上是嗅觉印象的接受器件，也是使嗅觉意识影响动物行为得以实现的装置。当一只原始脊椎动物，比如狗鲨，闻到诱人食物的气味并去追逐时，追逐的结果是捕获食物并鉴定其气味。这与导致追逐开始并主导其过程的初始嗅觉体验十分类似，因而追逐过程中的所有事件逐渐整合成一次体验，进而给出了一致性和意义。从此开始有了预见给定行为过程之结果的能力，以及在记忆中回想各事件之间的联系的能力。

因此我们必须假定，原始皮层不仅仅与嗅觉意识和分辨不同类型气味的能力有关，而且还与嗅觉体验的情感方面有关，包括任何气味的令人喜欢或厌恶之处，以及这些情感体验对于决定某一具体气味所能引起的反应本质的影响。考虑到嗅觉完全不具备任何空间属性，因此原始动物的大脑皮层是不能指导运动的。当动物闻到诱人食物的气味时，它从嗅觉中得不到任何关于提供刺激的物体在空间中所处位置的信息。它仅仅是激发行动，由其他神经机制负责控制和指导因此产生的活动。可以说，大脑皮层仅仅是一个释放脑活动并且刺激和指导运动的扳机。

大脑半球中负责将上述刺激转化为行动的部分是纹状体，而纹状体是与丘脑相联系的，后者接受来自于机体——即皮肤、双眼、两耳以及肌肉与关节——的脉冲，这些脉冲调节并指导动物展开行动时所产生的运动。丘脑将这些刺激的影响传输到纹状体，从而调整肌肉运动行为。对于诸如眼睛等器官来说，其首要功能并不仅仅是对光的意识，还包括对外部世界中运动的意识，或者更恰当地说，是外部世界中的物体相对于机体自身的运动。眼睛在脑中将它们整合，一种复杂的机制使它们得以自动地指导机体针对外部世界之事件的运动。但是又远不止于此，眼睛还向丘脑的一部分（外侧膝状体）传输脉冲，这些脉冲负责对光线刺激的意识，而且影响机体并使丘脑赖以成为一个整体，以及依次影响纹状体的功能和动物的运动。

我们必须假定，在原始脊椎动物中，丘脑的作用如同一个具有除嗅觉以外的所有感觉的情感器官，并且作为一种结构使生物体受到由感觉经验带来的愉快的或不愉快的影响，还要假定在与嗅觉相关的相同功能上大脑皮层起着类似的但是更具主导性的作用。在大多数原始脊椎动物中，大脑皮层的主导性部分是海马结构，并且，如果假设皮层的首要功能是决定动物的行为，那就有理由假设，原始海马体的目的

is to determine the behaviour of the animal, it is perhaps justifiable to assume that the purpose of the primitive hippocampus is to make possible the adequate association of the affective qualities of smell and to translate them into action by playing a dominant part in determining the animal's behaviour.

It is perhaps not without significance in this connexion that the efferent fibres from the hippocampal formation, after passing out of the cerebral hemisphere, terminate in the hypothalamus, that part of the brain which controls the visceral system (sympathetic and para-sympathetic) and thereby regulates the activity of the viscera. It is, in fact, that part of the brain which is intimately related to the functions of the appetites. Nor is it surprising that the particular part of the hypothalamus in which the hippocampal fibres terminate should be linked up with the thalamus, so as to provide a neural circuit in which the total affective qualities of all the senses are brought into relationship in such a way that they can influence through the striatum the motor responses of the body.

The researches of Prof. Le Gros Clark have established the fact that the thalamus contains three kinds of cell groups (Fig. 2). Those forming the ultimate termini of certain of the sensory pathways, which according to Sir Henry Head form the essential organ of the thalamus, are the instrument whereby we become aware of sensory experience and appreciate its affective qualities. Secondly, there is a group of cells (ventral nucleus) which receives the great sensory paths coming up from the other parts of the brain and the spinal cord, and transmits the impulses either to the corpus striatum or in mammals to the neopallium. In the third place, there is a group of nuclei in the thalamus which become well developed only in the higher mammals. They do not receive afferent impulses directly, but only from the intermediation of the ventral nucleus. The highest type of thalamic cells, known as the lateral nucleus (Fig. 3), establishes connexions with the parietal area of the neopallium, which intervenes between the sensory cortical areas for touch, vision and hearing (*P*, Fig. 1), and presumably confers upon this area the ability to provide sensory experience with spatial and discriminative qualities. All three categories of thalamic elements are intimately joined together by numerous fibre tracts so as to form a closely integrated functional whole the proper working of which is essential for cortical functions.

Integration of the Dispositions of the Mind

The common practice of psychologists of segregating the three dispositions of the mind, cognitive, affective and conative, and attempting to study them as isolated units, is devoid of justification. All three are indissolubly united in the working of the mind. To give them cohesion it is necessary to assume the existence of a circulation of nervous impulses from the thalamus to the cortex and to the widespread and complex mechanisms concerned with muscular activities.

In the growth of a concept conation plays a fundamental part. Man learns from experimentation. By the exercise of his manual dexterity he acquires knowledge of the properties of things, the nature of forces, and the means for interpreting (and in some measure understanding) the world in which he lives. The surprisingly large part of the

可能是使嗅觉的情感属性能够得以充分联系，并且通过在决定动物行为的过程中起主导性作用而将它们转化为行动。

下面这个联系可能不是毫无意义的，即由海马结构发出的传出纤维在经过大脑半球之后终止于下丘脑，下丘脑是大脑中控制内脏系统（交感神经和副交感神经）从而调控内脏活动的部分。事实上，正是脑中的这个部分与欲望的功能密切关联。同样不会令人惊奇的是，下丘脑中的特定部位，即海马纤维终止处，应该与丘脑相联系，这样才能提供一条神经循环，使得所有感觉的全部情感属性都能形成关联，以这样一种方式它们能够通过纹状体影响机体的运动反应。

勒格罗·克拉克教授的研究已确定了如下事实，丘脑中包含三种类型的细胞群（图 2）。那些构成了某些感觉传导通路之最终目的地的细胞群——根据亨利·黑德爵士的看法，它们形成了丘脑的核心组件——是使我们得以意识到感觉经验并鉴别其情感属性的结构。第二，还有一群细胞（腹侧核）接收来自脑和脊髓其他部位的大量感觉传导通路，并且将脉冲传输到纹状体或者哺乳动物的新皮层。第三，丘脑中还存在一组核——只有在高等哺乳动物中丘脑才会变得如此发达。它们并不直接接收传入脉冲，而是只能借助腹侧核的媒介作用。最高级类型的丘脑细胞，即我们所说的外侧核（图 3），建立了与新皮层顶部区域的联系，这个区域插入到触觉、视觉和听觉的感觉皮层区（P，图 1）之间，据推测，这就使该区域具有了为感觉体验提供空间属性和分辨属性的能力。全部三类丘脑成分都通过大量纤维束紧密地联系在一起，以形成严密整合的功能性整体——它的正常运转对于皮层功能是至关重要的。

思维倾向的整合

心理学家的常见做法是分离认知、情感和意动这三种思维倾向并企图把它们作为独立单元加以研究，这些都是缺乏论证的。所有这三者在思维的运行过程中都是不能分解地结合在一起的。要使它们结合，就必须假定存在一个从丘脑到皮层的神经脉冲循环，以及与肌肉活动有关的一套普遍而复杂的机制。

在概念的产生过程中，意动起到了极为基础性的作用。人类从经验中学习。通过练习手的灵活性，人类获得了关于事物性质、力的本质和解释（在某种程度上是理解）其所处世界之方法的知识。大脑皮层中有大得令人惊讶的一部分来负责对肌

cerebral cortex that is concerned with the regulation of muscular functions and the multitude of its fibre-connexions with the cerebellum affords an impressive testimony of the vast significance of action in mind-making and emphasises what Prof. T. H. Pear has well called "the intellectual respectability of muscular skill". It is a truism that we learn by doing. In man, thought is a prerequisite for action, and action a corrective of thought. The biological justification for the evolution of the high degree of visual discrimination, whereby man knows the world and the society in which he lives, is the motor efficiency it makes possible.

The most significant factor in the evolution of the mind was effected when the direction of movements was transferred from the midbrain to the neopallium (see *Nature*, **125**, p. 820; 1930) and from being an unconscious automatism became a consciously directed process. For the neopallium not only established a direct control over the motor nuclei of the whole central nervous system, but it also became linked up with all the complicated machinery in other parts of the brain which are concerned with muscular activities.

This concentration of control in the neopallium implies a circulation of nervous impulses throughout the brain to effect cohesion between the living instruments of the conative dispositions with those of the affective (thalamus) and cognitive (neopallium) dispositions of the mind. A circulation such as Mr. Campion postulates is essential to the working of the mind.

This circulation in turn involves the hypothalamus, which presumably confers the emotional tone that plays a part in all mental and muscular activity in particular in artistic expression and the self-knowledge which is one of the most distinctive qualities of man and his thinking.

Anthropological investigations, the results of which I have summarised in chaps. v and vi of my "Human History" (1930), suggest that in primitive man there is an innate goodness and truthfulness, the awareness of which we call conscience. These qualities of the mind are responsible for character and personality. The terrible experiments which the incidence of diseases such as sleepy sickness (encephalitis lethargica) provides, has shown that these amiable qualities can be destroyed by minute injuries of certain parts of the brain in or in the neighbourhood of the hypothalamus. We must suppose that these parts of the brain are responsible for the maintenance of the innate goodness of human nature, the goodwill of normal man, seeing that their destruction causes so profound an alteration of character. Mr. Campion's hypothesis of a widespread circulation of nervous impulses provides an explanation of how these various dispositions of the mind and character may be integrated into the living human personality.

Before I close this discourse, I must express my gratitude to Mr. George Campion for his stimulating suggestions and to Prof. J. S. B. Stopford, of Manchester, for help in giving them neurological expression.

(**133**, 245-252; 1934)

肉功能的调节，而且它那些与小脑相连的大量纤维为思维发生行为的非凡重要性提供了令人瞩目的证据，并且强调了皮尔教授所称的"肌肉技能的智力品德"。我们通过做事而学习这是不言而喻的。对于人类而言，思考是行为的先决条件，而行为则可以修正思考。关于高程度的视觉辨别能力——人类藉此了解其生活的世界和社会——的进化的生物学依据，是由于进化而获得可能性的动作效率。

当对运动的指导从中脑转移到新皮层（参见《自然》，第125卷，第820页；1930年）并且从一种无意识的自动作用转变为一种有意识的指导过程时，思维进化过程中最重要的因素就形成了。因为新皮层不仅建立了对于整个中枢神经系统的运动核的直接控制，而且还和脑中其他与肌肉活动有关的部位的全部复杂系统建立了连接。

新皮层中的这种集中控制意味着有一个遍布脑中的神经脉冲循环，它可以实现意动倾向的作用结构与思维中情感倾向（丘脑）和认知倾向（新皮层）的作用结构之间的联系。就像坎皮恩先生所提出的那样的循环对于思维的运行来说至关重要。

这个循环自然涉及下丘脑，据推测它负责感情属性，这种属性在所有的精神和肌肉活动中，尤其是在艺术表现和自我认识方面——这是人类及其思考所具有的最与众不同的属性之一——都有作用。

人类学研究——我在《人类的历史》（1930年）的第五章和第六章中总结了其研究结果——指出，在原始人类中存在一种先天的善良与坦诚，这种意识就是所谓的良心。这种思维品质决定了品性与人格。由诸如昏睡症（昏睡性脑炎）之类的疾病的发生提供的很糟的实验表明，发生在脑的下丘脑之中或者其邻近区域中的某些部位的微小损伤就能摧毁这些美好的品质。考虑到它们的损坏会导致非常深远的品性变化，我们就必须假定，大脑的这些部位是与保持人性中先天善良品性（即普通人的善意）相关联的。坎皮恩先生关于神经脉冲普遍循环的假说对于上述各种思维与品性之倾向如何被整合成活生生的人性提供了一种解释。

在我结束这次演讲之前，我必须向乔治·坎皮恩先生表达感激之情，感谢他提供了启发性的建议，另外我还要感谢曼彻斯特的斯托普福德教授在向他们提供神经学表述方面给予的帮助。

（王耀杨 翻译；刘京国 审稿）

A Velocity-Modulation Television System

Editor's Note

In the mid 1930s, many groups were developing technology for transmitting visual images over long distances. Here *Nature* reports on a recent advance. Most approaches produced an image by scanning a cathode ray rapidly over a fluorescent screen. Modulations of the ray intensity translate into lighter or darker parts of the image. But improved images could be obtained by modulating the velocity of the ray, rather than its amplitude, with the screen being naturally darker where the ray passes more quickly. The article notes that engineers had recently reported on advances in such a system, and demonstrated in laboratory tests that intensity modulation could be used in addition to improve the contrast of the images.

MANY of the investigators who are seeking at the present time to develop a practical system of television make use of the cathode ray oscillograph tube in one form or another, since the electron beam in such a tube provides an easily controlled means of scanning the picture to be transmitted. At the receiving end, the cathode ray tube is employed to build-up the received picture by varying the intensity of the beam in accordance with the light and dark portions of the picture. The ordinary type of cathode ray tube, however, gives only a small range of intensity control without the accompaniment of loss of focus of the spot on the fluorescent screen, and special electrode systems have to be arranged to obtain good intensity modulation in this manner. As an alternative to this method, the intensity of the cathode ray beam may be kept constant but its tranverse velocity may be varied as it moves over the picture, the beam being speeded up over the dark portions of the picture and slowed down over the light portions. The corresponding motion of the cathode ray beam at the receiving end thus gives varying illumination according to the speed of travel of the spot on the fluorescent screen, and with the aid of the phenomenon of persistence of vision, a true impression of the shades and contrasts in the picture received is obtained.

The conception of this velocity-modulation principle, or variable-speed cathode ray television, dates back to 1911, when it was described in a British patent by B. Rosing. Since that date the principle appears to have fallen into oblivion until it was revived in Germany by R. Thun in 1929. The first practical realisation of the method was achieved by M. von Ardenne in 1931 and reference was made to this work in *Nature* of October 7 last (p.573).

During the development of cathode ray oscillograph tubes for general scientific and technical purposes, the staff of Messrs. A. C. Cossor Ltd. realised the possibilities of the

一个基于速度调制的电视系统

编者按

20世纪30年代中期，许多研究组都在发展远距离传输可视图像的技术。《自然》的这篇文章介绍了当时的最新进展。大多数技术是通过使用阴极射线快速地扫描荧光屏来产生图像的。调制阴极射线的强度可以反映出图像的亮区和暗区。但是，相对于调制振幅而言，通过调制阴极射线的速度可以得到更加清晰的图像，当射线扫描速度较快时，扫过的区域会自然的较暗。这篇文章介绍了工程师们最近报道的这类系统的进展，同时也指出了在实验室测试中还可以用强度调制来增强图像的对比度。

目前，许多致力于开发实用电视系统的研究者们都在使用各种形式的阴极射线示波管，因为这种示波管中的电子束提供了一种很容易控制的方法来对将要传输的图片进行扫描。在接收端，阴极射线管根据原始图片的明暗区域相应地改变电子束的强度，以实现对接收图片的构建。然而，如果不考虑在荧光屏上聚焦点的发散作用，那么一般的阴极射线管能控制电子束的强度范围是很小的，要用这种方式，就必须使用特殊的电极系统才能获得良好的强度调制效果。作为这种方式的一个替代方案，可以保持阴极射线束的强度不变，而使其横向速度在扫过图片时发生变化：通过图片的暗区时，速度加快；通过明区时，速度变慢。于是，根据荧光屏上点的运动速度，接收端的阴极射线束的相应运动就会给出不同的照射强度，借助于视觉暂留现象，人们就能获得对于接收到的图片的明暗区域与对比度的真实现象。

这种速度调制或者变速的阴极射线电视的概念可以追溯到1911年，当时有一个名为罗辛的人在他的英国专利中提到过。之后这个理论概念就被人们遗忘了，直到1929年德国的图恩再次提起。这一理论的第一次实用化是在1931年由冯·阿登完成的，与此相关的参考文献发表在去年10月7日的《自然》上（第573页）。

在以一般科学和技术为目的的阴极射线示波管的发展过程中，科索尔有限公司的员工们认识到了上述电视系统的可行性，并且将之前在18个月中完成的大量深入

above system of television, and an account of the development work carried out during the past eighteen months was presented in a paper entitled "A Velocity-Modulation Television System", read before the Wireless Section of the Institution of Electrical Engineers by Messrs. L. H. Bedford and O. S. Puckle on February 7.

Consideration of the basic principles outlined above shows that it is impossible to realise a velocity-modulated picture from a uniformly scanned object; the scanning at the transmitter must also be of the variable-speed or velocity-modulated type, and must therefore be carried out by a cathode ray. It follows that a cathode ray oscillograph must serve as the source of light at the transmitting end, and, with oscillographs of the ordinary low-voltage type, the conditions of scanning-light economy will restrict the picture subject matter to cinematograph film material. This, however, is not considered to be a disadvantage of the method; many of the television systems being developed at the present time make use of a film as an intermediary, and processes are being devised in which the interval between the photography of the subject and the projection of the picture through the transmitter is reduced to the bare minimum.

The transmitting arrangements described by Messrs. Bedford and Puckle comprise the projection of light from the fluorescent screen of the oscillograph through the film picture on to a photoelectric cell. The output of the photo-cell amplifier operates, through a screen-grid valve and a thyratron, an electrical time-base circuit which supplies the potential difference to one pair of the deflecting plates of the oscillograph. The light from the cathode ray tube is thus swept in a straight line across the picture with a velocity which varies according to its transparency at different points. At the end of each scanning line, the discharge of the thyratron provides a "fly-back" action to the spot sufficiently rapid to be invisible. Simultaneously with this operation, a second valve and thyratron circuit provides a traversing time-base potential difference to the second pair of deflecting plates of the oscillograph tube. By this means the scanning line is traversed across the picture in successive steps.

From this description it will be realised that an image of the picture being transmitted is built up on the fluorescent screen of the cathode ray oscillograph, and this is found to be a useful feature of the system for monitoring purposes. Furthermore, for the reproduction of the image on the screen of another oscillograph tube at a distant receiving station, it is merely necessary to transmit to the second tube the voltages being applied to the two pairs of deflecting plates of the first tube. If these voltages are sent through two separate channels, the received picture is automatically synchronised with that at the transmitting end.

The authors of the paper referred to above have modified this arrangement to some extent, however, to enable all the intelligence to be sent along a single channel. Using a picture frequency of 25 per second with a detail corresponding to 120 or 160 scanning lines, the transmitted signals require a frequency band of the order of 240 kilocycles per second; and special amplifiers have been developed to give uniform amplification over this range. The size of the picture received depends upon the deflector voltages which

的研究工作都写在了一篇名为《一个基于速度调制的电视系统》的文章里，这篇文章于 2 月 7 日由该公司的贝德福德和帕克尔在电气工程师学会无线电分会上进行了宣读。

根据上面概括的基本原理可以看出，对物体进行匀速扫描是不可能得到速度调制的图片的；在发射端的扫描也一定是速度变化型或是速度可调型的，因此一定也要通过阴极射线来实现。在发射端，阴极射线示波器充当了光源的角色，当使用普通低压型的示波器时，这种扫描光较弱的情况会使扫描图片的材料受到限制，只能使用电影胶片。然而，并不能认为这是此方式的缺点，因为目前正在发展的许多电视系统都把胶片当成一种媒介，过程是这样设计的：将实际物体的相片和通过发射端的相片投影之间的距离减小到几乎为零。

贝德福德和帕克尔描述的传输设置是将来自示波器的荧光屏的光通过胶片图像投影到光电管上。光电管放大器的输出通过一个屏栅阀和一个闸流管来控制一个电子时基电路，它为示波器的一对偏转片施加电位差。于是，从阴极射线管出来的射线以一条直线扫过图片，根据图片不同位置透光率的不同，扫过的速度也不一样。在每一条扫描线的末端，闸流管的放电产生一个"回扫"的动作使之回到原点，而且速度极快以至于肉眼难以观察到。在进行这个操作的同时，第二个屏栅阀和闸流管电路也对示波管的第二对偏转片施加一个时基的电位差。通过这种方式，扫描线就一条一条地覆盖了整幅图片。

从上面的描述中可以看出，在阴极射线管的荧光屏上产生了待传输图片的图像，而且这被认为是一个对监视很有用的特点。此外，为了在更远处的接收端的另一个阴极射线管的荧光屏上再现图像，我们只需要将施加在第一个射线管的两对偏转片上的电压传送到第二个射线管中就可以了。如果这两路电压通过不同的通道传输，那么接收的图片就会自动地与发射端的图片进行同步。

但是，文章的作者们在谈及上面的问题时，对这种设置进行了某种程度的修改，使所有的信息都通过一个信道进行传输。如果使用的图片频率为每秒 25 张，每幅图 120 或 160 条扫描线，那么传输信号需要的频带的数量级就为每秒 240 千周；并且他们发展出了一些专用的放大器以保证在这个范围内对信号进行均匀放大。接收图

may be applied to the oscillograph electrodes, and it is anticipated that future design and manufacture will enable a suitable receiver tube with a 9-inch screen to be produced. Among the advantages of the method described above over that employing intensity-modulation are the increased picture brightness for a given receiving oscillograph and the concentration of detail in the light portions of the picture.

Although Messrs. Bedford and Puckle's experiments have so far been limited to transmission over wire lines, no particular difficulty is anticipated in applying the necessary signals to radio transmission, at least on the ultra-short wave-length of a few metres where such a large frequency band as 240 kc./sec. may be permitted. At the reading of the paper, a cinematograph film was shown illustrating typical pictures received in a laboratory test of the whole system. Among the features brought out in this demonstration was the fact that, when required to obtain a better contrast ratio in the received picture, intensity modulation may be superimposed with advantage upon the velocity-modulation signals, and means of achieving this very satisfactory combination are being investigated.

(**133**, 263; 1934)

片的大小取决于施加在示波器电极上的偏转电压的大小，而且可以预见到，未来的设计和制造技术将会生产出具有 9 英寸屏幕的接收管。上述方法相对于强度调节的优点包括：对于给定的接收示波管而言，接收到的图片的亮度会提高，图片亮区的清晰度也会提高。

虽然到现在为止，在贝德福德和帕克尔的实验中仍只限于用金属线进行传输，但是可以预见到利用无线电传输所需的信号时不会出现其他特殊的困难，至少在波长为几米的超短波长的范围内，频带达到每秒 240 千周是可以实现的。在读这篇文章的时候，我们已经在整个系统的实验室测试中使用电影胶片得到了典型的图片。从实验中呈现出来的特征可以看出：当接收的图片要求较高的对比度时，强度调制要优于速度调制，而将这两者完美结合还需要进一步探讨。

（刘东亮 翻译；赵见高 审稿）

The Positron*

C. D. Anderson

Editor's Note

In September 1932, Carl Anderson had announced the observation of the positron, a positively charged particle having the same mass as the electron. Here he reviews the discovery and what has been learned since that time. The definitive observation had been made possible, he notes, by having cosmic rays impinge upon a lead target and observing tracks in a cloud chamber held in a high magnetic field. In April 1933, other physicists had shown that a gamma ray in the strong field of a nucleus can create electron-positron pairs. Anderson reviews these experiments in some detail, and notes that the inverse process—the annihilation of an electron and a positron, producing gamma radiation—should also be important, although it had not yet been observed.

THE existence of free positive electrons or positrons was first reported by me in September 1932[1], from cosmic ray experiments carried out at the California Institute of Technology. In the original paper, all possible alternative interpretations of the effects there presented were discussed in detail, and it was shown that only by calling upon the existence of free positive electrons could those effects be logically interpreted.

As a part of Prof. R. A. Millikan's programme of cosmic ray research, in particular to make energy measurements of the cosmic ray particles by the use of a vertical cloud chamber in a very powerful horizontal magnetic field, photographs were first taken in August 1931 in such an apparatus involving the maintenance of a field of strength up to 20,000 gauss over a space measuring 17 cm. × 17 cm. × 3 cm. As reported in lectures in Paris and Cambridge, England, in November 1931 and published in March 1932 by Millikan and myself[2], this work brought to light for the first time the fact that nuclear effects are of primary importance in the absorption of cosmic rays, as demonstrated by the frequent occurrence of associated tracks or showers containing particles of positive charge as well as those of negative charge.

Through the insertion in May 1932 of a lead plate across the centre of the cloud chamber, it was possible to show definitely in several cases that the mass of these particles of positive charge could not possibly be as great as that of the proton. The direction of motion of the particles was given in two ways: first, by allowing them to pass through the lead plate and suffer a loss in energy, and secondly, by the observation in several instances of two or more tracks all originating at one small region in the material surrounding the chamber. For a given curvature of track, the specific ionisation showed that the mass was small compared with the proton mass, but even more definite evidence was gained from an observation of

---

* Address delivered at the Symposium on Nuclear Physics of the American Physical Society meeting in Boston, Mass., on December 27, 1933.

正电子*

editor按

1932 年 9 月，卡尔·安德森声明发现了正电子，一种与电子质量相同且带有一个正电荷的粒子。在这篇文章中他回顾了正电子的发现和从那时起所学到的知识。他指出，通过宇宙线轰击铅靶并在强磁场内的云室中观察产生的径迹，便可确认这一发现。1933 年 4 月，另外有物理学家发现，在核的强场中 γ 射线可产生电子 – 正电子对。安德森详细地回顾了这些实验，并指出相反的过程应该也是非常重要的，即电子和正电子的湮灭产生 γ 辐射，尽管这一现象当时还未被观测到。

1932 年 9 月，根据在加州理工学院进行的宇宙线实验，我本人首次报道了自由正电子或者正电子的存在 [1]。对于发生的那些效应，所有可能的解释都在这篇最初的文章中进行了详细讨论，该文还指出只有通过引入自由正电子的存在，才能从逻辑上解释那些效应。

作为密立根教授的宇宙线研究计划（具体来说就是利用在非常强的水平磁场内的垂直云室做宇宙线粒子能量的测量）的一部分，这种测量于 1931 年 8 月首次拍得照片，当时的装置情况是云室 17 cm × 17 cm × 3 cm，磁场强度保持在 20,000 高斯。正如 1931 年 11 月在巴黎和英国剑桥的讲座中所报道的，以及密立根和我本人 [2] 于 1932 年 3 月发表的结果一样，这项研究首次揭示了一个事实，即在宇宙线的吸收过程中核效应是最重要的。伴生的带正电荷和负电荷的粒子的径迹或簇射的频繁发生可以证明这一点。

1932 年 5 月将铅板插入云室中心的实验能够明确说明，在几种情况下，这些带正电荷的粒子的质量不可能像质子的质量那么大。这些粒子的运动方向可以由以下两个过程来确定：首先，允许它们通过铅板，并损失部分能量；随后，对同样来自云室周围物质中某个小区域的两条或多条径迹进行观测。对于一条给定曲率的径迹，比电离显示该粒子的质量小于质子质量，而从粒子射程的观测则获得了更加确定的

---

* 本演讲发表于 1933 年 12 月 27 日在美国马萨诸塞州波士顿举行的美国物理学会会议的核物理分会上。

the range of the particles. The observed ranges were several times, in some instances more than ten times, greater than the possible ranges of proton tracks of the same curvature.

These considerations were the basis of the report announcing the existence of the free positive electron or positron published in September 1932. Within the next five months a large number of confirmatory photographs revealing unambiguously the existence of positrons was taken, and a second report was published in March 1933[3] in which fifteen of these photographs were discussed. The specific ionisation exhibited by the positron tracks on these photographs showed that the magnitude of charge of the positron could not differ by as much as a factor of two from that of the free negative electron, and it was, therefore, concluded, unless one admits fractional values of the elementary unit of charge, that the free positive and negative electrons were exactly alike in magnitude of charge. This fact, together with the curvatures measured in the magnetic field of a positron before and after it penetrated a plate of lead, fixed its mass as not greater than twenty times that of the free negative electron.

Since then[4], an observation of a collision between a moving positron and a free negative electron in the gas of the chamber revealed, on the basis of the conservation laws, that its mass was equal to that of the free negative electron with an error of not more than 30 percent. More recent measurements[15] of the specific ionisation of the positives and negatives for both high and low speed particles, by actual ion-counts on the tracks in the magnetic field, showed the specific ionisation of the positives and the negatives to be equal to within 20 percent. This fixes the limits of difference between the positives and negatives with regard to their charges and masses at 10 percent and 20 percent respectively. Further details of the history of this discovery were presented at the American Association for the Advancement of Science meeting in Chicago in June 1933[4].

In March 1933 confirmatory evidence for the existence of positrons was presented by Blackett and Occhialini[5], based on similar experiments with a vertical cloud chamber operating in a magnetic field of 3,000 gauss and actuated by the responses of Geiger-Müller counters. In April 1933 Chadwick, Blackett and Occhialini[6], Curie and Joliot[7], and Meitner and Philipp[8] reported that the bombardment of beryllium by α-particles can produce radiation which results in the production of positrons, though in these experiments it was not possible definitely to identify the nature of the radiation producing the positrons. By absorption experiments, however, Curie and Joliot showed that the yield of positrons decreased approximately as was to be expected if the γ-ray rather than the neutron component of the radiation were responsible for their production.

The first experiments proving directly that a γ-ray photon impinging upon a nucleus gives rise to positrons were carried out at the Norman Bridge Laboratory, using the γ-rays from thorium C'', and reported in April 1933[9]. In this paper the fact that free electrons of both positive and negative sign are produced simultaneously by the impact of a single γ-ray photon, an observation of considerable theoretical import, was first presented. Preliminary results of energy measurements were given in June 1933 by Neddermeyer and myself[10].

证据。所观测到的该粒子的射程比相同曲率的质子径迹的可能射程要大好几倍，在某些情况下甚至超过了 10 倍。

1932 年 9 月发表的宣称自由正电子或正电子存在的报道正是基于上述思考。在此后的五个月内又拍摄到了大量的验证性照片，这些照片明确地揭示了正电子的存在。1933 年 3 月刊登的第二篇报道 [3] 对其中的 15 张照片进行了探讨。这些照片上的正电子径迹所展现出的比电离显示，正电子的电荷大小与自由负电子的电荷大小相差不到两倍。因此除非我们允许电荷的基本单位为分数值，否则我们可以断定自由正电子和负电子的电荷大小是完全相同的。根据这个事实，连同在磁场中正电子穿透铅板前后测量到的曲率一起，就可以确定出其质量不会比自由负电子的质量高出 20 倍。

上述结论得出之后 [4]，对发生在云室气体中的一个运动正电子和一个自由负电子间的碰撞的观测表明，根据守恒定律，正电子的质量和自由负电子的质量是相等的，其误差不超过 30%。通过在磁场中的径迹上进行真实离子计数，得到的与高速和低速的正负电子的比电离有关的更多最新测量结果 [15] 表明，正电子和负电子的比电离差别不会超过 20%。这样就确定了对于电荷和质量，正电子和负电子的最大差值分别为 10% 和 20%。有关这个发现过程的更多细节发表于 1933 年 6 月在美国芝加哥举行的美国科学促进会的会议上 [4]。

1933 年 3 月，基于运行在 3,000 高斯磁场内的垂直云室中的类似实验，并利用盖革 – 米勒计数器的响应来启动云室，布莱克特和奥恰利尼 [5] 给出了正电子存在的确定性证据。1933 年 4 月，查德威克、布莱克特和奥恰利尼 [6]、居里和约里奥 [7] 以及迈特纳和菲利普 [8] 均指出，用 α 粒子对铍进行轰击可以产生辐射，从而导致正电子的产生，不过这些实验尚不能完全确定产生正电子的辐射的本质。然而通过吸收实验，居里和约里奥指出，如果正电子的产生是 γ 射线而不是辐射的中子组分造成的，那么产生的正电子的数量大体上会像预期中的那样减少。

首批直接证明 γ 射线光子撞击原子核会产生正电子的实验是在诺曼桥实验室进行的。该实验发表于 1933 年 4 月 [9]，所使用的 γ 射线来源于钍 C″。这篇文章首次报道了具有重要理论意义的观测，即用单个 γ 射线光子的碰撞会同时产生带有正电和负电的自由电子。1933 年 6 月，尼德迈耶和笔者 [10] 给出了能量测量的初步结果。

Curie and Joliot[11] in May 1933, and Meitner and Philipp[12] in June 1933, all of whom used γ-rays from thorium C″, also reported the detection of positrons from the same source. Curie and Joliot[13] have also shown that positrons are produced directly in the disintegration of aluminum and boron by α-particle bombardment. The positrons in the case of aluminum cannot here be produced by the internal conversion of a γ-ray photon unless the probability of such internal conversion is vastly greater than that to be expected on theoretical grounds[14]. Rather do these experiments indicate that an elementary positive charge is actually removed from the disintegrating nucleus and appears as a positron.

The foregoing furnishes in brief a historical survey of the early experimental work on positrons and their production.

A detailed study of the energy distribution and frequency of production of free positive and negative electron pairs by filtered thorium C″ γ-rays is of particular value because of the relative simplicity of these effects as compared with those appearing in the cosmic ray range of energies.

γ-Ray Effects

A discussion will now be given of experimental evidence as it bears on the theory suggested by Blackett and Occhialini on the basis of the Dirac electron theory, which postulates the creation of a free positive-negative electron pair out of the absorption of a photon impinging upon a nucleus. The nucleus itself in this picture undergoes no disintegration, but plays merely the rôle of a catalytic agent. This discussion will be given in the light of (1) new statistical studies by Neddermeyer and myself on the thorium C″ γ-ray effects, and (2) new experiments on cosmic ray showers by Millikan, Neddermeyer, Pickering and myself.

The work of Curie and Joliot, and of Chadwick, Blackett and Occhialini on the radiation from thorium and that excited in beryllium by α-particle bombardment, together with our own work on the cosmic radiation[15], has shown that the absorption process which gives rise to positrons becomes increasingly important with high energy radiations and heavy absorbing materials. Further, we have made a statistical study based on a total of more than 2,500 tracks of single electrons, both positive and negative, and positive-negative pairs ejected from plates of lead, aluminum and carbon by γ-rays from radiothorium filtered through 2.5 cm. of lead (in some cases with unfiltered rays for comparison) to determine the frequency of occurrence of pairs and single positrons, and their energy distribution for absorbing materials of different atomic numbers. The ejection of the particles was observed from lead plates of 0.25 mm. thickness, aluminum plates of 0.5 mm. thickness and a graphite plate of 1.4 cm. thickness (used also for cosmic ray studies). The magnetic field was here adjusted to 825 gauss.

We will consider first of all the energies. Both the single positives and the pairs (the sum of the energies of the positive and negative components being taken) ejected from the

居里和约里奥 [11] 以及迈特纳和菲利普 [12] 分别于 1933 年 5 月和 1933 年 6 月，采用了钍 C″ 的 γ 射线，并同样报道了从 γ 射线源可检测到正电子。居里和约里奥 [13] 还指出，经 α 粒子轰击后在铝和硼的蜕变中可直接产生正电子。就铝而言，这里的正电子不能由 γ 射线光子的内转换来产生，除非这种内转换的概率远大于理论预期值 [14]。这些实验确实能够表明，基本正电荷实际上是从蜕变的原子核中转移出来的，并表现为一个正电子。

前面的论述简要地回顾了有关正电子及其产生的早期实验工作。

用过滤的钍 C″ 的 γ 射线对自由正电子和负电子对的能量分布和产生频率进行详细研究具有特殊的价值，因为这些效应与在宇宙线能区出现的效应相比较为简单。

γ 射线效应

现在将就支持布莱克特和奥恰利尼的理论的实验证据进行讨论，该理论以狄拉克的电子理论为基础，它假设光子撞击原子核的吸收过程会产生出一个自由的正负电子对。在此图像中，核本身不发生蜕变，而只是起催化剂的作用。讨论将依据以下两点：(1) 由尼德迈耶和笔者对钍 C″ 的 γ 射线效应所进行的新的统计研究；(2) 由密立根、尼德迈耶、皮克林和笔者对宇宙线簇射所做的新实验。

居里和约里奥以及查德威克、布莱克特和奥恰利尼关于钍发出的辐射和用 α 粒子轰击铍而激发出的辐射的研究，以及我们关于宇宙辐射的研究 [15] 综合表明，产生正电子的吸收过程随着高能辐射和高吸收材料的发展而变得越来越重要。此外，我们基于总共超过 2,500 条单电子（包括正电子和负电子）和正负电子对的径迹进行了统计研究，这些单电子和电子对是由放射性钍通过 2.5 cm 厚的铅板过滤得到的 γ 射线照射铅板、铝板和石墨板而发射出来的（某些情况下会使用未过滤的射线以进行比较）。通过该研究可测定正负电子对和单个正电子产生的频率，以及它们对不同原子序数的吸收物质的能量分布。我们的观测中采用的是 0.25 mm 厚的铅板、0.5 mm 厚的铝板和 1.4 cm 厚的石墨板（它们也同样被用于宇宙线的研究）。所使用的磁场为 825 高斯。

我们首先来考虑能量。从铅板上发射出来的单个正电子和电子对（取正负电子的能量之和）所显示的最大能量均约为 1.6 MV（MV= 兆电子伏），80% 的单个正电

lead plates showed a maximum energy of about 1.6 MV (MV = millions of electron-volts), 80 percent of the single positrons having an energy less than 0.8 MV. For the case of the unfiltered γ-rays, the positrons and the pairs, though occurring in relatively fewer numbers compared with those ejected by the filtered rays, showed also a maximum energy of 1.6 MV. Further, in the case of the positives and pairs ejected from the plates of aluminum, the maximum energy was about 1.6 MV.

The maximum energy of the single negative electrons in all cases was about 2.5 MV. Since the errors in the energy measurements may be as high as 15 percent, this is in good agreement with the highest energy to be expected for extra-nuclear electrons resulting from Compton encounters or photoelectric absorption of the 2.65 MV photons.

A maximum energy of 1.6 MV for the positives and the pairs, both from the lead and the aluminum, is in good accord with that to be expected on the Dirac picture if 1 MV is allowed for the energy required to create a pair of electrons. There occurred, however, one pair the total energy of which was 2.9 MV; it is conceivable, though not likely, that it may have been produced by cosmic rays, or again it may represent the rebound of an electron against the under surface of the lead plate.

Of equal importance with the distribution in energy is the distribution in number of single positive electrons and pairs as compared with the single negative electrons. Out of a total of 1,542 electrons ejected from the 0.25 mm. lead plate by γ-rays from radiothorium filtered through 2.5 cm. of lead, there were 1,387 single negatives, 96 single positives and 59 pairs. From an aluminum plate 0.5 mm. thick and ejected by the same radiation there were, out of a total of 943 electron tracks, 916 single negatives, 20 single positives and 7 pairs.

The negatives may be assumed to have arisen in general from Compton and photoelectric encounters with extra-nuclear electrons in the lead or aluminum. But the single positives and the pairs must all, of course, correspond to nuclear encounters. If we assume that on the average an equal number of positives and negatives results from nuclear impacts, we can calculate the ratio of the nuclear to extra-nuclear absorption. This amounts to about 20 percent for lead and about 50 percent for aluminum. These values are in reasonably good agreement with those obtained by Chao[16], Meitner[17] and Gray and Tarrant[18] by entirely different methods in the matter of the excess absorption shown by lead over that shown by aluminum and also in the general relation of nuclear to extra-nuclear absorption in both metals.

That the nuclear absorption in carbon is very small for the thorium C″ γ-rays is shown by the fact that, as compared with 415 negatives, there appeared only 2 pairs and 6 single positives.

On the whole, the energy relations of the positives and pairs, from both the aluminum and the lead, appear to be quite consistent with the pair-creation hypothesis, as are also the approximate values of the excess absorption in lead and aluminum calculated on this

子的能量小于 0.8 MV。与使用过滤的射线的情况相比，在未使用过滤的 γ 射线的情况下，尽管发射出来的正电子和电子对的数量相对较少，但最大能量也显示为 1.6 MV。此外，在使用铝板的情况下，发射出的正电子和电子对的最大能量也约为 1.6 MV。

在所有情况下，单个负电子的最大能量都约为 2.5 MV。由于能量测量中的误差可能高达 15%，因此其与康普顿碰撞或 2.65 MV 光子的光电吸收后产生的核外电子的最高预期能量符合得很好。

如果 1 MV 是产生一个电子对所需要的能量，那么来自铅和铝的正电子和电子对的最大能量 1.6 MV 就能与狄拉克图像的预期很好地吻合。然而，产生一个电子对所需的总能量是 2.9 MV；虽然不太可能，但可以想到的是，它也许已经由宇宙线产生，再或许是它表示了一个电子对铅板下表面的反弹。

与能量分布同等重要的是，与单个负电子相比，单个正电子及电子对的数目分布。放射性钍通过 2.5 cm 厚的铅板过滤得到的 γ 射线照射 0.25 mm 厚的铅板，总共可发射出 1,542 个电子，其中有 1,387 个单个负电子、96 个单个正电子和 59 个电子对。用相同的 γ 射线照射 0.5 mm 厚的铝板，总共有 943 个电子径迹，其中 916 个单个负电子、20 个单个正电子和 7 个电子对。

通常可以认为负电子源于铅或铝中核外电子的康普顿碰撞和光电碰撞。但是单个正电子和电子对必然都对应于核的碰撞。如果我们假定在一般情况下由核碰撞产生的正负电子个数相等，那么我们便可以计算出核吸收与核外吸收之间的比值。对铅板而言，这个值约为 20%，而对铝板而言约为 50%。这些值与赵忠尧 [16]、迈特纳 [17] 及格雷和塔兰特 [18] 在关于铅的吸收远超过铝的吸收以及在两种金属中核吸收与核外吸收的普遍关系的研究中采用完全不同的方法得到的值相当吻合。

钍 C″ 的 γ 射线照射石墨板时，碳的核吸收是非常小的，这可以通过以下事实体现出来，即产生了 415 个负电子的同时，只出现了 2 个电子对和 6 个单个正电子。

总的来说，来自铝和铅的正电子和电子对的能量关系，似乎与有关电子对产生的假说非常一致，同样也与基于这个假说而计算得到的在铅和铝中的过剩吸收的近

assumption.

The ratio of the observed numbers of single positives compared with the pairs is also of great importance in this connexion. Whether a positive is always formed paired with a negative, or whether a positive not accompanied by a negative can in some cases be produced, is a question difficult to answer from the data so far obtained. An accurate calculation of the probability of removal of the negative, if a pair is generated, so that only the positive emerges from the plate, is not simple to make, depending as it does on energy loss and plural scattering in the plate, and on the initial space and energy distribution of the components of the pairs. But on the basis of very approximate considerations, it appears somewhat difficult to reconcile the appearance, for example, in the case of aluminum, of 20 single positives and only 7 pairs with the view that they are always formed in pairs. Experiments now planned in which the particles are ejected from very much thinner plates should decide this question.

One case should be cited in which two negatives and two positives were all observed to originate at one point in the lead plate. The possibility that this can represent two pairs accidentally associated in time and position is so remote that it is taken as evidence that *photons of energy even so low as those of the thorium C" gamma-rays can occasionally give rise to showers such as are a common feature of the cosmic rays*[9].

Cosmic Ray Effects

Our recent stereoscopic photographs taken in a 17,000 gauss magnetic field show numerous showers of more than thirty electrons, some positives and some negatives, originating in lead plates placed across the chamber. In all the observed cases of shower production, it was clearly seen from the photographs that non-ionising particles produced the showers. Also photographs taken in a magnetic field of only 800 gauss showed many examples of single negatives, single positives, pairs and triplets, of energies of the order of only a million or two electron volts, ejected from plates of lead by the impact of non-ionising particles. These low energy ejections are in all respects identical with those produced by the thorium C" γ-rays and are undoubtedly due to low energy photons. These electron effects cannot be ascribed to ordinary neutrons since a considerable study of neutrons in this very range of energies has shown that their absorption results in projected nuclei and not in electron projection or shower formation. The appearance of several such small electron showers on one photograph which contains evidences of showers which occurred above the chamber, brings to light a new fact, namely, that *in the absorption of the cosmic rays there are produced, in addition to the electron showers, in some instances, sprays of large numbers of secondary photons*. The evidences for this conclusion were presented at the November 1933 meeting of the National Academy of Sciences by Millikan, Neddermeyer, Pickering and myself[19], and a full discussion together with the photographs will appear shortly in the *Physical Review*. In one case, more than eighty low energy electron tracks simultaneously projected were photographed, their positions and orientations in the chamber showing that they must have arisen from nearly as many separate centres in

似值相一致。

就能量关系而言，观测到的单个正电子的数目与电子对数目之比也是非常重要的。一个正电子形成的同时是否总是伴随着一个负电子的形成，或者在某些情况下是否正电子产生的同时不伴随负电子的产生，这是一个难以通过目前所掌握的数据来回答的问题。当一个电子对产生时，板中只发出正电子，这时要对负电子移出概率进行精确计算并不容易，因为这受到多种因素的影响，其中包括发生这种情况时在板内的能量损失和多次散射，以及电子对组分的起始空间和能量分布。但是根据非常粗略的分析，结果似乎很难与实际情况相符，例如，对铝而言，有 20 个单个正电子，另外仅有 7 个电子对，而理论上来说它们应该总是成对出现的。在现在计划进行的实验中，粒子将从很薄的板上发射，这应当能对这个问题做出判定。

应当指出的一个例子是，实验中观测到两个负电子和两个正电子都在铅板的同一点产生。这表明在时间和位置上偶然出现关联的两个电子对的概率是极低的，因此这个现象可以证明，**即使能量像钍 C″ 的 γ 射线那样低的光子偶然也会产生簇射，如同宇宙线所具有的普遍特征一样** [9]。

宇宙线效应

我们最近在 17,000 高斯的磁场中拍摄的立体照片显示，大量多于 30 个电子的簇射（有些是正电子，有些是负电子）产生于穿过云室放置的铅板上。从照片中可以清楚地看到，在所有观测到的产生簇射的情况中，仅非电离粒子产生簇射。同样在仅为 800 高斯的磁场中拍摄的照片也显示了许多通过非电离粒子的碰撞，从铅板发射出单个负电子、单个正电子、电子对和三电子组的例子，它们的能量量级仅为 1 或 2 兆电子伏。这些低能的发射物在各个方面都与那些钍 C″ 的 γ 射线产生的发射物一致，并且无疑是由于低能光子产生的。这些电子效应不能归属于普通的中子，因为对这个能区的中子的大量研究已经表明，它们的吸收会导致核的发射，而不是电子的或簇射的形成。在一张照片中有几个这样的小型电子簇射的出现，这也是在云室之上出现簇射的证据，这一现象揭示了一个新的事实，即**在宇宙线的吸收中，除了电子簇射之外，在某些情况下，还会产生大量次级光子的喷射**。密立根、尼德迈耶、皮克林和笔者 [19] 于 1933 年 11 月在美国国家科学院的会议上给出了此结论的相关证据，结合这些照片所做的一个全面的讨论也将于近期发表在《物理学评论》上。在其中一个示例中，超过 80 个同时发射的低能电子的径迹被拍摄下来，它们在云室中的位置和方向表明，它们一定产生自包围云室的材料的许多分立中心，因此

the material surrounding the chamber, and must therefore be ascribed to such a spray of secondary photons.

That pair production or shower formation by a fast electron (positive or negative) is a relatively rare event is shown by the fact that more than a thousand fast electrons have been observed to traverse a 1 cm. lead plate, and only in one instance was a definite pair projected from the lead by a fast electron, while a large number of secondary negative electron tracks appeared as the result of close encounters with the extra-nuclear electrons in the lead plate. The immediate secondaries of fast electrons are therefore seen to consist largely of negative electrons and only in rare cases of positrons.

Because of the powerful magnetic field we are using, it is possible to deflect all but a very small number of the electrons projected in the showers by the photon impacts. In general, in a shower a pronounced asymmetry is noted in the numbers of positive as compared with negative electrons emerging from the lead plates, in one instance 7 positives and 15 negatives, and in a second case 15 positives and 10 negatives. These effects are only with some difficulty reconciled with the Dirac theory of the creation of pairs out of the incident photon. Rather might they indicate the existence of a nuclear reaction of a type in which the nucleus plays a more active rôle than merely that of a catalyst, as for example the ejection from it of positive and negative charges which then appear in the showers as free positive and negative electrons. The essential difference, however, between these two points of view may be merely that in one case the nucleus may change its charge, and in the other it does not do so.

To study nuclear absorption in a light element, more than four hundred successful photographs were taken in which a carbon plate of 1.4 cm. thickness replaced the lead plate. Many of these showed showers originating in a block of lead placed above the chamber, but in no instance was a secondary shower observed in the carbon plate. This indicates, in agreement with the thorium C'' data, the relatively small probability in comparison with lead of a carbon nucleus absorbing a photon by shower production.

A consequence of the pair-theory is that, in a suitably dense environment of negative electrons such as obtains in ordinary matter, a positron shall have a high probability of combining with a negative electron, resulting in the annihilation of both particles and the conversion of their proper and kinetic energies into radiation. The theory, though at present incomplete, states that the mean free path for annihilation is in general greater than the range of the positron, so that such annihilation should be evidenced by the appearance of quanta of about half a million electron-volts energy and a very small number of quanta of about one million electron-volts energy when positrons pass through matter[20]. The experiments by Gray and Tarrant[18] on the scattering of thorium C'' γ-rays showed the existence of secondary radiation of such energies, but some of the more recent experiments on the scattering of hard γ-rays fail to show a secondary radiation which can be attributed to the annihilation of positrons. Our cosmic ray photographs show that in the electron showers there are present large numbers of secondary photons, many of

这一定是由次级光子的喷射而产生的。

由快电子（正的或负的）产生电子对或形成簇射是相当罕见的事件，这可由以下事实说明，观测到多于 1,000 个快电子穿过 1 cm 厚的铅板，仅有一例确定是从铅板上由快电子射出的电子对，而大量的次级负电子径迹似乎均为在铅板中与核外电子近距离碰撞的结果。因此快速电子的即时次级发射似乎是由大量负电子构成的，而正电子仅是不多见的情况。

由于我们所用的磁场很强，因此除了由光子碰撞产生的簇射中发射出的极少量的电子没有发生偏转外，可能所有的电子都发生了偏转。通常在一个簇射中可注意到，从铅板发射出的正电子数目与负电子数目明显不对称。其中一个簇射中，有 7 个正电子和 15 个负电子，而在另一个簇射中，则有 15 个正电子和 10 个负电子。这些效应遭遇的唯一困难是，很难与入射光子产生电子对的狄拉克理论取得一致。很可能这些效应表明存在一类核反应，其中核的作用不仅是催化剂而是比之更加活跃，例如，正电荷和负电荷从核中发射出来，然后作为自由正电子和负电子出现在簇射中。然而，这两种观点本质上的区别可能只不过是，其中一个认为核是可以改变其电荷的，而另一种观点则认为其电荷不会改变。

为了研究在轻元素中的核吸收，于是将铅板替换为 1.4 cm 厚的碳板并成功地拍摄了 400 多张照片。许多照片显示出，位于云室上面的铅块中会产生簇射，但在所有情况下都没有在碳板上观测到次级簇射。这与钍 C″ 的数据得出的结论一致，即与铅相比，碳核经由簇射产生吸收光子的概率较小。

电子对理论的结论是，在负电子适当稠密的环境中（如同在普通物质中存在的那种），正电子与负电子有很高的概率相互结合，从而导致两种粒子的湮灭，而它们的固有能量和动能将转换为辐射。尽管这种理论目前还不完善，但它表明发生湮灭的平均自由程通常大于正电子的射程，因此，当正电子通过物质时，这类湮灭应当可以通过具有大约 0.5 兆电子伏能量的量子以及少量具有约 1 兆电子伏能量的量子的出现来证实 [20]。格雷和塔兰特 [18] 关于钍 C″ 的 γ 射线的散射实验显示，存在具有这种能量的次级辐射，但在最近的一些硬 γ 射线的散射实验中却没有观测到次级辐射，这可以归因于正电子的湮灭。我们的宇宙线照片表明，在电子簇射中存在大量的次级光子，其中许多是在这个能区中，但还不能确定它们是否部分地产生于正电

which are in this range of energy, but it is not yet certain if they are produced in part by the annihilation of positrons. In two very recent papers, Joliot[21] and Thibaud[22] report the observation in experiments with artificially produced positrons of secondary photons of the energies to be expected if they arise from the annihilation of positrons. By control experiments with negative electrons, they showed that a beam of positrons impinging upon matter results in the production of a considerably greater quantity of photons than does an equal number of negative electrons.

(**133**, 313-316; 1934)

Carl D. Anderson: California Institute of Technology, Pasadena, Calif.

References:

1. Anderson, *Science*, **76**, 238; 1932.

2. Millikan and Anderson, *Phys. Rev.*, **40**, 325; 1932. See also Anderson, *Phys. Rev.*, **41**, 405; 1932: and Kunze, *Z. Phys.*, **80**, 559; 1933.

3. Anderson, *Phys. Rev.*, **43**, 491; 1933.

4. Millikan, *Science*, **78**, 153; 1933.

5. Blackett and Occhialini, *Proc. Roy. Soc.*, A, **139**, 699; 1933.

6. Chadwick, Blackett and Occhialini, *Nature*, **131**, 473, April 1, 1933.

7. Curie and Joliot, *C.R.*, **196**, 1105; 1933.

8. Meitner and Philipp, *Naturwiss.*, **21**, 286; 1933.

9. Anderson, A.A.A.S. meeting, April 28, 1933, and *Science*, **77**, 432; 1933.

10. Anderson and Neddermeyer, *Phys. Rev.*, **43**, 1034; 1933.

11. Curie and Joliot, *C.R.*, **196**, 1581; 1933.

12. Meitner and Philipp, *Naturwiss.*, **24**, 468; 1933.

13. Curie and Joliot, *C.R.*, **197**, 237; 1933.

14. Oppenheimer and Plesset, *Phys. Rev.*, **44**, 53; 1933. Beck, *Z. Phys.*, **83**, 498; 1933.

15. Anderson, *Phys. Rev.*, **44**, 406; 1933.

16. Chao, *Proc. Nat. Acad. Sci.*, **16**, 431; 1930. *Phys. Rev.*, **36**, 1519; 1930.

17. Meitner and Hupfield, *Naturwiss.*, **19**, 775; 1931.

18. Gray and Tarrant, *Proc. Roy. Soc.*, A, **136**, 662; 1932.

19. Anderson, Millikan, Neddermeyer and Pickering, *Proc. Nat. Acad. Sci.* Autumn meeting Nov. 20, 1933. See also abstract by Anderson and Neddermeyer, A.A.A.S. meeting, Dec. 30, 1933.

20. Fermi and Uhlenbeck, *Phys. Rev.*, **44**, 510; 1933.

21. Joliot, *C.R.*, **197**, 1623; 1933.

22. Thibaud, *C.R.*, **197**, 1629; 1933.

子的湮灭。在最近的两篇文章中，约里奥[21]和蒂博[22]报道了如果次级光子是由于正电子的湮灭产生的，则观测利用预期能量的次级光子人工产生正电子的实验是可行的。通过用负电子控制实验，他们表示，与相同数量的负电子相比，一束正电子与物质碰撞时所产生的光子要多很多。

（沈乃澂 翻译；张焕乔 审稿）

Production of Induced Radioactivity by High Velocity Protons

J. D. Cockcroft *et al.*

Editor's Note

By the mid 1930s physicists were routinely producing new radio-isotopes by bombarding elements with alpha particles and protons. Here Cockcroft and colleagues describe the bombardment of graphite with high-energy protons, producing radioactivity that decreases with a half-life of about ten minutes. This suggested that the proton beam had created a significant amount of some radionuclide, presumably ^{13}N. Some of the emitted particles were positrons, although most were ordinary electrons with high energies that might be explained as due to "kicks" by gamma rays. These in turn might have been created by annihilation of positrons in the chamber walls. This was among the first observations of electron-positron annihilation, a process that was not well understood until the 1940s.

CURIE and Joliot[1] have reported that a number of new radioactive isotopes can be produced by the bombardment of various elements with α-particles, these isotopes emitting positive electrons. In particular, they showed that boron when bombarded by α-particles was transformed to the isotope N^{13}, radio-nitrogen, this isotope having a half life of 14 minutes. They suggested that the isotope might be produced by the bombardment of carbon with heavy hydrogen, the product, N^{14}, disintegrating with the emission of a neutron to radio-nitrogen.

We have bombarded a target of Acheson graphite with *protons* of 600 k.v. energy and have used a Geiger counter to search for any radiations produced after the bombardment ceased. After bombardment for 15 minutes with a current of about 10 microamperes of protons, the target was removed from the apparatus and placed against the Geiger counter. We then observed about 200 counts per minute, being about forty times the natural effect. The number of counts decayed exponentially with time, having a half life of 10.5±0.5 minutes.

We then carried out an experiment similar to that performed by Becquerel, in which the source was placed on one side of a 9 mm. thick lead plate with the counter on the opposite side, the whole being placed in a magnetic field, so that any electron emitted could only reach the counter by applying a field of appropriate sign and magnitude. We found that when the field was such that positive electrons could reach the counter, the number of counts increased by a factor of 3; when the field was in the reverse direction no definite increase was observed. We conclude, therefore, that the radiations consist in part at least of positive particles.

由高速质子产生的感生放射性

考克饶夫等

编者按

直到 20 世纪 30 年代中期，物理学家通常使用 α 粒子和质子轰击多种元素以产生新的放射性同位素。这篇文章中考克饶夫和他的合作者们描述了一种使用高能质子轰击石墨的实验，该实验产生了以半衰期约为 10 分钟的速率衰减的放射性。这表明质子束产生了某种数量可观的放射性核，有可能是 ^{13}N。发射出来的粒子中有一些是正电子，当然，大部分是高能的普通电子，普通电子可以解释为是由 γ 射线引起的"反冲"造成的。反之 γ 射线可能是由于正电子在云室壁上湮灭产生的。这是首次观察到的电子 – 正电子湮灭现象之一，而这一过程直到 20 世纪 40 年代才被人们很好地理解。

居里和约里奥[1] 曾经报道，许多新的放射性同位素可以用 α 粒子轰击各种元素来获得，这些同位素会放射出正电子。他们特别指出，当用 α 粒子轰击硼时，硼会转变为氮的同位素 ^{13}N，即放射性氮，这种同位素的半衰期是 14 分钟。他们认为，有可能通过重氢轰击碳产生的 ^{14}N 在放射出一个中子后衰变为这种放射性氮。

我们用 600 千电子伏能量的**质子**对艾奇逊人造石墨靶进行了轰击，并使用盖革计数器探测在轰击停止后产生的辐射。用强度约为 10 微安的质子流轰击 15 分钟后，将石墨靶从装置上移开并放置在正对着盖革计数器的地方。这时，我们观测到的计数约为每分钟 200 个，约为正常值的 40 倍。计数随时间呈指数衰减，其半衰期为 10.5 ± 0.5 分钟。

然后，我们做了一个与贝克勒尔所做实验类似的实验，在这个实验中，放射源放在 9 mm 厚的铅板一侧，计数器放置在另一侧，整个装置放在磁场内，只有当磁场的方向和大小都合适时，发射出来的电子才能到达计数器。我们发现，当磁场能使正电子到达计数器时，计数增加到原来的 3 倍；当磁场反向时，未观测到计数的明显增加。因此我们认为，至少部分辐射是由带正电的粒子组成的。

We have also taken about 250 Wilson chamber photographs in a field of 2,000 gauss, placing the activated source against the outside of the chamber wall, which was about 3 mm. thick. Under these conditions, we observed only two electrons of positive curvature which could possibly have come from the source, these electrons having energies of the order of 500 k.v. We observed, on the other hand, 48 tracks of Compton electrons starting in the gas, having energies ranging from 100 k.v. to 500 k.v., suggesting the emission of γ-rays of energy between 500 k.v. and 1 million volts. These γ-rays may result from the annihilation of the positive electrons, presumably in the glass wall of the chamber. The deflection experiments, whilst not at present precise, tend to confirm that few of the positive electrons would have sufficient energy to penetrate the glass walls. Further experiments will, therefore, be carried out with the source inside the chamber.*

The observations suggest that the unstable isotope N^{13} is produced by the addition of a proton to C^{12}. The difference between the half life observed and that reported by Curie and Joliot may be due to the formation of N^{13} in a different excited state.

No marked increase in the number of counts was observed when a mixed beam of heavy hydrogen ions and protons was substituted for the proton beam.

We are very much indebted to Dr. K. T. Bainbridge, who supplied the Geiger counter with which the observations were made.

(**133**, 328; 1934)

J. D. Cockcroft, C. W. Gilbert and E. T. S. Walton: Cavendish Laboratory, Cambridge, Feb. 24.

Reference:
1. *Comptes rendus*, **198**, 254; 1934.

---

* February 27. Experiments carried out with a counter having a mica window of small stopping power gave a great increase in the number of counts owing to the positive electrons now entering the counter. The absorption curve of the positive electrons is similar to that of negative electrons of 800 k.v. energy.

在 2,000 高斯的磁场中，我们将活化后的放射源放在约 3 mm 厚的云室壁的外侧，并拍摄了 250 张威尔逊云室的照片。在这种条件下，我们只观测到了两条正曲率的电子径迹，这些径迹可能是由放射源发射出的粒子形成的，而这些电子的能量在 500 千电子伏的数量级上。另一方面，我们观测到了从气体中发出来的 48 条康普顿电子的径迹，其能量分布在 100 千电子伏到 500 千电子伏的范围内，这表示 γ 射线的发射能量范围在 500 千电子伏与 1 兆电子伏之间。这些 γ 射线可能是由于正电子的湮灭而产生的，这一过程很可能发生在云室的玻璃壁内部。尽管偏转实验目前并不精确，但它仍然倾向于肯定少量的正电子将具有足够的能量穿透玻璃壁。因此，下一步的实验将把放射源置于云室内进行。*

观测到的这些现象表明，不稳定的同位素 ^{13}N 是由于 ^{12}C 增加一个质子而产生的。我们观测到的半衰期与居里和约里奥报道的数据不同，这可能是由于形成的 ^{13}N 处于不同的激发态。

当我们用重氢离子与质子的混合束代替质子束时，并未观测到计数的明显增多。

我们非常感激班布里奇博士，他提供了我们实验必需的盖革计数器。

（沈乃澂 翻译；夏海鸿 审稿）

---

* 2 月 27 日，在使用具有微小制动力的云母窗口计数器的实验中，正电子的进入使得计数器的数量极大地增加。正电子的吸收曲线与 800 千电子伏能量的负电子的吸收曲线相似。

Designation of the Positive Electron

H. Dingle

Editor's Note

As of 1934 there was no consensus about how to name the positive electron, discovered two years earlier. The popular (and ultimately the prevalent) choice seemed to be "positron", against which Herbert Dingle here argues. It is ugly and offends the literary sense with its hybrid character, he says, and moreover it suggests that the electron ought to be unhappily renamed the "negatron". Dingle suggests instead the poetic name "oreston", alluding to the sister and brother Elektra and Orestes of Greek myth. It never caught on.

I have been hoping that, following Lord Rutherford's proposal of a name for the heavy isotope of hydrogen, someone would suggest a more satisfactory word than "positron" for the positive electron. Since, however, no better qualified reformer has appeared, may I raise the question before it is too late? "Positron" is ugly; it offends literary purists by its hybrid character; and it not only bears no relation to the established name of the associated particle, the electron, but even suggests that that particle should be called the "negatron", which fortunately it is not.

In order to balance destructive by constructive criticism, I venture to propose the name "oreston" for the newcomer. The word is euphonious, pure Greek, and since, in one of the most beautiful of Greek stories, Orestes and Elektra were brother and sister, it implies an appropriate relation between the two particles. The name found favour among many physicists in Pasadena where Anderson first obtained evidence of the particle, when I mentioned it there last year. I do not propose, however, further to urge its claims, the purpose of this letter being mainly to cleanse the language of "positron", and only incidentally to nominate a substitute.

(**133**, 330; 1934)

Herbert Dingle: Imperial College, South Kensington, S.W.7, Feb. 12.

正电子的命名

丁格尔

编者按

截至 1934 年，物理学家对于两年前发现的带正电的电子的命名问题仍未达成一致。通常情况下（也是极为普遍的）会使用"positron"（正电子）一词，而这篇文章中赫伯特·丁格尔就此发表了反对意见。他认为这个单词是丑陋的，这种复合词的方式违背了文学的原则，此外，这还意味着"electron"（电子）应该不幸地被重命名为"negatron"。丁格尔建议代之以一个更加诗意的名字"oreston"，暗指希腊神话中的厄勒克特拉和俄瑞斯忒斯姐弟。然而这个名字并未流行起来。

在卢瑟福勋爵提议给氢的重同位素命名之后，我一直希望有人可以给带正电的电子起一个比"positron"更令人满意的名字。不过既然目前仍没有人给出更好的新命名，我是否可以在这里及时地提出这一问题？坦白而言，"positron"这个单词是丑陋的；它采用的复合词的形式在文学纯化论者看来是很反感的事情；它不仅与相关的粒子，即电子已确定的名字没有什么关系，甚至还容易让人以为电子（electron）应该被称为"negatron"，不过幸好大家没有这么做。

为了早日改变这一现状，在此我大胆建议为刚发现的带正电电子采用一个新的命名"oreston"。这个词非常悦耳并且是纯希腊语，此外还因为在最动听的希腊故事之一中，厄勒克特拉和俄瑞斯忒斯是亲姐弟，因此采用这一命名可以恰当地表达这两种粒子之间的关系。帕萨迪纳是安德森首次证实新粒子存在的地方，去年，当我在那里提议采用这个名字的时候，那里的物理学家都很赞成。然而，我并不会进一步要求大家非要接受这一命名。事实上，本文的主要目的是想消除"positron"这一命名，并顺便推荐我的命名。

（金世超 翻译；朱永生 审稿）

Hormones of the Anterior Lobe of the Pituitary Gland

Editor's Note

In the 1930s, biochemists spent much effort in identifying the vitamins necessary for healthy human life and which are not produced in the body, and also the hormones secreted by various glands in the body (such as insulin in the pancreas), which similarly sustain the whole body. This article, a digest of a book published in California, is a thumbnail account of the hormones of the anterior lobe of the pituitary gland.

IT is now generally admitted that the functions of the pituitary gland (or hypophysis) are mediated by the secretion of a number of hormones from its different parts; although no active principle has yet been isolated in the pure state, the fractionation of extracts has led to the preparation of solutions having only a part of the physiological activity of the original extract. Differences of opinion exist as to the number of hormones actually present, which can only be settled when they are finally isolated as chemical individuals. Our knowledge of the functions of the posterior lobe preceded that of the anterior, but within the last few years, with improvement in both chemical and surgical technique, and also following the discovery that hormones regulating certain of the sexual activities of the body are excreted in the urine, great advances have been made also in our knowledge of the functions of the anterior lobe.

It appears probable that a number of different hormones are secreted by this lobe, but attention has been directed especially to those stimulating growth and the sexual glands. One of the pioneers in this work has been H. M. Evans, of the University of California; the results of his researches, carried on over the last decade, are now available for study, in the form of a detailed monograph*. Although the association of overfunction of the pituitary with body overgrowth (gigantism or acromegaly) and of its underfunction with dwarfism has been frequently confirmed, it was not until 1921 that Evans and Long succeeded in preparing an extract of ox anterior lobes which stimulated growth in mammals. This was due to the facts that the growth hormone is a complex substance chemically resembling the proteins, is extraordinarily labile and can only be detected when administered frequently and parenterally to suitable animals. Adult female rats more than five months old (which have therefore ceased to increase in weight), are injected

---

* The Growth and Gonad-Stimulating Hormones of the Anterior Hypophysis. By H. M. Evans, K. Meyer and M. E. Simpson, in collaboration with A. J. Szarka, R. I. Pencharz, R. E. Cornish and F. L. Reichert. Memoirs of the University of California. Vol. 11. pp. 446. (University of California Press Berkeley, California, 1933.)

垂体前叶激素

编者按

20世纪30年代，生物化学家们花了大量的精力鉴定对于人类生命健康必需的维生素以及激素，前者在体内不能合成，后者由体内各种腺体分泌（比如胰腺分泌胰岛素）。这篇摘自于一部在加利福尼亚出版的图书的文章简略介绍了垂体前叶激素。

垂体的功能是通过其不同部位分泌的多种激素介导的，这一观点目前已经得到了普遍的认可；尽管目前还没有分离出纯的活性成分，但是对垂体提取物进行分级分离可以制备出具有原始提取物的部分生理活性的溶液。关于垂体实际分泌多少种激素存在不同的意见，只有将这些激素以化合物单体的形式分离出来之后，才能消除这些分歧。我们对于垂体后叶功能的认识领先于对垂体前叶的认识，但是，在过去的几年内，随着化学技术和外科手术技术的进步，以及调控机体某些性行为的激素会从尿液中排出这一现象被发现，我们对于垂体前叶功能的认识也已经取得了很大的进展。

看来垂体前叶很有可能分泌多种不同的激素，但是人们主要将注意力集中在那些促生长和促性腺的激素上。这个领域的先驱之一是加州大学的埃文斯，他在过去十年间所做研究的结果已经被编撰成一本详细的专著[*]供研究参考。尽管垂体功能亢进与身体过度生长（巨人症或者肢端肥大症）以及其功能减退与侏儒症之间的关系已经被多次证实，但是直到 1921 年，埃文斯和朗才成功地从牛垂体前叶中制备出了能够刺激哺乳动物生长的提取物。这是由于生长激素是一种化学结构类似于蛋白质的复杂物质，特别不稳定，只有当其被频繁地以肠道外给药的方式施加于适宜的动物时才能被检测到。向 5 月龄以上的雌性成年大鼠（体重已经不再增加）腹腔内注射生长激素，每日一次，持续 20 日；每组 4~6 只，每 5 天称一次体重。随给定的注

---

[*]《前垂体的生长和性腺刺激激素》，埃文斯，迈耶，辛普森，与绍尔卡，潘查兹，科尼什，赖歇特合著。《加州大学回忆文集》第 11 卷，第 446 页。（加州大学出版社：伯克利，加利福尼亚，1933 年。）

intraperitoneally daily for a period of 20 days; groups of four to six animals are used and they are weighed every five days. Gains in weight of 25-100 gm. can be obtained according to the dose given; the relationship between the logarithm of the dose and the gain in weight was found to be approximately linear. E. Bierring and E. Nielsen (*Biochem. J.*, **26**, 1015; 1932) have compared the composition of injected growing rats with that of normal growing rats and find that the former show a greater retention of water, but that the solid matter assimilated to the body tissues contains a much greater proportion of protein and less of ash and fat than that laid down by normal animals. About three quarters of the gain in weight of the injected animals is due to water retention, and three quarters of the dry matter deposited consists of protein.

The method of extraction recommended by Evans and his co-workers is briefly as follows: frozen ox anterior lobes are minced and extracted with water made alkaline with baryta; the mixture is centrifuged and the solution brought to pH8 with sulphuric acid and again centrifuged. The solution is then acidified and poured into excess of acetone; the precipitate is filtered off and dried. This powder is stable but still contains the gonad stimulating hormone. On extraction with 95-98 percent acetic acid, the latter is destroyed and the growth hormone can be precipitated from solution by acetone in the presence of quinine sulphate. Trichloracetic acid precipitates the growth hormone and part of the gonad stimulating hormone from aqueous solutions of the powder; in the supernatant fluid the latter can be obtained free from the former by precipitation with flavianic acid, which is then removed by 80 percent alcohol containing 1-2 percent ammonia. The purer growth hormone preparations are highly active in a daily dose of 5 mgm.

Hypophysectomised rats show a greater response to the growth hormone regardless of age or length of time after removal of the gland. Experiments with a hypophysectomised puppy are also described; the pituitary gland was removed when the animal was 8 weeks old; the operation was followed by complete cessation of growth. Daily intraperitoneal injections of the growth hormone resulted in a marked increase in weight and size, so that the animal finally became larger than its litter mate control. Signs of acromegaly, however, did not develop. The ovarian follicles showed considerable development and the thyroid was hyperplastic. Similar injections into a normal female resulted in the development of partial acromegaly, some gigantism and diabetes mellitus. A male, however, only developed adiposity. In dachshunds, the injections increased the size of the animals owing to increase in size of the skull and vertebrae, but the achondroplastic form of the short extremities was not altered; a male developed diabetes. The only outstanding acromegalic feature was a folding of the skin of the head and extremities. These results lend strong support to the generally accepted view that gigantism and acromegaly in human beings are due to over-secretion by the anterior lobe of the pituitary gland.

The gonad stimulating hormone (or hormones) is responsible for the normal development and maintenance in a state of functional activity of the sex glands, with the accessory organs and secondary sex characters. In the female the ovaries themselves respond readily

射剂量的不同，体重可以增加 25~100 g 不等；注射剂量的对数值与体重的增加几乎呈线性关系。比林和尼尔森（《生物化学杂志》，第 26 卷，第 1015 页，1932 年）对注射了生长激素的大鼠和正常生长的大鼠的组织进行了比较，结果发现：前者水潴留更加明显，但是被吸收到机体组织中所含固形物中所含蛋白质的比例更高，所含矿物质和脂肪的比例更低。注射激素的大鼠增加的体重中 3/4 是由于水潴留，而且 3/4 的干物质沉积是由蛋白质组成的。

埃文斯及其同事推荐的提取生长激素的方法简述如下：将冰冻的牛垂体前叶切碎，用氢氧化钡碱溶液进行萃取；将混合物离心，上清液用硫酸中和到 pH=8，再次离心。将上清液酸化并倒入过量的丙酮中；过滤沉淀物并将其干燥。由此获得的粉末是稳定的，但是仍然含有促性腺激素。用 95% ~ 98% 的醋酸萃取后，促性腺激素会被破坏，在有硫酸奎宁存在的条件下，就可以用丙酮将生长激素从溶液中沉淀出来。三氯乙酸能够将生长激素和部分促性腺激素从粉末的水溶液中沉淀出来；从上清液中单独获取促性腺激素的方法是用黄胺酸进行沉淀，然后用含有 1% ~ 2% 氨的80% 乙醇除去上清液中残留的酸。通过这种方法最终制备得到较纯的生长激素制剂，每天注射 5 mg，就能够发挥很高的活性。

垂体被切除后的大鼠对生长激素的反应更加明显，而且与年龄以及腺体移除后的时间长短无关。用垂体被切除的幼犬进行的实验如下所述：当幼犬 8 周龄时，摘除垂体；手术后，幼犬的生长完全停止。每日向其腹腔内注射生长激素会导致幼犬体重明显增加和体型明显增大，以至于最终比作为对照的同窝同伴长得更大。不过，并没有出现肢端肥大症的迹象。卵巢卵泡明显发育，并且甲状腺也出现增生。对一例正常的雌性个体进行类似的注射，该个体出现了一定程度的肢端肥大以及部分巨人症和糖尿病的症状。但是，经过同样处理的一例雄性个体则只出现了肥胖症。在对达克斯猎狗进行的实验中，激素的注射增加了颅骨和椎体的大小，从而增大了动物的体型，但是细小肢端软骨发育不全的状况没有改变；一例雄性个体患上了糖尿病。肢端肥大症唯一的显著特征是头部和肢端皮肤皱褶。这些结果强有力地支持了那个已被普遍接受的观点，即人类的巨人症和肢端肥大症是由垂体前叶的过度分泌造成的。

促性腺激素负责性腺的正常发育，并通过附属器官及第二性征使性腺功能活性维持在某个水平上。在雌性个体中，卵巢本身容易对该激素产生反应；在雄性个体

to the hormone; in the male the accessory organs show the most striking effects. Immature female rats were used by Evans and his colleagues for the assay of their preparations; injections were made on three days, the vaginal orifice examined on the fourth and fifth days, smears being taken as soon as it had opened, and the animals killed and examined about 96-100 hours after beginning treatment.

The hormone was prepared from ox anterior lobe (a poor source), from the serum of pregnant mares (a good source), and from the urine of pregnant women. The acetone powder from the alkaline extract of anterior lobes is dissolved in water and the reaction of the solution adjusted to give maximum precipitation: the greater part of the hormone remains in solution and is precipitated by flavianic acid, which can be removed afterwards by use of alcohol-ammonia mixture. Alternatively, the powder may be extracted with 50 percent pyridine, 50-60 percent alcohol or acetone containing 2-4 percent ammonia; the hormone is then precipitated by increasing the alcohol or acetone to 85 percent and adding a little acetic acid or salt. Pregnant mare serum was treated directly with acidified acetone and the powder purified by the methods used in the case of preparations from anterior lobes. From the urine of pregnant women the hormone (called prolan by Aschheim and Zondek its discoverers), was precipitated by excess of alcohol. The precipitate was extracted with dilute acid and the prolan reprecipitated with alcohol; the powder was purified by extraction with acetone-ammonia mixture. The minimum dose of the purest preparations was about 0.05 mgm.

Although preparations from these different sources all stimulate the gonads, yet they show differences in their chemical properties and biological effects. Prolan, for example, is more sensitive to both acid and alkali than preparations from pregnant mare serum; the latter, but not the former, give off hydrogen sulphide on treatment with alkali. However, the differences in chemical properties may be due to differences in the associated impurities. Differences in the biological effects produced are not so easily explained. Even though the minimal doses of different preparations may be the same, larger doses may have widely different effects on the ovary: thus increasing the dose of prolan increases the size of the ovaries at most four times, whilst with preparations from pregnant mare serum, there is a rough proportionality between dose and size up to about twenty-five times the minimal dose.

Evans and his co-workers have not been able to separate the gonad stimulating hormone into follicle stimulating and luteinising factors, corresponding to the prolans A and B of Aschheim and Zondek. A solution which is predominantly follicle stimulating at one dose level may produce corpora lutea at another level or when the injections are continued beyond the usual three-day period; the predominant effect may depend on the amount of purification to which the extract has been subjected. The type of response also depends in part on the time at which the examination is made after beginning the injections. There are indications that the presence of corpora lutea inhibits further development of the ovary: the occurrence of ovulation depends on the size of the ovary and the dose given. Hypophysectomised female rats were less sensitive than normal animals and

中，附属器官表现出最显著的反应。埃文斯及其同事用未成熟的雌性大鼠来检验他们的促性腺激素制剂；连续注射 3 天，在第四天和第五天时检查阴道口，阴道口一打开就立刻进行涂片，在开始处理之后大约 96 ～ 100 小时杀死这些大鼠并进行检查。

激素可由牛垂体前叶（比较差的来源）、怀孕母马的血清（比较好的来源）以及孕妇的尿液制备。将来自垂体前叶碱性萃取物的丙酮粉末溶解在水中，调节溶液中发生的反应使其能够产生最大量的沉淀物：大部分激素存留在溶液中，然后用黄胺酸使其沉淀，随后用乙醇 – 氨的混合溶液清除黄胺酸。另外也可以用 50% 的吡啶、50% ～ 60% 的乙醇或者含有 2% ～ 4% 氨的丙酮对此粉末进行萃取；然后提高乙醇或者丙酮的浓度到 85% 并加入少量醋酸或者食盐将激素沉淀出来。怀孕母马的血清则直接用酸化的丙酮处理，并用从垂体前叶制备激素的方法对粉末进行纯化。来自孕妇尿液的激素（其发现者阿什海姆和邹德克称之为绒毛膜促性腺激素）通过过量的乙醇进行沉淀。用稀释的酸萃取沉淀物，然后用乙醇将绒毛膜促性腺激素再沉淀下来；再用丙酮 – 氨的混合溶液进行萃取来纯化该粉末。所制得的最纯制剂的最小剂量大约是 0.05 mg。

尽管从这些不同的来源制备得到的样品都能刺激性腺，但是它们在化学特性和生物学效应上的表现并不相同。比如，绒毛膜促性腺激素比从怀孕母马血清中制备得到的激素对酸和碱都更加敏感；后者用碱处理时会释放出硫化氢，而前者不会。不过，化学特性方面的差异可能是由于含有的杂质不同。生物学效应方面的差异就不是这么容易解释了。尽管制备得到的各种样品的最小剂量几乎是相同的，但是，较大的剂量对于卵巢会有非常不同的作用：增加绒毛膜促性腺激素的量可以使卵巢的体积最多增大 4 倍，而对于从怀孕母马血清中制备得到的激素来说，剂量和卵巢的体积之间差不多成正比，卵巢的体积最大可达到最小剂量时的 25 倍左右。

埃文斯及其同事还不能将促性腺激素分离成卵泡刺激素和黄体生成素，分别对应于阿什海姆和邹德克所说的绒毛膜促性腺激素 A 和 B。激素溶液在一定剂量水平下可以显著地刺激卵泡的溶液，而在另一个剂量水平下或者连续注射超过通常的 3 天周期时就会产生黄体；其主导效应可能取决于提取物纯化的程度。产生效应的类型在某种程度上也依赖于开始注射后多长时间进行检查。一些现象提示黄体的存在抑制了卵巢进一步的发育：排卵的发生频率取决于卵巢的大小和注射剂量。垂体被切除的雌性大鼠的敏感性比正常大鼠低，而且对绒毛膜促性腺激素的反应要远远低

the response to prolan was much less than that to extracts of pregnant mare serum; simultaneous administration of the growth promoting hormone diminished the response. Substitution therapy failed to induce the rhythmic changes in the vagina characteristic of the oestrous cycle, a continuous oestrous reaction only being obtained. Pregnancy was not observed owing to failure of implantation, but it could be maintained in animals, hypophysectomised after implantation, by injection of mixtures of growth- and gonad-stimulating hormones.

In hypophysectomised female dogs, prolan had no effect on the genital system even in large doses, and when the system showed a marked degree of atrophy, an anterior lobe extract also had no effect. A mixture of the two preparations, however, stimulated the genitalia within ten days; the vulva increased to a size greater than that observed in normal oestrus in a litter mate control, the mammary gland and uterus showed marked development and the ovary was much enlarged and contained many corpora lutea. This result may be contrasted with some experiments on the hypophysectomised ferret recently published by M. K. McPhail (*Proc. Roy. Soc.*, B, **114**, 128; 1933). Anterior lobe extract alone produced extensive theca luteinisation of small follicles, but no development of large follicles: prolan alone caused many follicles to undergo partial growth, which, however, terminated in atresia: the vulva showed partial oestrous swelling. A mixture of the two preparations produced usually only theca luteinisation.

Without referring to other work in detail, it maybe stated that several workers in addition to Aschheim and Zondek have adduced evidence that the follicle stimulating and luteinising hormones from the anterior lobe are separate entities. The synergistic action with prolan may depend on the proportions of these factors present in different preparations. Apart from the chemical difficulties of preparing the hormones in a pure state, the facts that they act in succession, or if really a single entity initiate a series of reactions, introduces a complication into the evaluation of the biological tests, which only further work with a standardised technique can clarify.

In immature male rats, doses of gonad stimulating hormone sufficient to produce enlargement of the ovaries in immature females produced little or no increase in the weight of the testes, although the accessory organs grew markedly and attained the size characteristic of these organs in young adults. Larger doses of hormone, however, increased the weight of the testes. Senile males also responded by increase in weight of the accessory organs. In hypophysectomised males injections of the hormone caused regeneration of the atrophied testes, the seminal vesicles became enlarged and filled with fluid and spermatogenesis was resumed; the replacement therapy was complete since normal litters were sired, and the testes appeared normal on histological examination.

The atrophy of the thyroid and adrenal glands after removal of the pituitary was not repaired by injection of gonad stimulating hormone, but extracts containing the growth hormone maintained or restored the weight of these organs, although histologically the

于对怀孕母马血清提取物的反应；同时给予促生长激素可以减弱这种效应。替代治疗不能诱发发情周期中阴道特征的周期性变化，而只能获得持续的发情反应。因为胚胎不能着床，所以观察不到怀孕现象。但是如果在胚胎着床后切除垂体，则可以通过注射促生长激素和促性腺激素的混合物来维持动物的怀孕。

在垂体被切除的雌狗中，即使大剂量的绒毛膜促性腺激素也不能对生殖系统产生作用。当生殖系统表现出显著萎缩时，垂体前叶的提取物也不能发挥作用。但是，这两种物质的混合物能够在 10 天内刺激生殖器；外阴增大得比同窝作为对照的同伴正常发情期时还明显，乳腺和子宫明显发育，卵巢明显增大并含有大量黄体。这个结果和最近麦克费尔发表的在垂体被切除的雪貂上完成的一些实验的结果（《皇家学会学报》，B 辑，第 114 卷，第 128 页，1933 年）截然不同。单独用垂体前叶提取物能够使小卵泡的膜广泛黄体化，但是不能导致大卵泡的发育；单独用绒毛膜促性腺激素能够使许多卵泡部分发育，但是最终还是以闭锁告终；外阴表现出部分的发情期肿胀。两者的混合物常常只能引起膜黄体化。

不用再详细介绍其他研究工作，我们也可以说，除阿什海姆和邹德克以外其他一些研究人员也已经得到证据可以证明来自垂体前叶的卵泡刺激素和黄体生成素是两种不同的物质。它们与绒毛膜促性腺激素的协同作用可能与制备得到的不同样品中存在的这些物质的比例有关。除了制备纯净的激素存在化学方法上的困难之外，这些激素是顺次发生作用抑或是一种激素引发一系列的反应，这些事实都使得对生物学实验结果的评估变得更加复杂，只有通过标准化的实验技术进行更深入的研究才能澄清混乱。

将可使未成熟雌性大鼠卵巢增大的剂量的促性腺激素作用于未成熟的雄性大鼠后，其睾丸的重量增加很少或不增加，尽管附属器官的体积明显增大并且达到了年轻成年鼠的水平。不过，更大剂量的激素能够增加睾丸的重量。老年雄鼠也有反应，主要是附属器官重量增加。对于垂体被切除的雄鼠，注射激素能使萎缩睾丸再生，精囊增大并充满精液，精子发生过程重新开始；替代治疗获得了成功，因为已经能够生育出正常的幼崽，而且睾丸在组织学检查上也表现正常。

垂体被切除后，注射促性腺激素不能修复甲状腺和肾上腺的萎缩，但是含有生长激素的提取物则可以保持或者恢复这些器官的重量，尽管它们在组织学上不能完

normal structure was not completely regained. Evans's results do not show whether it is the growth hormone or some other active principles in the extracts which are responsible for these effects. The cachexia commonly observed in hypophysectomised rats was also relieved by injections of the growth hormone.

The data on which the workers in the University of California base the conclusions briefly reviewed above are available in detail in the monograph now under notice. The methods described should be of value to other investigators and their results should form the basis of further research in this important field.

(**133**, 401-403; 1934)

全恢复正常结构。埃文斯的结果没有揭示产生这些效应的到底是生长激素还是提取物中的其他活性物质。注射生长激素还能缓解垂体被切除后的大鼠中非常常见的恶病质。

　　加州大学的研究者们得出上述结论所依据的具体数据可以在那本受人瞩目的专著中查到。书中介绍的方法对于其他研究者来说应该是有价值的，而他们得到的结果则将成为在这个重要的领域中进行更深入研究的基础。

（毛晨晖 翻译；金侠 审稿）

Transmutation Effects Observed with Heavy Hydrogen

M. L. Oliphant *et al.*

Editor's Note

While American physicists were calling the recently discovered isotope of hydrogen "deuterium", their British colleagues persisted with "diplogen". Here Mark Oliphant and Paul Harteck, working with Rutherford in Cambridge, describe experiments that seem to involve the reaction of two diplogen nuclei ("diplons"). They substituted diplogen for hydrogen in ammonium compounds and bombarded them with low-energy diplogen. The researchers note that if two diplogen nuclei combine to form a helium nucleus, its atomic mass would be slightly greater than the known atomic mass of helium. So the resulting nucleus would be highly unstable and would immediately decay, throwing out protons and neutrons. Identifying the putative decay products (helium-3 and hydrogen-3, or tritium) awaited further experimental refinement.

WE have been making some experiments in which diplons have been used to bombard preparations such as ammonium chloride (NH_4Cl), ammonium sulphate (($NH_4)_2SO_4$) and orthophosphoric acid (H_3PO_4), in which the hydrogen has been displaced in large part by diplogen. When these D compounds are bombarded by an intense beam of protons, no large differences are observed between them and the ordinary hydrogen compounds. When, however, the ions of heavy hydrogen are used, there is an enormous emission of fast protons detectable even at energies of 20,000 volts. At 100,000 volts the effects are too large to be followed by our amplifier and oscillograph. The proton group has a definite range of 14.3 cm., corresponding to an energy of emission of 3 million volts. In addition to this, we have observed a short range group of singly charged particles of range about 1.6 cm., in number equal to that of the 14 cm. group. Other weak groups of particles are observed with the different preparations, but so far we have been unable to assign these definitely to primary reactions between diplons.

In addition to the two proton groups, a large number of neutrons has been observed. The maximum energy of these neutrons appears to be about 3 million volts. Rough estimates of the number of neutrons produced suggest that the reaction which produces them is less frequent than that which produces the protons.

While it is too early to draw definite conclusions, we are inclined to interpret the results in the following way. It seems to us suggestive that the diplon does not appear to be broken up by either α-particles or by proton bombardment for energies up to 300,000 volts. It therefore seems very unlikely that the diplon will break up merely in a much less energetic collision with another diplon. It seems more probable that the diplons unite to form a new

通过重氢观察到的嬗变效应

奥利芬特等

编者按

当美国物理家们将新发现的氢的同位素（氘）称为"deuterium"的时候，他们的英国同行则坚持使用"diplogen"这一叫法。这篇文章中，马克·奥利芬特和保罗·哈特克在剑桥同卢瑟福合作，描述了一个似乎包含两个氘原子核（"氘核"）反应的实验。他们用氘置换铵化合物中的氢，然后用低能的氘去轰击它们。研究者们指出，如果两个氘核结合在一起形成一个氦核，那么这个氦核的原子质量会比已知的氦的原子质量略大。所以该反应得到的原子核会是高度不稳定的，并且会立即开始衰变，放出质子和中子。对假定衰变产物（氦–3和氢–3，后者或称为氚）的鉴别有待进一步的实验改进。

我们进行了以下的实验，用氘核轰击氯化铵（NH$_4$Cl）、硫酸铵（(NH$_4$)$_2$SO$_4$）、正磷酸（H$_3$PO$_4$）等样品，使得化合物中的大部分氢被氘置换。当这些氘化合物受到强的质子束轰击时，这些化合物和普通氢化合物没有表现出太大区别。然而，当用重氢离子轰击时，即便是在20,000电子伏的能量下也能探测到大量快质子发射。在100,000电子伏时，这个效应则太强以致于我们的放大器和示波器不能对其进行跟踪。质子群有14.3厘米的固定射程，对应3兆电子伏发射能量。除此之外，我们还观察到了一个射程约1.6厘米的单电荷粒子群，数量和14厘米的质子群相同。在不同的样品中，还观测到了其他弱的粒子群，但是到目前为止，我们还不能确定这些反应就是氘核之间的初级反应。

除了这两个质子群，我们还观察到了大量的中子。这些中子中能量最大的约为3兆电子伏。对产生中子数目的粗略估算表明，产生中子的反应比产生质子的反应的频度要低。

现在得出确切的结论还为时过早，我们倾向于用以下方式来解释这些结果。当能量高达300,000电子伏时，无论用α粒子轰击还是用质子轰击，氘核都不会发生破裂，这对我们来说似乎是具有启发性的。因此，当氘核在更小的能量下与另一个氘核发生碰撞时，似乎就更不可能发生破裂了。更有可能的是，两个氘核结合而形

133

helium nucleus of mass 4.0272 and 2 charges. This nucleus apparently finds it difficult to get rid of its large surplus energy above that of an ordinary He nucleus of mass 4.0022, but breaks up into two components. One possibility is that it breaks up according to the reaction

$$D_1^2 + D_1^2 \rightarrow H_1^3 + H_1^1$$

The proton in this case has the range of 14 cm. while the range of 1.6 cm. observed agrees well with that to be expected from momentum relations for an H_1^3 particle. The mass of this new hydrogen isotope calculated from mass and energy changes is 3.0151.

Another possible reaction is

$$D_1^2 + D_1^2 \rightarrow He_2^3 + n_0^1$$

leading to the production of a helium isotope of mass 3 and a neutron. In a previous paper we suggested that a helium isotope of mass 3 is produced as a result of the transmutation of Li^6 under proton bombardment into two doubly charged particles. If this last reaction be correct, the mass of He_2^3 is 3.0165, and using this mass and Chadwick's mass for the neutron, the energy of the neutron comes out to be about 3 million volts. From momentum relations the recoiling He_2^3 particle should have a range of about 5 mm. Owing to many disturbing factors, it is difficult to observe and record particles of such short range, but experiments are in progress to test whether such a group can be detected. While the nuclei of H_1^3 and He_2^3 appear to be stable for the short time required for their detection, the question of their permanence requires further consideration.

(**133**, 413; 1934)

M. L. Oliphant, P. Harteck and Rutherford: Cavendish Laboratory, Cambridge, March 9.

成一个新的氦核，其质量为 4.0272，电荷数为 2。这个新的原子核的过剩能量比质量为 4.0022 的普通氦核的大，这一过剩能量明显是很难去除的，除非分裂为两部分。一种可能性是按照以下的反应发生分裂：

$$_1^2D + _1^2D \rightarrow _1^3H + _1^1H$$

在这种情况下质子的射程是 14 厘米，而我们所观察到的 1.6 厘米的射程与根据动量关系估算出的 $_1^3H$ 粒子的射程吻合得很好。从质能关系计算得到这种新的氢同位素的质量为 3.0151。

另一种可能发生的反应是：

$$_1^2D + _1^2D \rightarrow _2^3He + _0^1n$$

其产生一个质量为 3 的氦同位素和一个中子。在之前的一篇文章中，我们指出，^{6}Li 被质子轰击后会转变为两个带双电荷的粒子，这样就产生了质量为 3 的氦同位素。如果最后的这个反应是正确的，那么 $_2^3He$ 的质量应为 3.0165，利用这个质量和查德威克给出的中子质量进行计算，得出中子的能量约为 3 兆电子伏。根据动量关系，反冲的 $_2^3He$ 粒子的射程应该约为 5 毫米。由于存在很多干扰因素，观测并记录这样短射程的粒子是困难的，但是正在进行中的实验正试图去探测这样的粒子群。在探测所需的短时间内，$_1^3H$ 和 $_2^3He$ 原子核似乎是稳定的，它们的持久性问题还需要更进一步地探讨。

（王静 翻译；张焕乔 审稿）

Liquid Crystals[*]

W. Bragg

Editor's Note

The molecular-scale origins of the curious behaviour of liquid crystals were becoming clear in the early 1930s, thanks largely to the X-ray crystallography methods developed by William Bragg and others. These substances are composed of rod-like molecules which tend to become aligned while still mobile, combining crystalline and liquid properties. Here Bragg, in the transcript of a Royal Institution discourse, summarizes the state of knowledge, describing the disposition of molecules in the three main liquid-crystal states (smectic, nematic, cholesteric). The last of these involves a screw-like twist in orientation which can rotate the plane of polarization of light, later used as the basis for some liquid-crystal display devices.

THERE are substances which are liquid in their mobility and crystalline in their optical behaviour. The latter property suggests that there must be some degree of arrangement of the component molecules, and the former that this arrangement is readily disturbed though it may be as readily renewed. Such substances are generally described as "liquid crystals". It is argued, especially by Friedel, to whom we owe so much of our knowledge of their properties, that the title is bad, because the substances are neither perfect crystals nor perfect liquids. Friedel would call them mesomorphs, which is much more logical, since the conditions to be described are intermediate between other conditions that are well known. The term "liquid crystals" is, however, simple and suggestive, and those who use it are not likely to be misled.

The first to give any full and clear account of the properties of liquid crystals was O. Lehmann[1]. Following him, a number of investigators have attacked the general problem from various sides, Vorländer, Schenck, Friedel, Grandjean, Mauguin, Oseen and others. Quite a large literature has grown up round the subject. Friedel has given a full account of his experiments in the *Annales de Physique*[2]. The present state of knowledge may be inferred from the account of the general discussion on liquid crystals and anisotropic melts held by the Faraday Society in April, 1933[3].

The characteristic properties of liquid crystals are connected with the peculiar form of their molecules. There are relatively complicated structures possessing a common feature in their lengthy, chain-like form. It is not surprising that such molecules should sometimes exist in a state intermediate between solid and fluid. If the form and influences of a molecule can be represented approximately by a sphere, an assemblage of such molecules

---

* From the Friday evening discourse delivered at the Royal Institution on November 24, 1933.

液晶[*]

布拉格

编者按

20 世纪 30 年代早期，关于液晶具有的奇特行为的分子尺度的根源已经逐渐清楚，这主要归功于威廉·布拉格以及其他研究者发展出的 X 射线晶体学方法。液晶由倾向于规则排列而又具有流动性的棒状分子组成，兼具晶体和液体的性质。本文为布拉格在英国皇家研究院的演讲记录，他总结了当时的知识现状，描述了在三种主要的液晶状态（近晶相、向列相、胆甾相）中分子的排列情况。胆甾相状态中分子的取向涉及一种类似螺旋的扭曲结构，它可以使光的偏振平面发生偏转，这一性质是后来一些液晶显示器件的基础。

有这样一种物质，就其流动性而言是液体，就其光学性质而言是晶体。后一性质意味着其组分分子必定存在某种程度的规则排布，而前一性质则意味着这种排布很容易被打乱，尽管它也可能很容易恢复。一般将这种物质称为"液晶"。有人——特别是夫里德耳，我们所知道的关于这类物质性质的很多知识都归功于他——认为这个称呼很糟，因为它们既不是完美的晶体也不是完美的液体。既然该状态被描述为我们所熟知的两种状态的中间状态，夫里德耳想称其为中间态，这个称呼更合乎逻辑。不过，"液晶"这个词既简单又有启发性，不会对使用者造成误导。

最早对液晶的性质给出完整、清晰描述的人是莱曼[1]。在他之后，很多研究者从多个方面研究了相关的基本问题，其中包括福伦德、申克、夫里德耳、格朗让、莫甘、奥森和其他一些研究者。围绕这一主题的文献也大量涌现。夫里德耳在《物理学年鉴》[2]中给出其实验的完整介绍。当前对这个领域的了解都反映在 1933 年 4 月法拉第学会组织的关于液晶与各向异性熔体的全面讨论[3]里。

液晶的本征性质与其分子特定的形态有关。它们具有相对复杂的结构，其共同特征就在于长长的链状形态。这样的分子在某些时候会以介于固体和液体之间的中间状态存在，这并不奇怪。如果一个分子的形态和变化可近似为球形的话，这种分子的聚集体就会在某些特定温度下分解成独立个体。这是因为所有与邻近分子的连

---

[*] 1933 年 11 月 24 日，英国皇家研究院的周五晚间演讲。

will resolve itself into individuals at some definite temperature. That is because all the links with neighbouring molecules are similar and break down together. But when the molecule is relatively long and narrow, the linkages in different parts of it may be of different strengths. Some may be broken at a lower temperature than others. There must then be one or more intermediate states of greater but not complete mobility. A sufficiently high temperature will bring about the dissolution of the remaining molecular associations, and then a truly liquid state is reached. Though the intermediate phases lack the complete ordering of the crystal, that which remains has necessarily its optical effects.

It is an important fact that the changes from solid to liquid crystal, and from liquid crystal to liquid, are as sharp and definite as the change from solid to liquid in the more general case.

These optical effects possess in many cases a singular beauty, in respect both to colour and to form (*see* Figs. 1, 12 and 13*). Most of them, but not all, can be explained in comparatively simple terms which, however, are rarely described in treatises on optics. Writers have confined themselves to true crystals and true liquids, and the more complicated problem is discussed only in isolated papers. In what follows a brief account is given of this peculiar optics and of the consequent inferences as to the liquid crystal structure.

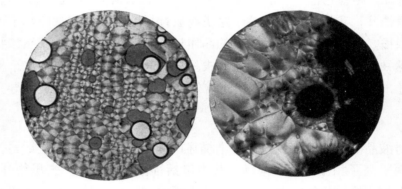

Fig. 1. Enlarged photomicrograph of a liquid crystal. A Nicol prism is used as analyser; there is no polariser. The substance is ethyl *para*-azoxybenzoate, temperature 114-120°C. Notice the polygons and the appearances of cones within them. The white circles are air-bubbles: the grey portions are liquid. The diameter of the original before magnification is 0.075 cm.

Smectic Crystals

Friedel divides liquid crystals into three classes: in his own words, there are three mesomorphous phases. The first of these he calls "smectic", thereby implying a parallelism with the soaps. Their special feature is their stratification. In each layer the molecules are arranged side by side, like corn in a field, the thickness of the layer being the length of

---

*The photographs are due to Mr. W. J. Green.

接都是类似的，会同时断开。但是当分子相对细长时，其不同部位的连接就可能具有不同的强度，某些部位可能会比其他部位在更低的温度下断开。那样就必定会出现一种或多种具有较高但并非完全流动性的中间状态。充分高的温度会使剩下的分子缔合体解离，进而达到一种真正的液态。虽然这些中间相缺乏晶体的完全有序性，但是剩余的有序性仍足以产生光学效应。

　　一个重要的事实是，从固态到液晶和从液晶到液态的变化，与更一般情况下的从固态到液态的变化是同样敏锐和确定的。

　　不论是就其颜色还是形式（**参见**图 1、图 12 和图 13*）而言，在很多情况下，这些光学效应具有一种非凡的美感。其中绝大部分，但不是全部，可以用相当简单的术语加以解释，但却很少在有关光学的文献中被提及。作者们将其自身局限于真正的晶体和真正的液体中，只在零星的论文中讨论过更为复杂的问题。下面所给出的是一份关于液晶结构的特殊光学性质及对其合理推论的简要描述。

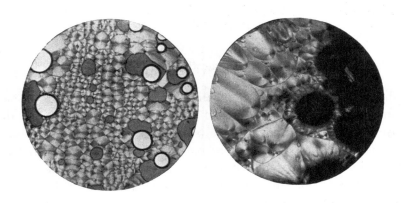

图 1. 放大了的液晶显微照片。用一块尼科尔棱镜作为检偏器；没有使用起偏器。所用物质为对－氧化偶氮基苯甲酸乙酯，温度为 114℃ ~120℃。注意其中的多边形和锥状外观。白色的圆是气泡，灰色部分是液体。放大前的初始直径为 0.075 cm。

近晶相液晶

　　夫里德耳将液晶分为三种类型：用他自己的话说，有三种中间型的相。其中第一种他称之为"近晶相"，暗示着与肥皂有某种类似性。它们的特殊性质是其分层。在每一层中，分子肩并肩地排列，如同田野里的玉米一样；层的厚度就是分子的长

---

* 这些照片由格林先生提供。

the molecules. In the case of the soap bubble or film, we have such layers forming the surface inside and out. The side to side attractions of the molecules bind them together, so that the film has a certain surface energy of tension. If the film is made to grow larger in extent, other molecules of the sodium oleate slip into their places and increase the area. If the film contracts, molecules drop out and go back into the liquid.

Let us suppose now that such layers are formed in the substance ethyl azoxybenzoate, which shows the smectic phenomena very well. Each sheet is very flexible. If such a sheet could be suspended in space, free from gravity, it would take the form of a perfectly flat surface because the molecules would tend to lie parallel to one another. Their side to side attractions are relatively strong. If bent, it would straighten itself out again. If a number of such sheets were put together like the leaves of a book, they would tend to adjust themselves further, so that the ends of the molecules on the face of one sheet fitted exactly in some characteristic way on to the ends of the molecules on the next sheet. In this way the solid crystal would be formed, in which there is arrangement and regular repetition in every direction in space. But in the smectic state the temperature is high enough to ease the bonds between sheet and sheet, and yet not high enough to break up the sheets themselves. A single sheet does not necessarily behave like a separate crystal: it is rather to be considered as a two-dimensional fluid.

$$C_2H_5-O-CO-C_6H_4-N-N-C_6H_4-CO-O-C_2H_5$$
$$\diagdown\diagup$$
$$O$$

Ethyl *para*-azoxybenzoate
Solid $-114°C$ $-$smectic $-120°C$ $-$liquid.

A sheet of this nature can slide without hindrance on its neighbours. When a film of the above-mentioned substance is stretched over a small hole in a plate, the condition of parallel layers is in fact arrived at. It can also be reached when the substance rests on a plate, but unless the plate is carefully prepared it is apt to be interfered with by local attachments, as will be seen presently. In the simple form the substance may be examined in polarised convergent light, and will show the usual rings. With the aid of a quarter-wave plate it can be shown by well-known methods that the arrangement simulates a positive crystal. The full structure of the crystal is not realised because the separate sheets are not properly adjusted to each other. That, however, does not affect the examination in convergent light, which requires only that the axis of the beam shall be perpendicular to the layers. The experiment shows that the substance behaves like a positive crystal, such as quartz. In other words, the frequency of the light vibrations perpendicular to the layers (and parallel to the molecules) is less than the frequency when the vibrations are not perpendicular thereto. This is to be expected, because it is always found that vibrations along an extended molecule are slower than those across it.

The simple stratification lends itself also to study by X-rays, when it appears that the thickness of the layer agrees closely with what we know of the length of such molecules, based on exact X-ray measurements of other organic molecules. Friedel[4] gives the value

度。就肥皂泡或薄膜而言，我们已使这些层形成了内外表面。分子间的并排吸引力将它们束缚在一起，因此薄膜具有特定的表面张力能。如果将薄膜扩大，其他的油酸钠分子就会填补入位而增大表面积。如果薄膜收缩，分子就会离开并变回液态。

现在让我们假设这些层是由氧化偶氮基苯甲酸乙酯形成的，这种物质表现出很好的近晶相特征。每一层都很有弹性。如果能将这样一层悬在空中而不受重力影响，它将以完美的平面形式呈现，因为分子会倾向于彼此平行。它们之间的并排吸引力相当强。如果被弯曲后，它会自动地再次伸直。如果将很多这样的层像一本书的书页一样放在一起，它们还会进一步自我调整，使得某一层表面上的分子末端精确地与下一层的分子末端以某种特征方式相结合。通过这种方式就会形成固态晶体，其中，空间的每一个方向上都存在着规则排布和规律的重复。但是在近晶相状态中，温度高到足以削弱层与层之间的连接，却又没有高到足以破坏层本身。单一的层无须具有独立晶体的性质：它更应该被看作是一种二维流体。

$$C_2H_5 - O - CO - C_6H_4 - N - N - C_6H_4 - CO - O - C_2H_5$$

对 – 氧化偶氮基苯甲酸乙酯

固态 –114℃ – 近晶相 –120℃ – 液态

一个具有这种性质的层可以毫无阻碍地在它的邻近层之间滑动。将上述物质的薄膜在平板中的小洞上拉伸时，实际上就可以满足平行层的条件。将该物质静置于平板上时，也可以达到要求，但是平板必须是精心制造的，否则局部的附着很容易就会造成干扰，如同我们不久将会看到的那样。处于简单形式中的该物质可以用偏振的汇聚光来检验，并会显示出正常的环。在四分之一波片的帮助下，通过众所周知的方法可以显示出其排布类似于正晶体。此类晶体的完整结构还未被了解，因为分离的各层之间无法进行适当的调整。不过，这并不影响汇聚光的检验，因为检验只需要光束的轴与层垂直即可。实验表明，该物质的行为类似于诸如石英等正晶体。换言之，垂直于层（从而与分子平行）的光的振动频率比不垂直于层时的振动频率小。这是可以预期的，因为我们经常发现沿着分子伸展方向的振动比穿过分子的慢。

这种简单分层还使其适合于通过 X 射线进行研究，层的厚度看起来与我们已知的该分子的长度相当一致——分子长度基于对其他有机分子精确的 X 射线测量。夫里德耳[4] 给出的值为 19.9 Å。在固态晶体中发现层的厚度为 16.2 Å。二者的差异

19.9 A. In the solid crystal the thickness of the layer is found to be 16.2 A. The difference is due to the fact that in the layers of the solid the molecules are inclined and not upright as in the liquid crystal.

In general, however, the substance, when placed between glasses, as is usual when examination is to be made under the microscope, and when raised to the proper range of temperature, or cooled from the melt, does not assume the simple form. The strata are crumpled. Attachments between substance and glass are strong, and at various points these attachments compel the arrangement of the molecules in different directions. The general arrangement has to accommodate itself to enforced conditions in various places. Moreover, nuclear associations of molecules are formed at various points in the liquid when it is passing into the liquid crystals phase; and these must be fitted to one another as they grow and meet together. There is something like the contortion of strata in a geological formation; but the smectic arrangement is simpler, because the layers, while preserving their thickness exactly, can slide easily over one another and so can adjust themselves to surface conditions.

The optical peculiarities of the smectic state are caused by these contortions of the strata. We have therefore to consider in the first place the forms which the strata assume, and in the second their effect upon the transmission of light.

From direct observation it can be inferred, as will be seen presently, that the surfaces of the strata form series of the "cyclides" examined long ago by Dupin and known by his name. We must therefore consider their chief properties.

The locus of the vertices of the circular cones (cones of revolution) passing through a given ellipse is a hyperbola which passes through the focus of the ellipse and lies in a plane perpendicular to that of the ellipse. Conversely, the ellipse is the locus of the vertices of circular cones passing through the hyperbola. The ellipse and the hyperbola are described as "focal conics".

Surfaces can be drawn which are at right angles to all the straight lines which pass through both conics. These are Dupin's cyclides. They are peculiar in that any pair of surfaces is equally separated everywhere, the distance of separation being measured along the common normal. Obviously this makes it possible for the surfaces to coincide with the surfaces of sheets of uniform thickness.

It is easy to form an idea of the arrangement by considering a simple case. The ellipse may become a circle, in which case the hyperbola becomes the axis of the circle, that is to say, a straight line passing through the centre of the circle and perpendicular to its plane. The cyclides become "anchor rings" or "torse", intersected at right angles by every straight line that meets both circle and axis. The construction is shown in Figs. 2 and 3.

归因于下列事实：在固体的层中分子是倾斜的，不像在液晶中是竖直的。

但是一般来说，将这种物质置于玻璃之间时（如同在显微镜下检验常常做的那样），当温度升高到适当范围，或者从熔融态冷却时，它都不会呈现简单的形式。层变皱了。物质与玻璃之间的附着作用很强，在各个点上，附着作用会迫使分子以不同的方向进行排布。整体排布不得不进行自我调节以顺应各处的条件。此外，当液体进入液晶相时，各个点上都会形成分子的有核缔合；而这些缔合体在生长和聚拢时必须彼此保持一致。这种情况有些类似于地质组成中的地层扭曲；不过近晶相排布更简单些，因为各个层在精确保持自身厚度的前提下可以很容易地彼此滑动，因而能够自我调整以适应表面条件。

近晶态的光学特性是由层的褶皱造成的。由此我们不得不首先考虑层所呈现的形式，继而考虑其对光传播的影响。

如同现在就要看到的那样，我们可以通过直接观测推测出层的表面形成了一系列的"圆纹曲面"，这是很久以前迪潘检测到的，也是以他的名字来命名的。因此我们必须考虑它们的主要性质。

通过一个给定椭圆的一组圆锥体（指旋转锥体）的顶点轨迹是双曲线，它经过椭圆的焦点，并位于垂直于椭圆的平面内。反过来，椭圆则是经过抛物线的圆锥体的顶点轨迹。椭圆和抛物线称为"焦点圆锥曲线"。

我们可以将表面画成与所有同时经过两条圆锥曲线的直线呈直角，这就是迪潘的圆纹曲面。它们的特别之处在于，若沿着公法线测量其分隔距离，任何一对表面各处都是等间距的。很明显，这使得各个表面有可能与同样厚度的层表面相一致。

通过考虑一种简单情况，人们很容易形成一种排布观念。椭圆可以变成一个圆，这时双曲线变成圆的轴，也就是一条经过圆心并与圆所在平面相垂直的直线。圆纹曲面变成了"锚环"或"环面"，与每条同时过圆和轴的直线以直角相交。图 2 和图 3 显示了这种结构。

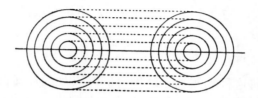

Fig. 2. Section of an anchor-ring in layers, which constitute a particular series of Dupin's cyclides.

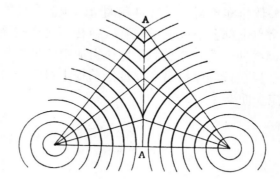

Fig. 3. An axis *AA* is now added to the ring of Fig. 2. Every straight line drawn from any point on *AA* to any point on the axial circle of the ring meets every layer at right angles. In this figure emphasis is laid on those parts of the layers which lie within the cone of which the upper point *A* is the vertex and the axial circle is the circumference of the flat base. Within the cone the layers are in equilibrium with each other. How one cone can be fitted to another is explained in the text.

When this simple case occurs in the liquid crystal, the strata are bounded by a succession of anchor rings equally separated. The straight lines that meet both circle and axis are perpendicular to the strata and therefore parallel to the long dimension of the molecule. As has been said above, the substance behaves like a uniaxial crystal, the axis lying along the molecule. The straight lines show therefore the direction of the optic axis at every point, being parallel to the molecules round about the point. It must not be supposed, however, that each such straight line is a chain of molecules; if that were the case converging lines of molecules would "jam" into one another.

It will be observed that no two of the straight lines intersect. We may pass from this special case to the general by imagining the circle to become an ellipse and the cones to be pushed over to the side as in Figs. 4 and 5. The anchor rings become distorted, but the characteristic properties of the cyclides are still maintained. Every straight line that meets both ellipse and hyperbola is normal at all points to a series of surfaces, and still any two of the surfaces are everywhere separated by the same distance, measured along the common normal.

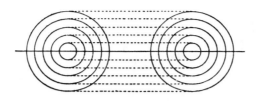

图 2. 层中的锚环截面，构成一系列特定的迪潘圆纹曲面。

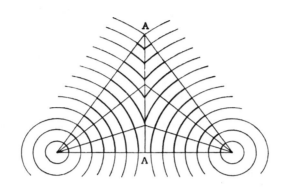

图 3. 现将轴 *AA* 添加到图 2 的环中。从 *AA* 上任意一点向环的轴圆上的任意一点画的每条直线都与每个层以直角相交。本图中所强调的是满足下列条件的各层的相应部分：它们位于以上面的 *A* 点为顶点、以底层圆周为轴圆的圆锥之间。在这一圆锥中，各层彼此取得平衡。正文中解释了一个圆锥如何与另一个相一致。

当这一简单情况出现在液晶中时，层受到一系列等间距锚环的约束。同时与圆和轴相交的直线是垂直于层的，因而平行于分子的纵向维度。如同上面已经提到过的，该物质表现得犹如一种单轴晶体，其轴平行于分子的方向。因而直线显示出各点的光轴方向，即与该点周围的分子平行。但我们绝对不能推断出每条这样的直线都是一个分子链；如果是那样的话，分子的汇聚线就会彼此"嵌入"。

我们将会看到，没有任何两条直线相交。想象圆变成椭圆而圆锥则被推向边界，如图 4 和图 5 所示，我们可以从这种特殊情况过渡到一般情况。锚环逐渐扭曲，而圆纹曲面的特征性质依然保留着。每条同时经过椭圆和双曲线的直线与一系列的表面在所有点正交，而且，若沿着公法线测量，任意两个表面仍然在各处都具有同样的距离间隔。

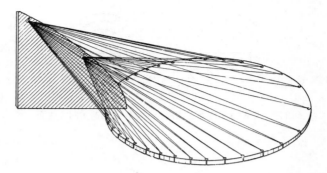

Fig. 4. A drawing of a model made to illustrate the structure of the interior of an oblique cone containing the smectic substance. The two sheets of zinc are cut into the form of an ellipse and part of a hyperbola, and are fastened together so that their planes are perpendicular to each other and each curve goes through the focus of the other. Slots are cut as shown, and strings join two points on the hyperbola to a number of points on the ellipse. If the ellipse were made into a circle, the hyperbola would become the axis of the circle as in Fig. 3. The strata, having the form of Dupin's cyclides, intersect every one of the strings at right angles.

If now we take any two points on the hyperbola, of which one may be the focus of the ellipse, and draw from each of them straight lines to every point on the ellipse, we include a region bounded by two cones, or in the special case one cone and its flat base, which can be divided by Dupin cyclides into a series of sheets of uniform thickness; and at all points on the surface of the space the sheets are perpendicular to the generators of the cones.

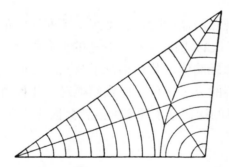

Fig. 5. A section of Fig. 4 in the plane of the hyperbola, showing parts of cyclides. Compare this with Fig. 3. The complete cyclide which in Fig. 3 was a uniform ring, the so-called "anchor ring", is now thicker on one side than on the other.

We are now going to see how, in imagination, we can divide a solid mass of material, such as that which lies on the microscope slide, into separate blocks, in each of which the substance is arranged on one or more sets of cyclides, while all the blocks can be fitted together so that the stratification runs continuously through the whole.

If two such conical regions are made to touch along a common generator, the cyclides in one region may be looked on as continuations of the cyclides in the other, though they come into contact only at the common generator. Any pyramidal space can be divided

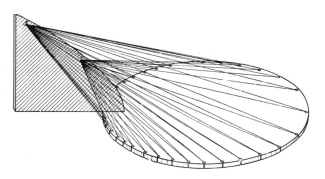

图 4. 描绘含近晶态物质的斜圆锥内部结构的模型图。将两张锌片裁割成椭圆和双曲线的一部分的
形式，再把它们固定在一起，使得它们所在的平面彼此垂直，并且每条曲线都经过另一条的焦点。
如图所示切开若干狭槽，用线将双曲线上的两个点与椭圆上的多个点连接起来。如果将椭圆变成圆，
那么双曲线就会如图 3 那样成为圆的轴。具有迪潘圆纹曲面形式的层与每条线以直角相交。

现在如果我们取双曲线上的任意两点，其中一点可以是椭圆的焦点，并从其中每
一点向椭圆上的各个点做直线，就包住了以两个圆锥为边界的区域，或者在特殊情况
下是由一个圆锥和它的底平面包围的区域，这个区域可以由迪潘圆纹曲面分隔成一系
列厚度相同的片层；并且在该空间表面的所有点上，这些片层垂直于圆锥的母线。

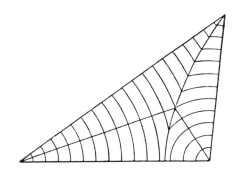

图 5. 图 4 中双曲线所在平面的一部分，呈现出圆纹曲面的局部。将其与图 3 相比较。图 3 中完整
的圆纹曲面是均匀的环，即所谓的"锚环"，而这里则一侧比另外一侧更厚些。

现在我们可以想象一下，如何将一块例如置于显微镜载物片上的实体物质分隔
成分离的块，每一块中该物质排布成一组或若干组圆纹曲面，而所有的块又可以结
合在一起从而使分层连续贯穿整个实体。

如果令两个这样的圆锥形区域沿着一条公共母线接触，一个区域内的圆纹曲面
就可以看成是另一区域中圆纹曲面的延续，不过它们只在公共母线处发生接触。任

147

into cones, large ones in the centre, smaller cones partially filling up corners that are left, and still smaller cones filling up corners that are still left, and so on. The pyramidal space can then be further sub-divided into strata of uniform thickness by sets of cyclides, one set to each cone, which all fit on to one another, and meet at right angles the straight lines drawn from the vertex to all the points on the polygon forming the base. In each of the cones the vertex and the focus of the ellipse forming its base are the two terminal points on the hyperbola belonging to that cone. Since all the hyperbolae lie on planes that are perpendicular to the bases of the cones, which bases are co-planar, and all pass through the vertex of the pyramid, the major axes of the ellipses all pass through the projection of the vertex on the basal plane.

A solid block can be divided into two sets of pyramids, half of which have their bases on each one of two opposite faces and vertices on the other, together with certain wedge-like spaces. This is readily seen if we consider such a division as is indicated in Fig. 6, where the pyramids are, for simplicity, set on square bases; and it appears that besides the pyramids there are wedges or tetrahedra such as *IJPQ*. Pyramids and wedges account for the whole. Now the top and bottom edges of each wedge can be looked on as portions of a pair of focal conics, and the space inside the wedge can be divided by cyclides which meet the other four edges at right angles and therefore pass continuously into cyclides in the adjoining pyramids. The top and bottom edges must have at least some small curvature. If straight lines be drawn from every point on the upper edge to every point on the lower, they are all normal to the set of cyclides which divide the space inside the wedge into layers of uniform thickness. Thus the whole of a solid block can be divided into uniformly thick contorted layers by Dupin cyclides belonging to a number of different sets which, however, fit on to each other perfectly.

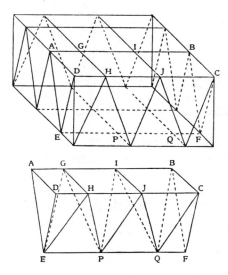

Fig. 6. The rectangular block is divided by saw-cuts into wedges; the division being made in two ways, parallel to two of the edges of the block. Below the block is shown one of the wedges obtained by cutting parallel to *AB*. The second set of cuts, parallel to *AD*, divides this larger wedge into pyramids such as *P*(*GHIJ*) and smaller wedges such as *IJPQ*.

何锥形空间都可以分隔成圆锥，较大的一些在中心，较小的圆锥部分地填充遗留空隙，更小的则填充剩下的遗留空隙，以此类推。那么，锥形空间就可以用若干组圆纹曲面进一步细分为同样厚度的层，每个圆锥对应一组，所有的圆纹曲面组合在一起，并且都与从顶点到构成底面的多边形上的所有点所做的直线以直角相交。在每个圆锥中，顶点和构成其底面的椭圆的焦点是属于这一圆锥的双曲线上的两个端点。由于所有的双曲线都位于垂直于圆锥底面（这些底是共面的）的平面上，并且都经过锥体的顶点，因此椭圆的长轴全都经过顶点在底面上的投影。

一个实心立方体可以分割成两组锥体，其中一半的锥体以两个对立面之一为底而顶点在另一个上，另外还有一些楔形空间。如果让我们来考虑图 6 中所示的这种分割，这是很容易看出来的。为简化起见，将其中的锥体置于正方形的底面上；看起来，除锥体外还有诸如 IJPQ 这样的楔形体或四面体。锥体和楔形体占据了全部。现在每个楔形体的顶部和底部的棱可以看作是一对焦点圆锥曲线的一部分，而楔形体内部的空间可用圆纹曲面进行分割，这些曲面与另外四条棱以直角相交，因而连续地穿入毗连的锥体内部的圆纹曲面。顶部和底部的棱必有一些小的曲率。如果从上方棱上的每个点向下方棱上的每个点做直线，则它们都与将楔形内空间分割成等厚度层的那组圆纹曲面正交。因而全部实心立方体可以用大量不同组的迪潘圆纹曲面分割成等厚度的褶皱层，从而各组之间可以完美地组合起来。

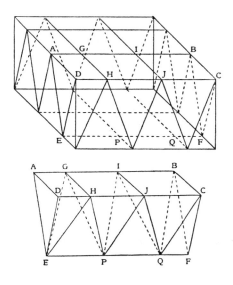

图 6. 用锯将矩形块分割成楔形：分割以两种与矩形块的两条棱平行的方式进行。矩形块下面显示的是平行于 AB 切割所得到的一个楔形。而第二组切割平行于 AD，将较大的楔形分割成像 P(GHIJ) 那样的四棱锥和像 IJPQ 那样较小的楔形体。

We have next to show that the optical effects are consistent with such an arrangement, and in fact establish its existence.

In a solid crystal the direction of the axes is constant throughout. In a liquid crystal this is not the case. Fortunately for our convenience in solving the new problem, there is only one axial direction at each point, namely, that which is perpendicular to the layer; it coincides with the straight line passing through the point and also through the tow focal conics. We may divide into two parts the problem of the path of a ray through a liquid crystal. Consider first the case when a continuous change in the direction of the crystal axis is taking place in the plane containing the path of the ray. Let that plane be the plane of the paper and let the axes be directed towards the point O in Fig. 7. Clearly a vibration which is perpendicular to the plane is always perpendicular to the axis wherever it is, and is never deflected. But a vibration in the plane of the diagram is that of an "extraordinary" ray and suffers continuous deflection. Its path was calculated by Grandjean[5] who showed that it moves on the curve $r \cos n\alpha = a$, where r and α are polar coordinates, O being the pole; n is the ratio of the refractive index of the extraordinary to that of the ordinary ray, and a $(=OA)$ is a constant. If $n=1$, the curve becomes a straight line, as it ought to do, since the substance would then behave as if isotropic, and a ray of light would go straight through. The curve in the figure has the two straight lines OP and OQ as asymptotes, and the angle $POQ = \pi/n$. An extraordinary ray approaching along a line originally parallel to OP but not directed at O is finally deflected along OQ. At the beginning and the end it is very nearly an ordinary ray. To sum up, ordinary rays consisting of vibrations normal to the diagram suffer no deflection, but extraordinary rays do.

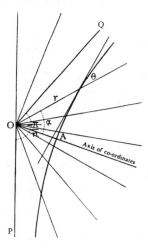

Fig. 7. The curved line shows the path of the extraordinary ray in a medium in which the axial direction at any point is directed towards O. The axes and the path lie in one plane.

Next we consider a ray passing through a region where the direction of the axis is changing continuously but is always normal to the direction of the ray. Such a structure may be termed a twisted or helicoidal structure. In any plane which is normal to the ray,

下面我们将指出，光学效应与这样一种排布是一致的，并且事实上也确证了这种存在。

在固态晶体中轴的方向始终保持不变，在液晶中却不是这样。幸运的是，对于我们解决这个新问题来说很方便的是，每个点只有一个轴方向，即与层垂直的方向；它与通过该点且通过两条焦点圆锥曲线的直线相一致。我们可以将通过液晶的射线的路径问题分成两部分。首先考虑的情况是晶轴线方向的连续变化发生在包含射线路径的平面内。令该平面为纸平面，并令轴指向如图 7 所示的点 O。显然地，垂直于平面的振动无论位于何处总是垂直于轴，绝无反射。但是图内平面中的振动是一条"异常"射线的振动，并遭受连续的反射。格朗让对其路径进行的计算 [5] 表明它在曲线 $r \cos n\alpha = a$ 上移动，其中 r 和 α 是极坐标，O 为极点；n 是异常部分的折射率与正常射线折射率的比值，而 a（$=OA$）则是一个常数。如果 $n = 1$，该曲线就变成直线，如同它本应如此的那样，由于接下来该物质会表现得如各向同性一般，因而光线将会直射而过。图中曲线以 OP 和 OQ 两条直线作为渐近线，角 $POQ = \pi/n$。一条异常射线沿着最初平行于 OP 但不指向 O 的方向接近，并最终沿着 OQ 而反射。在开始和结尾处它非常近似于一条正常射线。简而言之，与该图正交的振动组成的正常射线未发生反射，而异常射线则发生反射。

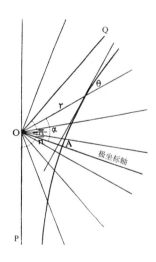

图 7. 曲线所示为异常射线的路径，其介质中任意一点处的轴向都指向 O。
各轴与路径位于同一平面内。

下面我们考虑射线通过一个轴向连续变化但总是与射线方向正交的区域。这种结构可以称为盘曲面或者螺旋面。在任一与射线正交的平面中，各点的轴向相

the direction of the axis is the same at every point but the direction changes continuously along the ray, as happens in a pack of cards to which a twist has been applied about an axis perpendicular to the plane of the cards.

It is not to be expected that a polarised ray would maintain unchanged the rectilinear character of its vibration during its passage through such a medium; in fact, Maxwell's equations of the electro-magnetic field cannot be satisfied by so simple an assumption. But if we try an elliptically polarised ray and suppose that the axes of the ellipse follow the twist, we find that the equations are satisfied for certain degrees of ellipticity and corresponding velocities. We have therefore found the solution of our problem.[*] A particular case is alone of importance to us here. In cases with which we are dealing, the wave-length λ is very small compared to p, the pitch of the screw. As Mauguin showed in the case of the nematic substances which we shall examine later, it is not possible to twist the medium so much as to make λ/p anything but a small fraction. It appears that the ellipticities are then small, and the result can be expressed as follows: —

Let K_1 and K_2 be the effective specific inductive capacities across and along the axis. Let c be the velocity in space, and $c/\sqrt{K}$ the velocity in the medium: let λ_0 and λ be the corresponding wave lengths. Let a and b be the axes of the elliptical vibration. Then *either*: —

$K = K_1$ to the second order of small quantities and $b/a = 2\,\lambda\,K_1/p\,(K_1 - K_2) = 2\,\lambda_0\sqrt{K_1}\,/p\,(K_1 - K_2)$ *or* $K = K_2$ and $a/b = 2\,\lambda_0\sqrt{K_2}\,/p\,(K_2 - K_1)$.

It appears therefore that in the twisted medium two elliptical vibrations can travel without change of form, each with its special velocity. When the twist is small we may assume that incident light is resolved into two linear vibrations, the ellipticity being negligible. These vibrations, however, follow the twist, so that the vibrations at any point are always along and perpendicular respectively to the crystal axis at that point. If exactness were necessary, we should have to recognise that incident light is always resolved into two elliptic vibrations of different ellipticities travelling with different speeds. For example, a polarised ray, in which the vibration is parallel to the crystal axis at the surface, is resolved into two elliptic vibrations which travel at different rates. The major axis of the larger lies in the direction of the incident vibration, that of the smaller is perpendicular to it and is equal to the minor axis of the larger. The two rotate in opposite directions. At regularly spaced depths in the medium the two again combine into a linear vibration.

It is to be observed that this effect is practically independent of the wave-length. The rate of rotation for all wave-lengths is that of the mechanical structure.

---

[*] A short proof is given in *Proc. Roy. Inst.*, 28, 90; 1934.

同但方向沿着射线连续变化，就像一摞卡片，围绕着垂直于卡片平面的轴盘成螺旋形。

我们不能预期一条极化的射线在通过这样一种介质时能保持其振动的线性特征不变；事实上，在如此简单的假设下，麦克斯韦的电磁场方程组无法得到满足。但是，如果我们尝试一下椭圆极化射线，并且假定椭圆的轴随着螺旋变化，就会发现特定程度的椭圆率与相应的速度可使方程组得以满足。由此可以找到我们问题的答案[*]。这里，有一种特殊情况对我们来说具有独特的重要性。在我们所处理的这些情况中，波长 λ 相比于螺距 p 是非常小的。如同莫甘在我们将在后面加以考察的向列相物质的情况中所指出的，不可能将介质盘曲到使 λ/p 值不可忽略的程度，它只是一个很小的分数。于是椭圆率看起来就会很小，其结果可以表示如下：

令 K_1 和 K_2 分别为垂直于轴和沿轴向的有效介电常数。令 c 为真空中的速度，$c/\sqrt{K}$ 为介质中的速度，λ_0 和 λ 为相应的波长。令 a 和 b 为椭圆振动的轴。那么，

或者 $K = K_1$ 到二阶小量并且 $b/a = 2\lambda K_1 / p (K_1 - K_2) = 2\lambda_0 \sqrt{K_1} / p (K_1 - K_2)$，
或者 $K = K_2$ 并且 $a/b = 2\lambda_0 \sqrt{K_2} / p (K_2 - K_1)$。

由此看来，两个各自具有特定速度的椭圆振动可以从盘曲的介质中通过而不发生形式变化。当盘曲很小时，我们可以假定入射光分解为两个线性振动，椭圆率可以忽略。不过，这些振动随着盘曲而变化，因而任一点处的振动总是分别沿着和垂直于该点处的晶轴线方向。如果必须考虑精确性的话，我们就不得不认为，入射光总是分解成两个以不同速度行进的具有不同椭圆率的椭圆振动。例如，一条振动与表面晶轴方向平行的极化射线分解为以不同速率行进的两个椭圆振动。较大振动的长轴位于入射振动的方向上，较小的则与其垂直并且等于较大振动的短轴。两个振动以相反的方向旋转。在介质中规则分布深度位置，它们再次结合为线性振动。

我们可以观测到，这种效应实际上与波长无关。对所有波长来说，旋转速率都是机制性的。

---

[*]《皇家研究院院刊》于 1934 年第 28 卷第 90 页中给出了一个简短的证明。

Any axial direction can be brought into coincidence with any other axial direction by a rotation in the plane containing the direction of the ray combined with a rotation about the ray. Thus we are able to say, as the result of the two cases considered, that the ordinary ray goes through the liquid crystal without any change in the direction of its path, no matter how the axis of the crystal alters its direction, provided that the latter alteration is continuous. The direction of the vibration changes in such a way that it is always perpendicular to the axis of the crystal. On the other hand, the extraordinary ray, though behaving like the ordinary ray in all other respects, continuously changes the direction of its path when there is any continuous change in the orientation of the crystal axis, which has a component in the plane containing the ray and the axis.

We can now proceed to examine the appearance of a smectic substance in the light of what we have just proved. Let us consider the photographs in Fig. 1. These are typical of the great variety of appearances presented by a thin layer of ethyl azoxybenzoate. It is in the smectic state, the temperature being held between the limits 114°C. and 120°C. The microscope is focused on the upper surface of the layer and is viewed through an analysing Nicol. There is no polariser. We observe at once the assemblage of polygons each with its content of ellipses. If we suppose that the substance is crumpled up into a combination of sets of cyclides as explained above, and also that these are grouped in cones, pyramids and wedges (see Figs. 4, 5, 6, 8 and 9) then the arrangement of the optic axes in the surface of the layer will be as in Fig. 9; with infinite possibility of variation in the number and sizes of the ellipses. The molecules on the surface lie always on straight lines, which show the directions of the crystal axes at every point, and in each ellipse radiate from the focus to the circumference.

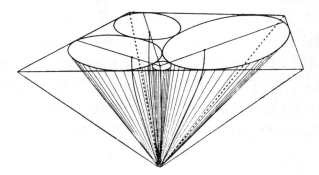

Fig. 8. The arrangement of a set of cones within a pyramid. It follows closely the actual arrangement within a polygon near the bottom and on the left of the left hand photograph in Fig. 1. It is to be remembered that the apparent cones in the photographs of Figs. 1 and 12 are not the cones of this figure though connected with them. Some lines are drawn in the figure in order to outline the cones. The hyperbolae belonging to the various ellipses meet at the vertex of the pyramid. The vacant spaces in the pyramid are filled with smaller cones or portions of cones.

任何一个轴方向都能由任何其他轴方向通过一个在包含射线方向的平面内的旋转加上一个关于射线的旋转而得到。因此我们可以说，作为所考虑两种情况的结果，不管晶体的轴向如何改变，只要该变化为连续，正常射线在经过液晶时就没有任何传播路径方向的变化。以这种方式变化的振动方向总是垂直于晶体的轴。另一方面，尽管异常射线的行为在其他所有方面都类似于正常射线，但只要晶轴的指向有任何连续变化，而且该指向在包含射线与轴的平面内有一个分量时，异常射线就会连续改变其路径方向。

现在我们可以着手检验一种近晶态物质在我们刚才已证明的光线中的样子。让我们来考虑图1中的照片。这些就是在氧化偶氮基苯甲酸乙酯薄层中所呈现出的大量不同外观中的典型样子。它们都处于近晶态，温度保持在114℃和120℃两个极限温度之间。显微镜聚焦于薄层的上表面，并透过一块检偏尼科尔棱镜进行观察。没有使用起偏器。我们立刻观察到内含椭圆的多面体的汇聚体。如果我们假定该物质由于起皱变成上面所解释过的一组圆纹曲面的结合体，并假定它们结合成圆锥、棱锥和楔形（见图4、图5、图6、图8和图9)，于是光轴在层表面中的排布就会如同图9中所显示的那样；椭圆的数目和大小都有无限多种可能性。表面上的分子总是位于直线之上，这些直线显示出各点处的晶轴方向，在每个椭圆中，分子从焦点辐射向圆周。

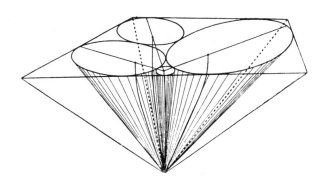

图 8. 一组圆锥在棱锥中的排列。它与图1中左边照片内左侧的底部多面体内的实际排布情况十分相似。应该记住的是，图1和图12中照片内所看到的并不是本图的圆锥，但是与其有一定的关系。图中某些线是为了勾勒圆锥形状而画出来的。属于各个椭圆的双曲线在棱锥的顶点相交。棱锥中的空隙部分由较小的圆锥或者圆锥的一部分所填充。

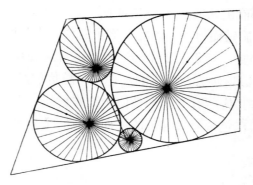

Fig. 9. This shows the base of the pyramid in Fig. 8: and the axial directions radiating from every focus at the base of the hyperbolae (see Fig. 8). The axes of the ellipses all meet at a point which is the projection of the vertex of the pyramid upon the base.

At every point the vibration in the ordinary ray as it emerges is perpendicular to the radius vector from the focus. The original beam divides into two on entering the substance, as usual, but the extraordinary ray quickly goes astray. If it gets through, its vibration is inclined to the radius vector, but its appearance is quite irregular. On the other hand, the ordinary ray appears uniformly at all parts of the field and gives the clear picture which is seen in the microscope. The analyser transmits vibrations parallel to its principal plane, and consequently each ellipse is crossed by a shadow which culminates at the focus. The central line of the shadow is parallel to the principal plane of the Nicol. It will be observed that when a polygon includes several ellipses, the major axes of those ellipses are all directed towards a single point, which, as already explained, is the projection upon the polygon of the vertex of the pyramid standing on the polygon. The vertex lies on the opposite face. When the microscope is adjusted so that the lower face is in focus, it is found that the point on which the major axes of the ellipses converge melts into a point where a number of edges of polygons meet. This is illustrated in Figs. 10 and 12.

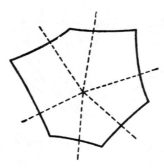

Fig. 10. This shows the disposition of polygon edges in one face of the lower left hand portion of Fig. 12 with respect to polygon edges in the other face.

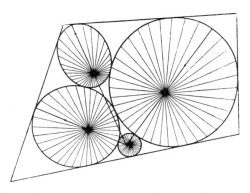

图 9. 这里所示的是图 8 中棱锥的底，以及从双曲线底上的每个焦点辐射出去的轴方向（见图 8）。
所有的椭圆轴的交点是棱锥顶点在底上的射影。

　　在每一点处，正常射线中的振动在射出时都垂直于从焦点出发的矢径。和正常情况一样，初始光束在进入物质时分成两束，但异常射线迅速偏离原路。如果它透过物质，则其振动向矢径倾斜，但外观很不规则。另一方面，正常射线在区域中的所有部分里看起来都是一样的，并且可以在显微镜中看到清晰图像。检偏器只允许平行于主平面的振动透过，结果是每个椭圆都与终结于焦点的一个投影相交。投影的中线与尼科尔棱镜的主平面平行。我们将会观察到，当一个多边形中包含若干个椭圆时，那些椭圆的长轴全都会指向一个单一的点，如同我们已解释过的，该点就是位于多边形之上的棱锥的顶点在多边形上的射影。顶点位于相反的面上。将显微镜调节到聚焦于下表面时，可以发现，椭圆的长轴所汇聚的交点转化为多边形的很多条边的交点，如图 10 和图 12 所示。

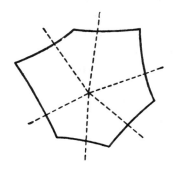

图 10. 本图显示的是图 12 左下方部分中一个面内的多面体棱相对于其他面内的多面体棱的排列。

The polygon edges of Fig. 1 vary in shade, some being light and some dark. It will be observed that the dark edges are more or less parallel to the middle line of the shadow in each polygon; and therefore also to the crystal axis along the edge. This is readily understood when we remember that the side of the polygon is the top edge of a wedge. Inside a wedge the axes run from every point on the top edge to every point on the bottom edge. Along the top edge the projection of the axes is therefore parallel to the edge as shown in Fig. 11. Somewhere in the edge, however, there is a point, unless the wedge is very skewed, where the axis is perpendicular to it, being the shortest distance between the top and bottom edges. At this point the extraordinary becomes equivalent to the ordinary ray. There is no separation when the light enters the medium, and the analyser does not quench it entirely. A black edge then shows a white spot in the middle.

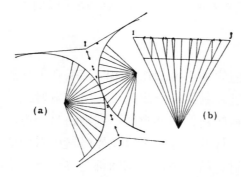

Fig. 11. This shows how the crystal axes in the edge of the wedge *IJ* are at right angles to the axes inside the ellipses where they touch the edge (*a*). About the middle of the edge, the axes are often vertical. This is very often the case in the left hand illustration in Fig. 1. The light from below gets through on this line without being resolved, and is only half darkened by the analyser. The section of *IJ* marked off by arrow-heads represents the direction and relative values of the axial projection on *IJ*; the manner of doing this is shown in (*b*).

From the general and close agreement between theory and observation, we may surely conclude that the smectic substance is indeed arranged in strata which take the form of Dupin's cyclides. There are, however, any number of other geometrical arrangements of sheets of uniform thickness. There must be a reason why the cyclides are preferred, and it must be based on energy considerations. A soap film stretched on a frame takes a form involving minimum energy; if the pressure is the same on both sides the total curvature is everywhere zero, and the edges comply with enforced boundary conditions. In the same way the strata in the smectic state must also, while obeying boundary conditions, arrange themselves so that the potential energy is a minimum.

Simplicity and symmetry imply less storage of energy than unnecessary complication and lack of symmetry. Let us consider possible methods of arrangement in declining order of symmetry.

图 1 中多边形的边在阴影中发生变化，有一些变亮而有一些则变暗。我们将会观察到，暗棱或多或少地与每个多边形中阴影的中线平行；因而也与沿着边的晶轴相平行。如果我们记得多边形的边是一个楔形体顶部的棱，就很容易理解这一点了。在楔形体内部，轴从顶部棱上的每个点到达底部棱上的每个点。因而轴的射影沿着顶部的棱与各边平行，如图 11 所示。但是在棱上的某处存在一个点（除非楔形体极为歪斜），在该点处的轴是垂直的，即为顶部和底部棱之间的最短距离。在这一点，异常射线变得与正常射线相当。光在进入介质时不存在分离，检偏器也不能完全抑制它。于是，一个白点出现在黑边的中部。

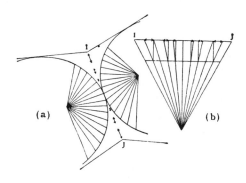

图 11. 本图显示出位于楔形体的棱 IJ 中的晶轴如何与椭圆内的轴在椭圆与棱接触的地方交于直角（a）。在棱中心附近，轴经常是竖直的。这在图1左图中是经常出现的情况。光线自下方通过此直线而不会被分解，经过检偏镜只变暗一半。由箭头所划分出的 IJ 部分代表轴在 IJ 上射影的方向和相对数值；（b）中显示了上述做法。

从理论与观测结果之间普遍且极好的一致性来看，我们可以确定地得出以下结论：近晶态物质确实采取迪潘圆纹曲面形式排列成层状。但是，还存在任意多种相同厚度的层的其他几何排布。圆纹曲面具有优势必然有一个原因，而这个原因必是基于能量的考虑。从一个框架上拉伸出的肥皂膜一定呈现具有最小能量的形状；如果其两边的压力相同，则总曲率处处为零，而其边则满足强制的边界条件。同样的道理，近晶态中的层必定也会在遵循边界条件的前提下进行排布，以使势能取最小值。

相对于不必要的复杂性和对称性缺失而言，简单性和对称性意味着储存较少的能量。让我们按照对称性逐渐减弱的顺序考虑各种可能的排布方法。

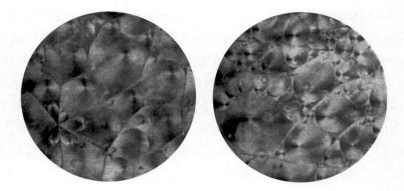

Fig. 12. Two photographs of the same portion of a smectic preparation, but in that on the right the upper surface is in focus, and in that on the left the lower. In the lower left hand portion of the photograph on the right is a fairly regular six-sided polygon, of which the centre is occupied by an ellipse which is nearly a circle. A number of smaller ellipses lie within the same polygon. The axes of all these ellipses are directed to a point. When the other surface is brought into focus this point is seen to be the meeting place of six polygon edges, as is shown by the illustration on the left. This point is the vertex of a pyramid standing on the six-sided polygon. The six lines that meet in a point on one face are the upper edges of wedges of which the lower edges are the sides of the polygon on the other face. They are separately at right angles to these lines because focal conics, however viewed, always seem to intersect at right angles. See Fig. 10.

If strata, originally plane and parallel to each other, are forced out of this arrangement, which is the simplest of all, they must tend to take the cylindrical form which comes next in simplicity. If the disturbing influences are complicated, the various attempts to adopt the cylindrical form must in some way be accommodated to each other. A set of strata of even thickness, bent into cylindrical form, is so grouped round the axis of the cylinder that the normals to the strata at all points intersect the axis at right angles. It is not possible, however, to divide a mass of the smectic substance into cylindrical groupings of this kind; the various groupings cannot be made conformable with each other.

In the next order of simplicity the normals to the strata still meet in a line, but are inclined to it, forming cones of revolution, the vertices of which are points on the line, the inclination being constant in all directions radiating from any point on the line. This is illustrated in various preceding figures, for example Fig. 4. Each cone is symmetrical about its axis.

It is this arrangement which is adopted. Every normal to the strata is anchored on two lines which are focal conics. Every boundary surface of the strata is as symmetrical as possible, being at right angles to series of cones of revolution; and the various sets of surfaces are conformable to each other as we have seen. The cyclides are the only surfaces which fulfil these conditions. The geometry of the cyclide was considered by Clerk Maxwell[6], who pointed out that if the rays in a beam of light pass through two focal lines, the lines are necessarily parts of focal conics. The wave surfaces are equally spaced cyclides to which all the rays are normal.

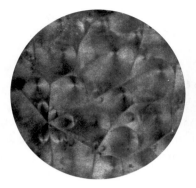

图 12. 某种近晶态制剂同一部分的两张照片，不过其中右边的一张是聚焦于上表面的，左边的则是聚焦于下表面。右边照片中的左下部分是一个相当规则的六边形，其中心由一个近似于圆的椭圆所占据。很多较小的椭圆也位于这个多边形中。所有这些椭圆的轴都指向一点。在聚焦于另一个表面时可以看到，这个点就是多边形六条边的交汇处，如同左边的图片中所显示的那样。这个点是以六边形为底面的棱锥的顶点。在某一表面上交于一点的六条线是楔形体顶部的棱，楔形体底部的棱则是位于另一表面上的多边形的边。它们分别与上述直线交成直角，因为焦点圆锥曲线无论怎样看似乎总是会交成直角。见图10。

如果原本为平面且彼此平行的层状被迫要改变这种最为简单的排布方式，它们必定会倾向于采取圆柱这一简单性次之的一种排布方式。如果扰动影响是复杂的，那么各种采取圆柱形式的尝试必须要以某种方式彼此调和。一组具有相同厚度的已弯曲成圆柱形式的层在圆柱的轴附近集聚，以满足层上所有点的法线和轴都相交成直角。但是，把大量的近晶态物质分成这种类型的圆柱形的组是不可能的；不同的组之间无法彼此契合。

简单性再降低一级，层的法线仍然相交于一条线，不过是倾斜着的，从而形成旋转锥体，锥体顶点为线上的点，其倾角在从线上任意一点辐射出来的所有方向上都是常数。这一点已在前面的多张图片中有所呈现，例如图 4 中。每个圆锥关于其轴都是对称的。

这就是实际采取的排布方式。层的每条法线均定位于两条焦点圆锥曲线之上。层的每个界面都是尽可能对称的，即与一系列旋转锥体交成直角；而各组表面之间则是彼此契合的，如同我们已经看到的那样。圆纹曲面是仅有的一种能满足上述要求的表面。克拉克·麦克斯韦 [6] 曾考察过圆纹曲面的几何性质，他指出，如果一束光中的射线通过两条焦线，焦线必须是焦点圆锥曲线的一部分。波面是等间距的圆纹曲面，所有射线都与其正交。

A useful list of substances which may exist in the smectic state is given by Friedel in the paper already referred to[2]. The azoxybenzoate is often taken as typical, as it is easily made to show all the smectic characteristics.

Nematic Crystals

The second of the three classes of liquid crystals outlined by Friedel, was called by him "nematic", from the singular appearance of mobile threads, either free in the interior of the substance or attached more or less to the bounding plates. These have none of the focal conic structures of the smectic substances, having in fact no stratification. They possess optical properties, however, and therefore some degree of molecular arrangement. What that arrangement is may well be inferred from a recent determination of the solid crystal structure by Bernal and Crowfoot[7]. *Para*-azoxyanisole and *para*-azoxyphenetole are typical nematic substances.

$$CH_3 - O - C_6H_4 - N - N - C_6H_4 - O - CH_3$$
$$O$$

Para-azoxyanisole

Solid $-116°C -$ nematic $-133°C -$ liquid

$$C_2H_5 - O - C_6H_4 - N - N - C_6H_4 - O - C_2H_5$$
$$O$$

Para-azoxyphenetole

Solid $-135°C -$ nematic $-165°C -$ liquid.

X-ray analysis shows that the molecules in the solid lie parallel to one another, but cannot be clearly separated into layers. They interleave one another, or, to use the description by the authors referred to, they are imbricated. Certain indications found on the X-ray photographs show also that the degree of interpenetration is not sharply defined but is variable about an average value. Since the change from solid to the "liquid crystal" form is so easy, there cannot be much variation in arrangement or bindings, and the natural inference is that, even more in the latter than in the former phase, the interpenetration lengthways is variable and easily effected. We should therefore conceive of the substance as owing its mobility to the facility with which the molecules can be drawn past each other, while retaining a strong tendency to acquire or retain a parallelism between the long dimensions of the molecules and the direction of drawing.

Another striking characteristic of the nematic state is the tendency for the molecules to be attached sideways to the slide or the coverslip. If once a solid crystal has formed between the two glass surfaces, it is difficult to remove all traces of its having done so. The substance may be completely melted and allowed to return to the nematic state, whereupon it will recrystallise more or less according to the same plan as before. The melting does not remove all the molecules adhering sideways to the glass, and enough

夫里德耳在前面已提到过的一篇论文 [2] 中给出了能够以近晶态形式存在的物质的一张有用的列表。氧化偶氮基苯甲酸酯经常被作为典型代表，因为它很容易呈现出所有近晶态特性。

向列相液晶

夫里德耳对三种液晶中的第二种进行了概述，他称其为"向列相"，因为它具有游动细丝这一特殊外观，或者是自由地处于物质内部，或者是或多或少地附着于有界的平板上。它们没有近晶态物质的焦点圆锥曲线结构，因而实际上也没有层结构。不过，它们拥有光学性质从而具有某种程度上的分子规则排布。通过贝尔纳和克劳福特最近关于固态晶体结构的一些论断 [7]，我们可以顺利地推测出这种排布是什么样的。对－氧化偶氮基苯甲醚和对－氧化偶氮基苯乙醚是典型的向列相物质。

$$CH_3-O-C_6H_4-N-N-C_6H_4-O-CH_3$$

对–氧化偶氮基苯甲醚

固态 –116℃ – 向外相 –133℃ – 液态

$$C_2H_5-O-C_6H_4-N-N-C_6H_4-O-C_2H_5$$

对–氧化偶氮基苯乙醚

固态 –135℃ – 向外相 –165℃ – 液态

X 射线分析显示，固态中的分子彼此平行地排列，但是无法明确地分离成层状。它们交织在一起，或者我们引述原作者的话来说，它们交叠在一起。X 射线照片中发现的某些迹象还指出，虽然无法清晰地勾画出互相渗透的程度，但它是围绕某一平均值而变化的。由于从固态到"液晶"形式的变化颇为容易，因此排布中不可能有太多变化或者说约束，自然的推论是，后一个相比前一个相中的纵向渗透更易变，而且易受影响。由此我们应该设想，这种物质的流动性源于分子的灵活性，因而可以在牵引下彼此穿越，同时又具有强烈的倾向使分子长度方向与牵引方向保持一致。

向列相状态的另一个令人惊讶的特性，是分子具有侧向附着在载玻片或盖玻片上的倾向。一旦固态晶体在两个玻璃表面之间形成，就很难再把它们彻底地去除。该物质可以完全熔化并能变回向列相状态，因此或多或少地会根据与以前相同的方式再结晶。熔化并不能除去所有侧向黏附在玻璃上的分子，足够的残余物会使分子回到它们此前在试剂中各个分离部分中的指向。将尼科尔棱镜交叉时，显微镜中的

remain to redirect the molecules in their former orientation in each separate part of the preparation. In the microscope, when the Nicols are crossed, the appearance is that of a map in which the different countries are differently tinted, because the general direction of the molecules in each part is peculiar to that part. In each part the direction may be the same right through the preparation from one glass surface to the other, especially if the layer is thin. If one or both of the Nicols are rotated, the alternations of light and dark are the same as if the preparation were a section of a uniaxial real crystal. Yet the substance is liquid (Friedel, *loc. cit*). If particles of dust or other intrusions wander through it they move freely, while the optical effects are unchanged. The orientations of the molecules are governed by those on the surface, and even if there is a stream flowing, they do not diverge from the common orientation of the section in which they are. But, if they move into another section, they change the old orientation for a new one.

Suppose now that the cover slip is moved, either by translation or by rotation with respect to the slide. In many places it must consequently happen that the orientation of the molecules on the top face is different from the corresponding orientation on the face below. The angle between them is α, let us say. It then appears that there is a gradual transition from one orientation to the other on the way through; the substance assumes a helicoidal or twisted arrangement. If a polariser is set parallel to the molecules on the lower surface, the analyser, in order to obtain extinction, must be set, not in the perpendicular direction but at an angle α thereto. We have a straightforward example of the twisted medium which we have already considered. Both ordinary and extraordinary rays follow the screw-like arrangement of the structure, the vibration in the one remaining always normal to the molecule, and therefore to the optic axis, while the other vibration is always parallel to it. In this case there is no deflection of the extraordinary ray.

The substance in the nematic state does not always assume the simple arrangement in plane sheets, in which the axes are parallel to the surface. If it is cooled quickly from the amorphous phase, or if less care is taken in the preparation of the glass plates, it becomes full of complicated vortices and intertwinings. Among these are the fine lines or threads from which the phase derives its name; they are especially obvious where the preparation is thick. The threads are lines of discontinuity giving rise to optical effects, in accordance with the calculations made above. A thread might be a line which is the meeting place of crystal axes at all points of its length, as in the smectic case. There is now no necessity, however, for the line to be part of an ellipse or hyperbola, because it has no companion with which to form a pair of focal conics. Or again, it might be a line round which the medium is circulating, corresponding to a vortex ring, which is either complete or anchored at two ends. The molecules and the optic axes are then tangential to circles having the line as axis. Sometimes a line marks the boundary between two portions in which the axial directions are different.

In these cases, the ordinary ray is not deflected as it passes by the thread, unless it passes very close to it. There must then be a deflection of the ordinary ray because the thread is

镜像犹如一幅不同国家区域染有不同颜色的地图，因为每部分分子的总体方向是该部分所特有的。在每个部分中，从一块玻璃表面到另一块表面之间的所有试剂可以具有同样的指向，尤其是在层很薄时。若将一块或两块尼科尔棱镜旋转，试剂会表现出明与暗的交替变化，如同一块真实的单轴晶体一样。但是该物质是液态的（夫里德耳，见上述引文）。如果有灰尘颗粒或其他侵入物质通过，它们可以自由移动，同时光学效应不变。分子的指向是受表面上的分子所支配的，即使有某种流量存在，分子也不会偏离其所在部分中的共同指向。但是，如果它们进入另一部分，原有的指向就会发生改变。

现在假定将盖玻片相对于载玻片移动，或平移或旋转。在很多情况下，这必定会导致上表面分子的指向不同于下表面分子相应的指向。两者之间的夹角我们不妨称为 α。接着就可以看到，沿途径会出现一种指向向另一种逐渐过渡；物质采取一种螺旋形或盘曲形的排布方式。如果将起偏器置于与下表面分子平行的方向，那么为了获得消光，就必定不能将检偏器置于垂直方向，而是要与垂直方向成 α 角。我们已经考虑过关于盘曲形介质的直接例子。正常的和异常的射线都允许结构螺旋状排布，其中一种振动总是保持与分子正交，从而也与光轴正交，而另外一种振动则总是与其平行。在这种情况下不存在异常射线的偏转。

处于向列态的物质并不总是采取简单排布方式，即轴与表面平行的平面层状。如果将其从非晶相快速冷却，或者在制备玻璃板时不够小心，就会出现很多复杂的旋涡和缠结。其中有细线或丝线形，这种相的名称即由此而来；在试剂较厚的情况下，它们显得格外显眼。根据前面所进行的计算，这些细丝是不连续的线，是它们引起了光学效应。一根细丝可能是一条线，即，其上所有的点都是晶轴的交汇处，如同近晶态中的情况那样。不过，现在这条线还未必就是椭圆或双曲线的一部分，因为它还缺少一个同伴以形成一对焦点圆锥曲线。或者，它可能也是介质所环绕的一条线，与一个或完整，或锚定于两个末端的涡环相一致。于是，分子和光轴就与以该线为轴的圆相切。有时，一条线标识出两个具有不同轴方向的部分之间的边界。

在上述情况下，正常射线经过细丝时不会偏转，除非它经过时过于靠近细丝。那样就必定会出现正常射线的偏转，因为细丝是可见的。假如有反射面的话，可能

visible. It may be that there is actually a hollow cylinder—perhaps vacuous—providing a reflecting surface; or it may be that the excessive strain of the medium close to the thread actually alters the refractive index of the ordinary ray.

The latter explanation would involve the introduction of a principle not used hitherto in these considerations. It has been sufficient, so far, to ascribe the optical effects to geometrical arrangement. The extraordinary ray, on the other hand, may be deflected, since it passes through a region in which the crystal axis is continuously changing its direction in the plane containing axis and ray.

From this point of view we see at once the explanation of a very remarkable and characteristic appearance of the nematic substances, which is illustrated in the photographs of Fig. 13. These are photographs of the same preparation, taken one after the other as quickly as possible so as to avoid changes due to the continuous movement of the liquid. The light entering from below is not polarised but passes through an analyser after crossing the preparation. The obvious difference between the two photographs is due to the fact that the analyser was rotated through about 90° between the two exposures. The threads that look narrow and clear in one photograph are distorted in the other; a close comparison will show that otherwise the two photographs are identical.

Fig. 13. The two photographs show the same substance, *Para*-azoxyphenetole in the nematic phase, at two moments separated by as short an interval as possible. The only difference is that the position of the analyser in one case is approximately at right angles to its position in the other. No polariser. The clearer portion of each photograph is seen by ordinary rays; and the other by extraordinary rays.

The remarkable feature which demands explanation is the fact that all the threads in one part of the picture should be clear simultaneously, while in another part they are all blurred. We remember, however, that there can be a skin or pellicle, to use Friedel's term, in contact with the glass surface; in other words, the previous existence of a solid crystal there has left molecules on the glass which all point the same way, like a flock of birds on the ground which all head up into the wind. This sets the orientation of other molecules in the near neighbourhood of the glass, and though the molecules may be orientated in all kinds of ways between the top and the bottom of the preparation, the change is never discontinuous except in the "thread" itself; even then the continuity passes round the

166

实际上会出现一个空心圆柱（可能是空的）；还有可能是，靠近细丝周围的介质的过度张力实际上改变了正常射线的折射率。

后一解释将会引入一个在前述考虑中未曾用到过的原理。到目前为止，我们足以将光学效应归结为几何排布的结果。另一方面，异常射线可能发生偏转，因为它经过了晶轴在轴和射线的平面内连续改变方向的区域。

从这个观点出发，我们立刻可以为向列相物质的极为显著且特有的外观找到解释——这种外观在图 13 的照片中呈现出来。它们是同一试剂的照片，以尽可能快的方式连续拍下，以避免由于液体的连续运动而导致的变化。从下方射入的光没有发生偏振，而在穿过试剂后再经过检偏器就不然了。两张照片之间的显著差别源于检偏器在两次曝光之间转过了大约 90°。在其中一张照片中，细丝看起来窄而清晰，在另一张中则发生变形；通过精细的比较显示两张照片在其他方面是一样的。

图 13. 两张照片显示的是同一种物质，是在间隔尽可能短暂的两个瞬间时，处于向列相的对－氧化偶氮基苯乙醚。唯一的差别在于检偏器的位置，其中一种情况下的位置与另外一种时的近似呈直角。没有起偏器。每张照片中较清晰的部分是借助于正常射线看到的，其余部分则是借助于异常射线。

一个需要解释的显著特征是，所有的细丝在图片的一部分中是清晰的，同时在另一部分中却是模糊的。不过我们还记得在与玻璃表面接触处存在着，用夫里德耳的话来讲，一层外壳或薄膜；换言之，先前存在于那里的固态晶体在玻璃表面留下一些分子，它们全都指向同一路线，如同地上的一群鸟同时抬首眺望风中。这确定了玻璃附近区域中分子的指向，而且，尽管试剂顶部和底部之间的分子能够以任何方式指向，但除去"细丝"本身之外指向变化绝不会是不连续的；即使是那样，如果不是穿过细丝的话，连续性仍然可以通过细丝的周围。结果是，正常射线伴随着

thread, if not through it. Consequently the ordinary rays emerge with their vibrations perpendicular to the axis of the pellicle at the point of emergence; though when the rays passed by the thread, the vibrations were all parallel or perpendicular to the thread, according to the view which we take of the nature of the thread. The vibrations of the extraordinary rays are all perpendicular to those of the ordinary. The analysing Nicol can therefore be set so as to extinguish all the extraordinary rays and transmit only the ordinary, so that the threads are seen clearly. If the Nicol is set so that the view is obtained by means of the extraordinary rays, the images are blurred because those rays are deflected out of their course by going near the threads.

The whole effect depends on the compelling power of the pellicle, setting an arrangement at the surface to which the internal arrangement, whatever it may be at a distance from the surface, must gradually conform as the distance from the surface diminishes. The vibrations have been orientated in a different direction at each point of the tortuous thread, but have all been pulled into one direction when they emerge. In Fig. 13 there are two regions; in one of them the molecular direction in the surface happens to be more or less at right angles to the direction in the other: so that when one part, seen by ordinary rays, is clear, the other, seen by extraordinary rays, is confused. The optical effects of nematic threads have been studied by H. Zocher and his colleagues[8].

When the *para*-azoxyanisole is cooling down from the liquid, the first appearance of a change of phase is the formation of separate groups of molecules, which between crossed Nicols give the effect illustrated in Fig. 14. Each group shows, besides finer details, a cross, the arms of which are parallel to the principal planes of the Nicols. A similar effect may be observed in certain solids, such as strontium carbonate or salicin, and occasionally lavas and glasses, and in organic substances such as cholesteryl acetate. It is an indication that in each group there is a nuclear point from which the axes of minute crystals radiate uniformly in all directions. In two of those directions, mutually at right angles, the axes of the crystals are parallel respectively to the principal planes of the crossed Nicols. If the preparation is rotated with respect to the Nicols, the cross does not move. The group is therefore independent of any pellicles; it is floating freely in the middle of isotropic liquid. The molecules either radiate from the nucleus in the centre, or are arranged along concentric circles as if there were a vortex. Either arrangement gives the cross. On one side of Fig. 14, the groups are coalescing and are attaching themselves to the glass above and below. The connexions are irregular but there are traces of the original simple arrangements of the groups. On the border between the liquid crystal phase are larger groups formed by the coalescence of smaller groups.

振动出现，振动方向垂直于出现位置处的薄膜的轴；不过当射线经过细丝时，根据我们所认识的细丝本质来判断，振动全部平行或垂直于细丝。异常射线的振动全都垂直于正常射线的振动。因此，可以通过设置检偏尼科尔棱镜来消除所有异常射线，只令正常射线透过，从而使细丝看起来更清晰。如果设置尼科尔棱镜以通过异常射线来获得图像，图像就会模糊，因为异常射线在经过细丝附近时会偏离方向。

整个效应取决于薄膜的强制力，即在表面设置一种排布，不管其内部距离表面有多远，内部排列都必须随着到表面距离的减小而与表面保持一致。在弯曲细丝的每一点，振动指向不同的方向，但在射出时都会被拖入同一方向。图13中有两个区域；在其中一个区域里，表面分子的方向恰好与另一个区域中的方向大致成直角：因此，当通过正常射线看到一部分清晰时，通过异常射线看到的另外那个部分就模糊了。措赫尔及其同事已对向列相细丝的光学效应进行了研究 [8]。

将对－氧化偶氮基苯甲醚从液态进行冷却时，首先出现的相变化现象是独立分子团的形成，图14显示了位于交叉尼科尔棱镜之间的物质所呈现出的效应。暂不考虑更具体的细节，每个分子团都呈十字形交叉，其两臂平行于尼科尔棱镜的主平面。在某些固体中可以观测到类似的效应，例如在碳酸锶和水杨苷中，有时也可以在熔岩和玻璃中，还可以在诸如胆甾醇乙酸酯等有机物中看到。这预示了每个分子团中存在一个核心，微小晶体的轴从这个点均匀地向所有方向辐射。在这些方向中的两个彼此垂直的方向上，晶体的轴分别平行于交叉尼科尔棱镜的两个主平面。当试剂相对于尼科尔棱镜旋转时，交叉结构并不移动，因而分子团独立于任何薄膜；它在各向同性液体的中心自由地漂流。分子或者从位于中心的核向外辐射，或者像旋涡一样沿着同心圆排布。每一种排布都会产生十字形结构。在图14的一侧，分子团正在合并，而且正在将自身附着于上方和下方的玻璃表面。虽然关联是不规则的，但存在着分子团最初的简单排布的痕迹。在液晶相边界上的是由较小分子团合并而形成的较大分子团。

Fig. 14. *Para*-azoxyanisole cooling, between crossed Nicols. On the left the nematic state is advancing. Small drops are forming in the liquid on the right. The arms of the crosses are parallel to the principal planes of the Nicols. The larger drops are formed by coalescence of the smaller.

Cholesteric Crystals

The third class of liquid crystals has been termed by Friedel the cholesteric. In some ways its properties resemble those of the smectic and nematic classes. But we meet here with a new effect, a brilliant coloration of which the causes and laws have never been fully explained.

We may take as an example

$$C_6H_5 - CH = CH - CO - O - C_{26}H_{43}$$

Cholesteryl cinnamate.

Solid $-156°C-$ cholesteric $-197°C-$ liquid.

When this substance is allowed to cool down from the liquid phase, it presents at first a confused appearance of a focal conic structure. But a slight mechanical disturbance causes it to assume a form in which it reflects brilliant colours like those of a peacock's feather. The colour depends on the temperature, being vivid green at the higher temperatures and golden-bronze at the lower. But the most remarkable effect is that the reflected or, more correctly speaking, scattered light, is circularly polarised. If the incident light is circularly polarised, it is reflected if the circulation is represented by a right-handed screw, and transmitted if the screw is left-handed. In the case of some other cholesteric substances this is reversed. More remarkable still is the fact that the scattered light is right-handed, like the absorbed light to which it is due. In all other known cases of the reflection of circularly polarised light the sense of the rotation is reversed.

These substances, when in their characteristic state, are optically active to an extraordinary degree, represented sometimes by as much as a whole turn in the hundredth of a millimetre.

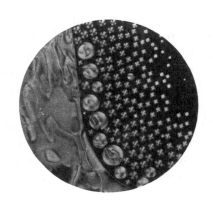

图 14. 位于交叉尼科尔棱镜之间的对－氧化偶氮基苯甲醚的冷却。左边，向列态正在推进。右边，小液滴正在液体中形成。十字交叉的两臂平行于尼科尔棱镜的主平面。较大液滴是由较小液滴合并形成的。

胆甾相晶体

夫里德耳将第三种液晶命名为胆甾相。在某些方面，它的性质类似于近晶相和向列相。但是这里我们遇到了一种新的效应，一种亮丽的着色效应，对于其原因和规律始终没能给出完整的解释。

我们可以用下列物质为例：

$$C_6H_5 - CH = CH - CO - O - C_{26}H_{43}$$

胆甾相肉桂酸
固态 −156℃ − 胆甾相 −197℃ − 液态

将这种物质从液相进行冷却时，它首先呈现出具有焦点圆锥曲线结构的模糊外观。但是，一个轻微的机械扰动就可以使它呈现出一种像孔雀羽毛般反射亮丽色彩的形态。其颜色取决于温度，在较高温度时为鲜艳的绿色，而较低温度时则是金黄色。但是更为显著的效应是，反射光——或者更准确的说法是散射光——是圆偏振的。当入射光为圆偏振光时，若其旋转方向为右手螺旋则被反射，为左手螺旋时则透过。在另外一些胆甾相物质中则与此相反。更引人注目的是，如同吸收光那样，散射光是右手螺旋的。而在所有其他已知的圆偏振光反射中，旋转方向都是相反的。

这些物质在处于其特征状态时，都具有极高的光学活性，有时能在百分之一毫米的范围内几乎完全反转。

This short account of the chief properties of "liquid crystals" is very far from complete. Nothing has been said of the influence of electrical and magnetic fields on molecular arrangement, which is strong in the case of substances in the nematic phase but absent in the smectic, except during the process of cooling from the liquid. Nor has reference been made to the peculiar facility with which the molecules of liquid crystals dispose themselves in particular directions on fresh cleavage faces of solid crystals. Nor have the viscosity effects been described. In spite of these omissions, the account may help as an introduction to the extensive literature of the subject, the more so because the accumulated observations are scattered over many scientific journals, and because also the various workers are far from agreement as to their interpretations.

(**133**, 445-456; 1934)

References:

1. O. Lehmann, "Über fliessende Kristalle," *Z. phys. Chem.*, **4**, 1889.

2. *Ann. Phys.*, 9, **18**, 273; 1922.

3. *Trans. Faraday Soc.*, **29**, 881; 1933.

4. *Comptes rendus*, **180**, 265; 1925.

5. *Bull. Soc. Min.*, **42**, 42; 1919. See also *Proc. Roy. Inst.*, **28**, 89; 1934.

6. Collected Researches, **2**, 144.

7. *Trans. Faraday Soc.*, **29**, 1032; 1933.

8. Zocher and Birstein, *Z. phys. Chemie*, A, **142**, 113.

这篇关于"液晶"主要性质的简要报告还远不够完全。这里没有提到电场和磁场对分子排布方式的影响，而在向列相物质中，这种影响是非常强烈的，而对近晶相物质则不是那样，除非是在从液态冷却的过程中。文中也没有提到液晶分子在将自身按特别的方向排布于固态晶体新鲜解理面上时所表现出的独特的灵活性。而且没有论及黏度效应。尽管有上述不足，这篇报告作为该主题的大量文献的导论应该还是有些帮助的，尤其是因为已积累的观测结果散见于多种科学期刊之中，而且不同的研究者远没有就其解释达成一致。

（王耀杨 翻译；赵见高 审稿）

Supraconductivity of Films of Tin

E. F. Burton

Editor's Note

Superconductivity had been discovered in 1911 by Heike Kamerlingh Onnes, who found that solid mercury lost its electrical resistance when cooled within a few degrees of absolute zero. Other materials such as tin and lead were soon also found to be "supraconductors", as they were then known, but there was no explanation for the phenomenon. Here E. F. Burton of the University of Toronto reported an important constraint on such a theory: a thin film of superconducting material such as tin loses its superconductivity when sandwiched between other materials that are not superconducting. Burton notes that the effect applies only to sufficiently thin superconducting films, less than a micrometre or so thick.

EXPERIMENTS on the relation of high frequency currents to the phenomenon of superconductivity led to work at Toronto with films of superconducting metals. The films (of tin) were produced by "tinning" the surface of fine wires which themselves were not superconducting: in the early experiments a coating of tin 2×10^{-4} cm. in thickness was "wiped" on constantan wire of 0.016 cm. diameter. In this way one obtains the equivalent of a thin cylinder of superconducting metal, and the resistance of the whole becomes zero below the transition temperature of the superconducting element used[1].

With the intention of studying further the effect of high frequency currents, samples of such coated wires were plated with other metals—for example, copper and nickel—which are not superconductors; an example of such a combination is constantan covered with tin and then plated with copper. The diameters of the wires forming the core were as follows: for constantan 0.056 cm., for copper 0.040 cm. and for nickel 0.045 cm.

Preliminary experiments were carried out on these samples to confirm their reaction with respect to direct currents—the ordinary superconductivity test—and it was found that thin films of tin cease to show superconductivity when these films are themselves plated over with a film of a non-superconducting metal, for example, copper or nickel. This surprising result shows itself only with thin films, but a number of repetitions of the experiments renders the results unmistakable. The accompanying table shows the nature of the phenomenon: so far, only the superconductor tin has been tested in this way.

174

锡膜的超导电性

伯顿

编者按

1911 年海克·卡默林·昂内斯发现了超导电性，他发现当温度低至绝对零度附近几度时固体汞的电阻会消失。随后另外一些材料诸如锡和铅也很快被发现是"超导体"，正如此后人们所知道的那样，但是当时并未能就这一现象给出解释。这篇文章中，多伦多大学的伯顿指出了超导理论的一个重要的限制条件：超导材料例如锡膜如果被夹在两层非超导的材料之间时，会失去它的超导电性。伯顿还指出这个效应只适用于足够薄的超导薄膜，厚度应小于或者等于 1 微米。

关于高频电流与超导电性现象之间关系的实验促成了在多伦多进行的对超导金属膜的研究。（锡）膜是在非超导材料制成的细线表面"镀锡"形成的：在早期的实验中，我们是将厚度为 2×10^{-4} 厘米的锡的镀层"包裹"在直径为 0.016 厘米的康铜丝上。按这种方法，我们得到了一个等效的超导金属的薄圆筒，而且当温度低于所用超导元素的转变温度时，整个薄圆筒的电阻会变为零[1]。

为了进一步研究高频电流的效应，我们给这类镀丝样品镀上其他一些没有超导电性的金属，如铜和镍；例如，在镀了锡的康铜丝外再镀上铜，作为芯的几种金属丝的直径如下：康铜，0.056 厘米；铜，0.040 厘米；镍，0.045 厘米。

我们最初做的实验是为了证实这些样品对直流电的反应，即普通的超导电性测试，在实验中我们发现，当这些锡膜镀上非超导金属膜（例如铜或镍）时，它们就不再显示超导电性。虽然这个奇怪的结果只有在膜非常薄时才能得到，但多次的重复实验都倾向于表明这个结果正确无误。下表显示出这种现象的规律：到现在为止，我们只用这种方法对超导体锡做了试验。

No.	Sample	Thickness of Tin Film (cm. $\times 10^{-5}$)	Thickness of outer layer (cm. $\times 10^{-5}$)	Superconductive Action, direct current of 200 ma.
1a	Constantan-Tin	10	0	Transition point 3.69°K
1b	Constantan-Tin-Copper	10	100	Not superconducting at 2°K
2a	Copper-Tin	9	0	Transition point 3.58°K
2b	Copper-Tin-Copper	9	100	Not superconducting at 2°K
3a	Nickel-Tin	9	0	Transition point 3.42°K
3b	Nickel-Tin-Copper	9	100	Not superconducting at 2°K
4	Constantan-Tin	6.8	0	Transition point 3.49°K
5	Constantan-Tin	2	0	Transition point 2.48°K
6	Constantan-Tin-Copper	18	40	Not superconducting at 2°K
7	Constantan-Tin-Copper	4	20	Not superconducting at 2°K
8	Constantan-Tin-Nickel	15	30	Not superconducting at 2°K
9	Constantan-Tin(wiped)	90	0	Transition point 3.68°K
9a	Constantan-Tin-Copper	90	80	Transition point 3.44°K
10	Constantan-Tin (electro-plated)	200	0	Transition point 3.76°K
10a	Constantan-Tin-Copper	200	80	Transition point 3.73°K
11	Tin Wire	diameter	0.085	Transition point 3.77°K

It is seen that as the film of tin increases in thickness, a point is reached at which the superconducting property of the tin film is not lost by surface plating. This phenomenon will undoubtedly be of importance in framing a satisfactory theory of superconductivity— a consideration of utmost importance in dealing with metallic conduction. This work is being carried on by J. O. Wilhelm and A. D. Misener.

(**133**, 459; 1934)

E. F. Burton: McLennan Laboratory, University of Toronto, Feb. 17.

Reference:

1. E. F. Burton, "Superconductivity" (University of Toronto Press, and Oxford University Press), p. 70. J. C. McLennan, *Nature*, **130**, 879, Dec. 10, 1932.

序号	样　品	锡薄膜的厚度（厘米 ×10⁻⁵）	外层的厚度（厘米 ×10⁻⁵）	超导作用，200 mA 的直流电流
1a	康铜－锡	10	0	转变点 3.69 K
1b	康铜－锡－铜	10	100	2 K 时无超导
2a	铜－锡	9	0	转变点 3.58 K
2b	铜－锡－铜	9	100	2 K 时无超导
3a	镍－锡	9	0	转变点 3.42 K
3b	镍－锡－铜	9	100	2 K 时无超导
4	康铜－锡	6.8	0	转变点 3.49 K
5	康铜－锡	2	0	转变点 2.48 K
6	康铜－锡－铜	18	40	2 K 时无超导
7	康铜－锡－铜	4	20	2 K 时无超导
8	康铜－锡－镍	15	30	2 K 时无超导
9	康铜－锡（焊接的）	90	0	转变点 3.68 K
9a	康铜－锡－铜	90	80	转变点 3.44 K
10	康铜－锡（电镀的）	200	0	转变点 3.76 K
10a	康铜－锡－铜	200	80	转变点 3.73 K
11	锡线	直径	0.085	转变点 3.77 K

　　我们发现，当锡膜厚度增加到一个点时，锡膜的超导性能不再因为表面镀层而丧失。这种现象对构造一个令人满意的超导理论无疑是极其重要的，这是处理金属电导时需要重点考虑的一个问题。威廉和麦色纳正在进行这项研究。

（沈乃澂 翻译；郑东宁 审稿）

177

Persistent Currents in Supraconductors

K. Mendelssohn and J. D. Babbitt

Editor's Note

Physicists in the early 1930s were struggling to understand superconductivity. Here Kurt Mendelssohn and J. D. Babbitt explored the surprising recent discovery by Walther Meissner and Robert Ochsenfeld that a superconductor expels magnetic flux from its interior. That finding confounded the expectation that persistent electrical currents in a superconductor would instead "capture" magnetic flux and sustain it even if the external magnetic field were removed. Yet the experiments reported here showed that the flux expulsion wasn't perfect: some magnetisation remains inside superconducting tin. This was the first evidence of persistent "supercurrents", although their value was only one-sixth of that predicted earlier.

UNTIL recently it was generally assumed that it was possible to predict, by the ordinary electromagnetic equations, the persistent current produced in a supraconductor cooled below the transition point in a constant external magnetic field after the field was switched off. Thus H. A. Lorentz[1] calculated the current induced in a supraconducting sphere, that is, the effective magnetic dipole when an external magnetic field is established.

According to results recently published by Meissner and Ochsenfeld[2], the matter is not so simple as might at first sight appear. Instead of the lines of force being "frozen in" as had been previously assumed would happen when a supraconductor was cooled below the transition point in a magnetic field, it appeared that the field increased in the neighbourhood of the supraconductor, which behaved as a body of zero permeability. If this were so, the flux of induction in the supraconductor should be zero and one might expect, in contradistinction to the old view, that no persistent current or effective induced dipole would be produced by switching off the external field.

The following experiments seem to show that although supraconductors do not conform to the older theory, neither do they behave as though they had zero permeability.

(1) A solid tin sphere of 1.5 cm. radius was cooled from 4.2°K. to 2.5°K. (the liquid helium was produced in a liquefaction apparatus utilising the expansion method of Simon) in a field of 70 gauss. When the field was switched off, the magnetic moment of the sphere was observed with a test coil. Its magnitude was about one sixth of that calculated according to the Lorentz equation.

The magnetic moment remained almost constant whilst the temperature of the sphere rose from 2.5° to 2.9°; with a further rise in temperature it decreased steadily, becoming

超导体中的持续电流

门德尔松，巴比特

编者按

20世纪30年代早期，物理学家们正在费尽心力地研究超导电性的产生机制。这篇文章中，库尔特·门德尔松和巴比特探讨了近期瓦尔特·迈斯纳和罗伯特·奥克森费尔德的惊人发现——超导体会将磁通量排除在外。在此之前人们猜想超导体中持续的电流应该能够"捕获"磁通量，并且即使外磁场被撤除，超导体中的磁通量也能够保持，但该发现否定了这一猜想。然而这篇文章中报道的实验显示磁通量的排除并不完全：超导态锡的内部仍保留有一定的磁化强度。这首次证明了持续的"超导电流"的存在，尽管它的大小只有之前预测值的1/6。

直至不久前，人们仍然普遍认为，根据一般的电磁方程就可以预测：在恒定外磁场中将超导体冷却至转变温度之下，关闭磁场时会产生持续的电流。据此，洛伦兹[1]计算出了超导球体中的感生电流，即在外磁场建立后的有效磁偶极。

按照迈斯纳和奥克森费尔德[2]最近公开发表的结果，事情并非如初看时那么简单。磁场中的超导体被冷却到转变点之下时，并不像我们以前假定的那样会将磁力线"冻结"，实验表明，超导体附近的磁场会增强，超导体表现得像一个完全的抗磁体。如果事实确实如此，那么超导体中的感应磁通量应为零，而且我们也可以推断出与旧观点相反的结论：关闭外磁场并不会在超导体中产生持续的电流或有效的感生偶极。

下列实验似乎表明，超导体虽然并不符合旧的理论，但也没有表现出磁导率为零的性质。

（1）在70高斯的磁场中，将一个半径为1.5厘米的固体锡球的温度从4.2 K冷却到2.5 K（液氦是在一个液化装置中利用西蒙膨胀法产生的）。当关闭磁场时，我们用实验线圈测量固体球的磁矩。测量得出的磁矩大小约为根据洛伦兹方程计算所得值的1/6。

当球的温度从2.5 K上升到2.9 K时，磁矩几乎保持恒定；而在温度进一步上升时，磁矩稳步减少，且在3.7 K时变为零，这个临界温度就是锡的正常转变点。对磁

zero at 3.7°, the normal transition point of tin. Plotting the magnetic moment against the temperature, one obtains a curve of similar shape to that found for the magnetic threshold values.

(2) The same sphere was cooled to 2.5° without any external magnetic field, a field of 230 gauss (higher than the threshold value at this temperature) was switched on and immediately switched off. The magnetic moment thus produced in the sphere at 2.5° was 8 percent greater than that produced in the previous experiment using 70 gauss, but as the temperature rose it decreased and at 2.9° it reached the same value as the magnetic moment at this temperature in the previous experiment. From 2.9° to 4° the curve coincided with that found in experiment (1).

(3) Similar experiments to those described above were carried out with a hollow tin sphere of the same radius, the spherical space in the middle being equal in volume to one half the volume of the sphere. The magnetic moments produced in the hollow sphere were two to three times greater than those obtained with the solid sphere.

In all these experiments the magnetic field was produced by a cylindrical coil in the middle of which the sphere was placed, all iron being excluded. Although the field near the sphere was thus fairly homogeneous, we think it possible that the observed phenomena may be influenced by slight inhomogeneities of the external field. In a completely homogeneous field it would seem possible that the method of cooling might affect the results. In order to test this, we cooled the spheres from the poles and also from the equator. This did not seem to make any difference, the magnetic moment observed being of the same order of magnitude in either case.

As a result of these experiments, it seems certain that the effective permeability of substances when they become supraconducting decreases, as observed by Meissner and Ochsenfeld. On the other hand, it appears clear that under our experimental conditions the permeability does not vanish entirely, as might be expected in view of the almost infinite conductivity, or if it does vanish, it only does so in certain regions and not throughout the whole volume of the supraconductor.

In conclusion, we would like to express our thanks to Mr. T. C. Keeley for his advice and assistance in various phases of the work.

(**133**, 459; 1934)

K. Mendelssohn and J. D. Babbitt: Clarendon Laboratory, Oxford, Feb. 17.

References:

1. Comm. Leiden, Suppl., Nr. 50 b, 1924.

2. *Naturwiss*, **21**, 787; 1933.

矩随温度变化的作图，我们得到一条与临界磁场随温度变化的曲线形状类似的曲线。

（2）同样的球体在无任何外磁场的情况下冷却到 2.5 K，打开并立即关闭 230 高斯的磁场（高于在此温度下的临界磁场）。结果在温度为 2.5 K 时产生的磁矩比上一实验中使用 70 高斯时产生的磁矩大 8%，而当温度上升时磁矩不断下降，在温度上升到 2.9 K 时，磁矩与在以前实验中温度为 2.9 K 时的磁矩值相同。在温度为 2.9 K~4 K 的范围内，得到的曲线与实验（1）中这个温度段的曲线重合。

（3）与上述实验类似，只是改用半径相同的空心锡球进行研究，中心的球型空心是整个球体积的一半。空心球产生的磁矩是实心球的 2~3 倍。

在所有这些实验中，磁场是由缠绕成圆筒状的线圈产生的，圆球置于线圈的中部，实验中没有使用任何铁质材料。尽管这样可以使圆球附近的磁场相当均匀，但我们还是认为，观测到的现象可能会受到外场细微的非均匀性的影响。而即便在一个完全均匀的磁场中，冷却方法也可能会影响到最终的结果。为了验证这一点，我们分别从圆球的两极和赤道位置对其进行冷却。然而这个做法并没有导致任何差异的产生，两种情况下观测到的磁矩的数量级是相同的。

根据这些实验的结果，我们似乎肯定，亦如迈斯纳和奥克森费尔德所观测的，当物质成为超导体时，它们的有效磁导率会减小。另一方面，很显然在我们当前的实验条件下，磁导率并不会如电导率趋于一个无限值状况所预期的那样完全消失，或者即便磁导率完全消失，那也仅是发生在部分区域内，而不会贯穿整个超导体。

最后，我们要感谢基利先生，他在我们工作的各个阶段都给予了建议和大量帮助。

（沈乃澂 翻译；郑东宁 审稿）

The Velocity of Light

M. E. J. Gheury de Bray

Editor's Note

There were many occasions in the early decades of the publication when *Nature* deliberately published items that were calculated to surprise and even challenge orthodox opinion. Thus the journal published in the 1930s three letters from a man called M. E. J. Gheury de Bray advocating the opinion that the velocity of light is not constant in time but that it had slowly decreased between 1924 and 1933. The possibility of a slow change in supposed "constants" of physics is now back in vogue among cosmologists, albeit so far without compelling evidence to support it.

IN 1927 there was published in these columns[1] a table of all the determinations of the velocity of light which I compiled from the original memoirs, together with a discussion, and I pointed out that except a pair of practically simultaneous values obtained in 1882 the final values (printed in heavy type) indicate a secular decrease of velocity. The last (and lowest) value given is 299,796 ± 4 km./sec. for 1926.

Since then, two determinations have been made: the first by Karolus and Mittelstaedt (1928) using a Kerr cell, to the terminals of which an alternating potential was applied, for interrupting periodically the luminous beam, instead of a toothed wheel[2]. A frequency can be obtained in this way, of the order of a million per second, which can be accurately calculated, thus permitting a very short base to be used (41.386 metre) without any loss of accuracy. The value found (mean of 755 measurements) was 299,778 ± 20 km./sec. The second recent determination is mentioned in *Nature* of February 3, p.169: it gives for the velocity of light in 1933 the value 299,774 ± 1 or 2 km./sec.

The determinations of this so-called constant made during the last ten years (the most accurate of the whole series) are therefore:

1924	..	..	299,802 ± 30 km./sec.
1926	..	..	299,796 ± 4 km./sec.
1928	..	..	299,778 ± 20 km./sec.
1933	..	..	299,774 ± 1 or 2 km./sec.

No physicist, looking at the above table, can but admit that the alleged constancy of the velocity of light is absolutely unsupported by observations. As a matter of fact, the above data, treated by Cauchy's method[3], give the linear law:

$$V_{km./sec.} = 299,900 - 4T_{(1900)\ years.}$$

光的速度

谷瑞·德布雷

编者按

在《自然》杂志发行的前几十年中，它对于发表那些旨在抨击甚至挑战传统观点的文章是非常慎重的，但事实上它仍然发表了很多这类文章。20 世纪 30 年代，《自然》就发表了一个名为谷瑞·德布雷的人的三篇通讯，他的观点是光速并不是永远恒定的，在 1924 年至 1933 年间光速随时间在缓慢地减小。天文学家中又掀起了这样一种风潮，即发现物理学中原以为"恒定"的事物存在缓慢变化的可能性，不过目前尚无确凿的证据证实这一观点。

本专栏在 1927 年 [1] 发表了我从原始文献中汇集的关于光速的全部测定结果的列表以及对此进行的讨论。我曾指出，除了一对几乎同时于 1882 年获得的数值之外，最终结果（黑体字印刷）显示出光速在不断地减少。表中所给出的最后一个（也是最小的一个）数值是 1926 年测得的 299,796±4 千米 / 秒。

在那以后，科学家又得到了两个测定结果：第一个来自卡罗卢斯和米特尔施泰特（1928），他们使用了克尔盒，并在其终端施加交变电压来代替齿轮，用以周期性地隔断光束 [2]。用这种方式可以精确地计算并得到每秒百万数量级的隔断频率，从而可以使用一个极短的基线（41.386 米）而丝毫不损失精确性。由此而得到的光速数值（755 次测量结果的平均值）为 299,778±20 千米 / 秒。第二个近期测定结果是在 2 月 3 日出版的《自然》杂志第 169 页给出的，它测定于 1933 年，值为299,774±1（或 2）千米 / 秒。

因此，可以将最近十年中对光速这一所谓常数的测定结果（整个序列中最为精确的）排列如下：

1924	..	..	299,802 ± 30 千米 / 秒
1926	..	..	299,796 ± 4 千米 / 秒
1928	..	..	299,778 ± 20 千米 / 秒
1933	..	..	299,774 ± 1（或 2）千米 / 秒

看过上面的表后，物理学家们不得不承认，所谓的光速恒定性显然没有得到观测结果的支持。事实上，经过柯西方法 [3] 处理后，上述光速测量值与测量年份满足线性关系：

$$V_{千米/秒} = 299,900 - 4T_{20世纪各年份}$$

When I first pointed out this fact (in 1924) it was objected that the data available were inconclusive, because the probable errors of the observations were greater than the alleged rate of change. Sir Arthur Eddington has dealt the death blow to the theory of errors[4] and "this theory is the last surviving stronghold of those who would reject plain fact and common sense in favour of remote deductions from unverifiable guesses, having no merit other than mathematical tractability"[5]. Even "die-hards", however, may fruitfully meditate over the 2nd and the 4th values in the above table.

(**133**, 464; 1934)

M. E. J. Gheury de Bray: 40 Westmount Road, Eltham, S.E.9.

References:

1. *Nature*, **120**, 603, Oct. 22, 1927.

2. *Phys. Z.*, 698-702; 165-167; 1929.

3. *Engineer*, Sept. 13, 1912.

4. *Proc. Phys. Soc.*, 271-282; 1933.

5. Dr. N. R. Campbell, *loc. cit.*, 283.

　　我第一次指出这一事实时（1924 年），有人反对说现有的数据是不确定的，因为观测中的或然误差大于所谓的变化速率。阿瑟·爱丁顿爵士曾对这一误差理论 [4] 施以致命一击："对于那些拒绝承认明确的事实与常识却喜欢从无法检验的猜测中得出间接推论的人来说，该理论是最后的生存堡垒，它除了数学便利性之外毫无优点可言" [5]。但是，即使是"老顽固们"也可能会对上表中第 2 和第 4 个值进行一番深刻的思考。

（王耀杨 翻译；张元仲 审稿）

Attempt to Detect a Neutral Particle of Small Mass

Editor's Note

In 1930, Wolfgang Pauli hypothesized that nuclear beta decay might involve a second particle being emitted from the nucleus in addition to the electron. He pointed out that the puzzling continuous variation in energy of beta-decay electrons could be understood if a second, electrically neutral particle carries away a varying amount of energy. Fermi named the proposed particle the neutrino, and here *Nature* reports on a failed attempt by Chadwick and colleagues to detect it. If such particles do exist, they found, they must have very small mass. Indeed they do, and because they interact so weakly with other particles, neutrinos are enormous difficult to detect. This was finally achieved in 1956. Physicists later discovered that neutrinos come in three flavours.

CHADWICK and Lea have recently published the negative result of an experiment designed to examine the possibility that the continuous β-ray spectrum is accompanied by the emission of penetrating neutral particles (*Proc. Camb. Phil. Soc.*, **30**, Part 1). The energies of these particles might be distributed in such a way that they combine with those of the β-particles to form a constant energy of disintegration, a low energy β-particle being associated with a high energy "neutrino". A strong source of radium D + E + F (radium E gives a well-marked continuous β-ray spectrum) was placed near a high-pressure ionisation chamber and an absorption curve was taken with lead screens. The radiation was all identified with the radium E and polonium γ-rays. If neutral particles are emitted, it is calculated that they cannot produce more than 1 ion pair in 150 kilometres path in air. A consideration of the possible nature of the particle shows that, if it exists, it must have small mass and zero magnetic moment.

(133, 466; 1934)

探测小质量中性粒子的尝试

编者按

1930 年，沃尔夫冈·泡利猜测原子核在 β 衰变过程中除了产生电子之外还会放出第二种粒子。他指出如果这第二种电中性的粒子携带了不同大小的能量，那么令人困扰的 β 衰变过程中电子能量的连续变化就可以得到解释了。费米将这一假想的粒子命名为中微子，《自然》在这篇文章中报道了查德威克和他的同事在探测中微子方面的一次失败的尝试。他们发现如果这一粒子确实存在，它们一定具有非常小的质量。事实正是如此，而且正因为中微子与其他粒子的相互作用非常微弱，所以中微子的探测异常困难。这一探测最终于 1956 年获得成功。之后物理学家又发现中微子有三种味。

最近，查德威克和利发表了他们实验得到的负面结果，设计该实验的目的是检验连续 β 射线谱伴随着发射出具有穿透性的中性粒子的可能性（《剑桥哲学学会会刊》，第 30 卷，第 1 部分）。上述中性粒子的能量可能是以这样的方式分布的：中性粒子能量与 β 粒子能量之和等于一个恒定的衰变能，由此把低能 β 粒子与高能"中微子"联系了起来。将一个包含镭 D、镭 E 和镭 F 的强放射源（镭 E 可以给出很清楚的连续 β 射线谱）置于高压电离室附近，并利用铅屏来获得吸收曲线。得到的谱线与镭 E 的射线谱及钋的 γ 射线谱是完全一致的。经过计算可得，即使有中性粒子发射，它们也不可能在空气中 150 km 的路径内产生出多于 1 个的离子对。对这种中性粒子可能的性质考虑得到的结果是，如果它们存在的话，其质量一定很小且磁矩为零。

（王耀杨 翻译；朱永生 审稿）

The New Hydrogen*

Editor's Note

Scientists had believed for more than a century that pure water is a well-defined chemical substance with molecular weight 18. That confidence was disturbed four years ago, Rutherford remarks in this lecture delivered at the Royal Institution, and there has now been a revolution in our picture of the constitution of water. Rutherford describes the means by which heavy water had been isolated to near perfect purity, enabling a determination of its physical properties. It was then unknown whether the deuterium nucleus was simple or composite, and there were many possible combinations of electron, positron, neutron and proton to consider. If the particle is a composite of neutron and proton, bombardment with sufficiently energetic alpha particles should break it apart.

FOR more than a century scientific men believed with confidence that pure water was a well-defined chemical substance, H_2O, of molecular weight 18. This belief was shown by the fact that the unit of mass, the kilogram, consisting of a cylinder of platinum-iridium, was initially chosen to be of the same mass as 1,000 cubic centimetres of water at the temperature of maximum density. Subsequent measurements showed that this was slightly in error, so that the unit of mass was defined in terms of the metal standard. It was only about four years ago that this confidence was slightly disturbed as a result of the study of the isotopic constitution of oxygen. Instead of being a simple element of mass 16, oxygen was found to contain in small quantity isotopes of masses 17 and 18. It was clear from this that pure water must contain some molecules of weight 19 and 20 as well as the normal 18. Since, however, it seemed very unlikely that the proportion of the isotopes could be sensibly changed in the processes of preparation of pure water, this result, while of much theoretical interest, did not appear to have any practical importance.

As a result of investigations during the last two years, there has been a revolutionary change in our ideas of the constancy of the constitution of water. This has resulted from the discovery that a hydrogen isotope of twice the normal mass is always present in preparations of ordinary hydrogen. While this isotope of mass 2 exists only in small proportion—only about 1 in 6,000 of the main isotope of mass 1—yet, on account of the marked difference in mass of the two components, the relative concentration of the two isotopes can be varied in a marked way by various physical and chemical processes. This is

---

* Discourse delivered at the Royal Institution on Friday, March 23.

氢的新同位素*

卢瑟福

编者按

一个多世纪以来，科学家们一直深信纯水是一种明确的化学物质，其分子量为 18。卢瑟福在这篇于英国皇家研究院的演讲中强调，这一信念在 4 年之前就被打破了，他还指出我们对于水的构成的认识正在经历一场革命。卢瑟福描述了一种可以分离出几乎完全纯净的重水的方法，这使得测定重水的物理性质成为可能。当时人们并不知道重氢的原子核是单一的粒子还是复合的粒子，曾经考虑过电子、正电子、中子和质子的多种可能的组合。如果该粒子由中子和质子构成，那么用足够能量的 α 粒子对其进行轰击将能够使之发生分裂。

一个多世纪以来，科学家曾深信纯水是一种明确的化学物质，其化学式为 H_2O，分子量是 18。这种信念可以体现在下列事实中，以前，千克标准原器，即由铂铱合金制成的圆柱体，其质量依据的是 1,000 立方厘米的水在其最大密度的温度下所具有的质量。随后的测量表明，以水的质量定义的标准千克是稍有误差的，因而后来质量单位就按照该合金的标准来定义。仅仅大约四年前，科学家们对水的这种明确定义的信念就因为氧同位素组分的研究而稍有动摇。人们发现氧的原子量不只是16，它还包括少量原子量为 17 和 18 的同位素。由此可见，除了分子量为 18 的纯水外，必然还有些纯水的分子量为 19 和 20。不过，既然在纯水的制备过程中同位素的比例似乎不大可能有明显的变化，那么这个结果尽管具有不少理论兴趣，但似乎没有什么实际重要性。

最近两年的研究结果使我们对水的组分稳定性的认识出现了革命性的变化。这种认识的变化来源于氢元素同位素的发现，这种质量两倍于普通氢元素的同位素总是出现于正常氢元素的制备中。尽管这类质量为 2 的同位素仅以很小比例存在（不过是质量为 1 的主要同位素的 1/6,000），然而考虑到这两种组分元素质量之间的明显差异，两类同位素的相对浓度可能会通过各种物理和化学过程而发生显著的改变。

---

* 演讲在 3 月 23 日（星期五）于英国皇家研究院发表。

seen by the fact that we are now able to obtain preparations of water in which the isotope of hydrogen of mass 1 is completely replaced by the isotope of mass 2. The density of the heavy water is about ten percent greater than ordinary water; while its freezing point is 3.8°C., and its boiling point 1.42°C., higher. Though in outward appearance this heavy water resembles ordinary water, yet in general its physical and chemical properties show marked differences. Not only does the vapour pressure vary markedly from the normal, but also the latent heat is considerably higher. Both the surface tension and specific inductive capacity are lower while the viscosity is much greater.

It is of interest to indicate briefly the almost romantic history of this rapid advance in knowledge, and to note that there are certain points of analogy between the discovery of heavy hydrogen and the discovery of argon in the atmosphere by the late Lord Rayleigh. In both cases the clue to the discovery depended on the recognition of the importance of small differences observed in accurate measurements of density.

When the relative abundance of the isotopes of oxygen was first measured, Birge and Mendel showed that there was a slight discrepancy—only about 1 in 5,000—between the ratio of the masses of the atoms of hydrogen and oxygen measured by Aston by the method of positive rays and the ratio deduced by direct chemical methods. They concluded that this small difference was greater than the probable experimental error in the measurements and in explanation suggested that hydrogen might contain in small quantity—about 1 in 4,000—an isotope of mass 2. Let us consider for a moment how the presence of such an isotope could be demonstrated by direct experiment. Both the H^1 and H^2 isotopes would have the same nuclear charge of 1, and have one external electron, and would thus be expected to give the same type of optical spectrum under the influence of the electric discharge. It is to be remembered, however, that the electron, the movements of which when disturbed give rise to its characteristic radiations, is coupled to the nucleus; and that the rates of vibration, although mainly governed by the nuclear charge, are slightly affected by the mass of the nucleus itself. On account of the greater mass of the H^2 isotope, it can readily be calculated that the Balmer lines in the spectrum of heavy hydrogen should appear slightly displaced towards the red. In the case of the α line, the displacement amounts to 1.78 angstrom units. When an electric discharge is passed through ordinary hydrogen, weak satellites should thus appear on the side towards the red. The presence of such weak satellites in the right position was first detected in experiments made for the purpose by Urey, Brickwedde and Murphy. The intensity of the satellite compared with the strong $H\alpha$ line was difficult to measure with certainty but was found to be of the order of 1 to 5,000.

Experiments were then made to enrich the H^2 isotope by fractional distillation of liquid hydrogen; and with some success. Another important observation was made by Urey and Washbourn, who found that the water in old electrolytic cells contained a larger proportion of heavy hydrogen than the normal. The concentration of H^2 was found to be rapidly enriched by continued electrolysis. This gave the key to a successful method of

比如现在我们在水的制备过程中，可以将质量为 1 的氢同位素完全用质量为 2 的同位素代替。重水的密度比普通水约大 10%；其凝固点是 3.8℃，沸点也比普通水高 1.42℃。虽然在表观上重水与普通水类似，但在物理性质和化学性质方面它们却有明显的差异。与普通水相比，重水不仅有明显不同的蒸汽压，而且潜热也相当高。其表面张力和介电常数都较低，黏度则相对较高。

在这里我很乐意简要地指出这段发生在知识领域飞速进步的近乎浪漫的历史，并且非常有意思的是重氢的发现与已故的瑞利爵士对大气中氩气的发现存在某些相似之处。这两个"发现"的线索都缘于对在密度的精确测量中观测到的微小差异的重要性的重视。

首次对氧同位素的相对丰度进行测定后，伯奇和门德尔指出，阿斯顿用阳极射线方法测得的氢氧原子质量的比值与直接用化学方法得出的比值之间存在着微小的差异，大约仅为 1/5,000。他们认为，这项微小的差异大于测量中可能的实验误差，他们对此的解释是，氢可能含有少量（约 1/4,000）原子质量为 2 的同位素。下面我们来想一下如何直接用实验来说明这类同位素的存在。同位素 ^1H 和 ^2H 的核电荷均为 1，并都有一个核外电子，因此可以预期在放电影响下会发出相同形式的光谱。然而应当清楚，受扰动的电子运动产生了特征辐射，而在这个运动的过程中，电子与原子核是耦合的；虽然其振动频率主要由核电荷决定，但也会受到原子核自身质量的轻微影响。由于 ^2H 同位素有较大的质量，因而很容易计算出重氢光谱中的巴耳末线将出现微小的红移。α 线的位移量为 1.78 埃。当电荷穿过普通氢原子时，向红侧应出现微弱的伴线。尤里、布里克韦德和墨菲在为此所做的实验中首次在正确位置上探测到了弱伴线的存在。与强的 Hα 线相比，伴线强度难以确切地测量，但实验发现其量级为 1/5,000。

随后的实验是通过液氢的分馏来浓缩 ^2H 同位素；该项实验取得了一定的成功。尤里和沃什伯恩进行了另一项重要的观测，他们发现了旧电解池中的水比正常情况下含有更大比例的重氢。通过持续的电解，^2H 的浓度很快上升。这是找到成功制得

obtaining heavy hydrogen in quantity. The processes involved were carefully investigated by Lewis and Macdonald, and the electrolysis of water was carried out on a comparatively large scale. Nickel electrodes were used, and sodium hydroxide as an electrolyte. In general, it was found that the escape of H^1 during electrolysis was five to six times faster than that of H^2 relative to their concentrations in the solution. There was in consequence a steady accumulation of the heavy isotope in the water in the process until nearly pure heavy water was obtained. Assuming that the initial concentration of H^2 in the water was 1 in 6,000, about 1 c.c. of pure heavy water should be obtained by electrolysis of 6 litres of water.

Lewis succeeded in preparing many cubic centimetres of heavy water in which ordinary hydrogen was present in very small quantity. He and his collaborators investigated the main physical and chemical differences between heavy water and ordinary water, to some of which I have already referred. Our congratulations are due to our American colleagues for the masterly way they have opened up and developed so rapidly this new field of knowledge, which it is certain will prove of great scientific and practical importance in many directions in the near future. Prof. G. N. Lewis, of the University of California, who was the first to prepare nearly pure heavy water, generously presented samples of this water to a number of investigators, not only in his own country but also in Europe, in order to give them an early opportunity of testing its properties. I am personally much indebted to Prof. Lewis for a sample of this heavy water with which we were able to make a number of experiments on the transformation of matter to which I shall refer later.

We are all aware of the important part that hydrogen plays in many chemical compounds and particularly in organic molecules. When reasonable supplies of heavy water are available to the experimenter, there will no doubt be great activity in preparing and studying many compounds in which H^1 in the molecule is wholly or partly replaced by H^2. Already a few investigations have been carried out, for example, with ammonia and with hydrogen iodide, in which H^1 is replaced by the heavy isotope. It has been found that in mixtures of light and heavy hydrogen gas, the atoms interchange on a nickel surface at a temperature of about 600°C. and the conditions of equilibrium and heat evolution have been investigated. During the next few years we may expect an intensive study to be made of the change of properties of compounds in which heavy hydrogen is used. It will be of particular interest to examine the changes in the rates of reaction at different temperatures when heavy hydrogen is substituted for ordinary hydrogen.

The discovery of the new water will be of great importance in another direction, namely, its effect on the processes occurring in animal and plant life. There has not yet been sufficient time to make more than a few preliminary experiments in this field, and then only on a small scale. Lewis finds that seeds of a certain tobacco plant did not germinate in pure heavy water but did so when the concentration of heavy hydrogen was about one half. In experiments by other observers, well-defined physiological effects have been obtained for quite small concentrations of heavy hydrogen in water. Further observations in this highly important field of inquiry will be awaited with much interest.

大量重氢的方法的关键一步。刘易斯和麦克唐纳仔细地研究了相关电解过程，并且较大规模下实现了水的电解。他们用镍作电极，以氢氧化钠作电解液。实验发现在一般情形下，相对于 ^1H 和 ^2H 在电解液中的浓度，电解期间 ^1H 的逸出是 ^2H 逸出的 5~6 倍。因此可知，在获得几乎是纯的重水之前，水中的重同位素一直在稳定地累积。假设水中 ^2H 的初始浓度为 1/6,000，电解 6 升水应该得到约 1 立方厘米的纯重水。

刘易斯成功制备了一定体积（单位为立方厘米）的重水，其中只含有极少量的普通氢。他和同事们研究了重水与普通水的主要物理性质和化学性质的差异，其中有些差异前文已经提到。我们向这些美国的同事表示祝贺，他们以娴熟的方法开创并迅速发展了新的知识领域，在不久的将来肯定会在许多方面证明其在科学与实用方面巨大的重要性。加州大学的刘易斯教授首次制得了纯度极高的重水，为了使相关的研究者能够及早地测试出其性质，他不仅为美国的研究者，也为欧洲的研究者慷慨地提供了重水的样品。我个人非常感谢刘易斯教授，利用他提供的一份重水样品，我们得以进行了许多物质转化的实验，这点我在后文还会提到。

我们都认识到氢在许多化合物中尤其是在有机分子中具有重要的作用。当实验工作者能够获得适当数量的重水时，一定会有很多人将重水用于混合物的制备并对其进行研究，而混合物分子中的 ^1H 则全部或部分被 ^2H 代替。一些实验者已经开展了一些研究，例如，制备氨水和碘化氢，其中的氢元素为重氢。人们已经发现在普通氢和重氢的混合氢气中，原子在温度约为 600℃ 的镍表面上相互交换，人们还研究了这个反应的平衡条件和放热。我们可以期待，在今后的几年中，对含有重氢的化合物的性质变化的研究将得到更广泛的开展。当用重氢代替了普通氢后，对于不同温度下反应速率的变化的测定将格外引起人们的兴趣。

这种新类型的水的发现将对另一个领域也造成重要的影响，即它在动物和植物的生命过程中的作用。在这个领域内我们还没有足够的时间来展开研究，仅在小范围内开展了一些初步实验。刘易斯发现，某种烟草植物的种子在纯重水中不会发芽，但当重氢的浓度稀释到一半时就会发芽。其他观测者的实验中还发现，水中低浓度的重氢可以引起明显的生理学效应。我们将诚挚地期待在这个意义重大的研究领域中有更进一步的观察。

It is widely recognised that the new hydrogen will prove of so much general importance to chemistry and physics that it is desirable to give it a definite name and symbol. Prof. Urey, its discoverer, has suggested that the isotope of mass 1 should be called "protium" and the isotope of mass 2 "deuterium" while the nucleus of heavy hydrogen, which has already been found very efficient as a projectile in transforming matter, should be called "deuteron" or "deuton". The question of a suitable nomenclature is one of general importance to scientific men and deserves careful consideration. The name "diplogen" (διπλους, double) for H^2 and "diplon" for the nucleus seemed to find some favour in England as an alternative. The symbol D for the heavy isotope seems appropriate.

While diplogen (or deuterium) may be separated in quantity from heavy water in nearly a pure state, it is of interest to refer to another method of separation employed by Hertz. By utilising a special diffusion method devised by him, he has been able to separate from ordinary hydrogen gas about 1 c.c. of diplogen in such purity that the Balmer lines of hydrogen were not visible in its spectrum. With such pure material, it should be possible to study in detail the complicated band spectrum of diplogen and compare it with that of hydrogen.

We have not so far considered the question of the nuclear structure of diplogen and its relation, if any, to that of ordinary hydrogen. We first of all require to know its mass with accuracy; this has been measured by Bainbridge by using a modification of the positive ray method, who found that the mass of the atom is 2.0136 while the mass of the hydrogen atom is 1.0078 in terms of the mass of the main isotope of oxygen taken as 16. This mass is slightly less than the combined mass of two H atoms. Sufficient evidence is not yet available to decide whether the D nucleus is simple or composite, and there are a number of possible combinations to consider between the four units, the electron, positron, neutron and proton. If we assume, as seems not unlikely, that the D nucleus consists of a close combination of a proton with a neutron, it can be shown from the masses concerned that its binding energy should be somewhat less than 1 million volts if we take the value 1.0067 for the mass of the neutron as estimated by Chadwick. If this be the case, we should expect the diplon to be broken up occasionally into a proton and neutron as a consequence of a close collision with a fast α-particle. Experiments to test this have so far yielded negative results. If this dissociation occurs at all, the probability of such an event must be very small. Lawrence, from a study of the bombardment of elements by diplons, suggests that the diplon may break up into a proton and neutron in the strong electric field close to the bombarded nucleus, but the interpretation of his results is not yet certain. At the moment, therefore, the experimental evidence is insufficient to give a definite decision with regard to the structure of the diplon.

By comparing the scattering of α-particles when passing through diplogen and hydrogen gas, Mr. Kempton and I have found that as the result of a head-on collision with an α-particle, the recoiling diplon travels about eight percent farther than the proton in a corresponding collision. Such a result is in agreement with calculation. It also seems clear that the field of force round the diplon must be very similar to that of the proton,

人们现已广泛认可，新的氢元素对化学和物理学意义重大，因而需要给它一个确定的名称和符号。其发现者尤里教授提议质量为 1 的同位素应称为 "protium"，质量为 2 的同位素称为 "deuterium"；而重氢的核应称为 "deuteron" 或 "deuton"，后者已被认为可在物质变换过程中用作非常有效的轰击粒子。合适的命名对科技工作者具有普遍的重要性，并且值得慎重地思考。另一种命名似乎在英国获得青睐，即将 ^{2}H 命名为 "diplogen"（διπλουs，意思为 "双"），将其原子核命名为 "diplon"。以 D 作为重同位素的符号似乎是非常合适的。

尽管重氢（或氘）可以从接近于纯态的重水中大量分离出来，不过我还是很乐意提一下赫兹所使用的另一种分离方法。他所发明的这种特殊的扩散法，使他已经能够从普通氢气中分离出体积约 1 立方厘米的氘，其纯度高到在它的光谱中看不到氢的巴耳末线。有了这种纯度较多的样品，这使得进一步详细研究氘的复杂带谱并与氢的谱线进行比较成为可能。

至今，我们还没有考虑氘核结构及其与普通氢核结构的关系问题。首先我们需要知道其准确的质量；班布里奇用改进的阳极射线方法已经对此做了测量，他发现如果将氧的主要同位素的质量取为 16，可得氢原子质量是 1.0078，氘原子质量是 2.0136。这个质量稍小于两个 H 原子的质量。尚未有足够的证据确认 D 核是单一核还是复合核，所以在电子、正电子、中子和质子四种粒子之间存在许多种可能的组合。如果我们假定（似乎极有可能）D 核是由一个质子与一个中子的紧密结合而组成的，并对中子的质量取查德威克估算的 1.0067，则由质子和中子的质量可以知道它们之间的束缚能应稍小于 1 兆电子伏。如果情况确实如此，我们应该可以预期，当与快速 α 粒子发生近距碰撞时，氘核偶尔可以分裂为质子和中子。不过检验上述预言的实验至今得到的结果是否定的。如果这类离解确实存在，那么其发生概率也必然很小。劳伦斯根据元素被氘核轰击的研究，提出氘核在强电场中与被轰击核接近时可以分裂为质子和中子，但他对结果的解释尚未确定。因此，目前的实验证据还不足以给出关于氘核结构的确定结论。

通过对穿过氘气和氢气时的 α 粒子的散射作比较，肯普顿先生和我发现，由于与 α 粒子发生正碰，反冲氘核比相应碰撞中的质子行进远 8%。这个结果是与计算一致的。这似乎也表明，围绕氘核的力场必定类似于围绕质子的力场，尽管可以预期当 α 粒子行进非常快时氘核与质子还是会有些差别，如果氘核的组成如我们设想

although it may be expected that some differences would be shown for very fast α-particles if the diplon is composite as we have supposed.

Transmutation of Elements

The discovery of heavy hydrogen has provided us with a new form of projectile which has proved markedly efficient in disintegrating a number of light elements in novel ways. It was a very fortunate coincidence that, when Prof. Lewis had prepared some concentrated diplogen, his colleague in the same University, Prof. Lawrence, had available his ingenious apparatus for producing high-speed protons and other particles with an energy as high as two million volts. When diplogen was substituted for hydrogen, the diplon (D^+) was found to be about ten times as efficient in promoting some transformations in lithium as H^+ of equal energy. It will be remembered that Cockcroft and Walton found two years ago that lithium, when bombarded with fast protons, was transformed, with the emission of swift α-particles. It seems clear that in this case the lithium isotope of mass 7 is involved. A proton is captured by the nucleus and the resulting nucleus breaks up into two α-particles, ejected in nearly opposite directions, according to the relation

$$\mathrm{Li}_3^7 + \mathrm{H}_1^1 \rightarrow \mathrm{He}_2^4 + \mathrm{He}_2^4$$

The emission of other particles of short range has also been observed but the exact nature of the transformation which gives rise to them is not yet clear.

When lithium is bombarded with diplons instead of protons, different types of transformation occur. In one case it seems that the lithium isotope of mass 6, after capturing a diplon, breaks up into two α-particles according to the equation

$$\mathrm{Li}_3^6 + \mathrm{D}_1^2 \rightarrow \mathrm{He}_2^4 + \mathrm{He}_2^4$$

In this case also, as has been shown beautifully by the expansion photographs obtained by Dee and Walton, the two α-particles are shot out in opposite directions and with a speed greater than the swiftest α-particle from radioactive substances.

Still another interesting type of complex transformation occurs in this element. Oliphant and Rutherford observed that lithium when bombarded by diplons gave, in addition to the group of fast α-particles first observed by Lawrence, a distribution of α-particles of all ranges from 7.8 cm. to 1 cm. in air. It is believed in this case that the isotope of mass 7 captures a diplon and then breaks up into two α-particles and a neutron according to the relation

$$\mathrm{Li}_3^7 + \mathrm{D}_1^2 \rightarrow \mathrm{He}_2^4 + \mathrm{He}_2^4 + n_0^1$$

This transformation is in close accord with the conservation of energy when the change of mass and the energies of the expelled particles are taken into account. The emission of neutrons from lithium has been observed by Lauritsen and also in our experiments. In addition, Lawrence has shown that a number of other light elements give rise under bombardment to groups of fast protons and in many cases also to α-particles and neutrons. While the interpretation of the experimental results is as yet only clear in a

的那样。

元素的嬗变

重氢的发现为我们提供了一种新型的轰击粒子，在用新方法分裂许多轻元素时证明，它是非常有效的。不能不说这是一个幸运的巧合，当刘易斯教授制备了一定量的浓缩氘时，和他同在一所大学的同事劳伦斯教授已用他的精妙的装置产生了能量高达 2 兆电子伏的高速质子和其他粒子。当用氘代替氢时，氘核（D^+）在促进锂的某些变换时的效率是相同能量的 H^+ 的 10 倍。人们应该不会忘记在两年前，考克饶夫和瓦耳顿发现在用高速质子进行轰击时，锂发生了伴随发射快速 α 粒子的嬗变。这似乎表明在这个过程中，质量为 7 的锂同位素发生了嬗变。核俘获了一个质子，新形成的核分裂为两个 α 粒子，相反的过程则会放出一个质子，关系式如下：

$$\ _{3}^{7}\mathrm{Li} + \ _{1}^{1}\mathrm{H} \rightarrow\ _{2}^{4}\mathrm{He} + \ _{2}^{4}\mathrm{He}$$

他们也观测到其他短程粒子的发射，但尚不清楚引起嬗变的确切机理。

当用氘核取代质子轰击锂时，发生了不同类型的嬗变。其中一种情况是，质量为 6 的锂同位素在俘获一个氘核后分裂成两个 α 粒子，如下式所示：

$$\ _{3}^{6}\mathrm{Li} + \ _{1}^{2}\mathrm{D} \rightarrow\ _{2}^{4}\mathrm{He} + \ _{2}^{4}\mathrm{He}$$

迪伊和瓦耳顿也用（云雾室）膨胀时的照片漂亮地证明了这种情况，实验中两个 α 粒子向相反的方向发射，比放射物质发射的最快的 α 粒子还要快。

这个元素还发生了另一种有趣的复杂嬗变。当锂被氘核轰击时，除了劳伦斯首次观察到的一组快速运动的 α 粒子之外，奥利芬特和卢瑟福还在空气中发现了射程分布于 7.8 厘米到 1 厘米之间不等的 α 粒子。可以确信，在这种情况下，质量为 7 的锂同位素俘获一个氘核后分裂成两个 α 粒子和一个中子，如下式所示：

$$\ _{3}^{7}\mathrm{Li} + \ _{1}^{2}\mathrm{D} \rightarrow\ _{2}^{4}\mathrm{He} + \ _{2}^{4}\mathrm{He} + \ _{0}^{1}n$$

当考虑了所发射粒子的质量和能量变化时，这种嬗变过程与能量守恒是非常一致的。劳里森和我们的实验中均观测到了从锂中发射的中子。此外，劳伦斯还指出，许多其他轻元素在氘核轰击下会产生快质子群，多数情况下，也会产生 α 粒子和中子。不过关于这类实验结果的原理，大部分还尚不明确，但是毫无疑问，重氢的应用在拓展我们关于嬗变方面的知识上的重要性将是不可估量的，因此这也为我们探索原

few cases, there can be no doubt that the use of heavy hydrogen will prove invaluable for extending our knowledge of transformations and thus in helping to throw light on the structure of atomic nuclei.

The importance of this new projectile in studying transformations is well illustrated by some recent experiments made in Cambridge with Oliphant and Harteck. When diplons were used to bombard compounds like ammonium chloride, NH_4Cl, and ammonium sulphate, $(NH_4)_2SO_4$, in which ordinary hydrogen was in part displaced by diplogen, enormous numbers of fast protons were found to be emitted, even for an accelerating voltage of 100,000 volts. In fact the number of expelled particles is far greater than that observed in any other type of transformation at this voltage. The main groups of expelled protons had a range in air of 14 cm., corresponding to an energy of 3 million volts. In addition to this group, another strong group of singly charged particles were observed of range in air only 1.6 cm. Both of these groups contain equal numbers of particles.

In order to account for these observations, it seems likely that, as the result of a close collision, the diplon occasionally unites with the struck diplon to form a helium nucleus of mass 4 and charge 2, but containing a large excess of energy over the normal helium nucleus. The new nucleus is in consequence explosive and breaks up into two parts, one a fast proton and the other a new isotope of hydrogen H_1^3 of mass 3. If this be the case, the proton and H^3 nucleus should fly apart in opposite directions. It can be simply calculated that the range of the recoiling H^3 nucleus under these conditions should be 1.7 cm.—a range agreeing closely with that actually observed. The changes occurring are illustrated by the equation

$$D_1^2 + D_1^2 \rightarrow He_2^4 \rightarrow H_1^3 + H_1^1$$

From the known masses of D and H^1 and the energy of the observed motion of the H^1 and H^3 particles, it can be deduced that the mass of this new hydrogen isotope is 3.0151.

In these experiments, large numbers of neutrons are also emitted. It appears probable that these arise from another mode of disintegration of the newly formed helium nucleus according to the relation

$$D_1^2 + D_1^2 \rightarrow He_2^4 \rightarrow He_2^3 + neutron,$$

an isotope of helium of mass 3 and a neutron being expelled in opposite directions. There is strong evidence that such an isotope of helium also appears when the lithium atom of mass 6 is bombarded by protons, and from this transformation it appears that the mass of this isotope is 3.0165. It is quite likely that the helium nucleus of mass 3 formed in this way is unstable and may possibly break up into H_1^3 and a positive electron. While the conclusions outlined above are to some extent provisional and require confirmation by other methods, there can be no doubt that the effects which follow the collisions of a swift diplon with another are of much importance and interest in throwing light on possible modes of formation of some of the lighter nuclei.

子核的结构带来一线曙光。

最近剑桥的奥利芬特和哈特克所做的一些实验对这类新型轰击粒子在研究嬗变中的重要性做了很好的说明。当用氘核轰击氯化铵 (NH_4Cl) 和硫酸铵 ((NH_4)$_2SO_4$) 这类化合物时，如果化合物中普通氢元素部分地被氘所替代，那么即便在加速电压为 100,000 伏特时，它们也会发射出大量快质子。实际上，射出的粒子数远大于在同样电压下任何其他嬗变中观测到的粒子数。发射出的主要质子群在空气中的射程为 14 厘米，其相当于 3 兆电子伏的能量。除此之外，我们还观测到另一组很强的带单位电荷的带电粒子群，其在空气中的射程仅为 1.6 厘米。这两组粒子群中包含了相同数量的粒子。

为了解释这些观测，似乎可以认为其是近距碰撞产生的结果。入射氘核有时会与被击中的氘核一起形成质量为 4、电荷数为 2 的氦核，但其能量大大超过正常氦核的能量。新的原子核继续爆炸并分裂为两部分，一部分是快质子，另一部分是质量为 3 的氢的新同位素 $_1^3H$。如果这种情况的确存在，那么质子和 ^3H 核应分别向相反方向飞出。这时可以简单计算出反冲 ^3H 核的射程应是 1.7 厘米，这与实际观测完全相符。出现的变化由下列方程说明：

$$_1^2D + _1^2D \rightarrow _2^4He \rightarrow _1^3H + _1^1H$$

根据 D 和 ^1H 的已知质量以及观测的 ^1H 粒子和 ^3H 粒子运动的能量，可以推导出氢的新型同位素的质量为 3.0151。

这些实验中也发射出了大量的中子，这可能源自新形成的氦核按照下列关系所进行的另一类形式的蜕变：

$$_1^2D + _1^2D \rightarrow _2^4He \rightarrow _2^3He + _0^1n$$

一个质量为 3 的氦同位素和一个中子以相反的方向发射。强有力的证据已表明，这样的氦同位素在质量为 6 的锂原子被质子轰击时也会出现，在这个嬗变中氦同位素的质量为 3.0165。不过以这种方式形成的质量为 3 的氦核是不稳定的，很可能会分裂成 $_1^3H$ 和一个正电子。上述结论在某种程度上而言还是不确定的，尚需要用其他的方法加以证实，而可以肯定的是，快速氘核与其他粒子碰撞后的这种结果为研究某些轻核可能的形成途径开辟了光明的道路，这个意义非常重大，并且也是非常有意思的。

It is of interest to speculate why the heavy isotope of hydrogen appears in many cases far more effective, for equal energies, in producing transformations than the lighter isotope. On the general theory of transformation proposed some years ago by Gamow, it is to be anticipated that, for equal energies of motion, the diplon on account of its heavier mass would have a smaller chance of entering a nucleus than the swifter proton. It may be, however, that normally only a small fraction of the protons which actually enter a nucleus are able to cause a veritable transformation, the others escaping unchanged from the nucleus. On this view, the greater efficiency of the diplon in causing transformation may be due to the fact that a much larger fraction of those which enter the nucleus are retained by it, leading to a violent disintegration of its structure. It may be too that the diplon on entering a nucleus breaks up into its component parts. The appearance of the proton as well as the neutron in some of the transformations may be connected with the composite structure of the diplon.

(**133**, 481-484; 1934)

　　值得深思的是，在引发元素嬗变方面，为何氢的重同位素在许多情况下比相同能量的轻同位素表现得更有效率。根据几年前伽莫夫提出的嬗变的一般理论可以推测，在动能相等的情形下，与快质子相比，质量较重的氘核进入原子核的概率较小。然而，正常情况下进入核内的质子只有小部分能产生真正的嬗变，而其他质子则从核内逸出并且没有发生变化。据此可以推断，氘核在引发嬗变方面所显现出的高效性可能源于下述事实：有很大比例的进入核内的氘核被原子核保留，因此导致了其结构的激烈蜕变。也可能是因为，进入核内的氘核分裂为其组成部分。质子与中子在某些嬗变中的出现可能与氘核的组成结构相关。

（沈乃澂 翻译；朱永生 审稿）

Developments of Television

Editor's Note

In a theatre in the West End of London on 20 March 1934, *Nature* reports here, shareholders of Baird Television Ltd. saw and heard the chairman address them from a studio at the Crystal Palace eight miles away. The feat relied on the a newly developed large cathode-ray oscilloscope, as well as high-quality photo-cells and amplifiers capable of processing signals over a wide frequency range. Transmissions from the Crystal Palace location could broadcast television signals to the whole of Greater London. The report notes that another demonstration is planned of a method reported earlier in *Nature* by which television images of topical events might be displayed on cinema screens and home receivers within only a few seconds of having happened.

AN application of science has enabled a chairman of a company to become a historic figure. At the annual general meeting of Baird Television, Ltd., held in a theatre in the west end of London on March 20, the shareholders heard and saw distinctly the chairman address them from a studio at the Crystal Palace, nearly eight miles distant. To the shareholders, and afterwards to representatives of the Press, the Baird Company arranged a programme of transmissions by radio from the Crystal Palace to enable the audience to see persons talking on various subjects, a cartoonist sketching at his easel, excerpts from popular films and "still" pictures. All these items were reproduced in the receiver with sufficient detail for an audience of more than a hundred persons to "look in", although the receiver was devised for use in the home rather than a theatre. The success of these demonstrations is attributed to the state of perfection of the large cathode ray oscillographs made exclusively for the Baird Co. by the research staff of a British industrial concern, the excellence of the photoelectric cells in use at the transmitting end, and the construction of amplifiers which are capable of dealing without phase distortion with a range of frequencies from 25 to 1,000,000 cycles per second. The subject matter to be televised is divided up into 180 lines (or strips) corresponding to 24 times the definition obtainable with the old 30-line apparatus. Vision is being transmitted from a dipole aerial on a wave-length of 6.0 metres, and sound on 6.25 metres.

Judging from the demonstrations given last week, the Baird Company's engineers have successfully overcome interference effects due to motors, lifts and other electro-magnetic disturbances met with at these short wave-lengths. A series of experiments have been carried out to ascertain the effective range of reception, as a result of which it is claimed that the Crystal Palace transmitting station can provide an ultra-short wave high definition television service for the whole of the Greater London area, which includes a population of about eight millions. Capt. A. G. D. West, who joined the board of the Baird Company last June to direct its technical development, is to be warmly congratulated on his

电视的发展

编者按

《自然》的这篇文章报道了 1934 年 3 月 20 日在伦敦西区一个剧院中，贝尔德电视有限公司的股东们观看并且听到董事会主席在 8 英里外的水晶宫演播室向他们进行的演讲。这一成就得益于最近研制出的大型阴极射线示波器、高质量的光电管和能够处理宽频率范围信号的放大器。从水晶宫输出的信号可以为整个大伦敦地区提供电视信号。这篇报道提到了《自然》先前报道的另一种计划用于电视方面的技术，该技术可以使时事新闻的电视图像在事件发生后的几秒内显示在电影院屏幕或者家用接收机上。

科学的一项应用使一家公司的董事长成为了历史性的人物。3 月 20 日，贝尔德电视有限公司的年会在伦敦西区的一个剧院内召开，会上股东们清楚地听到并看见董事长在将近 8 英里外的水晶宫演播室向他们发表演讲。贝尔德公司给股东们，随后给出版社代表们安排了一个节目，节目通过无线电波从水晶宫传送信号，观众们能够看到谈论着不同话题的人们、一个正在画架上素描的漫画家以及一些从流行电影和"静止的"图画上摘选的内容。所有这些内容都被细致地再现于接收机上，供 100 多名观众"观看"，尽管接收机原本是为在家里而不是在剧院使用设计的。这些演示的成功主要归于以下几个原因：英国一家工业公司的研究人员专门为贝尔德公司制造的大型阴极射线示波器堪称完美，在发射端使用的光电管的性能非常优秀，新造的放大器能够无相位失真地处理每秒 25 周到每秒 100 万周频率范围内的信号。通过电视播放的内容被分解成 180 线（或带），这样其清晰度就是以前只能分解成 30 线的老设备的 24 倍。图像从一个偶极子天线处以波长 6 米的信号传出，而声音则以波长 6.25 米的信号传出。

从上周进行的演示来判断，贝尔德公司的工程师们已经成功克服了由汽车、电梯以及在这些短波长范围内的其他电磁干扰所产生的干涉效应。另外，工程师们也进行了一系列实验来确定有效的接收范围，据称，实验结果表明水晶宫的发射台能够为拥有约 800 万人口的整个大伦敦地区提供超短波的高清电视服务。去年 6 月加入贝尔德公司董事会主管公司技术发展的韦斯特上尉一定会因其成就受到热烈的祝贺，贝尔德公司也会因首次公开演示了高清电视播送的可能性而被人们赞颂。我

achievement; and the Company on the first public demonstration of the broadcasting possibilities of high-definition television. We understand that a demonstration will shortly be given of the intermediate film-method, described by Major A. G. Church in *Nature* of September 30, 1933, by means of which televised images of topical events will be thrown on screens in cinema theatres as well as on home-receivers within a few seconds of their occurrence. Another series of experiments on a new system of "scanning" invented by Mr. Baird is nearing completion. These experiments aim at securing sufficient illumination in a studio to enable "crowd" scenes to be televised directly with detailed fidelity.

(**133**, 488-489; 1934)

们可以预计，很快就会出现使用中间胶片法进行的演示。在 1933 年 9 月 30 日的《自然》上丘奇少校曾描述过该方法，通过这种方法，时事新闻的电视图像能够在事件发生后的几秒内显示在电影院屏幕或者家用接收机上。在贝尔德先生发明的新"扫描"系统上进行的另一系列实验也快要完成了。这些实验的目的是确保演播室有足够的照明度，以使"拥挤"的镜头能直接高保真地在电视上播放。

（刘霞 翻译；赵见高 审稿）

A Rapid Test for the Diagnosis of Pregnancy

C. W. Bellerby

Editor's Note

In the 1930s, biologists were occupied with two important and novel searches, one for vitamins (essential constituents of the human diet usually manufactured by plants) and one for hormones (chemicals essential for the life of human beings but which have to be manufactured in the body from ingested food). This paper is one of the first to suggest that hormones may be effective in the diagnosis of pregnancy in women, based on the use of the South African clawed toad as test animal.

CURRENT biological tests for the diagnosis of pregnancy or detection of ovary-stimulating substances in gland extracts and body fluids have the main disadvantage that several days must elapse before a result can be obtained. Attempts have been made to remedy this by making use of the doe rabbit, because in this animal a response (ovulation) can be obtained in less than 14 hours[1]. The rabbit, however, requires a good deal of care in order to obtain consistent results. It is essential to know the previous history of does employed, and preferably only to use them a short time after parturition. Even so, variation in response to injection may be so great as to necessitate the use of more than one doe in order to be sure of the result.

The test described in the present note depends upon the observation by Hogben[2] that extraneous ovulation in the South African clawed toad (*Xenopus Loevis*) can be induced by injection of extracts of the anterior lobe of pituitary. *Xenopus* can be obtained easily and cheaply in large numbers. Several hundreds can be kept without difficulty at the sole cost of a few handfuls of raw meat once a week, provided that they are kept in a warm well-lit room and that their water is changed after feeding. Ovulation does not occur spontaneously in captivity. Ova shed as a result of injection are clearly visible and extruded in large numbers. No doubt exists, therefore, as to the validity of a response.

During the past two years, work has been carried out on the use of *Xenopus* for detecting and estimating ovary-stimulating substances in tissue extracts and body fluids such as pregnancy urine. The following main points have emerged[3].

(*a*) At a temperature of 20°C-25°C a single injection of an active preparation into the lymph sac is followed in the great majority of cases by complete ovulation within 9 hours. Very often a response is obtained in less than 6 hours.

(*b*) A given batch of toads can be used repeatedly, provided that a rest of at least one

一项快速诊断妊娠的实验方法

贝勒比

编者按

20 世纪 30 年代，生物学家致力于寻找两种重要而新颖的物质，一种是维生素（人类饮食必需的成分，通常由植物体合成），另一种是激素（人类生命必需的化合物，但是只能通过摄入食物在体内合成）。本文是最早提出激素可能可以用于诊断妇女妊娠的文章之一，其研究是以非洲爪蟾作为实验动物的。

当前用于诊断妊娠或者检测腺体提取物及体液中卵巢刺激物质的生物学方法，主要缺点在于检测结果需要等好几天才能获得。人们曾尝试用雌兔进行实验来弥补这个缺点，因为在雌兔体内不到 14 小时就可以检测到排卵反应 [1]。然而，要获得一致的结果，需要精心照料雌兔，必须清楚它们的成长过程，而且最好是只在分娩后很短一段时间内使用它们。即便如此，注射后排卵反应的差异也非常巨大，从而必须用多只兔子进行实验以确保结果的准确性。

本文所描述的实验基于霍格本 [2] 的发现，即注射垂体前叶的提取物可以诱发非洲爪蟾的体外排卵。非洲爪蟾很容易大批量低成本地得到。只要将它们养在温暖且光线充足的房间里，保证每次喂食后换水，只需每周一次放入少量生肉，数百只爪蟾就能很容易地生存下来。在这种养殖条件下，爪蟾不会自发排卵。对其注射刺激物质后，可以非常清楚地看到大量排卵的过程。因此，注射刺激物质可以诱发排卵反应这一点是毫无疑问的。

在过去的两年里，我们利用非洲爪蟾对组织提取物和体液（例如孕妇尿液）中的卵巢刺激物质进行了检测和估计。从这些实验中可以得出以下几点主要结论 [3]。

(a) 在 20℃~25℃下，往爪蟾淋巴囊内单次注射活性提取物后，绝大多数爪蟾在 9 小时内完全排卵。在 6 小时内排卵的情况也经常出现。

(b) 每一批爪蟾都可以重复使用，只要连续两次注射之间至少间隔一周。

week is allowed to elapse between successive injections.

(*c*) A definite quantitative relationship holds between dosage and response.

As a result of the first observation, a test for early pregnancy has been elaborated, the exact procedure of which depends upon the time which has elapsed from the last missed menstrual period : —

(1) If one month or more has elapsed, untreated urine from the suspected case is used. Ten toads are injected in the lymph sac with 1 ml. A positive diagnosis is made if ovulation occurs in at least 5 out of 10 animals within 9 hours. The correct temperature is obtained by keeping vessels containing the toads in a room heated to 20°C-25°C by means of an electric fire.

(2) If less than one month has elapsed, a sample of 100 ml. of urine is precipitated with acetone and centrifuged. The residue is suspended in 10 ml. of distilled water and 1 ml. of the suspension injected into each of 10 toads. A positive result is indicated as before. This procedure is necessary owing to the facts that in very early pregnancy there is an insufficient amount of ovary-stimulating substance in 1 ml. of urine to produce a response, and that a volume of fluid greater than 2 ml. cannot be injected into the lymph sac without risk of non-absorption.

A full account of this work will appear later. So far no incorrect diagnosis has been made. In view of the quantitative nature of the test, it is hoped to distinguish normal early pregnancy from ectopic pregnancy or conditions such as hydatidiform mole.

(**133**, 494-495; 1934)

C. W. Bellerby: Department of Social Biology, University of London, March. 19.

References:

1. Bellerby, C. W., *J. Physiol.*, **67**, Proc. xxxii; 1929.

2. Hogben, L. T., *Proc. Roy. Soc. S. Africa.*, March, 1930.

3. Bellerby, C. W., *Biochem. J.*, **27**, 615, 2025; 1933.

(c) 注射剂量和妊娠反应之间存在明确的定量关系。

基于上述实验的结果，我们精心设计了一种检测早孕的方法。具体的操作方法取决于距离上次月经结束的时间有多长：

（1）如果时间已经超过 1 个月，那么可以直接用被检对象的尿液。在 10 只爪蟾的淋巴囊内分别注射 1 ml 尿液。如果在 9 小时内，10 只爪蟾中至少有 5 只出现了排卵，那么结果就是阳性的。将装有爪蟾的容器放置在 20℃~25℃ 的房间里，通过电热装置来保证温度的准确性。

（2）如果时间还未到 1 个月，那么就取 100 ml 尿样，用丙酮使其沉淀并离心。将沉淀物溶解于 10 ml 蒸馏水中。在 10 只爪蟾的淋巴囊内分别注射 1 ml 这种悬浮液。阳性结果的判断方法同前。这个操作过程是必需的，因为在怀孕后最初的时期，1 ml 尿液中所含有的卵巢刺激物质的量不足以引起排卵反应，而且为了保证吸收，不能向淋巴囊内注射 2 ml 以上的体液。

我们随后将详细叙述这项工作的过程。目前为止还没有出现错误的诊断。考虑到这种检测方法的定量性质，我们希望可以通过它将正常的早孕与异位妊娠或者诸如葡萄胎那样的其他情况区分开来。

（毛晨晖 翻译；金侠 审稿）

The "Neutrino"

H. Bethe and R. Peierls

Editor's Note

Hans Bethe and Rudolf Peierls here discuss the implications of Wolfgang Pauli's proposal that radioactive beta decay involves a hitherto unknown particle, the neutrino. If such a particle had small mass and spin 1/2, the continuous spread of energy of electrons emitted in beta decay would make sense, and energy and momentum conservation need not be abandoned for nuclear processes. They suggest that the neutrino is created at the moment of decay, and that a neutrino may initiate a reverse beta decay when impinging upon nuclei. However, by their estimates a neutrino should interact so weakly with other matter that observing the latter would be most unlikely. Indeed, they can see no way yet to observe a neutrino.

THE view has recently been put forward[1] that a neutral particle of about electronic mass, and spin $\frac{1}{2}\hbar$ (where $\hbar=h/2\pi$) exists, and that this "neutrino" is emitted together with an electron in β-decay. This assumption allows the conservation laws for energy and angular momentum to hold in nuclear physics[2]. Both the emitted electron and neutrino could be described either (a) as having existed before in the nucleus or (b) as being created at the time of emission. In a recent paper[3] Fermi has proposed a model of β-disintegration using (b) which seems to be confirmed by experiment.

According to (a), one should picture the neutron as being built up of a proton, an electron and a neutrino, while if one accepts (b), the rôles of neutron and proton would be symmetrical[4] and one would expect that positive electrons could also sometimes be created together with a neutrino in nuclear transformations. Therefore the experiments of Curie and Joliot[5] on an artificial positive β-decay give strong support to method (b), as one can scarcely assume the existence of positive electrons in the nucleus.

Why, then, have positive electrons never been found in the natural β-decay? This can be explained by the fact that radioactivity usually starts with α-emission and therefore leads to nuclei the charge of which is too small compared with their weight. The artificial β-emission was found for two unstable nuclei (most probably N^{13} and P^{30}) formed by capture of an α-particle and emission of a neutron, and therefore having too high a charge for their mass.

A consequence of assumption (b) is that two isobares differing by 1 in atomic number can only be stable if the difference of their masses is less than the mass of electron and neutrino together. For otherwise the heavier of the two elements would disintegrate with emission of a neutrino and either a positive or negative electron. There will be only a

"中微子"

泡利认为放射性 β 衰变的过程中涉及了一种未知粒子——中微子，汉斯·贝特和鲁道夫·佩尔斯在这篇文章中对沃尔夫冈·泡利这一提议的含义进行了讨论。如果这种粒子质量很小且自旋为 1/2，那么 β 衰变中放出的电子能谱的连续性就是可以理解的，而且核反应过程也因此而能满足能量和动量守恒。他们认为衰变发生时产生了中微子，并且中微子冲击原子核时会引发 β 衰变的逆过程。然而，根据他们的估算，中微子与其他物质的相互作用非常弱，因而难以观测。实际上，他们当时仍然没有找到任何办法来实现对中微子的观测。

最近有观点认为 [1]，存在质量和电子差不多、自旋为 $\frac{1}{2}\hbar$ ($\hbar=h/2\pi$) 的中性粒子，而这种"中微子"是在发生 β 衰变时与电子一起发射出来的。以上这个假设使得能量和角动量守恒定律在核物理中也得以成立 [2]。衰变过程中发射出来的电子和中微子均可被认为是 (a) 衰变发生前就存在于核中，或 (b) 衰变发生时创生出来的。在最近的一篇文章中 [3]，费米利用假设 (b) 提出了一种 β 衰变的模型，而这一假设似乎得到了实验的证实。

按照 (a) 的解释，中子应该是由一个质子、一个电子和一个中微子组成的，而如果采纳 (b) 的解释，则中子和质子的作用就是对称的 [4]，因此在核转变中也有可能同时发射出正电子和中微子。人们不太可能接受原子核中存在正电子的观点，因此，居里和约里奥 [5] 用人工正 β 衰变的实验有力地证明了 (b) 的解释是正确的。

那么，为什么从未在天然 β 衰变中发现过正电子呢？这可以用以下事实进行解释：放射现象通常先出现 α 发射，从而导致核的电荷与其质量相比很小。而人工 β 发射发现于两种不稳定核（最可能是 ^{13}N 和 ^{30}P）的形成过程中，即吸收一个 α 粒子并发射出一个中子，因此相对其质量而言，该不稳定的核具有很高的电荷。

由假设 (b) 可得到以下结论：原子序数相差 1 的两个同量异位素只有在它们的质量差小于电子和中微子的质量之和时才是稳定的。否则，两个元素中较重的一个将发生蜕变并发射出一个中微子和一个正电子（或负电子）。两个同量异位素的质量

limited region on the mass defect curve, probably at medium atomic weight, where such small differences are possible. In fact, neighbouring isobares have only been found with the mass numbers 87, 115, 121, 123, (187), (203), while isobares with atomic numbers differing by 2 are very frequent. In the first case, one of the two nuclei (Rb) is known to emit β-rays. In each of the last two cases one of the two isobares is stated to be exceedingly rare and its identification might be due to experimental error. The other three cases actually lie close together and have medium weight. A particular case of isobares are proton and neutron. Since all experimentally deduced values of the neutron mass lie between 1.0068 and 1.0078, they are certainly both stable even if the mass of the neutrino should be zero.

The possibility of creating neutrinos necessarily implies the existence of annihilation processes. The most interesting amongst them would be the following: a neutrino hits a nucleus and a positive or negative electron is created while the neutrino disappears and the charge of the nucleus changes by 1.

The cross section σ for such processes for a neutrino of given energy may be estimated from the lifetime t of β-radiating nuclei giving neutrinos of the same energy. (This estimate is in accord with Fermi's model but is more general.) Dimensionally, the connexion will be

$$\sigma = A/t$$

where A has the dimension cm.^{2} sec. The longest length and time which can possibly be involved are $\hbar/mc$ and $\hbar/mc^2$. Therefore

$$\sigma < \frac{\hbar^3}{m^3 c^4 t}$$

For an energy of 2.3×10^6 volts, t is 3 minutes and therefore $\sigma < 10^{-44}$ cm.^{2} (corresponding to a penetrating power of 10^{16} km. in solid matter). It is therefore absolutely impossible to observe processes of this kind with the neutrinos created in nuclear transformations.

With increasing energy, σ increases (in Fermi's model[3] for large energies as $(E/mc^2)^2$) but even if one assumes a very steep increase, it seems highly improbable that, even for cosmic ray energies, σ becomes large enough to allow the process to be observed.

If, therefore, the neutrino has no interaction with other particles besides the processes of creation and annihilation mentioned—and it is not necessary to assume interaction in order to explain the function of the neutrino in nuclear transformations—one can conclude that there is no practically possible way of observing the neutrino.

(**133**, 532; 1934)

H. Bethe and R. Peierls: Physical Laboratory, University, Manchester, Feb. 20.

差如此之小的情况对应于质量亏损曲线上有限的区域，该区域大概位于中等原子量处。实际上，已发现的原子序数相差 1 的同量异位素的质量数只有 87、115、121、123、(187) 和 (203)，而原子序数相差 2 的同量异位素是很常见的。对应上述第一个质量数，已知两种核之一 (Rb) 会发射 β 射线。而对应最后两个质量数，每个质量数的两种同量异位素中的任何一种都可以说相当稀少，而且很可能是实验误差导致大家以为存在着该同量异位素。其他三个质量数实际上很接近，且都具有中等的原子量。质子和中子是同量异位素的特殊情况。由于所有实验导出的中子质量值均在 1.0068 和 1.0078 之间，所以即使中微子的质量为零，中子和质子也肯定都是稳定的。

产生中微子的可能性必然意味着湮没过程的存在。这些现象中最令人感兴趣的是以下过程：一个中微子撞击一个核后，中微子消失并产生一个正电子或负电子，核的电荷数改变了 1。

给定能量的中微子发生以上过程时，其散射截面 σ 可以通过放射出相同能量中微子的 β 衰变核的寿命 t 来估算。（这个估计与费米模型的结果一致，但更具有普适性。）在量纲上，以上两个物理量的关系式可写成

$$\sigma = A/t$$

式中 A 的量纲为 $cm^2 \cdot s$。该问题可能涉及的最长长度和时间分别是 $\hbar/mc$ 和 $\hbar/mc^2$。因此

$$\sigma < \frac{\hbar^3}{m^3 c^4 t}$$

当能量为 2.3×10^6 电子伏、t 为 3 分钟时，$\sigma < 10^{-44}$ cm^2（相应于在固体物质中 10^{16} km 厚的穿透能力）。因此对于核转变时产生中微子的这类过程，我们绝对不可能观测到。

随着能量的增加，σ 也随之增大（在费米模型 [3] 中，当能量较大时，与 $(E/mc^2)^2$ 相当），但即使假定能量急剧增大，甚至是宇宙射线的能量，σ 也几乎不可能大到足以被我们观测到的程度。

因此，如果中微子除了上述的产生和湮没过程外与其他粒子没有相互作用——而我们也没有必要通过假设这种相互作用的存在来解释中微子在核转变中的作用——则我们可以断言没有实际可行的观测中微子的方法。

（沈乃澂 翻译；刘纯 审稿）

References:

1. W. Pauli, quoted repeatedly since 1931, to be published shortly in "Rapports du Septième Conseil Solvay, Brussels", 1933.

2. C. D. Ellis and N. F. Mott, *Proc. Roy. Soc.*, A, **141**, 502; 1933.

3. E. Fermi, *La Ricerca Scientifica*, **2**, No. 12; 1933.

4. This point of view was first put forward by I. Curie and F. Joliot at the Conseil Solvay, 1933.

5. I. Curie and F. Joliot, *Nature*, **133**, 201, Feb. 10, 1934.

Disintegration of the Diplon

P. I. Dee

Editor's Note

The recent experiments of Oliphant, Harteck and Rutherford with "diplons" (nuclei of the hydrogen isotope deuterium) suggested that they might react in pairs to form ^{3}He and ^{3}H. A colleague at the Cavendish Laboratory, Philip Ivor Dee, here reports partial confirmation from cloud-chamber experiments. The nuclear reaction of two deuterium nuclei is one of the most basic in nuclear physics, featuring in the fusion processes in the Sun.

IT has been shown by Oliphant, Harteck and Lord Rutherford in a recent letter[1] that the bombardment by high-velocity diplons of compounds containing diplogen gives rise to three groups of particles—two groups of equal numbers of singly-charged particles of ranges 14.3 cm. and 1.6 cm., together with neutrons of maximum energy of about three million volts. They suggest as possible explanations of these results the reactions:

$$_1D^2 + {}_1D^2 \rightarrow {}_1H^1 + {}_1H^3 \qquad (1)$$
$$\text{and} \qquad _1D^2 + {}_1D^2 \rightarrow {}_2He^3 + {}_0n^1 \qquad (2)$$

an atom of $_1H^3$ of 1.6 cm. range and a proton of 14.3 cm. range satisfying the momentum relations in reaction (1). In this reaction it is to be expected that the proton and the isotope of hydrogen of mass 3 would recoil in opposite directions, except for a small correction due to the momentum of the captured diplon. The cloud track method is extremely suitable for an examination of this possibility, and I have recently taken expansion chamber photographs of the disintegration particles resulting from the bombardment of a target of "heavy" ammonium sulphate with diplons, to see if further information can be obtained.

The first set of experiments was made with a thin target contained in an evacuated tube at the centre of the chamber. Two opposite sides of the end of this tube were closed with mica windows of 6.3 mm. and 11.4 cm. stopping power respectively. The chamber was filled with a suitable mixture of helium and air to increase the lengths of the tracks of the short particles. Under these conditions, the particles of 14.3 cm. range emerging through the thick window and the particles of 1.6 cm. range emerging through the thin window end in the chamber and the usual reprojection permits precise determination as to whether the two tracks are co-planar and of the ranges. Owing to the fine structure of the grid supporting the thin window the efficiency of collection of pairs cannot be high; also the companion to a 14.3 cm. particle passing through the thin window would not be able to pass through the opposite thick window. In spite of these difficulties, opposite pairs of tracks of about 14.3 cm. and 1.6 cm. range are observed with far greater frequency than could be attributed to chance. The photograph reproduced as Fig. 1 is a fortunate

氘核的蜕变

迪伊

编者按

奥利芬特、哈特克和卢瑟福关于"氚核"（氢的同位素氚的原子核）的新近实验表明，它们可以成对发生反应生成 ^3He 和 ^3H。这篇文章中卡文迪什实验室的一位同事菲利普·艾弗·迪伊报道了来自云室实验的部分证据。两个氚核间的反应是核物理学中最基本的反应之一，它在太阳的核聚变过程中起着重要的作用。

在最近的一篇通讯[1]中，奥利芬特、哈特克和卢瑟福勋爵曾指出，用高速的氘核轰击含有重氢的化合物，可以产生三组粒子——其中两组射程分别为 14.3 厘米和 1.6 厘米的同等数目的单电荷粒子，以及一组最大能量约为 3 兆电子伏的中子。对于这些结果，他们提出下列反应作为可能的解释：

$$^2_1D + {}^2_1D \rightarrow {}^1_1H + {}^3_1H \qquad (1)$$
$$\text{和} \qquad {}^2_1D + {}^2_1D \rightarrow {}^3_2He + {}^1_0n \qquad (2)$$

其中射程为 1.6 厘米的 ^3_1H 原子和射程为 14.3 厘米的质子就能满足反应式（1）中的动量关系。在这个反应中除了因俘获氘核的动量而做了一个小修正外，可以预期质子和质量数为 3 的氢同位素原子会向相反的方向反冲。采用云室径迹法来检验这一可能性是非常合适的。最近，为了考察能否获取更进一步的信息，我拍摄了一些用氘核轰击硫酸"重"铵靶而产生蜕变粒子的膨胀云室照片。

第一组实验把一个薄靶置于云室中心的真空管中。管的两端用具有阻断功能分别为 6.3 毫米和 11.4 厘米的云母窗封闭。云室充有适当比例的氢和空气的混合物以增加短径迹粒子的径迹长度。在这些条件下，射程为 14.3 厘米的粒子从真空管的厚窗中穿出，射程为 1.6 厘米的粒子则从另一端的薄窗中穿出并进入云室，而通常出现的二次投影可以精确测定粒子的射程以及其径迹是否共面。由于支撑薄窗的栅格的精细结构，粒子对的收集效率不可能高；另外，若射程为 14.3 厘米的粒子从薄窗中穿出，那么射程为 1.6 厘米的粒子就不能从对面的厚窗中穿出了。尽管存在这些困难，但我们观测到射程约为 14.3 厘米和 1.6 厘米的反向径迹对的频率远高于由于随机事件所导致的频率。图 1 这样的复印照片是一个幸运的例子，其中位于右方

example, the short track on the right being due to the new hydrogen isotope of mass 3. Detailed measurements of the lengths of the tracks and the angles between them are being made and will be published later.

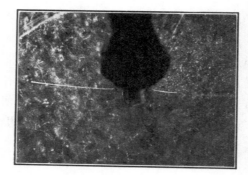

Fig. 1

To investigate the neutron emission, a second series of experiments has been made in which a target of the same material contained in a lead tube of 3 mm. wall thickness was bombarded in the same manner, the chamber being filled with a mixture of 50 percent helium in air. Under these conditions, thirty-one recoil tracks originating in the gas have been photographed. Assuming that these are due to impacts with neutrons, the latter appear to constitute an approximately homogeneous group of maximum energy of about 1.8 million volts. This energy appears to be in fair agreement with reaction (2) on substitution of the mass of $_2He^3$, which can be estimated from consideration of the energies of the short-range products resulting from the transformation of $_3Li^6$ by protons[2,3,4]. The $_2He^3$ group of reaction (2) with a possible range of about 5 mm. would not pass through the thinnest window used in these experiments, but special arrangements are being made to search for them in an expansion chamber.

These experiments are the first to be made with a new discharge tube constructed following a design due to Dr. Oliphant. I should like to acknowledge the much valuable advice which Dr. Oliphant has always so readily given me in the course of construction of this tube. I am also indebted to him for preparing the diplogen targets used in these experiments.

(133, 564; 1934)

P. I. Dee: Cavendish Laboratory, Cambridge.

References:
1. *Nature*, **133**, 413, March 17, 1934.
2. *Proc. Roy. Soc.*, A, **141**, 722; 1933.
3. *Nature*, **132**, 818, Nov. 25, 1933.
4. *Nature*. **133**, 377, March 10, 1934.

的短径迹是由质量数为 3 的氢的新同位素产生的。这些径迹的长度以及它们之间的夹角已被详细测量，稍后就会发表。

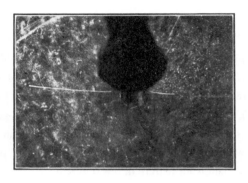

图 1

为了研究中子发射，我们进行了同系列的第二组实验，首先，云室中充入气体混合物为含氢量 50% 的空气，用相同材料的靶置于 3 毫米厚的铅管中并以相同的方式进行轰击。在这样的条件下，我们拍摄到了 31 条在气体中产生的反冲径迹。假定这些径迹是由于中子碰撞产生的，那么后者似乎构成一个最大能量约为 1.8 兆电子伏的近似单能峰。该能量似乎与反应式（2）中以 $_2^3$He 的质量代入获得的能量值相当，这个质量可以根据由质子引起 $_3^6$Li 蜕变产生的短射程产物的能量来估算 [2,3,4]。反应式（2）产生的 $_2^3$He 粒子群可能的射程约为 5 毫米，因此不能穿过这些实验中使用的最薄窗，但是我们正在制造一个特殊的实验装置以便能够在膨胀云室中找到它们。

我们的这些实验第一次使用了根据奥利芬特博士设计而制造出的新放电管。我还要感谢奥利芬特博士在我们制造放电管期间总是不厌其烦地给我们提供非常有建设性的建议。此外，我也很感激他在为上述实验准备氚靶时所提供的帮助。

（王耀杨 翻译；张焕乔 审稿）

Apparent Clustering of Galaxies

B. J. Bok

Editor's Note

Recent surveys of the placement of distant galaxies made it possible to begin describing their distribution. Here Bart Bok of the Harvard Observatory reviews evidence that galaxies are clustered, not distributed at random. This is particularly evident in statistical analyses of the number of galaxies brighter than a certain threshold within equal-area regions of each pole of the Galaxy. Two recent surveys of faint galaxies, from the Californian Mount Wilson Observatory and from Harvard, showed similar evidence of clustering, and Bok proposes that this should be considered a general and significant feature of our universe.

A considerable amount of material on the distribution of external galaxies has become available through the publication of the Harvard and Mount Wilson surveys. Shapley and Hubble have both discussed the observed irregularities in the distribution of these galaxies. Shapley emphasises the non-uniformity of the distribution of matter in the metagalaxy. Hubble finds that "statistically uniform distribution of nebulae appears to be a general characteristic of the observable region as a whole", and hesitates to admit the reality of clusters or groups of galaxies with the exception of the few that are readily recognised as such. Statistical analysis of the available material is now possible; and as the comparison between the observed distribution curves, corrected for the effect of dispersion in the limiting magnitudes, and the theoretical frequency curves, computed on the assumption of random distribution, has yielded some rather definite results, it seems worth while to communicate them in advance of publication in more detail.

The Shapley-Ames catalogue of galaxies brighter than the thirteenth magnitude[1] exhibits conspicuous deviations from a random distribution. Both galactic polar caps were divided into a number of equal areas (well-known clusters being excluded), and the number of galaxies was counted in each area. The observed frequency curve had a much larger dispersion than the theoretical curve, computed on the assumption of random distribution. The accompanying table shows conclusively that the irregularities in the distribution cannot have been caused by galactic or extragalactic absorption.

星系的视成团

博克

编者按

近来对于遥远星系位置的巡天观测使得我们可以开始描述它们的分布。本文中，哈佛天文台的巴特·博克评述了星系是成团而非随机分布的证据。特别是对银河系的两极方向相同面积区域内亮于某一定阈值的星系数的统计分析更是证明了这一点。近来分别由加州威尔逊山天文台和哈佛大学天文台所做的暗星系巡天观测显示出了类似的成团性证据，博克提出这应是宇宙普遍且重要的特征。

根据哈佛大学天文台和威尔逊山天文台所发表的巡天观测数据，人们可以得到大量关于河外星系分布的资料。沙普利和哈勃都曾就这些观测到的星系讨论过其分布的不规则性。沙普利强调了物质在总星系中分布的不均匀性。而哈勃则发现"星云统计上的均匀分布似乎是整个可观测区域的一个普遍特征"，但是除了少数容易识别者之外，他不愿意承认存在星系群或星系团的这一事实。现在已经能够对这些可用的资料进行统计分析；通过对极限星等弥散效应进行修正后得到的观测分布曲线和由随机分布的假设计算得到的理论频率曲线进行比较，我们已经得到了一些较为确定的结果，在更多细节发表之前，有必要先将这些结果公布出来。

亮于 13 星等的沙普利－艾姆斯星系表[1]中的星系显示出与随机分布存在明显的偏离。将银河系的两个极冠区平均分成若干区域（在去除了那些我们所熟知的星团后），并对每一个区域中的星系进行计数。观测到的频率曲线的弥散远远大于由随机分布假设计算得到的理论曲线的弥散。附表清楚地表明，分布中的不规则性不可能是由银河系或河外星系的吸收所造成的。

North Galactic Polar Cap.

No. of galaxies (Shapley-Ames)	$\overline{\log N}$ (Hubble)	No. of galaxies (Shapley-Ames)	$\overline{\log N}$ (Hubble)
$\frac{1}{2}$	1.92	15	1.79
$1\frac{1}{2}$	1.99	17	1.85
4	1.86	$18\frac{1}{2}$	1.87
$5\frac{1}{2}$	1.90	22	1.96
$6\frac{1}{2}$	1.88	24	1.95
10	1.87	26	1.87
$10\frac{1}{2}$	1.88	$29\frac{1}{2}$	1.86
$12\frac{1}{2}$	1.87	31	1.88
14	1.83	$31\frac{1}{2}$	1.86
$14\frac{1}{2}$	1.95	36	1.94
$14\frac{1}{2}$	1.93		

The first column of this table gives the number of galaxies counted for one of the areas in the Shapley-Ames catalogue. The centres of 9-13 survey fields used by Hubble in his study of the distribution of faint galaxies (down to mag. 19.5) fall within the limits of each area, and the second column of the table contains the mean value of log N for these faint galaxies. The absence of any progression in the values of $\overline{\log N}$ shows that the deviations from random distribution are due to a real clustering of galaxies and are not caused by the absorption of light in space.

Both the Mount Wilson[2] and Harvard[3] surveys of faint galaxies show evidence of clustering. The diagram (Fig. 1) gives a comparison between Hubble's observed distribution curve (dots), corrected for a dispersion of ±0.15 mag. in the limiting magnitude of the Mount Wilson plates, and the theoretical curve (crosses) computed on the assumption that the galaxies are distributed at random.

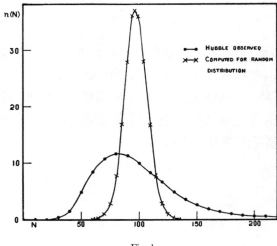

Fig. 1

银河系北极冠区

星系数（沙普利 – 艾姆斯）	$\overline{\log N}$（哈勃）	星系数（沙普利 – 艾姆斯）	$\overline{\log N}$（哈勃）
$\frac{1}{2}$	1.92	15	1.79
$1\frac{1}{2}$	1.99	17	1.85
4	1.86	$18\frac{1}{2}$	1.87
$5\frac{1}{2}$	1.90	22	1.96
$6\frac{1}{2}$	1.88	24	1.95
10	1.87	26	1.87
$10\frac{1}{2}$	1.88	$29\frac{1}{2}$	1.86
$12\frac{1}{2}$	1.87	31	1.88
14	1.83	$31\frac{1}{2}$	1.86
$14\frac{1}{2}$	1.95	36	1.94
$14\frac{1}{2}$	1.93		

此表格的第一列给出了沙普利 – 艾姆斯星表中每个区域中的星系数。哈勃在关于暗星系（暗至 19.5 星等）分布的研究中所使用的 9~13 巡天区域的中心，落在了每个区域的界限以内，而表格的第二列是这些暗星系数目的对数 $\log N$ 的平均值。$\overline{\log N}$ 的值的没有任何规律可循，这说明随机分布中的偏离是由实际中的星系成团造成的，而不是由光线在空间中被吸收所致。

威尔逊山天文台[2] 和哈佛大学天文台[3] 对暗星系的巡天观测都显示出星系成团的证据。图中（图 1）对哈勃观测得到的分布曲线（圆点表示）与理论曲线（叉号表示）进行了比较，其中哈勃观测的分布曲线是对威尔逊山天文台底板的极限星等进行 ±0.15 星等的弥散修正后得到的，而理论曲线则是在假设星系随机分布的基础上进行计算得到的。

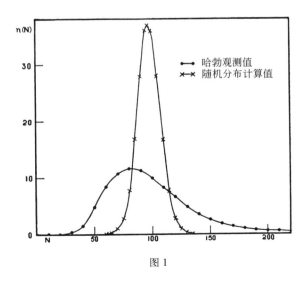

图 1

Similar deviations from random distribution are found in the Harvard material. The observed frequency curve in log N has, for the north galactic polar cap, a dispersion of ± 0.25, and as the maximum value of the error dispersion amounts to only ± 0.15 (most probable value ± 0.09), the true dispersion must be of the order of ± 0.20 in log N. The dispersion computed theoretically for random distribution is not larger than ± 0.03 in log N. For the south galactic polar cap the discrepancy is even greater. We should in addition consider Shapley's elegant and definite proof for the presence of clustering in nine regions[4].

We can scarcely escape the conclusion that a widespread tendency towards clustering among galaxies is one of the chief characteristics of our universe.

(**133**, 578; 1934)

Bart J. Bok: Harvard Observatory, Cambridge, Mass, Jan. 27.

References:
1. *Harv. Ann.*, **88**, No. 2; 1932.
2. *Astrophys. J.*, **79**, 8; 1934.
3. *Harv. Bull.*, 889; 1932. Harvard Reprint 90; 1933.
4. *Harv. Bull.*, 890; 1932.

在哈佛大学天文台的资料中也同样发现了相对于随机分布的偏离。银河系北极冠观测到的频率曲线，对 $\log N$ 有 ± 0.25 的弥散度，而误差的最大弥散值只有 ± 0.15（最可几值为 ± 0.09），因此 $\log N$ 的真实的弥散必定在 ± 0.20 量级。而理论计算得到的随机分布的 $\log N$ 的弥散则不会超过 ± 0.03。而在银河系的南极冠区这个差异则更加明显。另外我们还应该考虑沙普利对 9 个天区中星系成团的存在所做的简练而明确的证明 [4]。

我们很难回避这样一个结论，即星系成团的普遍趋势是宇宙的一个主要特征。

（周杰 翻译；邓祖淦 审稿）

The Inheritance of Acquired Habits

E. W. MacBride

Editor's Note

By the mid-twentieth century, Lamarckism—the idea that organisms can pass on traits developed in response to their environments—was out of favour. Paul Kammerer, whose work William MacBride cites here, killed himself in 1926, shortly after his studies on Lamarckian inheritance in the midwife toad were shown to have been faked. MacBride remained a believer until his death in 1940, but he was not a crank. The inheritance of acquired characters is now called epigenetic inheritance. Its importance in evolution is controversial, but several laboratory studies have demonstrated that environmental effects can cause traits that organisms pass onto their offspring by chemically modifying DNA—changing gene activity, for example—without changing the DNA sequence itself.

FOR the last five years, experiments to test the heritability of acquired habit have been in progress in the Zoological Laboratory of the Imperial college of Science under my supervision; and an account of the work may be of interest to readers of *Nature*.

The first part of the results of these experiments has been published by the Royal Society: the second part is almost ready for publication. Miss Sladden, who carried out the work, began by rearing the young of *Salamandra maculosa* and the eggs of *Alytes obstetricans*, thus endeavouring to repeat Kammerer's work. It became evident, however, that we did not possess the equipment necessary to provide the conditions which would induce these animals to breed. We succeeded in confirming some of Kammerer's statements about the effect of the environment on the habits of one generation. Thus it is quite possible to induce *Alytes*. normally a land animal, to adopt an aquatic life; and in regard to *Salamandra* we were enabled to explain Herbst's failure to obtain Kammerer's results.

There are two distinct races of *Salamandra maculosa*, an eastern and a western. In the latter, which inhabits the Jura and the Vosges, the yellow pigment is arranged in two longitudinal bands on the back, over a general body colour of black. Miss Sladden has reared animals of this race from birth to an age of three years in boxes painted inside with bright yellow and also in boxes painted deep black inside. In neither case could we detect any alteration in the amount of yellow pigment as a result of the colour of the background. In the eastern race, however, which formed the subject of Kammerer's researches, the yellow pigment is arranged as a series of spots over a black background; and by experiments conducted by Mr. E. Boulenger, then curator of reptiles in the Zoological Gardens, and by myself, during the years 1919–1924, we were able to show that animals of this race exposed for long periods to a black environment do show definite reduction of the yellow

226

获得性习性的遗传

麦克布赖德

编者按

到 20 世纪中叶，拉马克学说——认为生物体能够传递为适应自身环境而发展来的性状——已经不再受到关注。威廉·麦克布赖德在此引用了保罗·卡默勒的工作。1926 年，保罗·卡默勒在他的关于产婆蟾的拉马克式遗传的研究被指证为造假后不久便自杀了。麦克布赖德直到 1940 年去世时仍然坚信卡默勒的观点，不过他对此并不狂热。获得性特征的遗传现在被称为表观遗传。人们对它在进化方面的重要性仍有争议，但是有些实验研究已经表明环境影响能够导致生物体产生某些性状，通过 DNA 的化学修饰——例如，改变基因的活性——而并不改变 DNA 本身的序列，生物体可以将这些性状传递给他们的后代。

过去 5 年中，在我的指导下，我们一直在帝国理工学院的动物学实验室进行实验来验证获得性习性的遗传。现对该工作加以介绍以飨对此感兴趣的《自然》杂志的读者。

这些实验结果的第一部分已由皇家学会发表；第二部分也即将发表。实施这项研究的斯莱登小姐从培养斑点蝾螈的幼仔和产婆蟾的卵子开始，致力于重复卡默勒的工作。然而，很显然我们并不具备必要的设备来创造诱导这些动物进行繁殖的条件。但我们成功证实了卡默勒关于环境影响一个世代的习惯的一些论断。因此，我们很可能可以通过诱导使通常情况下陆生生活的产婆蟾适应水生生活；对于蝾螈，我们已经能解释为什么赫布斯特没能得到卡默勒的实验结果。

斑点蝾螈有两个不同的种类，一种东方的和一种西方的。后者生活于侏罗山脉和孚日山脉，其通身为黑色，背上的黄色素呈两排纵向条带排列。斯莱登小姐将各个不同阶段（从出生直至 3 岁）的这种动物分别饲养在内壁涂成亮黄色和深黑色的盒子中。结果我们在两种颜色背景的盒子里都没有检测到黄色素的量有任何变化。然而，东方种类，即卡默勒的研究对象，其黄色素呈一系列点状排布在黑色的体色背景上；通过 1919~1924 年布朗热先生进行的实验和动物园爬行动物馆的馆长随后进行的实验以及我自己的实验，我们能够证明，如果将这种动物长期暴露于黑色环境中，那么他们确实可以表现出黄色素的明显减少。但是，即使斯莱登小姐已经可以成功地使她饲养的动物进行繁殖，所需的时间长度也不能允许她进行实验，因为

pigment. But even if Miss Sladden had been successful in getting her animals to breed, the length of time involved would have been prohibitive, since the adult condition is only attained after four years' growth. Therefore we sought for a convenient experimental animal in which the generations succeeded each other more rapidly.

Some years ago (1912–1915), in conjunction with another pupil (Miss Jackson, afterwards Mrs. Meinertzhagen), I conducted experiments on breeding the stick-insect, *Carausius morosus*, and I found that this insect, whose normal food in England is privet, could be forced by starvation to feed upon ivy. I therefore suggested to Miss Sladden that she should test the development of this ivy-feeding habit. This insect offers great advantages when used as an experimental animal. It is parthenogenetic: males only appear in small numbers every five or six generations and when they do appear they are at once recognisable by their smaller size and different coloration. The parthenogenetic insect produces about 150 eggs a year which take about three months to develop: there is no metamorphosis and as there are no wings the nymph is morphologically similar to the adult.

The plan adopted was to isolate the just hatched young, keeping each one in a separate box. These boxes were made of metal: they were circular and had glass covers. In each box was placed a small piece of ivy leaf. At the end of two days about ten percent of the insects had begun to eat ivy, the rest had not touched it. If we had reared from these insects alone we should have been accused of selection: but we adopted a different plan (suggested by my colleague, Mr. Hewer). The ninety percent which refused ivy were given a bit of privet leaf to eat and so rescued from starvation. Then after one day the privet was removed and the insect was again provided with ivy. This second provision of ivy was called the "second presentation". If after two days more the insect still refused ivy, it was again given privet for a day. The majority of the insects accepted ivy at the second presentation, but some held out until the third, fourth, or even fifth, presentation and one recalcitrant held out until the tenth presentation.

We started the experiments with 125 females. All the young which accepted ivy at the same presentation, to whatever mother they belonged, were classed together, and when they in turn became adult the eggs of each class were mixed together. From each mixture 100 eggs were selected in order to rear the next generation. In the second generation, in place of ten percent no less than eighty percent of the insects accepted ivy when first presented, that is, at the first presentation: in all, 800 insects were tested. In the third generation ninety-five percent accepted ivy at the first opportunity and 2,000 insects were tested.

Thus with these insects, we reached exactly the same conclusions as those arrived at by Prof. McDougall with regard to induced habits in rats, namely, that when members of one generation are compelled to adopt a new habit, a residual effect of this habit is carried over to the next generation, so that the young insects adopt the new habit more quickly than did their parents. We claim, however, that the stick-insect gives more conclusive

这种动物要经过 4 年才能达到成年状态。因此，我们要寻找一种方便的可以更加快速地完成传代过程的实验动物。

多年前（1912~1915 年），我与另外一个学生（杰克逊小姐，后来成为迈纳茨哈根太太）合作进行了饲养竹节虫（印度棒䗛）的实验。我发现，这种在英国通常以女贞为食的昆虫迫于饥饿会以常春藤为食，因此我建议斯莱登小姐研究这种常春藤食性的发展过程。作为一种实验动物，这种昆虫具有很大的优势。它们是孤雌生殖的：每五六代中仅出现少量的雄性昆虫，并且一旦出现雄性，我们立刻就可以通过它们较小的体型和不同的颜色将它们辨别出来。孤雌生殖的昆虫每年大概产 150 个卵，这些卵的发育需要大约 3 个月的时间：发育不经过变态过程，而且因为没有翅膀所以蛹虫与成虫在形态上很相似。

采用的实验设计是：隔离刚孵化的幼虫，将其分别饲养在不同的盒子里。这些盒子是用金属制成的圆形盒子，并且有一个玻璃盖子。在每个盒子中放置一小片常春藤叶子。在第二天快结束时，约有 10% 的昆虫已经开始吃常春藤了，其他的昆虫一直没有碰过常春藤叶子。如果我们当时再将这些已经食用常春藤的昆虫单独喂养，那么可能就会有人指责我们引入了选择：不过，我们采用了另一种不同的方案（根据我的同事休尔先生的建议）。我们给 90% 的那些拒绝食用常春藤的昆虫提供少许女贞叶子以使它们不至于饿死。一天后将女贞叶子取出，再给它们提供常春藤。常春藤的第二次供应被称为"第二次给食"。如果两天之后昆虫仍拒绝吃常春藤，就再喂它们一天女贞叶子。实验发现，大部分昆虫在第二次给食时就接受了常春藤，有些则一直坚持到第三次、第四次、甚至第五次给食时才接受，有一只顽抗的虫子直到第十次才屈服。

我们开始实验时使用了 125 只雌性昆虫。所有在同一次给食时接受常春藤的幼虫，不论它们是不是来自同一个母亲，都被归为一类。当它们变成成虫时，将每种类型的卵混合在一起。从每类混合中选出 100 个卵来繁殖下一代。第二代中，至少有 80% 而不是只有 10% 的昆虫在第一次喂食常春藤（即第一次给食）时就接受了常春藤：我们总共检测了 800 只第二代的昆虫。到第三代时，我们检测了 2,000 只昆虫，95% 的昆虫在第一次给食时就接受了常春藤。

因此我们通过这些昆虫得到的结论与麦克杜格尔教授从对大鼠的诱导习性的研究中得到的结论完全一致，即，当一代成员被迫接受一种新习性时，这种习性的残余效应会延续至下一代，因此幼虫会比它们的父母更快地接受这种新习性。然而我们要说明的是，对竹节虫进行实验得到的结果比大鼠更具说服力，因为尽管我们认

results than the rat, because although we think that Prof. McDougall has overcome all his difficulties, yet there were very serious objections to be faced with rats, such as possible mass-suggestion, parental training, etc., which are obviously inapplicable to insects.

What many people fail to realise, however, is that this transference of a residual effect of habit is the central principle of Lamarckism, clearly and unequivocally expressed by Lamarck himself. He said that "the environment produces no direct effect on the animal", but by making new needs (for example, the necessity of eating ivy or starving) it forces the animal to make new efforts to satisfy them, and "if these needs *continue for a long time* then the animal's efforts become habits" and habits by causing the use of some organs more and others less bring about the enlargement of the former and the diminution in size of the latter; and these changes are preserved by reproduction.

This article is written in the hope that other investigators will take up this question and repeat the experiments using other animals, especially other insects, as subjects; for only by such experiments can this fundamental principle be settled. Indeed, experiments with the larvae of moths were begun some years ago by Dr. Thorpe, of Cambridge. The attractive feature about such experiments is that the percentage of mortality is very low, so that the agency of "chance" or "natural selection" is excluded. Prof. Woltereck, whose great book "Grundzüge einer allgemeinen Biologie" was reviewed in *Nature* of December 17, 1932, removed Cladoceran Crustacea from northern lakes to Lake Nemi in Italy. When he examined the transported stock after twenty years he found them much altered in shape: when he again re-transferred some of this stock to the post-glacial lakes of their ancestry they reverted to their original shape—but only *gradually during the course of several generations.*

The Linnean Society recently had the privilege of hearing Prof. Woltereck deliver an address on the fauna of recent lakes in many lands. Summing up the evidence, Prof. Woltereck concludes that the time since the recession of the ice of the last phase of the glacial age, that is, about 10,000 years, has only sufficed for the production of new races: for the production of new species we must go back to pre-glacial times possibly 500,000 years ago. As I remarked in my comments on the lecture it would be hard lines on the experimenter if he had to live and experiment for 10,000 years, before he could hope to produce a new heritable *structure*, but heritable changes of *habit* in small rapidly breeding animals may be observed after experiments lasting from five to ten years.

Students of mutation, that is, "geneticists", will naturally inquire what is the relation between these changes of habit and mutations. That is a question for future study; here only certain tentative suggestions can be offered. From the study of the few cases in which mutations have been experimentally produced by such agencies as X-rays and heat, it may be concluded that they are due to some damage to the developmental machinery of the nucleus in the germ cells. They, and not the Lamarckian changes, are the results of the "direct action of the environment". So long as malign conditions surrounding early

为麦克杜格尔教授已经克服了他所遇到的所有困难，但大鼠实验仍面临着非常严重的缺陷，例如可能存在集体暗示及亲代训练等，而昆虫显然不存在这些情况。

然而许多人没有意识到的是，这种习性残余效应的传递是拉马克学说的中心原则，拉马克本人对此进行了清晰而又明确的表述。他说"环境并不会对动物产生直接的影响"，而是通过创造新的需求（例如，食用常春藤或者挨饿的必需性）来迫使它们作出新的努力以适应这些新的需求，"如果这些需求**持续很长一段时间**，那么动物的努力就会变成习性"，这些习性通过更多地使用某些器官和更少地使用另外一些器官而使得前一种器官体积变大而后一种器官体积缩小；这些变化通过繁殖得以保留下来。

写这篇文章是希望其他研究者能够去研究这一问题并使用其他动物（特别是用其他昆虫）作为研究对象来重复这一实验；因为只有通过这样的实验才能确定这一基本原则。实际上，多年前剑桥的索普博士就开始用蛾的幼虫进行实验。这种实验吸引人的特征是死亡率很低，因此"偶然"或"自然选择"的影响可以被排除。著有重要书籍《普通生物学概述》（1932 年 12 月 17 日《自然》上有对此书的评论）的沃尔特雷克教授，将大型蚤从意大利的北部湖泊迁移到内米湖。20 年之后当他检查这一迁移蚤群时，他发现它们的形状发生了很大改变：当他把其中一部分再次转运回原来它们祖先生活的冰后期湖泊时，它们又恢复了原始的形状——不过是**经历了几代的时间逐渐恢复的**。

林奈学会最近有幸聆听了沃尔特雷克教授所作的关于陆地上新形成湖泊中的动物群的演讲。通过总结证据，沃尔特雷克教授推断，自从冰河时代最后一个冰期的冰川消退以来的大约 10,000 年的时间只够产生新的种系：对于新物种的产生，我们必须回溯到大约 500,000 年前的前冰河时代。正如我在对此演讲的评论中所写的，如果实验者希望通过实验产生新的可遗传的**结构**，那么他必须生活且实验 10,000 年，这对实验者来说是极其困难的，但是如果用能够快速繁殖的小型动物作为实验对象，那么经过持续 5~10 年的实验之后这些小型动物的**习性**的可遗传改变也许就可以被观察到了。

研究突变的"遗传学家"会自然地探寻习性的这些变化和突变之间有什么联系。这是将来要研究的一个问题；这里只能提供一些尝试性的建议。从几个通过 X 射线和加热等实验手段产生突变的实例研究，可以推断出突变是由于生殖细胞的细胞核的发育结构受到了某种损伤而产生的。它们和非拉马克式的改变都是"环境的直接作用"的结果。只要早期发育阶段持续存在恶性条件，那么突变就会忠实地遗传下

development persist, the mutations are faithfully inherited, but if the organism can be replaced in its natural environment, then in a limited number of generations they pass off and the original constitution reasserts itself. In 1790 Capt. Cook introduced the English domestic pig into New Zealand in order to induce the Maoris to abstain from cannibalism. The animals escaped into the woods, and by 1840 had increased to herds of at least 40,000 in number and had assumed all the characters of the ancestral wild boar, including the fierce tusks—although in New Zealand there were no enemies which required such weapons to drive them off. Mutations seemingly are more surface phenomena than racial habits: they are indeed what Johanssen the inventor of the word "gene" called them, "superficial disturbances of the chromosomes", but racial habits belong to the inmost core of the heritable constitution.

(**133**, 598-599; 1934)

去；但是如果将生物重新放在其自然的生存环境中，那么突变就会在经历有限的几代后终止，原来的构成得以重现。1790 年，为了使毛利人不再自相残杀，库克船长将英国的家猪引入新西兰。结果这些家猪逃进了树林，到 1840 年时已经增加到至少 40,000 头，并且都呈现出了原始野猪的所有特征，包括凶猛的獠牙——尽管在新西兰并不存在需要它们使用这样的武器来驱赶的敌人。貌似比起种系习性来，突变是更加表面化的现象：事实上突变正是被"基因"一词的发明者约翰森称为"染色体的表面扰乱"，而种系习性则属于可遗传组成的最核心的部分。

（刘皓芳 翻译；刘京国 审稿）

Commercial Production of Heavy Water

Editor's Note

A plant of Imperial Chemical Industries, *Nature* here reports, has begun commercial production of heavy water, producing as much as 5 grams per day with a purity of 30% (pure heavy water was refined at a later date). The plant uses electrolytic method, inspired by Harold Urey and Edward Washburn's discovery that the concentration of deuterium increases in water undergoing electrolysis. The company believes it will be able to supply all heavy water required for commercial purposes in the near future. Production of heavy water became a major focus of nations in the Second World War, given its potential use in nuclear reactors.

THE recently discovered "heavy water", which has created so much interest in popular as well as scientific circles, is to be produced commercially in England. Plant has been developed at the Billingham works of Imperial Chemical Industries, Ltd., which is capable of producing a continuous supply of heavy water of approximately 30 percent purity at the rate of 5 gm. per day, while approximately pure "heavy water" will be produced at a somewhat later date. I.C.I. anticipate that they will be able to meet any commercial demand that may arise. Urey and Washburn, in the United States, discovered that the residual water in old electrolytic cells contained a larger proportion of heavy hydrogen than the normal. It was further found that by continued electrolysis, the concentration of the "heavy water" was enriched, ordinary light hydrogen being given off preferentially, and "heavy water" accumulating. This gave the key to a successful method of preparing "heavy water" in quantity, and the electrolytic method is the one in use at Billingham. Large-scale production of "heavy water" is only possible where exceptional resources of power and raw materials exist together. At Billingham, not only ordinary hydrogen in large quantities, but also residues in which "heavy water" has accumulated, are readily available. These resources, together with cheap power and convenient research facilities, make Billingham a logical centre for the large-scale production of the new compound. Since its discovery in the United States, its probable uses are becoming more evident, and it is eloquent testimony to the vitality of British chemical technique that in so short a space of time it should have been translated from a scientific curiosity to a marketable commodity.

(**133**, 604; 1934)

重水的商业化生产

编者按

《自然》杂志在这篇文章中报道了帝国化学工业公司的一个工厂开始了重水的商业化生产，他们每天生产 5 克纯度为 30% 的重水（后来才精炼得到纯的重水）。哈罗德·尤里和爱德华·沃什伯恩发现重氢在水中的浓度会随着电解的进行而升高，受此启发，这个工厂使用电解的方法生产重水。该公司相信在不远的将来他们有能力满足所有对商业用重水的需求。由于其在核反应堆中的潜在应用价值，重水的生产成了第二次世界大战期间各国关注的焦点。

最近发现的"重水"引起了公众及科学界极大的兴趣，并即将在英格兰进行商业化生产。帝国化学工业有限公司（简称 ICI）已经在比林罕厂区建立了厂房，该厂可以以每天 5 克的速率持续供给纯度大约为 30% 的重水，不久以后将会生产接近纯净的"重水"。ICI 估计他们将可以满足任何商业需求。美国的尤里和沃什伯恩发现，在旧电解池中剩余的水比一般的水含有更高比例的重氢。他们进一步发现，通过连续电解可以提高"重水"的浓度，普通的轻氢会被选择性地除去而使"重水"得到累积。这个发现为成功地进行大规模的"重水"制备提供了关键思路，而比林罕的工厂使用的正是电解的方法。只有在优越的动力和原材料同时满足的情况下才有可能大量生产"重水"。在比林罕，不仅普通氢原料充足，而且有其中累积了"重水"的残液便于利用。这些资源与廉价的动力以及方便的研究设备，使比林罕自然而然成为一个大量生产新化合物的中心。自"重水"在美国发现以来，其可能的应用价值日益明显，这也是英国化学工业技术具有生命力的有力明证，即：在非常短的时间内，重水将从科学珍品转变为具有市场价值的商品。

（沈乃澂 翻译；李芝芬 审稿）

The Neutrino

H. Bethe and R. Peierls

Editor's Note

Bethe and Peierls again write on the perplexing matter of the neutrino. It seems very unlikely, they note, that this particle would create any detectable ionisation after emerging from a nucleus. Nevertheless, its existence might still be demonstrated experimentally. One way, they suggest, would be to measure the recoil of a nucleus during beta decay. Though this energy in natural beta decays would be too small, it could be much bigger in artificial decays, for example of ^{13}N. If the neutrino hypothesis were correct, its existence would be evident from the missing energy or momentum in individual decays. Although this was not how the neutrino's existence would ultimately be demonstrated, the suggestion showed that doing so was not considered hopeless.

ALTHOUGH it seems very unlikely that neutrinos, after having been emitted in a nuclear process, give rise to any detectable ionisation[1], we would like to point out that it is not impossible in principle to decide experimentally whether they exist.

One possible experiment would be to check the energy balance for the artificial β-decay. Take, for example, the process

$$B^{10} + \alpha \rightarrow N^{13} + \text{neutron}$$
$$N^{13} \rightarrow C^{13} + e^{+} + \text{neutrino}.$$

One can safely assume that if the positive electron is emitted with the greatest possible energy, the kinetic energy of the neutrino will just be zero. The balance of energy in this case will therefore determine the mass of the neutrino. For this purpose one would have to know the mass defects of B^{10}, C^{13} and the neutron*, the kinetic energy of the α-particles and the neutrons and the upper limit of the spectrum of the emitted positive electrons.

A second way of deciding the question would be to observe the recoil of the nucleus in β-decay. With natural β-rays this is in practice impossible because the recoil energy is too small, but the nuclei involved in artificial β-decay are much lighter. The kinetic energy of recoil of a disintegrating N^{13} nucleus would be of the order of some hundreds of volts if there were no neutrinos. If the neutrino hypothesis is correct, there would be a defect of momentum which would be uniquely connected with the lack of observable energy in each individual process.

---

* The accuracy with which the mass of the neutron can be determined at present is, however, far from being sufficient for this purpose.

中微子

贝特，佩尔斯

编者按

贝特和佩尔斯又一次描述了中微子令人困扰的一面。他们注意到，这种粒子从原子核中出现之后，似乎不可能引起任何可观测的电离过程。然而，中微子的存在仍需要实验的验证。他们提出的一个方法是，测量原子核在 β 衰变过程中的反冲能。尽管天然 β 衰变中的核反冲能量很小，但在人工衰变过程中这个能量可以大得多，比如 ^{13}N 核的衰变。如果中微子假说是正确的，那么各种衰变过程中的能量和动量缺失就是它存在的证据。尽管并不能通过这一方法最终证明中微子的存在，但他们的方法表明验证这点也并不是毫无希望的。

虽然核转变过程中发射出来的中微子似乎不可能给出任何可观测的电离效应 [1]，但我们要指出的是，原则上用实验来判断它们是否存在还是可能的。

一个可能的实验是检验人工 β 衰变前后能量是否守恒。例如下列实验过程：

$$^{10}B + \alpha \rightarrow {}^{13}N + 中子$$
$$^{13}N \rightarrow {}^{13}C + e^+ + 中微子$$

我们完全可以假设，如果正电子是以最大可能的能量发射的，则中微子的动能将是零。这种情况下，根据能量守恒可以确定中微子的质量。为此，我们还必须知道 ^{10}B、^{13}C 和中子* 的质量亏损，α 粒子和中子的动能以及发射正电子谱的上限。

判定中微子是否存在的第二种方法是观测 β 衰变中核的反冲能。用天然 β 衰变实际上是不可能实现这一目的的，因为反冲能量太小了，但是人工 β 衰变中所涉及的核要轻得多。如果不存在中微子，^{13}N 核发生蜕变时的反冲动能将是几百电子伏的量级。而如果确实存在中微子，则每个独立过程中都将出现与可观测到的能量亏损唯一相关的动量亏损。

---

* 目前可以确定中子的质量，但远未达到所需的精确度。

In addition to the nuclear processes mentioned in our previous communication, it may also be expected that a nucleus catches one of its orbital electrons, decreases by one in atomic number, and emits a neutrino. (A corresponding process with increase in atomic number is not possible because of the absence of positive electrons.) This process further limits the possible mass differences between stable neighbouring isobares, and particularly between neutron and proton. If the hydrogen atom is to be stable, we must have (for the masses):

$$\text{Proton} + \text{electron} < \text{neutron} + \text{neutrino}.$$

The probability of such a process is less than that of a process involving emission only, the energy of the neutrino being the same. The reason is that the momentum of the electron, which enters in the third power, is about a hundred times smaller. But even for a surplus energy of 10^5 volts, the life-period of hydrogen would be only 10^{10} years, which seems incompatible with experimental facts. If therefore the neutrino is not heavier than the electron, the neutron must be at least as heavy as the proton.

(**133**, 689-690; 1934)

H. Bethe and R. Peierls: Physical Laboratory, University, Manchester, April 1.

Reference:
1. H. Bethe and R. Peierls, *Nature*, 133, 532, April 7, 1934.

除了我们以前文章中提到的核转变过程外，我们还认为核可能会捕获核外的一个轨道电子，从而原子序数减小 1 并发射出一个中微子。（与之对应的原子序数增加的过程是不可能的，因为不存在正电子。）这个过程进一步限制了稳定的相邻同量异位素之间，特别是质子与中子之间可能的质量差。如果氢原子是稳定的，则必须满足（对其质量而言）：

$$质子 + 电子 < 中子 + 中微子$$

如果中微子的能量是相同的，则发生以上过程的概率小于只有发射的 β 衰变的概率。理由是以三次方形式出现的电子动量小了百倍。但即使多赋予电子 10^6 电子伏的能量，氢的寿命也仅为 10^{10} 年，这似乎与实验事实相矛盾。因此，如果中微子并不比电子重的话，则中子至少应与质子同样重。

（沈乃澂 翻译；刘纯 审稿）

Liquefaction of Helium by an Adiabatic Method without Pre-cooling with Liquid Hydrogen

P. Kapitza

Editor's Note

Russian physicist Pyotr Kapitza reports on a new technique for liquefying hydrogen and helium, developed by himself and colleagues in Cambridge. These substances, so useful for modern physics research, were still being liquefied by methods dating from the beginning of the century. But his group had now developed a method based primarily on adiabatic expansion, in which no heat is lost or gained in the process. Their design eliminated the need for lubricants capable of working at such low temperatures, and could produce up to one litre per hour. The method would soon provide abundant supplies of liquid helium and hydrogen for low-temperature physics.

THE methods for the continuous liquefaction of hydrogen and helium at present in use are essentially the same as those originally used by Dewar and Kamerlingh Onnes when these gases were first liquefied. These methods are based on the use of the Joule-Thomson effect, combined with a regenerating heat exchange after the gas has been cooled below its conversion temperature by liquid air or hydrogen. Since these processes are essentially nonreversible, the efficiency of the method is very low: for example, Meissner[1] calculates that to produce liquid helium, one hundred times more power is required than if the process could be done reversibly. The advantages to be gained by using adiabatic expansion for the cooling of liquefying gases have long been realised, but owing to technical difficulties this method has only been used up to the present to liquefy small amounts of gas by a single expansion. Thus in 1895, Olszewski was the first to obtain a fog of liquid hydrogen drops by a sudden expansion of compressed hydrogen. Recently, Simon[2] has produced appreciable quantities of liquid helium also by a sudden expansion of highly compressed helium.

The technical difficulties in constructing an apparatus for continuous liquefaction by adiabatic expansion lie chiefly in the designing of a cooling expansion engine which will work at low temperatures. Two principal types of expansion engine can be considered. The first is a turbine, but this involves a number of technical difficulties which have not yet been overcome. The second type of machine is a reciprocating moving piston expansion engine; this also involves great difficulties, chiefly arising from the difficulty of finding a lubricant which will make the piston tight in the cylinder and retain its lubricating properties at the very low temperatures. Claude, however, managed to make such an expansion engine which would work at the temperature of liquid air by using the

无液氢预冷的绝热法氦液化

卡皮查

编者按

俄罗斯物理学家彼得·卡皮查报道了一种将氢和氦液化的新技术，这一技术是由他和他在剑桥的同事们共同研发的。这些对现代物理学研究非常有用的物质，仍在使用20世纪初的液化技术。卡皮查的研究小组发展出了一种主要基于绝热膨胀的技术，在绝热膨胀过程中，既没有热量失去也没有热量获得。他们的设计无须使用必须能够在同样的低温下工作的润滑剂，而且可以将产量提升至每小时1升。这种方法很快就为低温物理实验提供了充足的液氦和液氢。

目前所用的氢和氦连续液化方法，本质上与杜瓦和卡默林·昂内斯首次将这些气体液化时所用的方法相同。这些方法是基于焦耳－汤姆孙效应，并结合了再生式热交换，即利用气体被液态空气或液氢冷却到低于其转变温度后的部分返回气体实现的。由于这些过程本质上是不可逆的，因此这种方法的效率非常低：例如，迈斯纳[1]对这一过程的液氢产生效率进行了计算，发现它所需要的能量比可逆过程高出一百倍以上。人们很早以前就已了解到用绝热膨胀的方法对被液化气体进行冷却的优势，但由于技术上的困难，这类方法至今仅用于通过单次膨胀实现少量气体的液化。1895年，奥尔谢夫斯基通过将被压缩的氢突然膨胀的方法首次获得了液氢滴雾。最近，西蒙[2]同样采用将高度压缩的氦突然膨胀的方法，产生了数量可观的液氦。

制造通过绝热膨胀实现连续液化的设备，其技术难点主要在于对低温下工作的冷却膨胀机的设计。有两种主要的膨胀机类型可以考虑。第一类是涡轮机，但这涉及许多尚未攻克的技术难题。第二类机器是往复运动的活塞膨胀机；这也有很大的困难，主要是难以找到一种可以使活塞紧密贴近汽缸，同时在极低温下保持润滑的润滑剂。但克劳德通过采用被液化的气体作为润滑剂的方法，设法使这一类型的膨胀机可以在液态空气的温度下工作。不过，这个方法对于氢和氦的液化似乎并不

liquefied gas as the lubricant. This method, however, does not appear to be practicable for liquefying helium and hydrogen.

During the last year, in our laboratory we have been working on the development of a reciprocating expansion engine working on a different principle which does not require any lubrication of the piston at all, and which will work at any temperature. The main feature of the method is that the piston is loosely fitted in the cylinder with a definite clearance, and when the gas in introduced into the cylinder at high pressure, it is allowed to escape freely through the gap between the cylinder and the piston. The expansion engine is arranged in such a way that the piston moves very rapidly on the expanding stroke, and the expansion takes place in such a small fraction of a second that the amount of gas escaping through the gap is very small and does not appreciably affect the efficiency of the machine.

Fig. 1. Helium liquefaction apparatus at the Royal Society Mond Laboratory.

The principal difficulty in constructing such a machine was concerned with the valves in the expansion engine, which had to let in a considerable amount of gas in a small fraction of a second. Another difficulty was to find metals with the necessary mechanical properties for use at these low temperatures. All these difficulties have now been successfully overcome, and the liquefier is shown in the accompanying photograph (Fig. 1). The expansion engine is placed in the middle of the evacuated cylindrical copper casing, the dimensions of which are 75 cm. long and 25 cm. diameter. The casing also contains heat-exchanging spirals and a container of liquid air for the preliminary cooling of the

可行。

去年，我们实验室在研制一种基于不同原理工作的往复式膨胀机，它完全不需要对活塞进行任何润滑，并可以在任何温度下工作。这种方法的主要特征是，活塞宽松地装配于气缸中，之间留有一定的空隙，当气体在高压下被引入气缸时，允许其通过气缸与活塞之间的间隙自由地逸出。膨胀机被设计成在膨胀冲程内活塞运动得非常快，并且膨胀过程发生在远小于 1 秒的时间内，使得通过间隙逸出的气体量很少，不会明显地影响机器的效率。

图 1. 皇家学会蒙德实验室的氦液化装置

制造这种机器所遇到的主要困难是膨胀机中的阀门，它必须在远小于 1 秒的时间内让大量的气体进入。另一个困难是寻找在这样低的温度下具有必要力学性能的一些金属。现在所有这些难题均已成功得到解决，液化器如照片（图 1）中所示。膨胀机置于抽空的圆筒形铜制壳体的中间，其尺寸为长 75 cm，直径 25 cm。壳体内还包含热交换螺旋管，以及用于盛预冷氦的液空的容器。氦被压缩到 25～30 个大气压，并先被冷却到液态空气的温度，然后用膨胀机和再生式热交换螺

helium. Helium is compressed to 25–30 atmospheres and is first cooled to the temperature of liquid air and then cooled by the expansion engine and regenerating spiral to about 8°K. ; the final liquefaction is produced by making use of the Joule-Thomson effect. This combination proves to be the most efficient method of liquefaction. The liquid helium is drawn off from the bottom of the liquefier by means of a tap.

Following the preliminary cooling to the temperature of liquid nitrogen, the liquefier starts after 45 minutes to liquefy helium at a rate of 1 litre per hour, consuming about 3 litres of liquid air per litre of liquid helium. This output we hope will shortly be increased, but even now it compares very favourably with the original method of making liquid helium, in which, according to Meissner (*loc. cit.*), the consumption is 6 litres of liquid air plus 5 litres of liquid hydrogen per litre of liquid helium. It is also evidently a considerable advantage to be able to dispense with liquid hydrogen as a preliminary cooling agent. Theoretically it would be possible in our case also to dispense with liquid air, but the size of the liquefier would then be impracticably large. Using liquid hydrogen as a cooling agent, the output of the liquefier could be increased about six times.

The same liquefier has also been used for liquefying hydrogen, which was passed through a special circuit under a pressure of a few atmospheres.

A detailed description of the apparatus will shortly be published elsewhere.

(**133**, 708-709; 1934)

P. Kapitza: F.R.S., Royal Society Mond Laboratory, Cambridge.

References:
1. "Handbuch der Physik." Geiger and Scheel, vol. 11, p. 328.
2. *Z. Phys.*, **81**, 816; 1933.

旋管冷却到 8 K ；最终的液化是利用焦耳 - 汤姆孙效应实现的。这种组合方式被证明是最有效的液化方法。液氦通过阀门从液化器的底部抽取出来。

在预冷到液氮温度之后，液化器在 45 分钟后开始以每小时 1 升的速率液化氦，每升液氦约消耗 3 升液态空气。我们期望产量很快会得到提高，不过即使是现在这样的水平，与原有的生产液氦的方法相比也是非常有优势的，按迈斯纳（在上引文中）的计算，原有方法每制备 1 升液氦要消耗 6 升液态空气加 5 升液氢。显然，新方法不使用液氢作预冷剂是一个非常大的优势。理论上讲，我们的方法中也可以不用液态空气，不过这样会使液化器的尺寸大得无法实现。如果用液氢作为冷却剂，液化器的产量大约可以增加六倍。

同样的液化器也已被用于氢的液化，其中氢气会在几个大气压下通过一个特殊管路。

有关装置的详细描述将于近期发表在其他文章中。

（沈乃澂 翻译；陶宏杰 审稿）

Mass of the Neutron

I. Curie and F. Joliot

Editor's Note

James Chadwick had estimated the neutron mass by analysing a reaction in which an alpha particle stimulates the transformation of boron into nitrogen with emission of a neutron. His calculations required the experimental values for the masses of several nuclei. Here wife-and-husband physicists Irène Curie and Frédéric Joliot report a more accurate and higher value for the neutron mass by examining other reactions, and without using any nuclear mass other than that of the proton. This higher value suggested that one might interpret nuclear beta decays as being triggered by the decay of a neutron into a proton within the nucleus, with the ejection of an electron and a neutrino, which today remains the modern view.

THE mass of the neutron has been calculated by Chadwick on the assumption that the neutrons of boron are emitted by the isotope $^{11}_{5}$B, according to the nuclear reaction

$$^{11}_{5}\text{B} + {}^{4}_{2}\text{He} = {}^{14}_{7}\text{N} + {}^{1}_{0}n$$

Using the exact masses of $^{11}_{5}$B, $^{4}_{2}$He and $^{14}_{7}$N and the maximum energy of the neutron excited by the α-rays of polonium, one may calculate for the neutron a mass 1.0068 (taking ^{16}O $= 16$).[1]

We have suggested[2] that the emission of the neutron of boron is due to the isotope $^{10}_{5}$B and not to $^{11}_{5}$B. The nucleus $^{10}_{5}$B can suffer two kinds of transmutation under the action of the α-particles of polonium, one with the emission of a proton, one with the emission of a neutron and a positive electron, according to the equations:

$$^{10}_{5}\text{B} + {}^{4}_{2}\text{He} = {}^{13}_{6}\text{C} + {}^{1}_{1}\text{H}$$
$$^{10}_{5}\text{B} + {}^{4}_{2}\text{He} = {}^{13}_{6}\text{C} + {}^{1}_{0}n + \overset{+}{\varepsilon}.$$

Our latest experiments on the creation of new radio-elements have confirmed our interpretation of the transmutation of boron. Similar reactions are observed with the nucleus $^{27}_{13}$Al and with $^{24}_{12}$Mg. The reactions can be divided in two steps:

$$^{10}_{5}\text{B} + {}^{4}_{2}\text{He} = {}^{13}_{7}\text{N} + {}^{1}_{0}n \qquad {}^{13}_{7}\text{N} = {}^{13}_{6}\text{C} + \overset{+}{\varepsilon}$$
$$^{24}_{12}\text{Mg} + {}^{4}_{2}\text{He} = {}^{27}_{14}\text{Si} + {}^{1}_{0}n \qquad {}^{27}_{14}\text{Si} = {}^{27}_{13}\text{Al} + \overset{+}{\varepsilon}$$
$$^{27}_{13}\text{Al} + {}^{4}_{2}\text{He} = {}^{30}_{15}\text{P} + {}^{1}_{0}n \qquad {}^{30}_{15}\text{P} = {}^{30}_{14}\text{Si} + \overset{+}{\varepsilon}$$

$^{13}_{7}$N, $^{27}_{14}$Si, $^{30}_{15}$P being unstable nuclei that disintegrate with the emission of positrons.

中子的质量

居里，约里奥

编者按

詹姆斯·查德威克通过分析 α 粒子引发的硼转变为氮并放出一个中子的反应，估算出了中子的质量。他的计算用到了几种原子核质量的实验值。在这篇文章中，物理学家弗雷德里克·约里奥和伊雷娜·居里夫妇通过对其他反应的研究给出了一个数值更为精确并且较大的中子质量值，并且他们的计算仅使用了质子的质量而没有用到其他任何原子核的质量。根据这一较大的中子质量数值，我们可以推测原子核的 β 衰变是由原子核中一个中子衰变为一个质子所引发的，同时放射出一个电子和一个中微子，这一观点一直沿用至今。

查德威克计算了中子的质量。在计算中，他假设硼放出的中子是由同位素 $_5^{11}B$ 放出的，对应于核反应：

$$_5^{11}B + _2^4He = _7^{14}N + _0^1n$$

利用 $_5^{11}B$、$_2^4He$ 和 $_7^{14}N$ 的精确质量，以及钋放射出的 α 射线所激发出的中子最大能量，可以计算出中子的质量是 1.0068（取 $^{16}O = 16$）[1]。

但我们认为 [2]，放射出中子的是同位素 $_5^{10}B$，而不是 $_5^{11}B$。$_5^{10}B$ 的原子核在钋放射出的 α 粒子的作用下，可以发生两种嬗变，其中一种放射出一个质子，另一种放射出一个中子和一个正电子，核反应方程分别为：

$$_5^{10}B + _2^4He = _6^{13}C + _1^1H$$
$$_5^{10}B + _2^4He = _6^{13}C + _0^1n + \overset{+}{\varepsilon}$$

最近我们关于产生新的放射性元素的实验证实了我们对硼嬗变的解释。在 $_{13}^{27}Al$ 和 $_{12}^{27}Mg$ 中也观察到了类似的反应。反应可以分成两步：

$$_5^{10}B + _2^4He = _7^{13}N + _0^1n \qquad _7^{13}N = _6^{13}C + \overset{+}{\varepsilon}$$
$$_{12}^{24}Mg + _2^4He = _{14}^{27}Si + _0^1n \qquad _{14}^{27}Si = _{13}^{27}Al + \overset{+}{\varepsilon}$$
$$_{13}^{27}Al + _2^4He = _{15}^{30}P + _0^1n \qquad _{15}^{30}P = _{14}^{30}Si + \overset{+}{\varepsilon}$$

其中，$_7^{13}N$、$_{14}^{27}Si$、$_{15}^{30}P$ 是不稳定的原子核，它们会发生衰变，同时放出正电子。

The complete reactions, with the masses and energy of all the particles are, for the two modes of transmutation of boron:

$$^{10}_{5}B + {}^{4}_{2}He + W_{\alpha} = {}^{13}_{6}C + {}^{1}_{1}H + W_H + W_R,$$
$$^{10}_{5}B + {}^{4}_{2}He + W_{\alpha} = {}^{13}_{6}C + {}^{1}_{0}n + \overset{+}{\varepsilon} + W_n + W_{\varepsilon} + W_R'$$

where W_{α}, W_H, W_n, W_{ε}, W_R, W_R' are the energies of the α-particle and the corresponding energies of the ejected particles and of the recoil atoms in the reactions. Subtracting the first of these equations from the second gives:

$$^{1}_{0}n = \text{mass of proton} - \text{mass of positron} + Q,$$

where $Q = W_H + W_R - W_n - W_R' - W_{\varepsilon}$.

One gets exactly the same equation using the transmutations of aluminium and magnesium.

Thus these equations enable us to calculate the mass of neutron without using the exact masses of any nucleus, except the proton.

According to our most recent measurements, the positrons emitted by the new radio-elements form a continuous spectrum of maximum energy 1.5×10^6 e.v. for $^{13}_{7}N$, 3×10^6 e.v. for $^{30}_{15}P$ and approximately 1.5×10^6 e.v. for $^{27}_{14}Si$. The emission of positrons is probably accompanied by the emission of neutrinos, but if the positrons have their maximum energy, the neutrinos will have a very small energy; the most recent hypotheses on the nature of this particle admits of a mass which is zero, or very small. So we need not take this particle into account in the calculations. The energy of the recoil atom in the disintegration with emission of a positron is negligible.

For the irradiation with the α-rays of polonium we have the following numerical values for the energies (expressed in 10^6 e.v.). One gets for the mass of neutron three values: 1.0098, 1.0092, 1.0089. These values agree approximately. Yet the first, deduced from boron, is the most precise. The energies of the neutrons of aluminium and magnesium and the energy of the positrons of magnesium are not well known.

	W_H	W_R	W_n	W_R'	W_{ε}	Q (10^6 e.v.)	Q in units of mass
B	8.05	0.23	3.3	0.59	1.5	+2.89	0.0031
Al	7.56	0.11	2	0.33	3.0	+2.34	0.0025
Mg	4.82*	0.21	1	0.48	1.5	+2.05	0.0022

*The maximum energy possible for the positrons does not correspond to a group effectively observed, but has been deduced by F. Perrin from the experiments of Bothe and Klarman, by the consideration of the energy balance relative to the groups of protons.

硼嬗变的两种模式的完整的反应方程式如下，其中包含了所有粒子的能量和质量：

$$^{10}_{5}B + ^{4}_{2}He + W_\alpha = ^{13}_{6}C + ^{1}_{1}H + W_H + W_R$$
$$^{10}_{5}B + ^{4}_{2}He + W_\alpha = ^{13}_{6}C + ^{1}_{0}n + \overset{+}{\varepsilon} + W_n + W_\varepsilon + W'_R$$

其中，W_α、W_H、W_n、W_ε、W_R、W'_R 分别是反应中 α 粒子的能量、放出粒子的相应能量，以及反冲原子的相应能量。用第二个反应方程式减去第一个反应方程式，可以得到：

$$^{1}_{0}n = 质子的质量 - 正电子的质量 + Q,$$

其中，$Q = W_H + W_R - W_n - W'_R - W_\varepsilon$。

利用铝和镁的嬗变反应方程式，也可以得到完全相同的方程。

这样，我们不必用到除质子以外的其他任何原子核的质量，就可以计算出中子的质量。

根据我们最近的测量，新形成的放射性元素放出的正电子的能量分布为连续谱，对 $^{13}_{7}N$、$^{30}_{15}P$ 和 $^{27}_{14}Si$ 而言，连续谱的最大能量分别是：1.5×10^6 eV、3×10^6 eV 和大约 1.5×10^6 eV。放出正电子时大多伴随着中微子的放出，但是如果正电子有其最大能量，那么中微子的能量将非常小。而且最近关于中微子性质的假说认为中微子的质量为 0，或者非常小。因此，在计算中我们不需要考虑中微子。在放出正电子的衰变过程中，反冲原子的能量也可以忽略不计。

我们得到钋放射的 α 射线的能量数值（单位是 10^6 eV），如下表所示。由此，我们分别得到三个中子质量：1.0098、1.0092、1.0089。这些值基本一致。但是第一个值最精确，即从硼原子推导出的中子质量。镁和铝中的中子能量以及镁中正电子的能量都还不是十分确定。

	W_H	W_R	W_n	W'_R	W_ε	Q (10^6 eV)	Q 以质量为单位
B	8.05	0.23	3.3	0.59	1.5	+2.89	0.0031
Al	7.56	0.11	2	0.33	3.0	+2.34	0.0025
Mg	4.82*	0.21	1	0.48	1.5	+2.05	0.0022

---

* 这个正电子能量的最大可能值与实际观测并不相符，但是通过考虑与质子组的能量平衡，佩兰已经从博特和卡拉曼的实验中推导出了这个最大值。

From considerations on the stability of the nucleus $^9_4$Be, the mass of the neutron should have a minimum value 1.0107. But an error of 0.001 in the determination of the mass of Be seems quite possible.

We may adopt for the mass of the neutron a value 1.010, in which the error probably does not exceed 0.0005.

With the mass 1.010 for the neutron, the maximum energy of the neutron ejected from beryllium by α-particles from polonium should be about 9×10^6 e.v. The emission of slow neutrons when lithium is bombarded with α-particles from polonium, according to the reaction $^7_3$Li $+ ^4_2$He $= ^{10}_5$B $+ ^1_0 n$, cannot be explained unless the mass adopted for $^{10}_5$B is too great, namely, by about 0.003.

If atomic nuclei contain only protons and neutrons, then the β-emission might be the consequence of the transformation of a neutron into a proton inside the nucleus, with the ejection of the negative electron and a neutrino, as has been suggested by several authors. The inverse processes would also be possible: transformation of a proton into a neutron with the ejection of a positron and a neutrino.

With the mass 1.010 for the neutron, the energy liberated in the transformation neutron $\rightarrow$ proton $+ \bar{\varepsilon}$ is 2.1×10^6 e.v.; the energy absorbed in the transformation proton $\rightarrow$ neutron $+ \overset{+}{\varepsilon}$ is 3.1×10^6 e.v.

(**133**, 721; 1934)

I. Curie and F. Joliot: Institut du Radium, Paris, 5.

References:
1. Chadwick, *Proc. Roy. Soc.*, **136**, 692; 1932.
2. I. Curie and F. Joliot, *C.R.*, **197**, 237; 1933.

考虑到 $_4^9$Be 原子核的稳定性，中子的质量本应该有一个最小值 1.0107。但是在确定 Be 的质量时很可能存在 0.001 的误差。

我们可以取中子质量为 1.010，这个值的误差大概不会超过 0.0005。

取中子质量为 1.010 时，铍被钋放出的 α 粒子轰击所放出的中子的最大能量约为 9×10^6 eV。根据反应 $_3^7$Li + $_2^4$He = $_5^{10}$B + $_0^1n$，除非认为我们采用的 $_5^{10}$B 的质量太大，超过真实值 0.003，否则就无法解释当锂被钋放出的 α 粒子轰击时，会放射出慢中子的事实。

如一些作者所设想的那样，如果原子核只包含质子和中子，那么当核内部一个中子转变成一个质子，并放射出负电子和中微子的反应可能就是 β 发射产生的原因。相反的过程也有可能发生：一个质子转变成一个中子，并放出一个正电子和一个中微子。

取中子质量为 1.010 时，一个中子转变为一个质子和一个负电子的反应所释放的能量是 2.1×10^6 eV；一个质子转变成一个中子和一个正电子的反应所吸收的能量是 3.1×10^6 eV。

（王静 翻译；王乃彦 审稿）

The Explanation of Supraconductivity

J. Frenkel

Editor's Note

Superconductivity involves a transformation to a state of zero electrical resistance, apparently equivalent to an infinite conductivity. But here Russian physicist Yakov Frenkel suggests instead considering that the dielectric constant—a measure of a material's response to electric fields, due to polarisation—becomes infinite. While ordinary electrical current involves electrons moving freely through the material, a "polarisation current" might arise if the polarisation of atoms created by an applied electric field became infinite. Then, electrons could hop between atoms, creating coherent motion of one-dimensional chains of electrons sliding over the atomic lattice. Although Frenkel's contribution did not explain superconductivity, it did further an ultimately fruitful idea: that the phenomenon is somehow linked to coherent motion of charge carriers.

IT is customary to describe the supraconductive state of a metal by setting its specific electric conductivity σ equal to infinity. I wish to direct attention to another possibility, namely, that the supraconductive state can be described much more adequately by setting equal to infinity the *dielectric constant* ε of the substance, its conductivity σ remaining finite or even becoming equal to zero.

The actual meaning of the new definition can be seen from a comparison of the mechanism of ordinary electric conduction (σ finite) and ordinary polarisation (ε finite). In the former case the electrons called "free" move *independently*, the conduction current being constituted by a drift motion due to the action of an external electric field and superposed on the unperturbed random motion of the individual electrons. In the second case the electrons called "bound" are displaced by the electric field simultaneously in the same direction, the polarisation current being due to an orderly collective motion of all the electrons. Under normal conditions the displacement of the electrons with regard to the respective atoms remains small compared with the interatomic distances; this corresponds to a finite value of the dielectric constant. The assumption that the latter becomes infinite means that under the action of an infinitesimal field the electrons are displaced simultaneously over finite distances, each of them passing successively from an atom to the next one, like a chain gliding over a toothed track.

Such a collective motion of the "bound" electrons will constitute an electric current just as much as the individual motion of the free electrons, but a *polarisation* current rather than a *conduction* one. The electrostatic mutual action of the electrons moving collectively in a chain-like way will stabilise them against the perturbing action of the heat motion of the crystal lattice, which will result in the permanence of the polarisation current

超导电性的解释

弗伦克尔

编者按

超导电性涉及一个电阻突降为零的转变过程，而电阻为零似乎意味着一个无穷大的电导。但是在这篇文章中，俄国物理学家雅科夫·弗伦克尔则认为应该将介电常数视为无穷大，介电常数是表征材料由于极化引起的对电场响应程度的物理参数。虽然通常电流的形成就是电子自由通过材料的过程，但是如果由于电场导致的原子极化变为无穷大的话，也会产生"极化电流"。这样，电子可以在原子间跳跃，产生电子的一维链在原子晶格上滑移的相干运动。尽管弗伦克尔的这篇文章并没有解释清楚超导电性，但它确实促成了一个全新的想法：这一现象与载流子的相干运动存在某种联系。

在描述金属的超导状态时，我们习惯于将金属的电导率 σ 定义为无穷大。我希望能够引导大家关注另外一种可能性，而这有可能是对超导状态更加合适的描述，即设物质的**介电常数** ε 为无穷大，而电导率 σ 保持为有限值，甚至等于零。

这个新定义的真正含义可以从普通电传导（σ 为有限值）与普通电极化（ε 为有限值）机制的比较中看出。就前者而言，电子可被看成是在**独立地"自由"**运动，传导电流是由外电场作用引起的漂移运动和单个电子无干扰的随机运动叠加而形成的。而对后者而言，受"束缚"的电子在电场的作用下沿同一方向同时产生位移，极化电流是由所有电子有序的集体运动产生的。一般情况下，电子相对于各自所属原子的位移比原子间的距离要小；这对应于介电常数是有限值的情形。如果我们假设介电常数的值为无穷大，那就代表，在无穷小电场的作用下，所有电子会同时移动一段有限的距离，每个电子连续地从一个原子穿越至下一个原子，就像一根链子在锯齿形的轨道上滑动一般。

"束缚"电子的这类集体运动所形成的电流与自由电子的单个运动形成的电流大小相等，但它是**极化**电流，而不是**传导**电流。以类链方式集体运动的电子之间的静电相互作用会克服由晶格热运动引起的扰动，从而使电子的这种运动稳定下来，这

after the disappearance of the electric field by which it was started[1]. This permanence, which has been erroneously interpreted as corresponding to an infinite value of the specific conductivity, must be interpreted in reality as corresponding to an *infinite value of the dielectric constant*. Now, how is it possible to explain the occurrence of such an infinite value? This turns out to be a very simple matter, the appropriate mechanism having been considered already by Hertzfeld, who, however, failed to give it the correct interpretation. Consider a chain of equally spaced atoms with a polarisation coefficient α. This means that an isolated atom assumes under the action of an external field E an electric moment $p = \alpha E$. If the field E is acting in the direction of the chain, then in computing the polarisation of a certain atom we must add to it the field E' produced by all the other atoms in virtue of their induced electric moments. All these moments being the same, we get

$$E' = \frac{2p}{a^3} 2 \sum_{n=1}^{\infty} \frac{1}{n^3} = 4.52 \frac{p}{a^3} \, ;$$

and consequently

$$p = \alpha \left(E + 4.52 \frac{p}{a^3} \right),$$

whence

$$p = \frac{\alpha E}{1 - 4.52 \alpha / a^3} = \alpha' E. \tag{1}$$

We thus see that with a finite value of α for an isolated atom, an infinite value of the effective polarisation coefficient α' for the atom-chain is obtained if

$$4.52 \alpha \geqq a^3. \tag{2}$$

The sign $>$ corresponding to a negative value of α' need not be distinguished from the sign $=$; in both cases the atom chain is characterised by the instability of the electron chain connected with it. This instability, which has been noticed previously by Hertzfeld, was interpreted by him as an indication of the fact that the electrons no longer remain bound, but become free "conduction" electrons. Thus the inequality (2) was considered as characteristic of the metallic state in general. I believe that it is characteristic not of the metallic state but of the supraconductive state, a supraconductor being rather a dielectric with freely movable electron chains (that is, with $\varepsilon = \infty$) than a metal.

According to a theory of the metallic state developed in a rather qualitative way by Slater[2] and recently greatly improved and generalised by Schubin[3], the normal conductivity of a metal is due to a *partial ionisation* of the atoms, a certain fraction s of all the atoms becoming positive ions, and an equal portion (to which the corresponding electrons are attached) negative ions. If these electrons are bound very weakly, they may be considered as "free" in the usual sense of the word. The conductivity of a metal is equal to the sum of the conductivities due to these free electrons or negative ions on one hand and the positive ions or "holes" on the other. The mechanism of electrical conduction consists in the *individual* jumping of an electron from a negative ion to one of the neutral atoms surrounding it (which is thus converted into a negative ion), or from a neutral atom to a positive ion, which thus becomes a neutral atom, its rôle being switched over to the "donor". We meet with the same type of electric conduction in electronic semi-conductors[4]. The chief distinction between a metal and a semi-conductor consists in the fact that in the former

使得在引发了该运动的电场消失后，极化电流还将一直持续 [1]。这种电流的持续性曾经被错误地解释为是特定情况下电导率无穷大所致，而实际上应该用**介电常数无穷大**来进行解释。那么现在如何来解释介电常数无穷大的出现呢？事实上很简单，赫茨菲尔德已经想到了合适的机制，但是他并没有给出正确的解释。下面我们考虑由极化系数为 α 的等间距的原子组成的链。于是，在外场 E 的作用下，单个原子的电偶极矩就为 $p = \alpha E$。如果电场 E 沿链的方向，则在计算某一个原子的极化时，我们必须加上由于其他所有原子的感生电偶极矩所产生的电场 E'。假设所有这些电偶极矩都相等，我们得到

$$E' = \frac{2p}{a^3} 2 \sum_{n=1}^{\infty} \frac{1}{n^3} = 4.52 \frac{p}{a^3}$$

因此

$$p = \alpha \left(E + 4.52 \frac{p}{a^3} \right)$$

所以

$$p = \frac{\alpha E}{1 - 4.52\alpha/a^3} = \alpha' E \tag{1}$$

由此可见，对于 α 是一个有限值的单个原子来说，如果

$$4.52\alpha \geq a^3 \tag{2}$$

我们得到原子链的有效极化系数 α' 的值为无穷大。

(2) 式中符号 ">" 相当于 α' 是负值，与符号 "=" 没有区别；在这两种情况下，原子链可以用与其相连的电子链的不稳定性来表征。赫茨菲尔德以前就注意到了这种不稳定性，他还把这种现象解释为是电子不再受到束缚，而成为自由"传导"电子这一事实的一个标志。因此不等式 (2) 一般被认为是金属态的特征。我相信这并不是金属态的特征，而是超导态的特征，超导体是一种具有可自由运动电子链（即 $\varepsilon = \infty$）的电介质，而非金属本身。

按照由斯莱特 [2] 发展出的定性的金属态理论，以及最近由舒宾 [3] 对该理论的改进和推广，金属的正常导电性是由于原子的**部分电离**引起的，某一部分原子 s 变成正离子，而相等的另一部分（携带相应电子的部分）变成负离子。如果这些电子受到的束缚很微弱，通常可以称其是"自由的"。金属的电导率等于由这些自由电子或负离子产生的电导率加上正离子或"空穴"产生的电导率之和。电传导的机制主要是一个电子从一个负离子**单个地**跳到附近的一个中性原子上（于是这个中性原子就转换成一个负离子），或从一个中性原子跳到一个正离子上，于是正离子就成为中性原子，充当"施主"的角色。半导体 [4] 中具有相同类型的电传导机制。金属和半导体的主要区别在于：前者在温度（T）达绝对零度时，$s > 0$；而后者在 $T = 0$ 时，$s = 0$， case $s > 0$ at the absolute zero of temperature (T) whereas in the latter case $s = 0$ at $T = 0$, increasing according to the Boltzmann equation ($s = ce^{-W/kT}$ where W is the ionisation energy) with the temperature.

The elements which are likely to become supraconductors form an intermediary group in the sense that at ordinary temperatures they are relatively poor conductors, like the ordinary semi-conductors; the dependence of their conductivity on the temperature is, however, of the same character as that of typical metals (negative temperature coefficient). This means that in the case of these intermediary elements or "half-metals", we have to do with substances which are characterised by a practically constant value of the ionisation fraction s. Their small conductivity can be explained either by a small value of s or by a small mobility of the individual electrons (which seems the more probable alternative in view of the correlation between supraconductivity and the Hall effect discovered by Kikoin and Lasareff). The fact that, in ordinary circumstances, that is, above the "transition temperature" T_c, these substances are not supraconductive, can be explained by the finite value of their dielectric constant as determined by the polarisability of ions stripped of the conduction electrons. The nature of the transition which takes place when the temperature T is decreased below T_c can thus be very simply interpreted by assuming that, at this temperature, s suddenly falls from a certain rather high value to *zero*, and that the polarisation coefficient α of the resulting *normal* atoms with their full complement of bound electrons satisfies the inequality (2)*. The very fact that the substance loses its conductivity (σ falling to zero along with s) thus transforms it from a metal into a dielectric with $\varepsilon = \infty$, that is, it becomes a supraconductor.

Both the necessity and the sharpness of the transition $s \to 0$ (that is, $\sigma \to 0$ and $\varepsilon \to \infty$) can be easily understood if we assume that the state $s = 0$ has a smaller energy than the state $s > 0$. It results from Slater's and especially from Schubin's calculations that the *lowest* energy level for polar (ionic) states *may* correspond to a *finite* value of s, whether this lowest level lies below or above the energy level corresponding to $s = 0$. It can further easily be seen that the distance between the successive levels in a band of levels corresponding to a given value of s is very small compared with kT, even for extremely low temperatures (of the order of a few degrees K.). If, further, the *total* width of the band was also small compared with kT, the entropy of the state $s > 0$ could be calculated as $k \lg g$, where g is the statistical weight of the whole band, that is, the number of ways in which the state s is realised. Taking all possible distributions of the ns electrons (negative ions) and ns positive holes (positive ions) between the n atoms, we get

$$g = \left[\frac{n!}{(ns)!\,(n - ns)!} \right]^2.$$

The transition $0 \to s$ is thus connected with an *increase* of entropy

* This inequality is probably satisfied for all metals, although not all of them are supraconductors, because for true metal s remains finite (and practically constant) down to the absolute zero of temperature, while for supraconductors it jumps to a finite value slightly above it .

且按照玻尔兹曼方程（$s = ce^{-W/kT}$，其中 W 是电离能）s 随着温度的上升而增大。

从某种意义上来说，能够成为超导体的元素形成了一个过渡状态的元素组，常温下，它们是传导性能相对比较差的导体，类似于普通的半导体；然而它们的电导率与温度的变化关系又和典型的金属（负温度系数）相同。当考虑这些过渡状态的元素或者"半金属"元素时，我们必然会遇到一些电离分数 s 实际为常数的物质。它们的弱导电性可以用很小的 s 值来解释，也可以用单个电子很小的迁移率来解释（考虑到基科因和拉萨雷夫共同发现的霍尔效应与超导电性之间的关系，这似乎是一个更合适的选择）。在通常情况下，也就是温度在"转变温度"T_c 以上时，这些物质不再是超导体，这一事实可以利用它们的介电常数为有限值来解释，这个有限值是由失去了传导电子的离子的极化率来决定的。对于当温度由 T 降至 T_c 之下时发生的相变的本质，我们可以简单地用以下两点假设进行解释：第一，在这个温度下，s 突然由某一相当高的值突变为**零**；第二，相应的带着所有束缚电子的**普通**原子的极化系数 α 满足不等式（2）*。物质失去导电性（σ 与 s 变为零），于是由金属转变为 $\varepsilon = \infty$ 的介质，也就是变成了超导体。

如果我们假设 $s = 0$ 的态比 $s > 0$ 的态所具有的能量小，那么 $s \to 0$ 转变（即 $\sigma \to 0$ 和 $\varepsilon \to \infty$）所具有的必然性和陡峭特点就很好解释了。这样的结论可以从斯莱特尤其是从舒宾的计算中得到，这个计算显示：无论**最低**能级处于 $s = 0$ 对应能级之上或之下，极化（离子）态的最低能级都**可能**对应于**有限**的 s 值。从而我们很容易看出，即使在极低的温度下（几 K 量级），给定 s 值对应能带中连续能级的间距远小于 kT。如果能带的**总带宽**也小于 kT，那么就可以按式子 $k\lg g$ 来计算 $s > 0$ 的态的熵，其中 g 是整个能带的统计权重，即得到态 s 所有方式的数目。考虑 n 个原子间 ns 个电子（负离子）和 ns 个正空穴（正离子）所有可能的分布，我们得到：

$$g = \left[\frac{n!}{(ns)!\,(n - ns)!}\right]^2$$

因此，与 $0 \to s$ 转变相应的熵**增加**是

---

* 这个不等式几乎对所有金属来说都是成立的，尽管并不是所有的金属都是超导体，因为对于真正的金属而言，在温度下降到绝对零度的过程中，s 将保持一个有限值（实际上是常数），然而对超导体而言，它会跳跃成为比先前略大的一个有限值。

$$\Delta\eta = 2k\left[n\lg n - ns\lg ns - (n - ns)\lg(n - ns)\right]. \tag{3}$$

In reality, the width of a band is of the order of 1 volt and therefore at least a thousand times larger than kT at the transition point. This will result in a much smaller entropy increase $\Delta\eta$.

So long, however, as $\Delta\eta > 0$ it follows that the state $s = 0$ must be stable at low temperatures and the state $s > 0$ at higher ones.

The transition temperature T_c as determined by the equality of the free energies of the two states is given by

$$T_c = \frac{\Delta\varepsilon}{\Delta\eta}\,(\Delta\varepsilon = \varepsilon_s - \varepsilon_0). \tag{4}$$

Taking $s = \frac{1}{2}$ (which is probably an exaggeration) and calculating $\Delta\eta$ with the help of (3), we get $\Delta\eta \doteq 1.7k_n$. If $T = 4°$ (say) the transition energy $\Delta\varepsilon$ should be of the order of 14 small calories per gram atom. This value is greatly reduced if the width of the energy band under consideration is large compared with nT, its effective weight being accordingly small compared with g.

We thus see that the second condition for supraconductivity is expressed by the inequality $\varepsilon_s > \varepsilon_0$ at $T = 0$. But this is not all. Equation (1) is a good approximation so long as the chain-like displacement of the electrons x is small compared with the interatomic distance a. When x approaches $\frac{1}{2}a$, the electrons are pushed back by a force which varies more rapidly than the first power of x and can be overcome through the quantum mechanism of the tunnel effect. If a large number of electrons N are moving together in a chain-like way, they behave like a particle with an N-fold mass, the transition probability being correspondingly reduced. Now in his second theory of supraconductivity, Kronig[5] has shown that a chain or, as he puts it, a "linear lattice", of electrons, bound to each other in a quasi-elastic way, can be displaced through a periodic field of force (with a period a equal to the average spacing between the electrons) under the condition

$$h/b\sqrt{m} > a^2, \tag{5}$$

where h is Planck's constant, m the mass of an electron and b is the rigidity coefficient of the "electron lattice". Putting $b = \tau e/a^{3/2}$ where τ is a numerical coefficient of the order 1, Kronig finds that the condition (5) is fulfilled if a is of the order of less than a few Ångström units. This seems to show that a "linear lattice", that is, chain of electrons, is practically *always movable* with respect to the corresponding chain of atoms, provided the condition (2), which is much more restrictive, is fulfilled also. In fact, the latter condition seems to be the mathematical formulation of the possibility of treating the (bound) electrons as a kind of lattice. I do not believe in the reality of the three-dimensional lattices postulated by Kronig in his first paper. He has himself shown that such lattices, even if they exist, could not be moved through the ionic lattice. As a matter of fact, one-dimensional lattices or rather movable *chains* of bound electrons fully suffice for the explanation of supraconductivity. Such chains need not be movable in all directions. It is sufficient to assume that they should be movable in one particular crystallographic direction corresponding to the smallest spacing between the atoms, the dielectric constant being infinite for this direction and preserving a finite value for all the others.

$$\Delta\eta = 2k\left[n\lg n - ns\lg ns - (n-ns)\lg(n-ns)\right] \tag{3}$$

实际上，带宽的数量级是 1 电子伏，因此在温度处于转变点时，带宽至少是 kT 的一千倍。这将得到一个非常小的熵的增加量 $\Delta\eta$。

然而，只要 $\Delta\eta > 0$，$s = 0$ 的态在低温下一定是稳定的，$s > 0$ 的态在更高的温度下也一定是稳定的。

转变温度 T_c 由两个态的自由能相等决定，由下式给出：

$$T_c = \frac{\Delta\varepsilon}{\Delta\eta}\,(\Delta\varepsilon = \varepsilon_s - \varepsilon_0) \tag{4}$$

取 $s = \frac{1}{2}$（它可能是一个夸大值），根据 (3) 式计算 $\Delta\eta$，我们得到 $\Delta\eta = 1.7k_n$。假设 $T = 4$ K，则转变能 $\Delta\varepsilon$ 应是每克原子 14 卡的量级。如果在考虑的范围内能带的带宽比 nT 大，那么这个值会大幅度降低，其有效权重会相应地比 g 小。

于是，我们发现，超导电性的第二个条件应该表示为在 $T = 0$ 时满足不等式 $\varepsilon_s > \varepsilon_0$。但这还不是全部。只要电子的类链位移 x 小于原子间距 a，(1) 式就是一个很好的近似。当 x 约等于 $\frac{1}{2}a$ 时，电子则被一个力推回去，这个力比 x 的一次幂变化更快，并能被量子机制的隧道效应所克服。如果大量电子 N 以类链方式整体运动，它们就犹如具有 N 倍质量的一个粒子一样，转变概率将显著下降。克罗尼格[5] 在他的第二个超导理论中已指出，电子链（他所说的"线形晶格"）以准弹性方式彼此束缚，在满足条件（5）式的情况下可以通过力的周期场（周期 a 等于电子之间的平均距离）。

$$h/b\sqrt{m} > a^2 \tag{5}$$

式中，h 是普朗克常数，m 是电子质量，b 是"电子晶格"的刚性系数。令 $b = \tau e/a^{3/2}$，其中 τ 是一个量级为 1 的系数，克罗尼格发现，如果 a 的量级小于几埃，则条件 (5) 式是满足的。这似乎表明，当限制性更强的条件 (2) 式也满足时，"线性晶格"即电子链相对于相应的原子链实际上**总是可运动的**。实际上，后一条件似乎是能否将（束缚）电子当作一种晶格来处理的可能性的数学描述。我并不认为，克罗尼格在他的第一篇文章中假设的三维晶格是真实存在的。他自己也表明，这类晶格即使存在也不能穿过离子晶格。事实上，一维晶格或可运动的束缚电子**链**完全可以解释超导电性。这类链并不需要在所有方向上都能运动。它们只要做如下的假设就足够了，即它们在一个特殊的晶体学方向上应该是可运动的，这个特殊方向对应于原子间的距离最小，而且介电常数在这个方向上为无穷大，而在其他方向上总保持一个有限值。

In spite of its shortcomings, Kronig's theory is certainly the nearest approach to the correct explanation of supraconductivity published hitherto, the present theory differing from it more in form than in essence. The theory I advanced before, which was based on the supposed stabilisation of the free electrons (against heat motion) by their *electromagnetic* action, was wholly erroneous in this particular respect. It was correct, however, in describing the motion of the electrons in the supraconductive state as an organised "collective" motion. This led to the result that a metal must possess when in this state an enormous diamagnetic susceptibility. This corollary subsists in the new theory and is corroborated by the fact recently discovered by Meissner that the magnetic permeability μ of a metal in the supraconducting state drops to zero. A supraconductor can thus be described as a body with $\mu = 0$ and $\varepsilon = \infty$, its electrical conductivity σ in the exact sense of the word being either finite or even zero.

A more complete account of the present theory will be published elsewhere.

($\mathbf{133}$, 730-731; 1934)

References:

1. The effects of heat motion of the crystal lattice on the individual electrons are mutually cancelled. Cf. R. Kronig, *Z. Phys.*, **80**, 203; 1933.

2. *Phys. Rev.*, **35**, 509; 1930.

3. In the press.

4. Cf. J. Frenkel, *Nature*, **132**, 312, Aug. 26, 1933.

5. *Z. Phys.*, **80**, 203; 933.

克罗尼格的理论虽然存在不足，但它确实是迄今发表的对超导电性最接近正确的解释，我的理论与其的差别更多是在形式上，而非本质上的。我以前提出的基于假设在**电磁**作用下自由电子（相对于热运动）的稳定性的理论在这个特定方面是完全错误的。但是，在将超导态中电子的运动描述为有组织的"集体"运动这点是正确的。这就要求金属在这种态下必须具有巨大的抗磁性的磁化率。这个推论在新理论中成立，而且被迈斯纳最近发现的事实所证实，迈斯纳的实验显示金属的磁导率 μ 在超导态中会下降到零。因此超导体可以被表述为 $\mu = 0$ 和 $\varepsilon = \infty$ 的物体，更确切地说，其电导率 σ 或者是一个有限值，或者就是零。

这一理论更完整的叙述将在其他地方发表。

（沈乃澂 翻译；郑东宁 审稿）

Modern Ideas on Nuclear Constitution

G. Gamow

Editor's Notes

George Gamow here reviews advances in the theory of nuclear structure. With the discovery of the neutron, physicists now considered stable nuclei to be composed of neutrons and protons. As Gamow points out, Heisenberg's theory of nuclear structure suggested that small nuclei should have roughly equal numbers of the two particles, and that an imbalance toward more neutrons should grow with increasing atomic mass, thereby counteracting the electrical repulsion between protons. Gamow considers the stability of nuclei to both beta and alpha decay, which could be understood only partially in current theory. The approximate proportionality of nuclear radius to the cube root of the atomic mass suggested that the density of the nucleus remains roughly constant.

WHEN the complexity of atomic nuclei was proved by the existence of spontaneous and artificial nuclear transformations, a very important question arose: From which of the elementary particles are the different nuclei built up? It seemed that this question could be simply answered as there were only two particles with pretensions to be elementary: the proton and the electron. The protons had to account for the main part of the nuclear mass and the electrons had to be introduced to reduce the positive charge to the observed value. For example, the nucleus of bismuth, with atomic weight 209 and atomic number 83, was considered to be constructed from 209 protons and $209 - 83 = 126$ electrons. It was also accepted as very probable that these elementary particles build up inside the nucleus certain complex units constructed from four protons and two electrons each (α-particles). All this construction was in good agreement with the experimental evidence, as electrons, protons and α-particles were really observed being emitted in nuclear transformations.

The theory treating the nuclei as constructed of α-particles, some protons and a certain number of electrons, was worked out by Gamow. Although this theory gave some interesting results as to the general shape of the mass-defect curve and the conditions of emission of α-particles, it met with serious difficulties. It was very difficult to understand, on the basis of the quantum theory of the electron, how the electron can exist in a space so small as that limited by the nuclear radius. It was also not clear why the nuclear electrons, behaving in quite a strange and obscure way, do not affect the processes of emission of the heavy nuclear particles, protons and α-particles.

About two years ago, it was shown by Chadwick that the experimental evidence forces us to recognise the existence of a new kind of particle, the so-called neutron, also with claims to be held to play an important rôle in nuclear structure. The discovery of neutrons

262

核组成的现代思想

伽莫夫

编者按

在这篇文章中，乔治·伽莫夫回顾了核结构理论的发展状况。随着中子的发现，现在物理学家认为稳定的原子核由质子和中子构成。正如伽莫夫指出的那样，海森堡的核结构理论认为小的原子核应该含有大体相等数量的两种粒子，但随着原子质量的增加平衡会被打破，中子的数目会变得更多，这会抵消质子间的静电斥力。伽莫夫认为当前的理论只能部分解释原子核相对 α 衰变和 β 衰变的稳定性。原子核半径与原子质量的立方根粗略成正比表明原子核的密度大致保持不变。

当自发和人工的核转变的存在证明了原子核的复杂性时，一个很重要的问题出现了：不同的原子核是由哪些基本粒子组成的？这个问题似乎可以简单地回答，因为自命是基本粒子的只有两类：质子和电子。原子核的质量主要是由质子贡献的，而电子的引入是为了减少正电荷以便符合实验的观测值。例如，原子量 209、原子序数 83 的铋原子核被认为是由 209 个质子和 209 - 83=126 个电子组成的。大家还认为这些基本粒子在原子核内构建某种由四个质子和两个电子组成的复合单元（α 粒子）也是很有可能的。所有这些结构都与实验结果吻合得很好，因为我们确实在核转变的实验中观测到了所放出的电子、质子和 α 粒子。

伽莫夫发展了一种理论，即原子核由 α 粒子、一些质子和一定数目的电子组成。虽然这个理论给出了一些有趣的结果，如原子核质量亏损曲线的一般形状和原子核发射 α 粒子的条件，但同时也遇到了严重的困难。根据电子的量子理论，我们难以理解电子如何能存在于原子核半径所限制的微小空间内。我们也不清楚原子核中电子的行为为何如此奇怪，且难以理解原子核的电子为何不会影响重核的粒子（质子和 α 粒子）的发射过程。

约两年前，查德威克指出，实验证据使我们不得不承认存在一类新的粒子，即所谓的中子，它们在原子核结构中扮演了重要角色。中子的发现大大简化了原子核内

263

considerably simplified the difficulties about electrons in nuclei. One could now suppose that the nuclei were completely constructed of neutrons and protons (for example, the nucleus of bismuth from 83 protons and 209–83=126 neutrons) which probably sometimes unite to form an α-particle (two neutrons and two protons). Thus the first of the above-mentioned difficulties was, so to say, hidden inside the neutron, while the second one was actually removed.

On the basis of these new ideas, Heisenberg succeeded in building up a general theory of nuclear structure, accounting for the main features of nuclear stability. The basis of his theory is certain assumptions about the forces acting between neutrons and protons. It seems most rational to accept the view that the interaction between particles of the same kind is only due to electric charges (that is, no forces between two neutrons and the usual Coulomb repulsion between two protons), while between two different particles (neutron and proton) strong exchange forces come into play. These last forces are probably of the same kind as the forces between atoms playing the main rôle in quantum chemistry, and may be considered as due to the exchange of charge between the two particles in question.

This hypothesis explains at once why the number of nuclear neutrons for heavy elements is considerably greater than the number of protons (that is, why the ratio of atomic weight to atomic number increases for heavier elements). In fact, if we neglect the coulomb forces, the most stable state of the nucleus will correspond to equal numbers of neutrons and protons, as in this case all the possibilities of binding (by attracting exchange forces), between protons and neutrons are saturated. The presence of the Coulomb repulsion between protons will, however, shift the optimum in the direction of a smaller number of protons and the position of lowest potential energy of our system will correspond to the larger proportion of neutrons. As the importance of the Coulomb forces increases with the nuclear charge, one can understand that an equal number of neutrons and protons is possible only for the lightest elements (first ten elements of the periodic system), while for heavier ones the number of neutrons predominates (126 neutrons and only 83 protons in bismuth).

Accepting the simplest form for the law of variation of the exchange forces with distance:—

$$I = a \cdot e^{-br} \qquad (1)$$

and applying the quantum statistical method, Heisenberg calculated the behaviour of the nuclear model constructed from n_1 neutrons and n_2 protons. The result is that the particles are rather uniformly distributed inside a certain volume proportional to the total number of particles. This result fits very well with evidence otherwise obtained, that the density inside the nucleus is rather uniform and does not depend greatly on the atomic weight. The formula obtained for the total binding energy E of the nucleus as a function of n_1 and n_2 looks rather complicated and depends, of course, on the numerical values of the coefficients a and b in the expression (1) for the exchange force. Comparing this formula with experimental values of the mass defects of different nuclei, one can estimate the values of a and b. One finds thus: $a = 4.05 \times 10^{-5}$ erg; $b = 1.25 \times 10^{12}$ cm.$^{-1}$.

有关电子的困难。现在我们可以假设原子核完全是由质子和中子组成的（例如，铋元素的原子核是由 83 个质子和 209–83=126 个中子组成），而质子和中子有时也可能结合成一个 α 粒子（两个质子和两个中子）。因此，可以这么说，上面提到的第一个困难被隐藏在中子内部，而实际上第二个困难这时已经被排除。

根据这些新的思想，海森堡成功地建立了一个原子核结构的普遍理论，用来解释原子核稳定性的主要特征。他的理论基础是建立在某些关于质子和中子之间存在相互作用力的假设上的。看起来最合理且可接受的观点是，认为同类粒子之间的相互作用仅由电荷产生（即在两个中子之间不存在力的作用，而在两个质子之间通常有库仑排斥力），而在两类不同的粒子（中子和质子）之间有强的交换力起作用。这后一种力很可能与量子化学中起主要作用的原子间的作用力类同，可以认为是由相关的两个粒子之间电荷交换产生的。

以上的假设立即解释了为何重元素原子核中的中子数远大于其质子数（即为何原子量与原子序数之比对较重元素而言是逐渐增大的）。实际上，如果我们忽略库仑力，原子核最稳定的状态将相应于质子数与中子数相等的情况，在这种情况下，质子与中子之间所有可能的结合方式（通过吸引的交换力）趋于饱和。但是，由于质子之间存在库仑排斥现象使得原子核偏离最佳状态朝向较小的质子数，这时，系统的最低势能状态将对应于较大比例的中子数。由于库仑力的重要性随着核电荷的增大而增加，这时人们可以理解只有对那些最轻的元素（元素周期表中的前 10 个元素），同等数目的中子和质子才是可能的；而对于较重的元素，其中子数在数量上就会占优势（如铋元素由 126 个中子和 83 个质子组成）。

对交换力随距离变化的规律采用最简单的形式：

$$I = a \cdot e^{-br} \tag{1}$$

并应用量子统计方法，海森堡计算出了由 n_1 个中子和 n_2 个质子所构建的核模型的行为。结果是，在与粒子总数成正比的确定体积内，粒子的分布相当均匀。这项结果与从其他途径得到的结果是非常吻合的，即核内的密度分布相当均匀，且与原子量无太大关系。而以原子核总的结合能 E 作为 n_1 和 n_2 的函数得到的关系式似乎非常复杂，当然，E 与交换力表达式（1）中的系数 a 和 b 的数值也是有关的。将这个公式与不同原子核的质量亏损的实验值进行对照，我们可以估算出 a 和 b 的值，得到的结果是：$a = 4.05 \times 10^{-5}$ erg，$b = 1.25 \times 10^{12}$ cm^{-1}。

Very interesting consequences can also be obtained from Heisenberg's theory concerning the question of nuclear stability. It is easily understood that nuclei with a high positive electric charge must tend to emit positive particles. From the point of view of the energy balance, the most favourable case for such emission is the emission of an α-particle, as this removes from the nucleus a large amount of negative energy (the binding-energy of the α-particle itself), which is equivalent to the supply of an equal quantity of positive energy. The condition for the possibility of α-emission can be simply formulated if we consider it as a simultaneous subtraction of two neutrons and two protons from the nucleus in question. The work necessary for such subtraction is evidently

$$\frac{\delta E}{\delta n_1}\, \Delta n_1 + \frac{\delta E}{\delta n_2}\, \Delta n_2$$

or, as
$$\Delta n_1 = \Delta n_2 = -2,$$

$$-2\left(\frac{\delta E}{\delta n_1} + \frac{\delta E}{\delta n_2}\right).$$

To make a spontaneous α-disintegration possible, this quantity must be smaller than the above mentioned energy-supply due to the binding energy $\Delta M_\alpha c^2$ of the α-particle from neutrons and protons. (The difference appears as the kinetic energy of the emitted particle.) Thus the condition for α-decay will be:

$$-2\left(\frac{\delta E}{\delta n_1} + \frac{\delta E}{\delta n_2}\right) < \Delta M_\alpha c^2 \tag{2}$$

In Fig. 1, the ratio of the number of neutrons to the number of protons is plotted against the number of protons for all known isotopes. The α-stability curve as calculated from formula (2) is represented by a broken line (curve I) and one can see that it is situated too low. One notices, however, that the theoretical curve, apart from absolute values, gives a good idea of the general form of this stability limit. We may notice that the condition for the spontaneous emission of a proton:

$$-\frac{\delta E}{\delta n_2} < 0 \tag{2'}$$

will give us a stability limit located very far to the right of the α-stability curve, which means that spontaneous proton decay could only take place for very heavily charged nuclei (atomic number > 200). On the other hand, the condition for the emission of a neutron:

$$-\frac{\delta E}{\delta n_1} < 0 \tag{2''}$$

is never fulfilled, which can easily be understood if we remember that neutrons, having no charge, are not at all repelled by nuclei.

We must now turn our attention to the question of the emission of light particles. From the point of view of the neutron-proton model of the nucleus, we must accept the view that the process of ordinary β-emission is due to the transformation of a nuclear neutron into a proton with the liberation of negative charge in the form of an electron:

$$n \rightarrow p + \bar{e}.$$

从海森堡有关核稳定性问题的理论中，我们也能获得很有趣的结果。我们很容易理解具有高正电荷的原子核必然趋于发射出带正电的粒子。根据能量守恒的观点，对这类发射最有利的情况是发射一个 α 粒子，即从核中带走了大量的负能量（α 粒子自身的结合能），这相当于给原子核提供了同样多的正能量。如果把 α 粒子的发射认为是从相关的核内同时减去两个中子和两个质子，则 α 粒子发射的可能性条件可以被简单地表述出来。显然，这类过程扣除所需的能量为

$$\frac{\delta E}{\delta n_1} \Delta n_1 + \frac{\delta E}{\delta n_2} \Delta n_2$$

或，当 $\Delta n_1 = \Delta n_2 = -2$ 时，

$$-2\left(\frac{\delta E}{\delta n_1} + \frac{\delta E}{\delta n_2}\right)$$

要使一个自发的 α 衰变成为可能，这个量必须小于上述由中子和质子形成 α 粒子时放出的结合能 $\Delta M_\alpha c^2$。（两者的能量差将作为放出的粒子的动能。）因此，α 衰变的条件是：

$$-2\left(\frac{\delta E}{\delta n_1} + \frac{\delta E}{\delta n_2}\right) < \Delta M_\alpha c^2 \qquad (2)$$

图 1 中画出了所有已知同位素的中子数和质子数的比值与其质子数的关系。根据公式 (2) 计算得到的 α 稳定性曲线用虚线（曲线 I）表示，从中可以看到，它所处的位置非常低。然而我们注意到，不考虑绝对值的大小，理论曲线还是让我们对 α 稳定性的界限有了很好的了解。我们可能会注意到，质子的自发发射条件为：

$$-\frac{\delta E}{\delta n_2} < 0 \qquad (2')$$

这里给出的发射质子的稳定性界限远离 α 稳定性曲线的右边，这意味着只有很重的带电核（原子序数大于 200）才能发生自发的质子衰变。另一方面，对中子发射的条件：

$$-\frac{\delta E}{\delta n_1} < 0 \qquad (2'')$$

是永远不可能满足的，如果想到不带电荷的中子绝不被原子核排斥，我们将很容易理解这一点。

现在我们必须将注意力转回到轻粒子发射的问题上来。根据核的中子 – 质子模型，我们必须采纳以下观点，即通常的 β 发射过程是由于核的中子以电子的形式释放出负电荷而转变为质子所引起的：

$$n \to p + \bar{e}$$

On the other hand, the recent discovery of the Joliots of elements emitting positive electrons suggests the possibility of the reverse process:

$$p \rightarrow n + \overset{+}{e}.$$

We can easily estimate the stability limits for such processes if we consider the emission of a nuclear electron as the subtraction from the nucleus of a neutron and simultaneous addition of a proton. The condition for the positive energy balance of such a transformation will evidently be:

$$-\frac{\delta E}{\delta n_1} + \frac{\delta E}{\delta n_2} < \Delta M_n \cdot c^2, \tag{3}$$

where ΔM_n is the mass defect of a neutron as constructed from a proton and an electron. In an exactly analogous way we obtain for the possibility of emission of a positive electron the condition:

$$-\frac{\delta E}{\delta n_2} + \frac{\delta E}{\delta n_1} < \Delta M_p \cdot c^2, \tag{4}$$

where ΔM_p is the mass defect of a proton as constructed from a neutron and a positive electron. From (3) and (4) we can conclude that the nucleus can be stable relative to electron emission only if

$$- \Delta M_p c^2 < -\frac{\delta E}{\delta n_1} + \frac{\delta E}{\delta n_2} < \Delta M_n c^2,$$

conditions which correspond in the stability diagram (Fig. 1) to a very narrow band (curves II and III)*, in contradiction with the experimental evidence.

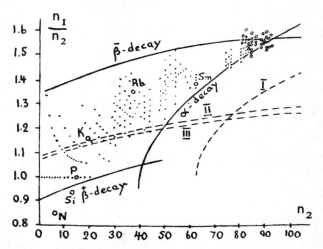

Fig. 1. A map of all known nuclei. Stable nuclei are indicated by full points, unstable nuclei by small circles.

---

* From the equations $n = p + \bar{e} + \Delta M_n c^2$ and $p = n + \overset{+}{e} + \Delta M_p c^2$, we obtain $\Delta M_n c^2 - (- \Delta M_p c^2) = \Delta M_n c^2 + \Delta M_p c^2 = \bar{e} + \overset{+}{e} = 2mc^2 = 1.6 \times 10^{-6}$ erg. This corresponds in Fig. 1 to a breadth of the stable region of about 0.016 units along the ordinate.

另一方面，约里奥夫妇最近发现了发射正电子的元素从而揭示了以上逆过程出现的可能性：

$$p \rightarrow n + \overset{+}{e}$$

只要我们认为核电子的发射相当于从原子核内拿走一个中子同时加入一个质子，则我们很容易估计出这个过程的稳定性极限。这种转变的正能量守恒条件显然将是：

$$-\frac{\delta E}{\delta n_1} + \frac{\delta E}{\delta n_2} < \ \Delta M_n \cdot c^2 \tag{3}$$

式中，ΔM_n 是一个质子和一个电子构成一个中子的质量亏损。通过严格类比，我们得到可能发射正电子的条件为：

$$-\frac{\delta E}{\delta n_2} + \frac{\delta E}{\delta n_1} < \ \Delta M_p \cdot c^2 \tag{4}$$

式中，ΔM_p 是一个中子和一个正电子构成一个质子的质量亏损。根据 (3) 式和 (4) 式，我们可以断定，仅在以下条件下，即

$$- \ \Delta M_p c^2 < -\frac{\delta E}{\delta n_1} + \frac{\delta E}{\delta n_2} < \ \Delta M_n c^2$$

核相对电子发射可能是稳定的，这个条件对应于稳定性图（图 1）中一条很窄的带（曲线 II 和曲线 III）*，这与实验结果相矛盾。

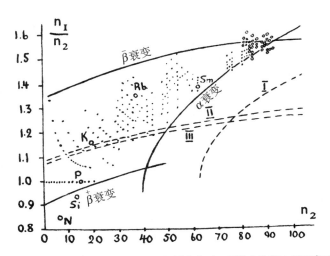

图 1. 所有已知原子核的图。稳定核用黑点表示，不稳定核用小圆圈表示。

---

* 从等式 $n = p + \overset{-}{e} + \Delta M_n c^2$ 和 $p = n + \overset{+}{e} + \Delta M_p c^2$ 中，我们可得到 $\Delta M_n c^2 - (- \ \Delta M_p c^2) = \Delta M_n c^2 + \Delta M_p c^2 = \overset{-}{e} + \overset{+}{e} = 2mc^2 = 1.6 \times 10^{-6}$erg。在图 1 中由纵坐标上的一个约 0.016 单位稳定宽度范围所反映。

The stability region can, however, be made much broader if we consider more closely the energy conditions connected with electronic emission from nuclei. The point is that for a given total number of neutrons plus protons (that is, for given atomic weight) the nuclei are considerably more stable if the number of protons is even (even atomic number). The reason for this is that, with the increasing number of protons, each second one will lead to the formation of a new α-particle, and consequently correspond to larger liberation of energy. Thus if we plot the binding energy of isobaric nuclei against the atomic number (Fig. 2), the points corresponding to even-numbered elements will lie on a lower curve than those corresponding to the odd numbers. As can be seen from the diagram, this will have the result that for a series of elements extending some way both to the left and to the right side of the minimum, the emission of one electron (either negative or positive) will be energetically impossible. In such cases only the simultaneous emission of two electrons can be considered, but, as can be estimated from general theoretical considerations, such a double emission has extremely small probability. The possibility is not excluded that the natural β-activity of potassium and rubidium has its origin in such a double process, which would easily explain their extremely long period of life.

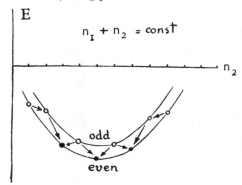

Fig. 2. Mass defect curves for typical isobaric nuclei. ●, stable nuclei; ○, unstable nuclei.

According to these considerations we must push the limit of $\overline{\beta}$-stability upwards and the limit of $\overset{+}{\beta}$-stability downwards, and thus get a considerably broader stability region. It can be seen from Fig. 1 that theoretical limiting curves give a good idea of the form of the actual stability limits, although, just as in the case of α-decay, the curves go again too low. It seems that both discrepancies have a common origin.

In Fig. 1, the points corresponding to unstable nuclei are shown by small circles. One notices that in the region of the heavy elements, where α- and β-stability curves run rather close to one another (and possibly cross), the sequences of α-disintegrations followed by two β-disintegrations are possible. For the lighter elements only a few cases of spontaneous disintegration are at present known. Samarium (most probably its lightest isotope) emits α-particles of about 1.5 cm. range and has an average life of about 10^{12} years. The lightest isotopes of nitrogen, silicon and phosphorus (N_7^{13}, Si_{14}^{27}, P_{15}^{30}), unknown in Nature and produced artificially by the Joliots by α-bombardment of boron, magnesium and aluminium, give $\overset{+}{\beta}$-particles with an energy of 1-2 million volts and possess life-periods of several minutes.

然而，如果我们进一步考虑与原子核的电子发射有关的能量条件，以上讨论的稳定区域可以变得更宽。问题在于对一个给定的中子和质子的总数（即对于给定的原子量），如果质子数是偶数（偶原子序数），那么原子核是相当稳定的。理由是，随着质子数的增加，每两个质子将导致一个新的 α 粒子的形成，从而释放更多的能量。因此如果我们画出同量异位核的结合能相对其原子序数的关系图（图 2），则对应于偶数元素的点位于比奇数元素相应点更低的曲线上。如图所示，结果将是，对延伸到位于最小值两侧的一系列元素从能量角度上来看是不可能发射电子（不管是负电子或正电子）的。在这种情况下，只能认为两个电子同时发射。正如根据一般的理论估计的那样，这类成对电子发射的概率是很小的。但并不排除元素钾和铷的天然 β 放射性源于这类成对电子的发射过程，这也容易解释它们为何具有极长的寿命。

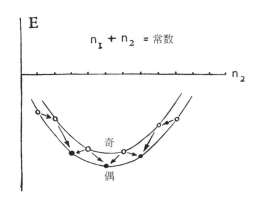

图 2. 典型的同量异位素核的质量亏损曲线。● 稳定核；○ 不稳定核。

根据以上的考虑，我们必须将 $\bar{\beta}$ 稳定性的极限向上推，而将 $\overset{+}{\beta}$ 稳定性的极限向下推，从而得到相当宽的稳定性区域。由图 1 可见，尽管与 α 衰变的情况一样，曲线的位置仍然很低，但是理论的极限曲线对实际的稳定性极限形状有一个很好的认识作用。似乎以上两类差异都出于相同的原因。

在图 1 中，对应的不稳定核用小圆圈表示。我们注意到，在重元素区域内 α 和 β 的稳定性曲线彼此很接近（可能有交叉），发生 α 衰变后紧接着两次 β 衰变的顺序是可能的。对于较轻的元素，目前我们只知道存在少数的自发衰变情况。如钐（极有可能是最轻的同位素）放出射程约为 1.5 cm 的 α 粒子，且平均寿命约为 10^{12} 年。而氮、硅和磷各自最轻的同位素（$^{13}_{7}N$，$^{27}_{14}Si$，$^{30}_{15}P$）在自然界中不存在，而是由约里奥夫妇利用 α 粒子分别轰击硼、镁和铝人工产生的，这些人工同位素放出能量为 1~2 兆电子伏，寿命约为几分钟的 $\overset{+}{\beta}$ 粒子。

The $\bar{\beta}$-emission from potassium and rubidium must be explained either as a double electron emission from their heavier isotopes (K_{19}^{41} and Rb_{37}^{87}) or as due to some unknown isotopes of chlorine and bromine resulting from a very short range α-emission of the above mentioned elements (probably from K_{19}^{40} and Rb_{37}^{86}). As these ranges in air, as calculated theoretically from the value of the corresponding decay constants, are 0.24 cm. and 0.63 cm. respectively, one can understand why the α-particles have not yet been detected. Thus we see that our general theoretical considerations fit rather nicely with the experimental evidence.

We now turn our attention to the details of the processes of emission of α-particles and electrons, and the connexion of the disintegration energy with the average period of life. The process of α-emission can be explained on the basis of the ordinary wave equation of Schrödinger as the velocities of the emitted α-particles are small compared with the velocity of the light. It was shown by Gamow, and independently by Gurney and Condon, that the long life of α-decaying bodies is due to the fact that the α-particle leaving a nucleus must cross a very high potential barrier, the transparency of which is extremely small and decreases very rapidly with the decrease of the energy liberated in the disintegration. Theory leads us to the following formula for the decay-constant λ as a function of the α-particle velocity v:

$$\lambda = \frac{4h}{mr_0^2} e^{-\frac{8\pi^2 e^2}{h}\frac{(Z-2)}{v} + \frac{16\pi e\sqrt{m}}{h}\sqrt{Z-2}\sqrt{r_0}} \tag{5}$$

where Z is the atomic number of the disintegrating element and r_0 the nuclear radius. Accepting r_0 for radioactive elements to be of the order of magnitude 10^{-12} cm., one obtains very good agreement between the calculated and measured values of λ and can explain theoretically the empirical relation between $\lg\lambda$ and v found by Geiger and Nuttall.

For complete agreement one must, however, accept the view that the nuclear radius r_0 changes from one element to another in such way that the density of the nucleus remains constant $(r_0 \sim \sqrt[3]{A})$. Formula (5) permits us also to estimate one of the values λ or v if the other is measured. Thus, for example, the range of the α-particles of radium C, estimated from this formula to be equal to 4 cm., is in good agreement with the value found later by Rutherford, and the period of life of the very short lived product radium C' given by this formula (10^{-3} sec.) fits well with the recent measurements of Jacobsen.

It is also interesting to notice that formula (5) may be successfully applied in the region of the lighter elements. According to (5) the period of life of samarium as estimated from the velocity of its α-particles must be about 10^{12} years, in good agreement with the observed value.

In the process of α-decay, it may often happen that the nucleus of the product of disintegration is constructed in an excited state, which corresponds to the emission of α-groups with slightly smaller energy (fine-structure of α-rays). The formula helps us to understand the relative intensities of such α-groups and also permits us to draw certain

钾和铷的 $\bar{\beta}$ 发射一定也可以解释成要么是它们较重的同位素（$^{41}_{19}K$ 和 $^{87}_{37}Rb$）发生了双电子发射，要么是源于上述元素（可能来自 $^{41}_{19}K$ 和 $^{87}_{37}Rb$）非常短射程的 α 粒子发射的一些氯和溴的未知同位素。根据相应的衰变常数进行理论计算，可以得到它们在空气中的射程分别为 0.24 cm 和 0.63 cm，这样我们就可以理解为何 α 粒子尚未被探测到。这里我们看到，通常的理论推算与实验结果较好地符合了。

我们现在将注意力转到 α 粒子和电子发射的详细过程以及衰变能量与平均寿命的关系上来。α 粒子发射过程基于普通的薛定谔波动方程可以解释为，发射的 α 粒子的速度是小于光速的。格尼、康登他们与伽莫夫都曾独立地指出，α 粒子衰变体的长寿命是由于从核中逃逸的 α 粒子必须穿过很高的势垒，而势垒的透射率极小，且随着衰变过程释放出能量的减小而迅速减小。理论导出以衰变常数 λ 作为 α 粒子速度 v 函数的公式：

$$\lambda = \frac{4h}{mr_0^2} e^{-\frac{8\pi^2 e^2}{h}\frac{(Z-2)}{v} + \frac{16\pi e\sqrt{m}}{h}\sqrt{Z-2}\sqrt{r_0}} \tag{5}$$

式中，Z 是衰变元素的原子序数，r_0 是核半径。采用放射性元素的 r_0 是在 10^{-12}cm 的量级，这使得 λ 的计算值与测量值得到很好的符合，而且可以在理论上解释由盖革和努塔耳得到的 lgλ 和 v 之间的经验关系式。

然而，为了使理论和实验可以完全符合，我们必须采用以下观点，在核的密度保持恒定（$r_0 \sim \sqrt[3]{A}$）的条件下，不同元素之间的核半径 r_0 是变化的。如果 λ 和 v 两个值中一个被测量，则通过式 (5) 我们可以估算出另一个值。例如，我们从式（5）估算得到镭 C 放出的 α 粒子的射程为 4 cm，这很好地符合了卢瑟福后来得到的数值，而由该公式得到很短存活产物镭 C' 的寿命（10^{-3} 秒）与最近雅克布森的测量值也符合得很好。

有趣的是我们还注意到，公式 (5) 也完全适用于较轻元素。根据（5）式，从钐放出的 α 粒子的速度可估算出钐的寿命约为 10^{12} 年，与观测值非常一致。

在 α 衰变过程中，衰变的产物的原子核通常总是处于激发态的，它对应于具有较小能量的 α 粒子群的发射（α 射线的精细结构）。这个公式有助于我们理解这类 α 粒子群的相对强度，也允许我们确认核的不同激发能级的量子数。另一方面，这

important conclusions about the quantum numbers of the different excited nuclear levels. On the other hand, it also explains the small number of so-called long-range α-groups corresponding to the disintegration of excited nuclei.

In contrast with the theory of α-decay, the understanding of the process of β-disintegration presents serious difficulties. First of all, the electrons emitted in β-decay possess a continuous distribution of energy, which seems to be in contradiction with the law of conservation of energy. It was pointed out by Bohr that the law of conservation of energy need not necessarily hold for processes involving nuclear electrons for which the modern quantum theory is not applicable. But, as was shown by Landau, the rejection of the conservation law for energy will be connécted with very serious difficulties in the general gravitational theory, according to which the mass present inside a certain closed surface is entirely defined by the gravitational field on this surface. It was proposed by Pauli that one might retain the energy conservation law by the introduction of a new kind of particle called a "neutrino". These neutrinos, having no electric charge and possessing very small (or even vanishing) mass, would be practically unobservable in all experiments and could easily take away the surplus energy of β-decay. The existence of such particles is, however, at present rather doubtful.

An attempt to construct a theory of β-disintegration on the basis of Dirac's relativistic wave equation, treating the emission of a nuclear electron in a similar way to the emission of light quanta by an atom, has recently been made by Fermi. In this theory, one accepts the view that the transformation of a nuclear neutron into a proton is connected with the creation of an electron and a neutrino, which, being born, leave the nucleus, dividing between them the energy liberated in this transformation. Accepting a definite value for the interaction energy giving rise to such transformations (of the order of magnitude of about 10^{-14} erg), Fermi obtains reasonable values for the decay constants of β-disintegrating elements and a good fit with the correlation curve between the decay constant and the maximum energy of the β-particles as found by Sargent.

An interesting consequence of this theory, which, however, is much more general and will hold for every theory treating electron emission as the result of the transformation of a neutron into a proton, is a definite exclusion rule for β-decay. According to this rule, β-transformations in which the original nuclei and those produced possess different spins are not all permitted, and can only happen with a rather reduced probability (about a hundred times less often than transformations in which the spin does not change). This explains at once the two different curves obtained by Sargent as due to permitted and not permitted transformations. It has been shown by Gamow that the application of the above mentioned exclusion rule for β-decay to the analysis of radioactive families gives very good results and permits us to give definite spin values to normal and excited states of radioactive nuclei.

(**133**, 744-747; 1934)

个公式也解释了少量的所谓长程 α 粒子群对应于激发态核的衰变。

与 α 衰变理论相比较，理解 β 衰变过程存在严重的困难。首先，β 衰变发射的电子具有连续的能量分布，这似乎与能量守恒定律相矛盾。玻尔曾指出，由于现代量子理论不适用于涉及核电子的过程，因此，能量守恒定律并不适用于该过程。但正如朗道所指出的，在广义引力理论中，某个闭合曲面中的质量完全是用该曲面上的重力场来定义的，违反能量守恒定律在广义引力理论中将会遇到非常严重的困难。泡利提出，我们可以通过引入称之为"中微子"的一类新粒子来保证能量守恒定律。这些中微子没有电荷，只有很小（甚至趋于零）的质量，实际上在所有的实验中都没有观测到它，但很可能就是它带走了 β 衰变多余的能量。但是，这类粒子存在与否目前尚存在争议。

最近，费米尝试在狄拉克相对论波动方程的基础上构建一套 β 衰变的理论，类比原子的光量子发射方式来处理原子核的电子发射。在该理论中，人们接受这种观点，即原子核的一个中子转变成一个质子，伴随产生了一个电子和一个中微子，它们一旦产生就会离开原子核，并将这个转变过程中释放的能量在它们之间分配。对导致这类转变的相互作用，能量采用某个确定值（约为 10^{-14}erg 的量级），费米由此得到了 β 衰变元素合理的衰变常数的值，并与萨金特得到的 β 粒子的衰变常数和最大能量的关系曲线吻合得很好。

然而，费米这套理论的一个有趣的结果是对 β 衰变给出了确定的不相容定则，这个结果是非常普遍的，适用于任何理论，即把电子发射认为是中子转变成质子的结果。按照这一定则，最初的原子核和产生具有不同自旋的那些原子核的 β 衰变过程并不都是允许的，且只能以较小的概率（约为自旋不变的转变概率的百分之一）发生。这立即解释了由萨金特获得的两条不同的曲线正是分别对应于允许转变和不允许转变。伽莫夫已指出，将上述的 β 衰变的不相容定则应用于分析放射族得到了很好的结果，并且允许我们给出放射性核正常态和激发态确定的自旋值。

（沈乃澂 翻译；张焕乔 审稿）

Radioactivity Induced by Neutron Bombardment

E. Fermi

Editor's Note

The impact of neutrons could induce radioactivity in many nuclei, as Enrico Fermi here reports. In experiments, he and colleagues had exposed a number of different elements to a source of neutrons, and found that in almost every case the exposed substances became radioactive. They found particularly strong effects with phosphorus, aluminium, silver, iodine and chromium, and measured half-lives varying from a few seconds to several hours. Fermi notes that it seemed likely nuclei were absorbing neutrons, which later transform into protons with ejection of an electron, thereby returning the nucleus to stability. Although very indirectly, these experiments hinted at the possibility of sustained nuclear reactions.

EXPERIMENTS have been carried out to ascertain whether neutron bombardment can produce an induced radioactivity, giving rise to unstable products which disintegrate with emission of β-particles. Preliminary results have been communicated in a letter to *La Ricerca Scientifica*, **5**, 282; 1934.

The source of neutrons is a sealed glass tube containing radium emanation and beryllium powder. The amount of radium emanation available varied in the different experiments from 30 to 630 millicuries. We are much indebted to Prof. G. C. Trabacchi, Laboratorio Fisico della Sanità Pubblica, for putting at our disposal such strong sources.

The elements, or in some cases compounds containing them, were used in the form of small cylinders. After irradiation with the source for a period which varied from a few minutes to several hours, they were put around a Geiger counter with walls of thin aluminium foil (about 0.2 mm. thickness) and the number of impulses per minute was registered.

So far, we have obtained an effect with the following elements:

Phosphorus—Strong effect. Half-period about 3 hours. The disintegration electrons could be photographed in the Wilson chamber. Chemical separation of the active product showed that the unstable element formed under the bombardment is probably silicon.

Iron—Period about 2 hours. As the result of chemical separation of the active product, this is probably manganese.

276

由中子轰击引发的放射性

费米

编者按

就像恩里科·费米在这篇文章中报道的一样，中子的碰撞会使许多原子核产生放射性。在实验中，他和其合作者们将许多种不同的元素暴露于中子源的辐射之下，发现几乎每一种实验中暴露的材料都会具有放射活性。并且他们在磷、铝、银、碘和铬中观察到了尤为强的效应，并测量得到它们的半衰期在数秒到几个小时之间不等。费米注意到似乎是原子核吸收了中子，并释放了一个电子，进而转变为质子，然后使原子核趋于稳定。这些实验尽管非常间接，但却隐含了持续核反应发生的可能性。

为查明物质在中子的轰击下是否会产生感生放射性的实验已经完成了，该实验产生不稳定的产物，而该产物将继续发生蜕变并放射出 β 粒子。初步的结果发表在 1934 年《科学研究》杂志第 5 卷第 282 页的通讯中。

中子源是一个密封的内含氡和铍粉末的玻璃管，在不同实验中，氡的用量从 30 到 630 毫居里不等。我们非常感谢公共卫生物理实验室的特拉巴基教授，他为我们提供了如此强的中子放射源。

把某些元素或含有这些元素的化合物压制成小的圆柱体形状，用放射源辐照其数分钟到几个小时不等，之后将它们放在以薄铝箔（厚约 0.2 mm）为壁的盖革计数器周围，并记录每分钟的脉冲数。

迄今为止，我们已获得了下列元素在中子轰击下所产生的效应：

磷——强效应。半衰期约 3 小时。由磷物质蜕变放射出的电子可在威尔逊云室中被拍摄到。对放射性产物的化学分离情况显示，在中子的轰击下产生的不稳定元素可能是硅。

铁——半衰期约 2 小时。根据对其放射性产物进行化学分离的结果分析，产生的元素可能是锰。

Silicon—Very strong effect. Period about 3 minutes. Electrons photographed in the Wilson chamber.

Aluminium—Strong effect. Period about 12 minutes. Electrons photographed in the Wilson chamber.

Chlorine—Gives an effect with a period much longer than that of any element investigated at present.

Vanadium—Period about 5 minutes.

Copper—Effect rather small. Period about 6 minutes.

Arsenic—Period about two days.

Silver—Strong effect. Period about 2 minutes.

Tellurium—Period about 1 hour.

Iodine—Intense effect. Period about 30 minutes.

Chromium—Intense effect. Period about 6 minutes. Electrons photographed in the Wilson chamber.

Barium—Small effect. Period about 2 minutes.

Fluorine—Period about 10 seconds.

The following elements have also given indication of an effect: sodium, magnesium, titanium, zirconium, zinc, strontium, antimony, selenium and bromine. Some elements give indication of having two or more periods, which may be partly due to several isotopic constituents and partly to successive radioactive transformations. The experiments are being continued in order to verify these results and to extend the research to other elements.

The nuclear reaction which causes these phenomena may be different in different cases. The chemical separation effected in the cases of iron and phosphorus seems to indicate that, at least in these two cases, the neutron is absorbed and a proton emitted. The unstable product, by the emission of a β-particle, returns to the original element.

硅——非常强的效应。半衰期约 3 分钟。经辐照后产生的电子可在威尔逊云室中被拍摄到。

铝——强效应。半衰期约 12 分钟。经辐照后产生的电子可在威尔逊云室中被拍摄到。

氯——产生效应的周期比目前研究过的任何元素产生效应的周期都要长得多。

钒——半衰期约 5 分钟。

铜——效应很小。半衰期约 6 分钟。

砷——半衰期约 2 天。

银——强效应。半衰期约 2 分钟。

碲——半衰期约 1 小时。

碘——超强效应。半衰期约 30 分钟。

铬——超强效应。半衰期约 6 分钟。产生的电子可在威尔逊云室中被拍摄到。

钡——效应小。半衰期约 2 分钟。

氟——半衰期约 10 秒钟。

下列元素也显示出存在效应的迹象：钠、镁、钛、锆、锌、锶、锑、硒和溴。其中有些元素显示出两个或多个半衰期，这可能是由于某些元素存在多种同位素，也可能是由于某些元素发生了连续的放射性衰变。为了验证以上这些实验结果并将该研究拓展到其他元素，相关实验仍在继续进行中。

由上述实验现象所引起的核反应在不同情况下可能是不同的。铁和磷这两种元素的化学分离效应似乎表明，至少在中子轰击这两种元素时，原子核吸收了中子并放射出一个质子。在中子轰击下产生的不稳定产物通过放射出一个 β 粒子又转变为初始的元素。

The chemical separations have been carried out by Dr. O. D'Agostino. Dr. E. Amaldi and Dr. E. Segrè have collaborated in the physical research.

(**133**, 757; 1934)

Enrico Fermi: Physical Institute, Royal University, Rome, April 10.

化学分离的工作由达戈斯蒂诺博士完成。阿马尔迪博士和塞格雷博士合作进行了物理方面的研究。

（沈乃澂 翻译；夏海鸿 审稿）

X-Ray Photographs of Crystalline Pepsin

Editor's Note

The division of proteins into two structural types—the compact or globular and the extended or fibrous—stems from these papers by J. Desmond Bernal and Dorothy Crowfoot at Cambridge and by William Astbury and R. Lomax at Leeds. Broadly speaking, globular proteins are enzymes, while fibrous proteins are structural, comprising biological tissues. Bernal, like Astbury a protégé of William Bragg, and Crowfoot (later a Nobel laureate for her work on biomolecular crystallography) express doubts here about whether the globular molecules of the enzyme pepsin consist of continuous polypeptide chains, but Astbury and Lomax suggest that the chain is "folded in some neat manner". This principle of protein folding is now central to the relation of structure to function in globular proteins.

FOUR weeks ago, Dr. G. Millikan brought us some crystals of pepsin prepared by Dr. Philpot in the laboratory of Prof. The Svedberg, Uppsala. They are in the form of perfect hexagonal bipyramids up to 2 mm. in length, of axial ratio $c/a=2.3\pm 0.1$. When examined in their mother liquor, they appear moderately birefringent and positively uniaxial, showing a good interference figure. On exposure to air, however, the birefringence rapidly diminishes. X-ray photographs taken of the crystals in the usual way showed nothing but a vague blackening. This indicates complete alteration of the crystal and explains why previous workers have obtained negative results with proteins, so far as crystalline pattern is concerned[1]. W. T. Astbury has, however, shown that the altered pepsin is a protein of the chain type like myosin or keratin giving an amorphous or fibre pattern.

It was clearly necessary to avoid alteration of the crystals, and this was effected by drawing them with their mother liquor and without exposure to air into thin capillary tubes of Lindemann glass. The first photograph taken in this way showed that we were dealing with an unaltered crystal. From oscillation photographs with copper $K\alpha$-radiation, the dimensions of the unit cell were found to be $a=67$ A., $c=154$ A., correct to about 5 percent. This is a minimum value as the spots on the c row lines are too close for accurate measurement and the c axial length is derived from the axial ratio. The dimensions of the cell may still be multiples of this. Using the density measured on fresh material[2] as 1.32 (our measurements gave 1.28), the cell molecular weight is 478,000, which is twelve times 40,000, almost exactly Svedberg's value arrived at by sedimentation in the ultracentrifuge. This agreement may however be quite fortuitous as we have found that the crystals contain about 50 percent of water removable at room temperature. But this would still lead to a large molecular weight, with possibly fewer molecules in the unit cell.

胃蛋白酶晶体的X射线照片

编者按

蛋白质可以划分为两种结构类型——紧实型（或者说球形）和伸展型（或者说纤维状），这种划分来源于剑桥大学的德斯蒙德·贝尔纳和多萝西·克劳福特以及利兹大学的威廉·阿斯特伯里和洛马克斯的这些文章。一般来说，球形的蛋白质是酶，而纤维状的蛋白质是结构性的，用来构成生物组织。与阿斯特伯里（威廉·布拉格的学生）和克劳福特（由于在生物大分子晶体学方面的工作她后来获得了诺贝尔奖）一样，贝尔纳在这里对胃蛋白酶的球状分子是否包含连续多肽链表示了怀疑，阿斯特伯里和洛马克斯则认为链是"以某种巧妙的形式折叠的"。蛋白质折叠的这种原理是当前对球蛋白结构和功能之间关系研究的核心。

四个星期以前，米利肯博士带给我们一些由乌普萨拉的斯韦德贝里教授实验室的菲尔波特博士制备的胃蛋白酶晶体。它们具有完美的六方双锥形状，长度达到2毫米，轴率 $c/a=2.3\pm0.1$。当对处于母液中的晶体进行检测时，它们表现出适度的双折射和明显的单轴性，显示出良好的干涉图像。不过，当晶体被暴露于空气中时，其双折射迅速减弱。用一般方法得到的该晶体的 X 射线照片显示出一片模糊的黑影。这表明晶体彻底改变，从而解释了以前的研究者用蛋白质（仅就晶体形式而言）进行实验却得到阴性结果 [1] 的原因。不过，阿斯特伯里指出，改变后的胃蛋白酶是像肌球蛋白或角蛋白那样的链状蛋白，衍射结果表现出非结晶形的或纤维状的结构特征。

很明显，我们必须避免晶体的改变，而要做到这一点，则需要将其与母液一起提取出来，并在不与空气接触的条件下置于林德曼玻璃毛细管中。以此方法得到的第一张照片表明，我们所处理的是未改变的晶体。通过铜 $K\alpha$ 辐射得到的回摆照相结果表明，单位晶胞的大小为 $a=67Å$，$c=154Å$，准确至约 5%。这是最小值，因为 c 列上的点过于接近而无法精确测量，c 轴的长度是由轴率得到的。晶胞的大小可能仍然是它的倍数。对新制备的样品进行测量 [2] 得到其密度是 1.32（我们的测量结果是 1.28），利用此数值可以计算出晶胞的分子量为 478,000，是 40,000 的 12 倍，与斯韦德贝里用超速离心机通过沉降所得到的数值几乎完全一致。不过这可能是很偶然的，因为我们发现这些晶体中含有约 50% 可在室温下被除去的水。但这可能还会导致分子量更大，因为单位晶胞中可能只有更少的分子。

Not only do these measurements confirm such large molecular weights but they also give considerable information as to the nature of the protein molecules and will certainly give much more when the analysis is pushed further. From the intensity of the spots near the centre, we can infer that the protein molecules are relatively dense globular bodies, perhaps joined together by valency bridges, but in any event separated by relatively large spaces which contain water. From the intensity of the more distant spots, it can be inferred that the arrangement of atoms inside the protein molecule is also of a perfectly definite kind, although without the periodicities characterising the fibrous proteins. The observations are compatible with oblate spheroidal molecules of diameters about 25 A. and 35 A., arranged in hexagonal nets, which are related to each other by a hexagonal screw-axis. With this model we may imagine degeneration to take place by the linking up of amino acid residues in such molecules to form chains as in the ring-chain polymerisation of polyoxy methylenes. Peptide chains in the ordinary sense may exist only in the more highly condensed or fibrous proteins, while the molecules of the primary soluble proteins may have their constituent parts grouped more symmetrically around a prosthetic nucleus.

At this stage, such ideas are merely speculative, but now that a crystalline protein has been made to give X-ray photographs, it is clear that we have the means of checking them and, by examining the structure of all crystalline proteins, arriving at far more detailed conclusions about protein structure than previous physical or chemical methods have been able to give.

J. D. Bernal and D. Crowfoot

(**133**, 794-795; 1934)

*   *   *

It is now some time since we first took X-ray powder photographs of crystalline pepsin kindly sent by Prof. J. H. Northrop, but no really satisfactory interpretation of these photographs presented itself because they show features which we have learnt recently to associate with the fibrous proteins[3]: even single crystals, so far as we could judge with the minute crystals available, appeared to give results similar to those produced by many crystals in random orientation. The two chief rings have spacings of about 11.5 A. and 4.6 A. at ordinary humidity, corresponding to the "side-chain spacing" and the "backbone spacing", respectively, of an extended polypeptide[3].

It was difficult, of course, to reconcile such findings with external morphology and the Law of Rational Indices, but the photographs of Bernal and Miss Crowfoot, taken before the degeneration which we now see the crystals must have undergone on drying, clear up this long-standing problem at once. Furthermore, their photographs tend to confirm the suggestion[4] that the numbers 2, 3, 4, and 6 occurring in Svedberg's multiple particle weights are fundamentally of *crystallographic* significance, even though their conclusions to date appear to be against the chain mechanism proposed for the building-up of the various crystallographic groups[4].

这些测量结果不仅证实了蛋白质分子具有大分子量，而且给出了相当多的关于蛋白质分子性质的信息，在进一步的分析中无疑将会提供更多的信息。通过中心附近点的强度，我们可以推断蛋白质分子是比较密集的球体，也许通过共价桥结合在一起，但不管怎样，都是被相对较大的含水空间隔离开的。通过距离更远的点的强度，可以推断出蛋白质分子中内部原子的排布也是完全确定的（尽管没有纤维蛋白所特有的周期性）。观测结果与直径约为 25 Å 和 35 Å 的排列成六边形网格的扁圆球形分子是一致的，它们通过六方螺旋轴而彼此关联。利用这个模型我们可以想象，通过这种分子中氨基酸残基连接而形成链（就像聚甲醛的环链聚合作用那样），变性就可以发生。通常意义上的多肽链可能只存在于密度更高的蛋白或纤维蛋白中，而原生的可溶性蛋白质分子可能会将它们的重要组成部分更加对称地汇聚在非蛋白质基核周围。

现阶段，这些观点还仅仅是猜测，但既然已经制备出了一种结晶蛋白质并得到了它的 X 射线照片，那么很显然我们有办法来检测它们，并且通过考察所有结晶蛋白质的结构，就可以得到比以前用物理和化学方法所能给出的关于蛋白质结构的结果更为详细的结论。

贝尔纳，克劳福特

*　　*　　*

从我们第一次对诺斯罗普教授惠赠的结晶胃蛋白酶进行 X 射线粉末照相到现在已经有一段时间了，但是对于这些照片的真正令人满意的解释仍没有出现，因为我们最近才了解到照片呈现出的一些特征与纤维蛋白有关 [3]：即使是单晶——就我们根据现有的微小晶体所能做出的判断而言——看起来似乎也能给出类似于由多种随机取向的晶体得到的结果。在一般湿度条件下，两个主环具有约 11.5Å 和 4.6Å 的间距，分别对应于一条伸展的多肽链中的"侧链间距"和"骨架间距" [3]。

当然，要使这些发现与晶体的外观形态以及有理指数定律相一致是很困难的，但是，贝尔纳和克劳福特小姐在蛋白质变性——现在我们知道这是晶体在干燥过程中一定会发生的现象——之前照的照片立刻解决了这一长期存在的问题。此外，他们的照片还倾向于确认如下提议 [4]：出现在斯韦德贝里的多重粒子重量中的数字 2、3、4 和 6 具有重要的晶体学意义，即便目前为止他们的结论看起来似乎违背了针对各种结晶体群的构成而提出的链机制 [4]。

We are left now with the paradox that the pepsin molecule is both globular[5] and also a real, or potential, polypeptide chain system, and the immediate question is whether the chains are formed by metamorphosis and linking-up of the globular molecules, or whether the initial unit is the chain itself, which is afterwards folded in some neat manner which is merely an elaboration of the intra-molecular folding that has been observed in the keratin transformation[3]. What is either an exceedingly valuable clue or else only a fantastic coincidence is found in the fibre photograph of feather keratin[6], a study of which will be published shortly; for if, as Bernal thinks, the pepsin molecules are piled, perhaps in a screw, along the hexad axis, their length in this direction is 140/6, that is, about $23\frac{1}{2}$ A., which is almost exactly the strongest period along the fibre-axis of feather keratin, a period which is again repeated probably six (or a multiple of six) times before the fundamental period is completed! The innermost equatorial spot of the feather photograph also corresponds to a side-spacing of about 33 A. (though this is probably not the maximum side-spacing), which again is in simple relation to the side dimensions of the pepsin unit cell. As just said, these resemblances may be only accidental, but we cannot afford to overlook anything in such a difficult field, and it is not impossible that we have here an indication of how very long, *but periodic*, polypeptide chains can arise by the degeneration and linking-up of originally globular molecules.

W. T. Astbury and R. Lomax

(**133**, 795; 1934)

J. D. Bernal and D. Crowfoot: Department of Mineralogy and Petrology, Cambridge, May 17.

W. T. Astbury and R. Lomax: Textile Physics Laboratory, University of Leeds.

References:

1. G. L. Clark and K. E. Korrigan (*Phys. Rev.*, (ii), **40**, 639; 1932) describe long spacings found from crystalline insulin, but no details have been published.

2. J. H. Northrop, *J. Gen. Physiol.*, **13**, 739; 1930.

3. W. T. Astbury, *Trans. Faraday Soc.*, **29**, 193; 1933. W. T. Astbury and A. Street, *Phil. Trans. Roy. Soc.*, A, **230**, 75; 1931. W. T. Astbury and H. J. Woods, *Nature*, **126**, 913, Dec. 13, 1930. *Phil. Trans. Roy. Soc.*, A, **232**, 333; 1933. W. T. Astbury and W. R. Atkin, *Nature*, **132**, 348, Sept. 2, 1933.

4. W. T. Astbury and H. J. Woods, *Nature*, **127**, 663, May 2, 1931.

5. J. St. L. Philpot and Inga-Britta Eriksson-Quensel, *Nature*, **132**, 932, Dec. 16, 1933.

6. W. T. Astbury and T. C. Marwick, *Nature*, **130**, 309, Aug. 27, 1932.

现在留给我们的是一个悖论，即胃蛋白酶分子既是球形的 [5]，又是一个真正的或者潜在的多肽链体系，并且随之而来的问题是，链是否是由球状分子通过变性以及连接而形成的，或者是否最初单位就是链本身，随后链以某种巧妙的方式进行折叠，其方式不过是对我们在角蛋白的转变中所观测到的分子内折叠的精致化 [3]。羽毛角蛋白的纤维照片中的发现，可能是一条非常有价值的线索，也可能只是某种奇异的一致性 [6]，关于这一点的研究不久将会发表；按照贝尔纳的想法，如果胃蛋白酶分子沿着六次轴堆叠（也许是以螺旋形式），那么它们在这个方向上的长度是 140/6，也就是大约 $23\frac{1}{2}$Å，这几乎恰好就是沿羽毛角蛋白纤维轴的最强周期，该周期可能会重复 6 次（或者 6 的倍数），直到基本周期完成为止！羽毛照片中最靠内的赤道点也对应于大约 33Å 的旁侧间隔（尽管这可能不是最大的旁侧间隔），它与胃蛋白酶单位晶胞的侧向尺度也简单关联。如同刚才所说的，这些类同之处可能只是偶然的，但是在一个如此困难的领域中我们绝不能忽视任何事，而且对于如何通过最初的球状分子的变性以及连接形成非常长的、**但具周期性的**多肽链，我们也可能会从这里获得某种启发。

阿斯特伯里，洛马克斯

（王耀杨 翻译；周筠梅 审稿）

Production of Large Quantities of Heavy Water

L. Tronstad

Editor's Note

Nature had recently reported on the establishment of a British plant for the manufacture of heavy water. Here Leif Tronstad of the Institute of Inorganic Chemistry in Norway tells of a similar project already undertaken by the Norwegians. Large quantities of heavy water were being produced from a facility run by Norsk Hydro near Rjukan in the Telemark region. In principle, this facility could produce up to 10 litres of heavy water in a single day, if this came to be demanded by increasing research activity in physics, chemistry and biology. The plant was sabotaged by the Norwegian resistance during the Second World War to prevent heavy water being used to develop a German atomic bomb.

FROM the discussion recently held in the Royal Society[1], and from several communications on heavy hydrogen published in *Nature*, it is obvious that larger quantities of heavy water are at present much needed for investigations in several branches of physics, chemistry and biology. To meet this demand, Imperial Chemical Industries, Ltd., is to undertake commercial production at Billingham[2]. It may also be of interest to report in this connexion, that various concentrates of the new water are now produced on a large scale in Norway by Norsk Hydro-Elektrisk Kvaelstofaktieselskab, Oslo. Large quantities of "1:300-water" can be obtained from the above company, and richer concentrates will be available at a later date.

This company at its works in Rjukan has one of the largest electrolytic hydrogen plants of the world, with a capacity of about 20,000 m.[3] per hour. Assuming the efficiency of separation by electrolysis so low as 10 percent[3], a quantity of about 10 litres of "pure" heavy water a day can be produced if the consumption requires.

In full agreement with other investigators, it has been found that the efficiency is only slightly affected by the conditions of the electrolysis[1,4]. However, certain difficulties arose using sulphuric acid with lead electrodes, due to the formation of porous lead on the cathodes and to the formation of fog. The efficiency of separation in both acid and alkaline solution agree fairly well with that found, for example, by Harteck[5]. Further details of the experimental results are to be published shortly in the *Zeitschrift für Elektrochemie*.

(**133**, 872; 1934)

Leif Tronstad: Institute of Inorganic Chemistry, Norwegian Technical High School, Trondhjem, Norway, May, 4.

重水的大量生产

特龙斯塔

编者按

《自然》最近对一个生产重水的英国工厂进行了报道。这篇文章中挪威无机化学研究所的莱夫·特龙斯塔指出，由挪威人承担的一个类似的项目已经启动了。大量的重水正在由泰勒马克行政区留坎附近挪威海德鲁公司运营的装置生产出来。原则上，这一装置每天可以生产多达 10 升的重水，以满足日益增长的物理学、化学和生物学研究的需求。这一工厂在第二次世界大战期间曾被挪威抵抗组织破坏，以防止重水被德国用来研制原子弹。

根据皇家学会近期举办的有关重氢的讨论会 [1] 以及在《自然》上发表的几篇关于重氢的通讯，我们可以明显地感觉到，目前在物理学、化学和生物学若干分支的科学研究中对重水有很大的需求。为了满足这种需求，帝国化学工业有限公司在比林罕进行了商业化生产 [2]。目前挪威奥斯陆的挪威水电氮气有限公司（即现在的挪威海德鲁公司）大规模生产各种新水的浓缩物，对此进行报道也有可能引起人们的兴趣。从上述公司可以得到大量的"1:300 的水"，今后将可以获得浓度更高的浓缩物。

这家公司在留坎的制造厂拥有一个全球最大的电解氢工厂，其产量约为每小时 20,000 立方米。假定通过电解分离的效率只有 10%[3]，如果有消费需求，每天大约可以生产 10 升"纯净的"重水。

已经发现电解条件对其效率仅有轻微的影响 [1,4]，这与其他研究者的结果完全一致。然而，由于会形成雾气以及在阴极上会形成多孔铅，在硫酸与铅电极一起使用的过程中出现了某些困难。正如哈特克 [5] 的发现，酸溶液和碱溶液两者的分离效率与上述发现非常一致。对实验结果更加详细的说明将于近期发表在《电化学杂志》上。

（沈乃澂 翻译；李芝芬 审稿）

References:

1. *Proc. Roy. Soc.*, A, **144**, 1; 1934.

2. *Nature*, **133**, 604, April 21, 1934.

3. Taylor, Eyring and Frost, *J. Chem. Phys.*, **1**, 823; (1933).

4. Compare, for example, Topley and Eyring, *Nature*, **133**, 292, Feb. 24, 1934. Bell and Wolfenden, *ibid.*, p.25.

5. Harteck, *Proc. Roy. Soc.*, loc. cit. and *Proc. Phys. Soc.*, **40**, 277; 1934.

Possible Production of Elements of Atomic Number Higher than 92

E. Fermi

Editor's Note

Physicists bombarding matter with charged particles had for the most part achieved induced radioactivity only with fairly light elements, because it was hard to reach the energies required to achieve an effect with heavier elements. But as Fermi here points out, this limitation did not apply to neutrons, which he had recently shown could induce radioactivity in a wide range of elements. Fermi describes new experiments with heavy elements, especially uranium. The resulting radiation showed half-lives from 10 seconds up to around 40 minutes. Experiments had ruled out the formation of isotopes of uranium, palladium, thorium, actinium, radium, bismuth and lead. The resulting radioactive isotope apparently had atomic number higher than 92, the maximum then known for any element.

UNTIL recently it was generally admitted that an atom resulting from artificial disintegration should normally correspond to a stable isotope. M. and Mme. Joliot first found evidence that it is not necessarily so; in some cases the product atom may be radioactive with a measurable mean life, and go over to a stable form only after emission of a positron.

The number of elements which can be activated either by the impact of an α-particle (Joliot) or a proton (Cockcroft, Gilbert, Walton) or a deuton (Crane, Lauritsen, Henderson, Livingston, Lawrence) is necessarily limited by the fact that only light elements can be disintegrated, owing to the Coulomb repulsion.

This limitation is not effective in the case of neutron bombardment. The high efficiency of these particles in producing disintegrations compensates fairly for the weakness of available neutron sources as compared with α-particle or proton sources. As a matter of fact, it has been shown[1] that a large number of elements (47 out of 68 examined until now) of any atomic weight could be activated, using neutron sources consisting of a small glass tube filled with beryllium powder and radon up to 800 millicuries. This source gives a yield of about one million neutrons per second.

All the elements activated by this method with intensity large enough for a magnetic analysis of the sign of the charge of the emitted particles were found to give out only negative electrons. This is theoretically understandable, as the absorption of the bombarding neutron produces an excess in the number of neutrons present inside the nucleus; a stable state is therefore reached generally through transformation of a neutron

原子序数大于92的元素的可能生成

费米

编者按

物理学家使用带电粒子对物质进行轰击，大部分情况下会产生感生放射性，而这仅仅是对于轻元素而言的，因为很难获得足以对重元素产生效应的能量。但费米在这篇文章中指出，使用中子进行轰击时不受此限制，他最近的研究表明中子可以使更大范围内的元素产生感生放射性。费米在本文中描述了关于重元素尤其是铀的新实验。得到的放射性元素的半衰期从10秒至40分钟左右不等。该实验排除了产生铀、镤、钍、锕、镭、铋和铅的同位素的可能。得到的放射性同位素的原子序数明显大于92，这是当时已知的最大的原子序数。

人工嬗变得到的原子总是对应于一个稳定同位素，这一观点直到现在仍被广泛认可。但是约里奥夫妇首次通过实验结果证实事实并不完全是这样；在某些情况下，产生的原子具有放射性并具有可测量的平均寿命，且只有在放射出一个正电子之后它才达到稳定的状态。

由于库仑斥力的存在，只有轻元素可以发生嬗变，因此不论是用 α 粒子(约里奥)、质子（考克饶夫、吉尔伯特、瓦耳顿）还是用氘（克兰、劳里森、亨德森、利文斯通、劳伦斯）来轰击，可以被活化的元素的数目都必然要受到上述事实的限制。

但是在用中子轰击的情况下，这样的限制就失效了。中子引发蜕变的高效性完全弥补了中子源相对 α 粒子源或质子源较弱的缺点。事实上，不论原子量的大小，许多元素（截至目前试验过的 68 种元素中的 47 种）都可以被一个由铍粉和辐射剂量为 800 毫居里的氡填充的小玻璃管构成的中子源所活化[1]。这个中子源每秒释放出大约一百万个中子。

用这种方法活化的元素，其放射性强度强到足以通过磁学手段去分析放射出的粒子所携带的电荷符号，我们通过观察发现这些元素只能放出负电性的电子。这一点在理论上是可以理解的，由于轰击的中子被吸收而使核内的中子数增加；而只有当一个中子转变为一个质子时，体系才会达到稳定态，这个过程还会相应地放射出一个 β

into a proton, which is connected to the emission of a β-particle.

In several cases it was possible to carry out a chemical separation of the β-active element, following the usual technique of adding to the irradiated substance small amounts of the neighbouring elements. These elements are then separated by chemical analysis and separately checked for the β-activity with a Geiger-Müller counter. The activity always followed completely a certain element, with which the active element could thus be identified.

In three cases (aluminium, chlorine, cobalt) the active element formed by bombarding the element of atomic number Z has atomic number $Z-2$. In four cases (phosphorus, sulphur, iron, zinc) the atomic number of the active product is $Z-1$. In two cases (bromine, iodine) the active element is an isotope of the bombarded element.

This evidence seems to show that three main processes are possible: (a) capture of a neutron with instantaneous emission of an α-particle; (b) capture of the neutron with emission of a proton; (c) capture of the neutron with emission of a γ-quantum, to get rid of the surplus energy. From a theoretical point of view, the probability of processes (a) and (b) depends very largely on the energy of the emitted α- or H-particle; the more so the higher the atomic weight of the element. The probability of process (c) can be evaluated only very roughly in the present state of nuclear theory; nevertheless, it would appear to be smaller than the observed value by a factor 100 or 1,000.

It seemed worth while to direct particular attention to the heavy radioactive elements thorium and uranium, as the general instability of nuclei in this range of atomic weight might give rise to successive transformations. For this reason an investigation of these elements was undertaken by the writer in collaboration with F. Rasetti and O. D'Agostino.

Experiment showed that both elements, previously freed of ordinary active impurities, can be strongly activated by neutron bombardment. The initial induced activity corresponded in our experiments to about 1,000 impulses per minute in a Geiger counter made of aluminium foil of 0.2 mm. thickness. The curves of decay of these activities show that the phenomenon is rather complex. A rough survey of thorium activity showed in this element at least two periods.

Better investigated is the case of uranium; the existence of periods of about 10 sec., 40 sec., 13 min., plus at least two more periods from 40 minutes to one day is well established. The large uncertainty in the decay curves due to the statistical fluctuations makes it very difficult to establish whether these periods represent successive or alternative processes of disintegration.

Attempts have been made to identify chemically the β-active element with the period of 13 min. The general scheme of this research consisted in adding to the irradiated

粒子。

在某些情况下，利用通常采用的加入少量相邻元素的技术，可以对具有 β 放射性的元素进行化学分离。然后通过化学分析的手段将这些元素分离，并用盖革－米勒计数器分别检验它们的 β 放射性。这种放射性通常伴随着一个完全确定的元素，通过这个元素可以确定具有放射性的元素。

在三种情况下（铝、氯、钴），轰击原子序数为 Z 的元素会形成原子序数为 Z–2 的放射性元素。在四种情况下（磷、硫、铁、锌），放射性产物的原子序数为 Z–1。在两种情况下（溴、碘），产生的放射性元素是被轰击元素的一种同位素。

上述证据似乎表明，可能有三种主要过程：(a) 俘获一个中子，即时放出一个 α 粒子；(b) 俘获一个中子，放出一个质子；(c) 俘获一个中子，放出一个 γ 量子，以带走过剩的能量。从理论上讲，过程 (a) 和 (b) 发生的概率主要依赖于放出的 α 粒子或 H 粒子的能量；元素的原子量越大，依赖程度越强。根据目前的核理论，我们只能对过程 (c) 发生的概率做出很粗略的估计；然而，这个估计值比观测值小 100 或 1,000 倍。

对于放射性重元素钍和铀给予特别的关注似乎是必要的，因为在这个原子量的范围内，原子核普遍的不稳定性会引发一系列的元素间的变换。基于这个原因，笔者与拉塞蒂和达戈斯蒂诺合作对这些元素进行了相关研究。

实验表明，在除去常见的放射性杂质之后，这两种元素都可以在中子轰击下被强烈活化。在我们实验中，使用盖革计数器对初始阶段感生放射性的强度的测量结果为每分钟约 1,000 个脉冲，这个计数器用 0.2 毫米厚的铝箔制得。这种放射性的衰减曲线表明这种现象是相当复杂的。对钍元素放射性的粗略观测表明，在这个元素的感生放射性的衰减过程中至少有两个周期。

铀得到了更好的研究；已经确定存在的周期包括 10 秒、40 秒和 13 分钟，还包括介于 40 分钟到 1 天之间的至少两个以上的周期。统计涨落导致衰减曲线具有很大的不确定性，这使得人们难以确定这些周期是代表链式反应的衰变过程还是代表并行反应的衰变过程。

我们尝试对周期为 13 分钟的 β 放射性元素进行化学识别。这项研究的总体方案是向被辐照的物质（除去了衰变产物的硝酸铀的浓溶液）中加入一定量的普通 β 放

substance (uranium nitrate in concentrated solution, purified of its decay products) such an amount of an ordinary β-active element as to give some hundred impulses per minute on the counter. Should it be possible to prove that the induced activity, recognisable by its characteristic period, can be chemically separated from the added activity, it is reasonable to assume that the two activities are not due to isotopes.

The following reaction enables one to separate the 13 min.-product from most of the heaviest elements. The irradiated uranium solution is diluted in 50 percent nitric acid; a small amount of a manganese salt is added and then the manganese is precipitated as dioxide (MnO_2) from the boiling solution by addition of sodium chlorate. The manganese dioxide precipitate carries a large percentage of the activity.

This reaction proves at once that the 13 min.-activity is not isotopic with uranium. For testing the possibility that it might be due to an element 90 (thorium) or 91 (palladium), we repeated the reaction at least ten times, adding an amount of uranium X_1+X_2 corresponding to about 2,000 impulses per minute; also some cerium and lanthanum were added in order to sustain uranium X. In these conditions the manganese reaction carried only the 13 min.-activity; no trace of the 2,000 impulses of uranium X_1 (period 24 days) was found in the precipitate; and none of uranium X_2, although the operation had been performed in less than two minutes from the precipitation of the manganese dioxide, so that several hundreds of impulses of uranium X_2 (period 75 sec.) would have been easily recognisable.

Similar evidence was obtained for excluding atomic numbers 88 (radium) and 89 (actinium). For this, mesothorium-1 and -2 were used, adding barium and lanthanum; the evidence was completely negative, as in the former case. The eventual precipitation of uranium-X_1 and mesothorium-1, which do not emit β-rays penetrating enough to be detectable in our counters, would have been revealed by the subsequent formation respectively of uranium-X_2 and mesothorium-2.

Lastly, we added to the irradiated uranium solution some inactive lead and bismuth, and proved that the conditions of the manganese dioxide reaction could be regulated in such a way as to obtain the precipitation of manganese dioxide with the 13 min.-activity, without carrying down lead and bismuth.

In this way it appears that we have excluded the possibility that the 13 min.-activity is due to isotopes of uranium (92), palladium (91), thorium (90), actinium (89), radium (88), bismuth (83), lead (82). Its behaviour excludes also ekacaesium (87) and emanation (86).

This negative evidence about the identity of the 13 min.-activity from a large number of heavy elements suggests the possibility that the atomic number of the element may be greater than 92. If it were an element 93, it would be chemically homologous with manganese and rhenium. This hypothesis is supported to some extent also by the observed fact that the 13 min.-activity is carried down by a precipitate of rhenium sulphide

射性元素，使得它们在计数器中给出每分钟几百个脉冲的计数。通过其特征周期可以对感生放射性成分进行辨认，而如果感生放射性成分可以与加入的放射性成分进行化学分离的话，那么就可以合理地认定这两类放射性并不是源于多种同位素。

下面的反应能使我们能够将周期为 13 分钟的产物与大多数最重的元素分离开。将被辐照的铀溶液用 50% 的硝酸稀释；加入少量的锰盐，在沸腾的溶液中加入氯酸钠使锰以二氧化物（二氧化锰）的形式沉淀出来。二氧化锰沉淀物携带了大部分的放射性。

这个反应同时也证明了周期为 13 分钟的放射性物质不是铀的同位素。为了验证该放射性是否来源于 90 号元素（钍）或 91 号元素（镤），我们至少重复了 10 次这个反应，加上适量的铀-X_1 和铀-X_2，它们的放射性强度相当于每分钟约 2,000 个脉冲；为了稳定住铀-X 还加入了一些铈和镧。在这样的条件下，锰的反应只会携带周期为 13 分钟的放射性；尽管我们将测量过程控制在二氧化锰沉淀产生后 2 分钟之内完成，因为这样的条件下源自铀-X_2（周期 75 秒）的几百个脉冲应该是很容易检测到的，但我们在沉淀物中没有追踪到源自铀-X_1（周期 24 天）的 2,000 个脉冲，也没有发现铀-X_2 的脉冲。

利用类似的证据我们排除了原子序数为 88（镭）和 89（锕）的元素的可能性。在实验中，我们使用了新钍-1 和新钍-2，并加入了钡和镧；与前述情况类似，证据完全是否定性的。铀-X_1 和新钍-1 的最终沉淀物原被解释为分别生成了铀-X_2 和新钍-2，但实验中我们的计数器并未探测到 β 射线。

最后，我们向经辐照的铀溶液加入一些非放射性的铅和铋，这证明了二氧化锰沉淀反应的条件可以通过这种方法进行调整，从而得到具有周期为 13 分钟的放射性二氧化锰沉淀，且不含有铅和铋。

通过这样的方法，我们已排除了周期为 13 分钟的放射性是源于铀的同位素（92）、镤（91）、钍（90）、锕（89）、镭（88）、铋（83）和铅（82）的可能性，其行为也排除了钫（87）和氡（86）的可能性。

周期为 13 分钟的放射性可能来自一系列重元素的否定性证据，为我们指出了另一种可能性，即该放射性元素的原子序数可能大于 92。如果它是 93 号元素，那么它将与锰和铼同族。这个假设在某种程度上得到了以下观测事实的支持，即周期为

insoluble in hydrochloric acid. However, as several elements are easily precipitated in this form, this evidence cannot be considered as very strong.

The possibility of an atomic number 94 or 95 is not easy to distinguish from the former, as the chemical properties are probably rather similar. Valuable information on the processes involved could be gathered by an investigation of the possible emission of heavy particles. A careful search for such heavy particles has not yet been carried out, as they require for their observation that the active product should be in the form of a very thin layer. It seems therefore at present premature to form any definite hypothesis on the chain of disintegrations involved.

(**133**, 898-899; 1934)

E. Fermi: Royal University of Rome.

_____

Reference:
1. E. Fermi, _Ricerca Scientifica_, 1, 5, 283; 6, 330. _Nature_, 133, 757, May 19, 1934. E. Amaldi, O. D'Agostino, E. Fermi, F. Rasetti, E. Segrè, _Ricerca Scientifica_, **8**, 452; 1934.

13 分钟的放射性可以随不溶于盐酸的硫化铼沉淀而出。然而，由于还有其他一些元素也很容易以这种形式产生沉淀，因此，我们不能认定其为一种强有力的证据。

该元素原子序数为 94 或 95 的可能性很难与前述可能性相区分，因为它们的化学性质可能相当类似。此过程中包含的有价值的信息可以通过研究可能存在的重粒子发射行为而获得。不过对这类重粒子的仔细探索尚未展开，因为它们需要在薄层形式的放射性产物中进行观测。因此在目前情况下，我们还不能对所涉及的衰变链做出任何确定的假设。

（沈乃澂 翻译；朱永生 审稿）

The Factor $\frac{137}{136}$ in Quantum Theory

A. S. Eddington

Editor's Note

Arthur Eddington developed speculative theories to account for the values of the fine structure constant (which determines the strength of electrical forces) and the mass ratio of the proton to electron. In his theory these values were exactly 1/137 and 1847.6, in good agreement with experiments. But the measured ratio of electron charge to mass was slightly smaller than predicted, by a factor of more or less precisely 136/137. Here Eddington tries to explain how this extra factor might arise from the indistinguishability of electrons, which could cause overestimation of the electron mass by a factor of 137/136. Eddington's speculations did not stand the test of time, but reflected a preoccupation with finding simplicities among the known fundamental constants.

IT has been suggested by W. N. Bond[1] that, in some or all of the attempts to determine e/m experimentally, the quantity actually found is $\frac{136}{137}e/m$; for if the experimental results are corrected in accordance with this hypothesis, they are found to be in satisfactory accordance with my theoretical values of the fine-structure constant (137) and mass-ratio (1847.6). R. T. Birge[2] has confirmed this; and, quoting three important recent determinations of e/m, he has shown that the agreement is extremely close.

On theoretical grounds it seems likely that Bond's hypothesis is right. In my earliest paper on the subject[3], I gave the value of the fine-structure constant as 136, since I found the Coulomb energy of two elementary particles to be $1/136r$ in natural quantum units. This energy was $\frac{137}{136}$ times too large, because I had not allowed for the 137th degree of freedom arising from the indistinguishability of the particles. Bond's hypothesis implies that I am not the only victim of this mistake; current quantum theory in deriving from observational data the proper-energy or mass m of an electron has also obtained an energy $\frac{137}{136}$ times too large. If so, the cause is presumably the same, namely, neglect to take into account the degree of freedom due to indistinguishability.

There is nothing mystical in the effect of indistinguishability. It occasions, not an objective difference of behaviour, but a difference in what we can ascertain about the behaviour, and hence a difference of treatment. In the dynamics of two particles, we have to describe the change with time of the positions, momenta and spin-components (or of a probability distribution of them) of the particles which we call No.1 and No. 2; and also we have to describe a growing uncertainty whether the particle, called No.1 at the time t, is the original No.1. If the probability that it is the original No.1 is $\cos^2\theta$ (so that the probability

量子理论中的137/136因子

爱丁顿

编者按

阿瑟·爱丁顿发展了一套推测性的理论，用来说明精细结构常数（其决定了电场力的强度）以及质子与电子的质量比的重要性。在爱丁顿的理论中，以上两个值与实验结果很好地吻合，分别严格等于1/137和1847.6。但测量得到的电子荷质比略小于理论预期值，相差了大约136/137这个因子。本文中爱丁顿试图用电子的不可分辨性来解释这个多出来的因子，正是电子的不可分辨性导致估算得到的电子质量是实值的137/136倍。爱丁顿的假设虽然没有经得住时间的考验，但这反映出他当时专注于在已知的基本常数中寻求简单性。

邦德[1]提出，在某些或者说全部试图测定荷质比e/m值的实验中得到的结果都是真实的荷质比e/m值的$\frac{136}{137}$；如果实验结果按此假设进行修正，则其与我从理论计算得到的精细结构常数（137）以及质子与电子的质量比（1847.6）的值是完全吻合的。伯奇[2]已经证实了这个结论；他引用了三次最近对荷质比e/m的重要测量，表明这些结果都是非常一致的。

在理论计算的基础上，邦德的假设看起来似乎是正确的。我在关于这方面研究的早期文章中[3]给出了精细结构常数的值为136，因为我发现两个基本粒子的库仑能量可以用自然量子单位表示成$1/136r$。事实上，我所得到的这个能量值相对而言远大于真实的结果，是真实值的$\frac{137}{136}$倍，原因是我没有考虑与粒子的不可分辨性相对应的第137个自由度。邦德的假设表明，我并不是这个错误的唯一受害者；目前的量子理论从观测数据得到电子的固有能量或质量m的结果表明，观测得到的结果也远大于真实值，是真实值的$\frac{137}{136}$倍。如果事实确实如此，则原因估计是相同的，即都没有考虑到与粒子的不可分辨性相对应的自由度。

粒子的不可分辨性本身并没有什么神秘之处。它不会使粒子的行为出现客观本质上的变化，而是引起了我们对粒子行为的主观推断的变化，进而使我们的处理方式有所不同。处理两个粒子的动力学行为时，我们必须给出这两个粒子的位置、动量和自旋分量随时间变化的情况（或者这些量的概率分布），我们把这两个粒子命名为1号粒子和2号粒子；另外，我们还必须考虑t时刻的1号粒子是否仍为原来的1号粒子这种不确定性的增长。如果t时刻的1号粒子是原来的1号粒子的概率是

that it is the original No. 2 is sin²θ) the permutation variable θ will be a function of the time and have all the properties of a dynamical variable, giving therefore an extra degree of freedom of the system and having a momentum (energy of interchange) associated with it. When, however, the particles are distinguished without uncertainty, θ is constrained to be zero, and this degree of freedom is lost.

Thus for the treatment of two indistinguishable particles, we have to start with an a priori probability distributed over a closed domain of 137 dimensions, whereas for two distinguishable particles it is distributed over a closed domain of 136 dimensions. Naturally, the average values of characteristics of the distribution are slightly different in the two treatments. In particular, the energy tensor of the a priori probability distribution, which is identical with the metrical tensor $g_{\mu\nu}$ of macroscopic theory, is different. Hence *the two kinds of treatment are associated with different metrics of space-time*. It seems clear that a factor $\frac{137}{136}$ (neglected in current quantum theory) will be introduced by the change of metric when we equate the space occupied by the indistinguishable particles of quantum theory to the space occupied by the distinguishable parts of our measuring apparatus.

It may be asked: Why does this factor affect the mass of the electron but not that of the proton? The discrimination is, I think, not strictly between the proton and electron, but between the resultant mass $(M + m)$ which is nearly the mass of a proton, and the reduced mass of the relative motion $Mm/(M + m)$ which is nearly the mass of an electron; for it is in the relative motion that the question of distinguishing the two ends of the relation arises. It may also be asked why the factor $\frac{137}{136}$, which refers especially to a system of two particles, applies irrespective of the number of particles. The answer is that the metrical ideas of quantum theory are borrowed from those of relativity theory; and since the latter are based on the interval between two points, the former refer correspondingly to the wave function of two particles.

(**133**, 907; 1934)

A. S. Eddington: Observatory, Cambridge, June 5.

References:

1. W. N. Bond, *Nature*, **133**, 327, March 3, 1934.

2. R.T. Birge, *Nature*, **133**, 648, April 28, 1934.

3. A. S. Eddington, *Proc. Roy. Soc.*, A, **122**, 358; 1929.

cos²θ（因而是原来的 2 号粒子的概率便是 sin²θ)，则置换变量 θ 将是时间的函数，并具有力学量的所有性质，因此系统多了一个与动量（能量交换）相关的自由度。然而，如果不考虑不确定性，即粒子可分辨时，θ 值就只能为零，系统就没有这类自由度了。

因此，在处理两个不可分辨的粒子时，我们在 137 维的闭域内利用先验的概率分布来处理问题；而对于两个可分辨的粒子的情况，则以 136 维的闭域内先验的概率分布为出发点。自然地，两类处理情况下的概率分布的平均特征值稍有差别。尤其是与宏观理论的度规张量 $g_{\mu\nu}$ 等价的先验概率分布的能量张量在这两种情况下是不同的。因此，**两类处理是与时空的两个不同度规相关的**。似乎很明显可见，当我们将量子理论中由不可分辨的粒子所占据的空间与由测量装置中可分辨的粒子所组成的空间视为等同时，由于两个空间度规的不同将引入 $\frac{137}{136}$ 这个因子（在目前的量子理论中是忽略该因子的）。

可能有人会问：为何这个因子会影响电子的质量，而不影响质子的质量？我认为以上的两种质量并不是严格的质子和电子的质量，而是合成质量 $(M+m)$ 与相对运动的约化质量 $Mm/(M+m)$，前者几乎是质子的质量，而后者几乎是电子的质量；正是由于考虑了相对运动，使得我们在辨别质量关系的两种极限时出现了问题。也许有人还会问，为何从两个粒子所组成的系统这一特殊情况中推出的因子 $\frac{137}{136}$ 也适用于其他系统，而与组成系统的粒子数无关。原因是量子理论中度规的想法是借用相对论中度规的概念而来的；后者是基于两点之间的间隔，而前者与两个粒子的波函数有关。

(沈乃澂 翻译；李军刚 审稿)

Exchange Forces between Neutrons and Protons, and Fermi's Theory

Ig. Tamm

Editor's Note

Soviet physicist Igor Tamm, a pioneer in nuclear science and future Nobel laureate, here comments on Enrico Fermi's recent theory of beta radioactivity, which assumes that protons and neutrons can be transmuted into one another while emitting or absorbing electrons, positrons and neutrinos. As Tamm argues, Fermi's scheme suggests that the force binding nuclei might be an "exchange force" between nuclear particles, originating in the exchange of light particles in direct analogy to the photon-exchange process mediating the electromagnetic force. But a simple estimate of the magnitude of such a force yields a value that is far too small. Tamm's result implied that physicists were still seeking another fundamental force, which would later became known as the nuclear strong force.

FERMI[1] has recently developed a successful theory of β-radioactivity, based on the assumption that transmutations of a neutron into a proton and vice versa are possible and are accompanied by the birth or disappearance of an electron and a neutrino.

This theory implies the possibility of deducing the exchange forces between neutrons and protons, introduced more or less phenomenologically by Heisenberg. (This idea occurred also quite independently to my friend, D. Iwanenko, with whom I have since had the opportunity of discussing the question.) Consider two heavy particles a and b, a being in a neutron and b in a proton state. If a becomes a proton and b a neutron the energy remains unchanged. Now these two degenerate states of the system may be linked up by a two-step process: the emission of an electron and a neutrino by the neutron a which becomes a proton, and the ensuing re-absorption of these light particles by the proton b which becomes a neutron. The energy of the system will be in general not conserved in the intermediate state (compare the theory of dispersion). The emission and re-absorption of a positron and neutrino may also take place[2]. In this way the two degenerate states of the system considered are split into two energy states, differing by the sign of the exchange energy.

Since the rôle of the light particles (ψ-field) providing an interaction between heavy particles corresponds exactly to the rôle of the photons (electromagnetic field), providing an interaction between electrons, we may adapt for our purposes the methods used in quantum electrodynamics to deduce the expression for Coulomb forces.

Putting $\psi = \psi_0 + g\psi_1 + g^2\psi_2 + \ldots$, where g is the Fermi constant ($\sim 4 \times 10^{-50}$ erg. cm.[3]),

质子中子之间的交换力与费米理论

塔姆

编者按

苏联物理学家伊戈尔·塔姆是核科学界的先驱，并在之后获得了诺贝尔奖，这篇文章中他评论了恩里科·费米新近的β衰变理论，费米假定质子和中子可以相互转化，并在此过程中放出或者吸收电子、正电子和中微子。事实正如塔姆所质疑的那样，费米的理论方案表明束缚原子核的作用力可能是一种原子核粒子间的"交换作用"，这一想法源于对电磁相互作用中以光子交换过程为媒介的交换的直接类比，但是对于这种相互作用大小的粗略估算得到数值过小。塔姆的结果表明物理学家仍在寻找另一种基本相互作用，而这种相互作用后来被称为强相互作用。

最近，费米 [1] 成功地发展了一套关于β衰变的理论。这个理论基于这样的假设：中子转变为质子或质子转变为中子都是有可能的，并且在此过程中伴随着一个电子和一个中微子的产生或消失。

这一理论意味着推导出质子和中子之间的交换力是有可能的，交换力这一概念在某种程度上是由海森堡唯象地引入的。（这个概念也曾独立地出现在我的朋友伊万年科的脑海中，我曾有机会和他讨论过这个问题。）设有两个重粒子 a 和 b，a 处于中子态，b 处于质子态。如果 a 变成一个质子，而 b 变成一个中子，系统能量保持不变。这样，系统的这两个简并态就可以通过以下两个步骤联系起来：首先，中子 a 放出一个电子和一个中微子，变成一个质子；其次，质子 b 再吸收这些轻粒子，变成一个中子。整个系统的能量在中间态（与色散理论相比）并不守恒。正电子和中微子的发射和再吸收同样也有可能发生 [2]，因此以这种方法所考虑的系统的两个简并态就劈裂成交换能符号不同的两个能态。

由于轻粒子（ψ 场）在重粒子相互作用中所扮演的角色与光子（电磁场）在电子相互作用中所扮演的角色非常类似，所以，我们可以采取量子电动力学中推导库仑力表达式的方法来研究我们的问题。

设 $\psi = \psi_0 + g\psi_1 + g^2\psi_2 + \cdots$，其中 g 为费米常数（$\sim 4 \times 10^{-50}$ 尔格·立方厘米），

and using the theory of perturbations and retaining only that part of ψ which corresponds to the absence of light particles in the initial and final states, we obtain

$$\left(H_0 - i\hbar\frac{\partial}{\partial t}\right)\psi_2 \sim \left(K \mp \frac{1}{16\pi^3\,\hbar\,cr^5}I(r)\right)\psi_0,$$

where K is an infinite constant, r is the distance between a and b and $I(r)$ is a decreasing function of r, which is equal to 1 when $r \ll \hbar/mc$ (m is the mass of the electron). Neglecting K, one would obtain the same result if one introduced directly in the wave equation of the heavy particles an exchange energy $A\,(r)$:

$$A(r) = \pm\frac{g^2}{16\pi^3\,\hbar\,cr^5}I(r),$$

the sign of $A(r)$ depending on the symmetry of ψ in respect to a and b. Introducing the values of $\hbar$, c and g, we obtain

$$\left|A(r)\right| \ll 10^{-85}r^{-5}\ \mathrm{erg.}$$

Thus $A(r)$ is far too small to account for the known interaction of neutrons and protons at distances of the order of $r \sim 10^{-13}$ cm.

If the difference of masses of the neutron and of the proton is larger than the sum of the masses of an electron and a neutrino, the emission of light particles by a heavy particle may take place without violation of the conservation of energy. But again the corresponding value of the exchange energy may be shown to be far too small

$$\left|A(r)\right| < g\left(\frac{mc}{\hbar}\right)^3 \sim 10^{-18}\ \mathrm{erg.}$$

Our negative result indicates that either the Fermi theory needs substantial modification (no simple one seems to alter the results materially), or that the origin of the forces between neutrons and protons does not lie, as would appear from the original suggestion of Heisenberg, in their transmutations, considered in detail by Fermi.

(**133**, 981; 1934)

Ig. Tamm: Physical Research Institute, State University, Moscow.

References:

1. Fermi, *Z. Phys.*, **88**, 161; 1934.

2. Wick, *Rend. R. Nat. Acad. Lincei*, **19**, 319; 1934.

用微扰理论，且只保留初末态中与轻粒子的缺失有关的那部分 ψ，可以得到：

$$\left(H_0 - i\hbar\frac{\partial}{\partial t}\right)\psi_2 \sim \left(K \mp \frac{1}{16\pi^3}\frac{1}{\hbar cr^5}I(r)\right)\psi_0,$$

其中，K 是一个无限大的常数，r 表示 a 和 b 之间的距离，$I(r)$ 是 r 的单调下降函数，当 $r \ll \hbar/mc$ 时，$I(r)$ 等于 1（m 是电子的质量）。不考虑常数 K，如果将交换能 $A(r)$ 直接引入重粒子的波动方程，我们将会得到相同的结果。$A(r)$ 的表达式为：

$$A(r) = \pm\frac{g^2}{16\pi^3}\frac{1}{\hbar cr^5}I(r)$$

$A(r)$ 的符号取决于由 a 和 b 决定的 ψ 的对称性。将 $\hbar$、c 和 g 的值代入上式，我们得到：

$$|A(r)| \ll 10^{-85}r^{-5} \text{ 尔格}$$

因此，如果中子和质子的距离 $r \sim 10^{-13}$ 厘米量级，那么 $A(r)$ 的值就太小了，以致于无法解释中子和质子之间已知的相互作用。

如果中子和质子之间的质量差大于电子和中微子的质量和，那么重粒子发射轻粒子的过程就可能不违反能量守恒原理，但是，相应的交换能的值仍然太小：

$$|A(r)| < g\left(\frac{mc}{\hbar}\right)^3 \sim 10^{-18} \text{ 尔格}$$

我们得到的负面结果表明，不是费米理论需要根本的修正（因为使结果有实质上的改变绝非易事），就是中子和质子之间作用力的源头根本不像海森堡最初设想，且由费米细致考虑的那样存在于它们的相互转变之中。

（王静 翻译；王乃彦 审稿）

Interaction of Neutrons and Protons

D. Iwanenko

Editor's Notes

Russian physicist Dmitri Iwanenko here argues that Fermi's recent theory of beta radioactivity, while successful in some regards, makes some erroneous predictions. For decays observed in light nuclei, the theory gives a roughly correct link between the rate of decay and the maximum energy of the ejected particles. However, if one uses the theory to consider nuclear binding as an exchange of force-mediating particles similar to the electromagnetic force, one finds the force is only large enough at a distance between nucleons of about 10^{-17} m, which is far too small. Iwanenko concludes that Fermi's theory is thus only a very crude approximation.

AS electrons and positrons are expelled in some reactions from nuclei, we can try to treat these *light* particles like the photons emitted by atoms. Then the interaction of *heavy* particles (protons, neutrons) can be considered as taking place *via* light particles described by the equations of a ψ-field in the same manner as electromagnetic, for example, Coulomb, interaction takes place through an electromagnetic field, or photons.

The *first* order effects are the expulsion (or absorption) of an electron, which case was treated recently by Fermi, or of a positron. We may remark that the application of Fermi's formalism to positron disintegration of light nuclei (which we get by changing the sign of the charge number and taking for the latter the appropriate value) gives results which fit, though not very accurately, the observed relation between the half-period and the maximum energy of the disintegration particle[1]. Though there seems to be a quantitative disagreement between Fermi's theory (applied to positrons) and positron disintegration, on the other hand the calculated values for K and Rb support Fermi's assumption of the existence of quadripole transitions of heavy particles, giving too big values for the half periods in comparison with the usual dipole disintegrations. The exceptional position of K and Rb is in some way rather *anschaulich*. We may remark that the Sargent-Fermi rule, in contrast to the Geiger-Nuttall law, shows a less pronounced dependence on the charge number, so that for qualitative considerations even the wave functions of free particles can be used.

The *second* order effects give specially the probability of production of pairs, which is in the case of the ψ-field less effective than in the electromagnetic case, as the charge, e, is much bigger than Fermi's coefficient, g (the "charge" for the ψ-field). The most important second order effect is the subsequent production and annihilation of an electron and positron, in the field of proton and neutron, which leads to the appearance of an interaction *exchange* energy (Heisenberg's *Austausch*) between proton and neutron,

中子和质子的相互作用

俄国物理学家德米特里·伊万年科在这篇文章中指出费米新近关于β辐射的理论尽管在某些方面获得了成功，但它也给出了一些错误的预测。对于在轻原子核中观察到的衰变现象，虽然该理论给出的衰变速率和放出的粒子的最大能量之间的关系是大致正确的，但是，如果使用该理论时考虑束缚核的相互作用，从而认为其是类似于电磁相互作用的作用——媒介粒子的交换，人们会发现这种作用力只有在核子之间的距离大约为 10^{-17} 米时才足够强，而这个距离太短了。因此，伊万年科得出结论认为费米的理论只是一个非常粗略的近似理论。

　　由于电子和正电子都会在一些核反应中被原子核排斥出来，所以我们可以试着像处理原子所放射的光子一样处理这些**轻**粒子。于是，我们可以认为重粒子（质子、中子）之间的相互作用是通过 ψ 场方程所描述的轻粒子来实现的。这种相互作用与以电磁场或光子为介质的电磁相互作用（如库仑相互作用）具有相同的形式。

　　一阶效应是电子的释放（或吸收），费米最近研究过这个问题，当然正电子的情况类似。我们注意到，将费米理论应用到产生正电子的轻核衰变时（我们是通过改变电荷数的符号并且赋予后者适当的数值来实现这一过程的），得到的理论结果与实验观察到的衰变粒子的半衰期和其最大能量之间的关系 [1] 相符合，但不是精确吻合。虽然正电子的衰变和费米理论（应用于正电子）计算的结果似乎在数值上吻合得不是很好，但是从另一方面来看，K 和 Rb 的计算结果却支持费米关于存在重粒子四极裂变的假设，由其计算给出的四极裂变的半衰期要远大于通常的偶极裂变的半衰期。K 和 Rb 的特殊地位从某种程度上说可谓非常**直观**。我们注意到对照盖革－努塔耳定律，萨金特－费米规则反而很少依赖于电荷数，因此在做定性分析时，甚至可以用自由粒子的波函数。

　　二阶效应特别给出了产生粒子对的可能性。由于电荷 e 要远远大于费米系数 g（对应 ψ 场的"电荷"），所以相对于在电磁场中，在 ψ 场中产生粒子对的可能性要小。最重要的二阶效应是：在质子和中子场中，电子和正电子的产生和湮灭，导致了中子和质子之间相互作用的**交换**能（海森堡**交换**）的出现。这正如库仑相互作用可以看作是由两个电子之间光子的产生和吸收所导致的。不同于库仑作用中的比值

quite in the same way as Coulomb interaction can be conceived as arising from the birth and absorption of a photon in the case of two electrons. Instead of e^2/r one gets here an interaction of the order g^2/chr^5, which is easily verified dimensionally. The exact calculations were first carried out by Prof. Ig. Tamm, who also insisted on development of this method. With $g \sim 10^{-50}$ (the computations were carried out by V. Mamasichlisov), which value is required by the empirical data on heavy radioactive bodies, we get an interaction energy of a million volts, no at a distance of 10^{-13} cm. but only at $r \sim 10^{-15}$ cm., which is inadmissible. We may ask about the value of r, which would give a *self-interaction* energy of the order of the proper energy of a heavy particle. This value is of the order 10^{-16} cm., which is that of the classical radius of a proton.

The appearance of these small distances is very surprising and can be removed only by some quite new assumptions. Fermi's characteristic coefficient g appears to be connected also with distances of this order of magnitude.

(**133**, 981-982; 1934)

D. Iwanenko: Physical-Technical Institute, Leningrad.

Reference:
1. cf. D. Iwanenko, *C.R. Ac. Sci. U.S.S.R.*, Leningrad, 2, No. 9, 1934.

e^2/r，重粒子的交换能与 g^2/chr^5 成正比，这个值可以很容易地从数量级上进行验证。塔姆教授首先进行了准确计算，他仍在坚持发展这一方法。根据重放射性物质的经验数值的要求，取 $g \sim 10^{-50}$（由麻马斯克索夫计算得出），我们得到相互作用能为一兆电子伏，而这是在距离 $r \sim 10^{-15}$ cm 而不是距离 $r \sim 10^{-13}$ cm 时得到的，但是这个距离是不合理的。我们可能会对距离 r 值产生疑问，距离 r 应该给出一个对于重粒子来说数量级合理的**自作用**能量。这个值在 10^{-16} cm 量级，即质子的经典半径的量级。

出现这么小的间距实在是让人吃惊，只有引入某种新的假设才能解决这个问题。费米特征系数 g 也与这个间距的数量级大小有关。

（王静 翻译；王乃彦 审稿）

A "Nuclear Photo-effect": Disintegration of the Diplon by γ-Rays

J. Chadwick and M. Goldhaber

Editor's Note

In 1934, some physicists still doubted if the neutron were a genuine subatomic particle, or a composite of the proton and the electron. Here James Chadwick and Maurice Goldhaber describe their experimental determination of a significantly more accurate neutron mass. They used photons to induce the disintegration of a "diplon"—a nucleus of heavy hydrogen—into a proton and neutron. As the masses of the atoms of hydrogen and heavy hydrogen were known very accurately, it was then easy to deduce a value for the mass of the neutron. This experiment suggested that the diplon is composed of a neutron and proton, and helped cement the status of the neutron as a fundamental particle.

BY analogy with the excitation and ionisation of atoms by light, one might expect that any complex nucleus should be excited or "ionised", that is, disintegrated, by γ-rays of suitable energy. Disintegration would be much easier to detect than excitation. The necessary condition to make disintegration possible is that the energy of the γ-ray must be greater than the binding energy of the emitted particle. The γ-rays of thorium C'' of $h\nu = 2.62 \times 10^6$ electron volts are the most energetic which are available in sufficient intensity, and therefore one might expect to produce disintegration with emission of a heavy particle, such as a neutron, proton, etc., only of those nuclei which have a small or negative mass defect; for example, D^2, Be^9, and the radioactive nuclei which emit α-particles. The emission of a positive or negative electron from a nucleus under the influence of γ-rays would be difficult to detect unless the resulting nucleus were radioactive.

Heavy hydrogen was chosen as the element first to be examined, because the diplon has a small mass defect and also because it is the simplest of all nuclear systems and its properties are as important in nuclear theory as the hydrogen atom is in atomic theory. The disintegration to be expected is

$$_1D^2 + h\nu \rightarrow {}_1H^1 + {}_0n^1 \tag{1}$$

Since the momentum of the quantum is small and the masses of the proton and neutron are nearly the same, the available energy, $h\nu - W$, where W is the binding energy of the particles, will be divided nearly equally between the proton and the neutron.

The experiments were as follows. An ionisation chamber was filled with heavy hydrogen of about 95 percent purity, kindly lent by Dr. Oliphant. The chamber was connected to a linear amplifier and oscillograph in the usual way. When the heavy hydrogen was exposed to the γ-radiation from a source of radiothorium, a number of "kicks" was recorded by

一种"核的光效应"：γ射线引发的氘核蜕变

查德威克，戈德哈伯

编者按

1934 年，仍有一些物理学家对于中子是真正的亚原子粒子抑或是电子和质子的结合体而感到疑惑。这篇文章中，詹姆斯·查德威克和莫里斯·戈德哈伯描述了他们对于中子质量更为精确的实验测定。他们用光子引发"氘核"（重氢的原子核）蜕变为一个质子和一个中子。由于氢原子和重氢原子的质量已经有了非常精确的数值，所以据此可以很容易推算出中子的质量。这一实验表明氘核由一个中子和一个质子构成，该实验也更加牢固地确立了中子是一种基本粒子的理念。

根据原子在光的照射下可以发生激发和电离，人们可以以此类推出，任何具有复杂结构的原子核都会被具有适当能量的 γ 射线激发或者"电离"（即蜕变）。蜕变要比激发容易探测得多。蜕变发生的必要条件是 γ 射线的能量大于所放出的粒子的结合能。钍 C″ 放射出的 γ 射线的能量为 $hv = 2.62 \times 10^6$ 电子伏，这是能够得到的且具有足够强度的射线中能量最高的，因此，人们期望核蜕变可以产生某种重粒子（例如中子、质子等），而只有在蜕变中质量亏损较小或者为负值的原子核才能产生这种蜕变；像 ^2D、^9Be 以及放射性原子核则放射出 α 粒子。由 γ 射线引起的正电子或负电子发射很难被探测到，除非形成的原子核具有放射性。

首先选择重氢作为研究对象，因为氘核的质量亏损小，并具有最简单的核系统，而且氘核在核理论中的重要性就如同氢原子在原子理论中的一样。我们预期的蜕变反应是：

$$^2_1D + hv \rightarrow ^1_1H + ^1_0n \tag{1}$$

由于光量子动量非常小，而且质子和中子的质量几乎相等，所以可获取的能量 $hv - W$（W 是粒子的结合能）几乎会在质子和中子间平分。

实验过程如下：向电离腔中充满纯度为 95% 的重氢（重氢是奥利芬特博士慷慨赠予的），我们依照常规的方法将电离腔与一个线性放大器和示波器相连。当我们用放射性钍所放射的 γ 射线辐照重氢时，示波器就会记录到很多"突跳"。实验证明，

313

the oscillograph. Tests showed that these kicks must be attributed to protons resulting from the splitting of the diplon. When a radium source of equal γ-ray intensity was employed, very few kicks were observed. From this fact we deduce that the disintegration cannot be produced to any marked degree by γ-rays of energy less than 1.8×10^6 electron volts, for there is a strong line of this energy in the radium C spectrum.

If the nuclear process assumed in (1) is correct, a very reliable estimate of the mass of the neutron can be obtained, for the masses of the atoms of hydrogen and heavy hydrogen are known accurately. They are 1.0078 and 2.0136[1] respectively. Since the diplon is stable and can be disintegrated by a γ-ray of energy 2.62×10^6 electron volts (the strong γ-ray of thorium C″), the mass of the neutron must lie between 1.0058 and 1.0086; if the γ-ray of radium C of 1.8×10^6 electron volts is ineffective, the mass of the neutron must be greater than 1.0077. If the energy of the protons liberated in the disintegration (1) were measured, the mass of the neutron could be fixed very closely. A rough estimate of the energy of the protons was deduced from measurements of the size of the oscillograph kicks in the above experiments. The value obtained was about 250,000 volts. This leads to a binding energy for the diplon of 2.1×10^6 electron volts, and gives a value of 1.0081 for the neutron mass. This estimate of the proton energy is, however, very rough, and for the present we may take for the mass of the neutron the value 1.0080, with extreme errors of ± 0.0005.

Previous estimates of the mass of the neutron have been made from considerations of the energy changes in certain nuclear reactions, and values of 1.007 and 1.010 have been derived in this way[2,3]. These estimates, however, depend not only on assumptions concerning the nuclear processes, but also on certain mass-spectrograph measurements, some of which may be in error by about 0.001 mass units. It is of great importance to fix accurately the mass of the neutron and it is hoped to accomplish this by the new method given here.

Experiments are in preparation to observe the disintegration of the diplon in the expansion chamber. These experiments should confirm the nuclear process which has been assumed, and therewith the assumption that the diplon consists of a proton and a neutron. Both the energy of the protons and their angular distribution should also be obtained.

If, as our experiments suggest, the mass defect of the diplon is about 2×10^6 electron volts, it is at once evident why the diplon cannot be disintegrated by the impact of polonium α-particles[4]. When an α-particle collides with a nucleus of mass number M, only a fraction $M/(M + 4)$ of the kinetic energy of the α-particle is available for disintegration, if momentum is to be conserved. In the case of the diplon, therefore, only one third of the kinetic energy of the α-particle is available, and this, for the polonium α-particle, is rather less than 1.8×10^6 electron volts. The more energetic particles of radium C′ should just be able to produce disintegration, and Dunning[5] has in fact observed a small effect when heavy water was enclosed in a radon tube.

这些突跳是氘核蜕变产生的质子引起的。如果我们用相同强度的镭源 γ 射线照射重氢，观察到的突跳就很少。由此我们推断，能量小于 1.8×10^6 电子伏的 γ 射线无法引发显著的蜕变，因为在镭 C 能谱的这个能量位置上有一条很强的线。

如果式（1）中假设的核反应过程是正确的，因为氢原子和重氢原子的质量都是精确已知的，其值分别是 1.0078 和 2.0136[1]，所以我们可以对中子质量进行可靠的估算。由于氘核是稳定的，而且可以由能量为 2.62×10^6 电子伏的 γ 射线（钍 C″ 放射的强 γ 射线）引发蜕变，所以中子质量一定在 1.0058 和 1.0086 之间；如果镭 C 发射的能量为 1.8×10^6 电子伏的 γ 射线不能引发蜕变，那么中子质量一定大于 1.0077。如果蜕变反应式（1）中释放的质子能量是可以测量的，那么中子质量就能较为精确地确定了。通过测量上述实验中示波器上突跳的大小可以对质子的能量进行粗略估算，由此得到的能量数值约为 250,000 电子伏。由这个值导出氘核的结合能为 2.1×10^6 电子伏，中子质量为 1.0081。不过，这种对质子能量的估算非常粗略，目前我们取中子质量为 1.0080，最大误差为 ± 0.0005。

之前根据某些核反应的能量变化估算出来的 [2,3] 中子质量值为 1.007 和 1.010。然而，这些估算值不仅依赖于对于核过程的假设，还需依赖质谱测量，而有些质谱测量的误差会达到约 0.001 个质量单位。精确确定中子质量是十分重要的，我们希望这里给出的新方法能够成功解决这个问题。

对膨胀云室中氘核蜕变进行观测的实验正在筹备之中。这些实验将会证实前面假设的核反应过程，进而证实氘核是由一个质子和一个中子构成的。质子的能量以及它们的角分布也都将被测得。

正如我们的实验所表明的那样，如果氘核的质量亏损约为 2×10^6 电子伏，那么氘核不能在钋放射出的 α 粒子的轰击下发生蜕变[4] 的原因就会立刻清楚了。当 α 粒子和一个质量数为 M 的原子核发生碰撞时，如果碰撞过程中动量是守恒的，那么在 α 粒子的动能中只有 $M/(M+4)$ 可以用于诱发蜕变。因此，在参与碰撞的原子核为氘核的情况中，α 粒子的动能只有 1/3 可用于蜕变，而对于钋放射出的 α 粒子，这个能量小于 1.8×10^6 电子伏。而镭 C′ 发射出的能量更高的粒子刚好可以引发蜕变，事实上，邓宁 [5] 已经在将重水封装于氢管里的实验中观察到了微弱的蜕变效应。

Our experiments give a value of about 10^{-28} sq. cm. for the cross-section for disintegration of a diplon by a γ-ray of 2.62×10^6 electron volts. In a paper to be published shortly, H. Bethe and R. Peierls have calculated this cross-section, assuming the interaction forces between a proton and a neutron which are given by the considerations developed by Heisenberg, Majorana and Wigner. They have obtained the transition probability in the usual quantum-mechanical way, and their result gives a value for the cross-section of the same order as the experimental value, but rather greater, if we take the mass of the neutron as 1.0080. If, however, we take the experimental value for the cross-section, the calculations lead to a neutron mass of 1.0085, which seems rather high. Thus the agreement of theory with experiment may be called satisfactory but not complete.

One further point may be mentioned. Some experiments of Lea[6] have shown that paraffin wax bombarded by neutrons emits a hard γ-radiation greater in intensity and in quantum energy than when carbon alone is bombarded. The explanation suggested was that, in the collisions of neutrons and protons, the particles sometimes combine to form a diplon, with the emission of a γ-ray. This process is the reverse of the one considered here. Now if we assume detailed balancing of all processes occurring in a thermodynamical equilibrium between diplons, protons, neutrons and radiation, we can calculate, without any special assumption about interaction forces, the relative probabilities of the reaction (1) and the reverse process. Using our experimental value for the cross-section for reaction (1), we can calculate the cross-section for the capture of neutrons by protons for the case when the neutrons have a kinetic energy $2(h\nu - W) = 1.0 \times 10^6$ electron volts in a co-ordinate system in which the proton is at rest before the collision. In this special case the cross-section σ_c for capture (into the ground state of the diplon—we neglect possible higher states) is much smaller than the cross-section σ_p for the "photo-effect". It is unlikely that σ_c will be very much greater for the faster neutrons concerned in Lea's experiments. It therefore seems very difficult to explain the observations of Lea as due to the capture of neutrons by protons, for this effect should be extremely small. A satisfactory explanation is not easy to find and further experiments seem desirable.

(134, 237-238; 1934)

References:

1. K. T. Bainbridge, *Phys. Rev.*, **44**, 57; 1933.

2. J. Chadwick, *Proc. Roy. Soc.*, A, **142**, 1; 1933.

3. I, Curie and F. Joliot, *Nature*, **133**, 721, May 12, 1934.

4. Rutherford and A. E. Kempton, *Proc. Roy. Roc.*, A, **143**, 724; 1934.

5. *Phys. Rev.*, **45**, 586; 1934.

6. *Nature*, **133**, 24, Jan. 6, 1934.

我们的实验给出了能量为 2.62×10^6 电子伏的 γ 射线所引发氘核蜕变时的碰撞截面为 10^{-28} 平方厘米。在近期即将发表的一篇论文中，贝特与佩尔斯假设中子和质子之间相互作用力符合海森堡、马约拉纳和维格纳提出的设想，从而计算出这个截面的数值。他们使用通常的量子力学方法计算了蜕变的概率，其理论计算给出的碰撞截面数值与实验值具有相同的数量级，但如果我们取中子质量为 1.0080，计算值就会相当大了。然而，如果我们设碰撞截面为实验值，那么计算得到的中子质量就是 1.0085，这个值似乎太大了。因此，我们只能说理论和实验基本相符，而并非完全一致。

另外还有一点需要提及。利[6] 的一些实验表明，用中子轰击固体石蜡发射出一种硬 γ 射线，这种射线比单独轰击碳原子产生的射线的强度更强且量子能量更高。对此的解释是，中子和质子发生碰撞有时会结合成氘核，并释放出 γ 射线。这一过程是我们这里所研究的反应的逆过程。现在，如果我们假定氘核、中子、质子三者各自与射线之间的热力学平衡所涉及的所有过程都达到细致平衡，那么无需任何有关相互作用力的假定，我们就能计算出反应式（1）与其逆过程发生的相对概率。用我们在实验中测得的反应式（1）的截面数据，当中子具有 $2(h\nu - W) = 1.0 \times 10^6$ 电子伏的动能，且质子在碰撞前静止时，可以计算出质子俘获中子的俘获截面。在这种特殊情况下，俘获截面 σ_c（在这里我们只考虑俘获后氘核处于基态的情况，忽略了可能存在的更高的激发态）要比"光效应"截面 σ_p 小很多。对于利的实验中相关的快中子，俘获截面 σ_c 不可能会非常大。因此，似乎很难将利在实验中的观测解释成为质子俘获了中子的结果，因为这个效应应该是非常微弱的。要想找到一个令人满意的解释并不是很容易，这似乎有待更进一步的实验。

（王静 翻译；王乃彦 审稿）

Quantum Mechanics and Physical Reality

N. Bohr

Editor's Note

In May 1935, Einstein, Podolsky and Rosen published a landmark paper arguing that quantum mechanics must be considered incomplete. They had described a thought experiment in which the values of some physical variables could be known before they were measured, implying that some aspect of physical reality must correspond to those variables, which quantum mechanics however failed to describe. Here Niels Bohr argues that their argument was flawed owing to an essential ambiguity in quantum mechanics, which demands that physical reality cannot be considered independently of the conditions that define an experiment. So began an argument over the completeness of quantum theory, and its apparent "non-local" character (the possibility of action at a distance), which continues to this day.

IN a recent article by A. Einstein, B. Podolsky and N. Rosen, which appeared in the *Physical Review* of May 15, and was reviewed in *Nature* of June 22, the question of the completeness of quantum mechanical description has been discussed on the basis of a "criterion of physical reality", which the authors formulate as follows: "If, without in any way disturbing a system, we can predict with certainty the value of a physical quantity, then there exists an element of physical reality corresponding to this physical quantity".

Since, as the authors show, it is always possible in quantum theory, just as in classical theory, to predict the value of any variable involved in the description of a mechanical system from measurements performed on other systems, which have only temporarily been in interaction with the system under investigation; and since in contrast to classical mechanics it is never possible in quantum mechanics to assign definite values to both of two conjugate variables, the authors conclude from their criterion that quantum mechanical description of physical reality is incomplete.

I should like to point out, however, that the named criterion contains an essential ambiguity when it is applied to problems of quantum mechanics. It is true that in the measurements under consideration any direct mechanical interaction of the system and the measuring agencies is excluded, but a closer examination reveals that the procedure of measurements has an essential influence on the conditions on which the very definition of the physical quantities in question rests. Since these conditions must be considered as an inherent element of any phenomenon to which the term "physical reality" can be unambiguously applied, the conclusion of the

量子力学和物理实在

玻尔

编者按

1935 年 5 月，爱因斯坦、波多尔斯基和罗森一起发表了一篇具有里程碑意义的论文，他们认为量子力学应该是不完备的。他们描述了这样一个理想实验，其中有些物理变量的值在测量前就是已知的，这意味着这些物理量对应于某些物理实在，但量子力学无法描述这些物理量。本文中尼尔斯·玻尔认为他们的理论有缺陷，因为在量子力学中有一个重要的地方未阐述清楚，即需要说清楚的是，不可能独立于实验所处的环境来考虑物理实在。由此引发了关于量子理论完备性和量子理论明显"非局域"特征（超距作用的可能性）的讨论，直到今天，这方面的讨论仍在继续。

最近，爱因斯坦、波多尔斯基和罗森在 5 月 15 日的《物理学评论》上发表了一篇文章，6 月 22 日的《自然》杂志对该文章进行了评论。基于"物理实在的判据"，他们在文章中讨论了量子力学描述的完备性问题并对该问题作了如下阐述："假如系统没有受到任何形式的干扰，我们就可以确切地预言物理量的值，并且认为存在某个物理实在的要素与该物理量相对应。"

正如以上作者所述，像经典理论那样，在量子理论中通过对与所研究的系统有短暂相互作用的其他系统进行测量，可以预言与描述该力学系统有关的任何一个变量；但与经典力学不同的是，在量子力学中永远不可能同时给出两个共轭变量的确定值，上述文章的作者们根据其判据认为，物理实在的量子力学描述是不完备的。

然而，我想要指出的是，当把所谓的判据应用于量子力学的问题时将会出现基本定义模糊不清的问题。确实，前面已经假设在测量过程中不考虑系统与测量仪器之间任何直接的力学相互作用，但是进一步的研究表明，测量过程对现在我们所讨论的物理实在的确切定义有重要的影响。只有考虑测量过程对系统的影响并把这些影响看成是任何一个物理现象的内在属性，我们才可以明确地使用"物理实在"这个术语，因此，以上提到的那些作者们的结论似乎就不太合理了。不久，进一步完

above-mentioned authors would not appear to be justified. A fuller development of this argument will be given in an article to be published shortly in the *Physical Review*.

(**136**, 65; 1935)

N. Bohr: Institute of Theoretical Physics, Copenhagen, June 29.

整地论证这个问题的文章将发表在《物理学评论》上。

（沈乃澂 翻译；李军刚 审稿）

Isotopic Constitution of Uranium

A. J. Dempster

Editor's Note

Uranium has the highest atomic weight of any naturally occurring element, and exists predominantly in the form of uranium-238. Here, however, physicist Arthur Dempster of the University of Chicago reports that about 0.4% of the element is an unstable isotope uranium-235. This isotope, he suggests, is the origin of the actinium series of radioactive elements, as the elements protactinium-231, actinium-227, francium-223 and so on can be generated by radioactive alpha and beta decays. Dempster also notes that another isotope, uranium-234, appears to exist in traces of 0.008%. Uranium-235 would soon become very important as the only natural fissile isotope: one capable of sustaining a nuclear chain reaction driven by slow moving neutrons, thus making nuclear power and atomic bombs conceivable.

THE analysis of uranium rays from the volatile hexafluoride by Dr. Aston[1] has shown a single line at atomic weight 238. The element appeared to be simple to at least two or three percent, but its properties were not favourable for study in the gas discharge. As uranium is of great importance for the subject of radioactivity, the spark source described in *Nature* of April 6 (**135**, 542) was tried with uranium metal and gold as electrodes, and also with an electrode made by packing a nickel tube with pitchblende. It was found that an exposure of a few seconds was sufficient for the main component at 238 reported by Dr. Aston; but in addition on long exposures a faint companion of atomic weight 235 was also present. With two different uranium electrodes it was observed on eight photographs, and two photographs with the pitchblende electrode also showed the new component. The relative intensity could be only roughly estimated on account of the irregularity of the spark, but it appeared to be less than one percent of the intensity of the main component.

This faint isotope of uranium is of special interest as it is in all probability the parent of the actinium series of radioactive elements. In discussing Dr. Aston's analysis[2] of the isotopes in lead from radioactive minerals, Lord Rutherford[3] pointed out that the lead isotope of atomic weight 207 is probably the end product of the actinium series, so that the atomic weight of protoactinium would be 231, (207+6×4). This value has been verified by the recent chemical determination of the atomic weight by v. Grosse[4]. Protoactinium itself may be formed by α- and β-ray transformations from a hypothetical isotope of uranium, actino-uranium, with an atomic weight of 235 or 239[3]. The relative amount of actino-uranium at present on the earth would be 0.4 percent of the uranium according to a recalculation by Dr. v. Grosse[5,6]. The present observations thus support this theory, with the atomic weight of 235 for the isotope actino-uranium. A third isotope, uranium II, of

铀的同位素构成

登普斯特

编者按

自然界中存在的元素中，铀具有最大的原子量，且绝大部分以铀–238 的形式存在。而在这篇文章中芝加哥大学的物理学家阿瑟·登普斯特指出，约有 0.4% 的铀是不稳定的同位素铀–235。他认为这种铀的同位素是锕系列放射性元素的起源，因为镁–231、锕–227、钫–223 等锕系放射性元素可通过该同位素的 α 衰变和 β 衰变而获得。同时登普斯特还注意到了铀的另一个同位素——铀–234，它只占 0.008%。作为仅有的天然可裂变的同位素，铀–235 很快变得非常重要：它可以维持一个由慢中子驱动的链式核反应，这使得核能和原子弹成为可能。

阿斯顿博士 [1] 对挥发性六氟化铀中的铀离子束的分析显示出一条对应于原子量为 238 的单线。至少在 2% 或 3% 的精度上讲这种元素的同位素构成是简单的，但是它的性质却很不适于利用气体电离的方法进行研究。鉴于铀对于放射性研究的巨大重要性，我们使用了 4 月 6 日发表于《自然》第 135 卷第 542 页的论文中所描述的火花源的方法，我们以金属铀和金作为电极，还使用了填充沥青铀矿的镍管为电极。实验发现，对于阿斯顿博士所报道的原子量为 238 的主要成分来说，几秒钟的曝光时间就已足够；但是除此之外，在长时间曝光后，一个原子量为 235 的微弱伴线也出现了。采用两个不同的铀电极，我们在八张照片中观察到了这条伴线，同时在两张使用沥青铀矿电极的照片中也显示了这一新成分的存在。由于火花的不均匀性，对新成分的相对强度只能进行粗略地估算，不过它的强度似乎不到主要成分的 1%。

铀的这种少量的同位素引起了我们特别的关注，因为它很可能是锕系放射性元素的母体。在就阿斯顿博士对放射性矿物中铅同位素的分析结果 [2] 进行讨论时，卢瑟福勋爵 [3] 指出，原子量为 207 的铅同位素可能是锕系元素的最终产物，因此镁元素的原子量应为 231，即（207+6×4）。冯·格罗塞 [4] 采用新近的原子量化学测定法对这个值进行了确认。镁本身可以由一种假定的铀同位素（锕铀，原子量为 235 或 239）通过 α 衰变或 β 衰变而形成 [3]。根据冯·格罗塞博士的重新计算 [5,6]，目前地球上的锕铀的相对含量大约为铀的 0.4%。因此，就原子量为 235 的同位素锕铀而言，目前的观测结果是支持该理论的。第三种同位素——原子量为 234 的铀 II，理论上

atomic weight 234 amounts theoretically to only 0.008 percent of the uranium, and would be too faint for observation by the mass-spectrograph.

(**136**, 180; 1935)

A. J. Dempster: University of Chicago, July 12.

References:
1. Aston, *Nature*, **128**, 725; 1931.
2. Aston, *Nature*, **123**, 313; 1929.
3. Rutherford, *Nature*, **123**, 313; 1929.
4. A. v. Grosse, *Proc. Roy. Soc.*, **150**, 363; 1935.
5. A. v. Grosse, *Phys, Rev.*, **42**, 565; 1932.
6. A. v. Grosse, *J. Phys. Chem.*, **38**, 487; 1933.

只占铀总量的 0.008%，这个量对于质谱观测来说可能过少了。

（王耀杨 翻译；汪长征 审稿）

Form, Drift, and Rhythm of the Continents[*]

W. W. Watts

Editor's Note

Here W. Watts surveys what was known about changes through geological time in the disposition of continents and oceans. Features such as submerged fossil forests and raised fossil beaches showed that what was once sea is now land and vice versa. What ultimately drives this shifting Earth? Could it be a cycle of thermal swelling caused by radioactive decay within the planet? That popular idea was wrong, but contained the germ of rightness in linking continental motions to heat-driven convection. Watts also mentions the theory of continental drift recently advocated by Alfred Wegener on the basis of the matching shapes of opposite coastlines. Watts points out that Wegener's critics bemoaned the lack of a plausible mechanism for such drift, but in fact all the ingredients are already here: continental wandering is now known to be caused by convection currents in the hot mantle.

IT is now sixty-seven years since the British Association enjoyed the hospitality of the city of Norwich, a privilege which is being renewed under the most happy auspices.

At that meeting we find the scientific community was particularly interested in underground temperatures and tidal phenomena, in the application of the spectroscope to celestial objects, and in the discovery of the oldest Cambrian fossils and the earliest fossil mammals then known. Many papers were read on local natural history, including those on Norfolk farming and the drainage of the county and of the Fens.

In his address at the meeting the president, Sir Joseph D. Hooker, made special reference to the work of Charles Darwin: not to the "Origin of Species" which had been acrimoniously discussed by the Association on previous occasions, and notably at Oxford in 1860, but to some of the work that followed.

It should be remembered that Hooker was one of the three scientific men, representing botany, zoology and geology, whom Darwin had selected as judges with whose opinion on the soundness of his theory of the origin of species he would be content. The others were Huxley and Lyell; and of the three Lyell was the hardest to convince, chiefly because the record of life in the past then furnished by the rocks was manifestly so incomplete and unsatisfactory that its evidence was insufficient to warrant a definite verdict.

---

[*] Presidential Address delivered at Norwich on September 4, 1935.

大陆的形成、漂移及节律*

沃茨

编者按

这篇文章中沃茨概括了当时已知的陆地与海洋在地质历史期间的位置变迁。根据一些特征（如被淹没并石化的森林和升高并石化的海滩）可以推断，现在是陆地的地方可能曾经是一片汪洋，反之亦然。是什么最终驱动了地球上的这种变迁？这是否是由这个行星内部的放射性衰变导致的一个周期性的热膨胀过程呢？这一当时流行的观点是错误的，但是其中包含着的将大陆运动与热驱动的对流联系起来的思想是正确理论的萌芽。沃茨也提到了当时阿尔弗雷德·魏格纳刚刚创立的大陆漂移学说，这个学说是基于两侧海岸线形态吻合性而提出的。沃茨指出，魏格纳的批评者对缺乏可靠的机制来解释这种漂移感到惋惜，但实际上所有的要素都已经摆在这里了：现在我们知道大陆漂移是地幔热对流造成的。

在诺里奇城主办方的热烈邀请下英国科学促进会又一次在这里召开，这距离上次在此地顺利召开已时隔 67 年了。

在那次会议上，我们发现科学界特别感兴趣的论题主要包括：地下的温度和潮汐现象、分光镜在天体观测中的应用，以及当时所知的最古老的寒武纪化石与最早的哺乳动物化石的发现等等。会上还看到了很多关于当地自然史的论文，其中有关于诺福克郡的农业和郡内以及费恩（英格兰东部沼泽地带）的排水系统等内容。

当时，会议主席约瑟夫·胡克爵士在他的致辞中特别提到了查尔斯·达尔文的工作，不过不是《物种起源》，而是在它之后的一些工作，《物种起源》在之前的会议上已被详细讨论过了，并且早在 1860 年就已闻名牛津。

大家应该记得，胡克就是当时达尔文分别从植物学、动物学和地质学界选出的鉴定其物种起源理论可靠性的三位科学家之一。另外两位分别是赫胥黎和赖尔。而这三人之中最难说服的就是赖尔，这主要是因为当时由岩石提供的古生物记录显然是不完整并且无法令人满意的，以致没有足够的证据来获得明确的结论。

---

* 1935 年 9 月 4 日在诺里奇的主席致辞。

Uniformitarianism

Lyell had set out to "treat of such features of the economy of existing nature, animate and inanimate, as are illustrative of geology", and to make "an investigation of the permanent effects of causes now in action which may serve as records to after ages of the present condition of the Earth and its inhabitants". By laborious study of the work of others, and by his own extensive travel and research, he had been able to enunciate, for the inorganic world, the principle of uniformitarianism, which in its original form we owe to Hutton. This principle involved that the history revealed by the rocks should be read as the effect of the slow but continuous operation of causes, most of them small, such as could be seen in action in some part or other of the world today. This was set in opposition to the opinion of the older geologists, who had postulated a succession of catastrophes which, by flood, fire and convulsion, had periodically wrecked the world and destroyed its inhabitants; each catastrophe necessitating a new creation to provide the succession of life on the Earth as it then was known.

But in the organic world, Lyell, like Hutton, had failed to detect any analogous principle, and, as he rejected all the theories of transmutation of species then in vogue, he had to accept their absolute fixity; and to suppose that, as species became extinct one after another, replacement by special creations followed. Yet the reading today of the chapters devoted to this branch in the earlier editions of Lyell's great work produces the haunting feeling that a better explanation had only just eluded him. It was the story revealed in Lyell's work, Darwin tells us, the new conception that the Earth had been in existence for vast aeons of time, the proof that it had been continuously peopled by animals and plants, and that these had steadfastly advanced and improved throughout that time, which showed him the necessity for an explanation of the progression of life, and gave him the first hints of his theory. When he had enunciated this, he was enabled to repay his master with the principle of organic evolution, which brought changes in the animate world into harmony with those of the inanimate.

His "Antiquity of Man" shows that by 1863 Lyell had become a convert, and he afterwards rewrote much of the second volume of his "Principles" accepting the new point of view. This change earned from Hooker a testimonial in the 1868 address which, if not unique, must certainly be one of the most magnificent ever awarded to a scientific work:

"I know no brighter example of heroism, of its kind, than this, of an author thus abandoning, late in life, a theory which he had regarded as one of the foundation stones of a work that had given him the highest position attainable amongst contemporary scientific writers. Well may he be proud of a superstructure, raised on the foundation of an insecure doctrine, when he finds that he can underpin it and substitute a new foundation: and, after all is finished, survey his edifice, not only more secure, but more harmonious in proportions than before."

均变论

赖尔已经着手"论述现存大自然生态系统中的种种特征，不管是有生命的还是无生命的，都可以看作地质学上的证据"，并且研究了"当今正在作用的过程所产生的永久性效应，这些效应许多年以后可能会成为现今地球及其寄居生物条件状况的地质记录。"根据其他学者的实验研究及他本人的广泛游历和调查，赖尔阐明了适用于无机世界的均变论原理，当然该理论的雏形最早是由赫顿提出的。该原理认为：地壳岩石所揭示的历史应当看成是缓慢连续的地质作用的结果，其中绝大多数的地质作用都很微弱，正如今天我们在地球上某些地方所看到的正在发生的那些作用一样。这与前辈地质学家们的观点正好相反，他们认为应该存在一系列的灾难，包括洪水、火灾、地震等，周期性地破坏地球并毁灭生物；而当时人们认为每次灾难都促使新生物的诞生，以使地球上的生命得以延续。

但在有机世界，赖尔同赫顿一样，也没能探索出类似的原理。而且，由于他摒弃了所有当时流行的关于物种变化的理论，所以只好接受其绝对不变性；并假设随着物种的逐渐灭绝，会有后继的专门物种来替代。然而今天阅读赖尔那部伟大著作的早期版本时，其中关于该问题的章节部分总是让人觉得一种更好的解释曾与他擦肩而过。达尔文告诉我们，在赖尔的著作中已经揭示出了一个新的观念，即地球存在的时间已经长达数十亿年了，并指出有证据表明动植物一直遍布整个地球，且随时间的推移稳步地发展变化着。所有这些让达尔文觉得需要为生命的进化发展寻找一种新的解释，而这也为他的理论提供了最初的灵感。当达尔文阐明了这一点时，他也终于能够以生物进化论来报答他的老师，而这一理论将有生命与无生命的物质的变化和谐地统一了起来。

《人类始祖》一书表明，到 1863 年时，赖尔其实已经转变了原来的观念，随后他重新编写了《地质学原理》第二卷中的许多内容，并纳入了这种新的观点。因为这一改变，胡克在 1868 年的致辞中对他给予了高度评价。这对于一本科学著作来说即便不是空前绝后，也一定是有史以来最高的奖励了：

"我再也找不出比这更能诠释勇敢的例子了，一位作者在晚年放弃了一个理论，而这个理论曾被他视为自己著作的基石之一，要知道这一著作曾给他带来同时代科技著作者所能获得的最高荣誉。他可能曾经以这种建立在并不可靠的学说之上的作品为骄傲，但后来他发现新的学说可以更好地支撑其理论，便对先前的工作做了修改：当全部工作完成时，再审视自己的作品，不仅比以前更可靠，而且各部分之间也更加协调了。"

Although infinitely richer than when Darwin wrote, the geological record still is, and must from its very nature remain, imperfect. Every major group of animal life but the vertebrates is represented in the Cambrian fauna, and the scant relics that have been recovered from earlier rocks give very little idea of what had gone before, and no evidence whatever as to the beginnings of life. But, from Cambrian time onward the chain of life is continuous and unbroken. Type after type has arisen, flourished, and attained dominion. Some of them have met extinction in the heyday of their development; others have slowly dwindled away; others, again, have not finished their downhill journey, or are still advancing to their climax.

Study of the succession of rocks and the organisms contained in them, in every case in which evidence is sufficiently abundant and particularly among the vertebrates and in the later stages of geological history, has now revealed that the great majority of species show close affinities with those which preceded and with those which followed them; that, indeed, they have been derived from their predecessors and gave origin to their successors. We may now fairly claim that palaeontology has lifted the theory of evolution of organisms from the limbo of hypothesis into a fact completely demonstrated by the integral chain of life which links the animals and plants of today with the earliest of their forerunners of the most remote past.

Further, the rocks themselves yield proof of the geographical changes undergone by the Earth during its physical history; and indicate with perfect clearness that these changes have been so closely attendant on variation in life, and the incoming of new species, that it is impossible to deny a relation of cause and effect.

Indeed, when we realise the delicate adjustment of all life to the four elements of the ancients which environ it, air, water, earth and fire; to their composition, interrelationships and circulation; it is perhaps one of the most remarkable facts established by geology that, in spite of the physical changes which we know to have occurred, the chain of life has never snapped in all the hundreds of millions of years through which its history has been traced.

Rhythm of Sea and Land

The physical changes with which Lyell and his successors were most closely concerned were, first, the formation of stratified rocks on horizontal seafloors, situated in what is now often the interior of continents, far removed from the oceans of the present day, and thus indicating important and repeated changes in the position of land and water; and, secondly, the deformation of these flat deposits until they were rucked and ridged to build the mountain ranges.

Before and since Lyell's time, geologists have devoted themselves to working out the exact and detailed succession of these stratified rocks, translating their sequence into history and

虽然相对于达尔文创作《物种起源》时来说，地质记录已经丰富很多，但仅从自然遗迹来看仍不完整。除脊椎动物以外，所有主要动物种群都能在寒武纪动物中找到代表，然而从更早期的岩石中获得的那些少量的遗迹却无法解释从前到底发生了什么，也未发现任何有关生命起源的证据。不过，自寒武纪以来，生物链一直是连续的，并且从未间断。不同种类的生物前赴后继地出现、繁盛，进而占据统治地位。其中有的在其发展的全盛时期遭到了灭绝，有的则缓慢衰退消亡，还有的正走在衰退的路上，有的则正在向着繁盛的顶点前进。

在各种情形下，岩石及其内部包含的有机体都蕴藏着丰富的证据，特别是在地质历史的最近一个阶段，脊椎动物尤其丰富。通过研究岩石及其内部包含的有机体的连续性，发现绝大多数物种与其之前和之后的物种都有着密切的关系，实际上也就是说，它们是由其之前的物种进化而来，随后又进化为它们的继任物种。现在我们可以公正地说，古生物学利用一个完整的生物链将现在的动植物与其远古时期的祖先联系到了一起，从而将生物进化论从假说变成了事实。

此外，岩石本身也可以作为记录自然历史时期地球上发生的各种地理变化的证据；并且这些证据清楚地表明，每次地理变化都与生命形式的变化以及新物种的出现存在着密切关系，这种因果关系是无法否认的。

一切生命形式都会根据其周围的空气、水、土壤和火这四个基本要素做出微妙的调整；即根据这些要素的组成、相互间的影响和相互间的转化进行一定的调整；实际上，当我们意识到这些的时候，一个可能是极为重要的地质学事实便得到证实：尽管已经发生过这些已知的自然变化，但是在我们所追溯的几亿年的历史中，生物链还从未间断过。

海洋和陆地的节律

赖尔及其后继者们最关心的自然变化包括：第一，形成于平坦海底的层状岩石常出现在今天的内陆地区，远离现在的大洋，这说明海陆位置曾发生过重大且反复的变化；第二，这些平坦的沉积层发生变形，直到褶皱并隆起形成山脉。

无论是在赖尔时代之前还是之后，地质学家们一直致力于找出这些层状岩石确切详细的演替过程，从而根据其演替次序揭示地球历史，根据其特征探索地理变

their characters into terms of geography; the succession of physical conditions prevailing at the time of their formation. Further, although animals and plants migrate from place to place, the time occupied by the migrations of suitable forms is so negligible when compared with the length of the chapters of geological history that their fossil remains have proved to be the best means for correlating strata over broad stretches of the Earth's surface. This correlation has converted the fragments of local history thus revealed into at least the outlines of the geological story of the world.

It was not until 1885, however, that the accumulation of data of this type was sufficient to enable the great geologist, Suess, an Austrian, but born in Great Britain, to assemble and correlate them, and to deduce from them further principles which have been the mainstay and inspiration of his successors. We owe to Hertha Sollas and her father the rendering of this great work, "The Face of the Earth", into English; and to Emmanuel de Margerie and his colleagues a French translation enriched with a magnificent series of maps and sections such as could only have been brought together by one with the most remarkable bibliographic knowledge: a veritable recension of the original.

The nature and associations and the distribution in time and space of modern changes in the relative levels of land and sea, as detected at sea-margins and by altitude survey, and of older changes betrayed by such evidence as submerged forests and raised beaches, had convinced geologists that the unstable element was not the fickle and mobile sea, but the solid if elastic earth-crust. They naturally applied the same explanation to those encroachments of the sea in the past which had resulted in the formation of our stratified rocks. But while some investigators were content with one form of movement—that due to lateral pressure—to explain both the formation of mountains and the rise and fall of the land, others called in a different cause for the latter. Without entering into a discussion of causes, it may be well for us to distinguish the orogenic or mountain-forming from the epeirogenic or continental movement.

The evidence collected by Suess proved that these last great land and sea changes had occurred simultaneously over whole continents or even wider regions. Such great submergences as those to which the Cambrian Rocks, the Oxford Clay, and the Chalk are due were of this character; while, in between, there came times of broad expansions of continental land and regressions of the sea. These changes were in his view on far too grand a scale to be compared with, or explained by, the trivial upheavals and depressions of land margins of the present day, which he showed could mostly be correlated with volcanoes or earthquakes, or with such incidents as the imposition or relief of ice-sheets on an elastic crust in connexion with glacial conditions.

It became necessary for him to replace or supplement oscillations of the earth-crust by a world-wide periodic ebb and flow of the oceans, to and from the continents; positive movements of transgression carrying the sea and its deposits over the lands, drowning them and their features under tens or hundreds of fathoms of water; and negative movements or regressions when the oceans retreated to the deeps, leaving the continents

化；并弄清它们形成时主要自然条件的演替。此外，虽然动植物不断从一个地方迁移到另一个地方，但特定种类的迁移时间相对于悠久的地质历史来说甚至可以忽略不计，所以其化石仍是证明宽广的地表上地层之间相互联系的最好证据。局部地区的地质历史片段被这种相互关系联系起来，据此至少可以描绘出全球地质历史发展的梗概。

然而直到 1885 年，伟大的地质学家——出生于英国的奥地利人修斯，才将这些不断丰富的数据收集并联系起来，由此进一步推引出一些原理，这些原理现已成为这个学科的基础并指引着他的后继者。赫莎·索拉斯与父亲共同将《地球的面貌》这部伟大著作翻译成了英文，而伊曼纽尔·德马尔热里与其同事们则译出了法语版本，并补充了大量的地图和章节，其内容之丰富，恐怕只有最富有文献学知识的人才能将这些内容整合在一起，因此是一部名副其实的修订本。

不管是在海缘所进行的观测以及利用高程测量得到的现代海洋与陆地的相对高程变化，还是被淹没的森林和升高的海滩等证据揭示出的过去的海陆变化，它们的性质组合和时空分布都使地质学家们确信，那个变动的因素并非是多变且具有移动性的海洋，而是虽然有些弹性但非常坚固的地壳。于是，他们很自然地也将这一点用于解释海洋的侵蚀作用，这一作用曾导致了层状岩石的形成。不过，当部分研究者满足于用水平压力引起的一种运动来解释山脉的形成以及陆地的隆起与下陷时，另一部分人则认为后者是由不同原因造成的。其实，不用详细讨论其原因，我们也可以将造山运动或者成山过程与造陆运动或者大陆漂移区别开来。

修斯收集到的证据表明，最后一次大规模的海陆变迁是在整个陆地甚至更大范围内同时发生的。例如寒武纪岩石、牛津黏土以及白垩岩的成因，即那些大规模的陆地下沉都具有这样的特点；在这些运动的间歇，则是陆地扩张及海洋消退的时期。修斯认为，这些变迁的规模之大是当今陆地边缘处的微小隆起和下沉所远远无法比拟的，并且无法用这样的现象对其进行解释。他认为，现今的陆地起伏多数是由火山、地震或者其他一些事件造成的，比如，冰川环境下冰盖对弹性地壳的荷载或者释压等。

这时修斯有必要利用世界范围内海洋相对于陆地的周期性涨落来取代或补充地壳的震荡运动；正向运动，即海进时，会携带海水及其沉积物于陆地之上，将陆地以及陆地的轮廓淹没在数十至数百英寻的海水之下；而当负向运动，即海退时，海洋会向深处退缩，留下光秃秃的或者覆盖了一层新沉积物的陆地。

bare or encrusted with recently formed sediments.

Although the facts cried out for this generalisation, Suess was at a loss to supply any mechanism competent to produce the wonderful rhythm. The problem was difficult because a liquid must maintain a horizontal, that is, an equipotential, surface. It was manifestly impossible to withdraw from the earth, and later to replace upon it, the vast quantity of water that would be required; and, though a shifted water-level, or even a varied water-surface relative to the continents, might be caused by polar ice-caps, by redistribution of the continents carrying their local effects on gravitation, by variations in the rate of the Earth's rotation, or other far-reaching causes, none of these would supply an explanation that fitted all the facts. Regressions of the sea could be to some extent explained if Suess's main postulate, that the great ocean basins had been slowly sinking throughout geological time, were granted. But this explanation only rendered more impotent the raising of ocean levels by deposits of sediment, and this was almost the only valid cause for transgressions that he had been able to suggest.

Further, it is not possible to ignore the definite relationship that exists between the pulsation of the oceans and the raising of mountains by lateral or tangential stress. Periods of positive movement or advance of the seas were times of comparative tranquillity, when tangential pressure was in abeyance. Periods of negative movement and retreat were invariably marked by the operation of great stresses by which the Earth's face was ridged and wrinkled in the throes of mountain-birth.

Mountain Ranges

The theory that continuous cooling and shrinkage of the interior of the Earth afforded an explanation of mountain ranges and other rugosities on its surface was a legacy from the nebular hypothesis. In spite of the homely simile of a shrivelling apple, this explanation has never received a very enthusiastic welcome from geologists, though, in default of other resources, they had to make use of it. As knowledge has grown, the difficulties have become insurmountable to them.

First, there is its inadequacy to explain the vast amount of lateral movement required to account for the greater mountain ranges; their rocks, originally spread over a wider area, having been folded and crushed into a narrower width. The shortening of the earth-curst thus effected has been estimated in the case of the Rocky Mountains at 29 miles, of the Himalayas at 62, the Alps at 76, and the Appalachians at the large figure of 200 miles.

Then there is the periodicity of mountain growth. The great epochs of mountain building, such as the Caledonian, to which the chief Scottish and Welsh mountains are due, the Hercynian, responsible for the Pennine and South Wales, and the Alpine, which gave us "the wooded, dim, blue goodness of the Weald", were associated with vast continental development; and each was separated from the next by a period of relative inactivity

尽管这种概括较好地解释了一些事实，但修斯未能提供这种奇妙节律的产生机制。这个问题非常困难，因为液体会始终保持在一个水平面，即等位面。海水撤离陆地，之后再重新覆盖陆地会需要大量的海水，因此很明显是不可能的；尽管极地冰盖的融化、陆块再分配对局部重力的影响、地球自转速率的变化以及其他一些影响深远的原因都有可能造成水平面变化或者水面相对于陆地变化，但所有这些都无法解释所有的事实。修斯理论的基本假设是：在整个地质历史上大洋盆地在缓慢下沉，如果这一假设成立，便能在一定程度上解释海退现象。但是这样一来，沉积物沉积导致海平面上升的说法就显得更加苍白无力了，而这种说法几乎是他所能找到的可以解释海进现象的唯一一个有现实依据的理由。

此外，海洋的律动与侧向应力或者剪应力所导致的山脉隆起之间存在着一定的关系，这点是不容忽视的。当剪应力消失时，海洋的正向运动期即海进期的时间是海洋相对平静期的几倍。而海洋的负向运动期又称海退期，则总是以强烈的应力作用为标志，在这种应力作用下，地球表面在山脉诞生的阵痛中发生隆起和褶皱。

山　脉

认为地球内部的不断降温和收缩可以为山脉以及地球表面其他褶皱的形成提供一种解释的理论是星云假说遗留的产物。只是，除了将地球表面比喻为干皱苹果的朴实笑脸这一点外，这一解释还从未受到地质学家们的热烈欢迎，但是由于没有其他选择，他们也不得不使用它。然而随着知识的积累，使用这一理论时所面临的困难开始变得无法克服了。

首先，上述理论不足以解释大规模的水平运动，而这种运动导致了较大的山脉的形成；形成山脉的那些岩石原本广泛散布在一个很大的区域内，它们受到褶皱、挤压，聚集在一个狭窄的范围内从而最终形成了山脉。地壳收缩就是这样实现的，这已经在许多山脉中得到验证，包括落基山脉（地壳收缩了 29 英里）、喜马拉雅山脉（62 英里）、阿尔卑斯山脉（76 英里）以及阿巴拉契亚山脉（足有 200 英里）等。

其次是山脉的周期性生长。强烈的造山运动期均与大规模的陆地活动有关，比如加里东期形成了苏格兰和威尔士的主要山脉，海西期形成了奔宁山脉、南威尔士的山脉，阿尔卑斯期则形成了"威尔德地区树木繁茂、朦胧阴郁的美丽景象"；而

lasting dozens of millions of years.

Further, there is the fact that the vigour of mountain building, of volcanoes, and of other manifestations of unrest, has shown no sign of senility or lack of energy. The geologically recent Alpine-Himalayan range is as great, as lofty, and as complicated in structure as were any of its precursors. The active volcanoes of Kilauea, Krakatao, or St. Pierre, and those recently extinct in northern Ireland and the Scottish Isles, were as violent and efficient as any of those of the Palaeozoic era. The Earth is "a lady of a certain age", but she has contrived to preserve her youth and energy as well as her beauty.

Age of the Earth

It was when Lord Kelvin's dictum struck from geology its grandest conception, time, that it became vital to re-examine the position. He had demonstrated that, if the Earth had been continuously cooling down at its present rate, its surface must have been too hot for the existence of life upon it a limited number of million years ago. The concept of geological time, indicated by Hutton in his famous saying that in this inquiry "we find no vestige of a beginning—no prospect of an end", had been confirmed by data accumulated through the painstaking researches of a host of competent and devoted observers all over the world. To them, familiar with the tremendous changes, organic and inorganic, that the Earth had passed through since Cambrian time, it was wholly impossible to compress the life-story of the Earth, or the history of life upon it, into a paltry twenty or thirty million years. The slow growth and slow decay of mountain range after mountain range, each built out of, and in some cases upon, the ruins of its predecessor; the chain of slowly evolving organisms, vast in numbers and infinite in variety; told plainly of long aeons of time. The duration of these aeons can be dimly realised when it is recalled that, within a small fraction of the latest of them, man, with the most primitive of implements and the most rudimentary culture, has succeeded in penetrating to the uttermost corners of the world, and developed his innumerable languages and civilisations.

Huxley took up the challenge in his address to the Geological Society in 1869, and asked the pertinent question, "but is the Earth nothing but a cooling mass 'like a hot water jar such as is used in carriages' or 'a globe of sandstone'?" He was able to point out at least some agencies which might regenerate the Earth's heat or delay its loss.

So it is only fitting that the great physicist, who imposed a narrow limit to geological time, should have prepared the way for those who have proved that the Earth possesses in its radioactive substances a "hidden reserve" capable of supplying a continuous recrudescence of the energy wasted by radiation, thus lengthening out the time required to complete its total loss. These later physicists have given us time without stint; and, though this time is the merest fraction of that envisaged by cosmogonists and astronomers, we are now so much richer than our original estimates that we are

这些造山运动之间则都有一个持续上千万年相对平静的过渡期。

再者，还有一个事实就是，无论是造山运动、火山爆发还是其他形式的动荡等等，它们在气势上都没有表现出任何衰弱或者缺乏能量的迹象。从地质年代上看，最近形成的阿尔卑斯–喜马拉雅山系在规模、高度、构造的复杂性方面都不逊于早期形成的山系。无论是活火山，如基拉韦厄、喀拉喀托、圣皮埃尔，还是北爱尔兰和苏格兰岛上那些新近形成的死火山，都与古生代的那些火山同样的猛烈和高效。地球是"一位半老徐娘"，但她仍在想方设法保持其青春活力以及美貌。

地球的年龄

在计算地质时间这一重要的地质学参数时，开尔文勋爵的推断与现实相去甚远，这时就有必要重新检验这一计算方法。开尔文认为，如果地球是以现在的速度持续变冷的，那么，在仅仅几百万年前，其表面的炎热程度就已无法适宜生命的存在了。赫顿首先阐释了地质年代的概念，他在那句著名的格言中说：在这个问题上，"我们既找不出起始的痕迹，也看不到结束的迹象"，来自世界各地的许多出色的、富有奉献精神的学者经过艰苦的研究积累了大量数据，这些都进一步证实了这一观点的正确性。寒武纪以来，无论是有机世界还是无机世界都发生了巨大的变化，熟知这些的地质学家都知道，根本不可能将地球的生命或者地球上生物的发展史压缩到微不足道的两千万或三千万年。山脉一个接一个地不断缓慢地生长、衰退，新的山脉在旧的山脉中孕育而生，甚至就在旧的山脉的废墟上拔地而起；有机体的演化链持续缓慢地发展，数量巨大，种类繁多；这一切都清楚地表明了地质年代的漫长。回顾人类的发展史，我们可以对地质年代的持续时间有一个大概的认识，人类产生于最近的一个地质年代的最近一小段时间，却已从仅拥有最原始的生产资料和最初级的文化，成功发展到遍及地球的每一个角落，并且创造出了无数的语言和文明。

赫胥黎在 1869 年地质学会上的演讲中挑战了这一难题，他一针见血地指出："难道地球仅仅是一个在不断变冷的物体，'就像马车上用的热水罐'或者'一块球形砂岩'吗？"同时他还认为，至少存在一些作用可以使地球的热量再生或延缓其衰减。

所以，我们只能说，这位给地质年代加上了一个狭窄界限的伟大物理学家，为后继的物理学家们做了准备工作，后者已经证明，地球在它的放射性物质中存储了一种"隐藏的储备"，这使得由于放射性而损失的能量可以持续再生，并由此延长完全衰变所需的时间。后来的这些物理学家推算出的地球年龄要长得多；尽管对于宇宙进化论者和天文学家们来说这段时间是微不足道的，但已经比我们原先预想的

embarrassed by the wealth poured into our hands. So far from the last century's urge to "hurry up our phenomena", we are almost at a loss for phenomena enough to fill up the time.

The far-sighted genius of Lord Rutherford and Lord Rayleigh first saw the bearing of the rate of disintegration of radioactive substances in the minerals of rocks on the age of the parts of the earth-crust built of them. The extension and supplementing of this work, by Joly, Holmes and others, has now enabled us to look to the disintegration of uranium, thorium and potassium, as the most promising of many methods that have been used in the endeavour to ascertain the age of those parts of the earth-crust that are accessible to observation. These methods also promise a means of dating the geological succession of Eras and Periods in terms of millions if not hundreds of thousands of years.

The Earth Pulse

The decline and early death to which Lord Kelvin's dictum had condemned the Earth, according so little with the vigour displayed in its geological story, is now transformed into a history of prolonged though not perennial youth. It was for Joly, of whose work the extent, variety and fruitfulness are scarcely yet fully appreciated, to take the next step and see in the release of radioactive energy a mechanism which could drive the pulse that geologists had so long felt, and that Suess had so brilliantly diagnosed. As Darwin found the missing word for Lyell, so Joly in his theory of thermal cycles has indicated the direction of search for a mechanism to actuate the rhythm of Suess.

In Joly's conception, the running down of the Earth's energy, though a continuous process, was, through the intervention of radioactivity, converted into a series of cycles, during each of which relative movements of sea and land must occur; downward movements of the continents, associated with positive encroachments of the sea; upward movements, with retreat of the sea, the formation of wide land masses, and the ridging of strata to form mountain ranges. Thus he forged a link that could unite the continental or epeirogenic movement with orogenic or mountain movement.

The visible parts of mountains and continents, as well as their lower and hidden portions, or "roots", are made of comparatively light rocks. In order to stand up as they do, their roots must be embedded in denser matter, in which they "float" like icebergs in water. A far larger mass must exist below than is visible above, and the bigger the upstanding part the bigger the submerged root. Over the larger area of the ocean floor, on the other hand, the thickness of material of low density must be very slight, and the denser layer must come close to the surface.

Thermal Cycles

The study of earthquakes, to which the Seismology Committee of the British Association

要长得多了，以至于我们为突然涌入自己手中的财富而感到不安。从上个世纪提出"加速我们对地质现象的认识"的口号到现在，我们几乎无法用现象将地质年代填满。

富有远见的天才卢瑟福勋爵和瑞利勋爵首先发现了岩石矿物中放射性物质的衰变速率与它们所在的那部分地壳的年龄之间的关系。乔利、霍姆斯和其他一些学者对这方面的工作做了扩展和补充，这使得可以通过铀，钍和钾的衰变来确定可观测到的地壳的年龄，这也是众多方法中最可靠的一个。该方法还可以用于地质年代序列中代和纪的确定，而代和纪的时间跨度为几十万年甚至几百万年。

地球的脉动

衰落和早亡是开尔文勋爵对地球所持的观点，这种判断与地质历史上地球所表现出的活力不相符合，现在人们转而认为地球虽不是青春永驻，但其寿命也比原来预计的要长得多。乔利的著作虽然缺乏广度、多样性以及实用性，但却受到了普遍赞赏，这是因为他相比开尔文又进了一步，在放射性能量的释放中观察到了一种可以驱动地球脉动的机制，而这种脉动早已被地质学家们所感知，并且修斯也曾英明地指出过这种脉动。如同达尔文为赖尔所做的补充工作一样，乔利在他的热循环理论中，也表现出了寻找修斯所称的律动的驱动机制的倾向。

乔利认为，地球能量的消耗虽然是一个连续的过程，但可以通过放射性活动的介入转化为一系列的循环，每个循环期间，海陆的相对运动必定出现；陆块的下沉运动对应着海侵；陆块的上升对应海退，形成了宽广的陆地，地层脊状隆起形成了山脉。由此，他成功地将大陆的运动或造陆作用与山脉的运动或造山运动关联起来。

山脉与陆地的可见部分及其下部的隐藏部分，即"根部"，都是由相对较轻的岩石构成的。而为了能够保持它们今天的屹立不倒，其根部必须嵌在密度大一些的物质中，就像冰山浮在水中一样。下部质量要远远大于上部的可见部分，并且外部直立的部分越大埋没的根部也就越大。而另一方面，在广阔的大洋底部，低密度物质的厚度必然会很小，而密度较大的层也必然会离地表很近。

热 循 环

英国科学促进会地震学委员会为地震研究作出了卓越贡献，他们通过研究振动

has made outstanding contributions, has yielded, from the times taken in transmission of vibrations through the Earth, the best information as to the nature and state of the interior. It has proved that the dense layer is solid at the present time. It is probably no coincidence that the Earth is also but just recovering from what is possibly the greatest period of mountain building, if not the greatest negative movement of ocean retreat, that it has ever experienced.

But solidity cannot be the permanent condition of the substratum. Heat is generated in it by its own radioactivity, but, according to the terms of the hypothesis, cannot escape, in consequence of the higher temperature generated in the continental rocks which cover it. It is therefore retained in the substratum and stored as latent heat of liquefaction, so that, within a period which has been calculated approximately in millions of years, complete melting of the sub-crust must ensue.

The resulting expansion of the liquefied stratum will have at least two effects of great importance to us. In the first place, the unexpanded superficial layers will be too small to fit the swelling interior. They will, therefore, suffer tension, greater on the ocean floor than on land, and cracking and rifting will occur, with intrusion and extrusion of molten rock. In the second place the continental masses, now truly floating in a substratum which has become fluid and less dense than before, will sink deeper into it, suffering displacement along the rift cracks or other planes of dislocation. As a result the ocean waters, unchanged in volume, must encroach on the edges of the continents, and spread farther and farther over their surfaces.

Thus we have the mechanism which Suess vainly sought, causing positive movements of the oceans, their waters spreading over wide stretches of what was formerly continental land, and laying down as sediment upon it the marine stratified rocks which are our chief witness of the rhythmic advances of the sea.

This condition, however, cannot be permanent, for by convection of the fluid basic substratum, supplemented by the influence of tides within it, and the slow westward tidal drag of the continental masses towards and over what had been ocean floor, there will now be dissipation of its heat, mainly into the ocean waters, at a rate much faster than it has been or could be accumulated. Resolidification ensues, and again there are two main consequences. First, the stratum embedding their roots having now become more dense, the continental masses rise, and as they do so the ocean waters retreat from their margins and epicontinental seas, leaving bare as new land, made of the recently deposited sediments, the areas previously drowned. Secondly, the expanded crust, left insufficiently supported by the withdrawal of shrunken substratum, will suffer from severe tangential stress, and, on yielding, will wrinkle like the skin of a withering apple. The wrinkles will be mountain ranges, formed along lines of weakness such as those at continental margins; and they will be piled up and elevated, to suffer from the intense erosion due to water action upon their exposed and upraised rocks.

穿过地球的时间，得到了最好的关于地球内部性质和状态的信息。已经证实地球的高密度层目前处于固体状态。而地球目前可能刚从有史以来最大规模的一次海退中恢复过来，还有可能是刚从最长周期的造山运动中恢复过来，关于这一点学界可能还没有达成一致。

不过，固体状态并非是地层下部的永久状态。因为根据这一假说，由于其上覆盖的陆地岩石中具有较高的温度，所以地层下部因其本身的放射性而产生的热量便无法逃逸。这些热量会一直保留在地层下部中，并成为潜在的液化热量，这样经过一段时间以后，据推算约为几百万年，地壳下部就会被完全融化了。

对于我们来说，因地层液化导致的膨胀至少会在两方面造成重大的影响。首先，未发生膨胀的最表层会由于太小而无法适应内部的胀大。因此，最表层将受到张力作用，这种作用在洋底要比在陆地上更强烈，并进而产生裂缝和断陷，同时伴随着熔岩的侵入和喷出。其次，地层下部成为液体且密度减小，这时真正漂浮在地层下部中的陆块会向更深处下陷，并沿断开的裂缝或其他断层面发生位移。这导致海水在体积不变的情况下向陆地边缘侵入，并沿陆表不断向内陆蔓延。

这样我们便获得了修斯费尽心思探寻而未果的海洋正向运动的产生机制，海水漫过曾经是陆地的广袤区域，并将海洋中的层状岩石沉积于陆地上，而这正是我们判定节律性海进运动的主要证据。

但是这种状态不会永远持续下去，因为流体状态的基性的地层下部的对流作用，再加上海洋内部潮汐作用的影响，以及缓慢的西向引潮力拖拽着陆块向着或者越过曾经的洋底运动，都会导致热量消散，消散的热量主要被海水吸收，而这种消散的速率要比热量累积的速率快得多。随后发生再次固化，同样会造成两个主要结果。第一，嵌入到根部的地层的密度此时已经变大，陆块上升，因此海水由陆地边缘和陆缘海向后退却，先前被淹没的陆地又重新浮出水面，光秃秃的一片就像是新的陆地一样，其上覆盖着新沉积下来的沉积物。第二，膨大的地壳不足以被收缩的地层下部所支撑，还将受到强烈的剪应力作用，从而导致地壳表层如干瘪的苹果皮一样布满褶皱。这些褶皱会在薄弱地带，例如沿着大陆的边缘形成山系；山系不断地堆积和升高，而裸露出来的被抬高的岩石则面临着水作用带来的强烈侵蚀。

In this, again, we have a mechanism which supplies what was needed by Suess, and one, moreover, which secures the required relationship between continental and mountain movement, between the broader extensions of continental land and the growth of mountains with their volcanoes and earthquakes and the other concomitants of lateral thrust.

Thus a thermal cycle may run its full course from the solid substratum, through a period of liquefaction accompanied by crustal tension, back to solidification and an era of lateral stress: and the stage is set for a new cycle.

Prof. Arthur Holmes, in checking Joly's calculations, has concluded that the length of the cycles in a basic rock substratum should occupy 25-40 million years, a period much too short to fit the major periods of mountain movement, as determined by him from the radioactivity of minerals contained in the rocks. On this evidence the Alpine movement should date back 20-60 millions of years ago, the Hercynian 200-250 millions, and the Caledonian 350-375 million years.

In a preliminary attempt to modify Joly's hypothesis, Holmes postulated the occurrence of similar, but longer cycles (magmatic cycles) in a denser, ultra-basic layer underlying the basic one, the rhythm of which would be nearer to 150 million years. The shorter cycles due to the basic layer are held in part responsible for periods of minor disturbance, and also to account for the individual variations in effect, duration and intensity of the larger ones. Each of the later movements has also evidently been limited and conditioned by the results of foregoing ones, and especially by areas of fracture and weakness on one hand, and by large stable masses composed of rocks intensely consolidated, or already closely packed, on the other.

More recently, Holmes has developed the possibility that the loss of heat is mainly due to convection in the liquid substrata, and that convection is the leading cause of the drifting and other movements of the crust, and the disturbances that have occurred in it. He says:

> "Although the hypothesis involving sub-crustal convection currents cannot be regarded as established, it is encouraging to find that it is consistent with a wide range of geological and geophysical data. Moreover, it is by no means independent of the best features of the other hypotheses. It requires the local operation of thermal cycles within the crust, and it necessarily involves contraction in regions where crustal cooling takes place. It is sufficiently complex to match the astonishing complexities of geological history, and sufficiently startling to stimulate research in many directions".

The phenomena are difficult to disentangle as the number of operating causes has been so great and many of them are not fully understood. But, underlying them all there is

就这样，我们又找到一种修斯所需要的机制，而且该机制确保了陆地和山脉的运动之间的必然关系，以及陆地的广泛扩张和与火山、地震及其他侧向逆冲现象相伴的山脉崛起之间的必然关系。

如此，一次热循环算是完成了它的全过程，从固态的地层下部开始，经过一段时期的液化，其间伴随着地壳拉张，最后再回到固态和侧向应力作用的时期：当然这一阶段又是一个新的循环的开始。

阿瑟·霍姆斯教授利用乔利的计算方法得出，基性岩石的地层下部的循环周期应在两千五百万到四千万年之间，而这个周期太短，与他利用岩石中矿物的放射性测得的山脉运动的周期不相符。根据放射性测年，阿尔卑斯造山运动应该发生在两千万到六千万年以前，海西运动在两亿到两亿五千万年之前，而加里东运动则在三亿五千万到三亿七千五百万年之前。

在一项改进乔利假说的初步尝试中，霍姆斯假定在基性层之下的密度更大的超基性层中，存在一个类似的、但周期更长的循环（岩浆旋回），其节律周期大约为一亿五千万年。基性层的短周期循环是形成较小的周期性扰动的原因之一，同时也造成大的循环周期在效果、持续时间和强度方面的个别变化。很明显，后一次运动会受到前一次运动结果的限制和制约，特别是前一次运动形成的断裂和薄弱的区域，以及由强烈固结的岩石或是已经紧密压实了的岩石构成的较大的稳定陆块。

最近霍姆斯详尽论述了热量损失可能主要是由于液态的地层下部的对流所致，并且这种对流很可能就是造成地壳的漂移和其他运动及其内部扰动的首要原因。他说：

"尽管不能说已经建立起了关于地壳下部对流的假说，但是已发现它与一系列的地质和地球物理数据相一致，这是令人鼓舞的。此外，它还融合了其他假说的优点。该假说要求地壳内部存在局部的热循环作用，在地壳温度降低的地区还会发生收缩。其复杂性足以与地质历史的惊人复杂性相匹配，并且可以促进多个研究方向的发展，这也是十分令人惊叹的。"

由于作用原因非常之多，并且其中有很多还未被理解，因此这些现象还很难解释。但是毫无疑问，隐藏在这些现象之下的就是存在于修斯所看到的地球内部的脉

unquestionably the pulse within pulse which Suess saw, and of which Joly pointed the way to explanation.

The view at which we have arrived is neither strictly uniformitarian nor strictly catastrophic, but takes the best from each hypothesis. As Lyell showed, most of the phenomena of geology can be matched somewhere and sometime on the Earth of today; but it would appear that they have varied in place, intensity, phase and time. And, as Lyell was driven to accept *evolution* to explain the history of life on the Earth, so must we employ the same word to express the life-processes of the Earth itself, as was suggested by Huxley in 1869 and strongly advocated by Sollas in 1883.

The Atlantic and Pacific Oceans

The contrast in outline and structure between the Atlantic and Pacific Oceans had long been noted when Suess formulated and used the differences as the basis of his classification.

The Pacific is bounded everywhere by steep slopes, rising abruptly from profound ocean depths to lofty lands crowned with mountain ranges, parallel to its shores and surrounding its whole area. On the American side the coast range is continued by the Andes. On the Asiatic side chains of mountainous peninsulas and islands, separated from the continent by shallow inland seas, extend in festoons from Kamchatka and Japan to the East Indies, eastern Australia and New Zealand. This mountain ring, as Charles Lapworth said, "is ablaze with volcanoes and creeping with earthquakes", testifying that it has been recently formed and is still unfinished.

The Atlantic Ocean, on the other hand, is not bordered with continuous ranges, but breaks across them all: the Scottish and Welsh ranges, the Armorican range, the continuation of the Pyrenees and Atlas; and, on the American side, the uplands of Labrador, Newfoundland and the eastern States, and the hill ranges of Guiana and Brazil. The Atlantic is in disconformity with the grain of the land, while the Pacific conforms with it. The Pacific has the rock-folds of its ranges breaking like ocean waves towards it as though the land were being driven by pressure to advance upon it, while the Atlantic recalls the effects of fracture under tension.

The middle and southern edges of the Atlantic, however, agree to some extent with the Pacific type. The Caribbean Sea, with the Antilles and the rest of its border girdle, recalls the similar structure of the Mediterranean, as it stretches eastwards, with breaks, to the East Indian Archipelago; while the Andes are continued to Antarctica in a sweeping curve of islands. The rest of the Indian Ocean is of Atlantic type, as seen in the shores of eastern Africa and western Australia.

344

动之中的脉动，而乔利指明了解释它们的方法。

我们所得到的观点，既不是严格的均变论也不是严格的灾变论，而是汲取了两者的优点。正如赖尔所展示的那样，大多数地质现象可以与现今地球上某些地方某个时候的现象相符；但在地点、强度、阶段和时间上会有所不同。并且正如赖尔不得不接受**进化**一词来解释地球上的生命史一样，我们也不得不用同一个单词来表达地球本身的生命过程，这一观点由赫胥黎于 1869 年提出并在 1883 年得到了索拉斯的强烈支持。

大西洋和太平洋

人们早已注意到大西洋和太平洋在轮廓和构造上的差别，后来修斯对此进行了详尽的描述并将这些差别视为大洋分类的基础。

太平洋的边界布满了陡坡，这些陡坡由大洋深处陡峭地上升至被山系环绕着的高高的陆地上，平行于海岸线并环绕着整个太平洋。其中在美洲一侧，海岸山脉与安第斯山脉相连。而在亚洲一侧，则是一连串多山的半岛和岛屿，浅水内陆海将其与大陆分开，它们从堪察加半岛到日本，一直延伸到东印度群岛、澳大利亚东部和新西兰。如查尔斯·拉普沃思所说，该环太平洋山系"喷发着火山、孕育着地震"，这证明，这里刚刚形成并且这个过程尚未结束。

大西洋的边界则没有连着连续的山系，而是将下列山系和地区分割开来：苏格兰和威尔士山系、阿莫里凯山系、比利牛斯山脉以及阿特拉斯山脉的延伸等等；在美洲一侧为拉布拉多高地、纽芬兰岛与美国东部地区以及圭亚那与巴西的丘陵。大西洋与陆地呈假整合状态，而太平洋与陆地之间则表现为整合状态。太平洋边界的山脉发育有岩层的褶皱，就像海水朝着它冲击，仿佛陆地正在压力作用下向着它运动，而大西洋则在张力作用下发生断裂。

不过，大西洋的中部和南部边缘在一定程度上与太平洋类型一致。加勒比海，包括安的列斯群岛以及其他边缘带与地中海的构造类似，均向东延伸，中间存在断裂，一直到东印度群岛。安第斯山脉则是通过一个巨大的岛弧链与南极洲相连。印度洋的其余部分属大西洋型，这正如在非洲东部和澳大利亚西部海岸所看到的那样。

Continental Drift

Another feature of the Atlantic is the parallelism of much of its eastern and western coasts, the meaning of which has often attracted the speculations of geologists and geographers. With a little stretch of the imagination, and some ingenuity and elasticity of adjustment, plans or maps of the opposite sides may be fitted fairly closely, particularly if we plot and assemble the real edges of the continents, the steep slopes which divide the "shelves" on which they stand from the ocean depths. This has suggested the possibility that the two sides may once have been united, and have since broken and drifted apart until they are now separated by the ocean.

This view, outlined by others, has been emphasised by Wegener and dealt with by him in full detail in his work on "The Origin of Continents and Oceans", and it now plays a leading part in what is known as the Wegener theory of continental drift. The hypothesis is supported by the close resemblances in the rocks and fossils of many ages in western Europe and Britain to those of eastern North America; by community of the structures by which these rocks are affected; and by the strong likeness exhibited by the living animals and plants on the two sides, so that they can only be referred to a single biological and distributional unit, the Palaearctic region.

The hypothesis, however, did not stop at this; and in the South Atlantic and certain other areas Wegener and his followers have also given good reasons for believing that continental masses, once continuous, have drifted apart.

Broad areas in southern Africa are built of rocks known as the Karroo Formation, of which the lower part, of late Carboniferous age, is characterised especially by species of the strange fern-like fossil plants *Glossopteris* and *Gangamopteris*. Associated with them are peculiar groups of fossil shells and fossil amphibia and reptiles. Similar rocks, with similar associations and contents, in Peninsular India have been named the Gondwana Formation. Comparable formations also occupy large regions in Australia, Tasmania and New Zealand, in Madagascar, in the Falkland Islands and Brazil, and in Antarctica.

The correspondence between these areas is so close that Suess supposed they must at that date have been connected together by lands, now sunk beneath the sea, and he named the continent thus formed Gondwanaland after the Indian occurrences. The break-up of this land can be followed from a study of the rocks, and it was a slow process, its steps occupying much of Mesozoic time. Dr. A. L. du Toit's comparison of South African rocks with those of Brazil and elsewhere in South America favours even a closer union than this between the units now scattered.

One of the most remarkable features shown by these rocks in all the areas mentioned, but to varying extents, is the presence of conglomerates made of far-travelled boulders, scratched like those borne by the modern ice-sheets of Greenland and the Antarctic,

大陆漂移

大西洋的另一个特征是其东海岸和西海岸的大部分相互平行，其中的意义常常引起地质学家和地理学家的思考。其实只需稍加想象，在此基础上再发挥一点儿创造力和灵活性，那么大西洋两岸的平面图或地图就变得非常吻合了，尤其是当我们将实际的大陆边缘，即将"大陆架"与大洋深处分割开来的陆峭的斜坡绘出并拼到一起的时候，上述结论就变得更加明显了。这表明大西洋两侧曾经很可能是一体的，只是后来发生破裂并漂移开来，直到现在被大洋所分开。

这个前人总结出的观点，后来得到魏格纳的特别强调，并在其著作《海陆起源》一书中做了详细分析，现在这一观点已成为魏格纳大陆漂移学说的最核心部分。该学说得到了许多证据的广泛支持，包括：欧洲西部和大不列颠岛与北美东部多个地质时期的化石和岩石极为相似；影响这些岩石的构造是一致的；此外，两岸现存动植物也表现出强烈的相似性，由此可推断出，它们都属于同一个生物学单元和分布单元，即古北区。

但这一学说并未止于此；魏格纳及其追随者们在南大西洋和其他一些地区也找到了充分的证据证明大陆块曾经是一个整体，后来才漂移开来。

非洲南部的广阔区域由卡鲁岩系组成，其下部形成于晚石炭纪，以舌羊齿属和圆舌羊齿属奇特的似蕨类植物化石为特征。同时还伴有罕见的壳体化石和两栖类与爬行类化石群。而在印度半岛上也有含有相似群落及物种的岩系，被称为冈瓦纳岩系。另外，在澳大利亚、塔斯马尼亚、新西兰、马达加斯加、福克兰群岛（阿根廷称马尔维纳斯群岛，英国与阿根廷争议地区）以及巴西和南极大陆等地区也有大片类似的岩系。

这些地区之间具有如此惊人的相似性，这使得修斯认为，那个时候这些地区是由陆地联系在一起的，而现在这些陆地已被大海淹没，他根据印度冈瓦纳地区的地质产状将他构建的这个大陆命名为冈瓦纳古陆。可以通过对岩石的研究来探求该大陆的分裂过程，但这是一个缓慢的过程，其各个步骤占据了中生代的大部分时间。迪图瓦博士对南非与巴西及南美洲其他地区的岩石作了比较，发现它们之间的关系比它们与现在分散于其旁边的那些岩石的关系还要密切。

所有上述地区的岩石所表现出的一个最显著的特征就是，不同程度地存在着由经过长途搬运的漂砾所构成的漂砾，这些漂砾被刮擦的痕迹与格陵兰岛及南极地区

associated with other deposits of a glacial nature, and often resting upon typical glaciated surfaces. There is no possible escape from the conclusion that these areas, now situated in or near the tropics, suffered an intense glaciation. This was not a case of mere alpine glaciers, for the land was of low relief and not far removed from sea-level, but of extensive ice-sheets on a far larger scale than the glaciation of the northern parts of the New and Old Worlds in the Pleistocene Ice Age. I have never seen any geological evidence more impressive or convincing than that displayed at Nooitgedacht, near Kimberley; while the illustrations and other evidence published by David and Howchin from Australia are equally striking.

Du Toit's work on these glacial deposits brings out two remarkable facts; first, that the movement of the ice was southerly, pole-ward and away from the equator, the opposite to what would be expected and to the direction of the Pleistocene ice-movement; secondly, that the ice in Natal invaded the land from what is now sea to the north-east.

When it is realised that at this period there is no evidence of glacial action in northern Europe or America, but a climate in which grew the vegetation that formed the coal seams of our Coal Measures, it is clear that we are not dealing with any general refrigeration of the globe, even if that would produce such widespread glaciation: we are face to face with a special glaciation of Gondwanaland.

On both sides of the Atlantic these glacial episodes in Carboniferous times were followed by dry and desert climates in Triassic time, and these by violent volcanic outbursts. Nor are the rocks alike only in mode of formation: the structures by which they are traversed correspond; while even in details there is remarkable agreement, as in the peculiar manganese deposits, and the occurrence of diamonds in "pipes" of igneous rock, both east and west of the Ocean.

Rather than face the difficulties presented by the subsidence of lands connecting the severed portions of Gondwanaland, as pictured by Suess, Wegener has preferred—and in this he is supported by Du Toit and many other geologists—to bring into contact these severed parts, which could be fitted together as nearly as might be expected, considering the dates of severance. Du Toit's map of the period places South America to the west and south of South Africa, Madagascar and India to the east, Antarctica to the south, and Australia farther to the south-east. Such a grouping would form a continent much less wide in extent than that envisaged by Suess, and would offer some explanation of the more remarkable features of the glaciation in the several areas, as well as the problems of the rocks, fossils and structures involved.

In its application to the geology of Gondwanaland the modified hypothesis of Wegener cuts a Gordian knot; but it still leaves a great climatal difficulty, unless we take his further step and conceive that at this date the terrestrial south pole was situated within Gondwanaland. No shift in the axis on which the Earth rotates would, of course, be

的现代冰盖所携带的漂砾类似，并伴有其他一些冰川沉积物，且常常位于典型受到冰川作用的表面上。由此可以得出结论，即现在位于热带或热带附近的这些地区曾遭受过强烈的冰川作用。由于这块陆地的起伏较低并且离海平面也不远，应该不只是高山冰川的作用，而是还涉及广阔的冰盖，其规模比更新世冰期的新大陆和旧大陆北部地区的冰川作用要大得多。在所有我见过的地质学证据中，发现于金伯利附近的努伊特赫达赫的证据最具震撼力和说服力；而戴维和豪钦所发表的在澳大利亚获得的图件和其他一些证据也同样令人惊叹。

迪图瓦关于冰川沉积的工作指出两个值得关注的事实：首先，冰川是向南运动的，远离赤道向极地运动，这与我们的预期以及更新世时冰川的运动方向正好相反；其次，纳塔尔的冰川是从现今是海洋的地方向东北方侵入陆地的。

在北欧和美洲没有发现任何证据表明这一时期受到过冰川作用，相反这一时期的气候适宜植被生长，从而形成了我们现在的煤系中的煤层。当我们意识到这一点时，显然，可以确定，这里所遇到的并不是全球性的变冷，尽管那样可以形成如此广泛分布的冰川；实际上我们面对的是一次冈瓦纳古陆上的特殊的冰川作用。

在大西洋两岸，这些石炭纪的冰川事件之后紧接着的都是三叠纪的干旱的荒漠气候，随后是强烈的火山爆发。岩石也不仅仅在成因类型上相似：根据它们的构造，横向也是可以对比的；此外在细节上也存在显著的一致性，例如在大洋的东西两侧，均有罕见的锰沉积，并且在火成岩的"管道"中发现有金刚石。

修斯提出，因陆地下沉而导致了冈瓦纳古陆的分离，这一观点带来了一系列的问题，但是魏格纳并没有纠缠于这一问题，而是倾向于将各个分离的部分联系起来，并且这一想法得到了迪图瓦和许多地质学家的支持。考虑到已经分开了如此久远的年代，这些陆块之间的吻合程度几乎与预期的一样好。迪图瓦绘制的这一时期的地图中，南非的西面和南面为南美洲，东面为马达加斯加和印度，南面为南极大陆，东南面稍远处为澳大利亚。这一组合构成的大陆在范围上比修斯所预想的要小，并且能够解释在几个地区都见到的更为明显的冰川作用的特征，也能就相关的岩石、化石和构造问题给出一些解释。

将改进后的魏格纳假说应用到冈瓦纳古陆的地质概况中，一些难题便迎刃而解了；但是仍旧遗留了一个气候方面的大难题，若使其得到合理解释，除非我们进一步假设在这一时期地球的南极位于冈瓦纳古陆内部。当然，地球的自转轴很可能没

possible, nor is it postulated: only a drifting at that date of continental land across the pole.

If a hypothesis of drift be admitted for Gondwanaland, it would be illogical to deny its application to other regions, including the north Atlantic. I have already mentioned some facts in its favour. Others are the resemblances of all sedimentary rocks on the two sides from the Cambrian to the Ordovician, and from the Devonian to the Trias; the links between the structures of the land, as, for example, between Ireland and Newfoundland; and the instance given by Prof. E. B. Bailey in his address to Section C in 1928. As Bailey then pointed out, the great Caledonian range which crosses Scotland, northern England and Wales from north-east to south-west on its course from Scandinavia is affected and displaced by the east to west Armorican (Hercynian) chain extending across from Brittany to South Wales. "The crossing of the chains, begun in the British Isles, is completed in New England"; and from here the Armorican structure continues its westerly course. This is where it should cross if the continent of North America were brought back across the Atlantic and placed in the position which, according to Wegener, it would fit into in the European coast! Can the Pilgrim Fathers have ever dreamed of such a link between the Old England and the New?

The hypothesis of continental drift gave rich promise of solving so many difficult problems that it was hailed by many classes of investigators almost as a panacea. Geographers have seen in it an explanation of the forms of continents and the position of peninsulas, islands and mountains; meteorologists have found it the solution of some of the problems of past climates and their anomalies of distribution over the world; biologists hope to get help with the intense complexities in the distribution of forms of life and many strange facts in migration, and palaeontologists with similar difficulties among the ancient faunas and floras as revealed by their fossil remains; geodesists have welcomed escape from the rising and sinking of the crust, so difficult to reconcile with the demands of isostatic equilibrium; and it has been already stated that drift forms a vital factor in Joly's thermal cycles.

But there has been no lack of criticism in all these directions. It has been assailed on one hand for the detail attempted in its geographical restorations, and on the other hand for its vagueness. Prof. Schuchert quotes Termier as saying that it is "a beautiful dream, the dream of a great poet. One tries to embrace it, and finds that he has in his arms but a little vapour or smoke: it is at the same time alluring and intangible". It has been objected that "no plausible explanation of the mechanics involved has been offered"; that the continental connexions postulated present by no means so close a match, when fitted together, as has been claimed, in the structure or the nature of either igneous or sedimentary rocks; that there is good evidence of extensive vertical movements in recent earthquakes, in the accumulation of tremendous thicknesses of sediment indicative of shallow-water from base to summit, and in the growth of coral reefs; that Central America and the Mediterranean are a difficult obstacle; and that the known distribution of the Karroo fossil reptiles is not by any means what the hypothesis demands.

有发生过移动,也不能假设它发生了移动:唯一的可能是那时大陆漂移并穿过了极点。

如果承认了冈瓦纳古陆的漂移这一假设,那么否定这一原则在其他地区包括北大西洋地区的应用就是不符合逻辑的。关于这一点,我在前面已经提到了一些有利的事实。此外还包括:北大西洋两侧从石炭纪到奥陶纪、从泥盆纪到三叠纪的所有沉积岩都非常相似;大陆构造之间的联系,例如,纽芬兰岛和爱尔兰之间;以及贝利教授在 1928 年 C 分会的致辞中给出的那个例子。正如贝利当时指出的那样,巨大的加里东山脉从斯堪的纳维亚起,由东北向西南依次穿过苏格兰、北英格兰以及威尔士,它受到东西向的从布列塔尼延伸至南威尔士的阿莫里凯(海西)山系的影响,并发生位移。"两列山系的交叉始于不列颠群岛,止于新英格兰";阿莫里凯山系从新英格兰又继续向西延伸。根据魏格纳的理论,如果将北美大陆从大西洋彼岸移过来,那么这里就是它应该的位置,并且能够与欧洲海岸相吻合!那些于 1620 年移居美国的清教神父们做梦也想不到新、旧英格兰之间会有这样一种联系吧?

大陆漂移学说为许多难题的解决带来了曙光,因此受到多个学科的研究者的热烈欢迎,几乎把它看成了包治百病的灵药。地理学家们认为可以利用它来解释大陆的形成以及半岛、岛屿和山脉位置所在;气象学家们已经利用它解决了古气候中的一些疑问以及全球气候分布的异常;生物学家们则希望它可以有助于理解生命形式分布的极端复杂性以及许多奇特的迁移现象,对于古生物学家们来说,它有助于解决化石遗迹所揭示的古代动、植物群落中存在的类似难题;大地测量学家们则摆脱了地壳上升与下沉难以符合地壳均衡状态的问题;另外,大陆漂移也是乔利的热循环理论中一个非常重要的因子。

不过,在上述各个方面也不乏批评的声音。质疑一方面针对其地理复位的细节问题,另一方面则是针对它的模糊性。舒克特教授引用泰尔米埃的话说,这是"一个美丽的梦想,一个伟大诗人的梦想。当你试图去拥抱它时,却发现仅仅是一缕烟雾在怀:它迷人但又难以捉摸"。反对者们认为它"没有对大陆漂移的机制给出可靠的解释";如果真将大陆拼在一起,那么无论是火成岩还是沉积岩,其构造和性质所反映出来的大陆之间的联系决不会像所宣称的那样如此吻合;近期的地震活动、从低地变为山峰的浅海相巨厚沉积物的堆积以及珊瑚礁的生长都可以很好地证明大规模垂直运动的存在;中美洲和地中海也是一个难以逾越的障碍;而已知的卡鲁化石中爬行类化石的分布也与该学说完全不符。

If the idea of drift be accepted, it cannot be regarded as a royal road out of all our difficulties, nor can it be the only form of earth-movement to be reckoned with. The late J. W. Gregory, whose life was sacrificed to geological discovery, studied exhaustively the geological history of the Atlantic and Pacific Oceans, both as revealed by the sedimentary rocks and fossils on their borders, and by the distribution of life today. He found that, according to our present knowledge, in the two oceans, facilities for migration have fluctuated from time to time, periods of great community of organisms alternating with periods of diversity. Again, at some times connexion seems to have been established north of the equator, at others to the south; and we cannot ignore the possibility of migration across polar lands or seas when terrestrial climates have differed from the present. The facts of life distribution are far too complex to be explained by any single period of connexion followed by a definite breaking apart, even if that took place by stages. Mrs. Reid, too, has pointed out that resemblances between the Tertiary floras of America and Europe actually increased at the time when the Atlantic should have been widening. Unless continental drift has been a more complicated process than anyone has yet conceived, it seems impossible to escape from some form of the "land bridges" of the older naturalists:

> "Air-roads over islands lost—
> Ages since 'neath Ocean lost—"

We have no right to expect greater simplicity in the life of a planet than in that of an organism.

As the question of drift must in the last appeal be one of fact, it is not unnaturally expected that the real answer will come from measurements of longitude and latitude with greater exactness and over periods longer than has yet been possible. None of the measurements hitherto made has indicated variations greater than the limits of errors of observation. Two things, however, may militate against a definite answer from this source. Many parts of the crust, such as the shield-like masses of Archaean rock, may have completed their movement, or be now moving so slowly that the movement cannot be measured. Careful selection of locality is essential, and at present we have little guidance. Also, as the displacement of crust must be dependent on the condition of its substratum, it will be a periodic phenomenon and the rate of movement may vary much in time. According to the theory of thermal cycles the sub-crust is at present solid, and may not permit of drift. Drift, according to Joly and Holmes, is a cyclical phenomenon; if present-day observations were to give a negative result they would not necessarily disprove it.

The occurrence of recumbent rock-folds, and nearly horizontal slides or "nappes" in mountain regions, gives positive proof that parts of the upper earth-crust have moved over the lower. In the North-west Highlands of Scotland, a sliding of at least ten miles was proved by Peach and Horne, and in Scandinavia it amounts to sixty miles. For mountain packing as a whole the figures already given are far larger, while in Asia, Argand has stated that packing of more than 2,000 miles has occurred. Thus, when all is said and done, movements on a colossal scale are established facts, and the question

352

即使大陆漂移的观点被接受，也不能把它当作是解决所有难题的终南捷径，也不能将大陆漂移视为地球运动的唯一形式。将毕生都献给地质探索事业的已故的格雷戈里，对大西洋和太平洋的地质历史做了详细研究，研究对象为两者边界处的沉积岩和化石以及现今的生物分布。他发现，根据我们现有的知识，在两个大洋中，迁移的路径是随时间而变化的，生物的大群落周期与多样性周期交替出现。此外，一些生物之间的关联有时是在赤道以北建立的，有时则在赤道以南；当陆地气候不同于现在时，我们不能忽略生物有穿过极地大陆或大洋而迁移的可能性。生物分布的实际情况非常之复杂，所以我们不能用任何最初相互关联而后以特定的方式分离这样的单一周期来解释，即使这种过程是阶段性发生的。里德夫人也曾指出，实际上当大西洋变宽以后，美洲和欧洲大陆上的第三纪植物越来越相似了。除非大陆漂移比所有现已构想出的过程还要复杂，否则将不可能摆脱前辈博物学者们提出的诸如"陆桥"等的形式：

> "大洋底部的通道消失了——
> 很久以后，岛屿之间的空中通道也消失了——"

我们没有任何理由期望一个行星的生命过程会比一个生物的生命过程还简单。

对于漂移的疑问最终一定会出现，因此我们很自然地会期望通过在尽可能长的时间间隔内对经纬度的精确测量来找出答案。然而迄今为止，还未测到任何大于观测误差极限的变化。因为可能有两方面的问题妨碍了通过这个途径找到确定的答案。首先，地壳的很多部分，比如太古代岩石构成的地盾状物质等，可能已经完成了运动过程，或者现在已经运动得非常缓慢以致根本无法测定。所以，仔细地选择观测点是很有必要的，而现在我们没有任何相关的线索。再者，由于地壳的位移取决于其地层下部的状态，所以它应该是一种周期性现象，并且其运动速率随时间的变化也很大。根据热循环理论，目前地壳下部处于固态，所以可能不会发生漂移。按照乔利和霍姆斯的观点，大陆漂移是一种循环现象，因此即使现在观测到的结果与该理论不符，也不足以用来反驳这一理论。

平卧褶皱以及山区近乎水平的滑动构造或"推覆体"的存在，为部分上地壳在下地壳之上运动提供了有力证据。皮奇和霍恩证实，在苏格兰西北高地上，滑动距离至少有 10 英里，而在斯堪的纳维亚则达到了 60 英里。因为山脉是作为一个整体进行堆叠，因此这些数字已经相当之大，而阿尔冈指出，在亚洲有些地方堆叠距离超过 2,000 英里。因此归根结底，大规模的运动已是不争的事实，而接下来的问题是，

of the future is how far we shall accept the scheme of drift due to Wegener, or one or other of the modifications of it. It is for us to watch and test all the data under our own observation, feeling sure that we shall have to adapt to our own case Galileo's words "e pur si muove".

Rock Folding and Mountain Birth

Ever since it was realised that the inclination and folding of rocks must be attributed to lateral or tangential stress and not solely to uplift, shrinkage of the interior of the Earth from its crust has been accepted as the prime mover, and whichever of the current theories we adopt, we cannot deny the efficacy of so powerful a cause.

The general course of events in the formation of a mountain range is fairly well known: the slow sinking of a downfold in the crust during long ages; the filling of this with sediment *pari passu* with the sinking, and associated softening of the sub-crust due to accumulated heat; the oncoming of lateral pressure causing wave-like folds in the sediments and the base on which they rest; the crushing of folds together until, like water waves, they bend over and break by over-driving from above or, it may be, under-driving from below; fracture of the compressed folds and the travelling forward for great distances of slivers or "nappes" of rock, generally of small relative thickness but of great length and breadth, and sliding upon floors of crushed rock; the outpouring and intrusion of igneous rocks, lubricating contacts and complicating the loading of the sediments; metamorphism of many of the rocks by crystallisation at elevated temperatures and under stress, with the development of a new and elaborate system of planes of re-orientation and movement; and elevation of the whole, either independently or by thickening with compression and piling up to bring about a fresh equilibrium.

Such a course of events would be brought about by lateral pressure developed during the consolidation phase of each of the thermal or magmatic cycles. At each period of their building, mountains have arisen along lines of weakness in the crust, especially coast lines and the steep slopes marking the limits between continents and ocean basins. This is consistent with Joly's theory that the thrust of ocean beds against land margins is the cause.

The advocates of continental drift point to the siting of ranges across the paths along which the drifting movement is supposed to have occurred, and they consider that the moving masses are responsible; and indeed that the ridging and packing of the crust has in the end checked and stopped the movement. They note that the great western ranges of America occur in the path of any western drift of that continent, the Himalayas in the course of the postulated movement of India, the East Indies in front of Australia; and that the Alpine ranges of Europe may be linked with the crushing of Africa towards the north.

The "nappes" of rock, cut off from their origin and sliding for dozens of miles, are a constant source of wonder to all who have considered the mechanics of mountain

我们能够在多大程度上接受魏格纳所设想的大陆漂移理论，或是其改进的版本。我们需要通过我们自己的观察来审视和检验所有的数据，我们确信伽利略的那句名言同样适用于我们的工作，那就是"地球依然在动着"。

岩石的褶皱与山脉的诞生

岩石的倾斜与褶皱是由于侧向或剪应力作用而不仅仅是抬升作用的结果，当人们认识到这一点以后，地球内部相对于地壳的收缩就被视为这种运动的主要原动力，并且，套用任何一个现已得到承认的理论，我们都不能否认这个强有力的原动力的效力。

山脉形成过程中各事件发生的一般过程已为大家所熟知，即：在相当长的一段时间内，地壳中向下褶皱的缓慢下沉；沉积物对下沉区的填充随下沉**同时**进行，并伴随着由于热量累积而导致的地壳以下部分的软化；继之而来的侧向应力造成沉积物与其依赖的基底发生波状褶皱；在来自上部的上部驱动力或者来自下部的下部驱动力的作用下，水波状褶皱向一起挤压，直到发生弯曲或直接断裂；受挤压的褶皱产生断裂，而岩石薄板或"推覆体"会向前移动很长一段距离，通常这种岩石很长很宽但比较薄，它们会在碎裂的小石块组成的底面上滑行；火成岩的喷出和侵入，使沉积物之间的接触松动并导致沉积物的荷载复杂化；在温度升高和压力作用的条件下，结晶作用导致许多岩石发生变质，并形成一个经过重新定向和移动的晶面构成的新的复杂体系；然后整体升高，这个升高要么单独完成，要么同时伴随着挤压增厚或者堆叠，并最终达到一个新的平衡。

上述过程可能是由于每次热循环或岩浆循环中，固化阶段形成的侧向压力作用导致的。在造山运动的各个阶段，山脉都是沿着地壳的薄弱线隆起的，特别是在位于大陆与洋盆交界处的海岸线以及陡峭的斜坡附近。这与乔利的理论是一致的，他认为海底相对于陆地边缘的挤压是造成山脉隆起的原因。

支持大陆漂移学说的学者指出，山脉坐落在假定的大陆漂移的路径上，他们认为这是运动的陆块所致；实际上，正是地壳的脊状隆起和堆叠最后阻碍并阻止了大陆的继续漂移。他们还指出，美国西部的巨大山系出现在美洲大陆向西漂移的路径上，而喜马拉雅山系位于印度即将要运动的线路上，东印度群岛处于澳大利亚的前缘；此外，欧洲的阿尔卑斯山系可能也与非洲向北的挤压运动相关。

对于研究山脉形成机制的人们来说，岩石的"推覆体"脱离原来的位置并发生几十英里的滑动，这一直是一个疑点。与其巨大的长度和宽度相比，这些岩石是如

formation. They are so thin as compared with their great length and breadth, that it seems impossible to imagine them moved by any force other than one which would make itself felt throughout their every particle. Such a force is gravitation, and it is of interest that some Alpine geologists and Dr. Harold Jeffreys have used it in explanation of them. Prof. R. A. Daly has also adopted gravitation on an even greater scale in his theory of continental sliding: and one cannot fail to notice the increasing use of the term "crust-creep" by those working on earth-movement.

Is there no other force, comparable in its method of action to gravitation, but capable of producing movement of the earth-crust in a direction other than downhill? Is it not possible, for example, that the tidal influence of the Moon and Sun, which is producing so much distortion of the solid Earth that the ocean tides are less than they would be otherwise, and, dragging always in one direction, is slowing down the Earth's rotation, may exert permanent distorting influence on the solid Earth itself? May it not be that such a stress, if not sufficiently powerful to produce the greater displacements of continental drift and mountain building, may yet take advantage of structures of weakness produced by other causes, and itself contribute to the formation of nappes and to other movements of a nature at present unexplained?

Geological Surveying

Our knowledge of geology has been gained by the survey of the rocks, the study of their structures, and the delineation of both upon maps and sections. This work is being accomplished by geologists all over the world, and Great Britain and the Empire have contributed their full share. It is therefore opportune to note that there has just been celebrated the centenary of the Geological Survey of Britain and, with it, the opening of the new Geological Museum at South Kensington.

A century ago H. T. de la Beche, one of the devoted band of pioneer workers then studying the geology of the country, offered to "affix geological colours to the new maps of Devon and Cornwall" then in course of issue by the Ordnance Survey. His offer was accepted, and, at his own expense and on his own feet, he carried out a geological survey of some 4,000 square miles. In 1835 he was appointed to continue this task, with a small salary and a few assistants. Thus was started the first official geological survey, an example widely followed by other nations and dominions. De la Beche's conception included also a Museum of economic and practical geology, a Library, a Record of Mines, for which he secured support from a strong committee of the British Association in 1838, and a School of Mines for the scientific and technical education of those to be employed in the survey or exploitation of mineral resources. In these objects, and especially the last, he was warmly supported by the Prince Consort. He lived to see his visions all come true, as he collected round himself that wonderful band of surveyors, investigators, writers and teachers, which included such men as Playfair, Logan, Ramsay, Aveline, Jukes, Forbes, Percy, Hooker, and Huxley.

356

此之薄，除非这个力能作用到"推覆体"上每一点，否则很难想象是什么力能让它运动。而这个力就是重力，有趣的是，一些研究阿尔卑斯山脉的地质学家以及哈罗德·杰弗里斯博士已经用重力来解释这个现象了。戴利教授在其大陆滑动理论中，更大范围地应用了重力；而且，人们一定会注意到研究地球运动的学者们正越来越频繁地用到"地壳蠕动"这一术语。

难道就不存在这样一种力，其作用方式与重力相当，却能够造成地壳在某一方向上运动而不只是向下运动？比如我们知道太阳和月球引起的潮汐作用使固体地球发生了巨大的扭曲，从而在一定程度上降低了海洋潮汐作用，并且这种潮汐作用总是向着一个方向拖拽，那么难道就不存在这样一种可能，即这种潮汐作用使地球的自转速度减缓，并对固体地球造成永久性的扭曲效应？难道就不能是下面这种情况，即存在这样一种应力，虽然不足以使大陆漂移的距离更大或形成山脉，但却能在其他原因造成的薄弱构造上，作用形成推覆或者目前还无法解释的其他运动？

地质调查

我们的地质知识是通过对岩石的调查、对其构造的研究以及地图和剖面图的描绘获得的。这项工作是由全世界的地质学家共同完成的，同时得到了英国政府及皇室的大力支持和帮助。而凑巧，英国地质调查局刚举行过其百年庆典，同时一个新的地质博物馆在南肯辛顿开馆。

一个世纪以前，当英国地形测量局出版德文郡和康沃尔郡的地图时，当时研究国家地质的先驱者之一亨利·德拉贝什提议"将德文郡和康沃尔郡的新地图加上地质颜色"。他的这一建议得到了采纳，并且他还自费徒步完成了 4,000 平方英里的地质调查。1835 年，他奉命继续完成这项任务，但仅有少量的薪水和几个助手。第一次官方地质调查就这样开始了，而这也成为后来其他国家和地区广泛效仿的榜样。亨利·德拉贝什的设想还包括建立一座经济地质学和应用地质学的博物馆、一座图书馆、一份矿物记录，而在 1838 年，他的设想得到了强大的英国科学促进会的支持，另外还有一所矿业学校愿意对已被雇佣的即将参与矿产资源勘探的人员进行科技教育。他的这个设想，尤其是最后一个，得到了女王丈夫的热情支持。在他有生之年，他看到了自己的梦想都变为现实，因为他组建的这个团队吸纳了众多优秀的调查员、研究人员、作家和教师，其中包括普莱费尔、洛根、拉姆齐、阿夫利娜、朱克斯、福布斯、珀西、胡克以及赫胥黎等人。

Some of the schemes planned by de la Beche have budded off and grown into large and important entities, rendering conspicuous service to scientific record, education, and research. But the main duties of the Geological Survey remained with it, and have been carried on for a century. These are to map the geology of the country on the largest practicable scale, to describe and interpret the structure of the land, to preserve the evidence on which conclusions have been founded, and to illustrate for students and other workers the geology of the country and its applications to economics and industry. The broad detail of the structure of the whole country is now known, but much new work must be done to keep abreast of or to lead geological thought. For example, the study of the cloak of "superficial deposits", which often cover and conceal the structure of the more solid rocks below, is essential for the proper understanding of soils and agriculture; and a knowledge of the deep-seated geology of the country, which is often widely different from that nearer the surface and thus very difficult to interpret, is vital to the community for the successful location and working of coal and iron, and for tracing supplies of water and oil and other resources at depth.

Evolution of Life

Evolution of life on the Earth has been by no means uniform; there have been periods of waxing and waning which may be attributed to geographical, climatological, and biological influences. The development of large land areas, ranged longitudinally or latitudinally, the invasion of epicontinental seas, the isolation of mediterraneans or inland seas, the splitting of continental areas into archipelagos or the reunion of islands into continuous land, the making of barriers by the rearing of mountain chains or the formation of straits or arms of the sea, the oncoming of desert or glacial climates; all such factors and many others have been of importance in quickening or checking competition, and in accelerating or retarding the evolution of life.

Probably, however, even greater effects have followed the interaction of groups of biological changes on one another. As an example I might recall Starkie Gardner's estimate of the results following upon the first appearance of grasses in the world. This seems to have been not earlier than Eocene, and probably late Eocene times. By the Oligocene they had made good their hold, peculiarities in their growth and structure enabling them to compete with the other vegetation that then existed; and gradually they spread over huge areas of the Earth's surface, formerly occupied by marsh, scrub and forest. They have, as Ruskin says, "a very little strength ... and a few delicate long lines meeting at a point ... made, as it seems, only to be trodden on today, and tomorrow to be cast into the oven"; but, through their easy growth, their disregard of trampling and grazing, and by reason of the nourishment concentrated in their seeds, they provided an ideal and plentiful source of food.

On the establishment of the grasses, we find that groups of animals, which had previously browsed on shrubs and trees, adopted them, with consequent alterations and adaptations

亨利·德拉贝什的部分设想已变为现实并发展壮大成为重要的机构，同时为科学记录、教育和研究等方面提供了重要的帮助。不过地质调查局的主要职责没有变，迄今已履行了一个世纪之久。这些职责就是，以尽可能大的比例尺绘出本国的地质图，用以描述并解释陆地构造、为已确立的结论保留证据、为学生和其他工作者阐释本国的地质状况及其在经济和工业上的应用。对于整个国家的构造，已经掌握了大量详细的资料，不过还有许多新的工作要做，以便跟上甚至引领地质学思想的发展。例如，对掩盖并封闭了许多岩石构造的"浅表沉积"的遮盖物的研究，这一研究对于正确理解土壤和农业是很有必要的；而关于本国的深源地质方面的知识，则对那些需要成功定位和研究煤矿、铁矿以及寻找水源、石油和其他深部资源的组织非常重要，而深部地质通常与近表层地质有很大不同，因此解释起来也非常困难。

生命的进化

地球上生命的进化绝不是一成不变的；受地理、气候、生物等因素的影响，进化周期时长时短。贯穿东西南北的大面积陆地的形成、陆表海的侵入、地中海或内陆海与海洋的隔绝、大陆分裂为群岛以及岛屿重新联合形成整块的陆地、山系抬高导致屏障的产生以及海峡或海湾的形成、正在形成的沙漠或冰川气候等，所有这些因素和其他许多因素一起，共同加剧或阻止了生物的竞争，加速或延缓了生命的进化。

不过，已发生生物学变化的群落之间的相互作用可能会造成更大的影响。我可以引用斯塔基·加德纳对禾本科植物在地球上首次出现造成的结果的评价来作为一个例子。这一事件发生的时间似乎不会早于始新世，很有可能在始新世晚期。到渐新世时这种植物已经成功适应了生长环境，其生长和结构的特性使它们能够与当时存在的其他植被相互竞争；渐渐地，它们遍布了之前被沼泽、灌木和森林所占据的地球表面的广阔区域。正如拉斯金所说的那样，它们的叶子"并不强壮……数根纤弱的叶脉交汇于一点……因此它们似乎生来就是被践踏进而扔进火炉的命运"；然而，就是凭着易生长性、不怕被踩踏或被牧食，并且由于其种子上富集了营养，因而成为一种理想而丰富的食物来源。

我们发现，随着禾本科植物的繁盛，大群原来以灌木和乔木为食的动物开始食用禾本植物，并因此导致它们的牙齿及其他身体结构方面产生了变化和适应性。为

in their teeth and other bodily structures. To follow their food from over-grazed or sun-scorched regions they required to be able to migrate easily and quickly, and it was essential for them to discard sedentary defence and to flee from threatened danger. Such defence as was possible with heels, teeth or horns they retained; but the dominant modifications in their organisation were in the direction of speed as their vital need.

Side by side with this development, and in answer to increasing numbers, came bigger, stronger and speedier carnivores, to feed on prey now so much more abundant, but more difficult to catch. The answer of the grass-feeders, with their specialised hoofs, teeth and bones, better suited to flight than fight, was to seek safety in numbers, and thus develop the herd instinct, with its necessity for leadership and discipline; but this, in turn, provoked a like rejoinder from some types of their enemies.

When it is remembered how much of the meat and drink and life of mankind is bound up with the grasses, including wheat, maize, millet and other grains, sugar-cane, rice and bamboo, we must realise how close is his link with the development just outlined. Practically his whole food supply is provided by them, either directly by the agriculturist who grows little else but grasses, or indirectly by the herdsman whose domestic animals are fed chiefly on the same food. Nor must we forget that almost every one of our domesticated animals has been derived from the gregarious types just mentioned, which have accepted the leadership of man in place of that of their own species.

It is perhaps not too much to say that the magnificent outburst of energy put out by the Earth in the erection of the Alps, Andes and Himalayas in Tertiary times, was trivial in its influence for man's advent and his successful occupation of the Earth in comparison with the gentle but insidious growth of "mere unconquerable grass" and its green carpet of "wise turf", which in some form clothes by far the greater part of the land of the globe.

Development of Brain

The kind of developmental reaction of which this is but a single example must clearly have had influence on bodily features other than bones and horns, teeth and claws, speed and strength; and one of the most striking has been on intellectual development and the size and shape of brain.

We do not, and perhaps can never, know the quality of the material of which the brains of fossil creatures was made, for we have no instrument to pierce the veil of time as the spectroscope has penetrated the abysm of space. But we are even now learning something about their shapes and convolutions, and more about their mass in its relation to the size of the bodies controlled; from the time of the earliest Ordovician fishes, through the history of the amphibia, reptiles, birds and mammals, up to man himself.

了追逐食物，它们必须离开过度牧食地区或者干旱地区，因此它们需要具有灵活快速迁移的能力，而放弃原地的防守并从可能的危险中逃脱对它们来说也是非常必要的。像足跟、牙齿以及角这些可以作为防御工具的器官最终被保留了下来；不过它们机体中最显著的改变是，速度逐渐成为它们至关重要的需求。

与上述进化过程同时发生的是，随着上述动物数量的增长，相应出现了体形更大、更强壮、速度更快的食肉动物，它们以现在数量更多但更难捕获的动物为食。食草动物所特有的蹄、齿和骨骼更适于逃跑而不是战斗，于是它们开始以个体的数量来保障其安全性，并因此逐渐形成了群居的生活习性，同时还发展出了必要的领导者和纪律性；而这一点，反过来又促使它们的部分敌人也同样结群反击。

人类的食物、饮料和生活与禾本植物，包括小麦、玉米、黍子、其他谷物、甘蔗、大米以及竹子等等之间的关系十分密切，当我们想到这点时，我们一定会意识到人类与上述进化过程的关系是多么紧密了。实际上，人类的所有食物都是由它们提供的，有些直接来自于农民种植的禾本植物，有些则间接来自于牧民驯服的以禾本植物为食的动物。我们也一定还记得，我们所驯养的动物几乎全部来自于上面提到的群居动物，只是人类取代了它们的同类而成为其领导者。

悄然而迅速生长的"不屈不挠的小草"和由"聪明的草皮"形成的覆盖了地球上大部分陆地的草毯，相对于这些，似乎可以毫不夸张地说，在第三纪阿尔卑斯山脉、安第斯山脉和喜马拉雅山脉形成时，地球能量的强烈爆发对人类的出现以及人类成功占领地球所产生的影响简直是微不足道。

脑的进化

在所有进化中，脑的进化作用是一个特例，其不仅影响了骨骼与角、牙齿与爪子、速度与力量，更对整体有非常明显的影响；而其中最显著的影响是智力的发育以及大脑的尺寸和形状。

我们不知道，而且可能永远也不会知道化石中生物的脑是由何种性质的物质组成的，因为我们没有任何工具可以像分光镜穿透深空那样越过时间壁垒。不过现在我们已经知道了一些关于脑的形状和脑回的情况，以及脑的质量与它所控制的身体大小之间的关系；涉及范围从最早的奥陶纪鱼类开始，随后经历了两栖类、爬行类、鸟类以及哺乳类，最后发展到人类自己。

The brain of those gigantic if somewhat grotesque reptiles the dinosaurs, the tyrants of Mesozoic time, was relatively tiny. In *Diplodocus*, 80 feet in length and 20 tons in weight, the brain was about the size of a large hen's egg. It is true that there was a big supplementary sacral ganglion which may have taken chief charge of locomotion and helped to secure co-ordination throughout the hinder part of its huge length and bulk; but of true brain there was not more than a quarter of an ounce to control each ton of body and limb; and we begin to understand why they lost the lordship of creation.

The proportion of brain to body improved in those reptiles which took to flying, possibly in relation to their acquisition of warm blood, and in the birds evolved from reptiles; but it is only in mammals that a marked advance is seen. Here the brain of *Uintatherium*, a great rhinoceros-like animal of Eocene date, weighing 2 tons, was about the size of that of a dog. This proportion of half a pound of brain to each ton of body shows how far the mammals had gone, and still had to go. A twelve-stone man of the present day has about $3\frac{1}{2}$ pounds of brain—an amount not far short of half a hundredweight per ton.

Even though we can know nothing of its material, this steadfast growth in the guiding principle, through the millions of centuries that have gone to its development, is surely one of the most remarkable conclusions that we owe to geology. Of all the wonders of the universe of which we have present knowledge, from the electron to the atom, from the virus and bacillus to the oak and the elephant, from the tiniest meteor to the most magnificent nebula, surely there is nothing to surpass the brain of man. An instrument capable of controlling every thought and action of the human body, the most intricate and efficient piece of mechanism ever devised; of piercing the secrets and defining the laws of Nature; of recording and recalling every adventure of the individual from his cradle to his grave; of inspiring or of ruling great masses of mankind; of producing all the gems of speech and song, of poetry and art, that adorn the world, all the thoughts of philosophy and all the triumphs of imagination and insight: it is indeed the greatest marvel of all.

When we contemplate the time and energy, the sacrifice and devotion, that this evolution has cost, we must feel that we are still far from the end of this mighty purpose: that we can confidently look forward to the further advance which alone could justify the design and skill lavished on this great task throughout the golden ages that have gone.

(**136**, 369-379; 1935)

庞大的、并且有些奇怪的爬行动物——恐龙，是中生代的霸主，但它的脑相对来说却很小。例如梁龙，长约 80 英尺，重达 20 吨，而脑却仅仅相当于一只大母鸡的蛋那么大。虽然它还有一个较大的起辅助作用的骶骨神经节，主要负责运动并保证其又大又长的身体的整个后半部分的协调；但真正的脑却很小，平均每吨重的身体才只有不到 1/4 盎司的大脑控制着；由此我们就会明白为什么它们最终失去了统治万物的地位。

在会飞的爬行动物中，脑相对身体的比例有了提高，由爬行类进化而来的鸟类也是如此，前者很可能是因为它们已变为恒温动物；不过，只有在哺乳动物中这一比例才有了明显的增加。尤因他兽是始新世时期一种庞大的像犀牛的动物，体重约两吨，其脑的大小和狗的差不多。每吨躯体上分配的脑约为半磅，从这一比例可以看出其他动物与哺乳动物的差距了，而这个差距还在拉大。如今，一个 12 英石重的人，其脑可达 3.5 磅之重，这相当于每吨躯体上分配的脑将近半英担。

尽管我们对构成脑的物质仍一无所知，但几十亿年以来，大脑一直遵循这一原则稳步发育，这无疑是地质学获得的最引人注目的结论之一。在我们现在的知识范围内，从电子到原子，从病毒和细菌到橡树和大象，从最小的流星到壮丽的星云，所有这些宇宙奇迹都无法超越人脑。人脑能够控制人体所有思想和活动，完美地掌控其设计出的最复杂最有效的运行机制；它能够揭开自然的秘密，明确自然规律；它能够记录和回忆一生中所有难忘的经历；它能够鼓舞或者统治人类大众；它能够创造出精美的言语、歌谣、诗句和艺术，把这个世界装点得如此精彩，它创造出所有的哲学思想和所有的非凡的想象力与洞察力：它确实是宇宙中最伟大的奇迹。

如果仔细计算一下这项进化所耗费的时间和能量、牺牲和投入，我们就一定能感觉到，我们离这一伟大目标的实现还很遥远。不过，我们还是对未来能取得更大的成就充满信心，那些成就足以证明在已经过去的整个黄金时代中，花费在这项伟大任务上的构思和技能都是值得的。

（齐红艳 翻译；李三忠 审稿）

The Fundamental Paradox of the Quantum Theory

R. Peierls

Editor's Note

Rudolph Peierls here writes to counter a recent argument of George Temple, who had apparently demonstrated an inconsistency in quantum mechanics. Temple had assumed that one unique quantum-mechanical operator (a mathematical construct of the theory) must correspond to each of the classical variables of motion, such as positions and momenta. Peierls questions this assumption, noting that the order in which variables appear in the mathematical formalism matters in quantum theory, while it does not in classical theory. In this property of so-called non-commutation, in fact, lies the origin of Heisenberg's uncertainty principle.

THE question of the logical consistency of quantum mechanics has recently been discussed by Prof. G. Temple[1] and by Dr. H. Fröhlich and Dr. E. Guth[2]. Temple arrives at an apparent contradiction, starting from principles which he states to be an essential part of quantum theory. From these principles contradictory results follow, as Temple shows by a perfectly rigorous deduction. (The existence of this deduction seems to have been ignored by Fröhlich and Guth.)

The main assumption used by Temple is that to every function of the classical variables of motion (momentum, co-ordinate, etc.) there corresponds one unambiguously defined operator which may be taken as the representative of this function in quantum mechanics. Although this assumption can be found quite frequently in papers discussing the principles of quantum theory, and even in some text-books, I would like to emphasise that it is not at all necessary and—as one can see from Temple's argument—not even possible in quantum mechanics.

Quantum mechanics requires operators as representatives of physical variables for two purposes: to connect wave functions with experiments, actual or possible, and to calculate the time dependence of the wave function. In order to be able to apply quantum mechanics unambiguously to actual problems, one must, therefore, know (*a*) the operator representing the quantity measured by any given apparatus, and (*b*) the energy operator for any given physical system. Properly speaking, (*a*) is a special case of (*b*), for the properties of a measuring apparatus can always be analysed if its interaction energy with the object in question is known.

If, then, we had an apparatus built in such a way as to measure, say, qp^2q (p denoting the momentum, q the co-ordinate of a particle), this apparatus would be *different*

量子理论的基本佯谬

佩尔斯

编者按

鲁道夫·佩尔斯在本文中反驳了乔治·坦普尔最近的一个观点，当时坦普尔显然已经证明了量子力学中存在一个矛盾。坦普尔认为应该有唯一的量子力学算符（量子理论的数学表示）对应于每个经典的运动变量，如位置和动量。佩尔斯对坦普尔的这个结论表示质疑，他指出在量子理论中变量在数学表达式里的次序是很重要的，而在经典理论中是无关紧要的。事实上，海森堡测不准原理就是源于这种所谓的算符的不对易性。

最近，坦普尔教授[1]、弗勒利希博士和古思博士[2]都讨论了量子力学的逻辑一致性问题。坦普尔从他所陈述的量子理论的基本原理出发得出了一个明显的矛盾。这些矛盾的结果正是坦普尔从量子力学的基本原理出发通过严密精确的推导得到的。（弗勒利希博士和古思博士似乎并没有注意到坦普尔已做的相关推导。）

坦普尔的主要假设是：经典运动变量（如动量、坐标等）的每一个函数都有一个明确定义的算符与之相对应，这些算符可以被视为相应的函数在量子力学中的表示形式。虽然我们可以经常在讨论量子理论基本原理的文章中，甚至是相关的教科书中看到这个假设，但是，我想强调的是，从坦普尔的论证过程中可以看到，在量子力学中，这个假设并不必要，甚至是不合理的。

量子力学需要算符作为物理变量的表示形式有两个目的：一是将波函数与已经实现或可能实现的实验联系起来；二是计算波函数随时间的变化关系。为了能将量子力学明确地应用到实际的问题中，我们必须知道：(a) 任意给定装置所测量的量的对应算符，(b) 任意给定的物理系统对应的能量算符。严格地说，(a) 是 (b) 的特殊情况，因为如果测量装置与所考虑物体的相互作用能是已知的话，我们总可以对测量装置的性质进行分析。

譬如说，我们有这样一台用来测量 qp^2q（p 表示粒子的动量，q 表示粒子的坐标）这个量的测量装置，另外一台测量装置是用于测量 $\frac{1}{2}(p^2q^2 + q^2p^2)$ 的，虽然在经典力

365

from an apparatus measuring $\frac{1}{2}(p^2q^2 + q^2p^2)$, although in the limiting case of classical mechanics, where quantum effects are negligible, both would measure the same quantity.

Before applying such an apparatus (assuming, for the sake of argument, that it exists although it probably does not) one would have to make sure, either by experimental investigation or by applying quantum mechanics to its working mechanism, which operator actually is to be associated with it. In other words, an apparatus which is quite suitable for measuring a certain quantity in the classical limit may not satisfy our requirements if we rebuild it on a smaller scale, because then quantum effects will have to be taken into consideration.

That one never meets with any difficulty about the order of factors in the usual applications of quantum theory is due to the fact that only very simple operators occur in practice. The most typical of them is the energy of an electron in a field of force, $p^2/2m + V(q)$ (m = mass, V = potential energy). One generally assumes that the function in this exact form, without quantum corrections, has to be taken as the energy operator of a particle the energy of which would be given by the same expression in classical mechanics. This assumption seems very *natural*, but it cannot be *proved* on mere theoretical grounds. All one can say is that this expression is the *most plausible* amongst a variety of different expressions, which all become equal in the classical limit but differ by terms like, for example, $pV - Vp = (h/2\pi i)$ grad V (h = Planck's constant). It is for the experiment to show that the most plausible choice corresponds to reality and that such correction terms are absent.

That the absence of these correction terms cannot be inferred from mere theoretical considerations is proved by the fact that when relativity and spin corrections are taken into account, such terms actually *do occur*.

(**136**, 395; 1935)

R. Peierls: Physical Laboratory, University, Manchester, Aug. 5.

References:
1. *Nature*, **135**, 957, June 8, 1935.
2. *Nature*, **136**, 179, Aug. 3, 1935.

学的极限情况下，量子效应可以忽略不计，测量以上两个量的结果是一样的，但是以上两个测量装置本质上却是**不一样**的。

在应用这类测量装置之前（为了论证方便，虽然这个测量装置可能并不存在，但我们仍假定它存在）我们必须确定，不管是在实验研究中还是在应用量子力学的工作机制中，哪个算符与它们相联系。换句话说，一个在经典极限情况下适于测量某个量的装置，如果改装并放到小尺度空间中进行测量，则可能不符合测量要求，因为这时候我们需要考虑量子效应了。

我们在量子理论的日常应用中，并没在表达式中因子的次序上遇到问题，这是因为通常在实际情况中只会出现一些非常简单的算符。这些简单算符中最典型的是处在力场中电子的能量算符，$p^2/2m+V(q)$ （m 表示电子的质量，V 表示势能）。我们通常认为，不考虑量子修正的话，这个严格表达式中的函数是粒子的能量算符，并且该能量算符给出的系统能量与经典力学中的表达式是一致的。这个假设似乎**顺理成章**，但是单凭理论推导并不能**证明**这个假设是对的。我们只能说这个表达式是众多不同的表达形式中**看似最合理**的一个，而这些不同的表达形式一般在经典极限下是等价的，除非有如 $pV - Vp = (h/2\pi i)\, \nabla V$ （h 表示普朗克常数）的项存在时，它们才不一样。实验表明，关于表达式最合理的选择应与现实情况相对应，这时这些修正项便消失了。

实际上，当我们考虑相对论和自旋修正的时候，这些量子效应的修正项**的确出现了**，这表明我们不能单纯地从理论推导的角度得出这些修正项不存在的结论。

（沈乃澂 翻译；李军刚 审稿）

Uncertainty Principle and the Zero-Point Energy of the Harmonic Oscillator

R. A. Newing

Editor's Note

In 1913, Albert Einstein and Otto Stern suggested that measurements of the specific heat of hydrogen gas (a measure of how heat input changes its temperature) at low temperature could best be understood if the energy of the molecular vibrations could never be strictly zero, but had an irreducible residual energy. Theorists subsequently predicted such a residual, later known as the zero-point energy, from the equations of quantum mechanics. But the effect lacked intuitive justification. Here R. A. Newing shows that the zero-point energy can be seen as a consequence of Heisenberg's uncertainty principle, which forbids complete specification of position or momentum. Newing shows that the minimal possible value for the zero-point energy is consistent with that derived previously from quantum theory.

ACCORDING to quantum mechanics, an oscillator possesses a definite zero-point energy of vibration, and an attempt has been made to express this result *directly* in terms of some general principle. It has been found that the result may be deduced from the uncertainty principle, in view of the particular relation between position, momentum and energy in a simple harmonic field.

In a state of zero energy the vibrating particle would be at rest at the centre of the field, and its position and momentum would both be known accurately. But this would contradict the uncertainty principle, and the state is therefore not possible. The value of the minimum energy may be calculated from the uncertainty relation $\Delta p \Delta q \geqslant h/2\pi$. The linear harmonic oscillator is defined by the energy equation

$$W = \tfrac{1}{2}\mu\omega^2 q^2 + \tfrac{1}{2}p^2/\mu = \text{constant}.$$

If we interpret

amplitude of $q = \Delta q$ = uncertainty in position,

amplitude of $p = \Delta p$ = uncertainty in momentum,

then
$$W = \tfrac{1}{2}\mu\omega^2(\Delta q)^2 = \tfrac{1}{2}(\Delta p)^2/\mu,$$

giving
$$\mu\omega\Delta q = \pm\,\Delta p.$$

For real Δp the positive sign must be taken, and from the uncertainty relation, $(\Delta p)^2 \geqslant h\mu\omega/2\pi$,

368

测不准原理和谐振子的零点能

纽因

编者按

1913 年，阿尔伯特·爱因斯坦和奥托·斯特恩提出，如果在任何情况下，分子振动能量都不会完全等于零，而是存在着一个无法消除的残余能量，那么低温下氢气比热的测量（一项关于氢气温度随输入热量变化的测量）结果就能得到很好的解释了。紧接着，理论物理学家们从量子力学的方程中推导出了这一残余能量，其后来被称之为零点能。但是这一效应缺乏直观的合理性。这篇文章中，纽因认为零点能可以被看作是海森堡的测不准原理的推论，测不准原理认为不能同时精确的获知微观粒子的位置和动量。纽因的结果表明零点能的可能最小值与之前根据量子理论推导出的结果是一致的。

根据量子力学原理，一个振子具有确定的振动零点能，科学工作者也正在试图使用一些基本的原理来对这一结果进行**直接地**表述。在简单的谐波场中，考虑到位置、动量和能量之间的特殊关系，我们发现或许可以根据测不准原理推导出零点能。

处于零点能态的振动粒子如果会静止于场的中央，那么它的位置和动量都能准确地确定下来。但是这与测不准原理相矛盾，因此谐振子是不可能处于这种态的。我们可以根据测不准关系 $\Delta p \Delta q \geqslant h/2\pi$ 计算出能量的最小值。一维谐振子的能量是由下面的能量方程定义的

$$W = \frac{1}{2}\mu\omega^2 q^2 + \frac{1}{2}p^2/\mu = 常数$$

如果我们这样理解：

$$q\ 的大小 = \Delta q = 位置不确定度$$
$$p\ 的大小 = \Delta p = 动量不确定度$$

于是有
$$W = \frac{1}{2}\mu\omega^2 (\Delta q)^2 = \frac{1}{2}(\Delta p)^2/\mu$$

得出
$$\mu\omega\Delta q = \pm\,\Delta p$$

对于实数 Δp，必须取正号，根据测不准关系，我们推导出 $(\Delta p)^2 \geqslant h\mu\omega/2\pi$，因此可

and therefore $W \geqslant \frac{1}{2}h\omega/2\pi$. Taking the equality sign for the least value of the energy, it follows that the zero-point energy is $\frac{1}{2}h\omega/2\pi$.

(**136**, 395; 1935)

R. A. Newing: Department of Applied Mathematics, University, Liverpool, June 22.

得，$W \geqslant \frac{1}{2} h\omega/2\pi$。当求能量的最小值时取等号，于是得到零点能为 $\frac{1}{2} h\omega/2\pi$。

（沈乃澂 翻译；李淼 审稿）

Solar Magnetism

G. E. Hale

Editor's Note

On the occasion of Dutch physicist Pieter Zeeman's 70th birthday, American astronomer George Hale surveys applications of Zeeman's methods to the study of solar magnetism. These methods—based on how a magnetic field influences atomic energy levels, and hence the frequency of light an atom emits—had recently been used to document a 23-year cycle of sunspot activity, and also to show the existence of huge vortices of flowing material surrounding sunspots. The technique had also established that the Sun as a whole is also a large magnet. It is almost certain, Hale concludes, that these fields are all caused by charged particles in some kind of rotational motion.

THE recent celebration of Prof. Zeeman's seventieth birthday offers a favourable opportunity to describe current applications of his powerful method of research to the study of solar magnetism. Our latest results include the completion of the first observed 23-year magnetic cycle of sunspots and the conclusion of a long investigation of the Sun's general magnetic field, made for the purpose of checking beyond question the original measurements begun in 1912.

Zeeman Effect in Sunspots

As explained eleven years ago in *Nature*[1], I was led in 1908 to the discovery of magnetic fields in sunspots by a hypothesis based upon the results of two series of studies, begun at the Kenwood Observatory in 1890, and continued at the Yerkes and Mount Wilson Observatories. The first of these related to the nature of various phenomena of the solar atmosphere revealed by spectrographs and spectroheliographs. The hydrogen flocculi, as first shown by the H_α line at Mount Wilson in 1908, indicated the existence of immense vortices surrounding sunspots, and suggested that electrically charged particles might be whirled within the spots in such a way as to produce appreciable electric currents. Such currents would set up magnetic fields, possibly of sufficient strength to be detected by a powerful spectroscope. Zeeman had shown how the spectrum lines of luminous metallic vapours between the poles of a magnet are widened or split into several components, polarised in distinctive ways. Meanwhile our studies of sunspot spectra, supplementing those made with less powerful spectrographs by Young, had reached a point where many lines on our photographs were not only widened but also separated into apparent doublets or triplets. These had previously been regarded as reversed lines, due to the superposition of two vaporous layers of different temperature and density. Such reversals actually exist in certain cases, notably in the lines of hydrogen and calcium. Thus, the true understanding of the sunspot spectrum had been obscured.

太阳磁场

海耳

编者按

在荷兰物理学家彼得·塞曼 70 岁寿辰的庆典上，美国天文学家乔治·海耳综述了塞曼的方法在研究太阳磁场方面的各种应用。这些基于磁场如何影响原子的能级进而影响原子发光频率的方法近期被用于记录以 23 年为周期的太阳黑子活动，同时这种方法也表明在太阳黑子附近存在流动物质的巨大的涡旋。这一技术同时表明整个太阳是一个大磁体。海耳得出的结论认为，几乎可以肯定太阳磁场完全是由带电粒子的某种旋转运动造成的。

最近塞曼教授的 70 岁生日庆典为我们提供了一个很好的机会，对他提出的有效研究方法在太阳磁场研究方面的最新应用进行讨论。我们最新的应用结果包括首次完成的对太阳黑子 23 年磁周期的观测以及通过对太阳普遍磁场的长期观测得到的结论，这些观测是为了检验始于 1912 年的对太阳磁场的最初观测，1912 年的观测结果曾被人们认为是无可争辩的。

太阳黑子的塞曼效应

正如 11 年前在《自然》杂志上的[1]解释一样，1908 年，基于之前的两项研究成果，我做了一个假设，并由此发现了太阳黑子的磁场，这两项研究工作均于 1890 年在肯伍德天文台开始，后来在叶凯士天文台和威尔逊山天文台继续进行。其中第一项工作是关于太阳大气中一些现象的本质的研究，通过使用光谱仪和太阳单色光照相仪，我们对此有了一定的了解。1908 年，根据在威尔逊山天文台观测到的 H_α 线，人们第一次发现了太阳上的氢谱斑，这一现象意味着在太阳黑子附近存在巨大的涡旋，从而暗示了带电粒子在太阳黑子内部做回旋运动，并因此产生了可被测量的电流。而这些电流可以产生一个强度很大的磁场，足以被一台功能强大的分光镜观测到。塞曼已经为我们展示了在两个磁极之间的发光金属蒸汽的谱线是如何被展宽或分裂成不同部分并发生明显的极化现象的。同时，将我们对太阳黑子的光谱研究和扬用功能稍弱的光谱仪对太阳黑子所做的研究综合起来，可以得到这样一个结论：照片中的很多谱线不仅仅被展宽了，而且明显地分裂成了双线或三线。这种由温度和密度不同的两层蒸汽气体重叠所造成的谱线曾被前人称为反向线。这样的反向线在某些情况下确实是存在的，而在氢元素和钙元素的谱线中尤为明显。所以说，关于太阳光谱的正确解释在当时还不是十分明朗。

In the hope of disentangling the question, a new attack on sunspots was begun. Aided by the 60-foot tower telescope on Mount Wilson, equipped with a 30-foot grating spectrograph and suitable polariscopic apparatus, it was easy to test my hypothesis. The presence of magnetic fields was readily established in all the sunspots observed, and the polariscopic phenomena of the sunspot lines, varying as the solar rotation changed the angle between the lines of force and the line of sight, was quickly found to harmonise with Zeeman's laboratory results on the spectra of vapours. My solar work was greatly facilitated by experiments made in our own laboratory by King, provided with a Du Bois magnet and all the essential equipment.

Magnetic Polarity of Sunspots

The sunspot spectrum contains many thousands of lines, and its complete investigation is an extensive task. After a sufficient number of these lines had been examined in order to establish the existence, strength and general character of the magnetic fields, another phase of the problem was attacked.

Speaking broadly, sunspots in the northern hemisphere of the Sun were found to be opposite in polarity to those in the southern hemisphere. But occasional apparent exceptions indicated the need for a more careful analysis. The earliest drawings of sunspots, made by Galileo and Scheiner, suggest their complex character. They often appear at first as single spots, but soon develop into groups, frequently containing many components, large and small. No observer could fail to detect, however, a remarkable tendency of spots to occur in pairs, consisting of large spots with small companions, or of two groups of small spots. Here was an interesting chance for polarity tests, which showed that such pairs are almost invariably bipolar: that is, they consist of two spots or groups having opposite magnetic poles. The smaller spots that frequently cluster about the preceding (western) and following (eastern) major spots usually agree in polarity with the larger spots they accompany, though this is not an invariable rule.

From such characteristics a scheme of magnetic classification developed, which has been used ever since on Mount Wilson in recording the magnetic phenomena of thousands of spots examined with the 150-foot tower telescope and the 75-foot spectrograph. This long task, in which Nicholson, Ellerman, Joy and many others have taken part, has now covered more than two of the well-known sunspot cycles of approximately eleven years duration.

Law of Sunspot Polarity

It is well known that the first spots of each of these 11-year frequency cycles break out in comparatively high latitudes some time before the last of the spots of the previous cycle disappear near the equator. From 1908, the spots of the then existing cycle continued to show the same polarity, opposite in the two hemispheres, while slowly decreasing in mean latitude. Not long before the minimum of solar activity in 1912, the forerunners of the next 11-year cycle began to appear. To our surprise, their polarity was opposite to

人们怀着解决这个问题的期望迎来了又一轮太阳黑子的爆发。借助于威尔逊山天文台 60 英尺塔状望远镜、30 英尺光栅光谱仪以及合适的偏振光仪，很容易检验出我的假说是否正确。通过观测，我们确定在所有观测到的太阳黑子中都存在磁场。此外，当太阳旋转使磁力线方向和视线方向的夹角发生变化时，观测到的偏振光的偏振方向也随之改变，而且人们很快发现了这个变化关系与塞曼在实验室蒸汽谱线中发现的变化规律是相符的。我们实验室的金所做的实验大大推动了我在太阳磁场方面的研究工作，他在这个实验中使用了杜波依斯磁铁和其他相关的必要设备。

太阳黑子磁场的极性

太阳黑子的光谱中包含有成千上万条谱线，全面研究这些谱线所需的工作量很大。在对大部分的谱线进行了研究之后，我们确定了磁场的存在，并得到了磁场的强度和一般性特征。之后，我们又开始着手解决这个研究中的另一个部分了。

概括地说，我们发现太阳北半球上和南半球上的太阳黑子的磁场具有相反的极性。但是偶尔也会有例外出现，这表明对此现象我们还需要更加细致的分析。最早由伽利略和沙伊纳绘制的太阳黑子图显示了太阳黑子的复杂特性。它们起初通常是单个出现的，然后发展为一群，常常包含大大小小的不同部分。然而，黑子都有明显的成对现象，所有的观测者都注意到了这个现象，成对的现象可能表现为在大黑子的附近伴随有小的黑子，或者是两群小的黑子在一起。这些黑子对让人们有机会去检测磁场极性，人们发现这些黑子对总是具有不同的极性：即成对出现的两个或两群黑子的磁场极性总是相反的。较小的黑子经常聚集在前面（西部）和后面（东部）的大黑子的周围，并且与相伴的较大黑子呈现出相同的磁性，尽管这种模式并不是一成不变的。

人们从这些磁场的特性出发对磁场进行了分类，这种分类自从在威尔逊山天文台上被用来记录成千上万个黑子的磁现象之后，就一直被沿用至今，当时人们是通过 150 英尺塔状望远镜和 75 英尺光谱仪来观测黑子的磁现象的。这个工作已经开展了长达两个太阳黑子周期之久，众所周知，每个周期大约为 11 年，尼克尔森、埃勒曼、乔伊和很多其他科学家都曾参与了这项工作。

太阳黑子磁场极性的规律

众所周知，在每个 11 年的太阳活动周期开始时爆发的第一个黑子，总是在上一个周期的最后一个黑子在赤道附近消失之前出现在纬度相对稍高的地方。在 1908 年之后出现的这个太阳活动周期中，黑子的磁场极性一直保持不变，而在南北两个半球上黑子的磁极则是相反的，同时黑子的平均纬度慢慢变小。而在太阳活动极小年到来之前的 1912 年，就已经出现了下一个 11 年活动周期的先兆。令我们惊讶的是，

that of the spots of the preceding cycle. Moreover, the succeeding spots of the new cycle, which overlapped for a time the remnants of the old cycle in lower latitudes, retained the same reversed polarities for approximately eleven years. Then another frequency cycle commenced, with another reversal of polarity. Thus the complete magnetic cycle, bringing back spots of the same polarity as those first observed, occupies some twenty-two or twenty-three years, and comprises two frequency cycles. The northern and southern hemispheres represent this novel effect with opposite signs. The diagram shown in Fig. 1 summarises the changes of latitudes and polarities during the period 1908-35.

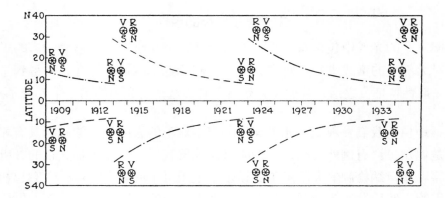

Fig. 1. Law of sunspot polarity. The curves represent the approximate variation in mean latitude and the corresponding magnetic polarities of sunspot groups observed at Mount Wilson form June 1908 until January 1935. The preceding spot is shown on the right.

A more detailed examination of the observations, many of which have been published in the *Astrophysical Journal* and the *Publications of the Astronomical Society of the Pacific*, would suffice to show that occasional exceptional phenomena complicate the explanation of these changes. About ninety-seven percent of consistent results, however, obviously point toward some general solution, applicable to the Sun and countless other stars, but still remaining in the form of the empirical law illustrated in Fig. 1.

General Magnetic Field of the Sun

Soon after the detection of strong magnetic fields in sunspots, I began to wonder whether the Sun as a whole might possess a general magnetic field. There was no very promising theoretical ground for such speculation, but the magnetic field of the Earth, with poles not far removed from the poles of rotation, was at least suggestive. Schuster had queried in 1891: "Is every rotating body a magnet?" and the structure of the solar corona resembles that of a magnetic field*. Thus while it was a far cry from the solid Earth to the vaporous Sun, it seemed worth while to undertake a trial.

The first attempts, made with the 60-foot tower telescope, were fruitless. In 1912, with the

---

* In the present brief statement no attempt is made to enumerate other speculations and theories.

在新一轮的周期中出现的黑子的磁场极性与前一个周期中的黑子的磁场极性完全相反。而且，在新的周期中最先出现的那些黑子与上一个周期中残存的黑子曾一度在低纬度发生重合，并且二者在约11年的时间里一直保持相反的极性。因此，具有另一种反向极性的太阳活动周期被提了出来。这使太阳黑子变回到与前一次观测时具有同极性的一个完整的磁场活动周期变成了大约是22或23年，即由两个11年的太阳活动周期组成。虽然太阳的南北半球中黑子磁场的极性相反，但都出现了这种奇特的现象。我们在图1中总结了1908～1935年黑子的纬度和磁场极性的变化情况。

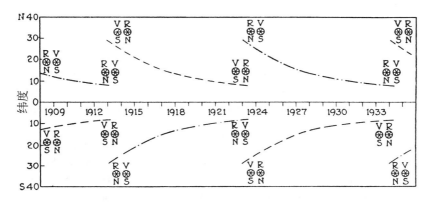

图1. 太阳黑子磁场极性的规律。这些曲线近似地表示了黑子群平均纬度的变化和相应的磁场极性。这些黑子群是1908年6月至1935年1月在威尔逊山上观测到的。前导黑子出现在右边。

《天体物理学杂志》和《太平洋天文学会会刊》上刊登了大部分关于太阳磁场的观测结果，而对所有的观测结果进行仔细研究后我们可以发现：偶尔出现的小概率现象增加了人们解释此种变化关系的难度。虽然97%的数据都一致明确指向了那些普遍的结论，该结论适用于太阳和其他无数的恒星，但是这种结论仍只是一种如图1所示的经验规律。

太阳的普遍磁场

在探测了太阳黑子中的强磁场后，我开始好奇整个太阳是否拥有一个整体的磁场。虽然我的这个猜想没有任何可靠的理论基础，但是地球磁场的磁极与转动极相差不远这一事实使我产生了这种联想。舒斯特曾在1891年提出这样的疑问："是不是所有的旋转物体都带有磁场？"太阳日冕层的结构与磁场的结构很像*。因此，虽然固态的地球与气态的太阳大不相同，但是这样的猜想还是很值得我们去尝试检验一下的。

我用60英尺的塔状望远镜进行了第一次的观测尝试，结果一无所获。1912年，

---

* 目前简单的声明论述中没有对其他猜想和理论进行列举。

completion of the 150-foot tower telescope and 75-foot spectrograph, a better opportunity offered itself. Obviously no such widening and complete splitting of lines as had been found in sunspots existed in regions away from spots. But by using a purely differential method, comprising a compound quarter-wave plate overlying a long Nicol prism on the slit, it seemed barely possible that minute magnetic displacements of suitable lines might be detected by measurements on successive strips. Assuming the magnetic poles of the Sun to correspond with the poles of rotation, and mounting the quarter-wave strips with their principal sections alternately at angles of $+45°$ and $-45°$ with the slit of the spectrograph, the displacements on odd and even strips should attain maximum values on the central meridian at about $45°$ north and south latitude, and decrease to zero at the poles and equator.

In the search for such minute displacements, every precaution was taken to obviate any possible bias on the part of the measurers. Thus the quarter-wave plates were frequently inverted, and the measurer was never allowed to know in advance in which position they stood, nor the hemisphere or latitude of the photographs under measurement.

Great difficulties attended this investigation, which was continued for several years. Many members of the Mount Wilson staff joined me in the task, including Seares, Anderson, Ellerman and van Maanen, together with Miss Lasby, Miss Richmond and Miss Felker, while check measures and tests were made by Adams, Babcock and others. Several different types of measuring machines were employed, and every possible means of avoiding personal or instrumental errors was adopted. The results, fully described in a series of papers in the *Astrophysical Journal*, seemed to leave no room for doubt regarding the existence, polarity and approximate strength of a weak general magnetic field of the Sun, having poles lying within a few degrees of the Sun's poles of rotation.

The fact remains, as pointed out in these papers, that some of the many measurers engaged in the work could not detect the general field, though the results of all those who succeeded were in agreement regarding its polarity and order of magnitude. The difficulties of measurement can be appreciated only by those who have endeavoured to detect such minute displacements of lines, rendered broad and diffuse by the great dispersion employed. The observed displacements ranged from zero near the equator and poles to maximum values of 0.001 A. at mid-latitudes.

Several years ago I renewed this investigation with the coelostat telescope (equivalent focal length 150 feet) and the 75-foot spectrograph of my solar laboratory in Pasadena. Having made a new series of photographs of the same dispersion as those previously taken on Mount Wilson, I endeavoured to measure them by several different instruments, including a Zeiss microphotometer and a tipping plate micrometer of the form used in our earlier work. The results showed little, if any, general magnetic field, and finally I thought it advisable to undertake new check measures of the plates made more than twenty years

当 150 英尺的塔状望远镜和 75 英尺的光谱仪的建成并投入使用后，我们刚好又遇到了一个极好的观测时机。显然在黑子以外的地方人们没有观测到谱线的展宽和完全的分裂。但若使用完全不同的方法，如把一个 1/4 波片和一个长的尼科尔棱镜重叠装在狭缝上，通过测量连续的条纹还是勉强有可能会观测到磁场在相应谱线上引起的微小位移。若假设太阳的磁极与旋转极是重合的，那么在装上一个与主截面成正 45 度角、与光谱仪狭缝成负 45 度角的 1/4 波片后，奇偶条纹之间的位移应该会在中心子午线南北纬 45 度左右的地方达到最大值，而在两极和赤道减小到为零。

为了测出这种微小的位移，我们采取了很多预防措施来避免任何可能在测量仪器上出现的偏差。因此我们要经常翻转 1/4 波片，并且在测量前不能预先知道其所处的位置，或照片上被测量区域所在的半球和纬度。

这项研究持续了几年，期间也遇到了很多困难。很多在威尔逊山天文台的工作人员都加入了我的这项工作，其中包括西尔斯、安德森、埃勒曼和范玛宁，还有拉斯比、里士满和费尔克三位女士。测试工作和测量结果的检验是由亚当斯、巴布科克等人来完成的。我们使用了几种不同类型的测量仪器，并采用了所有可能的办法来避免由人为和仪器所造成的误差。在《天体物理学杂志》上发表的一系列文章详细描述了我们的观测结果，这些结果明确阐述了太阳弱普遍磁场的存在、极性以及大概的强度，结果还表明太阳的磁极与其转动极的夹角只在几度的范围内。

正如我们在上述文章中所指出的，虽然所有成功的观测结果在太阳磁场极性和磁场强度的量级上都是吻合一致的，但事实上这项研究工作使用的很多测量仪器并不能探测到太阳普遍磁场的相关信息。只有那些致力于观测谱线微小位移的人们才能深刻地体会到测量过程中的困难，因为太阳磁场引起相应谱线的微小位移在使用的显著色散条件下变得很宽而散漫。所观测到的微小位移的变化范围从两极和赤道附近的零到中纬度附近的最大值 0.001 埃。

几年前，我利用帕萨迪纳太阳实验室中的（等效焦距为 150 英尺）定天望远镜和 75 英尺的光谱仪重新更新了这些研究数据。我用这些仪器观测得到了一系列新的照片，这些照片与之前在威尔逊山天文台观测到的照片呈现出一样的色散关系，我努力尝试用各种各样不同的仪器来测量这些照片，这些仪器包括蔡司显微光度计和一台形态上与我们先前使用过的仪器类似的有转动盘的千分尺。这些结果几乎没有显示出有关太阳普遍磁场的信息，即便有也是极少量的，所以我认为有必要对二十多年前在威尔逊山天文台观测得到的照片底片进行重新的检验测量工作。之后的测

ago on Mount Wilson. More difficulties were encountered, and most of the experienced measurers who had overcome them before were no longer available. However, others kindly enlisted, and a study lasting four years has at last yielded a sufficient number of independent confirmations to satisfy us of the validity of our former conclusions.

As before, some of the measurers have been unable to detect the general magnetic field shown by our old plates. On the contrary, Dr. John Strong with an improved Zeiss microphotometer, used visually, and Dr. R. M. Langer with the original tipping plate micrometer, have found systematic average displacements of the same sign. Mr. J. Evershed, who very kindly volunteered to assist, obtained excellent confirmatory measures of our original plates at his observatory in England, using his own admirable method of measurement. Within the last few weeks [date of communication, September 14, 1935], Dr. Langer has obtained two more unmistakable confirmations with the aid of a new type of combined measuring, recording and computing machine, built in my laboratory after a design due chiefly to himself. The chief advantages of this machine are its speed of operation, permitting a very large number of measures to be made in a short time, and its complete freedom from any possibility of bias.

Taken altogether, the evidence is overwhelmingly in favour of the existence, polarity and order of magnitude of the general magnetic field of the Sun given in our original papers. There is thus far no evidence of change of polarity at sunspot minima. As for any possible changes of intensity, every single determination is necessarily based upon thousands of measures, and hence represents mean values for many points on the Sun. Thus much time may elapse before the question of variability can be settled.

The striking magnetic phenomena of sunspots, and the evidence we have offered that the entire Sun is a magnet, would seem to have important bearings on the problems of terrestrial magnetism and the fundamental nature of magnetism itself. It is difficult to avoid the belief that the strong magnetic fields of the spots, and the much weaker general magnetic fields of the Sun and the Earth, arise from the same general cause, namely, the rotation of bodies carrying electrically charged particles. Many different hypotheses based upon this view have been tested, but there is much room for further work. While this will naturally deal at first with the simplest general assumptions, a detailed study of such anomalous phenomena as are presented by about three percent of all sunspots should not be overlooked.

(**136**, 703-705; 1935)

George E. Hale: Mount Wilson Observatory, Pasadena, California.

Reference:

1. "Sun-spots as Magnets and the Periodic Reversal of their Polarity", *Nature*, 113, 105, Jan. 19, 1924.

量工作中，我们遇到了更多的困难，而且大部分曾经克服过这些困难的经验丰富的工作人员也都不能再加入这项工作。不过，经过另外征集到的一些工作人员的努力，以及四年的研究最终得出了大量独立的证据，这些足以使我们相信以前的结论是有效的。

像前面提到的那样，有些测量仪器在老的照片底片上测不到太阳的普遍磁场。与之相反，约翰·斯特朗博士利用改良过的蔡司显微光度计、兰格博士利用早期的带转动盘的千分尺，通过目视都发现了由这一现象造成的系统平均位移。埃费希德先生非常主动且热心地帮助了我们，他在英国的天文台中，用他自己发明的绝妙的测量方法对我们最初的照片底片进行了测量，并得到了极好的确定的测量结果。在过去的几周内 [1935 年 9 月 14 日，通信日期]，兰格博士借助于一种新型的复合仪器又获得了另外两组确凿无误的数据核实了上述结果，这种仪器兼容了测量、记录和计算三种功能，主要由兰格博士自己设计并在我们实验室制成。这台仪器的主要优点在于它的运行速度，它可以在短时间内进行大量的测量，并可以避免产生任何可能的偏差。

综上所述，在我们最初的文章中已经提供了充分确凿的证据来证实太阳普遍磁场的存在，并测得了它的极性和强度量级。即便如此，我们手头上还是没有任何关于磁场极性在太阳黑子极小年会改变的证据。由于我们做出的每一个判断都是基于成千上万次测量的结果，因此它反映的是太阳上很多点的平均值。因此，要彻底弄清太阳上磁场强度的变化还需要更多的时间。

在解决地球磁场和磁场本身基本性质的问题上，太阳黑子显著的磁现象和我们提供的整个太阳是一个磁体的证据似乎有很重要的意义。人们很难回避这样的想法，那就是太阳黑子的强磁场和相比之下弱得多的太阳和地球上的整体磁场是由相同的原因造成的，即载有带电粒子的物体的旋转。基于这种观点的很多不同假说都已被检验过了，但是进一步研究的空间仍然很大。当然，我们的工作会最先涉及一些最简单的普遍假设，但是也不应该放弃对那些由 3% 的太阳黑子所引起的反常现象的深入研究。

（史春晖 翻译；蒋世仰 审稿）

Crossing-Over and Chromosome Disjunction

S. Gershenson

Editor's Note

Genetic recombination, which allows large segments of DNA to move from one chromosome to another, happens naturally during meiosis (cell divisions that halve the number of chromosomes) when chromosomes "cross over". But in 1935 the link between this cross-over and normal meiotic chromosome separation was far from clear. Sergey Gershenson from Moscow's Academy of Sciences here examines cross-over and separation in abnormal X-chromosomes from hybrid *Drosophila* females, and concludes that normal chromosome separation does not depend directly on cross-over. "A third, more general factor," he says, may be required. It wasn't clear what this could be.

BRIDGES, Anderson, Mather, Gershenson and many others have shown that there is a definite relation between crossing-over and the disjunction of chromosomes. Their work has made it evident that, during meiosis, crossover chromosomes are distributed between the daughter nuclei more regularly than non-crossover ones. However, the exact nature of this relation is still by no means clear. Darlington thinks that crossing-over is, in general, a necessary condition of regular chromosome disjunction. On the other hand, a number of general considerations as well as some recent facts obtained by Gershenson, Beadle and Sturtevant and Stone and Thomas, are opposed to such an interpretation in the case of *Drosophila*.

In order to decide the latter question, I undertook an experiment in collaboration with Miss Helene Pogossiants, in which, by using certain rearranged chromosomes, it seemed possible to obtain somewhat more conclusive results than in previous work. Crossing-over and non-disjunction were studied in females of *Drosophila melanogaster* carrying an X-chromosome with the *ClB* inversion and another X-chromosome (translocation X-IV or "Bar-Stone"), most of the genetically active part of which was translocated to the fourth chromosome. Data on single crossing-over in the non-inverted region and the number of recovered double crossovers in the inverted region enabled us to conclude, with a high degree of certainty, that single crossing-over in the latter region (undetectable by direct methods) is very low. Possible undetected crossing-over in the genetically inert parts of the X-chromosomes could influence only the disjunction of the *ClB* chromosome and the right (non-translocated) part of the other X-chromosome, as the left part, translocated to chromosome 4, does not carry any of the inert region of the X-chromosome. Non-disjunction of the left part of this X-chromosome and the *ClB* chromosome is much lower than would be expected if Darlington's hypothesis applies to *Drosophila*, and seems therefore to show that regular disjunction of chromosomes is not absolutely conditioned by crossing-over.

染色体分离与交换

格申森

编者按

遗传重组使大片段 DNA 从一条染色体移动到另一条染色体，自然情况下这一过程出现在染色体发生"交换"的减数分裂（染色体数目减半的细胞分裂）期间。但在1935 年时人们对染色体的这种交换与正常减数分裂时染色体的分离之间的联系还很不清楚。莫斯科科学院的谢尔盖·格申森在这篇文章中分析了杂交的雌性黑腹果蝇中异常 X 染色体的交换和分离过程，并得出了正常染色体的分离并不直接依赖于染色体交换的结论。他认为可能需要"另外一个更普遍的因子"。但是这个因子是什么还不清楚。

布里奇斯、安德森、马瑟、格申森等人认为，染色体的分离与交换之间有明确的关系。他们的研究已经证实，在减数分裂期间，发生交换的染色体比不发生交换的染色体更经常性地分布于子细胞核之间。然而，出现这种关联的本质原因还不清楚。达林顿认为，一般而言，交换是染色体正常分离的必要条件。另一方面，大多数人的普遍观点以及最近格申森、比德尔、斯特蒂文特、斯通、托马斯关于果蝇相关方面的研究结果却与达林顿的观点相反。

为了解决上文中的最后一个疑问，我和海伦妮小姐共同合作利用某种重排的染色体进行实验，希望可以得到比先前的研究工作更有说服力的结果。我们利用雌性黑腹果蝇来研究染色体的交换和不分离现象，这种果蝇的一条 X 染色体上发生 ClB 倒位，而另一条 X 染色体上大部分的遗传活性部分被易位到第四条染色体上（X–IV 易位）。关于非倒位区的单交换数和倒位区恢复正常的双交换数的数据使我们可以确定无疑地得出一个结论，即倒位区发生单交换（不能通过直接方法检测到）的概率很低。X 染色体遗传惰性区域可能发生但无法被检测到的单交换只会影响 ClB 染色体和另一条 X 染色体的右臂（非易位区）的分离，因为被易位到第四条染色体上的左臂并不包含 X 染色体的任何遗传惰性区域。如果达林顿的假说也适用于果蝇的话，那么我们观察到的这条 X 染色体的左支与 ClB 染色体之间发生的不分离现象要少于它应有的比例，因此交换不是染色体正常分离的必要条件。

It seems clear that both crossing-over and chromosome disjunction are dependent on a third, more general factor, possibly on the intensity with which the conjugation of chromosomes takes place.

(**136**, 834-835; 1935)

S. Gershenson: Institute of Genetics, Academy of Sciences, Moscow.

很明显，染色体交换和分离都依赖于另一个更为普遍的因子，这个因子可能是染色体结合的强度。

（韩玲俐 翻译；王晓晨 审稿）

Crossing-Over and Chromosome Disjunction

C. D. Darlington

Editor's Note

English geneticist Cyril Dean Darlington of London's John Innes Horticultural Institution replies to Gershenson's opinion (see the previous paper). The Russian geneticist had suggested that normal chromosome disjunction does not depend on cross-over and that the two processes depend on a third, as yet unidentified factor. The finding contradicted Darlington's view that crossing-over is part of normal chromosome disjunction, so he suggests that the third factor may be Gershenson's use of hybrids, which were "bound to have a complicated effect on disjunction." Darlington basically pins this paper's results down to experimental artefact. In later years he went on to outline the mechanics of chromosomal crossover and its role in inheritance.

DOBZHANSKY[1], Gershenson (above) and others have concluded that the disjunction of chromosomes does not depend directly on the occurrence of crossing-over between them, as I assume to be the case in all homozygous organisms[2]. They maintain that some "other factor" is concerned in their experiments. But these experiments have necessarily made use of hybridity, without which genetical tests are impossible; and the particular kind of hybridity (structural hybridity) they have used is bound to have a complicated effect on disjunction. It is itself the "other factor". Thus reciprocal crossing-over within two relatively inverted segments should give normal chromosomes with normal disjunction, other things being equal.

But when we consider the structure of the bivalent given by such crossing-over, we see that the disjunction expected in straightforward bivalents will not necessarily follow (Fig. 1). The pull which is to separate the paired chromatids is parallel to the plane of their association and not perpendicular to it. Resistance to separation is therefore not a certain constant minimum, but a function of the length between the two chiasmata. I have observed failure of disjunction in these circumstances in an inversion heterozygote in *Stenobothrus parallelus*. Other kinds of crossing-over in dislocated segments give rise to lagging, interlocking and irregular breakage. It is not therefore surprising that Grüneberg[3] finds the "non-disjunction" that has previously been attributed to non-pairing and random segregation is often due to loss of both partners.

染色体分离与交换

达林顿

编者按

伦敦约翰·英纳斯园艺中心的英国基因学家西里尔·迪安·达林顿对格申森的观点（见前一篇文章）给予了回应。俄罗斯基因学家格申森认为正常的染色体分离并不依赖于染色体交换，这两个过程都依赖于另一个尚不明确的因子。这一发现反驳了达林顿的染色体交换是正常的染色体分离的一部分的观点。达林顿认为，另一个因子可能源于格申森采用了"会对染色体分离产生复杂影响"的杂合体。达林顿从根本上认为那篇文章的结果是实验假象。之后的几年中，他继续总结了染色体交换的机制及其在遗传中的作用。

多布赞斯基 [1] 和格申森（上文的作者）等人认为染色体分离并不直接依赖于染色体交换的发生，而我认为在纯合生物中染色体分离是依赖于染色体交换的 [2]。他们认为在他们的实验中需要考虑某种"其他的因素"。但他们的实验必须采用杂合体，否则就无法进行遗传检测。他们采用的特定的杂合形式（结构杂合）必定会对染色体分离产生复杂的影响。这本身就是所谓的"其他的因素"。因此在两个相对倒位的片段之间的相互交换将会产生能够正常分离的正常染色体，这种情况在其他的生物中也一样会发生。

但是当我们考虑到由这种交换形成的二价染色体的结构时，我们发现在简单的二价染色体中预期的染色体分离并不一定发生（图1）。配对染色单体分离时的拉力是与染色单体联会形成的平面相平行的，而不是相垂直的。因此，染色单体之间分离的阻力不是一个特定的恒定小量，而是两条交叉单体之间距离的函数。在这种情况下，我在草地蝗的杂合体倒位中观察到了染色体分离失败的例子。在染色体移位片段之间发生的其他种类的互换将使染色体片段发生滞后、互锁和不规则断裂等情况。因此，格吕内贝格 [3] 发现先前被认为是由染色单体之间不配对和随机分离导致的"非分离"片段通常是由这两个染色单体的丢失导致的，这就不足为奇了。

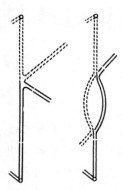

Fig. 1. The structure of bivalents with single (left) and double reciprocal crossing-over (right) between relatively inverted segments of homologous chromosomes.

This is merely one example of the special complications arising in structural hybrids. They have been described by Richardson for inversion hybrids and by myself for interchange hybrids in articles in the press[4]. They show the danger of arguing from the assumptions involved in an abstracted formal use of the terms "chromosome", "non-disjunction" and even "crossing-over" by the geneticist. They also show the difficulty the geneticist is faced with in dealing with the highly selected viable progeny of structural hybrids, a difficulty which can only be overcome by a close collaboration between those who are breeding the hybrids and those who are studying the structures found at meiosis in comparable material[2].

(**136**, 835; 1935)

C. D. Darlington: John Innes Horticultural Institution, London, S.W.19.

References:
1. *Z.I.A.V.*, **64**, 269–309.
2. *J. Genet.*, **31**, 185–212.
3. *J. Genet.*, **31**, 163–184.
4. *J. Genet.*, in the press.

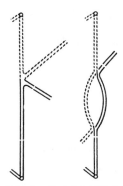

图 1. 同源染色体相对倒位区域之间发生单互换（左）
和双交叉互换（右）的二价染色体结构。

　　这仅仅是结构杂合体中存在特殊复杂性的一个例子。理查森曾论述过倒位杂合体中的这种特殊复杂性，我在即将发表的文章中 [4] 对互换杂合体的特殊复杂性也进行了描述。这些特殊复杂性表明，遗传学家们对"染色体"、"非分离"甚至"交换"这些术语抽象的正式用法所涉及的假设可能存在争议。同时，这些特殊复杂性也揭示了遗传学家们在处理结构杂合体的高选择性可存活后代时面对的困难。只有正在进行杂交育种的科学家们和正在研究那些相似物质的减数分裂时期出现的结构的科学家们 [2] 紧密合作，这些困难才有可能被克服。

（韩玲俐 翻译；王晓晨 审稿）

Chemical Detection of Artificial Transmutation of Elements

F. A. Paneth and H. Loleit

Editor's Note

By 1935 the transmutation of chemical elements by radioactivity was well established. Ernest Rutherford showed in 1919 that subatomic particles released in radioactive decay could transform non-radioactive atoms into new ones. But while such transmutations realised the dreams of alchemy, they had been verified only by physical means: by examining the radioactivity of the products. Chemists wanted to detect the new elements made this way with chemical methods. Here Austrian scientist Friedrich Paneth, with H. Loleit in London, uses chemical separation methods to isolate helium produced by the splitting of boron nuclei with neutrons, and identify it spectroscopically. Such chemical separation of the tiny amounts of material made by radiochemistry later proved vital in the search for wholly artificial elements.

IT has been our aim for years to prove the result of transmutation experiments by chemical analysis, and in a brief report[1] we have described our failure to find chemical evidence for the production of hydrogen or neon by bombardment with α-rays. In the meantime, many new ways of artificial transmutation have been found, and the discovery of artificial radioelements has enabled Curie and Joliot[2] to use the methods of radio-chemistry, that is, the combination of radioactive measurement with chemical operations, for the investigation of the chemical character of products of artificial transmutation. This line of work has been extended by Fermi and his collaborators and by many others. The quantity of newly formed matter has in general been much too small for any attempt at a purely chemical detection; the claim[3] of having separated and spectroscopically observed helium of atomic weight 3, made from heavy hydrogen, has been disproved by later work[4].

At present, for various experimental reasons, the best choice for the chemical detection of an artificially-produced element seemed to be helium originating from boron according to the reaction[5]

$$_5B^{10} + _0n^1 = _3Li^7 + _2He^4.$$

In a closed copper vessel we bombarded the methyl ester of boron with neutrons. These were produced near the centre of the spherical vessel by the decay of radon, mixed with beryllium, and were slowed down by the hydrogen atoms of the ester and of the water surrounding the metal flask. In a first experiment, by the decay of 450 mC. of radon, sufficient helium was produced for a spectroscopic observation. During a second experiment, lasting seven weeks, we procured enough radon to allow 2,200 mC. of it to

元素人工嬗变的化学检测

帕内特，洛莱特

编者按

在 1935 年之前，化学元素通过放射性衰变发生嬗变的机制已经确立起来了。欧内斯特·卢瑟福在 1919 年就指出放射性衰变中释放出的亚原子粒子能够使非放射性的原子转变为新的原子。这样的转变实现了炼金术的梦想，这一直以来只能用物理的方法进行证明——检测产品的放射能。化学家试图用化学手段去检测通过这种方式产生的新元素。这篇文章中奥地利科学家弗里德里希·帕内特与伦敦的洛莱特用化学分离的方法将中子轰击硼原子核使其分裂产生的氦分离了出来，并对它进行了光谱表征。这种将放射化学产生的微量物质进行化学分离的方法在后来研究人造元素的过程中被证明是非常有效的。

用化学分析的方法来证明嬗变实验的结果多年以来一直是我们的目标，我们曾在一份简要报告 [1] 中描述了寻找 α 射线轰击氢或氖的产物的化学证据时遭遇的失败。与此同时，人们还发现了很多人工嬗变的新方法，人工放射性元素的发现使居里和约里奥 [2] 得以使用放射化学方法——放射性观测与化学操作相结合的方法——对人工嬗变产物的化学特性进行研究。费米和他的同事以及很多其他研究者已在这项研究上取得了新的进展。然而，对于任何一种单纯的化学检测来说，新生成物质的量总的来讲都太少了。曾经有人宣称 [3] 已经分离出且用光谱方法观测到了由重氢原子得到的原子量为 3 的氦，但后来的研究 [4] 证明这一结果是错误的。

目前，由于各种实验上的原因，对人工制备的元素进行化学检测的最佳选择似乎就是由硼所产生的氦，反应如下 [5]：

$$^{10}_{5}B + ^{1}_{0}n = ^{7}_{3}Li + ^{4}_{2}He$$

在一个密闭的铜质容器中，我们用中子轰击硼的甲酯。这些中子是由掺杂了铍的氡在球形容器的中心附近发生的衰变产生的，并在酯和金属烧瓶周围的水中的氢原子的作用下减速。在第一次实验中，利用放射强度 450 毫居里的氡的衰变，生成了足以供光谱观测用的氦。在第二次持续 7 周的实验中，我们获得了足够多的氦，以至于它在装置中衰变时可产生 2,200 毫居里的放射强度。这一次我们不仅能用光谱方

decay in our apparatus. This time we were able not only to observe spectroscopically the helium produced but also to measure it; we found, to an accuracy of about 20 percent, 1.3×10^{-7} c.c. helium. A blank test run afterwards for nine weeks under exactly the same conditions, but without radon-beryllium tubes, showed not the slightest sign of helium production.

The copper vessel was a sphere of only 7.5 cm. radius; it is unlikely that more than half of the neutrons formed in the beryllium tubes were caught by the boron inside the vessel. A new experiment, making use of a larger flask, is in progress; but it can already be concluded from our preliminary figures (as one helium atom, according to the above equation, needs for its production one neutron) that a millicurie of radon, mixed with beryllium, produces more than 3,000 neutrons a second[6].

In this experiment—for the first time, so far as we are aware—an artificially produced element has been separated, spectroscopically observed, and measured. We presume that the old alchemistical goal can be achieved today in other cases also.

We wish to express our sincere thanks to Prof. F. L. Hopwood, director of the Radium Department, St. Bartholomew's Hospital, London, to Prof. S. Russ, director of the Radium Department, Middlesex Hospital, London, and to Prof. Stefan Meyer, director of the Institute for Radium Research in Vienna, for kindly supplying the radon-beryllium tubes; and also to Dr. E. Glückauf for assistance in the experiments.

(**136**, 950; 1935)

F. A. Paneth and H. Loleit: Imperial College of Science and Technology, London, S.W.7, Nov. 28.

References:

1. F. A. Paneth and P. L. Günther, *Nature*, **131**, 652; 1933. See also *Z. phys. Chem.*, *A*, **173**, 401; 1935.

2. I. Curie and F. Joliot, *C.R.*, **198**, 559; 1934.

3. G. P. Harnwell, H. D. Smyth and W. D. Urry, *Phys, Rev.*, **46**, 437; 1934.

4. H. D. Smyth, G. P. Bleakney and W. W. Lozier, *Phys. Rev.*, **47**, 800; 1935. F. A. Paneth and G. P. Thomson, *Nature*, **136**, 334; 1935.

5. J. Chadwick and M. Goldhaber, *Nature*, **135**, 65; 1935. *Proc. Cam. Phil. Soc.*, **31**, 612; 1935. H. J. Taylor and M. Goldhaber, *Nature*, **135**, 341; 1935. E. Amaldi, O. D'Agostino, E. Fermi, B. Pontecorvo, F. Rasetti and E. Segrè, *Proc. Roy. Soc.*, *A*, **149**, 522; 1935.

6. The ordinarily assumed yield of neutrons under these conditions is 1,000 neutrons per sec. (See, for example, E. Fermi and collaborators, *Proc. Roy. Soc.*, *A*, **146**, 483; 1934.) According to R. Jaeckel's observations (*Z. Phys.*, **91**, 493; 1934) the value 10,000 neutrons per sec. is more likely.

法观察到生成的氦，而且还可以进行测量——我们测量到了 1.3×10^{-7} 立方厘米的氦，精度达到 20%。后来在完全相同的条件下（只是没有了氡－铍管）进行了持续 9 周的空白实验，结果发现全部没有氦生成。

铜质容器是一个半径仅为 7.5 厘米的球体，容器中的硼所捕获到的在铍管中生成的中子不太可能超过一半。目前正在用更大的烧瓶进行一项新实验，但是利用我们的初期数据（根据上述方程式，生成一个氦原子需要一个中子）已经可以作出推断：1 毫居里掺杂铍的氡每秒钟可以产生超过 3,000 个中子 [6]。

在这项实验中，人类第一次（据我们所知）对一种人工制备的元素进行了分离、光谱观察以及测量。我们估计，就是古老的炼金术，今天也能够在某些条件下得以实现。

我们要对以下各位表达诚挚的谢意：伦敦圣巴托罗缪医院镭部主任霍普伍德教授，伦敦米德尔塞克斯医院镭部主任拉斯教授，以及维也纳镭研究所所长斯特凡·迈耶教授，他们热心地提供了氡－铍管；还要感谢格吕克奥夫博士在实验中给我们的帮助。

（王耀杨 翻译；汪长征 审稿）

The Slowing Down of Neutrons by Collisions with Protons

H. von Halban, Jr. and P. Preiswerk

Editor's Note

Fermi had recently shown that neutrons passing through substances containing hydrogen would be slowed by collisions with protons. Here Hans von Halban and Peter Preiswerk explore the process in detail. They note that neutrons of relatively low energy might well be slowed as they transfer energy to the molecules of the medium, in which case the slowing might be influenced by the molecular nature of the medium. So they passed neutrons through water, ethyl alcohol, benzene and liquid paraffin, measuring how the intensity of slow neutrons depended on distance travelled. The results showed that indeed the degree of slowing seemed likely to reflect differences in molecular motions. Slowing of neutrons was later to prove essential for controlled nuclear fission.

FERMI and others[1] showed that neutrons, passing through substances containing hydrogen, loose their energy by collisions with protons. It is of interest to discuss this process of slowing down somewhat further. So long as the energy of the neutron is higher than the energy with which the protons are bound in the molecules of the substance through which the neutrons pass, it seems evident that the latter give, on the average, half their energy to the proton at every collision. But when the neutrons are slowed down below this binding energy, they must excite rotation and oscillation of the hydrogen atom in the molecule in order to lose energy.

It is not certain whether the cross-section of protons for neutrons is a uniform function of the velocity of the neutrons, or if it shows discontinuities for energies comparable with the molecular bindings. In the latter case, it is possible that two substances, containing hydrogen held by different linkages, would show differences in slowing down the neutrons. We have carried out some experiments which indicate the existence of such differences.

Spheres with different radii (5-15 cm.) were alternately filled with water (0.11 gm. H/cm.³), ethyl alcohol (0.10 gm. H/cm.³), benzene (0.067 gm. H/cm.³) and a liquid paraffin (0.14 gm. H/cm.³). In the centre of the sphere a neutron source (radon + beryllium) was placed. The activation of a silver plate, which was fixed on the surface of the spheres and exposed for five minutes to irradiation, served as a measure of the intensity of slow neutrons.

Fig. 1 shows the number of slow neutrons per unit of the solid angle plotted against rd, where r is the radius of the sphere and d the quantity of hydrogen contained by 1 cm.³ of the liquid in question. The general aspect of these curves is already known. For small

与质子碰撞而导致的中子慢化

小哈尔班，普雷斯沃克

编者按

费米于近期指出中子穿过含氢物质时会与质子碰撞而减速。这篇文章中汉斯·冯·哈尔班和彼得·普雷斯沃克仔细探讨了这一过程。他们注意到能量相对较低的中子会由于将能量传递给介质分子而减速，在这种情况下，中子减速可能受到介质分子性质的影响。因此，他们使中子穿过水、酒精、苯和液体石蜡，以测量慢中子的强度是如何随穿透深度的变化而变化的。实验结果显示中子慢化的程度似乎反映出了介质分子运动的差别。后来，中子慢化被证明对于可控核裂变是非常关键的。

费米等人[1]指出，中子在通过含氢的物质时因与质子发生碰撞而损失能量。进一步深入地讨论这一慢化过程是有趣的。只要中子的能量大于它要通过的物质分子中质子的束缚能，中子平均在每一次的碰撞过程中就会有一半能量传给了质子，这点似乎是很明显的。但当中子的能量减少到这种束缚能以下时，中子就一定会激发分子中氢原子的转动和振动，从而使中子的能量减少。

不能确定的是：中子对质子的碰撞截面是否为中子速度的单调函数，或者当中子能量与分子的束缚能可比时，碰撞截面是否呈现不连续性。在后一种情况下，两种含有不同结合形式氢的物质在中子慢化的过程中可能会表现出差异性。我们已经进行了一些实验，结果显示出了这种差异性的存在。

用水（氢含量为 0.11 g/cm³）、乙醇（氢含量为 0.10 g/cm³）、苯（氢含量为 0.067 g/cm³）和液体石蜡（氢含量为 0.14 g/cm³）分别装满半径不同（5～15 cm）的球。在球的中央放置着一个中子源（氡＋铍），在球的表面安置一个银片并对其辐照 5 分钟，然后利用银片的放射性测量慢中子的强度。

图 1 显示了单位立体角中慢中子的数量随着 rd 的变化关系，其中 r 是球的半径，d 是 1 cm³ 液体的含氢量。这些曲线的一般意义是众所周知的。对小半径而言，随着

radii a rapid increase of the intensity with increasing radius is observed, due to the slowing down of neutrons by collisions with protons. After a certain point, an increase of the radius causes a reduction of the intensity. This clearly shows that not all neutrons which pass the surface of a sphere are reaching the next bigger sphere. The vanishing of slow neutrons must be ascribed to absorption.

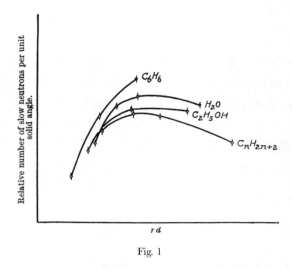

Fig. 1

The absorption of slow neutrons by paraffin and other substances containing hydrogen has been studied in detail by Bjerge and Westcott[2], who found that the number of slow neutrons is reduced to a half after diffusion through 1.6 cm. of water. By a different method we obtained the value of 2.5 cm. for paraffin in a preliminary experiment. A source of neutrons was placed in the centre of a paraffin wax cube of 14 cm. side. Five plates of paraffin wax, each 1 cm. thick, and finally a small silver plate were placed upon this cube. A screen of cadmium was interposed between the paraffin plates at different distances from the silver plate. The activity of the silver, obtained for equal times of irradiation, increased when the distance between the silver and the cadmium was increased. A curve was obtained which showed that influence of the absorption of the cadmium decreased to a half when the distance between the silver plate and the absorber was increased by 2.5 cm.

Fig. 1 shows that the maximum values of intensity are different for different liquids; these differences cannot be ascribed to the quantities of hydrogen contained by the liquids alone. Also, it is not possible to explain these results by absorption of slow neutrons by oxygen or carbon nuclei. A neutron has, for the same number of collisions with protons, passed twice the number of carbon atoms in benzene as in the liquid paraffin, and we see that the maximum value for the latter is much lower than for benzene, where the maximum seems to be just reached with the biggest sphere.

The differences in the influence of the four liquids examined, on the intensity of slow neutrons, cannot be ascribed to differences in the quantities of hydrogen, carbon or

半径的增大，观测到中子的强度显著增加，这是由于中子与质子碰撞而速度减慢。在某一个固定值之后，随着半径的增大，中子的强度反而减弱。这清楚地表明，并不是所有通过球表面的中子都会到达下一个更大的球面上。慢中子的消失必然是因为它被吸收了。

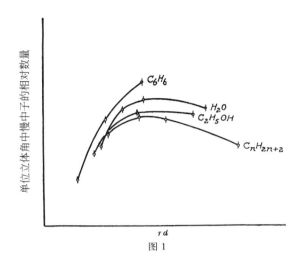

图 1

伯格和韦斯科特[2] 已经详细地研究了石蜡和其他含氢物质对慢中子的吸收，他们发现，其在通过厚 1.6 cm 的水之后，慢中子的数量减少了一半。在对石蜡进行的初步实验中，我们采用不同的方法得到的数值为 2.5 cm。把一个中子源放在边长为 14 cm 的立方体形石蜡的中心，在这个立方体石蜡上放置 5 个 1 cm 厚的石蜡板，最后放置一块小银板。在石蜡板之间插入一块镉片，并变换其位置以使其与银板的距离不同。在相等辐射时间内，当银板和镉板的距离增大时，银的放射性会增加。由实验得到的曲线表明，当银板与镉板之间的距离增大了 2.5 cm 时，镉吸收的影响减小到一半。

图 1 表明，对不同的液体，慢中子强度的最大值是不相同的；这些差别不能仅仅归因于液体中氢含量的不同。同样，也不能用氧核或碳核吸收慢中子来解释。在与质子碰撞次数相同的情况下，中子在苯中通过的碳原子数是在液体石蜡中通过碳原子数的两倍，而且我们还发现，液体石蜡中慢中子强度的最大值远远低于在苯中慢中子强度的最大值，而苯中的最大值似乎得用半径最大的球才刚能达到。

被测试的四种液体对于慢中子强度的影响力的差别，不能仅归因于是这些液体中氢、碳或氧含量的不同。这些液体的分子结构的不同也导致了它们之间的其他一

oxygen these liquids contain. Other differences between these liquids depend upon their molecular structure. Thus different probabilities for the slowing down of neutrons by excitation of rotation and oscillation of the hydrogen atoms in the different molecules may account for the discrepancies observed.

(**136**, 951-952; 1935)

Hans von Halban, Jr. and Peter Preiswerk: Institut du Radium, Laboratoire Curie, Paris, Nov. 5.

References:

1. Fermi and others, *La Ricerca Scientifica*, (v) 2, 1; 1934. (vi) 1, 1; 1935.
2. T. Bjerge and C. H. Westcott, *Proc. Roy. Soc.*, A, **150**, 709; 1935.

些差别。因此，或许我们可以这样解释观测到的差别，即不同分子中通过激发氢原子的转动和振动来减慢中子的概率不同。

（沈乃澂 翻译；王乃彦 审稿）

The Pattern of Proteins

D. M. Wrinch

Editor's Note

Although this paper presents an incorrect idea about protein molecular structure towards which biochemists now have a rather scathing attitude, it shows how unresolved that question was in the 1930s. The technique of X-ray crystallography was already being used by this time to look at proteins, notably by J. Desmond Bernal and his collaborators. Dorothy Wrinch was a mathematician with no formal training in chemistry, but her view, presented here, that protein backbones are built up of cyclic structures called "cyclols", gained support from some leading figures, especially the American chemist Irving Langmuir. This was partly due to Wrinch's energetic self-promotion, and *Nature* carried several subsequent elaborations of the idea, here presented only as a "working hypothesis".

ANY theory as to the structure of the molecule of simple native protein must take account of a number of facts, including the following:

(1) The molecules are largely, if not entirely, made up of amino acid residues. They contain —NH—CO linkages, but in general few —NH$_2$ groups not belonging to side chains, and in some cases possibly none.

(2) There is a general uniformity among proteins of widely different chemical constitution which suggests a simple general plan in the arrangement of the amino acid residues, characteristic of proteins in general. Protein crystals possess high, general trigonal, symmetry.

(3) Many native proteins are "globular" in form.

(4) A number of proteins[1] of widely different chemical constitution, though isodisperse in solution for a certain range of values of pH, split up into molecules of submultiple molecular weights in a sufficiently alkaline medium.

The facts cited suggest that native protein may contain closed, as opposed to open, polypeptides, that the polypeptides, open or closed, are in a folded state, and that the type of folding must be such as to imply the possibility of regular and orderly arrangements of hundreds of residues.

An examination of the geometrical nature of polypeptide chains shows that, *since all amino acids known to occur in proteins are α-derivatives*, they may be folded in hexagonal arrays. Closed

蛋白质结构模型

林奇

编者按

虽然这篇文章在蛋白质分子结构方面提出的观点是错误的，但它体现了 20 世纪 30 年代时人们对这个问题的探索，而现在生物化学家对于蛋白质分子结构已经有了相当严谨和清晰的观点。当时，X 射线晶体衍射技术已经被用于观察蛋白质，尤为著名的是德斯蒙德·贝尔纳及其合作者所做的工作。作为一个在化学方面没有接受过正规训练的数学家，多萝西·林奇在本文中提出的蛋白质骨架由环状结构（环醇）形成的观点却受到一些权威人物的支持，特别是美国化学家欧文·朗缪尔。这在一定程度上是由于林奇积极的自我完善。林奇对于这个观点的多次加工与完善相继发表在《自然》上，这篇文章所呈现的还只是一个"正在完善中的假说"。

关于简单天然蛋白质分子结构的任何假说都必须考虑如下所述的许多事实：

（1）蛋白质分子主要——即使不是全部——由氨基酸残基构成。这些氨基酸残基通过肽键相连，但通常除了侧链之外只有很少的氨基基团，有时可能完全没有。

（2）化学组成大不相同的蛋白质具有普遍一致的结构，这表明了氨基酸残基的排列顺序遵循一个简单普遍的原则。蛋白质晶体具有高度对称性，通常是三角对称。

（3）许多天然蛋白质呈"球形"。

（4）许多化学组成大不相同的蛋白质，虽然在一定 pH 范围内的溶液中均匀分散，但在碱性足够强的溶液中会分解成分子量为蛋白分子量约数的分子[1]。

上面列举的事实表明天然蛋白质可能包含闭合的而不是开环的多肽，并且无论是闭合的还是开环的，这些多肽都处于折叠状态，同时这种折叠类型必然意味着数以百计的氨基酸残基规则而有序的排列。

因为蛋白质中已知的氨基酸都是 α-衍生物，对多肽链的几何特性的研究表明多肽可能折叠成正六角形阵列。由 2、6、18、42、66、90、114、138、162······

polypeptide chains consisting of 2, 6, 18, 42, 66, 90, 114, 138, 162 ... $(18+24n)$ ... residues form a series with threefold central symmetry. A companion series consisting of 10, 26, 42, 58, 74, 90, 106, 122 ... $(10+16n)$ ... residues have twofold central symmetry. There is also a series with sixfold central symmetry: others with no central symmetry. Open polypeptides can also be hexagonally folded. The number of free —NH$_2$ groups, in so far as these indicate an open polypeptide, can be made as small as we please, even zero if we so desire. The hexagonal folding of polypeptide chains, open or closed, evidently allows the construction of molecules containing even hundreds of amino acid residues in orderly array, and provides a characteristic pattern, which in its simplicity and uniformity agrees with many facts of protein chemistry.

The stability of these folded polypeptide chains cannot be attributed to electrostatic attractions between the various CO, NH groups, for the appropriate distance between carbon and nitrogen atoms in these circumstances[2] lies between 2.8 A. and 4.2 A., whereas the distance in our case is at most 1.54 A. By using the transformation* suggested by Frank in 1933 at a lecture given by W. T. Astbury to the Oxford Junior Scientific Society,

$$\begin{array}{ccc} \diagdown \\ \diagup \end{array} C = O \qquad H-N \begin{array}{c} \diagup \\ \diagdown \end{array} \quad \text{to} \quad \begin{array}{c} \diagdown \\ \diagup \end{array} C(OH)-N \begin{array}{c} \diagup \\ \diagdown \end{array}$$

which has already proved useful in the structure of α-keratin[3], the situation is at once cleared up and we obtain (Fig. 1) the molecule "cyclol 6" (the closed polypeptide with six residues), "cyclol 18", "cyclol 42" (Fig. 2) and so on, and similarly open "cyclised" polypeptides (Fig. 3).

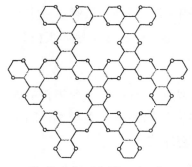

Fig. 1. The "cyclol 6" molecule.

Fig. 2. A "cyclol 42" molecule.

---

* The application of this transformation to these molecules was suggested to me by J. D. Bernal.

（18+24n）……个氨基酸残基构成的一系列闭合多肽链具有三重中心对称性。由10、26、42、58、74、90、106、122……（10+16n）……个氨基酸残基构成的一系列多肽链具有二重中心对称性。也有具有六重中心对称性的多肽链系列，其他多肽链没有中心对称性。开环的多肽也可以折叠成正六角形阵列。就自由氨基的存在意味着开环的多肽而言，我们可以按照自己的意愿使自由氨基的数目尽可能地减少，如果确有必要甚至可以使其为零。开环和闭合的多肽链都可以折叠成正六角形阵列，这就使得包含多达数百个氨基酸残基的分子的有序构建成为可能，同时也提供了一个特征性的模式，这种模式的简单性和一致性符合许多蛋白质化学的研究结论。

　　折叠多肽链的稳定性不能归因于各种羰基和氨基基团之间的静电作用。处于静电作用下的碳原子和氮原子之间的适宜距离[2] 在 2.8~4.2 埃之间，而我们的研究中这个距离最多只有 1.54 埃。在 1933 年参加阿斯特伯里为牛津初等科学学会所作的一场报告上，弗兰克提出了转化的方法*，

$$\diagdown C = O \qquad H - N \diagup \qquad 缩合为 \qquad \diagdown C(OH) - N \diagup$$

已经证明这种方法对于解析 α–角蛋白的结构是非常有用的[3]。通过使用这种方法，形势就立刻明朗起来了。我们得到了"六元环醇"分子（具有六个氨基酸残基的闭合多肽）（图1），"十八元环醇"分子和"四十二元环醇"分子（图2）等等，同时也得到了"开环"的多肽（图3）。

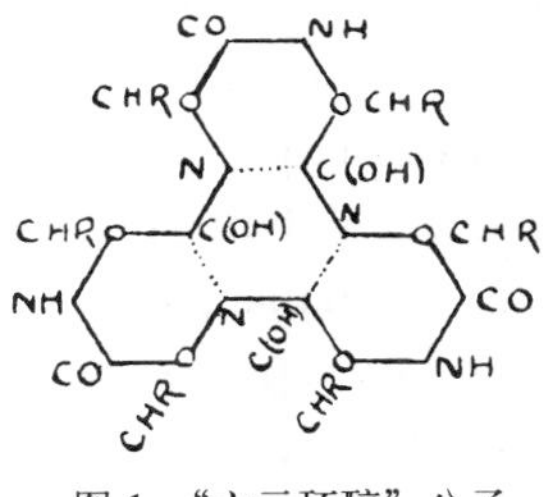

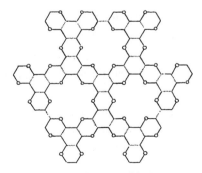

图 1. "六元环醇"分子

图 2."四十二元环醇"分子

---

* 贝尔纳建议我将转化的方法用在这些分子上。

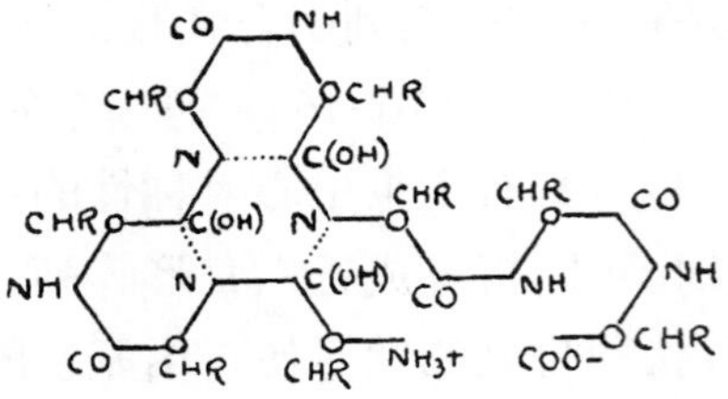

Fig. 3.

Hexagonal packing of polypeptides suggests a new *three dimensional* unit, $-\text{CHR}-\overset{\mid}{\text{C}}\,(\text{OH})-\text{N}\!\!<$, which may be used to build three-dimensional molecules of a variety of types. These are now being investigated in detail. At the moment we direct attention only to single cyclised polypeptides forming hexagons lying approximately in one plane. The cyclol layer molecule is a fabric the thickness of which is one amino acid residue. *Since all naturally occurring amino acids are of loevo type*[4] this fabric is dorsiventral, having a front surface from which the side chains emerge, and a back surface free from side chains. Both front and back carry trios of hydroxyls normal to the surface in alternating hexagonal arrays. Such a layer molecule and its polymers, formed also by the same transformation, can cover an area of any shape and extent. It offers suggestions as to the structure of the solid protein film when it is one amino acid residue thick. In its most compact form, the cyclol layer molecule gives an area per residue of about 9.9 A.[2]. Less dense layers can be built, for example, from polymers of cyclol 18 and of cyclol 66 respectively, where the corresponding areas per residue are 13.2 A.[2] and 16.2 A.[2] respectively. The figures for unimolecular films of gliadin, glutenin, egg albumin, zein, serum albumin, serum globulin range from 1.724×10^{-7} gm./cm.[2] for serum globulin to 1.111×10^{-7} gm./cm.[2] for serum albumin[5,6,7]. With an average residue weight of 120, these densities give an area per residue ranging from 11.48 A.[2] to 18.82 A.[2]. On the basis of the proposed hexagonal packing of polypeptides I therefore suggest that the upper limit of density of which a protein film is capable without buckling, provided that it is only one amino acid residue thick, is one residue per 9.9 A.[2]; further, that a higher density implies that the film, though it may still be unimolecular, is more than one amino acid residue thick.

Cyclol layers may also be used to build molecules and molecular aggregates with extension in three dimensions, since they may be linked front to front by means of the side chains, in particular, by cystine bridges, and back to back by means of hydroxyls[8]. The single-layer cyclol is a fabric capable of covering a two-dimensional area of any shape and extent; a three-dimensional array can then be built, layer upon layer, the linkage being alternately by means of side chains and hydroxyls. The idea that native proteins consist largely, if not entirely, of cyclised polypeptides therefore implies that some native proteins, including those of "globular" type, may have a layer structure.

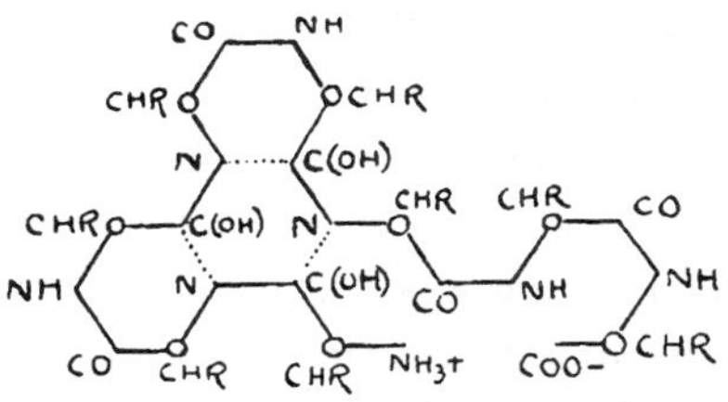

图 3

正六角形排列的多肽表明存在一个新的**三维结构**单元，$—CHR—\overset{|}{C}(OH)—N<$，可以用来构建多种类型的三维分子。现在正在对这些新的三维结构进行详细的研究。此刻我们关注的只是几乎在同一平面内形成六边形的单环多肽。这种层状环醇分子结构的厚度为一个氨基酸残基。**因为天然存在的氨基酸都是左旋型**[4]，因此这种结构呈背腹性，侧链出现在前表面而不是后表面。前后表面均有三个垂直于六角形表面的相间排列的羟基基团。这样的层状分子及其通过同样的转化方式形成的多聚体能够囊括蛋白质所有可能的形状。这为厚度只有一个氨基酸残基的固态蛋白质膜的结构提供了一些参考。在其最紧凑的结构中，层状环醇分子为每个氨基酸残基提供了约 9.9 平方埃的区域。在较为稀疏的结构中，例如，十八元环醇多聚体和六十六元环醇多聚体，每个氨基酸残基相应的区域大小分别为 13.2 平方埃和 16.2 平方埃。麦醇溶蛋白、麦谷蛋白、卵清蛋白、玉米醇溶蛋白、血清白蛋白和血清球蛋白形成的单分子膜的密度值的变化范围是从血清球蛋白的 1.724×10^{-7} 克 / 平方厘米到血清白蛋白的 1.111×10^{-7} 克 / 平方厘米 [5,6,7]。氨基酸残基的平均分子量为 120，因此从这些密度值推出每个氨基酸残基所占区域的变化范围是 11.48~18.82 平方埃。在前面已经提到的多肽的六角形排列的基础上，假如厚度只有一个氨基酸残基，那么我可以推算出在没发生折曲的蛋白膜中密度的上限为每 9.9 平方埃一个氨基酸残基；此外，较高的密度值意味着膜的厚度超过一个氨基酸残基，虽然它可能还是单分子的。

层状环醇结构也可以被用来构建在三维空间延伸的分子及分子聚集体。因为通过侧链（特别是胱氨酸桥）可以将环醇分子层状结构的前表面和前表面连接起来，也可以通过羟基把后表面与后表面相连接起来 [8]。单层的环醇结构可以囊括所有可能形状和程度的二维分子；通过环醇分子之间的侧链连接或者羟基连接，达到层与层的连接，我们就可以构建出三维阵列。天然蛋白质主要（即使不是全部）由环化多肽构成的观点意味着，包括那些"球形"蛋白质在内的许多天然蛋白质都可能具有层状结构。

Linkage by means of hydroxyls recalls the structures of graphitic oxide and montmorillonite, etc. Such a structure suggests a considerable capacity for hydration, an outstanding characteristic of many proteins. Further, since alternate layers are held together by means of hydroxyls, and contiguous molecules may also be held together in the same way, a protein molecular aggregate will, on this theory, necessarily be sensitive to changes in the acidity of the medium; in particular, a sufficiently high pH will cause such an aggregate to dissociate into single-layer units or into two-layer units joined by cystine bridges or side chains in covalent linkages. Svedberg's results, according to which a number of different native proteins break up into smaller molecules with sub-multiple molecular weights[1], here find a simple interpretation. The particular sub-multiples which occur may be regarded as affording evidence as to the type of symmetry possessed by the layers out of which the molecular aggregates are built.

The hypothesis that native proteins consist essentially of cyclised polypeptides thus takes account of the facts mentioned in (1), (2), (3), (4) above. Further, it derives support from the case of α-keratin, for with Astbury's "pseudo-diketopiperazine" structure[3] the polypeptides may be regarded as partially cyclised since they are cyclised at regular intervals, one out of every three (CO, NH) groups being involved. It is also suggestive in relation to a variety of other facts belonging to organic chemistry, X-ray analysis, enzyme chemistry and cytology. I cite the following:

(1) The rhythm of 18 in the distribution of amino acids in gelatin found by Bergmann[9], and the suggestion of Astbury[10] that in gelatin "the effective length of an amino acid residue is only about 2.8 A.".

(2) The low molecular weight not exceeding 1,000 found by Svedberg[11] for the bulk of the material from which lactalbumin is formed.

(3) Secretin[12], a protein with molecular weight of about 5,000, containing no open polypeptide chains.

(4) The nuclear membrane, which, consisting of proteins and lipoids, plays an important part in mitosis on account of its variable permeability.

(5) Bergmann's findings[13] with respect to dipeptidase; these suggest that the dipeptide substrate, upon which this enzyme acts, has a hexagonal configuration.

Finally, the deduction from the hypothesis of cyclised polypeptides, that native proteins may consist of dorsiventral layers, with the side-chains issuing from one side only, suggests that immunological reactions are concerned only with surfaces carrying side-chains. Hence, such reactions depend both on the particular nature and on the arrangement of the amino acids.

通过羟基连接形成分子的方式使我们想起了氧化石墨和蒙脱石等物质的结构。这种结构表现出了相当大的水合能力，而水合作用是许多蛋白质的典型特征。此外，因为相邻层是通过羟基相连的，所以相邻蛋白质分子之间也可以通过这种方式连接。根据这个理论，蛋白质分子聚集体必然对介质酸度的改变非常敏感；特别是足够高的 pH 值会导致聚集体分解成单层单元，或者由胱氨酸或侧链间的共价键连接在一起的双层单元。依据斯韦德贝里的研究，许多不同的天然蛋白质分解形成小分子，其分子量是原蛋白质分子量的约数 [1]，我们的理论对于这种现象提供了一种简单的解释。分子量为原蛋白质分子量约数的小分子的产生也可以为构成分子聚集体的单层单元所具有的对称性提供证据。

由此可见，天然蛋白质主要是由环化多肽构成的假说考虑到了前面（1）、（2）、（3）和（4）所述的事实。此外，基于阿斯特伯里的"伪二酮哌嗪"结构 [3]，可以认为 α-角蛋白多肽是部分环化的，其环化发生的位置之间具有固定的间隔，每三个基团（羧基和氨基）中有一个参与这种环化，这对于我们的假说也提供了支持。对于有机化学、X 射线分析、酶化学和细胞学的一些研究来说，此假说也是有启发性的。现总结如下：

（1）伯格曼 [9] 发现凝胶中的氨基酸分布呈现十八节律，阿斯特伯里 [10] 提出在凝胶中"氨基酸的有效长度大约只有 2.8 埃"。

（2）斯韦德贝里 [11] 发现，构成乳清蛋白的大部分物质的分子量很低，不超过 1,000。

（3）分子量约为 5,000 的促胰液素 [12] 中没有开放的多肽链。

（4）由于具有可变的渗透性，由蛋白质和类脂构成的核膜在有丝分裂过程中发挥着重要作用。

（5）伯格曼发现了一些关于二肽酶的结果 [13]；这些结果表明这种酶作用的二肽底物具有六边形构型。

最后，环化多肽假说的一个推论是天然蛋白质可能由背腹层构成，侧链仅在其一侧出现。这一推论表明对于免疫反应来说只有含侧链的表面是重要的。因此免疫反应既依赖于氨基酸的特定性质也依赖于其排列方式。

Full details of the work, which is to be regarded as offering for consideration, a simple *working hypothesis*, for which no finality is claimed, will be published in due course.

(**137**, 411-412; 1936)

D. M. Wrinch: Mathematical Institute, Oxford.

References:·
1. Svedberg, *Science*, **79**, 327 (1934).

2. International Tables for the Determination of Crystal Structure.

3. Astbury and Woods, *Phil. Trans. Roy. Soc.*, **232**, 333 (1933).

4. Jordan Lloyd, *Biol. Rev.*, 7, 256 (1932).

5. Gorter, *J. Gen. Phys.*, **18**, 421 (1935); *Amer. J. Diseases of Children*, **47**, 945 (1934).

6. Gorter and van Ormondt, *Biochem. J.*, **29**, 48 (1935).

7. Schulman and Rideal, *Biochem. J.*, **27**, 1581 (1933).

8. Bernal and Megaw, *Proc. Roy. Soc.*, A, **151**, 384 (1935).

9. Bergmann, *J. Biol. Chem.*, **110**, 471 (1935).

10. Astbury, Cold Spring Harbor Symposia on Quantitative Biology, **2**, 15 (1934).

11. Sjogren and Svedberg, *J. Amer. Chem. Soc.*, **52**, 3650 (1930).

12. Hammersten *et al.*, *Biochem. Z.*, **264**, 272 and 275 (1933).

13. Bergmann *et al.*, *J. Biol. Chem.*, **109**, 325 (1935).

我们的工作仅供参考，这只是一个**正在完善中的假说**，未成定论，此项工作的全部细节将会在适当的时间发表。

（赵凤轩 翻译；周筠梅 审稿）

A New Fossil Anthropoid Skull from South Africa

R. Broom

Editor's Note

For twelve years after Raymond Dart's discovery in 1924 of the infant *Australopithecus* at Taungs, the fossil record of human ancestry in Africa remained silent. Controversy reigned about whether the Taungs "baby" was a genuine intermediate in human evolution, or simply a juvenile ape, as many maintained. The impasse was broken by this announcement of the discovery of a fragmentary skull and brain-cast of an adult pre-human, by palaeontologist Robert Broom. It came from lime-workings near caves at Sterkfontein, soon to yield much more. Broom named the new form *Australopithecus transvaalensis*. The finding was the first step towards the acceptance of an ape-like intermediate in human evolution.

IT is nearly twelve years ago since Prof. R. A. Dart startled the world by the announcement of the discovery of a new type of fossil anthropoid found in a limestone cave at Taungs in Bechuanaland, South Africa. The specimen consists of most of the brain cast and the practically perfect face of a very young ape. The functional teeth are all of the milk set, though the first upper and lower molars have cut the gum but do not yet meet. Though the ape was only very young, Dart estimated the cranial capacity at more than 500 c.c., and considered that in an adult it might exceed 700 c.c. He believed that this little fossil ape is not very closely allied to either the chimpanzee or the gorilla, and that it is probably nearer to the ape from which man has been descended and thus to be practically the long sought for missing link.

Many European and American men of science considered that Dart had made a mistake, and that if he had had a series of young chimpanzee skulls for comparison he would have recognized that the Taungs ape is only a variety of chimpanzee. When after some years the lower jaw was detached from the upper and the crowns of the teeth could be examined fully, it was found that the milk teeth are not in the least like those of either the chimpanzee or gorilla, and that they agree entirely with those of man, though larger. In the gorilla and chimpanzee the first upper milk molars have each two cusps: in man and in *Australopithecus* there are three well-marked cusps in each. In the first lower milk molar of the gorilla there is only one large cusp; in the chimpanzee there is one large cusp and a second rudimentary cusp. In man and in *Australopithecus* there are four well-developed cusps.

I have constantly maintained since I first examined the skull in 1925 that Dart was essentially right in holding *Australopithecus* is not closely allied to either the gorilla or chimpanzee, and

410

发现于南非的一件新的类人猿头骨化石

布鲁姆

编者按

1924 年雷蒙德·达特于汤恩发现了幼年南方古猿，此后的 12 年间，再没有出现与非洲人类始祖的化石有关的报告。对于汤恩"幼儿"一直存在争议，即它究竟是人类进化过程中的过渡类型，还是仅仅只是一只幼年的猿类。古人类学家罗伯特·布鲁姆的发现打破了这个僵局，他发现了一件成年的史前人类的头骨残片以及脑模。第一件头骨残片是在斯泰克方丹岩洞附近的石灰岩矿场里发现的，随后又找到了更多的化石。布鲁姆将其命名为"南方古猿德兰士瓦属"。这一发现使人们开始接受人类进化过程中存在与猿相像的过渡种。

将近 12 年前，达特教授宣布，在南非贝专纳兰汤恩的一个石灰岩洞中发现了类人猿化石，当时这一消息震惊了世界。该标本来自于一只非常年幼的猿，它保存有大部分脑模和几乎完美的面部部分。功能性牙齿都是乳齿，尽管第一上臼齿和第一下臼齿都已经破龈而出，但还不能咬合在一起。尽管这只猿非常年幼，但据达特估计，其颅容量超过了 500 毫升，并认为成年猿的颅容量可能超过 700 毫升。他相信这具小猿化石既不属于黑猩猩，也不属于大猩猩，可能更接近于一种进化成人类的猿类，实际上就是长久以来一直在寻找的、在整个进化过程中缺失的一环。

许多欧美学者认为达特犯了一个错误，如果他对一系列幼年黑猩猩的头骨进行比较的话，他就会意识到汤恩古猿不过是黑猩猩的一种而已。若干年后，当下颌骨与上颌骨被分开后，人们才得以充分地检查其牙冠，并发现其乳齿与黑猩猩和大猩猩的一点也不像，而与人类的相比，除大一点以外，其他方面完全相符。大猩猩和黑猩猩的每颗第一上乳臼齿都有两个齿尖；人类和南方古猿的每颗上乳臼齿则有三个明显的齿尖。大猩猩的第一下乳臼齿只有一个大的齿尖；黑猩猩有一个大的齿尖和一个次尖。人类和南方古猿则有四个发育良好的齿尖。

达特认为：南方古猿与大猩猩和黑猩猩都没有亲缘关系，而是处于或接近于进化成人类的世系位置上。自 1925 年我初次研究汤恩古猿至今，我一直认为这一观点

is on or near the line by which man has arisen.

I do not know what is at present the opinion in Europe as to where *Australopithecus* ought to be placed. Gregory of New York regards it as fairly near to the origin of the human line; and Romer of Harvard says it is "clearly not a chimpanzee or a gorilla". But the most important thing to do seemed to be to get an adult skull. For the last three months, I have been busy working on the bone breccia of the limestone caves of the Transvaal largely in the hope of getting either a new "missing link" or a type of primitive man. I have so far found no trace of man, though I have discovered more than a dozen new species of fossil mammals, a number of which belong to new genera.

Two weeks ago [Dr. Broom's covering letter is dated August 8. —Ed.], when visiting the caves at Sterkfontein near Krugersdorp, Mr. G. W. Barlow, the very understanding manager of the lime works there and on whom I had impressed the importance of keeping his eyes open for a Taungs ape, handed me the brain cast of what appeared to be a large anthropoid (Fig. 1). It had been blasted out of the side of the cave a couple of days before. A search for some hours failed to find any other part of the skull, but we found the cast of the top of the head in the cave wall. A more extensive search on the following day with a large party of workers resulted in the discovery of most of the base of the skull, with the upper part of the face (Fig. 2). In the same matrix was found the detached right maxilla with three teeth, and the third upper molar was also found, though detached. The lower part of the face had been removed before fossilization; and so far no mandible or lower teeth have been found, though parts may yet be discovered in a mass of crushed and broken bones near the side of the head. As the bones are very friable, no attempt has as yet been made to remove them from the much harder matrix.

Fig. 1. Half side view of the brain cast resting on the imperfect base. The brow ridges are shown with parts of the frontal sinuses exposed. Part of the left cheek bone is also shown. About $\frac{1}{3}$ natural size.
Photograph by Mr. Herbert Lang.

本质上是正确的。

我不知道当前欧洲对于南方古猿的进化归属持什么观点。纽约的格雷戈里认为南方古猿应该与人类世系起源的位置特别接近；哈佛的罗默说南方古猿"很明显既不是黑猩猩，也不是大猩猩"。然而最重要的事情可能就是找到一个成年头骨。过去的三个月，我一直忙于研究德兰士瓦的石灰岩洞中的骨角砾岩，主要是希望能得到一个新的"缺失的环节"或者得到一种原始人类类型。尽管我已经发现了十多个哺乳动物新物种化石，其中有许多属于新的属，但一直没有发现人类的踪迹。

巴洛先生是一位非常了解克鲁格斯多普当地情况的石灰工厂经理，我曾让他一定要留心寻找汤恩古猿。两个星期前（布鲁姆博士的附信上注明的日期是 8 月 8 日。——编者注），当我考察此地附近的斯泰克方丹山洞时，他把一件好像是大型类人猿的脑模（图 1）交给了我。几天前这个山洞已经从外面给炸掉了。我们寻找了几小时也没有发现该头骨的其他部分，但是我们在洞壁上发现了该头骨顶部的脑模。第二天我们发动更多工人进行更大范围的搜索，结果发现了与脸上半部分相连的大部分颅底（图 2）。在同一埋藏成分中，我们发现了带有三颗牙齿的右上颌骨和一个脱落下来的第三上臼齿。脸下半部分在石化之前就已经缺失；因此目前为止还没有发现下颌骨或下边的牙齿，但是在发现头部侧面的地方附近有大量破碎断裂的骨头，也许从中还会有一些发现。因为这些骨头都非常脆弱易碎，所以我们现在还没有尝试将它们从那些坚硬的母质中取出来。

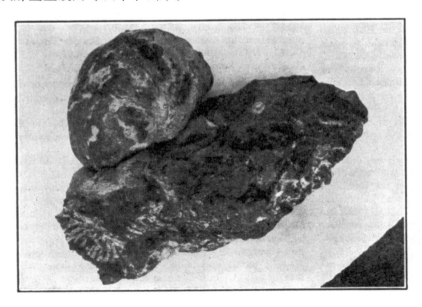

图 1. 置于不完整颅底上的脑模的半侧面图。图中展示了带有部分暴露的额窦的眉嵴。图中也可以看到部分左颧骨。该图大概是实际尺寸的 $\frac{1}{3}$。赫伯特·朗先生拍摄。

Fig. 2. Side view of right upper maxilla with the 2nd premolar and the 1st and 2nd molars. Parts of the roots of the canine and 1st premolar are shown. Slightly enlarged. Photograph by Mr. Herbert Lang.

Much of the cranial vault has been destroyed by the blast, but a large part of each parietal is preserved and a considerable part of the occiput. Unfortunately, the back of the brain cast is missing, and though the base of the skull is complete to the back of the foramen magnum, the contacts of the occipital fragment are lost.

The brain cast is perfect in its anterior two thirds. When complete it probably measured in length about 120 mm. and in breadth about 90 mm.; and the brain capacity was probably about 600 c.c. The skull probably measured from the glabella to the occiput about 145 mm., and the greatest parietal width was probably about 96 mm.

The brow ridges are moderately developed and there are fairly large frontal sinuses. The auditory meatus is 73 mm. behind the brow. It will be possible to make out much of the detailed structure of the base of the skull, but as yet no attempt has been made to clean it out as the bone is very friable and the investigation cannot be done in a hurry.

In the maxilla there are three well preserved teeth, the 2nd premolar and the 1st and 2nd molars (Fig. 3). The canine and 1st premolar are lost but the sockets are preserved. The canine has been relatively small. At its base it probably measured about 10 mm. by 8 mm. The 2nd premolar is somewhat worn. Its crown measured 11 mm. by 9 mm. Its pattern is well seen in Fig. 3.

图 2. 带有第二前臼齿、第一和第二臼齿的右上颌骨侧面图。可以从图中看到部分犬齿和第一前
臼齿的牙根。该图比实际尺寸略大。赫伯特·朗先生拍摄。

大部分颅顶都在爆炸中毁坏了，但是每块顶骨都有一大部分保留下来，此外还有一块相当大的枕骨残片。不幸的是，脑模的后面部分丢失了；尽管颅底直到枕骨大孔背部都是完整的，但是与枕骨片段相连接的部位丢失了。

脑模前部的 2/3 保存得很好。如果头骨完整的话，长度可能达到约 120 毫米，宽度约 90 毫米；脑量可能约有 600 毫升。头骨从眉间到枕骨大约 145 毫米，顶骨的最大宽度可能有 96 毫米左右。

眉峰处于中度发育水平，并有非常大的额窦。耳道位于眉骨后 73 毫米处。将来还有可能弄清楚这件头骨颅底的大部分详细结构，但是因为骨头非常脆弱，所以目前还没有将骨头清理出来，因此暂时不能对其进行研究。

上颌骨中有三颗保存完好的牙齿，分别是第二前臼齿、第一和第二臼齿（图 3）。犬齿和第一前臼齿缺失了，但是其齿槽保存了下来。犬齿相对较小，其基部可能约有 10 毫米×8 毫米大小。第二前臼齿有些磨损。其牙冠大小为 11 毫米×9 毫米。从图 3 中可以清楚地看到它的形态。

Fig. 3. Crowns of right upper 2nd premolar and 1st and 2nd molars. × about $\frac{3}{4}$.
Photograph by Mr. Herbert Lang.

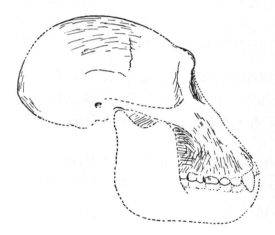

Fig. 4. Attempted restoration of skull of *Australopithecus transvaalensis* Broom. $\frac{1}{3}$ natural size.

Sufficient of the cranium is preserved to show its shape with certainty. Most of the right maxilla is preserved, but it is not in contact with the upper part of the skull, and there is thus a little doubt as to the relations.

The 1st molar is moderately large. Anteroposteriorly it measures 12 mm. and transversely 13 mm. It is of the typical Dryopithecid pattern—four well-developed cusps with a little posterior ridge and a well-marked posterior fovea. The tooth agrees fairly closely with that of the first molar of *Dryopithecus rhenanus*. The 2nd molar is exceptionally large. It measures 14.5 mm. in antero-posterior length and is 16 mm. across. It has four large cusps with a well-marked posterior fovea. The 3rd molar has been detached from the bone but it is preserved in perfect condition and unworn. It has three well-developed cusps, but the hypocone is relatively small owing to the invasion of the large fovea. The tooth measures antero-posteriorly 13.7 mm. and transversely 15.5 mm. The crown in this unworn condition is extremely wrinkled.

图 3. 右侧上部第二前臼齿和第一、第二臼齿的牙冠图。该图约为实际尺寸的 $\frac{3}{4}$。
赫伯特·朗先生拍摄。

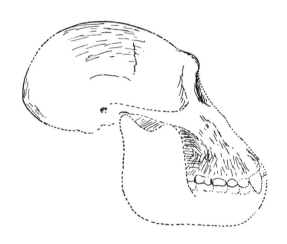

图 4. 布鲁姆对德兰士瓦南方古猿头骨的尝试性复原图。该图大小为实际尺寸的 $\frac{1}{3}$。

完整保存的颅骨确切地展示出它的形状。右上颌骨大部分保存下来了，但是与头骨的上半部分
没有衔接起来，因此对二者关系还有一点疑问。

　　第一臼齿稍大，前后长 12 毫米，横向长 13 毫米。这属于典型的森林古猿型——有
四个发育良好的齿尖并伴有一个小后嵴和一个明显的后凹。这颗牙齿与雷纳努斯森
林古猿的第一臼齿非常相似。第二臼齿特别大，其前后长 14.5 毫米，横向长 16 毫米，
有四个大的齿尖及一个明显的后凹。第三臼齿已经从上颌骨上脱落下来了，但是保
存状况非常好，没有任何磨损。该牙齿有三个发育良好的齿尖，但由于有一个大的
凹陷侵入，次尖相对较小。这颗牙前后长 13.7 毫米，横向为 15.5 毫米。未磨损的牙
冠上布满了大量的褶皱。

The whole premolar and molar series measures 59 mm.

This newly-found primate probably agrees fairly closely with the Taungs ape, but the only parts that we can compare are the brain casts and the 1st upper molars. The brain cast of the new form is considerably wider, especially in the frontal region, and the molar teeth differ in a number of important details. Further, the associated animals found at Taungs are all different from those found at Sterkfontein. I think the Taungs deposit will probably prove to be Lower or Middle Pleistocene, while the Sterkfontein deposit is most probably Upper Pleistocene. I therefore think it advisable to place the new form in a distinct species, though provisionally it may be put in the same genus as the Taungs ape.

This discovery shows that we had in South Africa during Pleistocene times large non-forest living anthropoids—not very closely allied to either the chimpanzee or the gorilla but showing distinct relationships to the Miocene and especially to the Pliocene species of *Dryopithecus*. They also show a number of typical human characters not met with in any of the living anthropoids.

(138, 486-488; 1936)

R. Broom: F.R.S, Transvaal Museum, Pretoria.

整个前臼齿和臼齿齿列长 59 毫米。

这个新发现的灵长类动物可能与汤恩古猿的亲缘关系非常近，但是我们能进行比较的部位还只有脑模和第一上臼齿。这种新型的脑模相当宽，尤其在额部，臼齿也在许多重要细节上有所不同。此外，在汤恩发现的伴生动物与在斯泰克方丹发现的伴生动物完全不同。我认为汤恩沉积物可能是早更新世或者中更新世的，而斯泰克方丹沉积更可能是晚更新世的。因此我认为将这种新类型列为一种新的物种是比较合理的，尽管它可能暂时被归在与汤恩古猿相同的属中。

这一发现表明，更新世时期在南非已经存在不生活于森林中的大型类人猿——它们不是黑猩猩或大猩猩的亲缘种，但是与中新世特别是上新世的森林古猿具有明显的关联。它们还具有许多典型的人类特征，这是任何现存类人猿都不具备的。

（刘皓芳 田晓阳 翻译；冯兴无 审稿）

Viscosity of Liquid Helium below the λ-Point

P. Kapitza

Editor's Note

Earlier experiments had noted strange behaviour in liquid helium at temperatures below about 2.18 K, where the liquid conducts heat with extraordinary efficiency. Here, physicist Pyotr Kapitza suggests that a dramatic decrease in the fluid's viscosity might explain the phenomenon, as it would make heat transport by convection much easier. Some recent experiments, he notes, had measured a decrease in the viscosity, but now his group, in a much more sensitive experiment, has found that the viscosity of the liquid below 2.18 K is at least 10,000 times smaller than that of any other known substance. Kapitza suggested this might be explained if liquid helium becomes a "superfluid" at low temperatures, perhaps even flowing with no viscosity at all.

THE abnormally high heat conductivity of helium II below the λ-point, as first observed by Keesom, suggested to me the possibility of an explanation in terms of convection currents. This explanation would require helium II to have an abnormally low viscosity; at present, the only viscosity measurements on liquid helium have been made in Toronto[1], and showed that there is a drop in viscosity below the λ-point by a factor of 3 compared with liquid helium at normal pressure, and by a factor of 8 compared with the value just above the λ-point. In these experiments, however, no check was made to ensure that the motion was laminar, and not turbulent.

The important fact that liquid helium has a specific density ρ of about 0.15, not very different from that of an ordinary fluid, while its viscosity μ is very small comparable to that of a gas, makes its kinematic viscosity $\nu = \mu/\rho$ extraordinary small. Consequently when the liquid is in motion in an ordinary viscosimeter, the Reynolds number may become very high, while in order to keep the motion laminar, especially in the method used in Toronto, namely, the damping of an oscillating cylinder, the Reynolds number must be kept very low. This requirement was not fulfilled in the Toronto experiments, and the deduced value of viscosity thus refers to turbulent motion, and consequently may be higher by any amount than the real value.

The very small kinematic viscosity of liquid helium II thus makes it difficult to measure the viscosity. In an attempt to get laminar motion the following method (shown diagrammatically in the accompanying illustration) was devised. The viscosity was measured by the pressure drop when the liquid flows through the gap between the disks 1 and 2; these disks were of glass and were optically flat, the gap between them being adjustable by mica distance pieces. The upper disk, 1, was 3 cm. in diameter with a central hole of 1.5 cm. diameter, over which a glass tube (3) was fixed. Lowering and raising this plunger in the liquid helium by means of the thread (4), the level of the liquid column in the tube

液态氦在 λ 点以下的黏度

卡皮查

编者按

在以往的实验中曾记录到一种奇怪的现象，当温度低于约 2.18 K 时，液氦的热导率惊人的高。在这篇文章中，物理学家彼得·卡皮查认为这一物理现象是由于液体黏度的急剧减小所造成的，因为这样会使得对流传热更加容易。他注意到最近一些实验测量到黏度的减小，但现在他的研究组通过更为精确的实验发现，低于 2.18 K 时液氦的黏度至少比其他已知物质的测量值小 10,000 倍。卡皮查认为如果液氦在这样的低温下变成了"超流体"，甚至流动时黏度为零，那么这个实验就能得到解释。

如同凯索姆首次观测到的那样，液氦 II 在 λ 点之下时表现出了异常高的热导率，这启发了我：也许可以用对流对它进行解释。如果这样解释的话就要求氦 II 的黏度非常小；到目前为止，仅有的对液氦黏度的测量是在多伦多进行的 [1]，测量结果显示，低于 λ 点时液氦的黏度比在常压下小 3 倍，而与略微高于 λ 点时相比则小 8 倍。然而，在上述实验中，并没有完全确认液氦的运动形式就是层流，而不是湍流。

重要的是，由于液氦的比重 ρ 大约为 0.15，与普通流体没有很大差别，但其黏度 μ 与普通气体相比却非常小，这样就使得液氦的动力黏度 $\nu = \mu/\rho$ 格外的小。于是，当液氦在普通黏度计中流动时，雷诺数可能会很高，然而只有雷诺数保持很小的值时，才能使运动保持层流形式，对于在多伦多所使用的测量圆柱振子阻尼的方法尤其是这样。但是多伦多实验并不满足这一条件，因此推导出来的黏度值应该对应于湍流运动，而这比真实值大多少都有可能。

液氦 II 的动力黏度很小，这就使得测量其黏度比较困难。为尽量保持层流，我们设计出了如下实验方法（见附图）。利用液体流经圆盘 1 和 2 之间空隙时的压强差可以测得黏度；其中两个圆盘是用玻璃制成的，并且是光学级平整的，它们之间的空隙可以利用云母隔离片进行调节。上面的圆盘 1 直径为 3 厘米，中间有一个直径 1.5 厘米的洞，洞上固定着一个玻璃管（3）。利用线（4）使这个装置在液氦中上升和下降，就可以令管 3 中液柱的水平位置高于或低于外围杜瓦瓶中液面（5）。利用测高

3 could be set above or below the level (5) of the liquid in the surrounding Dewar flask. The amount of flow and the pressure were deduced from the difference of the two levels, which was measured by cathetometer.

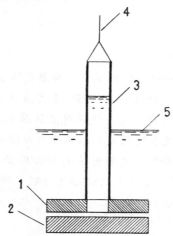

The results of the measurements were rather striking. When there were no distance pieces between the disks, and the plates 1 and 2 were brought into contact (by observation of optical fringes, their separation was estimated to be about half a micron), the flow of liquid above the λ-point could be only just detected over several minutes, while below the λ-point the liquid helium flowed quite easily, and the level in the tube 3 settled down in a few seconds. From the measurements we can conclude that the viscosity of helium II is at least 1,500 times smaller than that of helium I at normal pressure.

The experiments also showed that in the case of helium II, the pressure drop across the gap was proportional to the square of the velocity of flow, which means that the flow must have been turbulent. If, however, we calculate the viscosity, assuming the flow to have been laminar, we obtain a value of the order 10^{-9} C.G.S., which is evidently still only an upper limit to the true value. Using this estimate, the Reynolds number, even with such a small gap, comes out higher than 50,000, a value for which turbulence might indeed be expected.

We are making experiments in the hope of still further reducing the upper limit to the viscosity of liquid helium II, but the present upper limit (namely, 10^{-9} C.G.S.) is already very striking, since it is more than 10^4 times smaller than that of hydrogen gas (previously thought to be the fluid of least viscosity). The present limit is perhaps sufficient to suggest, by analogy with supraconductors, that the helium below the λ-point enters a special state which might be called a "superfluid".

As we have already mentioned, an abnormally low viscosity such as indicated by our experiments might indeed provide an explanation for the high thermal conductivity, and for the other anomalous properties observed by Allen, Peierls, and Uddin[2]. It is evidently possible that the turbulent motion, inevitably set up in the technical manipulation required

计读出两液面之间的差，我们就可以推导出流量和压力的大小。

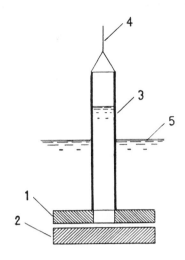

测量的结果相当明显。当两盘之间没有隔离片时，即令盘1和2接触（通过光学条纹的观测，估计其间距约为半微米），液氦流在高于λ点时需要经过几分钟才勉强能检测到，而在低于λ点时，液氦流动非常容易，管3中的液面在几秒钟内就稳定下来了。从这些测量我们可以推断，常压下氦II的黏度是氦I的1,500分之一。

实验还显示，氦II穿过空隙时的压强差正比于流动速度的平方，这表明这种流动一定是湍流。但是，如果我们假设它以层流的形式运动，并计算它的黏度，得到数量级为 10^{-9} 单位（厘米克秒制）的值，显然，这只是真实值的上限。按照这种估计，尽管间隙如此小，雷诺数仍然超过了50,000这个肯定会出现湍流的数值。

我们还在继续实验工作，期望进一步减小液氦II的黏度上限值，但是目前的上限（即 10^{-9} 单位（厘米克秒制））已经非常小了，因为它比氢气（过去认为是黏度最小的流体）的黏度至少小 10^4 倍。目前得到的极限也许足以表明，与超导体进行类比，氦在低于λ点时会进入一种特殊的状态，我们不妨称之为"超流体"。

如同我们之前提到的那样，我们的实验中显示的异常低的黏度，可能确实可以用来解释高热导率，以及由艾伦、佩尔斯和乌丁[2]所观测到的其他异常性质。在对液氦II进行所需的技术操作过程中，由于其具有较大的流动性，因此湍流的出现显

in working with the liquid helium II, might on account of the great fluidity, not die out, even in the small capillary tubes in which the thermal conductivity was measured; such turbulence would transport heat extremely efficiently by convection.

(**141**, 74; 1938)

P. Kapitza: Institute for Physical Problems, Academy of Sciences, Moscow, Dec.3.

References:
1. Burton, *Nature*, **135**, 265 (1935); Wilhelm, Misener and Clark, *Proc. Roy. Soc.*, A, **151**, 342 (1935).
2. *Nature*, **140**, 62 (1937).

然是无法避免的，即便在用于测量热导率的小毛细管中；而这种湍流运动将通过对流效率极高地传输热。

（王耀杨 翻译；于渌 审稿）

Flow of Liquid Helium II

J. F. Allen and A. D. Misener

Editor's Note

In Cambridge, physicists John Allen and Don Misener had come to the same conclusion as Kapitza (see the previous paper). As they announce here, they had also attempted to measure the viscosity of liquid helium below the so-called "lambda point" of 2.18 K in experiments where the fluid flowed through narrow capillaries. But their results could only place an upper limit on the viscosity, comparable to Kapitza's value. They note that the flow they observed is very strange, being independent of the pressure difference applied. It is possible, they speculate, that the liquid is actually slipping over the surface. These results would later be explained by a general theory of liquid helium as a superfluid, a state that arises from quantum-mechanical behaviour.

A survey of the various properties of liquid helium II has prompted us to investigate its viscosity more carefully. One of us[1] had previously deduced an upper limit of 10^{-5} C.G.S. units for the viscosity of helium II by measuring the damping of an oscillating cylinder. We had reached the same conclusion as Kapitza in the letter above; namely, that due to the high Reynolds number involved, the measurements probably represent non-laminar flow.

The present data were obtained from observations on the flow of liquid helium II through long capillaries. Two capillaries were used; the first had a circular bore of radius 0.05 cm. and length 130 cm. and drained a reservoir of 5.0 cm. diameter; the second was a thermometer capillary 93.5 cm. long and of elliptical cross-section with semi-axes 0.001 cm. and 0.002 cm., which was attached to a reservoir of 0.1 cm. diameter. The measurements were made by raising or lowering the reservoir with attached capillary so that the level of liquid helium in the reservoir was a centimetre or so above or below that of the surrounding liquid helium bath. The rate of change of level in the reservoir was then determined from the cathetometer eye-piece scale and a stopwatch; measurements were made until the levels became coincident. The data showing velocities of flow through the capillary and the corresponding pressure difference at the ends of the capillary are given in the accompanying table and plotted on a logarithmic scale in the diagram.

液氦 II 的流动

艾伦，麦色纳

编者按

在剑桥，物理学家约翰·艾伦和冬·麦色纳得出了与卡皮查相同的结论（见前一篇文章）。正如他们在这篇文章中介绍的，他们利用液体流过毛细管的实验，也试图去测量低于"λ点"（2.18 K）时液氦的黏度。但是与卡皮查的测量值相比，他们的结果仅仅得出了黏度值的上限。他们注意到他们观察到的流动现象非常奇特，它与两端施加的压力差无关。他们推测液体实际上是掠过表面。后来液氦超流态的普遍理论成功解释了这些现象，这是一种源于量子力学行为的状态。

对液氦 II 各种性质的探索促使我们更细致地研究它的黏度。本文作者之一[1]曾经通过测定振动圆柱的阻尼推导出液氦 II 黏度的上限为 10⁻⁵ 单位（厘米克秒制）。我们得到的结论与卡皮查在前文中叙述的相同；也就是说，由于测量过程中雷诺数很高，这一测量可能反映的是非层流的流动形式。

本文的数据是通过观测液氦 II 在长毛细管中的流动获得的。其间用到了两种毛细管；第一种毛细管带有一个半径为 0.05 厘米、长为 130 厘米的圆形孔道，并与一个直径为 5 厘米的储液管相接；第二种毛细管是温度计毛细管，长 93.5 厘米，具有椭圆形的横截面，其半轴长分别为 0.001 厘米和 0.002 厘米，整个毛细管与直径为 0.1 厘米的储液管相连。测量方法是：将连接毛细管的储液管上下移动，以便于使储液管中的液氦平面位于周围液氦平面的上方或下方约 1 厘米处。利用测高计的目镜刻度和秒表便可确定储液管中液面的移动速率；当内外液面一致时即可停止测量。附表中数据显示了流经毛细管时的速度和相应的毛细管两端的压力差，对它们分别取对数绘于图中。

Capillary I		Capillary II			
T=1.07°K.		T=1.07°K.		T=2.17°K.	
Velocity (cm./sec.)	Pressure (dynes)	Velocity (cm./sec.)	Pressure (dynes)	Velocity (cm./sec.)	Pressure (dynes)
13.9	183.5	8.35	402	0.837	36.6
11.5	154.5	6.92	218	0.757	31.3
10.3	127.7	6.88	143	0.715	26.1
9.0	105.0	6.30	101	0.685	21.1
8.2	83.5	6.05	56	0.655	16.4
7.5	65.7	5.55	30	0.609	12.1
6.9	49.3	4.70	11.3	0.570	8.3
6.1	34.1	4.39	9.2	0.525	4.3
5.2^5	20.3	3.92	13.0	0.433	0.9
4.5^5	15.2	2.88	7.2		

The following facts are evident:

(a) The velocity of flow, q, changes only slightly for large changes in pressure head, p. For the smaller capillary, the relation is approximately $p \propto q^6$, but at the lowest velocities an even higher power seems indicated.

(b) The velocity of flow, for given pressure head and temperature, changes only slightly with a change of cross-section area of the order of 10^3.

(c) The velocity of flow, for given pressure head and given cross-section, changes by about a factor of 10 with a change of temperature from 1.07°K. to 2.17°K.

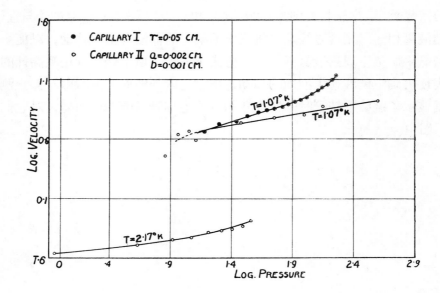

毛细管 I		毛细管 II			
$T = 1.07$ K		$T = 1.07$ K		$T = 2.17$ K	
速度 (厘米 / 秒)	压力 (达因)	速度 (厘米 / 秒)	压力 (达因)	速度 (厘米 / 秒)	压力 (达因)
13.9	183.5	8.35	402	0.837	36.6
11.5	154.5	6.92	218	0.757	31.3
10.3	127.7	6.88	143	0.715	26.1
9.0	105.0	6.30	101	0.685	21.1
8.2	83.5	6.05	56	0.655	16.4
7.5	65.7	5.55	30	0.609	12.1
6.9	49.3	4.70	11.3	0.570	8.3
6.1	34.1	4.39	9.2	0.525	4.3
5.2^5	20.3	3.92	13.0	0.433	0.9
4.5^5	15.2	2.88	7.2		

从上表明显可以看出:

（a）当压位差 p 大幅度改变时，流动速度 q 的变化不大。对于较细的毛细管，二者之间的关系近似为 $p \propto q^6$，但是在速度最低的时候，幂次似乎更高。

（b）对于给定的压位差和温度，当横截面面积以 10^3 数量级变化时，流动速度只发生微小的改变。

（c）对于给定的压位差和确定的横截面，在温度从 1.07 K 变化到 2.17 K 的过程中，流动速度变化了 10 倍左右。

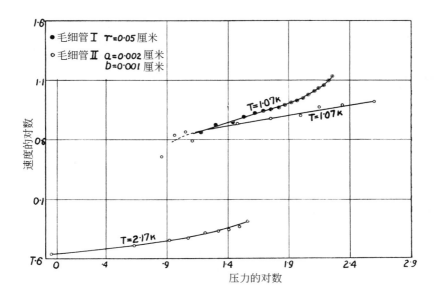

429

(d) With the larger capillary and slightly higher velocities of flow, the pressure-velocity relation is approximately $p \propto q^3$, with the power of q decreasing as the velocity is increased.

If, for the purpose of calculating a possible upper limit to the viscosity, we assume the formula for laminar flow, that is, $p \propto q$, we obtain the value $\eta = 4 \times 10^{-9}$ C.G.S. units. This agrees with the upper limit given by Kapitza who, using velocities of flow considerably higher than ours, has obtained the relation $p \propto q^2$ and an upper limit to the viscosity of $\eta = 10^{-9}$ C.G.S. units.

The observed type of flow, however, in which the velocity becomes almost independent of pressure, most certainly cannot be treated as laminar or even as ordinary turbulent flow. Consequently any known formula cannot, from our data, give a value of the "viscosity" which would have much meaning. It may be possible that the liquid helium II slips over the surface of the tube. In this case any flow method would be incapable of showing the "viscous drag" of the liquid.

With regard to the suggestion that the high thermal conductivity of helium II might be explained by turbulence, we have calculated that the flow velocity necessary to transport all the heat input over the observed temperature gradient in the Allen, Peierls and Uddin experiments[2] is about 10^4 cm./sec. On the other hand, the greatest flow velocity produced by manipulation and by the pressure difference along the thermal conduction capillary will not be likely to be greater than 50 cm./sec. It seems, therefore, that undamped turbulent motion cannot account for an appreciable part of the high thermal conductivity which has been observed for helium II.

(**141**, 75; 1938)

J. F. Allen and A. D. Misener: Royal Society Mond Laboratory, Cambridge, Dec, 22.

References:
1. Burton, E.F., *Nature*, **135**, 265 (1935).
2. Allen, Peierls and Uddin, *Nature*, **140**, 62 (1937).

(*d*) 在较粗的毛细管中，对于略高的流动速度，压力－速度之间的关系近似为 $p \propto q^3$，其中 q 的幂次随速度增加而降低。

为了计算出黏度的可能上限，我们假定层流运动的计算公式即 $p \propto q$ 成立，那么就可以得到 $\eta = 4 \times 10^{-9}$ 单位（厘米克秒制）。这个结果与卡皮查给出的上限是一致的，因为他使用的流动速度比我们所用的高很多，所以得出的关系式为 $p \propto q^2$，他最后给出的黏度上限是 $\eta = 10^{-9}$ 单位（厘米克秒制）。

不过，当流动速度与压力无关时，我们所观测到的这种流动类型一定不属于层流，甚至不属于普通的湍流。因此，根据我们的测量数据任何已知的公式都不可能给出一个很有意义的"黏度"数值。液氦 II 可能掠过管壁，在这种情况下，任何流动方法都无法显示出液体的"黏滞阻力"。

有人认为用湍流也许能够解释氦 II 的高热导率，对此我们计算的结果是，只有流速大约为 10^4 厘米／秒左右时，才足以在艾伦、佩尔斯和乌丁的实验 [2] 中观测到的温度梯度条件下传输所有输入的热量。而另一方面，在实验操作下沿着热传导毛细管的压力差所能产生的最大流速可能不会超过 50 厘米／秒。由此看来，无衰减的湍流运动并不能解释在氦 II 中观测到的高热导率。

（王耀杨 翻译；于渌 审稿）

The λ-Phenomenon of Liquid Helium and the Bose-Einstein Degeneracy

F. London

Editor's Note

In early 1938, *Nature* published the first reports of superfluidity in liquid helium, discovered independently by Pyotr Kapitza in Russia and by John Allen and Don Misener at Cambridge. Both reported that when cooled below 2.17 K, the viscosity of the liquid plunged apparently to zero. One proposed explanation was that the helium atoms adopted an ordered structure like that of diamond crystals. Here Fritz London proposes a radically different idea: that the phenomenon might be linked to the low-temperature quantum behaviour of particles of integer spin ("bosons"), whose collective statistical behaviour had been described by Bose and Einstein.

IN a recent paper[1] Fröhlich has tried to interpret the λ-phenomenon of liquid helium as an order-disorder transition between n holes and n helium atoms in a body-centred cubic lattice of $2n$ places. He remarks that a body-centred cubic lattice may be considered as consisting of two shifted diamond lattices, and he assumes that below the λ-point the helium atoms prefer the places of one of the two diamond lattices. The transition is treated on the lines of the Bragg-Williams-Bethe theory as a phase transition of second order in close analogy to the transition observed with β-brass. Jones and Allen in a recent communication to *Nature*[2] also referred to this idea. In both these papers, use is made of the fact, established by the present author, that with the absorbed abnormally great molecular volume of liquid helium (caused by the zero motion[3]) the diamond-configuration has the lowest potential energy among all regular lattice structures[4].

In this note, I should like first to show that the mechanism proposed by Fröhlich cannot be maintained and then to direct attention to an entirely different interpretation of this strange phenomenon.

(1) According to Fröhlich, a diamond lattice of He atoms, when partly formed, should offer, to any other He atom, a preference for being attached at those points which belong to the same diamond lattice, that is, the binding energy at a diamond point should be greater than anywhere else. It is, however, easy to see that just those points, which according to Fröhlich should become less favoured for low temperatures, have an appreciably greater binding energy. It is true these holes have four nearest neighbours at exactly the same distance (3.08 A.), as the lattice points of the diamond lattice have, but in addition they possess six second neighbours at the distance of 3.57 A. which the diamond lattice points do not possess, and these second neighbours contribute considerably to the binding energy just at the hole-places (about 50 percent to the potential energy).

液氦的 λ 现象和玻色–爱因斯坦简并

伦敦

编者按

1938 年初，《自然》刊载了两篇有关液氦超流动性的最早报告，那是俄国的彼得·卡皮查和剑桥的约翰·艾伦与冬·麦色纳各自独立发现的。两篇文章都提到当温度低于 2.17 K 时液氦的黏度似乎减小至零。有人认为这是由于氦原子排列成为类似金刚石晶体那样的有序结构。而这篇文章中弗里茨·伦敦提出了一个完全不同的看法：这种现象也许与某些具有整数自旋的粒子（"玻色子"）在低温下的量子力学行为有关，玻色和爱因斯坦曾经对玻色子的统计行为进行过描述。

弗勒利希最近的一篇文章中 [1] 试图将液氦的 λ 现象解释为在一个具有 $2n$ 个位置的体心立方晶格中，n 个空位和 n 个氦原子间的有序 – 无序相变。他认为，可以把一个体心立方晶格看作是由两套具有相对位移的金刚石晶格组合而成的，而且他假定在低于 λ 点时，氦原子更倾向于处在两套金刚石晶格中某一套的格点上。根据布拉格 – 威廉姆斯 – 贝特理论，这种转变被看作是一种二阶相变，非常类似于在 β 黄铜中发生的相变。琼斯和艾伦最近给《自然》的信 [2] 中也提到了这一观点。在这两篇文章中，都用到了本文作者确认的事实，即由于液氦占有的分子体积异常大（源于零点运动 [3]），所以在所有规则结构的晶格中，金刚石结构具有最低的势能 [4]。

在这篇短文中，我首先会说明弗勒利希提出的机制是不成立的，然后再引导大家关注对这种奇异现象的一种完全不同的解释。

（1）按照弗勒利希的观点，当 He 原子的金刚石晶格部分形成时，对于其他的 He 原子而言，属于同一套金刚石晶格上的格点应该更有优势，也就是说，金刚石晶格上的结合能应该大于其他点处的结合能。然而，我们很容易看出，按照弗勒利希的观点，在低温下对结合较为不利的那些位点反而具有比其他位点高得多的结合能。晶格中的空位在完全相同的距离（3.08 埃）处有 4 个最近邻，这与金刚石晶格的格点相同，但不同的是它们在距离 3.57 埃处还有 6 个次近邻，而且这些次近邻对空位的结合能贡献是很大的（约占势能的 50%）。因此，弗勒利希提出的这种合作现象是不会发生的。原子不仅易处于金刚石晶格的格点上，而且更易处于空位上，这意味

Therefore, actually no such co-operative phenomenon will appear as supposed by Fröhlich. The atoms would rather frequent the holes as much as the proper diamond lattice points, and this would signify that we have a body-centred lattice of $2n$ places for n atoms, every place being occupied with the probability $\frac{1}{2}$ only—even at the absolute zero. In this configuration every atom has on the average four nearest neighbours at a distance of 3.08 A, as in the diamond configuration, but in addition there are here on the average three second neighbours at the distance of 3.57 A. In the diamond lattice there are twelve second neighbours but at a distance of 5.04 A., where there is almost no Van der Waals field. It might be mentioned, by the way, that a face-centred lattice of $2n$ places for n atoms (on the average 6 first neighbours at a distance of 3.17 A.) has been found to have a still little lower energy than the configuration just discussed of the co-ordination number 4.

Complete numerical details cannot be given here; in any event it can be shown by such energetic discussions that a static spatial model of liquid He II of whatever regular configuration is certainly not possible. This has been previously suggested in consideration of the great zero point amplitude calculated for He⁴. The determination of the most favourable co-ordination numbers of the first and second neighbours, however, maintains a good physical meaning: it may be considered as a rough Hartree calculus which yields the self-consistent field and the corresponding probability distribution of the atoms belonging to the minimum of energy.

(2) It seems, therefore, reasonable to imagine a model in which each He atom moves in a self-consistent periodic field formed by the other atoms. The different states of the atoms may be described by eigen functions of a similar type to the electronic eigen functions which appear in Bloch's theory of metals; and, as in Bloch's theory, the energy of the lowest states will roughly be represented by a quadratic function of the wave number K,

$$E = \frac{\hbar^2}{2m^*}K^2,$$

the effective mass m^* being of the order of magnitude of the mass of the atoms. But in the present case we are obliged to apply Bose-Einstein statistics instead of Fermi statistics.

(3) In his well-known papers, Einstein has already discussed a peculiar condensation phenomenon of the "Bose-Einstein" gas; but in the course of time the degeneracy of the Bose-Einstein gas has rather got the reputation of having only a purely imaginary existence. Thus it is perhaps not generally known that this condensation phenomenon actually represents a discontinuity of the derivative of the specific heat (phase transition of third order). In the accompanying figure the specific heat (C_v) of an *ideal* Bose-Einstein gas is represented as a function of T/T_0 where

$$T_0 = \frac{h^2}{2\pi m^* k}\left(\frac{n}{2,615}\right)^{2/3},$$

With m^* = the mass of a He atom and with the mol. volume $\frac{N_l}{n} = 27.6$ cm.³ one obtains $T_0 = 3.09°$. For $T \leqslant T_0$ the specific heat is given by

$$C_v = 1.92\, R(T/T_0)^{3/2}$$

着对于 n 个原子来说，我们有 $2n$ 个位置的体心立方格子，每个位置被占据的概率即使在绝对零度下也仅为 1/2。每个原子在距离 3.08 埃处平均有 4 个最近邻，这与金刚石晶格结构相同，但除此之外，每个原子在距离 3.57 埃处平均还有 3 个次近邻。而在金刚石晶格中有 12 个次近邻，但距离是 5.04 埃，几乎没有范德瓦尔斯场。顺便提一下，对于 $2n$ 个位置，n 个原子的面心立方晶格（在距离 3.17 埃处平均有 6 个最近邻），其能量略低于刚才讨论过的配位数为 4 的结构。

在本文中我们不可能给出完整的数值计算过程；但是，通过对这种能量的讨论可以阐明，液体 He II 任何规则结构的静态空间分布模型肯定都是不可能的。这点在计算 He 巨大的零点振幅时就已被提出[4]。然而，确定最近邻和次近邻的最佳配位数却有着清楚的物理意义，其可以看作是粗略的哈特里计算，由此我们可得到自洽场和相对应的处于能量极小值的原子的分布概率。

（2）因此似乎可以构造这样一个模型，其中每个 He 原子在其他原子形成的自洽周期场中运动。用本征函数来描述原子不同的态，类似于在布洛赫的金属理论中用电子本征函数描述电子态；而且，类似于布洛赫理论，最低态的能量可以粗略地表示为波矢 K 的二次函数，

$$E = \frac{\hbar^2}{2m^*} K^2$$

其中有效质量 m^* 与原子质量的数量级相当。不过我们现在必须用玻色-爱因斯坦统计代替费米统计。

（3）在一些著名的文章中，爱因斯坦已经讨论了"玻色-爱因斯坦"气体特有的一种凝聚现象；但是，随着时间的推移，人们开始认为玻色-爱因斯坦气体的简并性不过是一种假象。因此可能很多人并不知道这种凝聚现象实际上表现为比热的导数的不连续（三阶相变）。在附图中，**理想**玻色-爱因斯坦气体的比热（C_v）可表示为 T/T_0 的函数，

$$T_0 = \frac{h^2}{2\pi m^* k} \left(\frac{n}{2,615} \right)^{2/3}$$

式中取 m^* = He 的原子质量，摩尔体积 $\frac{N_l}{n}$ = 27.6 立方厘米，可得 T_0 = 3.09 K。对于 $T \leqslant T_0$，所给出的比热为：

$$C_v = 1.92\ R\ (T/T_0)^{3/2}$$

and for $T \geqslant T_0$ by

$$C_v = \frac{3}{2}R\left[1 + 0.231\left(\frac{T_0}{T}\right)^{3/2} + 0.046\left(\frac{T_0}{T}\right)^3 + \cdots\right]$$

The entropy at the transition point T_0 amounts to $1.28\,R$ independently of T_0.

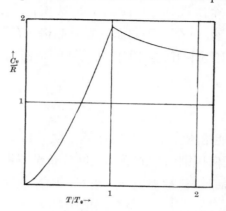

Specific heat of an ideal Bose-Einstein gas.

(4) Though actually the λ-point of helium resembles rather a phase transition of second order, it seems difficult not to imagine a connexion with the condensation phenomenon of the Bose-Einstein statistics. The experimental values of the temperature of the λ-point (2.19°) and of its entropy (~0.8 R) seem to be in favour of this conception. On the other hand, it is obvious that a model which is so far away from reality that it simplifies liquid helium to an ideal gas, cannot, for high temperatures, yield but the value $C_v = 3/2\,R$, and also for low temperatures the ideal Bose-Einstein gas must, of course, give too great a specific heat, since it does not account for the gradual "freezing in" of the Debye frequencies.

According to our conception the quantum states of liquid helium would have to correspond, so to speak, to both the states of the electrons and to the Debye vibrational states of the lattice in the theory of metals. It would, of course, be necessary to incorporate this feature into the theory before it can be expected to furnish quantitative insight into the properties of liquid helium.

The conception here proposed might also throw a light on the peculiar transport phenomena observed with He II (enormous conductivity of heat[5], extremely small viscosity[6] and also the strange fountain phenomenon recently discovered by Allen and Jones[2]).

A detailed discussion of these questions will be published in the *Journal de Physique*.

(**141**, 643-644; 1938)

F. London: Institut Henri Poincaré, Paris, March 5.

对于 $T \geqslant T_0$，比热为：

$$C_v = \frac{3}{2}R\left[1 + 0.231\left(\frac{T_0}{T}\right)^{3/2} + 0.046\left(\frac{T_0}{T}\right)^3 + \cdots\right]$$

在转变点 T_0，熵为 $1.28R$，与 T_0 无关。

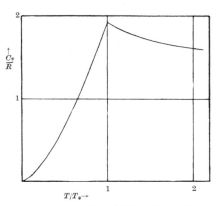

理想玻色－爱因斯坦气体的比热变化关系

（4）尽管氦的 λ 点实际上更类似于一种二阶相变，但还是很容易将其与玻色－爱因斯坦统计的凝聚现象联系起来。λ 点处的温度（2.19 K）和熵（~0.8R）的实验值似乎支持了这一猜想。另一方面，我们可以很明显地看出，把液氦简化为一种理想气体是一个脱离实际的模型，这个模型在高温时只能给出 $C_v = 3/2R$，而在低温区，理想的玻色－爱因斯坦气体也必然会给出过大的比热值，因为此模型并没有考虑德拜频率的逐渐"冻结"。

按照我们的构想，可以说液氦的量子态既对应于金属理论中的电子态又对应于晶格的德拜振动态。当然，我们必须要把这个特点涵盖在理论中，才能有望对液氦的性质有定量的了解。

本文提出的构想或许对理解 He II 中特别的输运现象有一点启发（巨大的热导率[5]，极小的黏度[6]，以及最近艾伦和琼斯观察到的奇异的喷泉现象[2]）。

有关这些问题的详细讨论将发表在《物理学杂志》上。

（沈乃澂 翻译；于渌 审稿）

References:

1. Fröhlich, H., *Physica*, 4, 639 (1937).

2. Allen, J. F., and Jones, H., *Nature*, 141, 243 (1938).

3. Simon, F., *Nature*, 133, 529 (1934).

4. London, F., *Proc. Roy. Soc.*, A, 153, 576 (1936).

5. Rollin, *Physica*, 2, 557 (1935); Keesom, W. H., and Keesom, H. P. *Physica*, 3, 359 (1936); Allen, J. F. , Peierls, R., and Zaki Uddin, M., *Nature*, 140, 62 (1937).

6. Burton, E. F., *Nature*, 135, 265 (1935); Kapitza, P., *Nature*, 141, 74 (1938); Allen, J. F. and Misener, A. D., *Nature*, 141, 75 (1938).

Discovery of an Additional *Pithecanthropus* Skull

G. H. R. von Koenigswald and F. Weidenreich

Editor's Note

Remains of a pre-human known as *Pithecanthropus* had been known from Java since Eugene Dubois's first discovery in 1891. In the early 1930s, fossils of a similar creature, *Sinanthropus*, were discovered in China. The relationship between the two forms was unclear until this brief announcement from Gustav von Koenigswald and Franz Weidenreich of discoveries from Java that looked much more like *Sinanthropus* than pithecanthropines typical of Java. This was an important step towards the recognition that all these east Asian forms belonged to *Homo erectus*, the earliest human definitively known to have ventured out of Africa.

D URING the systematic search for fossil man in Java, one of us (G. H. R. von K.) discovered, in 1937, in the Trinil formation of Sangiran (Central Java), an almost complete brain case of *Pithecanthropus*[1].

Amongst the material recently collected (July 1938) from the same area, a large fragment of an additional *Pithecanthropus* skull came to light. The fragment consists of the complete right parietal bone with the adjoining part of the left parietal bone and a small piece of the occipital bone. The three bones embrace in their original and entirely undisturbed arrangement a stone core composed of sandy tuft mixed with lapilli. The sagittal suture reaching from bregma to lambda is completely preserved. The right parietal bone also exhibits all the other sutures, only the sphenoidal angle being broken off. The coronal contour of the parietal bones is characterized by a very pronounced sagittal crest. Laterally there is a distinct depression reaching to the temporal line, from which the contour runs steadily outwards down to the squamous suture. The temporal line runs strikingly close to the sagittal suture.

These conditions entirely correspond to those which are characteristic of the Sinanthropus skulls. The pronounced flattening of the cap, so specific for the two *Pithecanthropus* skulls known hitherto, is completely missing in the case of this new *Pithecanthropus* skull. On the other hand, this skull has the following peculiarities in common with both *Sinanthropus* and *Pithecanthropus* skulls: the lowness of the entire cap and the position of the greatest breadth, the latter having undoubtedly been situated above the origin of the zygomatic arch, as is the case with all *Sinanthropus* and *Pithecanthropus* skulls.

According to the state of the sutures, the new skull belongs to a juvenile individual, in spite of the fact that the parietal bones show a thickness of more than 10 mm. near the bregma,

又一件爪哇猿人头骨的发现

孔尼华，魏登瑞

编者按

1891 年尤金·杜布瓦首次在爪哇发现了直立猿人化石，此后史前人类"爪哇猿人"化石便广为人知。20 世纪 30 年代初，在中国发现了一种与之类似的生物——"中国猿人"的化石。直到古斯塔夫·冯·柯尼希斯瓦尔德（孔尼华）和弗朗茨·魏登赖希（魏登瑞）发表了这篇简短的报告之后，这两种生物之间的关系才变得明晰，这篇报告中称，在爪哇发现了比典型的爪哇直立人看起来更接近中国猿人的化石。这对于认定所有的东亚猿人都属于"直立人"是非常重要的一步，而"直立人"是目前可以确定的从非洲迁徙出来的最早的人类。

我们对爪哇地区的化石人类进行了系统的搜寻，作者之一（孔尼华）于 1937 年在爪哇中部的桑吉兰特里尼尔地层组发现了一件几乎完整的爪哇猿人头盖骨[1]。

最近（1938 年 7 月）在同一地区采集的材料中，发现了另一件爪哇猿人头骨的一大块碎块。这一碎块由完整的右顶骨、相邻的部分左侧顶骨以及一小块枕骨构成。这三块骨头胶结在混杂有火山岩的沙质石核中，没有错位。这件头骨完整保留有从前囟点到人字点的矢状缝部分。除蝶角破损之外，右顶骨上其他所有的骨缝都可以看到。顶骨的冠状轮廓有一个非常明显的矢状脊，侧面有一个延伸至颞线的明显凹陷。从颞线处，头骨轮廓向外平稳扩展向下至鳞缝区域。颞线位置非常接近矢状缝。

这些特征与中国猿人头骨的特征完全相符。目前已知的两个爪哇猿人的头骨都明显地呈现出扁平的特征，但这一特征在本次新发现的爪哇猿人头骨上却没有出现。另一方面，这件头骨与爪哇猿人头骨以及中国猿人头骨在如下特征上是一样的：即整个头盖骨的低平程度以及最大宽度所在的位置。后者毫无疑问位于颧弓的起点之上，这与所有中国猿人和爪哇猿人头骨的情况都一样。

尽管新发现的这件头骨的顶骨在前囟处的厚度达十多毫米，并且其颞线很发达，但是根据骨缝的状态，它应该属于一个少年个体。枕骨圆枕区域仅有一小部分被保

and that the temporal line is well developed. The region of the occipital torus is preserved only to a very small extent, revealing only a faint swelling, apparently in correspondence with the age of the individual.

All the new *Pithecanthropus* finds demonstrate how important and promising it is to search for fossil man in Java, and to continue the work which has been made possible thanks to the generous support of the Carnegie Institution of Washington, D.C.

(**142**, 715; 1938)

G. H. R. von Koenigswald and Franz Weidenreich: Bandoeng, Java.

Reference:
1. *Proc. Kon. Akad. van Wetenschappen, Amsterdam,* 1938.

存下来，并显示出很微弱的隆起，这显然与该个体的年龄是相符的。

所有新爪哇猿人的发现证实了在爪哇寻找化石人类是非常重要和有前景的，能够继续该工作要感谢华盛顿卡内基研究院的慷慨支持。

（刘皓芳 翻译；刘武 审稿）

Mesotron (Intermediate Particle) as a Name for the New Particles of Intermediate Mass

C. D. Anderson and S. H. Neddermeyer

Editor's Note

In 1936, Carl Anderson and Seth Neddermeyer at the California Institute of Technology found evidence in cosmic-ray experiments for a particle having mass intermediate between those of the electron and proton. The particle carried one unit of charge, and penetrated matter much more strongly than the electron. Here the particle's discoverers propose a name for it. As its intermediate mass seemed the key property, they suggest the term "mesotron". This was later shortened to "meson", although the particle Anderson and Neddermeyer had discovered was actually what physicists today call the muon, a massive relative of the electron. The term meson later became used for intermediate-mass "hadrons" such as the pion or kaon, which are comprised of two quarks.

THE existence of particles intermediate in mass between protons and electrons has been shown in experiments on the cosmic radiation[1]. Since at present so little is known concerning the properties of these particles, for example, the exact value of the mass, the laws governing their production, their stability against disintegration, etc., it may yet be too early to assign to them a name. But inasmuch as several names have already been suggested, namely, dynatron, penetron, barytron, heavy electron, yukon and x-particle, it may be wise to consider the matter at this time.

The property which so far serves to distinguish the new particles from the other two types of particles which carry the same magnitude of electric charge, namely, the proton and the electron, seems to be the magnitude of their mass. Although from the experiments so far performed, it is not possible to say definitely whether the new particles exist with a unique mass only, or whether they occur with a range of masses, it does appear quite certain that the mass, whether unique or not, is greater than that of an electron and less than that of a proton. One must consider then three types of particles all carrying electric charges of equal magnitude: electrons, the new particles and protons. We should like to suggest therefore the word "mesotron" (intermediate particle) as a name for the new particles. It appears quite likely that the appropriateness of this name will not be lost, whatever new facts concerning these particles may be learned in the future.

(**142**, 878; 1938)

Carl D. Anderson and Seth H. Neddermeyer: California Institute of Technology, Pasadena, Sept. 30.

将介子（中间粒子）定为一种中间质量新粒子的名字

安德森，尼德迈耶

编者按

1936 年，美国加州理工学院的卡尔·安德森和塞思·尼德迈耶在宇宙射线实验中发现了一种质量介于电子和质子之间的粒子的径迹。这种粒子携带一个单位的电荷，穿透能力比电子强。本文中粒子的发现者提出为它命名。鉴于它的质量介于电子和质子之间是其重要性质，故建议选用单词"mesotron"，之后被缩写成"meson"，而安德森和尼德迈耶所发现的粒子实际上是今天物理学家所指的与电子有近亲关系的 μ 介子。介子（meson）一词后来用于表示中间质量的"强子"，例如由两个夸克组成的 π 介子和 K 介子。

在宇宙射线实验中发现了一种新粒子，其质量介于质子和电子之间 [1]。目前，人们对这种粒子的性质，例如粒子质量的精确值、产生的机制、对衰变的稳定性等了解甚少。因此现在给它们确定一个名字也许为时过早。但是，因为大家已经提出了几个候选的名字：（朝）代子、穿（透）子、重子、重电子、汤川子以及 x 粒子，所以也许现在来考虑这个问题是必要的。

迄今为止，只能通过质量的数值来区分这种新粒子与其他两种粒子——即携带相同数量电荷的质子和电子。虽然根据目前已做的实验尚无法肯定这种新粒子的质量是否有一个确定值，还是在一定的范围内变化，但可以肯定它们的质量，无论其数值是否唯一，都是大于电子而小于质子的，故可以认为三种类型的粒子，即电子、新粒子和质子，都带有相同数量的电荷。所以，我们建议用"mesotron"（中间粒子）作为这种新粒子的名称，这主要是因为我们认为这个名字的适用性不会因为将来发现了有关这个粒子的新性质而失效。

（胡雪兰 翻译；厉光烈 审稿）

Reference:

1. For historical summary see Wentzel, G., *Naturwiss.*, **26**, 273 (1938); and Bowen, Millikan and Neher, footnote, *Phys. Rev.*, **53**, 219 (1938).

Structure of Proteins

Editor's Note

This anonymous report describes a lecture on protein structure delivered by American chemist Irving Langmuir, in which Langmuir voiced support for the "cyclol" theory of proteins advocated by Dorothy Wrinch. This theory posited a cage-like structure for proteins, composed of polyhedra made from rings of amino-acid units. Langmuir's recognition of the role of "hydrophobic interactions" in protein structure is now seen as pivotal, which makes his support of Wrinch's fanciful theory seem all the more perverse. Notable here is his admission that the cyclol theory did not follow from the crucial X-ray crystallographic data on proteins collected by Dorothy Crowfoot and J. Desmond Bernal; and indeed, Bernal is recorded as a sceptical voice at the end of Langmuir's talk.

DESPITE the cold weather and the proximity of Christmas some hundred and thirty people attended a meeting of the Physical Society on December 20 at which Dr. Irving Langmuir delivered an address on the structure of proteins. He began by enumerating the facts which pure chemistry had succeeded in accumulating about these substances, which play such an important part in living Nature. By the union of two amino acids, with the elimination of a molecule of water, the polypeptide unit is built up. Chemically, this has two valence bonds free, one at each end, and thus seems adapted solely for the formation of chain compounds. If proteins are indeed chain compounds, it would be difficult to understand why they have apparently definite molecular weights (often multiples of 18,000), or why the molecule behaves approximately as a spherical one.

A few years ago, Dr. Dorothy Wrinch suggested that, instead of the polypeptide unit (I),

where R is one of a number of radicals, the unit might really be (II), which differs from it only in the position of a proton within the molecule. It has, however, four free valency bonds, which (being attached to nitrogen or carbon atoms) make angles of $109°$ with each other. Investigation of the spatial arrangements possible with such a unit shows that they can form closed "cages", the plane sides of which are constructed of a lacework of hexagons. The discrete molecular weights (and indeed the ratios of these) thus receive a natural explanation, as does the approximately spherical shape of the molecule.

蛋白质结构

编者按

这份没有署名的报告描述了美国化学家欧文·朗缪尔所做的一次关于蛋白质结构的演讲。在这次演讲中朗缪尔声称支持由多萝西·林奇提出的蛋白质的"环醇"理论。这个理论假定蛋白质为笼状结构，是由氨基酸单元形成的环构成的多面体。朗缪尔对蛋白质结构中"疏水作用"的认可现在看来很关键，这使得他对林奇的奇怪理论的支持显得更不合常理。值得注意的是，他承认环醇理论与多萝西·克劳福特和德斯蒙德·贝尔纳收集到的有关蛋白质结构的重要的 X 射线晶体衍射数据并不相符；另外，在朗缪尔演讲的最后部分，他也谈到了贝尔纳对此理论的质疑。

尽管天气寒冷且临近圣诞节，但是仍有 130 多位科学家出席了 12 月 20 日举行的物理学会会议，会上欧文·朗缪尔博士做了一个关于蛋白质结构的演讲。他首先陈述了在纯化学领域积累得到的关于这些物质的研究成果，这些物质在生物界起着非常重要的作用。两个氨基酸连接在一起，同时脱去一分子水，就构建出了多肽单元。从化学角度上讲，该物质具有两个自由的价键，分子两端各有一个，从而使得分子似乎完全适合于形成链状复合物。如果蛋白质真的是链状复合物，就很难理解为什么它们具有如此明确的分子量（通常是 18,000 的倍数），以及为什么蛋白分子表现得更像是一个球状物。

几年前，多萝西·林奇博士就曾指出，除了多肽单元（I）之外，

这里的 R 代表多种氨基酸侧链基团中的一个，结构单元还可能是如（II）所示的那样，与前者相比，两者之间的差别只在于分子内质子的位置不同。然而，它却具有四个自由的化学键，彼此（连在氮原子或碳原子上）之间的夹角为 109°。对这种结构单元可能形成的空间排布的研究显示，它们可以形成封闭的"笼状"结构，每一面由六边形构成。这样其分子量（事实上是它们的比率）离散分布以及其分子近似球形就都有了很自然的解释。

One cage in particular contains 288 amino-acid residues, which is equal to the number determined by physico-chemical methods in the case of egg albumin, within the limits of accuracy of these methods. In this particular case, the cage is a truncated tetrahedron which does not differ greatly from an octahedron.

Now proteins can be "denatured" by various mild treatments (shaking for three or four minutes, or heating to 65°C. for one or two minutes are sufficient in some cases) and then show markedly different properties from native proteins, but no change in molecular weight. It is suggested that these denatured proteins are in fact composed of the polypeptides which the chemist had discovered, since the treatment which he necessarily applies in order to make investigations would be sufficient to cause the change. The ease of denaturation, and the great alteration in properties, both follow naturally from this hypothesis, taken in conjunction with the "cyclol" hypothesis adopted for native proteins.

A particularly interesting fact which receives explanation by these theories is the insolubility in water of mono-molecular layers of proteins formed from soluble native proteins. The explanation lies in the positions of the side chains R, which in the cage structure are arranged around the edges of the hexagonal lacunae composing the plane sides of the cage, whereas in a mono-molecular layer, the cage is developed into a plane. When R is hydrophobe, the mono-molecular layer is formed with these radicals projecting; in the "cage" they project into the interior and are thus marked.

The last part of the lecture was devoted to the X-ray evidence, which is most complete in the case of insulin, since as shown by Crowfoot, this particular protein has but one molecule per unit cell, and the results are therefore more easily interpreted than would be the case with most proteins.

Dr. Langmuir stressed the point that the X-ray data, like many of the other facts explained by the theory, such as the appearance of α- but no β-amino acids, were not used as data in constructing it originally; nevertheless, the results of the X-ray investigation, in Dr. Langmuir's view, confirm many features of the structure to which the theory had led.

In the discussion which followed the address, Dr. Wrinch explained that the method used by Langmuir and Wrinch in interpreting the vector maps was a geometrical formulation of the classical picture of a crystal as a set of discrete units. Prof. J. D. Bernal uttered a word of caution against supposing that the theory was proved. He thought that certain features must be true, and others were possibly true, but in his view the X-ray data fail to confirm the proposed structure. He had had a vector map calculated for the latter, and found that it differed very markedly from that obtained experimentally. Prof. E. H. Neville showed the care that is needed in interpreting a vector map, by a simple example in which a map constructed from a given set of points appeared at first sight to correspond to quite a different type of distribution.

(**143**, 34-35; 1939)

特别是有一种笼状结构包含 288 个氨基酸残基，这与通过物理化学方法测定的卵清蛋白中氨基酸残基的数目是一致的，这些结果是在这些方法的精度范围内测定的。在此情况下，笼状结构是一个截顶四面体，和八面体没有太大的差别。

现在，可以通过各种温和的处理方法（振荡 3 ~ 4 分钟，在某些情况下 65℃ 加热 1 ~ 2 分钟足矣）使蛋白质变性，进而使其表现出与天然蛋白质截然不同的性质，但其分子量不发生改变。这表明这些变性的蛋白质实际上是由化学家已经发现的那些多肽链组成的，因为研究中必须用到的处理足以引起这些变化。综合考虑适用于天然蛋白质的"环醇"假说，蛋白质变性的易发生性及其性质上的巨大改变均可很自然地由此假说推导出来。

通过这些理论可以解释一个特别有趣的现象，即可溶性天然蛋白质在水中会形成不溶性的单分子层。其关键在于侧链 R 的位置。在笼状结构中这些侧链排布在六边形腔隙的边缘，构成笼状结构的侧平面，而在单分子层中，笼状结构转化为平面结构。当 R 基团是疏水基团时，单分子层由这些伸出的基团形成；在"笼状"结构中它们伸向内部，这也正是"笼状"结构的特征。

演讲的最后部分集中于 X 射线研究的证据，在这方面胰岛素的数据最为完整。就像克劳福特指出的那样，这种特殊的蛋白质在每一个单元晶胞中只含一个分子，因此相对于大多数蛋白质而言，胰岛素的结果更容易得到解释。

朗缪尔博士强调，就像许多其他可以被此理论解释的事实一样，例如 α–氨基酸而非 β–氨基酸的出现，在最初构建这种蛋白质结构理论时并没有用到 X 射线的研究数据。然而，在他看来，X 射线研究的结果验证了许多由此理论推导得出的结构特征。

在演讲之后的讨论中，林奇博士解释说，朗缪尔和林奇解析向量图时使用的方法是一种将晶体的典型图像看作一系列离散单元的几何学描述。贝尔纳教授说这个理论尚未被证实。他认为有些特征一定是真的，其他的则有可能是真的，但是依据他的观点，X 射线数据无法验证被提及的蛋白质的结构。他对后者的向量图进行了计算，发现与获得的实验结果有很大差别。内维尔教授通过如下一个简单的例子指出了在解析矢量图时要小心：从特定的一系列点出发构建得到的矢量图初看起来似乎对应着另一种非常不同的分布类型。

（刘振明 翻译；金侠 审稿）

Nature of the Cyclol Bond

I. Langmuir and D. Wrinch

Editor's Note

In the 1930s, the structure of protein molecules appeared to be a great mystery. That proteins are made from sub-units called amino acids (of which some 21 occur in natural proteins) was generally accepted, but the natural conformation of a protein molecule would have been a linear chain of amino acid "residues", which made it difficult for people to imagine how some protein molecules such as insulin appear to be roughly spherical in shape. One of the (incorrect) attempts to solve this problem was the so-called cyclol hypothesis, here advocated by Dorothy Wrinch, a British crystallographer, and Irving Langmuir, a distinguished American physical chemist.

I

THE confirmation by X-ray data[1,2] of C_2, the 288-residue cage structure proposed for the insulin molecule[3], makes it of interest to consider the nature of the cyclol bond, upon the postulation of which this structure and the cyclol theory of protein structure in general[4] depend. The making and breaking of a cyclol bond between an NH group of a polypeptide chain and a CO group of the same or of another polypeptide chain requires only the migration of an H atom thus:

$$\text{>NH} + \text{OC<} \rightleftharpoons \text{>N---(HO)C<}.$$

The making and breaking of a cyclol bond is therefore a prototropic tautomerism, inter- or intra-molecular, which indicates a special type of binding of the H atom. (A recent investigation has shown that a similar situation actually exists in crystalline diketopiperazine[5]). As a prototropic tautomerism, it is to be sharply contrasted with the making and breaking of a peptide link which, requiring the intervention of another molecule, say water, may be written:

$$\text{---NH---OC---} + \text{H}_2\text{O} \rightleftharpoons \text{---NH}_2 + \text{HOOC---}.$$

In order to direct attention to the fundamental difference between a prototropic tautomerism on one hand and a hydrolysis (or alcoholysis, etc.) on the other, it is convenient to talk in future of cyclol *bonds* and peptide *links*.

In current usage, the term protein is applied to anything having the chemical composition of amino acid condensation products. One class stands out as of paramount importance for the understanding of living matter, namely the crystalline globular proteins such as trypsin, pepsin and so on. These substances are already well defined in a number of ways, and it is with proteins belonging to this category that the cyclol theory is concerned.

452

环醇键的本质

朗缪尔，林奇

编者按

在 20 世纪 30 年代，蛋白质分子的结构仍是一个巨大的谜。当时人们普遍认为蛋白质是由被称为氨基酸（天然蛋白质中大约有 21 种氨基酸）的亚单元组成的。但这样一来，蛋白质分子的天然构象就应该是一条由氨基酸"残基"构成的线性直链，这样人们就很难想象为什么某些蛋白质分子（如胰岛素）是近似球形的。为了解决这一难题，人们进行了很多努力和尝试，其中之一就是由英国晶体学家多萝西·林奇和杰出的美国物理化学家欧文·朗缪尔提出的所谓环醇假说，但这种假说是错误的。

I

曾有人提出胰岛素分子具有由 288 个残基形成的 C_2 笼状结构 [3]，X 射线数据 [1,2] 对这一结构的确认使得人们对环醇键本质的关注变得很有意义，而胰岛素的分子结构以及蛋白质分子一般结构的假说 [4] 正是依赖于环醇键假说。一条多肽链中的 NH 基团与同一条或者另一条多肽链中的 CO 基团之间形成和断裂一个环醇键，只需要迁移一个 H 原子：

$$\text{>NH} + \text{OC<} \rightleftharpoons \text{>N—(HO)C<}$$

因此，环醇键的形成和断裂就是分子间或分子内质子转移的互变异构过程，这暗示了 H 原子的一种特殊键合方式。最近的一项研究显示，在晶态的二酮哌嗪（环缩二氨酸）中确实存在类似的情况 [5]。作为一种质子转移的互变异构过程，它与肽连接的形成和断裂形成了鲜明的对比。因为肽连接的形成和断裂需要另外一个分子（如水分子）的参与，可以写成下面的形式：

$$\text{—NH—OC—} + H_2O \rightleftharpoons \text{—NH}_2 + \text{HOOC—}$$

为了将注意力指向质子转移互变异构过程与水解过程（或者醇解等）二者之间的根本差异，简便起见，我们在以后的讨论中将它们称为**环醇键**和**肽连接**。

在目前流行的用法中，蛋白质一词可用于化学组成为氨基酸缩聚产物的任何物质。其中有一类对于理解生命物质最为重要，那就是具有结晶态的球蛋白，例如胰蛋白酶、胃蛋白酶等。这些物质在许多方面已有了详尽的定义，而环醇理论所关注的正是这一类蛋白质。

Among the properties by which the substances are already characterized are the following:

(1) They have definite molecular weights which are discretely arranged.

(2) They contain certain numbers of various particular amino acid residues and these numbers are frequently powers of 2 and 3.

(3) They are soluble in water or salt solutions, but their solubility is affected by changes in pH.

(4) They denature under very slight stimulus.

(5) They spontaneously form monolayers of extreme insolubility.

(6) They exhibit a high degree of specificity in biological reactions.

It has already been shown that the cyclol hypothesis explains (1), (2), (4). With regard to (3) and (5), we may point out that the extreme insolubility of the monolayer formed from a soluble protein[6,7,8] indicates that the globular protein has a structure in which hydrophobic groups can be completely masked, so leading directly to the idea of a cage structure which presented itself in the cyclol theory as a deduction from the geometry of polypeptide chains. The lacunae in the fabric allow ionized (and other) R groups to modify their positions profoundly in response to changes in pH, and indeed to lie inside or outside the cage. The spontaneous formation of protein monolayers from globular proteins in solution indicates that weak bonds only are broken. This we interpret to mean that, in the formation of monolayers, some or all of the cyclol bonds are opened, few or none of the peptide links being broken, so that protein monolayers consist of polypeptide chains partially or wholly decyclized, for the most part without open ends, the hydrophobic groups forming a separate phase in the surface. This type of structure explains many of their striking characteristics: for example viscosity, elasticity, etc.[7,8].

It may be emphasized that the breaking of cyclol bonds yields different degradation products according to the path of fragmentation. Thus cyclol-6 yields three diketopiperazine molecules or a single 6-residue chain (Fig. 1). In standard circumstances, a preferential path of fragmentation, probably largely determined by the R-groups, is to be expected[9], and it may be presumed that one and the same structure will under standard conditions break down in a unique way. Further, if preferential paths of breaking cyclol bonds be postulated, preferential paths of making cyclol bonds must also be postulated. Experiments have recently been reported purporting to disprove the cyclol hypothesis, in which glycyl leucine and leucyl glycine dipeptides were mixed and glycyl glycine and leucyl

下面列出的是这些物质已被确认的某些性质：

（1）它们具有呈离散分布的确定的分子量。

（2）它们包含一定数量的各种特定氨基酸残基，其数量往往成百上千。

（3）它们可溶于水或者盐溶液中，但 pH 的变化会影响其溶解性。

（4）它们会在很微弱的刺激下发生变性。

（5）它们可以自发地形成极难溶的单分子层。

（6）它们在生物反应中表现出高度的特异性。

以前已经证明，环醇假说可以解释（1）、（2）和（4）。至于（3）和（5），我们可以指出，可溶性蛋白质形成的单分子层的极度难溶性 [6,7,8] 意味着球蛋白具有一种能将疏水基团完全掩盖起来的结构，从而直接导致了在环醇理论中提出笼状结构的想法，这是从多肽链的几何特征中推导出来的。结构之间的缝隙允许离子化的（及其他的）R 基团随着 pH 的改变而大幅度地改变其位置，R 基团甚至可以位于笼的内部或外部。球蛋白在溶液中自发形成蛋白质单分子层，这表明只有弱键被打开了。我们对此的解释是，在形成单分子层的过程中，部分或全部环醇键被打开，但只有极少或没有肽连接断开，因而蛋白质单分子层是由部分或完全开环的多肽链组成，其中大部分没有开放的自由末端，疏水基团在表面形成了一个单独的相。这种结构解释了它们所具有的很多惊人特性：比如黏度、弹性等 [7,8]。

可能需要强调的是，根据断裂途径不同，环醇键打开后会产生不同的降解产物。因此六元环醇能够产生三个二酮哌嗪分子或者一条含有六个残基的链（图 1）。在标准条件下，可以预期一条优先的断裂途径（可能在很大程度上取决于 R 基团）[9]，并且还可以假定同一结构在标准条件下会以唯一的方式分解。另外，如果可以假定环醇键的优先断裂途径，那么相应地生成环醇键的优先途径也一定会被确定。最近报道的实验宣称推翻了环醇假说，实验中将甘氨酰亮氨酸与亮氨酰甘氨酸两种二肽混合，结果并没有形成甘氨酰甘氨酸和亮氨酰亮氨酸这两种二肽 [10]。即便有三嗪环形成（何况

455

leucine dipeptides were not formed[10]. Even if triazine rings were formed (and of this no evidence was offered), there seems no reason to suppose that the structure will break down to yield anything except the original molecules. We are therefore unable to accept these experiments as evidence against the cyclol hypothesis.

Fig. 1. Cyclol-6 (in centre) with its triazine ring dotted. The opening of this ring yields either three diketopiperazine molecules (shown on left) or a closed polypeptide chain of six residues (shown on right).

These suggestions of preferred paths of fragmentation apply equally to the globular proteins characterized, on the present view, by a specific set of amino acid residues, in a definite spatial interrelationship. They imply that for each protein there are one or more points at which the breaking of cyclol bonds normally starts. Thus an insulin molecule forming a monolayer would form a specific set of wholly (or partially) decyclized polypeptide chains. In this way, we can explain the highly characteristic films formed by different proteins, which permit an unknown protein to be recognized instantly as insulin or pepsin or papain and so on[6,7,8].

II

From the point of view of biology, cytology and immuno-chemistry, however, the most striking characteristic of the globular protein is its high degree of specificity. This, we suggest, indicates an organized structure with its own characteristic modes of vibration, which depend on the nature and arrangement of the various constituent amino acids. Since the breaking and making of cyclol bonds is a prototropic tautomerism, we anticipate that in appropriate circumstances there may be a kind of resonance in the molecule which accounts for the stability of the cyclol fabrics and the cyclol polyhedra. The cyclol fabric, a fragment of which is shown in Fig. 2, contains no double bonds and thus Frank[11] believed that "the cyclol molecule in itself offers no chance of constructing a resonant system". But each triazine hexagon has three parallel hydroxyls on the three carbon atoms, the next triazine hexagons in the fabric having their three hydroxyls on the other side of the fabric. With a symmetrical structure of this kind, it seems highly probable that the protons, instead of being attached to individual oxygen atoms, lie between the oxygen atoms serving as hydrogen bonds between them. There may thus be a marked resonance involving the three oxygens and the three hydrogens. Furthermore, resonance on a larger scale between neighbouring triazine groups may also be expected.

并没有证据支持这一点），似乎也没有理由推测该结构分解后会生成最初分子以外的任何其他物质。因此，我们无法接受把这些实验作为反对环醇假说的证据。

图 1. 六元环醇（位于中央）和它的三嗪环（由虚线表示）。如果把这个环打开，要么产生 3 个二酮哌嗪分子（示于左边），要么产生由 6 个残基组成的闭合多肽链（示于右边）。

根据当前的看法，关于优先断裂途径的说法同样适用于由具有明确空间互联关系的一组特定氨基酸残基构成的球蛋白。这些观点意味着，对于每种蛋白质来说，环醇键的断裂都有一个或多个正常的起点。因此，一个可以形成单分子层的胰岛素分子，会形成一组特定的完全（或部分）开环的多肽链。这样，我们就可以解释不同蛋白质所形成的高度特征化的薄膜，从而得以立即识别出一种未知蛋白质究竟是胰岛素、胃蛋白酶、木瓜蛋白酶，还是别的什么 [6,7,8]。

II

不过，从生物学、细胞学和免疫化学的角度来看，球蛋白最惊人的特征是它的高度特异性。我们认为，这意味着球蛋白是有序结构，并具有自身特定的振动模式，这种振动模式依赖于各种组分氨基酸的特性和排列方式。由于环醇键的断裂和形成都是质子转移的互变异构过程，我们预期，在某些适当的条件下分子中可能存在一种共振，这可以解释环醇织物与环醇多面体的稳定性。图 2 显示的是环醇结构的一个片段；环醇结构中不含双键，因此弗兰克 [11] 相信，"环醇分子自身没有构成共振体系的可能性"。但是，在每个三嗪六边形中，三个碳原子上都有三个平行羟基，而结构中下一个三嗪六边形也有三个羟基在结构的另外一侧。在这样一种对称结构中，看来极有可能的情况是质子并不是被束缚在单个氧原子上，而是位于两个氧原子之间并形成氢键将它们连接起来。因此可能存在一个涉及三个氧原子和三个氢原子的明显共振。此外，还可以预期，相邻三嗪基团之间可能存在更大规模的共振。

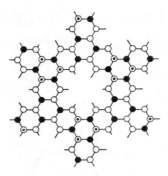

Fig. 2. A fragment of the cyclol fabric. The median plane of the lamina is the plane of the paper.
The lamina has its "front" surface above and its "back" surface below the paper.

● = N.

○ = C(OH), hydroxyl upwards.

⊙ = C(OH), hydroxyl downwards.

○— = CHR, direction of side chain initially outwards.

○— = CHR, direction of side chain initially upwards.

This suggestion of intramolecular hydrogen bonds in the cyclol fabric is in line with the intramolecular bonds already postulated in a wide variety of compounds, including ice, alum, natrolite and other zeolites, oxalic acid dihydrate and formic acid, in which oxygen atoms are shown, by crystal structure data, to lie abnormally close together[12]. Such a close distance of approach is evidence of considerable mutual energy of oxygen atoms, which can only be due to the presence of hydrogen between them[12]. For certain compounds, for example, salicylaldehyde and o-nitrophenol, the presence of intramolecular hydrogen bonds has been confirmed spectroscopically by the non-appearance of the hydroxyl band[13]. In these cases the oxygen-oxygen distance is about 2.5 A., considerably shorter than the distance of 2.7 A., that represents double the radius of the ion O^{2-} and very much shorter than that for neutral oxygen. In the case of the cyclol fabric, hydroxyls are carried by three carbons in a triazine ring, which lie at the distance apart of $\frac{2}{3}a\sqrt{6}$, which is equal to 2.45 A. if a, a length intermediate between the C-C and C-N distances is taken(as has so far been done)as 1.5 A.

One of the most extraordinary properties of proteins is their specificity in biological reactions. The haemoglobin in each different type of animal seems to differ in spectrum and in details of its behaviour with oxygen. We are thus forced to conclude that, in proteins, certain features of the molecule can transmit some effect to other parts of the molecule, particularly to prosthetic groups. Such transmission of chemical influence, although observable to some extent in such compounds as sterols, seems to exist in a unique degree in the proteins: in long-chain compounds, on the other hand, there is practically no evidence of such transmissions to distances of more than a few atoms. It is well known that in aromatic chemistry the resonance, for example in the benzene molecule, causes substituents in different parts of the molecule to have an effect on one another very different from what would be expected if no resonance occurred. The high specificity of the proteins therefore in itself seems to demand resonance to a degree

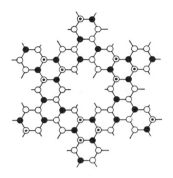

图 2. 环醇结构的片段。片层的中间平面为纸平面。片层的
"前"表面在纸的上方，"后"表面在纸的下方。
● = N。
○ = C(OH)，羟基向上。
⊙ = C(OH)，羟基向下。
○— = CHR，侧链方向原本向外。
○– = CHR，侧链方向原本向上。

环醇结构中存在分子内氢键的说法，是与大量不同化合物中存在分子内氢键的假定相符合的，这些化合物包括冰、明矾、钠沸石及其他沸石、二水合草酸和蚁酸等。晶体结构数据显示，这些化合物中的氧原子彼此间非常靠近[12]。如此近的距离是表明氧原子间具有相当强的相关能的证据，这只可能是由于两个氧原子之间存在氢原子的缘故[12]。对于某些化合物如水杨醛或者对邻硝基苯酚来说，分子内氢键的存在已经通过光谱学方法得到了证实，因为光谱图中没有出现羟基带[13]。在上述实例中，氧–氧原子间距约为2.5Å，明显短于氧离子 O^{2-} 半径的两倍即2.7Å，比起中性氧原子的半径就更是短很多。在环醇结构中,每一个三嗪环中的三个碳原子上都有一个羟基，间距为 $\frac{2}{3}a\sqrt{6}$，如果长度 a 的数值介于C–C与C–N间距之间（到目前为止人们都是这么处理的）即1.5Å的话，那么该间距等于2.45Å。

蛋白质最不同寻常的性质之一就是其在生物反应中的特异性。每一种不同类型的动物体内，其血红蛋白似乎都具有不同的光谱，并且在与氧发生作用的细节上有所不同。由此必然会推出，蛋白质分子的某些特征可以将某些效应传递到分子中的其他部分，特别是传递给辅基。这种化学效应的传递现象，虽然在某种程度上也可以在诸如固醇类化合物中被观测到，但它在蛋白质中出现的程度似乎是独一无二的；另一方面，在长链化合物中，完全没有证据表明这种传递可以超出几个原子的距离。众所周知，在芳香族化合物如苯分子中，共振会使分子中不同部位的取代基彼此间产生相互影响，而如果没有共振的话，可以预测这种影响会是大不相同的。由此看来，蛋白质自身的高度特异性似乎比其他已知化合物需要有更大程度的共振。看来，

greater than that in other known chemical compounds. It would seem that the cyclol polyhedral structure with its sets of rings within rings and its multiple paths of linkage between atoms (cf. Fig. 2) should be capable of just such a type of resonance.

May we not perhaps regard each diazine ring in the cyclol fabric as the analogue of an electrical resonant circuit, the natural frequency of which is determined by the character of the side chains in this ring? Then n resonant circuits coupled together would be characterized by n^2 frequencies, no one of which being exactly what it would be if the resonant units were separated from one another. An electrical network, the resonant circuits of which have the geometry of the cyclol polyhedra, would give very close coupling between the adjacent hexagonal units. Thus the structure as a whole should possess a wide range of frequencies. The situation is somewhat analogous to that in the Debye theory where a crystal has a large number of modes of vibration. So in the protein the cyclol structure may be characterized by a whole spectrum of frequencies definitely correlated with the symmetry of the structure as a whole. Thus if a single factor disturbs the symmetry, it might have a profound effect upon some of the characteristic frequencies. If we imagine that these frequencies are important in the interactions between proteins and in funnelling the energy to certain parts of the molecule, we have a possible reason for the important effects produced by apparently minor changes in the structure of the protein molecule.

III

It appears that a strong case can be made out for the cyclol theory, since its implications, derived by simple geometrical arguments, fits the facts summarized above. The theory depends upon one postulate which thus becomes of special interest, particularly as its formulation has occasioned some uneasiness in chemical circles. The question then arises as to the possibility of proving directly the existence or non-existence of cyclol bonds.

The work on protein monolayers indicates that only weak forces are required to open cyclol bonds. We are of the opinion that many chemical techniques are sufficient to rip open the cyclol fabric into polypeptide chains, so that the chemist by his very operations may destroy the structure he seeks to study. On this view, any apparent contradiction between the cyclol hypothesis (which regards the globular proteins as polypeptide fabrics) and the chemical data relating to proteins (which appear to show them to be polypeptide chains) disappears. The situation is thus reminiscent of that in quantum physics, where the conditions required for the observation of the position and velocity of an electron themselves modify the phenomena under study. Similarly, it has recently been suggested[14] that enzyme studies do not permit the deduction that cyclol bonds do or do not exist in globular proteins. Direct knowledge of protein structure must therefore depend upon physical methods of investigation such as X-rays and spectroscopy, etc.

The picture of a globular protein with hydrophilic groups on its outer surface and hydrocarbon groups in contact within the cage is strikingly akin to the picture of the

460

环醇多面体结构及其一系列的环内环和原子间的多重连接方式（参见图 2）应该是恰好可以产生这种共振的。

我们是否可以把环醇结构中的每个二嗪环视为一个共振电路的类似物，其天然频率由环内支链的特性决定？如果真是如此，那么偶连在一起的 n 个共振回路将由 n^2 种频率决定，并且其中没有一个会与这些共振单元彼此分离时呈现出来的频率严格一致。其共振回路具有环醇多面体几何特征的电网络会造成相邻六边形单元之间紧密偶连。因而其整体结构应具有大范围的频率。这有些类似于德拜理论中所提到的情况：一种晶体具有多种振动模式。因此，蛋白质分子中的环醇结构的特征就可以通过与整体结构对称性明确相关的一整套频率谱来明确描述。于是，如果有一个单一因素扰乱对称性时，那么它就可能对某些特征频率产生深刻影响。设想一下，如果这些频率对于蛋白质分子间的相互作用以及将能量集中于分子内特定部位的作用而言是重要的，那么我们就可能可以解释为什么蛋白质分子结构中看似很微小的变化也会导致重大的影响。

III

看起来似乎可以相信环醇理论了，因为从纯粹的几何学论据得出的该假说的推论与前面概述的各项事实都能吻合。环醇理论依赖于一个前提假设，这个假设因而吸引了人们的特别兴趣，一定程度上是因为它的表述方式引起了化学界的一些担忧，于是关于能否直接证明环醇键是否存在的问题就出现了。

对蛋白质单分子层的研究表明，只需要比较弱的作用力就可以打开环醇键。我们的看法是，有很多化学技术都足以使环醇结构断裂成多肽链，因此化学家所使用的特定操作很可能会破坏他试图研究的结构。这样一来，环醇假说（将球蛋白视为多肽结构）与蛋白质的化学数据（它们似乎显示球蛋白是多肽链）之间存在的任何矛盾都消失了。这种局面让人回想起量子物理学中的类似情况，即观测一个电子的位置与速度所需要的实验条件本身会改变正在被研究的现象。与此类似，最近有人提出 [14]，对酶的研究不能推测出环醇键是否存在于球蛋白中。因此，关于蛋白质结构的直接知识必须依赖于诸如 X 射线及光谱学等物理学的研究方法。

球蛋白的亲水基团位于外表面，而烃基则位于笼中相互靠近，这与最近研究得

structure of certain micelles to which recent studies have led[15]. Ions, such as cetyl trimethylammonium sulphate, which contain long hydrocarbon chains form micelles in very low concentration. It is found that the size of such particles corresponds to a sphere of radius about equal to the length of the individual molecules and it is shown that the micelles are spherical particles, in which the tails are crowded together in the interior and the hydrophilic heads form the outer surface. The micelles in soap solutions have a similar structure.

Little or nothing is known at present as to the path or the nature of protein synthesis. We see no reason to suppose that a cyclol fabric forms spontaneously from polypeptide chains. If on occasion such cross linking occurs, this is probably a relatively unstable state. The non-formation of cyclol bonds between simple molecules[10,16,17] is thus irrelevant to the cyclol hypothesis and to the problem of the formation of complete globular protein molecules. Using the information obtained in recent studies of protein monolayers formed spontaneously, we deduce that, in the globular state, the CH_2 groups are completely masked from the aqueous medium. The globular protein in water is thus pictured as having its outer surface predominantly hydrophilic, the hydrophobic groups lying close together in the interior of the cage. A protein molecule of the size of insulin must contain several hundred CH_2 groups to account for the insolubility of the monolayer which it forms. When two CH_2 groups come into contact, energy of the order of 2,000 calories per gram molecule is involved[18], totalling for a protein molecule of the size of insulin, containing at least 300 CH_2 groups, an energy of upwards of 600,000 calories. This suggests one possible factor in the formation of a protein cage molecule.

We would also direct attention to the difference between the stability to be expected when a single cyclol bond forms within or between polypeptide chains and when three cyclol bonds form a triazine ring, and to the still more striking difference to be expected between the stability of a piece of cyclol fabric and of a complete cyclol polyhedron. Undoubtedly there are a number of factors favouring the complete polyhedral structure over and above any uncompleted cyclol structure. These may account for the existence of cyclol cages even if there should be an intrinsic instability in isolated cyclol bonds.

(**143**, 49-52; 1939)

References:

1. Wrinch, *J. Amer. Chem. Soc.*, **60**, 2005 (1938).

2. Wrinch and Langmuir, *J. Amer. Chem. Soc.*, **60**, 2247 (1938).

3. Wrinch, *Science*, **85**, 566 (1937); *Trans. Far. Soc.*, **33**, 1368 (1937).

4. Wrinch, *Nature*, **137**, 411 (1936) *et seq.*

5. Corey, *J. Amer. Chem. Soc.*, **60**, 1598 (1938).

6. Langmuir and Schaefer, *J. Amer. Chem. Soc.*, **60**, 1351 (1938).

7. Langmuir, Cold Spring Harbor Symposium on Proteins, 8, 1938.

8. Langmuir, Pilgrim Lecture, Royal Society, 1938.

9. Wrinch, *Phil. Mag.*, **25**, 705 (1938); Cold Spring Harbor Symposium on Proteins, 8, 1938.

10. Meyer and Hoheneiser, *Nature*, **141**, 1138 (1938).

到的某些胶束的结构[15]惊人地相似。某些具有长烃链的离子，例如十六烷基三甲铵硫酸盐，能在极低浓度时形成胶束。已发现这种胶束微粒的大小相当于一个半径约为单个分子长度的球体，并且结果表明胶束是球状微粒，其中各个分子的尾部挤在球的内部，而亲水的头部则形成了外表面。肥皂溶液中的胶束具有类似的结构。

目前，我们对于蛋白质合成的途径或其性质所知甚少，或者一无所知。我们没有理由假定环醇结构是由多肽链自发形成的。即使偶然发生交联反应，这也很可能只是一种相对不稳定的状态。简单分子之间不形成环醇键这种说法[10,16,17]，与环醇假说以及完整球蛋白分子的形成问题并不相干。利用最近获得的关于蛋白质单分子层自发形成的研究结果，我们推测，在球形状态时，CH_2基团是完全与水介质隔离的。由此可以描绘球蛋白在水中的形象，其外表面几乎完全是亲水的，而疏水基团则彼此紧靠着处于笼的内部。一个与胰岛素大小差不多的蛋白质分子必定含有几百个CH_2基团，这样才可以解释它所形成的单分子层的不溶性。当两个CH_2基团彼此接触时，涉及的能量的数量级为每克分子 2,000 卡[18]，总计起来，一个与胰岛素大小差不多的蛋白质分子包含至少 300 个 CH_2 基团，总能量将达到 600,000 卡以上。这可能是形成蛋白质笼状分子的一个因素。

我们还应当把注意力转向可以预期的稳定性差异：如一个环醇键在多肽链内或多肽链间形成时的稳定性差异，三个环醇键形成一个三嗪环时的稳定性差异，以及可以料想到的存在于一个环醇结构与一个完整环醇多面体之间的更为惊人的差异。毫无疑问，与不完全的环醇结构相比，许多因素对完整的多面体结构的形成更为有利。这些因素也许可以解释环醇笼的存在，即便分离的环醇键也可能具有内在的不稳定性。

（王耀杨 翻译；顾孝诚 审稿）

11. Frank, *Nature*, **138**, 242 (1936).

12. Bernal and Megaw, *Proc. Roy. Soc.*, A, **151**, 384 (1935).

13. Hilbert, Wulf, Hendricks and Liddel, *Nature*, **135**, 147 (1935). Errera and Mollet *C.R. Acad. Sci.*, Paris, **200**, 814 (1935).

14. Linderstrøm-Lang, Hotchkiss and Johansen, *Nature*, **142**, 99 (1938).

15. Hartley and Runnicles, *Proc, Roy. Soc.*, A, 168, 401 (1938): Hartley *J. Chem. Soc.*, 1968 (1938).

16. Jenkins and Taylor, *J. Chem. Soc.*, 495 (1937).

17. Neuberger, Royal Society discussion on proteins, November 17 1938 (*Nature*, **142**, 1024; 1938).

18. Langmuir, *J. Amer. Chem. Soc.*, **39**, 1848(1917); Colloid Symposium Monograph 3, 48 (1925); "Colloid Chemistry", vol.1, 525 (1926).(Edited by J. Alexander, Chemical Catalog Co., N.Y.)

New Broadcasting System

Editor's Note

An engineer in the United States, *Nature* reports here, has developed a new kind of radio broadcasting system. Radio systems at that time worked by amplitude modulation, which encodes the signal, such as voice, in modulations of the amplitude of the carrier wave. In contrast, the new system developed by Edwin Armstrong encodes information in modulations of the frequency of the carrier wave. That gave a sharp reduction in radio interference, although there was a considerable increase in the receiver's complexity. Although the basic principles of this scheme of frequency modulation, or FM radio, had long been known, Armstrong brought it to fruition with valves and circuits. The first transmitting station, in Alpine New Jersey, began operating soon after.

ACCORDING to a recent report by the New York Correspondent of *The Times*, a new type of wireless transmission and reception will be used in an experimental station now being erected at Columbia University by Major E. H. Armstrong, professor of electrical engineering in the University, and inventor of the now well-known supersonic-heterodyne receiver. The station will use the frequency-modulation system of transmission, as distinct from the amplitude-modulation system at present used by all broadcasting stations. In the former method, the frequency of the emitted carrier wave is varied by the speech and music modulation; whereas in the methods so far employed, the frequency of the carrier wave remains constant and its amplitude is varied by the applied audio-frequencies. The principles of frequency-modulation have been known since the earliest days of radio-telephony, but it has remained for Prof. Armstrong to demonstrate how these may be brought into practical use with modern valves and circuit arrangements. Among the advantages claimed for the new system are that it effects a considerable reduction of interference in radio reception, and that a much larger number of broadcasting channels will become available in any given wave-length band. Against these, however, is the serious disadvantage that special receivers are necessary for frequency-modulated transmissions, and this factor is likely to involve serious delay in the introduction of the new system into modern broadcasting technique. The first transmitting station on the new system will be at Alpine, New Jersey, opposite New York City, and it has a licence to broadcast on a frequency of 40 megacycles per second (wave-length 7.5 metres). It is also understood that suitable receivers are already being manufactured, so that the result of this practical experiment will be awaited with interest.

(**143**, 152; 1939)

新的广播系统

编者按

《自然》的这篇文章对一位美国工程师发展出的一套新的广播系统进行了报道。当时的广播系统是通过调幅，即对载波的振幅进行调制而将声音等信号进行编码的。与之相对应的是埃德温·阿姆斯特朗研制的新系统，该系统通过对载波的频率进行调制而编码信息。尽管增加了接收机的复杂程度，但这一技术大大降低了广播信号间的相互干扰。虽然人们早已经了解了调频（FM）广播的基本原理，但是阿姆斯特朗用电子管和线路将这一理论变成了现实。第一个采用这种技术的发射台不久将在新泽西州的阿尔派投入使用。

根据《泰晤士报》驻纽约记者最新的一则报道，一家实验电台将采用一套新型的无线发射和接收系统，该实验电台目前正由哥伦比亚大学电子工程系教授阿姆斯特朗少校在该校架设，阿姆斯特朗教授也是目前广为人知的超外差接收器的发明者。目前所有广播电台使用的都是调幅系统，与此不同的是，正在建设中的这座电台将使用调频发射系统。在调频系统中，发射载波的频率会随着语音和音乐的声调变化而变化，而在目前使用的调幅系统中，载波的频率是恒定不变的，其振幅则随着所用音频的变化而变化。在无线电话问世之初，人们就已经知道了调频的原理。但是在阿姆斯特朗教授之前，没有人知道如何利用现代的电子管和各种电路元件将其带向实际应用。新系统的优点是：它大大减少了无线电接收中存在的干扰，也大幅增加了在任意给定的波长范围内可用的广播频道。然而，这种系统也有严重的缺点，人们必须用特殊的接收机才能接收调频发射的无线电信号，这一缺点很可能会严重减缓现代广播系统中应用这种新系统的速度。使用这种新系统的第一家发射台将设在新泽西州的阿尔派（与纽约市隔河相望），该发射台已经获得了在每秒 40 兆周（即波长 7.5 米）的频率上进行广播的授权。据悉，合适的接收机正在生产中，因此，大家都在饶有兴趣地等待着这项应用性实验的结果。

（刘霞 翻译；赵见高 审稿）

The Expanding Universe and the Origin of the Great Nebulae[*]

J. H. Jeans

Editor's Note

The astronomer James Jeans here criticises recent speculations of George Gamow and Edward Teller on the origins of galaxies. Gamow and Teller started from an estimate of the mass density of the universe, and reasoned that for the condensation of galaxies ever to have taken place, the average distance between galaxies must have once been 1,000 times smaller than today, a ratio curiously similar to that of the distance between galaxies to their typical diameters. Jeans rejects this argument as following from poor estimates of these quantities, and instead offers his own view: that current physics allows for the possibility of galaxy formation under a wide range of conditions, indeed so wide that nothing can be ruled out as impossible.

PROF. G. Gamow and Dr. E. Teller have propounded[1] an interesting view of the genesis of the nebulae, but I doubt if either their arguments or their calculations can survive criticism. In brief, they think that the average density of matter in the present universe is about 10^{-30}; that matter of this density, spread uniformly as a gas through space, could only condense into the present nebulae if the gas-molecules were at a temperature of "several million degrees, which seems to be very unlikely"; that for condensation to have taken place in the past, inter-nebular distances must have been less than now by a factor of about 1,000. "Since the present average distance between the nebulae is just about 1,000 times larger than their diameters, we conclude ..." and so on. Their whole cosmogony is based on the supposed equality of these two factors of 1,000. I believe both to be wrongly calculated.

The average internebular distance is about 2,000,000 light-years[2], but the average diameter of a nebula[3] is certainly more than 2,000 light-years. The true ratio here is probably nearer to 100 than to 1,000.

Recent investigations by Sinclair-Smith, Holmberg and others suggest that Hubble's estimate of 10^{-30} for mean density (which was anyhow only given as a lower limit), is emphatically on the low side. The average nebula appears to have a mass of at least 10^{11} Suns. This gives a mean density, for nebular matter alone, of 2.5×10^{-29}, which reduces the needed contraction from 1,000:1 to 40:1. But this is not all; in calculating the criterion for the formation of condensations, the authors neglect the gravitational field of all uncondensed matter outside the incipient condensation. My own calculations[4] indicate

---

[*]Translator's Note: "The Great Nebulae" in this paper refers to galaxies, which are different from the modern notion of nebulae as gas clouds.

膨胀的宇宙和大星云*的起源

金斯

编者按

本文中天文学家詹姆斯·金斯评论了近期乔治·伽莫夫和爱德华·特勒对星系起源的推测。伽莫夫和特勒从对宇宙中物质密度的估算开始，继而推测如果星系的塌缩曾经发生过，那么过去星系间的平均距离应该是今天的 1/1,000，这个比值非常接近于星系间的距离与它们的典型直径的比值。本文中，金斯认为这些估算数据的准确性太差从而否定了这个论据，并进一步提出了他自己的观点：根据现在的物理学，星系可以在一个极为广泛的条件下形成，甚至没有什么条件是不可能的。

乔治·伽莫夫教授和爱德华·特勒博士提出了 [1] 一个关于星云诞生的有趣观点，不过我怀疑他们的论据以及他们的计算能否经得起推敲。简而言之，他们认为在今天的宇宙中，物质的平均密度大约是 10^{-30}；而只有当这些气体分子处于"看似不可能的数百万度的"温度时，像气体一样均匀散布于空间中的这一密度的物质才能刚好塌缩成今天的星云；而由于过去曾发生了这种塌缩，因此过去星云间的距离应该是今天的 1/1,000。"因为今天星云之间的平均距离正好比它们的直径大差不多 1,000倍，所以我们可以得出……"等等。实际上，他们的整个宇宙演化论都是基于假定的这两个 1,000 因子是相等的。但我认为这两个因子都算错了。

星云间的平均距离大约是 2,000,000 光年 [2]，但是星云的平均直径 [3] 必定大于2,000 光年。因此两者之间真实的比值应该更接近 100 而不是 1,000。

辛克莱·史密斯、霍姆伯格以及其他人的最新研究认为，哈勃估算的平均密度值 10^{-30}（只是作为一个下限而言）无疑是偏低的。一般星云的质量至少是太阳质量的 10^{11} 倍。如果仅考虑星云物质，则给出的平均密度为 2.5×10^{-29}，这把所需的塌缩比从 1,000：1 降到了 40：1。不过这还不够全面；在计算塌缩产生的条件时，作者忽略了初始塌缩区域之外所有未塌缩物质的引力场。我自己的计算 [4] 表明，这会进一

---

* 译者注：这里的"大星云"指的是现在通常所说的星系，和现在通常说的星云的概念不同。

that this introduces a further wrong factor of $8\pi^2/9$, or about 9.

When all this is put straight, I find that the present universe, as it now stands, could be formed by the condensation of a gas with a "thermal" velocity of about 20 km. a second. To obtain this velocity, we need not postulate gas molecules (!) "at temperatures of several million degrees"; we can get it from hydrogen atoms at 19,000°C., or from free electrons at −260°C., or from a mixture of atoms and electrons at any temperature we choose between −260°C. and 19,000°C. The range is so wide that nothing can be ruled out as impossible.

The range of universes which could be formed by gas-condensation would appear, then, to include the actual present universe. If so, we cannot form any estimate of the epoch, or any picture of the manner, in which our universe was formed, from the considerations proposed by Gamow and Teller.

I believe other objections can be brought against their arguments without being hypercritical. For example, in the expanding universe of the theory of relativity, material particles gain kinetic energy during the process of expansion. But this gain must not be included in the equation of energy; if it is, there is no longer conservation of energy. This makes me think that the authors' arguments about velocity of escape are invalid.

(**143**, 158-159; 1939)

J. H. Jeans: Cleveland Lodge, Dorking.

References:
1. *Nature*, **143**, 116 (1939).
2. Hubble, "The Realm of the Nebulae", 189.
3. *Loc. cit.*, 178.
4. "Astronomy and Cosmogony" (second edit.), 348.

步引入一个 $8\pi^2/9$ 或者说大约为 9 的错误因子。

当所有这些都被纠正之后我发现，今天的宇宙的状态可以由"热运动"速度大约为 20 千米 / 秒的气体塌缩而成。为得到这个速度，我们不需要假设气体分子（！）"处于数百万度的温度"；我们可以从 19,000℃ 的氢原子，或者 −260℃ 的自由电子，或者处于我们选择的 −260℃ 到 19,000℃ 之间的任意温度的原子和电子的混合物中得到这个速度。这个范围如此之广，几乎在任何条件下都可以实现。

于是，由气体塌缩形成的宇宙范围就似乎包括了今天实际存在的宇宙。如果是这样，我们就不能根据伽莫夫和特勒提出的理论得到任何对演化时期的估算或者宇宙形成方式的图像。

我相信对他们的论据再提出一些反对意见还是很容易的。例如，相对论认为，在不断膨胀的宇宙中，物质粒子在膨胀过程中获得动能。但是，所获得的这份动能不包含在能量方程中；否则的话，就不再有能量守恒。这使我认为，作者关于逃逸速度的论点的推理是错误的。

（钱磊 翻译；何香涛 审稿）

Glaciological Results of the Jungfraujoch Research Party

T. P. Hughes *et al.*

Editor's Note

Max Perutz became one of the outstanding X-ray crystallographers of the period after the Second World War and won a Nobel Prize in 1962. In 1939, however, he had fled from his native Austria to avoid persecution by the German government, found himself an academic job at Cambridge and worked as a glaciologist. This Letter describes a detailed analysis of ice on a glacier at the Jungfraujoch, a prominent mountain in the Alps, south of the Swiss capital Berne. At this stage in his career, Perutz seemed to be committed to the study of ice and snow; his academic career was soon interrupted by his internment as an "enemy alien" on the Isle of Man.

LAST spring a note was published in *Nature* on the aims of our expedition to the Jungfraujoch to study glaciological problems. The working out of our results has now progressed so far that we are able to give a brief account of them.

The main part of the work was concerned with the study of the transition of snow into ice in glaciers, but the results obtained also threw considerable light on the mechanism of glacier flow.

The general scope of the work and results may be outlined as follows:

(1) *Transition of snow into glacier ice.* Specimens of firn and ice were removed from the walls of deep crevasses and artificial shafts in the interior of the glacier. Depths one hundred feet below the surface were explored. The samples were examined in a laboratory which had been excavated in stationary ice at the Jungfraujoch. The temperature of the laboratory remained at about $-4\,°C$. throughout the summer. The change in density with depth was determined at various points between the source and firn line of the Great Aletsch Glacier. From these results it was possible to draw a profile of the density distribution in the glacier and to define a transitional plane between firn and glacier ice. Usually the density increase on passing from early firn to glacier ice was found to be a gradual one. However, a transition point between the two could be distinguished at a density of about 0.84, since here the hitherto porous firn becomes impermeable to water by the freezing out of descending melt water and by a slow process of settling. Measurements indicate that the latter process is an important factor in increasing the density.

来自少女峰研究群体的冰川学成果

休斯等

编者按

第二次世界大战后，马克斯·佩鲁茨成了当时杰出的 X 射线晶体分析学家之一，并于 1962 年获得了诺贝尔奖。然而，在 1939 年，他为了躲避德国纳粹分子的迫害而逃离了自己的祖国奥地利，并在剑桥找到了一份学术性工作，开始从事冰川学研究。本文就是关于少女峰上一条冰川内冰层的详细分析。少女峰是阿尔卑斯山上的一座高峰，位于瑞士首都伯尔尼的南部。佩鲁茨这一时期的工作似乎一直致力于冰雪研究；不过不久后这段学术生涯就被迫中断了，原因是他被当作马恩岛的"异族敌人"而被扣留了起来。

去年春天，《自然》曾刊登过一条信息，内容涉及我们去少女峰考察并研究那里的冰川问题的目的。如今，我们的工作有了初步的结果，因此我们对此作了一个简短地总结。

我们的主要工作是研究冰川上由雪到冰的转化过程。不过所获得的研究结果也为我们提供了许多关于冰川流动机制方面的启发。

我们的工作内容及研究结果大致可概括如下：

（1）**由雪到冰川冰的转化**。粒雪和冰的样品均采自深层冰裂隙以及置于冰川内部的人工钻杆上。探测深度达 100 英尺。样品的分析是在少女峰固定冰层中挖掘而成的实验室内进行的。整个夏季，实验室的温度都保持在 $-4℃$ 左右。同时，还在大阿莱奇冰川发源地与永久雪线之间的多个点上测定了密度随深度变化的情况。根据上述结果可以对冰川内部的密度分布情况有个大致了解，并进而确定出粒雪与冰川冰之间的一个过渡界面。研究发现，一般情况下，从早期的粒雪到冰川冰，其密度是逐渐递增的。不过，可以认为密度值约为 0.84 时是两者之间的转折点，因为从这点开始，由于融水的减少以及缓慢的沉降作用，之前多孔渗水的粒雪变得无法使水透过。观测显示沉降作用是使其密度增大的一个重要因素。

(2) *Névé temperature*. By means of thermocouples buried at depths down to 30 m., it was found that the winter cold wave penetrated to about 15 m. depth. Below this depth it was concluded that the whole glacier was at the pressure melting temperature. The heating of the firn in summer is attributed to a downward percolation of melt water from the surface and it was found that the rate of temperature rise depended on the firn structure and its permeability to water.

(3) *Crystallographic studies*. Using the standard methods of optical crystallography, the size, shape and orientation of the crystals and the distribution of the air spaces were studied in thin sections cut from specimens which had been taken from the interior of the glacier. A statistical survey of the orientation of a large number of crystals in these sections gave evidence of the presence or absence of any preferred orientation. Although firn near the surface showed orientation due to growth in a unidirectional cold wave, this orientation was observed to disappear gradually at greater depths by the independent movement of firn grains during glacier flow and settling. Preferred orientation of crystals by plastic deformation due to shear was found in several places on glacier tongues.

(4) *Stratification bands*. Two types of bands are distinguishable in the *névé*, (*a*) dirt bands, which form on the surface and represent the boundary between the accumulation of successive years, and (*b*) ice bands, which are also of sedimentary origin; the crystal orientation of these is similar to that of pond ice. Other types of bands are to be seen in glacier tongues; of these the most important are the "blue bands" which are of tectonic origin. Bands of sedimentary origin are also found in the glacier tongues.

(5) *Glacier flow*. Fundamental differences were observed between the mechanism of flow in the *névé* region and in the ice of the tongue. Measurements of the differential movement in firn together with the crystallographic evidence showed conclusively that flow takes place by the haphazard motion of crystals or small crystal aggregates. Below the firn line, where the interlocking of crystals prevents their relative motion, the glacier flows by plastic deformation and also by laminar movement along thrust planes. Plastic deformation involves the slip of crystals along their basal glide planes and is accompanied by the growth and reorientation of crystals due to a molecular transfer across their grain boundaries.

Full accounts of the work will be published in the near future.

(**143**, 159; 1939)

T. P. Hughes: Laboratory of Physical Chemistry, Cambridge.

M. Perutz: Crystallographic Laboratory, Cambridge.

G. Seligman: The Athenaeum, London, S.W. 1.

（2）**粒雪的温度**。利用埋在冰面以下 30 米处的热电偶，我们发现冬季寒潮可以穿透到冰面以下 15 米处。而在该深度以下，整个冰川则处于压力融化温度。在夏季，粒雪的升温主要是由融水从地表向下渗透所致，而且我们发现，其温度升高的速度取决于粒雪的结构及其渗水性。

（3）**结晶学研究**。用晶体光学的标准方法，我们对采自冰川内部样本切割来的薄片中晶体的大小、形状和定向方位，以及孔隙的分布进行了研究。我们对切片中大量晶体定向方位的统计学研究，证明了是否存在优选定向的问题。我们观察到，虽然冰面附近的粒雪因在单向寒潮作用下形成而显示出了一定程度的定向性，但这种定向性会随深度的增加而逐渐消失，这是由粒雪颗粒在冰川流动作用与沉降作用下的独立运动导致的。另外，在冰舌上的某些地方还发现了由剪应力所致的塑性变形所造成的晶体的优选定向。

（4）**成层条带**。在粒雪中可以识别出两种不同类型的条带：(a）污化层带，它们形成于冰川表面，代表着多年连续沉积之间的界线；而（b）冰带，是由沉积作用形成的，它们的晶体取向类似于池冰。在冰舌中还见到了其他类型的带；其中最重要的是"蓝带"，它是构造作用形成的。在冰舌中同样也发现了沉积成因的带。

（5）**冰川的流动**。粒雪区和冰舌区的流动机制存在着根本性的差异。粒雪内部差异运动的测定结果以及结晶学证据确切地表明，其流动是由晶体的杂乱运动或小晶体的聚集引起的。在粒雪线以下，晶体间的互锁作用阻止了相对运动的发生，因而，冰川流动是由塑性变形和沿着逆冲面的层流运动造成的。塑性变形过程中，晶体会沿底滑面滑动，并且伴随着由分子沿颗粒边界迁移导致的晶体的生长和重定向。

关于该项工作的详细情况即将发表。

（孙惠南 齐红艳 翻译；李三忠 审稿）

Interpretation of Beta-Disintegration Data

H. A. Bethe *et al.*

Editor's Note

Enrico Fermi had recently proposed a theory for radioactive beta decay. As Hans Bethe and colleagues point out here, the theory disagrees with experimental data by predicting, for example, too few electrons emerging at low energies. An alternative theory, while accounting for this feature, introduces other problems. Yet a resolution, the authors suggest, may lie in supposing that Fermi's theory is correct but that experiments so far have not observed simple radioactive decays but instead mixed together decay processes leading to different nuclear states. Evidence for this idea might be found by scrutinizing the gamma rays emitted during beta decays.

FERMI'S original theory of β-decay[1] made a definite prediction as to the energy distribution of the electrons emitted from a β-active element. It was found[2] that the experimental distribution curves did not agree in shape with this prediction in the sense that the number of electrons of low energy (relative to the upper limit of the spectrum) was considerably greater in the experimental than in the theoretical curves. A modified theory was then proposed by Konopinski and Uhlenbeck (K.U.)[3] which introduced in the distribution curve another factor proportional to the square of the momentum of the emitted neutrino. This theory appeared to agree with the facts.

Further experimental evidence, however, revealed a number of facts which did not fit in well with the modified theory: (1) The shape of the observed energy spectra did not fit the K.U. law near the upper limit, but seemed there to follow the original law of Fermi, although the latter did not fit with any other part of the curve[4]; if one determined the position of the upper limit by extrapolation from the K.U. law, one obtained values that were difficult to reconcile either with the observed spectrum or with the other data on the energy balance[5]. (2) The Sargent curves (decay constant against disintegration energy) seemed to agree better with the Fermi theory[4]. (3) The probability of capturing a K-electron, as compared to that of emitting a positron, was found to be much smaller than the K.U. theory would predict, but in reasonable agreement with the Fermi theory[6]. (4) An attempt to develop the K.U. theory into a mathematically consistent scheme showed that it was, at any rate, far more complicated than that of Fermi, and no proof has as yet been given that it can be consistently carried further than to the first order of approximation[7].

We therefore investigated the view that the original theory of Fermi correctly represents the elementary law; but that the observed spectra, in so far as they belong to "allowed" transitions, do not represent the effect of a single nuclear transformation, but rather a superposition of different spectra belonging to transitions to different levels of the final

对 β 衰变数据的解释

贝特等

编者按

恩里科·费米最近提出了放射性 β 衰变理论。正如汉斯·贝特和他的同事在这里所指出的，该理论的预言与实验结果不符，例如，预言认为几乎没有出现低能电子。另一种理论虽能解决这个难题，但却引入了其他问题。本文作者给出的解答是，不妨假定费米理论是正确的，只是迄今为止的实验还没有观测到简单的放射性衰变过程，而观测到的是混在一起的导致不同核状态的衰变过程。如果仔细检查 β 衰变中放出的 γ 射线，或许可以发现支持这一观点的证据。

费米最初的 β 衰变理论 [1] 明确地预言了从 β 放射性元素发射出的电子的能量分布。但是，人们发现 [2] 实验中能量分布曲线的形状与费米理论的预言不一致：在能量分布实验曲线中，低能电子（相对于能谱上限来说）的数目明显多于理论预言值。因此，科诺平斯基与乌伦贝克 [3] 对费米理论进行了修正（修正后的理论称为 KU 理论），他们在能量分布曲线中引入了一个与所放射的中微子的动量平方成正比的因子。修正后的理论似乎与实验结果相符。

然而，进一步的实验证据揭示了很多与修正理论不符的现象：（1）所观测到的能谱形状在上限附近虽与 KU 理论不符，却与费米的原始理论一致，但费米理论并不能与曲线的其他部分相吻合 [4]。如果通过 KU 理论推出上限位置，那么人们得到的值既难于与观察到的能谱吻合，也难于与基于能量平衡 [5] 的其他一些数据吻合。（2）萨金特曲线（衰变系数依衰变能量变化的曲线）似乎与费米理论 [4] 符合得更好。（3）和放射一个正电子的概率相比，俘获一个 K 电子的概率要远小于 KU 理论的预计，但是却在合理范围内与费米理论 [6] 一致。（4）曾经有人尝试进一步发展 KU 理论，以求达到数学形式上的一致，然而这比对费米理论进行相同的尝试要复杂得多，并且到目前为止仍然没有证据可以支持比一阶近似更高的精确度 [7]。

因此，我们认为，费米的原始理论正确地表示了基本法则。但是，因为观测到的能谱属于"允许"跃迁，所以并不表示单核转变的结果，而是向末态原子核不同能级跃迁形成的不同能谱的叠加。这样就可以清楚地看出，能量分布结果包含的（相

nucleus. It is then clear that the resulting energy distribution will contain rather more electrons of low energies, compared to the upper limit of the spectrum, than a single Fermi curve. If the nucleus is left in an excited state, it must eventually lose its energy by radiation, and the crucial test for the suggested point of view is the presence of γ-rays of suitable energy and intensity from all those radioactive bodies which have "allowed" transitions and the energy spectra of which are known to be different from the simple Fermi curve. The γ-rays might in some cases be absent because the excited state of the nucleus might be a metastable isomer; but this could not be true for all such elements. The restriction to allowed transitions is necessary because in "forbidden" transitions the shape, even of a single curve, is affected by more complicated factors[8].

Interpreting from this point of view the electron spectra of ^{12}B, ^{20}F, ^{17}F, ^{13}N, ^{15}O, as given by Fowler, Delsasso and Lauritsen[9], we have estimated the energy and intensity of the γ-radiation to be expected. The results are given in the following table.

Active element	Product nucleus	Energy of γ-ray in Mv.	Number of γ-quanta per disintegration
^{12}B	^{12}C	5	0.5
^{20}F	^{20}Ne	2	0.7
^{13}N	^{13}C	0.27	0.8
^{15}O	^{15}N	0.5	0.4
^{17}F	^{17}O	0.9	0.6

No great accuracy is claimed for these results since the curve-fitting is very sensitive to the high-energy ends of the electron spectra, which are not very accurately known, and also because we have assumed that only one excited level is involved, whereas there might be more.

The presence of a γ-ray accompanying the disintegration of ^{13}N was indeed reported by Richardson[10], who gave its energy as 0.3 Mv. A γ-radiation from ^{20}F was reported by Burcham and Smith[11], and measurements of the energy of this radiation, which are being made by Bower[12], indicate a value of about 2.2 Mv. Although γ-radiations of the predicted energies from the other elements of our table have not been reported, it is interesting to notice that an energy level in ^{17}O at 0.83 Mv. is known to exist, since it is excited in a number of other nuclear reactions[11,13], and similarly an excited state of ^{12}C at 4.3 Mv. is known[13]. We are indebted to Mr. P. I. Dee for this discussion of the experimental data.

Finally, we would like to point out that, although one cannot consider the above evidence as convincing confirmation of the point of view we suggest, it is certainly incompatible with the K.U. theory, since the existence of γ-rays shows that the observed curves must be superpositions of at least two simple spectra, whereas their shapes are not such as could be represented as sums of two K.U. curves with endpoints differing by the energy of the γ-rays.

(**143**, 200-201; 1939)

H. A. Bethe: Physics Department, Cornell University.

对能谱上限来说）低能电子比一条单峰费米曲线包含的更多。如果原子核处于激发态，它最终将通过辐射来释放能量，因此可以验证我们观点的关键实验现象包括：存在从所有具有"允许"跃迁的放射性物质中放射出的具有适当强度和能量的γ射线，以及与单峰费米曲线不同的能谱。在某些情况下，γ射线也有可能不出现，因为原子核的激发态可能是一个亚稳的同质异能态，但是这种现象不可能对所有放射性元素都成立。对允许跃迁的限制是必要的，因为在"禁戒"跃迁中曲线的形状——即使是一条单峰曲线——都会受到更加复杂因素的影响 [8]。

用以上观点来解释福勒、德尔萨索以及劳里森 [9] 给出的 ^{12}B、^{20}F、^{17}F、^{13}N 和 ^{15}O 电子能谱，我们估算了γ辐射的能量和强度的期望值。下表给出了计算结果。

放射性元素	生成原子核	γ射线能量，单位兆电子伏	每次衰变辐射的γ量子数
^{12}B	^{12}C	5	0.5
^{20}F	^{20}Ne	2	0.7
^{13}N	^{13}C	0.27	0.8
^{15}O	^{15}N	0.5	0.4
^{17}F	^{17}O	0.9	0.6

我们没能给出非常精确的结果，因为曲线拟合对电子能谱的高能端非常敏感，而我们对此了解得又不够精确，并且我们在实验理论中假设只存在一个激发态，而事实上可能存在很多激发态。

理查森 [10] 曾报道过关于 ^{13}N 衰变伴随有γ射线出现的现象，并且给出γ射线的能量是 0.3 兆电子伏。伯彻姆和史密斯 [11] 报道过 ^{20}F 的γ辐射，其能量值由鲍尔 [12] 测得，约为 2.2 兆电子伏。虽然我们在表中列出的其他元素γ辐射的能量期望值还没有相关的实验报道，但有趣的是，^{17}O 的一个能级为 0.83 兆电子伏，这是已知存在的，因为它在其他很多核反应中是激发态 [11,13]，类似地，^{12}C 一个能级为 4.3 兆电子伏的激发态也是已知的 [13]。我们非常感谢迪伊先生与我们讨论了这些实验数据。

最后，需要指出的是，虽然不能将上述证据看作是对我们提出的观点的强有力证明，但是这些证据肯定与 KU 理论不符，因为γ射线的存在表明观察到的曲线一定至少是两条单峰能谱的叠加，然而它们的形状并不是两条由于γ射线能量造成其端点不同的 KU 曲线的叠加。

（王静 翻译；厉光烈 审稿）

F. Hoyle: Emmanuel College, Cambridge.

R. Peierls: University, Birmingham.

References:

1. Fermi, E., *Z. Phys.*, **88**, 161 (1934).

2. Kurie, F. N. D., Richardson, J. R., and Paxton, H. C., *Phys. Rev.*, **49**, 368(1936).

3. Konopinski, E. J., and Uhlenbeck, G. E., *Phys. Rev.*, **48**, 7 (1935).

4. Richardson, H. O. W., *Proc. Roy. Soc.*, A, **161**, 456 (1937).

5. Cockcroft, J. D., *Proc. Roy. Soc.*, A, **161**, 540 (1937).

6. Walke, H. (in the Press).

7. Fierz, M., *Helv. Phys. Acta*, **10**, 123, (1937).

8. Hoyle, F., *Proc. Roy. Soc.*, A, **166**, 249 (1938).

9. Fowler, W. A., Delsasso, L. A., and Lauritsen, C. C., *Phys. Rev.*, **49**, 569 (1936).

10. Richardson, J. R., *Phys. Rev.*, **53**, 610 (1938).

11. Burcham, W. E., and Smith, C. L., *Proc. Roy. Soc.*, A, **168**, 176 (1938).

12. Private communication.

13. Cockcroft, J. D., and Lewis, W. B., *Proc. Roy. Soc.*, A, **154**, 261 (1936).

Liquid Helium

J. F. Allen and H. Jones

Editor's Note

One of the sensations of the late 1930s was the discovery of the strange properties of liquid helium II—a form of liquid helium that appears when the ordinary material is cooled below 2.19K. The Royal Society Mond Laboratory was established in the early 1930s at the Cavendish Laboratory in Cambridge by Ernest Rutherford, who planned that it should be the workplace of Pyotr Kapitza. By 1939, however, when this article appeared, Kapitza had returned to Moscow, taking with him much of the electromagnetic equipment the Mond Laboratory had contained. One striking feature of the measurement described in this article is that the viscosity of liquid helium falls sharply as it is converted into helium II. The current explanation is that liquid helium II owes its distinctive properties to quantum mechanics and that the bulk of the liquid exists in the form of a "Bose-Einstein condensate"—essentially the liquid moves as an integrated whole.

THE properties of liquid helium can best be considered under two headings: (a) properties in thermal equilibrium, (b) transport effects. The equilibrium properties, which have been the subject of many careful investigations in Leyden and elsewhere, may be regarded as fairly well established. These include the determination of the specific heat for different temperatures, the variation of density with temperature at different constant pressures, and the relation of the saturated vapour pressure to the absolute temperature scale. The investigations of transport effects such as the flow of the liquid through tubes, heat conductivity and associated effects are still in an early stage of development, and no clear understanding of these phenomena has yet been reached. The subject was discussed at a meeting following the International Refrigeration Congress in July and also during the Cambridge meeting of the British Association. In this article we shall confine our attention largely to the interesting newly discovered transport effects, and give an account of recent experiments the results of which at present seem to find general acceptance.

Equilibrium Properties of Liquid Helium

Helium at atmospheric pressure liquefies at $4.22°$K.; the critical temperature is $5.2°$K. Generally speaking, the temperature range over which the properties of liquid helium have been measured extends only down to $1°$K., since this is the lowest temperature conveniently reached by lowering the vapour pressure over the surface of the liquid. At $2.19°$K. under its own vapour pressure, liquid helium undergoes a remarkable transformation. As the liquid is cooled through $2.19°$K., the specific heat jumps suddenly from a value of 0.4 cal. per gm. per degree to more than 5 cal. per gm. per degree,

液 氦

艾伦，琼斯

编者按

20 世纪 30 年代末的轰动事件之一，就是发现了液氦 II（普通液氦冷却到 2.19 K 以下出现的一种形式的液氦）的奇特性质。20 世纪 30 年代初，欧内斯特·卢瑟福在剑桥卡文迪什实验室建立了英国皇家学会蒙德实验室，他希望彼得·卡皮查教授能留在这个实验室工作。不过，到 1939 年这篇文章问世时，卡皮查已经携带蒙德实验室中的很多电磁学设备返回了莫斯科。本文所描述的液氦的一个显著的特性是，液氦在转化为氦 II 时黏度会迅速下降。目前利用量子力学解释氦 II 的这种独特性质，即液体的整体是以"玻色－爱因斯坦凝聚"形态存在——从本质上讲，就是液体作为一个整体在移动。

液氦的性质最好可以从以下两个方面来考虑：(a) 热平衡性质，(b) 输运效应。经过莱顿和其他实验室大量仔细的研究，平衡性质已得到充分证实，其中包括不同温度下比热的确定、不同恒压下密度随温度变化的关系、以及饱和蒸气压与绝对温标的关系。而有关输运效应的研究尚处在初级阶段，诸如液体在管中的流动、热导率及相关效应等，人们对于这些现象还没有一个清晰的认识。在七月国际制冷学大会之后的一次会议，以及在英国科协的剑桥会议上，人们对液氦的输运效应进行了讨论。本文中，我们将主要讨论这个新发现的有趣的输运效应，并介绍一些目前看来结果已获得公认的最新实验。

液氦的平衡性质

常压下，氦在温度为 4.22 K 时液化；临界温度为 5.2 K。一般来说，能观测液氦性质的温度下限仅能达到 1 K，因为这是用降低液面蒸气压的方法所能顺利实现的最低温度。在温度为 2.19 K 以及自身蒸气压下，液氦发生了显著的转变。当液氦被冷却至温度为 2.19 K 时，比热从 0.4 Cal/(g·K) 突跃到 5 Cal/(g·K) 以上，之后以近于 T^5 快速下降。最近，西蒙曾指出，在通过铁铵矾绝热退磁产生的极低温度

thereafter falling rapidly, approximately as T^5. Simon has recently shown that at very low temperatures (0.02°-0.05°K.) produced by adiabatic demagnetization of iron ammonium alum, the specific heat of liquid helium varies as T^3.

The transformation at 2.19°K. has also a remarkable effect on the expansion coefficient of liquid helium. Above that temperature it is positive, while below it is negative, although there is no discontinuity in the value of the density itself at 2.19°K.

Phase transformations of the type that liquid helium undergoes at 2.19°K. are known in other branches of physics; for example, the Curie-point transformation of a ferromagnetic, the order-disorder transformation of certain alloys, and the transition between the superconductive and the normal state of a metal. The temperature of the transformation in liquid helium is known as the λ-point, a name introduced by Ehrenfest. The modification of the liquid below the λ-point is generally referred to as helium II, that above the λ-point as helium I.

Liquid helium at 1°K. can be solidified under an external pressure of 25 atmospheres. At higher temperatures, greater pressures are required to produce the solid. The properties of liquid helium I are such as would be expected of an ordinary liquid of very low boiling point. It is far otherwise with liquid helium II. In the first place, it is an immediate inference from the phase diagram that liquid helium II under its own vapour pressure remains liquid at absolute zero, for even in the neighbourhood of 1°K. the boundary line between the solid and liquid phases tends to become parallel with the temperature axis at a pressure of approximately 25 atmospheres. Since dp/dt (the slope of the boundary line) approaches zero as the temperature is lowered, and since the volume change, Δv, is not zero, it follows from Clapeyron's equation $dp/dt = \Delta s / \Delta v$, that Δs, the change in entropy on passing from liquid to solid, also approaches zero. There can thus exist the paradoxical situation of a liquid with zero entropy. On this account the possibility has been considered by several investigators that condensed helium at absolute zero has a space-ordered structure, and that the λ-point is of the nature of an order-disorder transformation.

An experimental investigation of this point has been carried out by Keesom and Taconis. They examined the reflection of X-rays in a column of liquid helium II at about 1.6°K., as well as in helium above the λ-point. No essential difference between the reflections in the two cases could be observed. Confirmation of the space-ordered theory, therefore, is still lacking, although it should be borne in mind that at 1.6°K. an appreciable degree of disorder would in any event be expected.

We may mention here that F. London, in a very interesting letter to *Nature*, has recalled a prediction by Einstein that a perfect Bose gas at sufficiently low temperatures should show a discontinuity in the temperature derivative of the specific heat. Applying Einstein's formula to liquid helium, London shows that the discontinuity would occur at 3.09°K. Although Einstein's discontinuity is only in the temperature derivative of the specific heat,

（0.02 K ~ 0.05 K）下，液氦的比热随 T^3 变化。

温度为 2.19 K 时的这一转变对液氦的膨胀系数也有明显的影响。在该温度以上，膨胀系数为正，而在该温度以下则为负，但液氦的密度本身在温度为 2.19 K 时并没有出现不连续性。

类似液氦在温度为 2.19 K 时发生相变的情况在物理学其他分支中也遇到过；如，在居里点的铁磁转变、某些合金的有序–无序转变、以及金属超导态与正常态的转变。液氦的相变温度被称为 λ 点，这是埃伦费斯特给它命的名。通常将低于 λ 点的液氦相称为氦 II，高于 λ 点的称为氦 I。

在温度为 1 K 下，外加 25 个大气压可使液氦固化。在较高温度时，则需要加更大的外压来使其固化。液氦 I 的性质正如预期所料，即与具有极低沸点的普通液体一样，而液氦 II 的性质则大不相同。首先，从相图上可以直接推断出，处于自身蒸汽压下的液氦 II 在绝对零度时仍保持液态，因为大约 25 个大气压时，甚至在 1 K 附近，固相与液相的边界线与温度轴趋于平行。由于温度降低时边界线的斜率 dp/dt 趋近于零，而体积的变化量 Δv 不是零，利用克拉珀龙方程 $dp/dt = \Delta s/\Delta v$ 可以得到，其从液相到固相的熵变 Δs 也趋近于零。因此，可能存在一种具有零熵的奇怪液体。由于这个原因，很多研究者认为，可能凝聚态氦在绝对零度时具有空间有序结构，而 λ 点则是一种有序–无序转变的本质体现。

凯索姆和塔康尼斯已对这点做了实验研究。他们考察了温度约为 1.6 K 时一段液氦 II 液柱和高于 λ 点时一段液氦 I 液柱的 X 射线反射。然而并没有观测到这两种情况的反射有什么本质不同。因此，关于空间有序理论的确证仍然不足，不过应该清楚的是，在温度 1.6 K 时，应该预期到总会有可观的无序度出现。

本文中我们可以提一下，伦敦在致《自然》的一封有趣的信中回忆到，爱因斯坦曾做过一个预言，即理想玻色气体在温度足够低时，其比热对温度的导数应该是不连续的。伦敦将爱因斯坦给出的公式应用于液氦，推断出这个不连续点应该出现在 3.09 K。尽管爱因斯坦提出的不连续性只是关于比热对温度的导数而非比热本身，

not in the specific heat itself, London suggests that there may be some connexion with the λ-point of liquid helium. The advantage of such a theory of the λ-point is that it appears not to necessitate a space-ordered structure for the liquid at low temperatures.

Transport Effects

Flow Phenomena. Experiments designed to measure the viscosity of liquid helium II have led to the most surprising and apparently contradictory results. The first attempt in this direction was made at Toronto by Burton and Misener, who measured the damping of an oscillating cylinder immersed in the liquid. The value for the viscosity was found to drop suddenly at the λ-point from approximately 10^{-4} C.G.S. units for helium I to 10^{-5} C.G.S. units for helium II. Recent and more precise measurements by the similar method of an oscillating disk, made by MacWood at Leyden, give values varying from 3×10^{-5} C.G.S. units for helium II just below the λ-point to 2×10^{-6} C.G.S. units at 1.1°K. Liquid helium II thus appears to be very much less effective in damping the motion of a body immersed in it than helium gas at room temperature.

Attempts to measure the viscosity of helium II by measuring the rate of flow through a tube were first made by Kapitza* and by Allen and Misener in the Royal Society Mond Laboratory at Cambridge. On account of the anticipated low viscosity, the latter used very narrow tubes to lessen the rate of flow, with the extraordinary result that the rate of flow was far in excess of what would occur in a liquid of viscosity 10^{-5} C.G.S. units. Moreover, the velocity of flow did not vary linearly with the pressure head. Kapitza found a velocity proportional to the square root of the pressure head, and interpreted this as evidence that the flow was turbulent. He gave a value of 10^{-9} C.G.S. units as an upper limit to the viscosity of helium II. Giauque in California has also observed the flow of helium II through an annular tube and has obtained a temperature variation of viscosity of from 10^{-6} to 10^{-8} C.G.S. units. Allen and Misener endeavoured to reduce the velocity of flow by using finer capillaries to obtain more nearly the condition for stream-line flow, and found that the rate of flow varied as a power of the pressure head of even less than one half. It was found that the dependence of velocity on the pressure head decreased with decreasing capillary size. For glass capillaries of 0.0015 cm. radius, it was found that the velocity varied as the 1/6 power of the pressure, whilst for capillaries of 5×10^{-5} cm. in radius, obtained by packing a metal tube with parallel wires and then drawing the tube through dies, the velocity became absolutely independent of the driving pressure. In the latter case, the velocity increased very rapidly with decreasing temperature and reached a value of 20 cm. per second at 1.1°K. The flow also appears to be non-classical in the case of the variation of length of the capillary, since a variation of length by a factor of 70 produced only a fourfold change in the velocity.

On the other hand, experiments made by Burton in Toronto showed that with relatively wide and short tubes and rapid flow, the velocity is linearly proportional to the pressure

---

* Actually Kapitza used the essentially similar method of radial flow between two parallel plates with small separation.

486

伦敦还是认为这与液氦的 λ 点可能会有某种关联。这样一种 λ 点理论的优势在于，在低温下似乎并不要求液氦必须具有空间有序结构。

输运效应

流动现象。为测定液氦 II 黏度而设计的实验得到了令人非常惊讶且明显矛盾的结果。多伦多大学的伯顿和麦色纳在这个研究方向上最先进行了尝试，他们测定了浸在液氦中的振动圆筒的阻尼。研究发现，黏度值在 λ 点突然下降，从氦 I 的大约 10^{-4} 单位（厘米克秒制）迅速变到氦 II 的 10^{-5} 单位（厘米克秒制）。最近，麦克伍德在莱顿用类似的方法用振动盘进行了更精确的测量，得到的结果是氦 II 的黏度值从稍低于 λ 点时的 3×10^{-5} 单位（厘米克秒制）变到了 1.1 K 时的 2×10^{-6} 单位（厘米克秒制）。由此看来，在阻止浸入其中的物体的运动方面，液氦 II 的能力比室温下的氦气还要差很多。

卡皮查[*]和英国剑桥皇家学会蒙德实验室的艾伦与麦色纳率先进行了另一种尝试，通过测量氦 II 流经管子的速率来测定其黏度。由于预先考虑到氦 II 的低黏度，后者使用了非常细的管子以降低流速。实验结果非常出人意料，氦 II 的流速大大超过了黏度为 10^{-5} 单位（厘米克秒制）的液体应有的流速。此外，流速并不随着压位差的变化而线性变化。卡皮查发现，流速正比于压位差的平方根，他认为这是湍流的证据。他给出了氦 II 黏度的上限数值为 10^{-9} 单位（厘米克秒制）。加利福尼亚的吉奥克观测了氦 II 通过环形管的流动，得到黏度随温度变化的范围是从 10^{-6} 单位到 10^{-8} 单位（厘米克秒制）。艾伦和麦色纳使用更细的毛细管来尽量降低氦 II 的流速，使之更接近于流线流的条件，研究发现流速随着压位差的不到 1/2 次幂而变化。而且，毛细管越细，速度对于压位差的依赖性越小。对于半径为 0.0015 厘米的玻璃毛细管来说，速度随压力的 1/6 次幂变化，而在使用半径为 5×10^{-5} 厘米的毛细管（用平行金属丝将一根金属管子填充，再用一系列拉丝模把管子拉出，即可制得）时，速度变得与驱动压完全无关了。在后一种情况下，速度随着温度降低而非常迅速地增加，并在温度为 1.1 K 时达到 20 厘米 / 秒。流速随毛细管长度的变化也表现为非经典的，因为长度变化了 70 倍，而速度只变化了 4 倍。

另一方面，多伦多大学的伯顿所进行的实验指出，在使用相对粗而短的管子和更快的流速时，速度正比于压位差，并且由此确定的黏度值与通过振动盘阻尼方

---

[*] 实际上，卡皮查使用一种本质上类似的方法，即两个近距离平行盘之间的径向流。

head, and that the viscosity so determined agrees with the value obtained by the damping of oscillating disks. The anomalous features appear, therefore, when the flow takes place through very long and fine capillaries (radii less than 10^{-3} cm.).

A little light is thrown on these curious results by the experiments of Mendelssohn and Daunt on the creep of liquid helium II in the form of mobile films over solid surfaces. If an open vessel be partially immersed in liquid helium II, it was observed that liquid gradually collected in the vessel until the liquid levels in vessel and bath were coincident. The rate of filling increased rapidly with lowering temperature. The mechanism was found to consist not in evaporation and recon-densation, but in the transfer of liquid by means of surface films. At all temperatures in helium II the rate of transfer of liquid by means of the surface films was found to be independent of the difference in level. Both the thickness and the velocity of propagation of a film have been measured. The thickness is of order 5×10^{-6} cm. and the velocity increases from zero at the λ-point to 20 cm. per second at 1°K., which gives a rate of transfer of about 10^{-4} cubic centimeters per second per centimeter width of film. If films are formed above the λ-point, that is, by helium I, they are not more than 10^{-7} cm. thick.

A rough synthesis of the experimental results on flow of helium II can be attempted as follows. In flow through a tube, two distinct but by no means separate processes are taking place*: (a) the normal flow of a fluid with a viscosity (of order 10^{-4} C.G.S. units) which increases with decreasing temperature, and (b) creep along the inside walls of the tube by means of a surface film (of thickness of the order of 5×10^{-6} cm.), the velocity of which increases rapidly with decreasing temperature. For wide tubes, effect (a) predominates and the flow approximates to that of a normal viscous fluid. As the size of the capillary decreases, effect (b) becomes more pronounced, whilst for capillaries less than 10^{-4} cm. in radius, effect (a) becomes negligible and the quantity of liquid flowing per second is directly proportional to the circumference of the capillary.

Heat Conduction. The first experiments in the transport of heat through liquid helium II were made by Rollin and Keesom; their observations showed that helium II was a most efficient agent for the transport of heat, being far more effective than copper at the same temperature. It was observed later by Allen, Peierls and Uddin, and shown more convincingly by Keesom and Saris, that the rate of heat transport was not proportional to the temperature gradient. It is thus impossible to measure a true thermal conductivity for the liquid. The rate of heat transport is greater the smaller the gradient, and reaches a value corresponding to a conductivity several thousand times as great as that of copper at room temperature with gradients of the order of 10^{-5} of a degree per cm. For a given gradient the "conductivity" increases rapidly below the λ-point to a maximum at 2.0°K. and then falls again. Simon and Pickard of Oxford have found that the anomalously high conductivity disappears at the temperature at which the specific heat becomes normal.

---

* To be published shortly by J. F. Allen and A. D. Misener.

法得到的数值是一致的。由此看来，当氦 II 流经很长且很细的毛细管（半径小于 10^{-3} 厘米）时，才会出现反常特性。

门德尔松和当特进行了液氦 II 以流动膜形式沿固体表面爬行的实验，这为理解上述异常的结果带来了一线希望。如果将一端开口的空容器的底部部分地浸入液氦 II 之中，就可以观察到液体沿着容器壁逐渐流于容器中，直到容器内外液面持平。液体流进容器的速度随着温度降低而迅速加快。目前已经知道，这一行为的机制并非蒸发与再凝结，而是液体以表面膜的形式迁移。研究还发现，在任何温度下，氦 II 以表面膜形式迁移的速度都与液面高度差无关。现在已经测定了膜的厚度与其传播速度。厚度约为 5×10^{-6} 厘米的数量级，而传播速度则由 λ 点的静止不动，增大到 1K 时的 20 厘米 / 秒，从而给出每厘米膜宽度的迁移速率大约为 10^{-4} 立方厘米 / 秒。如果膜是在 λ 点以上形成的，即由氦 I 形成，那么其厚度不会超过 10^{-7} 厘米。

下面试着对关于氦 II 流动的实验结果做一大致的综述。在液氦流经管子的过程中，有两个截然不同却不可分割的过程在发生[*]：(a) 流体的正常流，黏度（为 10^{-4} 单位（厘米克秒制）的数量级）随着温度降低而增加；(b) 流体以表面膜（其厚度为 5×10^{-6} 厘米的数量级）方式沿着管内壁爬行，流体的流动速度随着温度降低而快速增大。对于粗管子来说，以 (a) 效应为主，流动近似为普通黏性流体的流动。随着毛细管尺寸减小，(b) 效应变得越来越显著，对于半径小于 10^{-4} 厘米的毛细管来说，效应 (a) 变得可以忽略，流动速度随着温度降低而增大，而每秒液体的流量与毛细管的周长成正比。

热传导。 罗林和凯索姆最早进行了液氦 II 的热输运实验；他们的实验观测表明，氦 II 是一种极为高效的热输运介质，比同温度下的铜还要高效很多。后来艾伦、佩尔斯和乌丁观测到，且经凯索姆和萨里斯令人信服地证明，热输运速率并不与温度梯度成比例。因此，不可能测得液体的真实热导率。热传递速率越大，温度梯度就越小且这个热传递速率相当于室温下，当温度梯度为 10^{-5} 厘米数量级时铜的热导率的几千倍。对于给定的温度梯度，"热导率"在 λ 点以下快速增大，在温度为 2.0 K 时达到最大值，此后再次减小。牛津大学的西蒙和皮卡德发现，反常高热导率出现在比热变为正常时的温度下。

---

[*] 艾伦和麦色纳将要发表的文章。

Fountain Effect. The fountain effect, which was discovered in the Mond Laboratory, shows in the most striking manner the fundamental difference between helium II and any other known liquid. In its simplest form, the effect may be described as follows. A tube is partly immersed in helium II; the lower end of the tube is a capillary; both ends are open and an arrangement is made to heat the liquid in the upper part. A steady flow of heat is thereby maintained down the capillary. Under these conditions, it is observed that the liquid inside the tube rises above the level outside, showing the existence of a pressure in the reverse direction to the heat flow. A more spectacular demonstration can be given by placing powder in the lower half of the immersed tube through which the heat flows. To produce the heat current in this case, it is sufficient to shine light on the powder. With this arrangement the liquid may be made to rise right out of the tube, and in fact a steady "fountain" several centimeters in height can easily be produced.

Quantitative measurements on the magnitude of the reaction pressure are very incomplete. Some data, however, are available from measurements* on the reaction to heat flowing in helium II through a tube filled with powder particles. The reaction pressure was found to attain a maximum value of approximately half an atmosphere for a gradient of $1°$ per cm. at $1.7°K$. The value of the heat conductivity through the powder-filled tube was lower by a factor of a hundred than that through a smooth capillary of the same open cross-section. It seems, therefore, that the very large conductivity observed for helium II when the heat flows through smooth tubes is caused by violent convection currents which are set up by the reaction mechanism. This might be the reason for the apparent variation of conductivity with temperature gradient.

A complete understanding of the fountain effect must naturally await a satisfactory theory of the constitution of liquid helium II. However, a few interesting deductions can be made. In the first place, in the simple arrangement described above, the force holding the liquid above the bath level can only come from some form of interaction of the liquid with the walls of the tube or the attached heating wire. No other support is available, and the vapour pressure above the bath and inside the tube are sensibly the same. Secondly, this interaction must result in a downward thrust on the tube equal to the weight of liquid above the bath level. From the atomic point of view, this means that the interacting atoms are steadily transferring momentum in a downward direction to the tube, just as the thrust on the walls of a vessel containing gas implies that the atoms steadily lose momentum to the walls as they are reflected. This has the interesting consequence that the main heat transport in helium II at these temperatures (below $2.19°K$.) cannot be due to the propagation of elastic waves as in ordinary liquids and solids, since elastic waves do not carry momentum.

Many and varied hypotheses have been made concerning the constitution of helium II. Michels, Bijl and de Boer and the present authors independently suggested that certain atoms which have more than the average energy in helium II have, as well, a larger than

---

* Proc. Cam. Phil. Soc. (in the Press).

喷泉效应。蒙德实验室发现了液氦 II 的喷泉效应，这一效应以非常惊人的方式表明了液氦 II 与其他任何一种已知液体的根本差别。这种喷泉效应最简单的形式可以描述如下：将一根管子部分浸入氦 II 中；管的下端为毛细管；两端都是开口的，并用一种装置给上半部分中的液体加热。由此保持着沿毛细管向下的热稳流。在此条件下，可以观测到管内液体上升到高于外部液面的位置，这表明在热流的相反方向存在着某种压力。关于喷泉效应更精彩的演示是，将一些粉末置于浸入管的下半部分，即有热流动的那一段。在这种条件下，为产生热流，只要将光照射于粉末之上就可以了。通过上述操作可以使液体直接上升到管口外，实际上很容易产生几厘米高的稳定"喷泉"。

对于反作用压力大小的定量测量还很不完善。不过，通过测定*氦 II 经过装满粉末颗粒的管子的热流的反作用力，已经得到一些数据。发现反作用压力，在温度为 1.7 K、温度梯度为每厘米 1 K 时反作用压力达到最大值，约为大气压的一半。与流经具有相同开口横截面的光滑毛细管相比，氦 II 流经装满粉末的管子的热导率数值要低一百倍。由此看来，热流经光滑管时，人们所观测到的氦 II 具有的极高热导率，是由反作用机制引起强烈对流所造成的。这可能就是热导率随温度梯度明显变化的原因。

当然，要完全理解喷泉效应，有待于一个令人满意的液氦 II 组成理论的出现。不过，现在已经可以对此作出一些有趣的推论。首先，在上面所描述的简单装置中，使管内液体保持在外部液池液面之上的力，只能来自于某种形式的相互作用，要么是液体与管壁之间，要么是液体与附着的加热导线之间。除此再没有其他支撑的可能，而且管内与液池上方的蒸气压也明显是相等的。其次，这种相互作用必然会在管壁上产生一个向下的推力，其大小等于高于液池液面之上的液体的重量。从原子层面来看，这意味着，参与相互作用的原子在向下的方向上向管壁稳定地传递着动量，就像盛有气体的容器器壁上所受的推力，即意味着原子在被反弹的过程中稳定地向器壁转移着动量。由此得到的有趣的结论是，在这些温度（低于 2.19 K）下，液氦 II 中的主要热输运不是像在普通液体或固体中那样归结为弹性波的传播，因为弹性波并不携带动量。

关于氦 II 的组合，目前已提出了各式各样的假说。米歇尔斯、比尔、德布尔以及本文作者各自独立地提出，氦 II 中某些具有高于平均能量的原子，在液体中也具

---

*《剑桥哲学学会会刊》（正在印刷中）。

average mean free path inside the liquid, and that heat flow represents a drift of these moving or "excited" atoms. Later, this idea of energetic particles moving through the unexcited or "condensed" atoms was developed by Tisza to include a theory of flow. This theory has not yet reached a quantitative stage, but has proved interesting and suggestive.

Note added in proof: Since this article was written, F. London has published (*Phys. Rev.*, 54, 947; 1938) an enlargement of the theory which he based on the consideration that helium at low temperatures exhibited Bose-Einstein condensation phenomena. His theoretical interpretation of the behaviour of liquid helium II appears to be quite in accordance with the experimental deductions given above, particularly with regard to the properties of flow of both heat and liquid.

(**143**, 227-230; 1939)

J. F. Allen: Royal Society Mond Laboratory.

H. Jones: Imperial College, London.

有较大的平均自由程,而热流则体现了这些运动的或"受激发的"原子的漂移。后来,这一具有活力的粒子在未激发的或"凝聚的"原子中运动的观点被蒂萨发展,并包含了流动理论。该理论尚未达到定量的程度,但已被证明是引人关注和有启发性的。

附加说明:自本文写就以后,伦敦考虑了氦在低温下出现玻色–爱因斯坦凝聚现象而发表了一篇文章对这一理论作了进一步的扩充(《物理学评论》,第 54 卷,第 947 页;1938 年)。他对于液氦 II 行为的理论解释,尤其是关于热和液体的流动性质,似乎与上面所给出的实验推论颇为吻合。

(王耀杨 翻译;陶宏杰 审稿)

Disintegration of Uranium by Neutrons: a New Type of Nuclear Reaction

L. Meitner and O. R. Frisch

Editor's Note

This is the first record in *Nature* referring to the stimulated disintegration of uranium nuclei by neutrons. Lise Meitner, an Austrian, had worked in Berlin with Otto Hahn until she was expelled in 1938 because of the German government's policy on people of Jewish origin. Otto Frisch, then working at Niels Bohr's institute in Copenhagen, was Meitner's nephew. The fission of uranium nuclei is of course the basis on which the first nuclear weapons were constructed.

ON bombarding uranium with neutrons, Fermi and collaborators[1] found that at least four radioactive substances were produced, to two of which atomic numbers larger than 92 were ascribed. Further investigations[2] demonstrated the existence of at least nine radioactive periods, six of which were assigned to elements beyond uranium, and nuclear isomerism had to be assumed in order to account for their chemical behaviour together with their genetic relations.

In making chemical assignments, it was always assumed that these radioactive bodies had atomic numbers near that of the element bombarded, since only particles with one or two charges were known to be emitted from nuclei. A body, for example, with similar properties to those of osmium was assumed to be eka-osmium ($Z = 94$) rather than osmium ($Z = 76$) or ruthenium ($Z = 44$).

Following up an observation of Curie and Savitch[3], Hahn and Strassmann[4] found that a group of at least three radioactive bodies, formed from uranium under neutron bombardment, were chemically similar to barium and, therefore, presumably isotopic with radium. Further investigation[5], however, showed that it was impossible to separate these bodies from barium (although mesothorium, an isotope of radium, was readily separated in the same experiment), so that Hahn and Strassmann were forced to conclude that *isotopes of barium ($Z = 56$) are formed as a consequence of the bombardment of uranium ($Z = 92$) with neutrons.*

At first sight, this result seems very hard to understand. The formation of elements much below uranium has been considered before, but was always rejected for physical reasons, so long as the chemical evidence was not entirely clear cut. The emission, within a short time, of a large number of charged particles may be regarded as excluded by the small penetrability of the "Coulomb barrier", indicated by Gamov's theory of alpha decay.

由中子引起的铀衰变：一类新型核反应

迈特纳，弗里施

编者按

这是《自然》中最早谈及铀核受中子激发而产生衰变的文章。奥地利学者莉泽·迈特纳曾在柏林与奥托·哈恩一起工作至 1938 年，后因德国政府的反犹政策而被驱逐。奥托·弗里施是迈特纳的侄子，当时在哥本哈根的尼尔斯·玻尔的研究机构中工作。当然，最早的核武器就是基于铀核裂变制造而成的。

费米及其合作者发现 [1]，用中子轰击铀核以后，至少会产生出四种放射性物质，其中两种放射性物质的原子序数均大于 92。通过进一步的研究 [2] 表明，事实上至少存在九种放射周期，其中有六种属于铀后面的元素，为了解释它们的化学行为及其衍生关系，必须假定存在核同质异能性。

人们在进行化学研究时，经常会假定这些放射性物质的原子序数与被轰击元素的原子序数相近，因为据目前所知，核受轰击后只会发射出带一个或两个电荷的粒子。例如，轰击铀核得到的类似于锇的化学性质的物质，被假定为类锇（$Z = 94$）而不是锇（$Z = 76$）或者钌（$Z = 44$）。

沿着居里和萨维奇 [3] 的观测结果继续探究下去，哈恩和施特拉斯曼 [4] 发现，中子轰击铀核时至少能形成三种放射性物质，它们的化学性质与钡类似，因而推测其为镭的同位素。然而进一步的研究显示 [5]，这些放射性物质几乎不能与钡分离（然而在相同的实验中，新钍——一种镭的同位素——很容易与钡分离），因此哈恩和施特拉斯曼被迫得出这样的结论：**用中子轰击铀（$Z = 92$）核的结果是产生了钡（$Z = 56$）的同位素。**

乍看起来，这个实验结果似乎让人很难理解。因为人们以前轰击铀核时，也曾考虑过存在比铀原子序数小很多的元素形成，但是在化学证据尚未完全明晰之前，这种想法总是因为一些物理原因而被排除。伽莫夫的 α 衰变理论指出，由于穿透"库仑势垒"的可能性极小，所以在短时间内要发射出大量带电微粒是不可能的。

On the basis, however, of present ideas about the behaviour of heavy nuclei[6], an entirely different and essentially classical picture of these new disintegration processes suggests itself. On account of their close packing and strong energy exchange, the particles in a heavy nucleus would be expected to move in a collective way which has some resemblance to the movement of a liquid drop. If the movement is made sufficiently violet by adding energy, such a drop may divide itself into two smaller drops.

In the discussion of the energies involved in the deformation of nuclei, the concept of surface tension of nuclear matter has been used[7] and its value has been estimated from simple considerations regarding nuclear forces. It must be remembered, however, that the surface tension of a charged droplet is diminished by its charge, and a rough estimate shows that the surface tension of nuclei, decreasing with increasing nuclear charge, may become zero for atomic numbers of the order of 100.

It seems therefore possible that the uranium nucleus has only small stability of form, and may, after neutron capture, divide itself into two nuclei of roughly equal size (the precise ratio of sizes depending on finer structural features and perhaps partly on chance). These two nuclei will repel each other and should gain a total kinetic energy of c. 200 Mev., as calculated from nuclear radius and charge. This amount of energy may actually be expected to be available from the difference in packing fraction between uranium and the elements in the middle of the periodic system. The whole "fission" process can thus be described in an essentially classical way, without having to consider quantum-mechanical "tunnel effects", which would actually be extremely small, on account of the large masses involved.

After division, the high neutron/proton ratio of uranium will tend to readjust itself by beta decay to the lower value suitable for lighter elements. Probably each part will thus give rise to a chain of disintegrations. If one of the parts is an isotope of barium[5], the other will be krypton ($Z = 92-56$), which might decay through rubidium, strontium and yttrium to zirconium. Perhaps one or two of the supposed barium-lanthanum-cerium chains are then actually strontium-yttrium-zirconium chains.

It is possible[5], and seems to us rather probable, that the periods which have been ascribed to elements beyond uranium are also due to light elements. From the chemical evidence, the two short periods (10 sec. and 40 sec.) so far ascribed to ^{239}U might be masurium isotopes ($Z = 43$) decaying through ruthenium, rhodium, palladium and silver into cadmium.

In all these cases it might not be necessary to assume nuclear isomerism; but the different radioactive periods belonging to the same chemical element may then be attributed to different isotopes of this element, since varying proportions of neutrons may be given to the two parts of the uranium nucleus.

不过，以目前关于重核 [6] 行为的观点为基础，对于这种新型核衰变过程，我们想到了一种完全不同、本质上又很经典的假设。它的大致内容如下：由于紧密堆积和强烈的能量交换，预期重核中的微粒会以整体方式运动，有些类似于液滴的运动。如果外加的能量能使这种运动变得足够剧烈，这个"液滴"就可能会分裂为两个较小的部分。

在讨论核变形过程中所涉及的能量问题时，需要用到核物质表面张力的概念 [7]，但人们只是在考虑核力存在的前提下估算过其数值。不过必须记住，带电微滴的表面张力因其所带的电荷而减小，并且核的表面张力随着核电荷的增加而减小，粗略的估计显示，当原子序数达到 100 时核的表面张力可能会减为零。

由此看来，铀核也许只具有较小的稳定性，因为其在俘获中子后可能会分裂为大小基本相同的两个核（两部分大小的精确比例取决于精细结构的特征，可能还有一部分偶然因素）。这两个核将彼此推斥，根据核半径与电荷进行计算，这两个核应该会获得约为 200 兆电子伏的总动能。似乎可以预期，这一能量值实际上可以利用铀与周期表中部元素的敛集率的差别计算得到。由于涉及的物质质量较大，所以相应的量子力学中的"隧道效应"产生的影响小到可以忽略不计，因此整个"裂变"过程可以使用经典的方式来描述。

具有高中子质子比的铀核分裂成两个新核以后，倾向于再进行 β 衰变，以使其调整到适合于较轻元素的较小比值。每个新核都可能会引起一条衰变反应链。如果其中一部分是钡 [5] 的同位素，另外一部分就将是氪（$Z = 92-56$）的同位素，氪可以经由铷、锶和钇衰变链一直衰变到锆。也许有一条或两条衰变链，我们假定其可能会发生钡－镧－铈衰变，而实际上发生的却是锶－钇－锆衰变。

有可能 [5]，并且在我们看来非常有可能的是，那些曾被归结为铀以后元素的放射周期也是轻元素的。根据化学证据，到目前为止被归结为铀－239 的两个短的放射周期（12 秒和 40 秒）可能来源于锝的同位素（$Z = 43$），其经钌、铑、钯和银衰变链衰变到镉。

在上述所有情况中，都不必假定存在核同质异能性；至于属于相同元素的不同放射周期则可以归因于该元素具有不同的同位素，因为铀核分裂形成的两部分可以获得各种不同比例的中子。

By bombarding thorium with neutrons, activities are obtained which have been ascribed to radium and actinium isotopes[8]. Some of these periods are approximately equal to periods of barium and lanthanum isotopes[5] resulting from the bombardment of uranium. We should therefore like to suggest that these periods are due to a "fission" of thorium which is like that of uranium and results partly in the same products. Of course, it would be especially interesting if one could obtain one of these products from a light element, for example, by means of neutron capture.

It might be mentioned that the body with half-life 24 min.[2] which was chemically identified with uranium is probably really ^{239}U, and goes over into an eka-rhenium which appears inactive but may decay slowly, probably with emission of alpha particles. (From inspection of the natural radioactive elements, ^{239}U cannot be expected to give more than one or two beta decays; the long chain of observed decays has always puzzled us.) The formation of this body is a typical resonance process[9]; the compound state must have a life-time a million times longer than the time it would take the nucleus to divide itself. Perhaps this state corresponds to some highly symmetrical type of motion of nuclear matter which does not favour "fission" of the nucleus.

(**143**, 239-240; 1939)

Lise Meitner: Physical Institute, Academy of Sciences, Stockholm.

O. R. Frisch: Institute of Theoretical Physics, University, Copenhagen, Jan. 16.

References:

1. Fermi. E., Amaldi, F., d' Agostino, O., Rasetti, F., and Segrè, E. *Proc. Roy. Soc.*, A, **146**, 483 (1934).

2. See Meitner, L., Hahn, O., and Strassmann, F., *Z. Phys.*, **106**, 249 (1937).

3. Curie, I., and Savitch, P., *C.R.*, **206**, 906, 1643 (1938).

4. Hahn, O., and Strassmann, F., *Naturwiss.*, **26**, 756 (1938).

5. Hahn, O., and Strassmann, F., *Naturwiss.*, **27**, 11 (1939).

6. Bohr, N., *Nature*, **137**, 344, 351 (1936).

7. Bohr, N., and Kalckar, F., *Kgl. Danske Vid. Selskab, Math. Phys. Medd.*, **14**, Nr. 10 (1937).

8. See Meitner, L., Strassmann, F., and Hahn, O., *Z. Phys.*, **109**, 538 (1938).

9. Bethe, A. H., and Placzek, G., *Phys. Rev.*, **51**, 450 (1937).

用中子轰击钍元素，得到了曾被认为是镭和锕的同位素所具有的放射性 [8]。其中某些元素的放射周期与轰击铀产生的钡和镧的同位素 [5] 具有的放射周期是近似相等的。因此，我们倾向于认为，上述放射周期应来源于钍的"裂变"，它类似于铀的裂变过程，并在一定程度上得到了相同的产物。当然，要是能从一种轻元素得到上述产物之一（例如，通过中子俘获的方式），那就更有趣了。

还要提一下，在化学上与铀相同且半衰期为 24 分钟 [2] 的那种元素，很可能就是真正的铀-239，它进而衰变为类铼。虽然类铼似乎没有放射性，但也可能是在缓慢地衰变，并有可能伴随着 α 粒子的发射。（根据对天然放射性元素已有的认识，铀-239 不可能发生超过一次或两次的 β 衰变；我们始终对观测到的衰变长链感到困惑。）这种物质的形成是典型的共振过程 [9]；复合态所具有的寿命一定比核分裂所需要的时间长一百万倍。也许这种状态适合于某些不会发生"裂变"的核物质的高度对称性的运动方式。

（王耀杨 翻译；鲍重光 审稿）

Theory of Mesons and Nuclear Forces

C. Møller and L. Rosenfeld

Editor's Note

Mesons were so-called because they are intermediate in mass between the electron and the proton. In 1935, in a Japanese journal, Hideki Yukawa and colleagues proposed that mesons could account for the strong forces between nucleons (protons and neutrons) much as photons account for the electrical forces between charged particles of all kinds. This article by Rosenfeld and Møller, both protegés of Niels Bohr at Copenhagen, suggests how physical considerations require particular forms of the mathematical expressions (called wave functions) that agree better with experiments on the decay of light elements emitting β-particles. This prediction proved correct.

AS was first pointed out by Yukawa, it is in principle possible to account for the short-range forces between nuclear particles by the assumption of virtual emission and absorption processes involving intermediary particles of integral spin, the so-called *mesons*[1], the mass of which is determined by the range of the forces. As has been shown by Kemmer[2], the simplest wave-equations for the mesons which satisfy, besides the claim of relativistic invariance, the condition of giving a positive definite expression for the energy, reduce to four types, characterized by different co-variance properties of the wavefunctions, and each allowing the existence of neutral as well as positively and negatively charged mesons. Starting from such wave-equations, including the interaction of the meson field with the heavy nuclear constituents, the estimation of the resulting expressions for the nuclear forces has hitherto been carried out by using the ordinary perturbation method of quantum theory, and taking into consideration only the first non-vanishing approximation, in spite of the well-known lack of convergence of the method. It would thus seem desirable to discuss more closely the reliability of such results, and for this purpose a possible method of attack is suggested by an analogous situation in quantum electrodynamics, where a suitable canonical transformation allows us to separate, from the expression of the total energy of a system consisting of electrons and an electromagnetic field, a term depending only on the coordinates of the electrons and representing the Coulomb potential energy.

A similar method[3] is, actually, applicable to a system consisting of nuclear particles and a meson field. For such a system it is, in fact, possible to find canonical transformations effecting the separation of a "static" interaction between the nuclear particles, defined as the part of the interaction which is obtained when one neglects the time-variations of the variables characterizing the positions, spins and proton or neutron states of the heavy particles. This static interaction is in all cases exactly the same as that obtained as

介子和核力理论

默勒，罗森菲尔德

编者按

介子因其质量介于电子和质子之间而得名。1935 年，汤川秀树及其合作者在一本日本杂志中指出，介子可以用来解释核子（质子和中子）间的强力，这与光子可以用来解释所有带电粒子之间的电力类似。哥本哈根的尼尔斯·玻尔的两位高徒——罗森菲尔德和默勒在这篇文章中阐述了怎样用能与轻元素衰变放射出 β 粒子的实验吻合得更好的特定数学表达式（或称波函数）来满足物理学研究的需要。这个预言后来被证明是正确的。

正如汤川秀树最先指出的，如果假设核子在虚拟的发射和吸收过程中包括具有整数自旋的媒介粒子，即所谓的"介子"[1]，其质量取决于作用力的范围，那么原则上就可对核子之间的短程作用力作出解释。凯默 [2] 的研究表明：可以把最简单的介子波动方程——既满足相对论所要求的不变性，又能给出一个正定的能量表达式——归纳为四种类型，以波函数协变性的不同进行区分，并且每一种类型都允许中性、带正电或带负电的介子存在。从这些包含介子场与重核子之间相互作用的波动方程出发，人们只能通过采用通常的量子力学微扰理论（仅考虑一阶不为零的近似值）来估算核力的最终表达式，尽管这种方法具有众所周知的非收敛性。因此对该结果的可靠性进行进一步的讨论就显得十分必要，为此有人提出也许可以参照量子电动力学对类似情况的处理方法，即用一个适当的正则变换使我们可从由若干电子和一个电磁场组成的系统的总能量表达式中将只与电子坐标有关的项与库仑势能项分开。

其实，同样的方法 [3] 也适用于核子和介子场组成的体系。对于这样的一个体系，实际上有可能找到一些正则变换使核子之间的"静态"相互作用被分离出来，其中静态相互作用指的是相互作用中忽略了表征重粒子位置、自旋以及质子或中子状态的一些变量随时间变化的部分。这种静态相互作用在任何情况下都与微扰理论中的一级近似完全一致，而且，对于两个相距足以使静态相互作用远大于非静态相互作

a first approximation in the perturbation method, and there exists a lower limit, smaller but unfortunately not much smaller, than the range of the nuclear forces, to the mutual distances between two heavy particles for which the static interaction is more important than the additional non-static contributions arising from the terms, in the transformed Hamiltonian, which describe the remaining interactions between the heavy particles and the meson field.

Although no improvement can, of course, be obtained in this way as regards the self-energy difficulties, it would seem that consistent results can be derived from the transformed Hamiltonian by considering only the last-mentioned interactions as a perturbation and applying a method of treatment analogous to the correspondence methods used in electrodynamics. It is especially to be noted that if, following Yukawa, we also introduce an interaction between the meson field and electrons and neutrinos, the transformed Hamiltonian contains a term which represents a direct interaction between the heavy particles and the electrons and neutrinos, and which, when treated as a small perturbation, immediately gives the probabilities of β-disintegration processes. It is perhaps to be regarded as a satisfactory feature of the point of view just outlined that, contrary to previous treatments, where the nuclear forces came out in the same stage of the perturbation method as the probabilities of β-decay, account is here taken at the outset of at least the static part of the nuclear forces.

As regards the form of these static interactions, it is well known that the type of potential resulting from the four-vector meson field generally considered hitherto has the defect of including a term of dipole interaction energy which is so strongly singular for infinitely small mutual distances of the nuclear particles that it would not in general allow the existence of stationary states for a system of such particles. In order to remedy this defect, it seems necessary[2] to introduce besides the four-vector wave-function a further pseudoscalar wave-function for the meson field which has the property of giving rise to a static interaction of a form just capable of cancelling the dipole interaction term without affecting the others. The consideration of such a pseudoscalar meson field would also seem to be useful from the point of view of the theory of β-decay. While, for example, the four-vector theory yields[4] exactly the same form of the β-spectrum as Fermi's original theory, the introduction of a pseudoscalar wave-function in addition to the four-vector one gives rise to a modification of the energy distribution of the β-rays which seems to open a new possibility of a better adaptation to the experimental results.

A detailed account of our work will appear shortly in the *Proceedings of the Copenhagen Academy*.

(**143**, 241-242; 1939)

C. Møller and L. Rosenfeld: Institute for Theoretical Physics, Copenhagen, Jan. 6.

用项的重粒子，它们之间的距离存在一个下限，然而不幸的是，这个下限与核力力程相比虽小但没有小很多。所谓非静态相互作用项，指的是在变换后的哈密顿量中那些用来描述重粒子与介子场之间剩余作用的项。

尽管这种方法并没有解决自能的困难，但是我们在仅考虑最后提到的剩余相互作用项作为微扰并应用与电动力学中类似的处理方法时，可以从变换的哈密顿量中得到自洽的结果。特别值得注意的是，如果按照汤川秀树的理论，我们也在介子场、电子和中微子之间引入一种相互作用，则变换后的哈密顿量就含有描述重粒子和电子及中微子之间直接作用的一项，当我们把它视为小微扰的时候，就可以立即给出发生 β 衰变的概率。对于上述理论来说，一开始就考虑了核力中的静态作用部分，这或许可以被认为是一个令人满意的构想，但这与以前的处理方法相反，之前核力是与 β 衰变概率在微扰法中的同一步中出现。

迄今为止，人们普遍认为，这些静态相互作用的形式来自四矢量介子场的这种类型的势存在一个缺陷，就是包含一个偶极相互作用能项，当核子之间的距离趋于无穷小时，它如此奇异以至于在一般情况下不能允许这种粒子的系统存在定态。为了弥补这个缺陷，看来除了四矢量波函数以外，还有必要 [2] 把一个赝标量波函数引入介子场，这个波函数的作用是引出一个静态相互作用，其作用刚好能够抵消偶极相互作用项而又不影响其他项。从 β 衰变理论的角度来看，考虑这种赝标量介子场似乎也是有意义的。举例来说，由四矢量理论得到 [4] 的 β 光谱与早先费米理论中的 β 光谱形式完全相同，把赝标量波函数叠加到四矢量波函数上后，β 射线的能量分布将被修正，这为与实验结果更好地吻合提供了新的可能。

我们的详细工作报告很快将发表在《哥本哈根学会学报》上。

（胡雪兰 翻译；厉光烈 审稿）

References:

1. See Bhabha, *Nature* (in the Press).

2. Kemmer, *Proc. Roy. Soc.*, A, **166**, 127 (1938); *Proc. Camb. Phil. Soc.*, **34**, 354 (1938).

3. Independently of our work, essentially the same method has been proposed by Stückelberg (*Phys.Rev.*, **54**, 889; 1938), to whom we are very thankful for the kind communication of his manuscript.

4. Yukawa, Sakata, Kobayasi, Taketani, *Proc. Phys. Math. Soc. Japan*, **20**, 720 (1938).

Physical Evidence for the Division of Heavy Nuclei under Neutron Bombardment

O. R. Frisch

Editor's Note

Otto Hahn and Fritz Strassmann in 1938 had found convincing chemical evidence for the fission of uranium nuclei. After bombarding uranium nuclei with neutrons, they had found traces of barium nuclei, with atomic weight 56, suggesting a roughly equal splitting of the nuclei. Here Otto Frisch of the Institute of Theoretical Physics in Copenhagen gives clinching physical evidence of the process. Calculations suggested that the fission fragments should have energies of perhaps 200 million electronvolts, and so should create significant ionization in a chamber. In experiments, Frisch had detected such ionization events and, from the level of ionization, estimated the atomic weight of the fragments as about 70, not too far from 56, and certainly less than uranium's 92.

FROM chemical evidence, Hahn and Strassmann[1] conclude that radioactive barium nuclei (atomic number $Z = 56$) are produced when uranium ($Z = 92$) is bombarded by neutrons. It has been pointed out[2] that this might be explained as a result of a "fission" of the uranium nucleus, similar to the division of a droplet into two. The energy liberated in such processes was estimated to be about 200 Mev., both from mass defect considerations and from the repulsion of the two nuclei resulting from the "fission" process.

If this picture is correct, one would expect fast-moving nuclei, of atomic number about 40-50 and atomic weight 100-150, and up to 100 Mev. energy, to emerge from a layer of uranium bombarded with neutrons. In spite of their high energy, these nuclei should have a range, in air, of a few millimetres only, on account of their high effective charge (estimated to be about 20), which implies very dense ionization. Each such particle should produce a total of about three million ion pairs.

By means of a uranium-lined ionization chamber, connected to a linear amplifier, I have succeeded in demonstrating the occurrence of such bursts of ionization. The amplifier was connected to a thyratron which was biased so as to count only pulses corresponding to at least 5×10^5 ion pairs. About fifteen particles a minute were recorded when 300 mgm. of radium, mixed with beryllium, was placed one centimetre from the uranium lining. No pulses at all were recorded during repeated check runs of several hours total duration when either the neutron source or the uranium lining was removed. With the neutron source at a distance of four centimetres from the uranium lining, surrounding the source with paraffin wax enhanced the effect by a factor of two.

中子轰击导致重核分裂的物理证据

弗里施

编者按

1938 年奥托·哈恩和弗里茨·施特拉斯曼发现了铀核裂变的可信的化学证据。他们在使用中子轰击铀核之后，发现了原子序数为 56 的钡原子核，这表明铀核几乎是对等地分裂为两半。这篇文章中哥本哈根理论物理研究所的奥托·弗里施给出了这个过程的明确的物理证据。计算表明裂变碎片应该具有大约 200 兆电子伏的能量，因此应该在电离室中产生显著的电离反应。弗里施在实验中已探测到了这种相关的电离情况，从电离的量级他估算出产生的碎片的原子序数应为 70 左右，与 56 相差不远，但明显小于铀的原子序数 92。

根据化学证据，哈恩和施特拉斯曼 [1] 作出了当中子轰击铀（原子序数 $Z = 92$）时会产生放射性钡核（原子序数 $Z = 56$）的结论。此前我们已经指出 [2]，这种现象可以解释为铀核的"裂变"，就像一个液滴一分为二那样。无论是根据质量亏损，还是根据"裂变"过程中产生的两核之间的排斥反应，都可估算出这一铀核"裂变"过程中释放出来的能量大约为 200 兆电子伏。

如果上述描述是正确的，那就可以预期，用中子轰击铀原子层时可以发出高速运动的原子核，其原子序数和原子量分别处于 40~50 和 100~150 的范围内，能量上达到 100 兆电子伏。尽管这些核的能量很高，但它们在空气中只有几毫米的射程，这是因为它们具有高的有效电荷（估计为 20），而这意味着具有极为密集的电离作用，每个这样的粒子会产生总计约 300 万个离子对。

利用一个与线性放大器连接的铀衬电离室，我成功证实了这种电离脉冲的出现。放大器与一个有偏置的闸流管相连，以便能对那些相当于至少 5×10^5 个离子对的脉冲计数。把 300 毫克混有铍的镭放置在距离铀衬一厘米处时，每分钟能记录到大约 15 个粒子。在重复进行的长达几个小时的检验测量中，无论是移走中子源还是移走铀衬，都根本记录不到任何脉冲。而当中子源距离铀衬 4 厘米远时，用石蜡包裹中子源却能使效应增加一倍。

It was checked that the number of pulses depended linearly on the strength of the neutron source; this was done in order to exclude the possibility that the pulses are produced by accidental summation of smaller pulses. When the amplifier was connected to an oscillograph, the large pulses could be seen very distinctly on the background of much smaller pulses due to the alpha particles of the uranium.

By varying the bias of the thyratron, the maximum size of pulses was found to correspond to at least two million ion pairs, or an energy loss of 70 Mev. of the particle within the chamber. Since the longest path of a particle in the chamber was three centimetres and the chamber was filled with hydrogen at atmospheric pressure, the particles must ionize so heavily, in spite of their energy of at least 70 Mev., that they can make two million ion pairs on a path equivalent to 0.8 cm. of air or less. From this it can be estimated that the ionizing particles must have an atomic weight of at least about seventy, assuming a reasonable connexion between atomic weight and effective charge. This seems to be conclusive physical evidence for the breaking up of uranium nuclei into parts of comparable size, as indicated by the experiments of Hahn and Strassmann.

Experiments with thorium instead of uranium gave quite similar results, except that surrounding the neutron source with paraffin did not enhance, but slightly diminished, the effect. This gives evidence in favour of the suggestion[2] that also in the case of thorium, some, if not all, of the activities produced by neutron bombardment[3] should be ascribed to light elements. It should be remembered that no enhancement by paraffin has been found for the activities produced in thorium[3] (except for one which is isotopic with thorium and is almost certainly produced by simple capture of the neutron).

Prof. Meitner has suggested another interesting experiment. If a metal plate is placed close to a uranium layer bombarded with neutrons, one would expect an active deposit of the light atoms emitted in the "fission" of the uranium to form on the plate. We hope to carry out such experiments, using the powerful source of neutrons which our high-tension apparatus will soon be able to provide.

(**143**, 276; 1939)

Otto Robert Frisch: Institute of Theoretical Physics, University, Copenhagen, Jan. 16.

References:
1. Hahn, O., and Strassmann, F., *Naturwiss.*, 27, 11 (1939).
2. Meitner, L., and Frisch, O. R., *Nature* [143, 239 (1939)].
3. See Meitner, L., Strassmann, F., and Hahn, O., *Z. Phys.*, **109**, 538 (1938).

现已证明脉冲数目与中子源的强度具有线性关系；这是为了排除脉冲源于偶然的较小脉冲累积而产生的可能性。当把放大器与示波器相连时，可以看到在铀发射的 α 粒子产生的非常小的脉冲背景之上有非常明显的大脉冲。

通过调节闸流管的偏压，可以发现最大脉冲幅度对应于至少 200 万个离子对，或者说相当于粒子在电离室内损失了 70 兆电子伏的能量。由于粒子在电离室内的最长路径只有 3 厘米，并且电离室内充满了一个大气压的氢气，因此，尽管粒子具有至少 70 兆电子伏的能量，但它们必定会发生强烈的电离以至于在相当于 0.8 厘米空气的路径上产生了 200 万个离子对。根据这一结果，假设原子量与有效电荷之间具有合理关联的话，我们就可以估算出电离粒子的原子序数应该至少是 70。这对铀核分裂成大小相当的两个部分似乎是个决定性的物理证据，正如哈恩和施特拉斯曼的实验结果所示。

用钍代替铀所做的实验给出了相当类似的结果，只是用石蜡包裹中子源后效应并没有增强，反而是略有减弱。先前我们曾提出 [2] 在钍的实验中用中子轰击所产生的某些（如果不是全部的话）放射性 [3] 应该归属为轻元素，上述实验结果为这一观点提供了有力的证据。同时我们还应该记住，在钍产生的放射性实验 [3] 中用石蜡包裹中子源后效应并没有增强（只有一次例外，那是因为使用了钍的某种同位素，并且几乎可以确定是由于单纯的中子俘获而产生的）。

迈特纳教授曾提出过另外一个有趣的实验。如果将一块金属板置于用中子轰击的铀层附近，就可以预期金属板上会形成铀"裂变"过程中所发射出的轻原子的放射性沉积物。我们希望实现诸如利用高压装置便能提供更强中子源的实验。

（王耀杨 翻译；张焕乔 鲍重光 审稿）

The Fundamental Length Introduced by the Theory of the Mesotron (Meson)[*]

H. J. Bhabha

Editor's Note

By 1939, physicists understood that the framework in which they discussed the behaviour of particles such as electrons and protons was in some sense incomplete. There was particular concern over the particles, called mesotrons, which were intermediate in mass between electrons and protons, but which carried electrical charge. Homi J. Bhabha was an Indian graduate student at Cambridge and Bristol. He was among the first to appreciate the wider implications of mesons. In the 1960s Bhabha returned to India and became the head of the Indian Atomic Energy Commission. He was killed in an air crash in 1966.

IT is well known that the vector theory of the meson[1] contains a fundamental length in the interaction of mesons with protons and neutrons determined by the fact that the mass of the meson appears explicitly in the denominator of some of the interaction terms. This circumstance has the result that in those elementary processes in which the momentum change is large compared with mc, m being the mass of the meson, the interaction becomes very large, leading to Heisenberg explosions, and to greater divergences in some second-order effects than is the case in radiation theory. This has led Heitler[2] and others to the view that the meson theory in its present form is quite incorrect for meson energies larger than about mc^2, and Heisenberg[3] to the position that quantum mechanics is competent to deal accurately with only those elementary processes in which the condition[4] due to Wataghin,

$$\left| \left(\frac{E_1 - E_2}{c} \right)^2 - (\boldsymbol{p}_1 - \boldsymbol{p}_2)^2 \right| \ll \left(\frac{\hbar}{r_0} \right)^2, \tag{1}$$

is satisfied, E and p being the initial and final energy and momenta of a particle concerned in the process, and r_0 a fundamental length of the order $\hbar/mc$. The purpose of this note is to bring forward an argument which, it seems to me, shows first that the limitation of quantum mechanics by the condition (1), if true, cannot be based on the explosions as derivable from the theory of the meson, and secondly, to throw some doubt on (1) itself as a limit to the correctness of quantum mechanics.

---

[*] The name "mesotron" has been suggested by Anderson and Nedder-meyer (*Nature*, **142**, 874; 1938) for the new particle found in cosmic radiation with a mass intermediate between that of the electron and proton. It is felt that the "tr" in this word is redundant, since it does not belong to the Greek root "meso" for middle; the "tr" in neutron and electron belong, of course, to the roots "neutr" and "electra". In these circumstances, it seems better to follow the suggestion of Bohr and to use electron to denote particles of electronic mass independently of their charge, and negaton and positon to differentiate between the sign of the charge. It would therefore be more logical and also shorter to call the new particle a meson instead of a mesotron.

510

介子理论中的基本长度[*]

巴巴

编者按

1939 年，物理学家认识到，讨论电子和质子等粒子行为的理论框架在某种意义上是不够完善的，尤其是对于一种叫介子的粒子，它的质量介于电子和质子之间而且携带电荷。霍米·巴巴是剑桥大学和布里斯托尔大学的印度籍研究生。他也是第一批对介子具有的更广泛含义进行认真思考的学者之一。20 世纪 60 年代巴巴回到印度并成为印度原子能委员会的主席。1966 年他在一次空难中不幸去世。

　　众所周知，介子矢量理论[1]包含介子与质子和中子相互作用的基本长度，它是由介子质量出现在一些相互作用项的分母中的事实所决定的。这种情况使得在一些动量变化大于 mc（m 为介子质量）的基本过程中相互作用变得非常大，从而导致了海森堡爆炸，同时也使一些二阶效应与辐射理论所得结果相比更加发散。这使海特勒[2]和其他一些人注意到介子理论的现有形式因给出介子能量大于 mc^2 而是完全错误的，海森堡[3]也指出，量子力学仅可以完美地解决那些满足瓦塔金条件[4]的基本过程，该条件如下：

$$\left| \left(\frac{E_1 - E_2}{c} \right)^2 - (\vec{p}_1 - \vec{p}_2)^2 \right| \ll \left(\frac{\hbar}{r_0} \right)^2 \tag{1}$$

式中 E 和 p 在这个过程中分别代表一个粒子初态和终态的能量和动量，r_0 为与 $\hbar/mc$ 具有同样量级的基本长度。我这篇短文的目的是要引出一个论点，首先该论点指出量子力学的应用范围如果真的仅限于条件 (1) 满足的情况，那么就不可能出现介子理论所预言的爆炸现象；其次，我对条件 (1) 本身作为量子力学正确性的限制条件表示质疑。

---

[*] "mesotron" 是安德森和尼德－迈耶（《自然》，142，874；1938）为在宇宙线中发现的新粒子所取的名字，该粒子的质量介于电子和质子之间。大家感觉 "tr" 在这个单词中是多余的，因为它并不属于前面表示 "中间" 的意思的希腊词根 "meso"，而中子和电子中的 "tr" 是属于词根 "neutr" 和 "electra" 的，在这种情况下最好接受玻尔的建议，即用电子表示与所带电荷正负无关的带电粒子，而用负电子和正电子来区分所带电荷的正负号。因此把这种新粒子命名为 "meson" 比将其称为 "mesotron" 更符合逻辑、也更简洁。

The argument runs as follows. Let us consider uncharged mesons[5] for simplicity, since this changes nothing essential to the argument, and consider the Hamiltonian given in A (49)[1]. The interaction (58 a) in this contains terms which become very large when the momentum change of the meson becomes large compared to mc in a suitable Lorenz frame. These terms, which lead to explosions, are due *as much to the transverse meson waves as to the longitudinal ones*, even in the limit when the proton may be considered to be moving non-relativistically. Further, the critical momentum above which explosions begin to appear becomes lower the smaller mc, and becomes vanishingly small when $mc \to 0$.

On the other hand, *the exact quantized equations of motion for the meson field derivable from this Hamiltonian* (A (14) and (15), with the appropriate simplifications for a neutral meson), namely,

$$G_{\mu\nu} = -\left(\frac{\partial}{\partial\chi^\mu}U_\nu - \frac{\partial}{\partial\chi^\nu}U_\mu\right) + \frac{g_2}{\hbar c}\psi + \gamma^\mu\gamma^\nu\tau_3\psi$$

$$\frac{\partial}{\partial\chi_\mu}b_{\mu\nu} = \frac{m^2c^2}{\hbar^2}U_\nu + \frac{g_1}{\hbar c}\psi + \gamma^\nu\tau_3\psi$$

go over continuously into the Maxwell equations when $m \to 0$. But one knows from electrodynamics that although there are circumstances in which the emission of a large number of quanta may be more probable than the emission of a single quantum, as in the so-called "infra-red catastrophe", this in no way sets a limit to the accuracy of quantum mechanics *and does not interfere with the calculation of less probable processes by the methods of perturbation theory*. Moreover, it is just those processes where the emission of a large number of quanta is very probable which can be calculated classically.

In view of the above circumstances, we must conclude that the appearance of the fundamental length determined by the mass of the meson in the interaction term in no way sets a limit to the accuracy of quantum mechanics. For example, in the collision of two protons with energy very large compared to mc^2, the probability becomes large for the simultaneous emission of a large number of mesons, which is the analogue of the "infra-red catastrophe" for quanta of finite rest mass, and hence quantum mechanics is none the less competent to deal with it. It can similarly be shown that *we can calculate the production of large explosions to a high degree of accuracy by treating the meson field quantities classically*, that is, as non-quantized magnitudes, for since mesons satisfy Einstein-Bose statistics, the meson field becomes a classical one just in the case where we are dealing with a large number of mesons.

Hence if a fundamental length r_0 exists which limits the applicability of present quantum mechanics to the cases satisfying (1), this length r_0 has nothing to do with the mass of the meson or the appearance of explosions. Quantum mechanics in its present form cannot be strictly valid since it leads to divergent results connected with the self-energies of point charges; but these limitations are probably due to the fact that it is not the quantization of the correct classical equations for point charges, and not to the existence of a fundamental length r_0. These equations have only recently been given by Dirac[6] and their quantization has not yet appeared.

这个论点具体如下：为了简单起见，我们考虑不带电荷的介子 [5] 的情况，因为带电情况的变化对这个论题没有本质上的影响，另外我们还用到 A(49) 式 [1] 中给出的哈密顿量。在适当的洛伦兹框架下，当介子动量的变化大到可以和 mc 相比拟时，表示相互作用的 (58 a) 式中的一些项就会变得非常大。即使在质子运动可能被认为是非相对论性的极限情况下，这些可引发爆炸的项也是一样由**横向介子波和纵向介子波**引起的。此外，爆炸开始出现时的临界动量在 mc 变小时也会变小，当 mc 趋于 0 时，临界动量会变得几乎为 0。

另一方面，**由哈密顿量**（A(14) 和 (15)，并在中性介子的假设下作适当简化）**导出的严格介子场量子化运动方程**，即：

$$G_{\mu\nu} = -\left(\frac{\partial}{\partial \chi^\mu} U_\nu - \frac{\partial}{\partial \chi^\nu} U_\mu\right) + \frac{g_2}{\hbar c}\psi + \gamma^\mu \gamma^\nu \tau_3 \psi$$

$$\frac{\partial}{\partial \chi_\mu} b_{\mu\nu} = \frac{m^2 c^2}{\hbar^2} U_\nu + \frac{g_1}{\hbar c}\psi + \gamma^\nu \tau_3 \psi$$

在 m 趋于 0 时会连续地过渡到麦克斯韦方程。但是根据电动力学，我们知道正如所谓的"红外灾难"，虽然发射大量量子的概率要大于发射单个量子的概率，但这决不会限制量子力学的适用范围，**也不会干预应用微扰理论计算小概率的过程**。而且正是那些可以用经典方法计算的过程有可能发射大量量子。

我们可以由此得出结论，取决于相互作用项中介子质量的基本长度绝不可能对量子力学的精确性有所限制。举例来讲，当两个能量大到足以和 mc^2 相比拟的质子发生碰撞的时候，同时发射大量介子的可能性就会变大，这类似于与具有有限静止质量的量子相关的"红外灾难"，因此量子力学仍然可以解决这类问题。同样我们可以指出，**用经典方法处理介子场量能够精确地计算出大爆炸的结果**，也就是说，既然介子满足爱因斯坦 – 玻色统计，那么当我们处理包括大量介子的问题时，对于非量子化的场量，介子场就变成了一个经典场。

因此，如果基本长度 r_0 的出现使现有的量子力学理论只能应用于满足式 (1) 的情况，那么这个长度 r_0 就与介子质量或爆炸的出现无关。量子力学的现有形式不可能是严格正确的，因为它在涉及点电荷自能问题时会产生发散的结果；但是，这种局限性可能是由于正确的经典点电荷方程没有量子化，而不是因为引入了基本长度 r_0。最近只有狄拉克 [6] 给出了这些方程，不过尚未得到这些方程的量子化形式。

Accordingly, we might expect that very fast protons (or neutrons) would produce explosions consisting of mesons of momenta roughly mc, while mesons with energy much larger than the proton rest-energy would *not* do so, and their scattering by protons would also decrease with increasing energy, in analogy with the Compton effect.

It can be shown that the classical retarded meson field and potentials due to the world line of a classically moving proton or neutron can be written as the sum of two parts. The first part has exactly the form that the corresponding electromagnetic quantities would have for a point charge and point dipole (represented by a six-vector) moving along a classical world line, and does not contain the mass of the meson. The second part has no singularity at any point of space including the world line of the proton, and goes to zero as the mass of the meson $m \to 0$. The meson singularities are therefore *identical* with the electromagnetic singularities, and it is possible to eliminate these to the same degree and in the same way as has been done by Dirac[6] for the electromagnetic field of a point charge.

The detailed calculations will be published elsewhere.

(**143**, 276-277; 1939)

H. J. Bhabha: Gonville and Caius College, Cambridge, Dec. 17.

References:

1. Kemmer, *Nature*, **141**, 116 (1938); *Proc. Roy. Soc.*, A, **166**, 127 (1938). Fröhlich, Heitler and Kemmer, *Proc. Roy. Soc.*, A, **166**, 154(1938). Bhabha, *Nature*, **141**, 117 (1938); *Proc. Roy. Soc.*, A, **166**, 501 (1938), referred to above as A; Yukawa, Sakata, and Taketani, *Proc. Phys. Math. Soc. Japan.* **20**, 319 (1938). Stueckelberg, *Helv. Phys. Acta*, **11**, 299 (1938).

2. Heitler, *Proc. Roy. Soc.*, A, **166** (1938).

3. Heisenberg, *Z. Phys.*, **110**, 251 (1938).

4. Wataghin, *Z. Phys.*, **66**, 650 (1931); **73**, 126 (1931).

5. Kemmer, *Proc. Camb. Phil.* Soc., **34**, 354 (1938).

6. Dirac, *Proc. Roy. Soc.*, A, **167**, 148 (1938). See also Pryce, *Proc. Roy. Soc.*, A, **168**, 389 (1938).

因此，我们可以预测快速运动的质子（或中子）会引发爆炸，放出动量大约为 mc 的介子，而当介子能量远大于质子的静止能量时则**不**可能引发爆炸，而且能量越大，质子对介子的散射越弱，这与康普顿效应类似。

这表明，由经典运动的质子或中子的世界线所决定的经典的推迟介子场和势能可以写成两部分之和。第一部分的具体形式为一个点电荷和点偶极子（用一个六维矢量描述）沿经典的世界线运动所对应的电磁场量，而不包含介子质量。第二部分在包括质子世界线在内的任何空间点上都不会出现奇异点，而且当介子质量 m 趋于 0 时它也变为 0。因此，介子的奇异点与电磁场的奇异点是**一样的**，可以参照狄拉克 [6] 对点电荷电磁场的处理方法以同样的方式、在同一程度上消除这些奇异点。

详细的计算结果将发表在其他地方。

（胡雪兰 翻译；厉光烈 审稿）

Energy Obtained by Transmutation

Editor's Note

This editorial comments on the possibility of deriving energy, perhaps in explosive form, from nuclear transmutation. The likelihood, it suggests, is remote. Meanwhile, recent experiments had demonstrated the artificial transmutation of most elements, including gold, though without any repercussions for world financial stability. The goal of harnessing nuclear energy seemed far off, partly because significant energy can be released only in processes involving the heaviest and rare elements. Yet the first atomic weapon was detonated only six years later, made possible by the enrichment of vast quantities of uranium with the easily fissionable isotope ^{235}U, which constitutes only 0.7% of the element naturally.

MR. Robert D. Potter, of "Science Service", Washington, D.C., points out that the confirmation of the artificial breakdown of uranium announced in New York (see also *Nature*, Feb. 11, p. 233) is in the direct succession of experiments carried out in recent years on the transmutation of the elements. For centuries, alchemists had dreamed of transmuting base metals into gold. It was imagined that enormous wealth would be at hand for the discoverer of this transmutation, and dire forecasts of the effects of this discovery were made, such as a complete revolution on the financial pattern of the world. We know that this transmutation has now been achieved for most of the known chemical elements. Transmutation's biggest result is the theoretical incentive it has provided for further physical researches. In a similar way, the dream of releasing the large amounts of energy locked inside atoms has been in the minds of men for many years. When the most efficient transformation of energy takes place in the atom of uranium so that a neutron can slip into it, the energy released is only one fifteenth of that required to bring it about. In fact, neutrons are so easily absorbed by all atomic nuclei that many of the neutrons produced with such poor efficiency will only go into atoms other than uranium. There need be little fear of an explosion in Nature due to uranium. The very heavy elements, in which such an energy release can be secured, occur only in very small amounts in the Earth's crust. The release of atomic energy can only be achieved by direct experiment with this end in view and with elaborate laboratory apparatus.

(**143**, 328; 1939)

嬗变产生的能量

编者按

这篇社论就从核嬗变中获取能量（或许以爆炸的形式）的可能性进行了评论。文中提出，这种可能性还很遥远。同时，最近的实验已经证实了包括金在内的大多数元素可实现人工嬗变，而这并未对世界金融的稳定造成影响。利用核能的想法似乎遥不可及，部分原因是只有最重且稀有的那些元素的嬗变过程才能释放出巨大的能量。然而仅在六年后，通过大量天然铀富集获得的铀–235 使得第一颗原子弹爆炸成功，而这种易裂变的同位素铀–235 仅占天然铀元素的 0.7%。

华盛顿特区科学服务社的罗伯特·波特先生指出，纽约宣布的铀的人工嬗变（也见《自然》2 月 11 日，第 233 页）是近年来对元素嬗变问题所进行的实验的直接延续。几个世纪以来，炼金术士都梦想将普通金属转变成金子。有人认为发现了这种嬗变，巨大的财富就会唾手可得，有人还对这个发现的结果做出了极端的预测，例如这将是一次世界金融格局的彻底变革。我们知道，现在对于大多数已知的化学元素，这类嬗变都已实现。嬗变的最大成效是，它为进一步的物理研究提供了理论发展的动力。同样，将禁锢在原子内部的大量能量释放出来，一直是人们心中多年以来的梦想。当铀原子中发生最有效的能量转化，并使一个中子进入其中时，所释放的能量仅是促使该过程发生所需能量的 1/15。实际上，中子很容易被各种原子核吸收，以至于许多如此低效的中子只能进入其他原子而不能进入铀。不必过于担心自然界的铀会引起爆炸。能够确保这种能量释放得非常重的元素在地壳中的含量很少。原子能量的释放只能用直接的实验来实现，为达到这样的目的而做的实验是要在精心制作的实验装置中进行的。

（沈乃澂 翻译；朱永生 审稿）

Cause, Purpose and Economy of Natural Laws* : Minimum Principles in Physics

M. Born

Editor's Note

In the 1920s, Max Born, based at the University of Göttingen, had been one of the founders of quantum mechanics. The German government's decision that Jewish people could no longer teach at German universities made it necessary for him to leave Germany; after a brief stay at Cambridge he settled in Edinburgh where he and his family remained for several decades. Born was an exceptionally lucid lecturer. This general lecture on the laws of physics is a model of its kind.

WITHOUT claiming to be a classical scholar, I think that the earliest reference in literature to the problems which I wish to treat here is contained in Virgil's "Aeneid", Book I, line 369, in the words "taurino quantum possent circumdare tergo."

When Dido landed at the site of the citadel of Carthage, she opened negotiations with the inhabitants for some land and was offered for her money only as much as she could surround with a bull's hide. But the astute woman cut the bull's hide into narrow strips, joined them end-to-end and with this long string encompassed a considerable piece of land, the nucleus of her kingdom. To do this she had evidently to solve a mathematical question—the celebrated "problem of Dido": to find a closed curve of given circumference having maximum area. We do not know how she solved it, by trial, by reasoning, or by intuition. In any event, the correct answer is not difficult to guess: it is the circle. But the mathematical proof of this fact has only been attained by modern mathematical methods.

In saying that the first appearance of this kind of problem in literature is that quoted above I am not, of course, suggesting that problems of minima and maxima had never occurred before in the life of mankind. In fact, nearly every application of reason to a definite practical purpose is more or less an attempt to solve such a problem: to get the greatest effect from a given effort, or, putting it the other way round, to get a desired effect with the smallest effort. We see from this double formulation of the same problem that there is no essential distinction between maximum and minimum; we can speak shortly of an "extremum", and "extremal" problems.

It was during Isaac Newton's lifetime, at the end of the seventeenth century, that geometrical and mechanical problems of extremals began to interest mathematicians,

---

* Substance of the Friday evening discourse delivered at the Royal Institution on February 10.

518

自然规律的起源、宗旨和经济性*：
物理学的极小原理

玻恩

编者按

20 世纪 20 年代，在哥廷根大学工作的马克斯·玻恩已经是量子力学的奠基人之一了。后来，德国政府关于犹太人不能再在德国大学任教的决定使他不得不离开德国；在剑桥短暂停留后，他最终定居爱丁堡，并和其家人在那里住了几十年。玻恩是一位思路极为清晰的讲演者，这篇关于物理定律的讲演就是其中的一个典范。

　　我并不是要表明自己是一名古典主义学者，不过我认为有关这里我要研究的问题的最早记录恐怕要追溯到维吉尔的《埃涅阿斯纪》，即第一册第 369 行所写的"用公牛皮围一块尽可能大的地"。

　　当狄多来到迦太基古城时，她与当地的土著人谈判，用一定量的金币换取一头公牛的牛皮能够围起来的土地。这个精明的女人把公牛皮割成细长条并将它们首尾相连，最终圈得一片相当大的土地，这就是她王国的核心。为了做到这点，显然她得解决这样一个数学问题——著名的"狄多问题"：如何使给定周长的闭合曲线所围成的面积达到最大。我们并不知道她是如何解决这个问题的，可能用试验或推理，也可能是靠直觉。无论如何，我们不难猜到这个问题的正确答案是：一个圆。但直到现代数学方法的出现才最终从数学方面给出了证明。

　　上面提到的内容是第一次在文字记载出现这类问题的相关记录，当然我不是指在此记录之前的人类历史中从未出现过这类求极小值和极大值的问题。实际上，每次应用推理达到某个明确实际的目标时，我们都或多或少在试图解决这样的问题：在一定的努力的基础上得到最大的效果，换句话说，即以最小的代价得到预期的效果。从以上对同一个问题的两种表述方式中我们看到，求极大值与极小值的问题之间并没有本质的区别；我们可以简单地称之为"极值"或"极值函数"问题。

　　在 17 世纪末的艾萨克·牛顿时代，极值函数的几何问题和力学问题开始引起数学家们的兴趣，在牛顿去世（1727 年）后不久，自然界的意义或经济性等形而上学

---

* 2 月 10 日周五晚上玻恩在英国皇家研究院发表演说的主要内容。

and shortly after Newton's death (1727) the metaphysical idea of purpose or economy in Nature was linked up with them.

One of the simplest examples is the optical "law of reflection" which can be expressed as a minimum principle: the beam of light from a point P_1 to another point P_2 selects just that reflecting point Q which makes the total path $P_1Q + QP_2$ as short as possible. The light behaves as if each beam had a tendency to contract, and the French philosopher, Fermat, has shown that all the laws of geometrical optics can be reduced to the same principle. Light moves like a tired messenger boy who has to reach definite destinations and carefully chooses the shortest way possible. Are we to consider this interpretation as accidental, or are we to see in it a deeper metaphysical significance? Before we can form a judgment, we must learn more about the facts and consider other cases.

The straight line is the shortest connexion between two points in space. But if we travel on our earth, we can never go exactly in a straight line since the earth's surface is not plane. The best we can do is to follow a great circle, which is the curve in which the sphere is intersected by a plane passing through the centre. The globe, however, is not an exact sphere, but is slightly flattened at the poles and bulges at the equator. What, then, about the shortest line on such a surface?

Gauss hit on this problem when occupied with a geodetic triangulation of his country, the electorate of Hanover. He attacked the problem from the most general point of view and investigated the shortest lines on arbitrary surfaces. But in remembrance of his starting point he called these lines "geodesics". They are in many ways of fundamental importance for physics.

Let us consider a point P on a surface and all curves through P which have the same direction at P. It is evident that there is among them a "straightest curve", that is, one with the smallest curvature. Hence the geodesic can be characterized by two somewhat different minimum properties: one which can be called a "local" or "differential" property, namely, to be as little curved as possible at a given point for a given direction; and the other, which can be called "total" or "integral", namely, to be the shortest path between two points on the surface.

This dualism between "local" and "total" laws appears not only in this simple geometrical problem, but also has a much wider application in physics. It lies at the root of the old controversy whether forces act directly at a distance (as assumed in Newton's theory of gravitation and the older forms of the electric and magnetic theories), or whether they act only from point to point (as in Faraday's and Maxwell's theory of electromagnetism and all modern field theories).

There seems to be no objection to extremal laws of the local type; but those of the integral type make our modern mind feel uneasy: although we understand that the particle may choose at a given instant to proceed on the straightest path, we cannot see how it can

的思想逐渐与这些极值问题联系起来了。

最简单的一个例子是光学中的"反射定律"，这个定律可以表述成极小原理：从某一点 P_1 传播到另一点 P_2 的光束所选择的反射点 Q 要满足总路程 $P_1Q + QP_2$ 为最短。光的行为性质表现为每束光都具有缩短路程的趋势，法国哲学家费马已经指出，几何光学的所有规律都可以归纳为这一原理。光的运动就像一个疲劳的信使，他会在到达确定的目的地之前谨慎地选择尽可能最短的路程。我们如何理解以上的解释呢？认为这是一种偶然的情况，还是我们可以从中发现更深刻的形而上学方面的意义？在我们做出判断之前，我们必须了解更多的事实，并考虑其他更多的情况。

空间中两点之间最短的连线是直线。但如果我们在地球上运动时，我们永远不能精确地沿直线行进，这是因为地球的表面不是平面。而最好的选择是沿着大圆的路径，这个大圆是大圆所在的球与某一穿过球心的平面相交的曲线。然而地球并不是一个精确的球体，它的两极稍微有些扁平、赤道略微凸起。那么在这样的球面上，最短的路线是什么样子的呢？

高斯利用大地三角测量方法对他所在的德国汉诺威选区进行测绘时也碰到了这个问题。他从最普遍的观点出发来处理问题，并研究了任意表面上最短的线。为了纪念他处理这个问题的出发点，他仍将这些最短的线称为"测地线"。对于物理学来说，"测地线"在许多方面都具有重要意义。

我们考虑球体表面上的一点 P，且通过 P 的所有曲线在 P 处方向相同。显然，在它们之中有一条"最直的曲线"，即曲率最小的曲线。因此，测地线可以用两种稍微不同的最小性原理来表征：第一种可被称为"局部的"或"微分的"性质，即经过某个定点并给定方向的曲线，其曲率最小；第二种被称为"整体的"或"积分的"性质，即表面上的两点之间路程最短。

"局部的"和"整体的"定律之间的二元论不仅出现在这类简单的几何问题中，而且在物理学中有着更加广泛的应用。它在早期争论物理学的基础时就已经出现，即力的作用是直接的超距作用（如牛顿引力理论和电磁理论早期形式中的假设），还是只能是点到点的作用（如法拉第和麦克斯韦的电磁学理论及所有的现代场论）。

人们对局部形式的极值定律似乎并无反对意见；但以我们现在的思维来说，我们还是不太能自然地接受总体形式的极值定律：虽然我们知道粒子将在给定的瞬间

quickly compare all possible motions to a distant position and choose the shortest one—this sounds altogether too metaphysical.

But before we follow out this line of thought, we must convince ourselves that minimum properties appear in all parts of physics, and that they are not only correct but also very useful and suggestive formulations of physical laws.

One field in which a minimum principle is of unquestionable utility is statics, the doctrine of the equilibrium of all kinds of systems under any forces. The centre of gravity tends to descend as far as possible; to find the configuration of stable equilibrium, one has only to look for the minimum of the height of the centre of gravity. This height, multiplied by the force of gravity, is called potential energy.

A chain hanging from both ends assumes a definite shape, which is determined by the condition that the height of the centre of gravity is a minimum. If the chain has very many links, we get a curve called the catenary. It can readily be shown by means of a heavy chain, the centre of gravity of which is marked by a construction of light levers, that disturbance of the equilibrium of the chain in any arbitrary way causes the centre of gravity of the chain to rise.

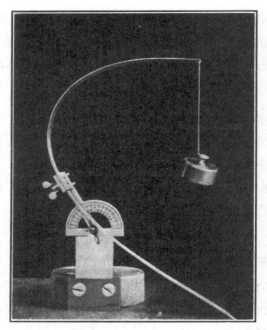

Fig. 1

Fig. 1 illustrates an example where gravity competes with another force, elasticity. A steel tape is clamped at one end and carries a weight at the other. This weight is pulled downwards by gravity, while the tape tries to resist bending in virtue of its elasticity. This

沿直线行进，但是我们并不明白它是如何迅速地对到达远处某个地方所有可能的路线进行对比并从中选择最短的一条的——这些听起来似乎都很形而上学。

但我们在探究以上想法之前，我们自己必须深信，在物理学的所有方面都存在最小性原理，它们不仅是正确的，而且是物理定律中很有用且具有启发性的公式。

毫无疑问，静力学，即各类系统在力的作用下最终都将处于平衡态的学说，成功应用了极小原理。重心趋向于处在尽量低的位置；为了得到稳定的平衡态结构，我们只能去寻求重心高度的极小值。重力乘以这个高度将得到所谓的势能。

两端悬挂的一条链将呈现出确定的形状，这个形状是在重心高度取极小值的条件下得到的。如果这条链有很多链环，我们将得到被称为悬链线的曲线形状。这很容易通过一条重的链条表示出来，它的重心是用光杠杆的测量方法进行标记的，用任何方式对链条的平衡位置进行扰动都会导致链条重心的上升。

图 1

图 1 描述了一个重力与另一种力即弹力相互竞争的例子。一根钢尺一端被夹紧固定住，另一端悬挂着一个砝码。这个砝码被重力往下拉，而钢尺由于具有弹性而

elastic force also has a potential energy; for a definite amount of work must be done to bend the tape into a given curved shape. Now there are definite positions of equilibrium in which the total energy, that of gravitation plus that of elasticity, is as small as possible. Generally there are two such positions. Changing the clamping angle carefully, a position is found when a jump suddenly occurs from one position to another on the opposite side. This instability is determined by the condition of minimum energy. We can summarize the facts connected with the limits of stability by drawing a graph, Fig. 2, not of the elastic lines themselves, but by plotting the angle of inclination against the distance from the free end. We obtain wave-shaped curves, all starting horizontally from the line representing the end carrying the weight. These curves have an envelope which separates the regions in which one or several curves are going through each point, and calculation shows that this envelope is just the limit of stability. We shall return to this example later when discussing the minimum principles of dynamics.

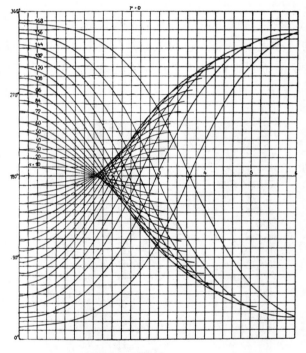

Fig. 2

Another example of the statical principle of minimum energy is provided by soap bubbles. Soap films have the property of contracting as much as possible; the potential energy is proportional to the surface area. Therefore soap films are surfaces of smallest area, or minimal surfaces. Nature is an expert mathematician, quickly finding the solution.

These experiments are not merely pretty toys without serious background. They have been chosen only for the sake of illustration. The real importance of the principle of minimum energy can scarcely be exaggerated. All engineering constructions are based on it, and also

抵制弯曲。因为必须做一定量的功才能使钢尺弯曲成一定形状的弧线，所以弹力也有相应的势能。事实上有一些确定的平衡位置，其总的能量即引力和弹力相应的势能之和取最小值。通常存在两个这样的平衡位置。慢慢地改变钢尺被夹的角度，我们可以找到这样一个位置，该位置上的钢尺可能突然朝反方向弯曲成相反的形状。这种不稳定性是由能量极小值的条件所决定的。我们总结了与稳定性极限相关的事实并用图形（图2）表示出来，图2所画的并不是弹性曲线本身，而是倾斜角与自由端到固定点距离两者的关系曲线。我们得到了波形曲线，这些曲线都是一端挂着砝码的曲线沿水平方向的变化曲线。这些曲线具有一个包络面，它把通过同一个点的一条或几条曲线与其他曲线分隔开来，相关的计算表明，包络面就是稳定性的极限条件。后面讨论到动力学的极小原理时我们将回来继续研究这个例子。

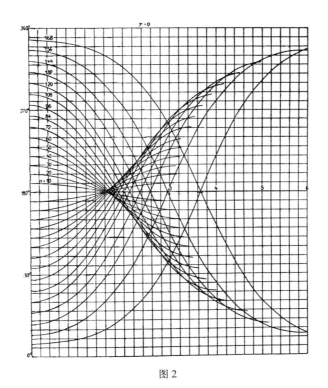

图 2

另一个证明极小能量静态原理的例子是肥皂泡。肥皂泡具有尽可能收缩变小的性质；其势能与表面面积成正比。因此，肥皂泡具有最小范围的表面，或者说极小的表面。自然界是一位专业的数学家，它很快就找到了这个问题的解决办法。

这些实验并不是不能应用于实际的玩具模型。选择它们只是为了便于说明。我们绝对没有夸大极小能量原理的实际重要性。它是所有工程建筑的基础，也是物理

all structural problems in physics and chemistry.

Models of crystal lattices provide examples of this. A crystal is a regular arrangement of atoms of definite kinds in space. Now the models representing the crystal lattices of two chemically similar compounds, namely, common salt (NaCl) and caesium chloride (CsCl) are different in structure. Why are they different? Because, as the caesium atoms are much larger than the sodium atoms, the potential energy differs in the two cases and its minimum is attained for different configurations.

Considerations of this kind, more or less quantitative, enable us to understand a great number of facts about the internal structure of solid matter.

Before we proceed to the consideration of minimum principles in dynamics, where the situation is not as clear and satisfactory as in statics, we must first mention another part of physics which in a sense occupies an intermediate position between statics and dynamics. It is the theory of heat, thermodynamics and statistical mechanics.

There is a very important extremum principle, discovered by Lord Kelvin, which governs irreversible processes: a quantity called "entropy" increases in the process and has a maximum for the final equilibrium state. It is not easy to describe this miraculous entropy in terms of directly observable quantities, such as volume, pressure, temperature, concentration, heat. But its meaning is immediately obvious from the point of view of atomic theory. A model will facilitate the explanation. Take a flat box like a little billiard table into which marbles can be put. If I carefully place them in the right-hand half, I have a state of partial order; if I shake the box they spread out over the whole box and attain a configuration of lower order. If I throw some marbles into the box one after the other so that their position is purely accidental, it is very improbable that they will all fall in the right-hand half. One can easily calculate the probability of a uniform distribution over the whole box as compared with one in which the majority of the marbles is in the right half; and one finds overwhelming odds in favour of the uniform distribution. Now the statistical theory of heat interprets the entropy of a system with the aid of the probability of the distribution of the atoms, and the tendency of entropy to increase is explained by the obvious fact that states of higher disorder have a higher probability.

Let us now come back to the minimum principles of dynamics.

The first problem of this kind—first both in historical order and in order of simplicity— was formulated at the end of the seventeenth century by Johann Bernoulli of Basle, one of a great family which produced many famous scholars and especially mathematicians. It is the problem of the curve of quickest descent or brachistochrone: given two points at different levels, not in the same vertical line, to determine a connecting curve in such a way that the time taken by a body to slide without friction under the action of gravity

学和化学中所有结构问题的基础。

晶格模型提供了这类例子。晶体是确定种类的原子在空间中规则排列形成的。由两种化学性质类似的化合物即普通的盐（NaCl）和氯化铯（CsCl）各自组成的晶格的模型在结构上是不同的。为什么二者会存在这样的差别呢？因为铯原子的尺寸远大于钠原子，所以两种情况下的势能不一样，而势能取极小值时对应的原子构型也不一样。

以上这类问题的考虑或多或少能从定量的角度帮助我们了解很多固体物质内部结构的情况。

由于动力学中的极小原理并不像静力学中的那样清楚和令人满意，因此，在开始考虑动力学的极小原理之前，我们有必要先提到物理学的另一部分，它在某种意义上来说是介于静力学和动力学之间的。这就是热学、热力学和统计力学的理论。

开尔文勋爵发现了控制不可逆过程的很重要的极值原理：被称为"熵"的物理量在不可逆过程中是不断增大的，并在最终的平衡态下达到最大值。很难用直接的可观测量，如体积、压力、温度、浓度和热量等来描述这个不可思议的熵。但是我们可以很容易地从原子理论的角度得到熵的物理意义。以下这个模型将帮助我进一步解释熵的意义。取一个如同台球桌那样扁平的可放入弹球的盒子。如果我们小心地把这些弹球摆在盒子的右半部分，这时得到的状态是部分有序；如果我们摇动盒子使这些弹球分布在整个盒子的范围内，得到的是一个更低序的状态。如果我将这些弹球一个接一个地扔进盒子里，则每个弹球的位置都是随机的，就不太可能出现所有的弹球都落到右半部分的情况了。我们可以很容易地计算出弹球在整个盒子内均匀分布的概率，并把这个概率与大部分弹球都位于右半部分的概率进行比较；人们发现均匀分布的情况存在压倒性的优势。热学的统计理论借助原子的分布概率解释了系统中的熵，而我们可以由越无序的状态出现的概率越大这个明显的事实来解释熵增加的趋势。

现在我们回来继续讨论动力学极小原理。

17 世纪末巴塞尔的约翰·伯努利阐述了我们要讨论的这类问题中的一个，这个问题不仅在历史顺序上是最早出现的，在这类问题中也是最简单的，伯努利家族是一个大家族，并且产生了许多著名的学者，尤其是数学家。这是一个关于最快速下降曲线或者说捷线的问题：给定两个不同水平高度上的点，它们不在同一竖直线上，为了确定这样一条曲线，使物体在重力作用下从较高点沿着该曲线无摩擦地滑到较

from the higher point to the lower is a minimum—compared of course with all possible curves through the two points. With a model having three paths, namely, a straight line, an are of a circle and an intermediate curve known as a cycloid, it can be shown that it is not the straight line on which a rolling ball arrives first, nor the steep descent of the circular arc, but the cycloid. If you were to try with any other curves, you would always find the same result, for the cycloid has been constructed according to the theoretical calculation.

The determination of this brachistochronic property of the cycloid was a very satisfactory piece of mathematics. It attracted much attention, and there is no philosopher of this period who did not test his analytical powers by solving similar extremal problems. Another member of the Bernoulli family, Daniel Bernoulli, developed at the beginning of the eighteenth century the minimum principle of statics and applied it to the catenary and the elastics line. Encouraged by these successes, he raised the question whether it was possible to characterize the orbit, and even the motion in the orbit, of a body subject to given forces—for example, a planet—by a minimum property of the real motion as compared with all other imagined or virtual motions. He put this question to the foremost mathematician of his time, Leonard Euler, who was very much interested in it and found, in the autumn of 1743, a solution which he explained with the help of various examples in a book published in 1744. It is the basis of the *principle of least action* which has played so prominent a part in physics right up to the present time.

The history of this principle, however, is an amazing tangle of controversies, quarrels over priority and other unpleasant matters. Maupertuis, in the same year, 1744, presented a paper to the Paris Academy of Sciences in which he substituted for Fermat's optical principle of the shortest light path, which we have already discussed, a rather arbitrary hypothesis, and extended the latter, in 1746, to all kinds of motions. He never gave a satisfactory proof of his principle (which is not surprising as it is incorrect), but defended it by metaphysical arguments based on the economy of Nature. He was violently attacked by Chevalier d'Arcy in Paris, Samuel König from Bern and others, who showed that if maupertuis's principle were true, thrifty Nature would be forced in certain circumstances to spend not a minimum but a maximum of action! Euler, whose principle is quite correct, behaved rather strangely; he did not claim his own rights, but even expressed his admiration for Maupertuis's principle, which he declared to be more general. The reasons for this attitude are difficult to trace. One of them seems to have been the publication by König of a fragment of an alleged letter of Leibniz in which the principle was enunciated. The genuineness of this letter could never be proved, and it seems probable that it was a forgery designed to weaken Maupertuis's position. This may have brought Euler over to the side of Maupertuis, who was at this time president of the Berlin Academy and a special favourite of the king, Frederic II, later known as the Great. The dispute was now carried over into the sphere of the court of Sanssouci and even into the arena of politics. Voltaire, friend of Frederic, who heartily disliked the haughty president of the Academy,

低点的过程中时间最短，我们当然要对通过这两点的所有可能曲线进行比较。使用一个具有三条路径的模型，三条路径分别为直线、圆的一段弧线和被称为摆线的中间曲线，可以看到，最先到达较低点的并不是沿着直线滚动的小球，也不是沿着圆弧的陡峭弧度滚动的小球，而是沿着摆线滚动的小球。如果你尝试其他任何曲线，你将会发现结果总是一样的，因为摆线就是按照理论计算所得出的时间最短的轨迹。

确定摆线的捷线过程在数学处理方面是完美、无可挑剔的。这类极值问题受到了广泛的关注，在那个时期，没有一个哲学家不是通过解决类似的极值问题来检验自己的分析结果的。18 世纪初，伯努利家族的另一个成员丹尼尔·伯努利发展了静力学的极小原理，并成功地把该原理应用到悬链线和弹性线的情况中。在以上这些成就的鼓舞下，他提出这样一个问题：通过真实运动情况的极小性质（与其他所有想象的或可能实现的运动情况相比较），是否可以描述出给定作用力情况下物体的运动轨迹，甚至是轨迹中物体的运动情况呢？例如描述一颗行星的运动情况。他向当时最有名的数学家伦纳德·欧拉提出了这个问题，欧拉对此很感兴趣并于 1743 年的秋天给出了这个问题的答案，之后，他在 1744 年出版的书中借助各类例子对此作了进一步的解释。这就是迄今为止在物理学中一直扮演着重要角色的**最小作用量原理**的基础。

与这个最小作用量原理有关的是一段充满混乱的不可思议的历史，其中出现了发现原理的优先权之争和其他不愉快的事件。同样是在 1744 年，莫佩尔蒂向巴黎科学院提交了一篇论文，文中他把我们前面已经讨论过的费马提出的最小光程的光学原理替换成一个他自己主观的假设，并于 1746 年把他的假设推广到所有的运动情况中。他并没有对他的原理给出满意的证明（这并不奇怪，因为他的原理本身就是不正确的），而是在自然经济性的基础上以形而上学的论据进行论证。他受到了巴黎的达西爵士、伯尔尼的塞缪尔·柯尼希和其他人的猛烈攻击，他们指出，如果莫佩尔蒂的主张是正确的话，那么一向经济节俭的自然在某些情况下将被迫做最大的而不是最小的功！欧拉提出的原理是正确的，但他的行为颇为奇怪；他非但没有声明自己发现该原理的优先权，反而对莫佩尔蒂的原理表示赞赏，并宣称这个原理是更普遍的。我们很难找到欧拉持这种态度的原因。其中的一个原因似乎是由于柯尼希公开了所谓的莱布尼茨信件的一部分，该部分对最小作用量原理也进行了阐述。这封信的真实性从未得到证实，似乎很有可能是伪造的，目的是用来削弱莫佩尔蒂的地位。这也许是使欧拉站在莫佩尔蒂这一边的原因，当时的莫佩尔蒂是柏林学院的院长并且特别受当时的国王弗雷德里克二世，也就是后来所谓的弗雷德里克大帝的喜爱。这场关于最小作用量原理的争辩不但在无忧宫的范围内展开了，后来甚至进入了政界的活动舞台。弗雷德里克的朋友伏尔泰非常讨厌傲慢的柏林学院院长莫

took the side of the "underdog", König, and wrote a caustic pamphlet, "Dr. Akakia", against Maupertuis. But the king, although he thoroughly enjoyed Voltaire's witty satire, could not sacrifice his grand president and was compelled to defend Maupertuis. This led at last to the disruption of their friendship and to Voltaire's flight from Berlin, as described in many biographies of Frederic and of Voltaire.

The curse of confusion has rested for a long period on the principle of least action. Lagrange, whose work was the culmination of the development of Newton's dynamics, gives an unsatisfactory formulation of the principle. Jacobi restricts it in such a way that the minimum condition determines the orbit correctly; the motion in the orbit must be found with the help of the energy equation. This was an important step. But the spell was at last broken by the great Irishman, Sir William Rowan Hamilton, whose principle is mathematically absolutely correct, simple and general. At the same time, it put an end to the interpretation of the principle expressing the economy of Nature. For there is, by a kind of fortunate mathematical coincidence, a statical problem for which the statical minimum principle for the potential energy coincides formally with Hamilton's principle of least action for the pendulum; this statical problem is the loaded steel tape considered before. The curves representing the angle of inclination of the elastic line as a function of the distance from the free end are exactly the same lines as those representing the angle of deflection of the pendulum as a function of time (see Fig. 2).

Now we have seen that only those regions of the graph which are simply covered by the lines correspond to a real minimum, a stable configuration of the elastic line. There are other regions, those beyond the envelope, where two or more lines pass through a given point. Only one of those lines corresponds to a real minimum. But both represent possible motions of the pendulum. Although the conditions at the ends of the elastic tape do not correspond exactly to those at the ends of the time interval in Hamilton's principle, there is this fact in common: if the length of the tape or the corresponding time interval in Hamilton's principle for the pendulum exceed a certain limit, there is more than one possible solution, and not each of them can correspond to a true minimum, though to a possible motion. In this way we come to the conclusion that the actual motion is not in every case distinguished by a genuine extremal property of action but by a less obvious mathematical property called "stationary" configuration.

Thus the interpretation in terms of economy breaks down. We may regard the idea of finding purpose and economy in natural laws as an absurd piece of anthropomorphism, a relic of a time when metaphysical thinking dominated science.

The importance of Hamilton's principle lies in a different direction altogether. It is not Nature that is economical, but science. All our knowledge starts with collecting facts; but proceeds by summarizing numerous facts by simple laws and these again by more general laws. This process is very obvious in physics. We may recall, for example, Maxwell's electromagnetic theory of light, by which optics became a branch of general electrodynamics. The minimum principles are a very powerful means to this end of

佩尔蒂，因此，他站到了"受压迫者"柯尼希的一边，并写了《阿卡基亚博士》这本小册子来讽刺莫佩尔蒂。虽然弗雷德里克非常欣赏伏尔泰机智的讽刺风格，但是为了不让自己尊贵的院长的利益受到损害，他不得不替莫佩尔蒂辩护。这最终导致了弗雷德里克和伏尔泰的友谊破灭，随后伏尔泰逃离柏林，这些在许多关于弗雷德里克或伏尔泰的传记中都有所描述。

如同受到了诅咒一样，人们在最小作用量原理上困惑了很长时间。拉格朗日的工作把牛顿力学发展到了极致，但是他给出的最小作用量原理的形式并不令人满意。雅可比给拉格朗日的形式加上了限制条件使得极小值条件可以给出物体正确的运动轨迹；但必须知道能量方程才能得到轨迹中具体的运动情况。这是极小原理发展历史上很重要的一步。最终，对这个原理的诅咒被伟大的爱尔兰人威廉·罗恩·哈密顿爵士打破了，他所表述的该原理在数学上是完全正确、简单且普适的。同时，他也结束了用自然的经济性来解释该原理的时代。由于幸运的数学巧合，势能的静态极小原理这个静力学问题与摆的哈密顿最小作用量原理在形式上完全符合；先前我们讨论的一端悬挂砝码的钢尺就是这种静力学情况之一。钢尺弯曲的倾斜角是其自由端到固定点距离的函数，而摆的偏转角是时间的函数，但是表示钢尺倾斜角的曲线与表示摆偏转角的曲线却是严格一致的（见图2）。

现在我们已经看到，图中只有那些被曲线简单覆盖的区域对应于实际的极小值范围，即对应弹性尺形变的稳定构型。而包络面以外的其他区域中存在两条或多条曲线穿过同一个给定点的情况。其中只有一条对应实际的极小值。以上两种对应实际极小值的情况都是摆可能的运动情况。虽然弹性钢尺端点的限制条件与哈密顿原理中每个时间间隔内端点的限制条件并不严格一致，但是在以下情况中它们有一样的规律：如果钢尺的长度或相应于哈密顿原理中钟摆模型的时间间隔超过一定的极限，将不止有一种可能的解存在，虽然这些解都对应于可能的运动情况，但并不是每一个解都存在真正的极小值与之对应。在这种情况下，我们得到的结论是：实际的运动情况是否存在并不总是以真正的作用量的极值性质作为判断依据的，而是以相对不明显的数学性质即所谓的"稳态"构型作为判断依据的。

因此从自然的经济性解释极小原理失败了。我们认为这种在自然规律中寻找目的和经济性的想法是一种可笑的拟人论的想法，它是形而上学的思维主导科学的时代留下的残余。

总而言之，哈密顿的极小原理的重要性体现在完全不同的方面。具有经济性的并不是自然而是科学。我们所有的知识都是从收集到的事实经验出发的；但我们进一步要做的是把这些无数的事实经验总结发展成为简单的规律，并把这些简单规律再次总结发展成为更加普适的规律。在物理学中这个过程是显而易见的。我们可以回想一下，例如在麦克斯韦关于光的电磁理论中，光学变成了广义电动力学的一个

unification. The ideal would be to condense all laws into a single law, a universal formula, the existence of which was postulated more than a century ago by the great French astronomer, Laplace.

If we follow the Viennese philosopher, Ernst Mach, we must consider economy of thought as the only justification of science. I do not share this view—there are other aspects and justifications of science. But I do not deny that economy of thought and condensation of the results are very important, and I consider Laplace's universal formula as a legitimate ideal. There is no question that the Hamiltonian principle is the adequate formulation of this tendency. It would be the universal formula if only the correct expressions for the potential energy of all forces were known. Nineteenth century thinkers believed more or less explicitly in this programme, and it was successful in an amazing degree.

By choosing a proper expression for the potential energy, nearly all phenomena could be described, including not only the dynamics of rigid and elastic bodies, but also that of fluids and gases, as well as electricity and magnetism, together with electronics and optics. The culmination of this development was Einstein's theory of relativity, by which the abstract principle of action regained a simple geometrical interpretation. The motions of the planets can be considered as "geodesics" in the four-dimensional space formed by adding time to our common space. Einstein's law of gravitation, which contains Newton's law as a limiting case, can also be derived from an extremum principle in which the quantity that is an extremum can be interpreted as the total curvature of the space-time world.

We call this period of physics which ends with the theory of relativity the classical period, in contrast to the recent period which is dominated by quantum theory. The new quantum mechanics assumes that all laws of physics are of statistical character. The fundamental quantity is a wave function which obeys laws similar to those of an acoustical or optical wave; it is not, however, an observable quantity, but determines indirectly the probability of observable processes. The point which interests us here is the fact that even this abstract wave function of quantum mechanics satisfies an extremum principle of the Hamiltonian type.

We are still far from knowing Laplace's universal formula, but we may be convinced that it will have the form of an extremal principle, not because Nature has a will or purpose or economy, but because the mechanism of our thinking has no other way of condensing a complicated structure of laws into a short expression.

(**143**, 357-361; 1939)

分支。在达到理论大统一的过程中，极小原理是一个强有力的手段。最理想的情况是把所有的规律浓缩成一个规律，一个普适的公式，而早在一个多世纪之前，法国伟大的天文学家拉普拉斯就已经提出过这种猜想了。

如果按照维也纳哲学家恩斯特·马赫的观点，则我们应该把是否具有经济性作为判断科学是否合理的唯一条件。我并不赞同这种观点——我认为还有其他判断科学合理性的方面和办法。这里我并不是认为思维的经济性和对结果的归纳不重要，而且我也认为拉普拉斯提到的普适的公式是一种合理的想法。毫无疑问，哈密顿原理是一个大家认可的倾向于成为普适规律的原理。如果已知所有作用力势能的正确表达式，哈密顿原理就将是一个普适的原理。19 世纪，几乎所有的思想家们都明确相信这个原理是普适的，而这个原理也确实取得了惊人的成功。

如果我们选择合适的势能表达式，哈密顿原理就可以描述几乎所有的现象，不仅包括刚体、弹性体的动力学，也包括流体、气体的动力学以及电学、磁学、电子学和光学。爱因斯坦的相对论是这个理论发展的极致，其中抽象的作用量原理又可以用简单的几何学进行解释了。在通常的空间中加入时间这个维度后，则我们可以认为行星的运动轨迹是这种四维空间中的"测地线"。牛顿运动定律作为一种极限情况被包含在爱因斯坦的引力定律当中，而我们也可以从极值原理导出后者，其中，极值原理中的极值这个量可以被解释为时空世界总的曲率。

我们把相对论出现之前的时期称为经典物理学的时期。与之相对的是最近以量子理论为主导的时期。新的量子力学假定所有的物理规律都具有统计特性。其中最基本的物理量是一个与声波和光波遵循类似规律的波函数；然而，它并不是一个可观测量，而是间接决定了可观测过程的概率。这里我们感兴趣的方面是，即便是量子力学中这个抽象的波函数也是满足哈密顿形式的极值原理的。

虽然要得到拉普拉斯所谓的普适公式还有很长的路要走，但我们深信最终我们将得到极值原理普适的形式，这并非出于自然界的愿望、宗旨或经济性，而是因为以我们现在的思维方式还没有其他办法能将复杂的结构规律浓缩成简单的表达式。

（沈乃澂 翻译；葛墨林 审稿）

Origin of the Earth's Magnetic Field

W. M. Elsasser

Editor's Note

Although much was known in the late 1930s of the behaviour of the Earth's magnetic field, there was no theory of how it is maintained. While observers were entirely ignorant of the fact that the Earth's magnetic field reverses its direction spontaneously at intervals of 100,000 years or so, this did not prevent Walter Elsasser from the California Institute of Technology from constructing a theory of how the Earth's magnetic field might be sustained. The modern view is that the Earth's magnetism derives from the supposedly metallic molten core of the Earth, that the magnetic field at the surface of the Earth is shaped by the movement of liquid metal in the core, and that the question will not be settled until there is a much clearer picture of how molten material moves in the Earth's core.

THERE is considerable physical evidence that the Earth possesses a metallic core[1]. Jeffreys[2] has estimated the viscosity of the core and finds it as low as 10^{10} C.G.S. units. If this value is correct, an intense thermal convection must be maintained in the core by the heat development of radioactive impurities, even if the amount of the latter is exceedingly small compared to their concentration in the Earth's crust.

I have developed a tentative theory of the magnetic field based on the assumption that this field is caused by *thermo-electric* currents in the core which owe their existence to the conditions created by the turbulent convection. The thermo-electric current density is

$$I = \sigma \, \mathrm{grad} \, \omega - B \, \mathrm{grad} \, T, \tag{1}$$

where σ is the conductivity, ω the potential of the space and surface charges, B the thermo-electric constant of the material and T the temperature. σ, B, T are functions of the co-ordinates. If they are given, ω follows as solution of the differential equation div $I = 0$ together with proper boundary conditions.

It might appear surprising that the local fluctuations of the currents (1) should sum up to yield a resultant magnetic momentum which is approximately parallel to the Earth's axis. The reason for this is found in the action of the *Coriolis force* upon the mechanical motions of the fluid mass. A glance at the hydrodynamic equations will show that for small values of the viscosity the Coriolis force is vastly preponderant as compared to all other dynamical effects. This causes a peculiar east-westerly asymmetry of the temperature variations at a given level. The latter variations are, in the usual way, produced by the vertical component of the convective motions.

地磁场的成因

艾尔萨瑟

编者按

20 世纪 30 年代末，虽然人们对地磁场的现象已经相当了解，但却并没有理论可以解释其成因。当时的研究者完全不知道地磁方向约 10 万年就会自发地发生一次反转，但这并没有影响加州理工学院的沃尔特·艾尔萨瑟提出地磁场成因的理论。现代观点认为，地磁场来源于推测出的地球熔融的金属内核，即地表磁场是由于地球内核液态金属的运动而产生的，不过若要彻底解决这一问题必须先弄清地核内的熔融物质是如何运动的。

大量物理证据表明地球具有一个金属质的内核 [1]。杰弗里斯 [2] 估算地核的黏度仅为 10^{10} 个单位（厘米克秒制）。如果这个估算值正确的话，那么地核内一定存在着由放射性杂质产生的热所引起的强烈的热对流，尽管放射性杂质的量相对于它们在地壳中的丰度来说非常小。

假设磁场是由地核内的"热电"流引起的，而热电流本身是由湍流对流所引发的环境所造成的。基于该假设，我给出了一个有关地磁场的尝试性理论。热电流的密度为：

$$I = \sigma \ \mathrm{grad} \ \omega - B \ \mathrm{grad} \ T \tag{1}$$

式中 σ 为电导率，ω 为电荷内部和表面的电势，B 为物质的热电常数，T 为温度。σ、B、T 为坐标函数。如果它们已经给定，则 ω 将是微分方程 $\mathrm{div} \ I = 0$ 在适当边界条件下的解。

有些令人吃惊的是，方程（1）中电流的局部起伏加起来可以形成一个近似与地轴平行的磁矩。这是因为流体的机械运动受到了**地转偏向力**的作用。看一下流体力学方程就会发现当黏度值较小时，相对于其他动力学因素，地转偏向力占绝对优势。在给定情况下，这就会引起一个明显的东西不对称温差。这种温差通常是由对流运动的垂直分量引起的。

For the further considerations, we shall confine ourselves to the second term on the right-hand side of equation (1), which presumably contributes the major part of the magnetic momentum. The discussion of the first term is closely analogous. It is readily seen that the magnetic dipole momentum vanishes, if, for a given depth, B is a constant. This means that in a homogeneous mass no temperature fluctuations would produce a magnetic momentum. In addition to the hypothesis of convective motions, we must therefore admit the existence of *inhomogeneities* in the Earth's core. Since any particle of the mass undergoes large pressure changes during vertical displacements, the inhomogeneities are best accounted for by phase transformations induced by the pressure changes which are a frequent occurrence at high pressures[3]. Perhaps there are also considerable chemical inhomogeneities present in the core, and while there would be a regular stratification in a state of rest, the distribution of the phases will become irregular under the constant stirring action of the convection.

No additional assumptions have been found necessary. An attempt has been made to estimate roughly the order of magnitude of the thermo-electric currents. Using some simple results of the theory of metallic conductivity, values of σ and B were estimated for iron under the physical conditions of the core. It was found that with temperature differences so low as $10°$ the current density is of the order of 10^{-6} amp./cm.^{2}. This is enough to explain the observed magnetic field as the result of a small one-sided excess in a current system of irregular distribution.

A full account of this investigation will appear shortly in the *Physical Review*.

(**143**, 374-375; 1939)

Walter M. Elsasser: California Institute of Technology, Pasadena, California.

References:

1. Jeffreys, H., "The Earth" (2nd ed., 1927, ch. VII).

2. Jeffreys, *Mon. Not. Roy. Astro. Soc., Geophys.* Suppl., 1, **371**, 416 (1926).

3. Bridgman, P. W., "The Physics of High Pressures" (London, 1931, ch. VIII).

为了深入分析，我们只关注方程（1）右侧的第二项，它应该是构成磁矩的主要部分。对第一项的讨论与此极为类似。于是我们可以很容易看出，如果 B 在给定的深度处为常数，那么磁偶极矩将变为零。也就是说，在一个均一的物体中，温度的变化不会导致磁矩的产生。因此，除了假设有对流运动之外，我们还必须承认地核内存在**不均一性**。地核内所有质点发生垂直位移时都经历了很大的压力变化，所以其不均一性的产生最有可能是由于压力变化引起的相变，这种相变在高压条件下很常见 [3]。地核中可能还存在很大的化学不均一性。地核在静止状态时会维持规则的分层现象，但对流的持续扰动会使各相的分布变得不均匀。

暂时未发现其他的必要假设。我还尝试对热电流的数量级作了大致估计。根据金属导电性理论的一些简单结论，估算了在地核物理条件下铁的电导率 σ 值和热电常数 B 值。研究发现，当温差仅为 10 度时，电流密度为 10^{-6} 安培 / 平方厘米。这足以说明观测到的磁场是由于不规则分布的电流体系中一个较小的单边过剩而产生的。

关于该项研究的详细情况将于近期发表在《物理学评论》上。

（齐红艳 蔡则怡 翻译；孟庆任 审稿）

The "Failure" of Quantum Theory at Short Ranges and High Energies

Arthur Eddington was by now the most distinguished astronomer in Britain. He had turned his attention to the problems thrown up by the new quantum mechanics. He quickly replied to Bhabha's claim that quantum mechanics could not accommodate the behaviour of atomic particles at high energy with an account of how he proposed to deal theoretically with nuclei of all kinds, concluding that quantum mechanics was not in need of revision. Both Bhabha and Eddington were, unfortunately, unaware of the complications that would arise from the introduction of mesons into their developing theory.

IN Dr. Bhabha's letter in *Nature* of February 18, reference is made to a breakdown of quantum theory at high energies and short intervals. This seems to be widely interpreted as setting a limit to the validity of our present physical conceptions. Some indeed would associate it with a fundamental discontinuity of structure of space and time. I have no occasion to criticize Dr. Bhabha's letter which, so far as it goes, is opposed to the more extreme interpretations. But I venture to suggest that an unnecessary mystery is being made of what is really an elementary point of relativity theory. In short, we know why the present theory has got into difficulties, and we know what must be taken into account if it is to get out of them.

Relativity theory begins with a denial of absolute motion. Every observed velocity dx/dt is a relative velocity of two physical objects. Likewise the "x" of which velocity is the time-derivative is a relative displacement of two physical objects. Both objects are connected with the space-time frame in the way pointed out by Heisenberg; namely, they are not locatable as points (or, in four dimensions, worldlines) but have an uncertainty of position and momentum.

Usually dx/dt and x are assigned to one of the objects (here called the object particle), the other being regarded as a reference body. In precise formulae, the reference body must evidently be a particle. The reference particle is then the physical "origin" from which the observable co-ordinate x of the object particle is measured. Current quantum theory has repeated the pre-relativity mistake of paying insufficient attention to the definition of the physical reference system to which its exact formulae are intended to apply. It enunciates formulae involving x and $\partial/\partial x$, but omits to specify the standard deviation (uncertainty) of position and momentum of the origin from which x is measured. Clearly, the formulae cannot be true for an arbitrary standard deviation; if true at all, they must hold for a

短程和高能中量子理论的"失败"

爱丁顿

编者按

阿瑟·爱丁顿是英国迄今为止最杰出的天文学家。后来他将注意力转向了新量子力学所引发的问题上。巴巴声称量子力学不适用于高能原子粒子的行为,爱丁顿随即对这一观点作出了回应。他阐述了理论上如何描述所有的原子核,进而认为量子力学没必要修正。不过遗憾的是巴巴和爱丁顿都没有意识到,当在他们的理论中引进介子后,相应会出现的一些新的问题。

在 2 月 18 日《自然》杂志上巴巴博士的文章中,提到了量子理论在短程和高能中存在问题。这似乎可以广泛的解释为需要对我们现有的物理概念的有效性做出限定。某些问题确实与基本的时间和空间结构的不连续性相关。现在严苛地质疑巴巴博士的文章还为时过早,就该文而言,它与更极端的解释相反。但我要冒昧地提出一个小的疑问,即究竟什么才真正是相对论的基本点。简言之,我们知道为什么现有的理论已经处于困境,并且我们也知道如果要克服这些困难必须要考虑什么。

相对论以否认绝对运动为出发点。每一个我们观测到的速度 dx/dt 都是两个物理对象的相对速度。同样地,"x"是两个物理对象之间的相对位移,而速度是"x"对时间的一阶导数。两个物体都与海森堡所指出的时空框架相联系;即它们并不是像三维空间中的点(或四维时空中的世界线)那样有确定的位置,它们的位置和动量具有不确定性。

通常,dx/dt 和 x 赋予其中一个物体(本文称之为实物粒子),另一个则被视为是参照物。显然,在精确的公式中,参照物必须是一个粒子。这个参照粒子即为物理"原点",我们可以由此测量实物粒子的可观测坐标 x。目前的量子理论已重复了相对论前时期的错误,即对精确公式所对应的物理参考系的定义不够重视。该理论虽然清楚地表达了包含 x 和 $\partial/\partial x$ 的公式,但却忽略了对 x 所参照的原点的位置和动量的标准偏差(不确定度)的测定。显然,公式并不可能对任意的一个标准偏差都是正确的;如果公式正确,它必然对应于特定位置的标准偏差 ε,并且这个标准偏

particular standard deviation of position ε which ought to have been specified. Since there is no explicit reference, the actual value of ε must be implicit in the empirical constants (such as h/mc) of the quantum formulae.

When two object particles with co-ordinates x_1 and x_2 are considered, the displacement ξ_0 of one relative to the other is observable independently of any origin of co-ordinates, being the original observable called "x" in our second paragraph. This must not be confused with the co-ordinate difference $\xi = x_2 - x_1$, which introduces twice over the uncertainty of the physical origin from which x_1 and x_2 are measured. We have (in the notation of the theory of errors)

$$\xi = \xi_0 \pm \varepsilon \sqrt{2}.$$

The failure of current theory is due especially to its omission to distinguish the two observables ξ and ξ_0.

The physical origin has uncertainty both of position and momentum; for if either were zero the other would be infinite, and the physical origin would not approximate to a geometrical origin with a definite world-line. An energy m_0c^2 corresponding to the mean square of the uncertain momentum is therefore associated with the origin. Except in two-body problems (in which one object particle is used as physical origin for the other) the practice is to treat all the object particles symmetrically; the physical origin must then be an additional *virtual* particle, that is, a particle inserted in the system as part of the apparatus of measurement, but not counted among the object particles, and only taken into account as representing the disturbance of the system which the carrying out of a measurement implies. The energy m_0c^2 belongs to the physical origin contemplated as a virtual particle, and gives it a proper mass m_0. In order that quantum equations may be definite, the uncertainty constants ε and m_0 of the physical origin must have standard values.

Naturally physicists who have neglected the uncertainty ε of the origin will find that their equations break down at distances of order ε. Nothing has gone wrong with space; it is the theorists who have failed to apply their own principles in relating the observable physical system to space. To state their failure summarily: there are two recognized principles of observability, namely, the quantum principle that an observable *object* has an uncertainty relation to the geometrical space-time frame, and the relativity principle that an observable *quantity* relates to two observable objects. Current theory recognizes these principles separately but not in combination; and in dealing with co-ordinates and momenta it pays attention only to the uncertainty at the object-particle end of the relation.

The remedy is obvious. I do not say that the application of the remedy is an easy matter; but, if it is clearly the thing most worth doing, that will not deter anyone. An astronomer, unable to solve his own "problem of three bodies", can only admire the success with which physicists tackle the more numerous closely interacting particles of the nucleus. But I think the advance would not be less rapid or less substantial if they gave up using the wrong formulae. My own work[1] (chiefly concerned with the momentum uncertainty m_0) has been

差也应当已确定。由于不存在明确的参照系，ε 的实际值必然隐含在量子公式的经验常数（例如 h/mc）中。

当考虑分别位于坐标 x_1 和 x_2 中的两个实物粒子时，一个粒子相对于另一个粒子的位移 ξ_0 是可观察的，这与任何坐标原点无关，也就是本文第二段中称为"x"的原始可观测量。一定不要把它与坐标差 $\xi = x_2 - x_1$ 相混淆，坐标差引入了测量 x_1 和 x_2 时所参照的物理原点两倍的不确定度。我们得到（用误差理论的符号表示）

$$\xi = \xi_0 \pm \varepsilon \sqrt{2}$$

目前理论的失败主要是忽略了两个可观测量 ξ 和 ξ_0 的区别所致。

物理原点具有位置和动量两种不确定度；因为如果其中任意一个物理量为零，那么另一个物理量必将是无穷大，那么物理原点就不会以有限的世界线接近几何原点。因此，存在一个对应于不确定动量均方值的能量 m_0c^2 与原点相联系。除了在二体问题中（其中一个实物粒子作为另一个的物理原点），实际上对所有的物体粒子都作无差别处理；我们用一个附加的**虚**粒子作为物理原点，即把一个粒子作为测量装置的一部分插入到系统中，但不计入实物粒子，而仅将其作为测量时所包含的系统扰动来考虑。能量 m_0c^2 对应于虚粒子考虑的物理原点，并给出其固有质量 m_0。为了可以确定量子方程，物理原点的不确定量 ε 和 m_0 必须具有标准值。

当然，忽略了原点不确定度 ε 的物理学家将会发现，他们的方程在量级为 ε 时会失效。空间本身没有问题；问题出在那些理论工作者身上，他们无法成功地应用自己的理论将可观测的物理系统与空间相联系。他们的失败可以概括地表述为：存在两个公认的关于可观测性的原理，即量子理论和相对性原理，在前者中可观测的**物体**对几何时空框架具有不确定关系，在后者中可观测的**量**与两个可观测的物体相关。目前的理论认为，这些原理相互独立无法结合；当我们处理坐标和动量时，仅需注意其关系中实物粒子端的不确定度。

补救措施是明显的。我并不是说完成修正是一件简单的事情；但是，如果它是一件最值得去做的事情，那就不会使任何人畏缩不前。一位不能解决自己"三体问题"的天文学家，只能羡慕物理学家处理原子核中大量存在短程相互作用的粒子时所取得的成就。但我认为，如果他们放弃使用错误的公式，不会使进展速度变缓，或使进展的实质性减弱。我自己的工作[1]（主要是关于动量不确定量 m_0）一直局限

confined to extra-nuclear problems; no insuperable difficulty has appeared, tough progress has not been easy.

I turn now to the actual values of ε and m_0. A geometrical frame of space-time is not a physical reference system, since its exactitude is incompatible with observability. (To assign infinite mass to the frame, so as to make both its position and velocity exact, would introduce infinite curvature, and defeat its use in a different way.) We turn it into a physical frame by associating with it uncertainty constants, namely, a particular length ε and a particular mass m_0. (In mathematical treatment we should assign to the frame a wave function describing a probability distribution corresponding to these constants.) These "put the scale into" physical systems, and all other natural lengths and masses will stand in a definite numerical ratio to them. Since we observe only relative scale, the arbitrariness of the initial choice of ε and m_0 is eliminated. From extra-nuclear investigations I have found that m_0 is 10/136 of the mass of a hydrogen atom; and ε, which is very simply related to certain magnitudes calculated in cosmological theory[2], has the value 1.10×10^{-13} cm. (For technical reasons, the constant more usually given is $k_0 = 2\varepsilon = 2.20 \times 10^{-13}$ cm.)

That the virtual particle of mass m_0, originally studied in extra-nuclear theory, is the particle now used in nuclear theory under the name of "mesotron", or "meson", admits, I think, of no doubt. But whether the usual assumption is correct, that nuclear mesotrons are the same as the actual mesotrons observed in a Wilson chamber, I have no means of judging. Since m_0 and ε are conjugate, it is optional which we treat as the more fundamental; but I would point out that to proceed *via* the mesotron mass is a roundabout way of getting at the range of nuclear forces, since the range is an immediate manifestation of the uncertainty of position of the origin. The nuclear force between two protons comes from an energy-singularity occurring when two protons coincide—a sink which (in uniform distribution) just compensates the Coulomb energy occurring when they do not coincide. The condition of coincidence $\xi = 0$ gives $\xi_0 = \pm \varepsilon \sqrt{2}$, which (for the calculated value of ε) agrees exactly with the range of force found by Breit, Condon and Present in their discussion of the scattering of protons.

(**143**, 432-433; 1939)

A. S. Eddington: Observatory, Cambridge, Feb. 27.

References:
1. Eddington, "Relativity Theory of Protons and Electrons", Chapters XI, XII.
2. Eddington, *Proc. Roy. Soc.*, A, **162**, 155 (1937).

于核外问题；在此过程中虽然尚未出现不能克服的困难，但也是举步维艰。

现在我回到 ε 与 m_0 的实际值问题的讨论。时空的几何框架并不是物理参考系，因为其精确性与可观测性互不相容。（设框架质量无限大，以使其位置和速度两者的值均是精确的，但这将引出无限曲率，使得该框架以另外一种方式失效。）我们将它转化为具有不确定性常数的物理框架，即其中的不确定性常数就是特定的长度 ε 和特定的质量 m_0。（在数学处理中，我们应赋予框架一个波函数来描述与这些常数相应的概率分布。）对物理系统"进行标度变换"，即所有其他自然长度和质量将以与其成确定比率的数值形式出现。由于我们仅观测相对标度，排除了 ε 和 m_0 最初选择的任意性。根据核外研究我发现，m_0 是氢原子质量的 10/136；ε 与宇宙论 [2] 中计算得到的确定量值有非常简单的关系，数值为 1.10×10^{-13} 厘米 (出于技术方面的考虑，通常将常数取为 $k_0 = 2\varepsilon = 2.20 \times 10^{-13}$ 厘米)。

最初在核外理论中研究的质量为 m_0 的虚粒子，正是现在核理论中的"介子"，我认为这种观点是毋庸置疑的。但通常的假设是否正确，即核介子是否与威尔逊云室中观测到的实际介子相同，我还无法做出判断。由于 m_0 与 ε 是共轭的，因此选择哪个作为基本量是任意的；但我要指出的是，由介子的质量出发确定核力的作用范围是一种不直接的方式，因为此范围是原点位置不确定性的直接表现。在两个质子之间的核力来自两个质子重合时产生的能量奇点——一个下陷，它（在均匀分布中）刚好可以补偿两个质子不重合时产生的库仑能。在刚好符合 $\xi=0$ 的条件时，有 $\xi_0 = \pm \varepsilon \sqrt{2}$，这（在 ξ 的计算值方面）与布莱特、康登和普雷森特在他们对质子散射的论述中建立的力的范围精确地一致。

（沈乃澂 翻译；鲍重光 李军刚 审稿）

A Living Fish of Mesozoic Type

J. L. B. Smith

Editor's Note

Imagine discovering a dinosaur carcass on a lonely country road. That is not as fanciful as it seems, given the discovery over Christmas 1938 of a coelacanth off the coast of East London, South Africa—a fish believed to have been extinct since the age of the dinosaurs, some 80 million years before. By the time that ichthyologist James Leonard Brierley Smith could get to the scene to make the observations reported here, the single specimen had badly decomposed, but enough remained for him to be sure that the strange fish he named *Latimeria chalumnae* was indeed a coelacanth similar to the Cretaceous form *Macropoma*. Smith's hope that another specimen might be captured was fulfilled—but not for another dozen years.

EX Africa semper aliquid novi. It is my privilege to announce the discovery of a Crossopterygian fish of a type believed to have become extinct by the close of the Mesozoic period. This fish was taken by trawl-net at a depth of about 40 fathoms some miles west of East London on December 22, 1938. It was alive when caught, and shortly after it died it was handed over to Miss Courtenay-Latimer, curator of the East London Museum. Miss Latimer wrote to me, enclosing a sketch and brief particulars of the specimen. Owing to the seasonal disorganization of the postal services, the letter did not reach me at Knysna, some four hundred miles away, until ten days later. It was obvious from the sketch and notes that the fish was of a type believed long extinct. Immediate telephonic communication with the East London Museum revealed that, owing to lack of preserving equipment at that Institution, the putrefied body had been disposed of beyond any hope of redemption, and the fish had been mounted by the local taxidermist.

Since the fish was unquestionably alive when caught, there is at least a possibility that this zoological tragedy may be ameliorated by the capture of another specimen. This is not so remote as might appear. After careful inspection of the mounted specimen, a responsible citizen-angler of East London stated that about five years ago he had found precisely such a fish, only considerably larger (*sic*), partially decomposed, cast up by the waves on a lonely part of the shore east of East London. When he returned with assistance, the monster had vanished with a risen tide. With regard to the present specimen, fortunately both Miss Latimer and the taxidermist were drawn to observe details of the carcass very closely, so that exhaustive independent questioning has left me with at least some definite information about the missing parts. Fortunately also, the terminal caudal portion of the vertebral column and part of the pectoral girdle remain. The skull is of course intact.

一种存活至今的中生代鱼类

史密斯

编者按

你是否设想过在一条荒凉的乡间小路上发现一具恐龙尸体。鉴于 1938 年圣诞节期间在南非的东伦敦海岸发现了腔棘鱼（人们原以为这种鱼在 8,000 万年前的恐龙时代就已经灭绝了），上述想法也就不像看上去那么荒诞了。当鱼类学者詹姆斯·里奥纳多·布莱尔利·史密斯到达现场进行本次观察时，这一标本已经腐烂得很厉害了，但是残余的躯体足以使他确信，这个被他命名为拉蒂迈鱼的奇怪鱼类确实与白垩纪大盖鱼属的腔棘鱼非常相似。史密斯希望能够捕获另一个标本的愿望最终得到了满足，但那已是十几年后了。

"在非洲总是可以发现新东西"。我很荣幸地宣布，我们发现了一种被认为在中生代末期就已经灭绝的总鳍鱼。它是在 1938 年 12 月 22 日于东伦敦以西几英里的深约 40 英尺的水中用拖网捕到的。刚被捕获时它还是活的，死后不久它就被移交到东伦敦博物馆馆员考特尼－拉蒂迈小姐的手中。拉蒂迈小姐给我写了一封信，随信附有该鱼标本的草图并简述了它的特征。由于邮政服务季节性的混乱，信件直到 10 天后才到达 400 英里外我所在的克尼斯纳。从信中的标本草图和记述可以明显看出，这条鱼属于一种之前被认为早已经灭绝的种类。我立即电话联系东伦敦博物馆，才发现由于博物馆没有相应的保存设备，腐烂的鱼体已经被处理过，并且没有修复的可能了，而鱼已经被当地的剥制师制作成标本了。

既然鱼在捕获时确实是活着的，那么至少存在这样一种可能性，那就是我们可以通过捕获另一条这种类型的鱼来弥补这一动物学遗憾。这件事情并不像表面看起来的那样难以实现。在对已经被制作成标本的鱼体进行仔细的观察之后，一位来自东伦敦地区的可靠的当地垂钓者声称，大约 5 年前他发现过一条一模一样的鱼，只不过那条鱼相对大一些，鱼体已经部分腐烂了，被海浪冲到东伦敦东部一个偏僻的海岸。当他带着帮手赶回那个地方时，那条鱼已经被上涨的潮水带走了。关于现在的标本，幸亏拉蒂迈小姐和动物标本剥制师都曾非常细致地观察过鱼体的细节，因此通过详尽的单独访问，我获得了一些有关标本缺失部分的明确信息。同样值得庆幸的是，脊柱尾部末端和部分胸带保留了下来。鱼的头骨也是完整无缺的。

The specimen is 1,500 mm. in total length, and weighed 127 lb. when caught. The colour was a bright metallic blue, which has faded to brown with preservation.

In major characters this remarkable specimen shows close relationship with the Mesozoic genus *Macropoma* Agassiz, of the family Coelacanthidae, order Actinistia. The gephyrocercal tail with protruding axial supplement, the normal first dorsal, the obtuse lobation of the remaining fins, the ganoin tubercle ornamentation on the scales and on some of the dermal bones of the head, the nature and arrangement of the dentigerous bones of the mouth, and the form of the dermal armour of the head, are all typically coelacanthid.

The skeleton was cartilaginous, the vertebral column apparently tubular, and the whole fish extraordinarily oily. The fish has small spiracles situated as shown in the accompanying illustration, and a definite though not very obvious lateral line, which continues uninterrupted to the end of the supplementary caudal. Other differences from the known coelacanthid fishes are the pronounced pedunculation of the lobate pectorals, the reduction of the dermal armour of the head, and the presence of two small heavily ornamented bones at the anterior lower corner of the opercular plate, which probably correspond with the more fully developed inter- and sub-opercula of teleosts, also a similar posterior post-spiracular ossicle. Dermal parafrontals are not visible. There is a free tongue composed of four fused segments covered with presumably ossified tubercles.

Coelacanthid Fish from East London, South Africa.
The small arrow shows the position of the spiracle, and the dotted line indicates
the position of a membrane behind the first dorsal fin.

It is probable that systematists will wish to propose a new family (some even a new order) for this fish, but I am at present satisfied that it is close enough to the Mesozoic Coelacanthidae to justify its inclusion in that family. It has been noted that certain coelacanthid fishes underwent little apparent change from the Devonian to the Cretaceous. It is therefore not surprising that this species, which presumably has survived from the Mesozoic, should still retain most of the features which characterize that family.

鱼被捕获时，全长 1,500 毫米，重 127 磅。全身原呈明亮的金属蓝色，但在保存过程中发生褪色而变为褐色。

这件珍贵标本的主要特征表明，它与中生代的腔棘目腔棘鱼科的大盖鱼属有着密切的关系。矛型尾具凸起的轴对称的中央尾叶，正常的第一背鳍，其他鳍呈钝圆形的缺刻结构，鱼鳞和鱼头部的一些真皮骨上装饰有硬鳞质结节，鱼口中带齿骨骼的特性和排列，及头部真皮骨的形态，这些都是腔棘鱼所具有的典型特征。

骨架为软骨，脊柱呈明显的管状结构，而整个鱼体格外油滑。鱼有小型的喷水孔，具体位置见本文的插图，一条确定的但并不明显的侧线一直延伸到中央尾叶的末端。与已知腔棘鱼相比，此鱼还具有如下不同：显著的胸鳍肉柄，头部真皮骨板减少，在鳃盖板的前下角有两块被严重修饰过的小骨，这两块小骨可能与硬骨鱼发育更全面的间鳃盖骨和下鳃盖骨相对应，此外还有一块类似于尾部后通气孔的小骨。真皮额顶骨不可见。游离的鱼舌由四个愈合部分组成，并覆有可能骨化的结节。

南非东伦敦发现的腔棘鱼。
小箭头显示喷水孔，虚线指示位于第一背鳍后软膜的位置。

也许分类学家们希望为这种鱼建立一个新科（甚至新目），但是目前我确信这种鱼与中生代腔棘鱼科非常相似，甚至足以证明它们属于同一科。这个可能从中生代一直存活至今的鱼种，竟然仍保留有它所在科的大部分特征，但是鉴于一些腔棘鱼从泥盆纪到白垩纪几乎没有发生明显的变化，因此这就不足为奇了。

For the fish described and figured above I propose the name *Latimeria Chalumnoe* gen. et sp. nov.; the full account of the species and of its taxonomic relationships will be published in the *Transactions of the Royal Society of South Africa*.

(**143**, 455-456; 1939)

J. L. B. Smith: Rhodes University College, Grahamstown.

　　根据以上对这个鱼的描述和绘图，我建议将其命名为拉蒂迈鱼（新属新种）；关于这个物种的更详细全面的记述及其在分类学上的关系将刊登在《南非皇家学会学报》上。

（张玉光 翻译；陈平富 审稿）

Element 43

E. Segrè

Editor's Note

Thanks to the diligence of chemists in the early decades of the twentieth century, most of the elements predicted by Mendeleev's table (Mendeléeff's table) had been discovered, but there remained gaps, one of which was element 43—predicted to be closely similar to the known element rhenium. Emilio Segrè was one of the team of physicists who built the first cyclotron at Berkeley, California. In this brief note, he describes how one of the cyclotron's first uses was to make tiny quantities of element 43 by bombarding the element molybdenum with neutrons. The new element was eventually called technetium. Segrè was awarded a Nobel Prize in 1959, not for this work but for the discovery of the antiproton.

EVERY time that physics has offered a new analytical tool to chemistry, the most striking success has been the discovery of new elements. Rubidium and caesium are thus offsprings of the use of the spectroscope, polonium and radium were discovered through the new methods of radioactivity, hafnium and rhenium were recognized through their X-ray spectra.

Mendeléeff's work, on the other hand, by classifying the chemical types, has in a way set a limit to the possibility of further discoveries and gives also a method of predicting rather exactly the properties of the missing elements. These are element 43, a lighter homologue of rhenium; element 61, a rare earth; element 87, a halogen; and element 89, an alkali. The search for these elements in the minerals, the only source at our disposal until a few years ago, has not been successful, and none of them seems to have been recognized with certainty in the earth's crust, in spite of considerable effort[1].

Artificial radioactivity has supplied chemistry with a powerful new instrument, and from the point of view of the discovery of new elements its most striking feature is that one is able now to create, by transmutation from other elements, the element one wants to study. The first achievement in this type of investigation was the discovery of transuranic elements by Fermi and his co-workers, continuing the periodic system above uranium (No.92), although, in view of recent work, confirmation of their existence is needed.

In the search for the four missing elements lower than uranium, we have now been able to prepare element 43 and study its properties in detail. The substance was produced in the Berkeley cyclotron, which thus remains for the time being the only "mine" of the element. It was made by bombarding molybdenum with deuterons or with neutrons[2].

43号元素

20 世纪前几十年，由于化学家的不懈努力，门捷列夫周期表所预言的绝大多数元素均已被发现，但是还有一些位置空缺，其中之一就是 43 号元素，人们预测它非常类似于已知元素铼。埃米利奥·塞格雷所在的物理学家小组在加州伯克利建造了第一台回旋加速器。在这篇短文中，他描述了回旋加速器的一次早期应用，即如何用中子轰击钼元素得到了少量 43 号元素，而这种新元素最终被命名为锝。塞格雷于 1959 年获得了诺贝尔奖，但不是因为这项工作，而是因为他发现了反质子。

每当物理学为化学提供一种新的分析工具时，最为轰动的成果往往是新元素的发现。铷和铯的发现就是应用分光镜的结果，钋和镭则是通过新的放射性方法发现的，而铪和铼是通过它们的 X 射线光谱找到的。

另一方面，门捷列夫对元素的化学类型进行分类的研究工作，已经在某种程度上限定了进一步发现的可能性，并且为准确预言尚未发现的元素的性质提供了一种方法。这些元素包括：43 号元素，它与铼同族但质量相对较轻；61 号元素，一种稀土元素；87 号元素，一种卤素；以及 89 号元素，一种碱金属。直到几年前，矿物还是我们仅有的进行实验的资源，尽管已经付出了相当多的努力 [1]，但在矿物中寻找上述元素的研究一直没有取得成功，目前还不能完全确定地壳中是否存在上述元素。

人工放射性已为化学研究提供了一种强有力的新工具，从发现新元素的角度来看，最令人惊奇的是，人们可以通过利用其他元素的嬗变来创造出想要研究的元素。这类研究的第一个成果是费米及其合作者发现的超铀元素，从而使元素周期表在铀（92 号元素）之后得以延续，尽管从近期的研究来看，还需要进一步确认这些元素的存在。

在寻找上述四种原子序数小于铀的元素的过程中，现在我们已经可以制备出 43 号元素并对其性质进行详细研究。该元素产生于伯克利的回旋加速器中，于是在当时这台加速器就成了寻找该元素的唯一"矿源"。现在我们用氘核或者中子 [2] 轰击钼就可以得到这种新元素。

At least five radioactive isotopes of atomic number 43 have been recognized[3] among the products of the bombardment, and some of them have a half-life long enough to permit a rather complete investigation of the chemical behaviour of element 43. Actually perusal of the periodic table may help to predict many of its chemical properties but, on the other hand, the finer details, often very important from the analytical point of view, may be found only by direct experiment.

The first properties to be studied obviously should be the analytical ones, in order to be able to identify the new element and separate it from all the others. Many of the separations are quite elementary and there is no need of any special study to devise them, but for the separation from the neighbouring elements things are more complicated, and emphasis has to be put on the separation from manganese, molybdenum, ruthenium and especially rhenium, which are the four elements closest to element 43 in the periodic table, and have most resemblance to it. The methods and principles of the chemistry of minute amounts of substance and of radioactive detection, as worked out by Curie, Rutherford, Soddy and others in their classical work on the natural radioactive elements, have been employed throughout and satisfactory methods of separation have been worked out. The fundamentals of the analytical chemistry of this element have thus been secured and can now be utilized for further progress.

Practically none of the many physical constants of the new element can be determined using amounts of the order of magnitude of 10^{-10} gm. of substance as produced artificially; but this situation prevails also for some of the natural radioactive substances, and there is at present no possibility of overcoming this difficulty. On the other hand, properties such as the volatility of certain compounds, partition coefficient in fractional crystallization, etc., can be determined even with such tiny amounts of substance, and some of these have actually been measured.

A fortunate circumstance allows us to detect even the $K\alpha$ line of the X-ray spectrum of element 43, though the amount of substance would not be sufficient to show, by ordinary methods of external excitation, this spectral line, or any optical line. One of the radioactive isotopes of 43 exists in two isomeric states and the upper state decays into the lower. By the mechanism of internal conversion of the gamma rays, these transitions eject the K electron of the atom 43, which is now in a condition to emit the characteristic X-ray line. This line has been identified by its absorption discontinuity in neighbouring elements[4], and more recently it has even been possible to photograph it in a bent crystal spectrograph[5]. This is the first time that the X-ray line of a new element, synthesized artificially, has been directly observed.

(**143**, 460-461; 1939)

在轰击产物中找到了至少五种原子序数为 43 的放射性同位素 [3]，其中一些元素的半衰期长到足以让我们对 43 号元素的化学行为进行相当充分的研究。实际上，仔细研究周期表可以帮助我们预言它的很多化学性质，不过从分析角度来看，极其重要且更为具体的细节常常只能通过直接的实验来发现。

我们首先应该研究的显然是分析性质，以便能够鉴定这种新元素，并把它从其他元素中分离出来。许多分离过程是很简单的，因此，不需要任何特殊的研究去设计；但是要从邻近元素中分离出所需要的元素，问题就复杂得多了。对于 43 号元素来说，重点是将其与锰、钼、钌特别是铼分离开，这四种元素在周期表中与 43 号元素位置最接近且性质也最为相似。由居里、卢瑟福、索迪和其他一些学者在研究天然放射性元素方面所进行的经典工作中提出的那些微量物质和放射性检测的化学方法与原理已经被广泛应用，理想的分离方法也已经被设计出来了。因此我们对该元素进行分析化学研究的基础已有保障，这些方法也可以应用于进一步的研究工作中。

实践中，利用人工制得的 10^{-10} 克量级这么少的物质根本无法确定这种新元素的任何物理常数；在某些天然放射性物质中同样存在这种困难，而且至今仍没有克服的办法。但另一方面，某些性质如特定混合物的挥发性、分级结晶的分配系数等，即使只用这么少量的物质也是可以确定的，实际上其中一些性质已经得到了测定。

一个有利的条件使我们能够检测到 43 号元素 X 射线谱中的 $K\alpha$ 线，但是在用普通的外部激发方法时，由于待测物质的量过少而不能给出这条谱线甚至任意一条光学谱线。43 号元素的一种放射性同位素存在两种同质异能态，其较高能态会衰变到较低能态。在上述跃迁过程中，43 号元素的原子通过 γ 射线内转换机制发射出 K 电子，这一状态下的 43 号元素的原子能够发射特征的 X 射线谱线。在邻近元素的 X 射线谱线中也发现了这种不连续吸收现象 [4]，最近还发现可以利用弯晶体光谱仪拍摄这条谱线 [5]。这还是第一次直接观测到一种人工合成的新元素的 X 射线谱线。

（王耀杨 翻译；郝项 审稿）

References:

1. See, however, Noddack, W., and Tacke, I., *Sitzb. Preuss. Akad. der Wissenschaften*, **19**, 400 (1925).

2. Perrier, C., and Segrè, E., *J. Chem. Phys.*, **5**, 712 (1937); and in the Press.

3. Cacciapuoti, B., and Segrè, E., *Phys. Rev.*, **52**, 1252 (1937); and unpublished results.

4. Segrè, E., Seaborg, G. T., *Phys. Rev.*, **54**, 772 (1938).

5. Abelson, P., unpublished results.

Liberation of Neutrons in the Nuclear Explosion of Uranium

H. von Halban, jun. *et al.*

Editor's Note

Recent experiments had shown that considerable energy was released in the explosion of uranium or thorium nuclei, triggered by impacting neutrons. The possibility of an energy-releasing chain reaction depended on whether such processes might release further neutrons. Here Hans von Halban, Frédéric Joliot and Lew Kowarski report experiments suggesting a positive answer. They sent neutrons into two substances, ammonium nitrate and uranyl nitrate, and measured the number of detected slow neutrons as a function of distance. A discrepancy between the two substances clearly seemed attributable to the presence of uranium and to additional neutrons being created in fission events. They could say little about the energy of the neutrons, but these observations were a step towards sustained nuclear fission.

RECENT experiments[1,2] have revealed the existence of a new kind of nuclear reaction: neutron bombardment of uranium and thorium leads to an explosion of the nucleus, which splits up into particles of inferior charge and weight, a considerable amount of energy being liberated in this process. Assuming a partition into two particles only, so that the nuclear mass and charge of uranium have to be distributed between two lighter nuclei, the latter contain considerably more neutrons than the heaviest stable isotopes with the same nuclear charges. (A splitting into, for example, ^{98}Rb and ^{141}Cs means an excess of 11 neutrons in the first, and of 8 neutrons in the second of these two nuclei.) There seem to be two possibilities of getting rid of this neutron excess. By the emission of a β-ray, a neutron is transformed into a proton, thus reducing the neutron excess by two units; in the example given above, five and four successive β-activities respectively would be needed to restore the neutron-proton stability ratio. In fact, the explosion products have been observed to be β-active and several periods have been recorded, so that a part, at least, of the neutron excess is certainly disposed of in this way. Another possible process is the direct liberation of neutrons, taking place either as a part of the explosion itself, or as an "evaporation" from the resulting nuclei which would be formed in an excited state.

In order to find some evidence of this second phenomenon, we studied the density distribution of the thermal neutrons produced by the slowing down of photo-neutrons from a Ra γ-Be source in a 1.6 molar solution of uranyl nitrate and in a 1.6 molar solution of ammonium nitrate (the hydrogen contents of these two solutions differ by only 2 percent). Plotting Ir^2 as a function of r (where r is the distance between the source and a given point, and I is the local density of thermal neutrons at the same point, measured by the activity induced in a dysprosium detector), a curve is obtained the area of which is

铀核爆炸时中子的释放

冯·哈尔班等

编者按

最近的实验显示由中子碰撞触发的铀核或钍核爆炸释放出相当多的能量。释放能量的链式反应发生的可能性依赖于这个过程是否释放更多的中子。本文中，汉斯·冯·哈尔班、弗雷德里克·约里奥和卢·科瓦尔斯基称实验给出了肯定答案。他们用中子轰击硝酸铵和硝酸双氧铀两种物质，对观测到的慢中子数目随距离的变化进行测量。在两种物质中产生的差异无疑是因为铀核的存在和在裂变中产生的额外中子。关于中子能量他们能讲得很少，但是这些观测是迈向持续核裂变研究的一步。

最近的实验 [1,2] 已经揭示了存在一种新的核反应：用中子轰击铀和钍会引发核爆炸，核分裂为电荷和质量较小的粒子，同时在这个过程中释放了相当大的能量。假设一次分裂仅产生两个粒子，则铀核的质量和电荷必定在两个更轻的核之间分配，与带有相同核电荷的最重的稳定同位素相比，两个轻核含有较多的中子。（例如，分裂为 ^{98}Rb 和 ^{141}Cs 意味着在两个核子中，第一个核子多出了 11 个中子，第二核子多出了 8 个中子。）似乎存在着两种可能性来消除这些过剩中子。通过发射 β 射线，一个中子转变为一个质子，这样就减少了两个单位的过剩中子；在上述给出的例子中，分别需要相继 5 次和 4 次 β 放射来恢复中子 – 质子的稳定率。实际上，已观测到的爆炸产物是具有 β 活性的，并且已经记录到了几个活性周期。因此，至少有一部分过剩的中子必定是通过这种方式去除的。另一种可能的过程是中子以部分爆炸产物的形式被直接释放，或从处于激发态的生成核中"蒸发"掉。

为了找到这类次级现象的某些证据，我们研究了 Ra γ-Be 光中子在 1.6 摩尔硝酸双氧铀溶液和 1.6 摩尔硝酸铵溶液中的减速所产生的热中子的密度分布（这两种溶液中的氢含量只相差 2%）。将 Ir^2 作为 r 的函数绘图（其中 r 是源点与给定点之间的距离，I 是热中子在相同点的局部密度，通过镝探测器中感生到的放射性进行测量），图中所得曲线的面积与 $Q \cdot \tau$ 成正比，Q 是每秒由中子源发射出的或在溶液中形

proportional to $Q \cdot \tau$, Q being the number of neutrons per second emitted by the source or formed in the solution and τ the mean time a neutron spends in the solution before being captured[3,4]. Any additional nuclei, which do not produce neutrons, brought into the solution, will increase the chances of capture and therefore decrease τ and the area. If, however, these dissolved nuclei are neutron-producing, Q will be greater and the area of the curve will tend to increase. Evidence of neutron production, as indicated by an actual increase of the area, will only be obtained if the gain through Q (neutron production) is greater than the loss through τ (neutron capture). This loss can anyway be studied separately, since it has been shown[5] that the introduction of nuclei which act merely by capture or by increasing the hydrogen content of the solution can affect the shape of the density curve only in a characteristic way: the modified curve can always be brought to coincide with the primitive curve by multiplying all abscissae by a suitable factor and all ordinates by another factor.

The accompanying graph shows the two curves obtained. At small distances from the source the neutron density is greater in the ammonium solution than in the uranyl solution; at distances greater than 13 cm., the reverse is true. In other words, the decrease of the neutron density with the distance is appreciably slower in the uranyl solution.

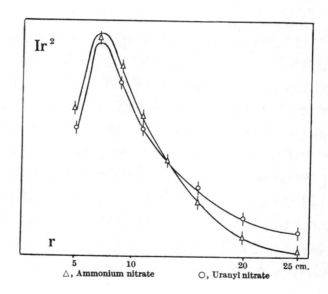

The observed difference must be ascribed to the presence of uranium. Since the two curves cannot be brought to coincide by the transformation mentioned above, the uranium nuclei do not act by capture only; an *elastic* diffusion by uranium nuclei would have an opposite effect: it would "contract" the abscissae, instead of stretching them. The density excess, shown by the uranyl curve beyond 13 cm., must therefore be considered as a proof of neutron production due to an interaction between the primary neutrons and the uranium nuclei. A reaction of the well-known $(n,2n)$ type is excluded because our primary neutrons are too slow for such a reaction (90 percent of Ra+Be photo-neutrons

成的中子数，τ 是中子被俘获之前在溶液中度过的平均时间 [3,4]。将任何其他不产生中子的原子核放入溶液中将会增加中子被俘获的概率，因此时间 τ 和面积也会相应减小。然而，如果溶液中的这些核是产生中子的，那么 Q 将更大，曲线的面积也将趋于增大。由面积的实际增大所表明中子生成的证据将仅在以下情况中才能获得，即由 Q（中子生成）所造成的增益比由时间 τ（中子俘获）所导致的损耗大的情况。我们可以通过各种方式来分别研究这项损耗，因为其已经表明 [5]，仅仅是通过俘获，或通过增加溶液中的氢含量而引入的核只通过一种特定的方式来影响密度曲线的形状，那么将原始曲线的所有横坐标乘上一个合适的因子，而将纵坐标乘上另一个合适的因子，修正的曲线总能与其相吻合。

　　附图显示了得到的两条曲线。在与源距离较近的位置，硝酸铵溶液中的中子密度大于硝酸双氧铀溶液中的密度；但在距离大于13厘米的位置时，情况则相反。换言之，在硝酸双氧铀溶液中中子密度随距离的减小明显较为缓慢。

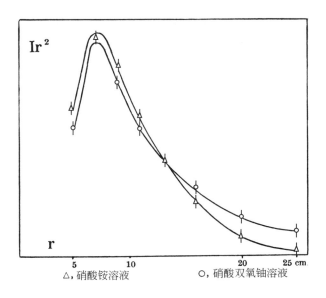

△，硝酸铵溶液　　　　　　　　　　　○，硝酸双氧铀溶液

　　观测到这样的差别一定是由铀的存在所致。因为这两条曲线不能通过上述修正而重合，所以铀核不仅仅起俘获的作用；由铀核所产生的**弹性**漫射将会起到相反的效果：它会"缩短"横坐标，而不是延长横坐标。因此，当距离超过 13 厘米时硝酸双氧铀曲线所示的密度超量，必定会被当作中子是由初级中子与铀核之间的相互作用的产物的证据。熟知的 $(n, 2n)$ 型的反应是被排除在外的，这是由于对于这类反应而言我们的初级中子的能量太小了（90% 的 Ra+Be 光中子的能量小于 0.5 兆电子伏，

have energies smaller than 0.5 Mev. and the remaining 10 percent are slower than 1 Mev.).

The degree of precision of the experiment does not permit us to attribute any significance to the small increase of the area in the uranyl curve (as compared to the ammonium curve), which we obtain by extrapolating the curves towards greater distances. In any event, an inferior limit for the cross-section for the production of a neutron can be obtained by assuming that the density excess due to this production is equal throughout the whole curve to the excess observed at $r = 25$ cm.; this limit, certainly inferior to the actual value, is 6×10^{-25} cm.^{2}.

Our measurements yield no information on the energy of the neutrons produced. If, among these neutrons, some possess and energy superior to 2 Mev., one might hope to detect them by a (n,p) process, for example, by the $^{32}S(n,p)^{32}P$ reaction. An experiment of this kind, Ra γ-Be still being used as the primary neutron source, is under way.

The interest of the phenomenon observed as a step towards the production of exo-energetic transmutation chains is evident. However, in order to establish such a chain, more than one neutron must be produced for each neutron absorbed. This seems to be the case, since the cross-section for the liberation of a neutron seems to be greater than the cross-section for the production of an explosion. Experiments with solutions of varying concentration will give information on this question.

(**143**, 470-471; 1939)

H. von Halban, jun., F. Joliot and L. Kowarski: Laboratoire de Chimie Nucléaire, Collège de France, Pairs, March 8.

References:

1. Joliot, F., *C.R.*, **208**, 341 (1939).

2. Frisch, O. R., *Nature*, **143**, 276 (1939).

3. Amaldi, E., and Fermi, E., *Phys. Rev.* **50**, 899 (1936).

4. Amaldi, E., Hafstad, L., and Tuve, M., *Phys. Rev.*, **51**, 896 (1937).

5. Frisch, O. R., von Halban, jun., H., and Koch, J., *Danske Videnskab. Kah.*, **15**, 10 (1938).

其余的 10% 小于 1 兆电子伏）。

实验的精度不允许我们对硝酸双氧铀曲线中面积的微小增加（与硝酸铵曲线比较）赋予任何含义，这样的增加是我们将曲线向距离更大的方向外推时得到的。在任何情况下，假设由于中子产生造成的密度增量等于在 $r=25$ 厘米处观测到的整个曲线的增量，则可得到中子产生的截面下限；这个极限肯定在实际值之下，为 6×10^{-25} 平方厘米。

我们的测量还无法给出关于所产生中子的能量的信息。如果在这些中子之中，某些中子具有的能量超过 2 兆电子伏，我们有望通过一个 (n,p) 过程来探测它们，例如，通过 $^{32}S(n,p)^{32}P$ 反应。初级中子源仍然为 Ra γ-Be 的这种实验正在进行之中。

我们所观测的现象使实现产生外能变换链向前迈进了一步，这个意义是很明显的。然而，为了建立这样的一个链条，每吸收一个中子，都必须再产生一个以上的中子。看起来事实就是如此，因为释放一个中子的截面似乎大于产生一次爆炸的截面。采用各种不同浓度的溶液进行的实验将给出该问题的相关信息。

（沈乃澂 翻译；王乃彦 审稿）

Products of the Fission of the Uranium Nucleus

L. Meitner and O. R. Frisch

Editor's Note

Lise Meitner and Otto Frisch here report new experiments probing the products of uranium fission experiments. Earlier work suggested that fission fragments should emerge with energies of several hundred million electron volts. Here the researchers sent neutrons into a sample of uranium hydroxide and attempted to collect the fission fragments 1 mm away, either in a paper surface or in water. They found evidence for a range of different fission fragments. It seemed most unlikely that the mere absorption of a neutron could give a uranium nucleus enough kinetic energy to reach their collecting surfaces. This new technique offered a route to the more detailed examination of the nuclear fragments created in fission processes.

O. Hahn and F. Strassmann[1] have discovered a new type of nuclear reaction, the splitting into two smaller nuclei of the nuclei of uranium and thorium under neutron bombardment. Thus they demonstrated the production of nuclei of barium, lanthanum, strontium, yttrium, and, more recently, of xenon and caesium.

It can be shown by simple considerations that this type of nuclear reaction may be described in an essentially classical way like the fission of a liquid drop, and that the fission products must fly apart with kinetic energies of the order of hundred million electron-volts each[2]. Evidence for these high energies was first given by O. R. Frisch[3] and almost simultaneously by a number of other investigators[4].

The possibility of making use of these high energies in order to collect the fission products in the same way as one collects the active deposit from alpha-recoil has been pointed out by L. Meitner (see ref. 3). In the meantime, F. Joliot has independently made experiments of this type[5]. We have now carried out some experiments, using the recently completed high-tension equipment of the Institute of Theoretical Physics, Copenhagen.

A thin layer of uranium hydroxide, placed at a distance of 1 mm. from a collecting surface, was exposed to neutron bombardment. The neutrons were produced by bombarding lithium or beryllium targets with deuterons of energies up to 800 kilovolts. In the first experiments, a piece of paper was used as a collecting surface (after making sure that the paper did not get active by itself under neutron bombardment). About two minutes after interrupting the irradiation, the paper was placed near a Geiger-Müller counter with aluminium walls of 0.1 mm. thickness. We found a well-measurable activity which decayed first quickly (about two minutes half-value period) and then more slowly. No attempt was made to analyse the slow decay in view of the large number of periods to be expected.

铀核的裂变产物

迈特纳，弗里施

编者按

莉泽·迈特纳和奥托·弗里施在这篇文章中报道了关于探测铀核裂变产物的新实验。早期的研究认为裂变碎片的产生会伴随有几百兆电子伏的能量出现。本文作者用中子轰击氢氧化铀样品，尝试在1毫米远的纸张表面或者水中收集裂变碎片。他们发现了一系列不同的裂变碎片存在的证据。可以看出，仅靠吸收一个中子似乎不能提供铀原子核足够的动能使其到达他们的收集表面。这项新技术提供了一个途径去更仔细地检测裂变过程中产生的原子核碎片。

哈恩和施特拉斯曼[1]发现了一种新型核反应，即在中子轰击下，铀核和钍核分裂为两个更小的核。以此他们证明了钡核、镧核、锶核、钇核以及最近又发现的氙核和铯核等裂变产物。

可以简单地以一种本质上经典的方式，比如类似于液滴分裂的形式，来描述这类核反应，并且分裂的产物必定以上百兆电子伏的动能飞离[2]。弗里施[3]首先给出这些高能反应的证明，几乎是在同一时间其他多位研究者也给出了证明[4]。

迈特纳已经指出（见参考文献3），像人们从α反冲中收集放射性沉积物那样，利用这些高能量来收集裂变产物是可能的。在此期间，约里奥已独立地进行了这类实验[5]。我们利用哥本哈根理论物理研究所最近制成的高压装置，现在已经开展了一些实验。

将一薄层氢氧化铀放在距收集表面1毫米的位置，并用中子对其进行轰击。中子是用能量高达800千电子伏的氘核轰击锂靶或铍靶而产生的。在第一个实验中，使用一张纸作为收集表面（已经确定纸在经过中子轰击后纸本身不具有放射性）。在辐照中断大约两分钟后，将纸放在具有0.1毫米厚铝壁的盖革－米勒计数器的附近。我们发现放射性可以很好地被测量到，并且开始时放射性衰变得很快（约两分钟的半衰期），然后会较为缓慢。鉴于估计其中存在数目繁多的周期，我们并不打算对缓慢的衰变进行分析。

The considerable intensity, however, of the collected activity encouraged us to try to get further information by chemical separations. The simplest experiment was to apply the chemical methods which have been developed in order to separate the "transuranium" elements from uranium and elements immediately below it[6]. The methods had to be slightly modified on account of the absence of uranium in our samples and in view of the light element activities discovered by Hahn and Strassmann[1].

In these experiments, the collecting surface was water, contained in a shallow trough of paraffin wax. After irradiation (of about one hour) a small sample of the water was evaporated on a piece of aluminium foil; its activity was found to decay to zero. It was checked in other ways, too, that the water was not contaminated by uranium. To the rest of the water we added 150 mgm. barium chloride, 15 mgm. lanthanum nitrate, 15 mgm. platinum chloride and enough hydrochloric acid to get an acid concentration of 7 percent. Then the platinum was precipitated with hydrogen sulphide, in the usual way; the precipitate was carefully rinsed and dried and then placed near our counter.

The results of three such experiments were found to be in mutual agreement. The decay of the activity was in one case followed for 28 hours. For comparison, a sample of uranium irradiated for one hour was treated chemically in the same way. The two decay curves were in perfect agreement with one another and with an old curve obtained by Hahn, Meitner and Strassmann under the same conditions. In the accompanying diagram the circles represent our recoil experiment while the full line represents the uranium precipitate. A comparison of the activity (within the first hour after irradiation) of the precipitate and of the evaporated sample showed that the precipitate contained about two thirds of the total activity collected in the water. After about two hours, however, the evaporated sample was found to decay considerably more slowly than the precipitate, presumably on account of the more long-lived fission products found by Hahn and Strassmann[1].

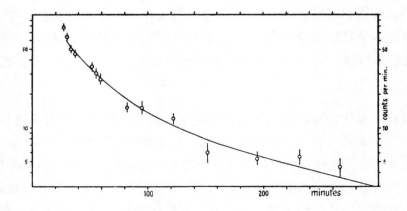

From these results, it can be concluded that the "transuranium" nuclei originate by fission of the uranium nucleus. Mere capture of a neutron would give so little kinetic energy to the nucleus that only a vanishing fraction of these nuclei could reach the water surface.

然而，收集到的放射性有相当大的强度，这促使我们试图通过化学分离的方法得到更进一步的信息。最简单的实验是采用一种化学方法，最初发展这种方法是为了把所谓的"超铀"元素从铀及紧邻它的较低的元素中分离出来[6]。考虑到在我们的样品中不存在铀，并鉴于哈恩和施特拉斯曼[1]发现的轻元素的放射性，这种实验方法必须稍做改进。

这些实验均以石蜡浅槽中的水作收集表面。在（大约一小时的）辐照后，少量样品水被蒸发到一片铝箔上；并且其放射性衰变为零。用其他方法也可证明这些水中并不含铀。在剩余的水中，我们加入 150 毫克氯化钡、15 毫克硝酸镧、15 毫克氯化铂和足够的盐酸，以便得到 7% 的酸浓度。采用通常的方法，用硫化氢将铂析出；析出的沉淀物经过精心漂洗和烘干，然后放在我们的计数器附近。

我们发现三个这样的实验得到的结果是相互一致的。在其中一种情况下，对放射性物质的衰变跟踪了 28 小时。作为对照，对经过一个小时辐照的铀样品，按同样方式进行化学处理。结果显示，这两条衰变曲线完全一致，并且它们与之前由哈恩、迈特纳和施特拉斯曼在相同条件下得到的曲线也完全符合。在附图中，圆圈表示我们的反冲实验，而实线表示铀的沉淀物。沉淀物与经过蒸发样品的放射性（辐照后的第一小时内）的对比表明，沉淀物大约含有水中收集到的总放射性的 2/3。然而，在大约两小时后，我们发现经过蒸发的样品比沉淀样品的衰变要更加缓慢，这大概是由哈恩和施特拉斯曼[1]所发现的更长寿命的裂变产物所致。

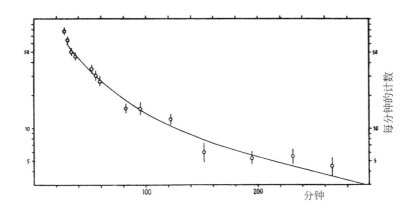

根据这些结果我们可以断定，所谓"超铀"核是由铀核裂变产生的。仅仅俘获一个中子只能为核提供极少的动能，因此这些核中没有一个能够达到水的表面。因

So it appears that the "transuranium" periods, too, will have to be ascribed to elements considerably lighter than uranium.

In conclusion, we wish to thank Dr. T. Bjerge, Dr. J. Koch and K. J. Brostrøm for putting the high-tension plant at our disposal and for kind help with the irradiations. We are also grateful to Prof. N. Bohr for the hospitality extended to us at the Institute of Theoretical Physics, Copenhagen.

(**143**, 471-472; 1939)

Lise Meitner: Physical Institute, Academy of Sciences, Stockholm.

Otto Robert Frisch: Institute of Theoretical Physics, University, Copenhagen, March 6.

References:

1. Hahn, O., and Strassmann, F., *Naturwiss.*, 27, 11, 89, and 163 (1939).

2. Meitner, L., and Frisch, O. R., *Nature*, 143, 239 (1939). Bohr, N., *Nature*, 143, 330 (1939).

3. Frisch, O. R., *Nature*, 143, 276 (1939).

4. Fowler, R. D., and Dodson, R. W., *Nature*, 143, 233 (1939). Jentschke, W., and Prankl, F., *Naturwiss.*, 27, 134 (1939).

5. Joliot, F., *C. R.*, 208, 341 (1939).

6. Hahn, O., Meitner, L., and Strassmann, F., *Chem. Ber.*, 69, 905 (1936); and 70, 1374 (1937).

而所谓"超铀"周期似乎也必然是由比铀轻得多的元素所致。

最后，我们要感谢伯格博士、科赫博士和布罗斯特伦，他们将高压设备交给我们自由使用并好心地对实验中的辐照提供了帮助。我们同样对玻尔教授在哥本哈根理论物理研究所对我们的热情款待表示感激。

(沈乃澂 翻译；张焕乔 审稿)

The Structure of the Globular Proteins

D. Wrinch

Editor's Note

Here the pugnacious Dorothy Wrinch defends her (incorrect) theory of the molecular structure of proteins against its critics. Wrinch maintained that proteins weren't simple chains of amino acids linked by peptide bonds, but were joined into hexagonal ring structures that are linked into cage-like forms. The serious problems with this theory were already evident—in particular, the "side chains" on some amino acids simply wouldn't fit, a problem not addressed here. Wrinch's arguments here are all circumstantial, but they are a reminder of how difficult it was to say anything definite about protein structure until X-ray crystallography began, over a decade later, to reveal it in earnest.

ON recent occasions a number of objections to the cyclol theory have been raised, to many of which replies have already been given, explicitly or implicitly, in a number of publications, notably in Langmuir's lecture to the Physical Society on December 20, 1938[1]. In view of the prominence which has been given to these criticisms, it seems desirable to summarize the replies.

It has been suggested that the number of theories such as the cyclol theory is so large that the *a priori* probability of any one is not sufficiently great for it to merit consideration[2,3]. It is difficult to give much weight to objections of this type until it proves possible to formulate, or failing this to establish the existence of, a sufficiently large number of independent theories, each of which leads to structures accounting for the definite and discretely arranged molecular weights of the native proteins, their capacity to denature to form spontaneously from solution highly insoluble monolayers and so on. So far as we are aware, no alternative structures have yet been proposed. Meanwhile, "the very large number of independent properties which are correlated by the cyclol theory and the extreme simplicity and the small number of postulates from which it is derived by purely logical processes"[1], seem to give it a considerable *a posteriori* probability.

It is suggested that there are grave objections on chemical grounds to the postulate of the four-armed unit $>N-CHR-COH<$[3] and indeed to the cyclol structure itself owing to the lack of precedent in organic chemistry for this diazine-triazine type of structure[4]. Proteins are so different from other substances that it is surprising that there is a reluctance to accept for them a structure for which no analogue in organic chemistry can be found. Globular proteins have not yet been synthesized in the laboratory. The fact that it has not proved possible to form ring structures from peptides[5] is therefore scarcely to be regarded as evidence against the cyclol hypothesis. Furthermore, we would not regard the lactam-lactim tautomerism of peptides as the chemical basis of the cyclol theory[4]. At present,

球蛋白的结构

林奇

编者按

针对批评，好斗的多萝西·林奇在本文中捍卫了她关于蛋白质分子结构的（不正确的）理论。林奇坚持认为蛋白质不是由氨基酸通过肽键连接形成的简单的链，而是由六边形的环状结构连接成为笼状的形式。这个理论面临的严重问题非常明显——特别是一些氨基酸上的"侧链"显然不能与这一理论吻合，但这一问题在本文中并未被提及。林奇在这里的辩解都是根据情况推测的，但是它提醒我们，要对蛋白质结构作出任何确定的描述有多么困难。直到十年之后 X 射线晶体学兴起，这一情况才得以改观。

最近在一些场合中，出现了一些反对环醇理论的意见；对于其中很多反对意见，已经有人在许多出版刊物上发表文章作出或明白或含蓄的答复，特别值得一提的是，1938 年 12 月 20 日朗缪尔在对物理学会的演讲中所作的回答 [1]。考虑到这些批评意见受到的重视，我觉得有必要在这里总结一下相关的答复。

有人提出，理论(例如环醇理论)的数目如此之多，以至于从先验的或然概率来说，任何一个理论都不足以引起人们的注意 [2,3]。要重视这类反对意见是很困难的，除非人们可以用公式表述足够大量的独立理论，或者如果做不到这一点的话，人们也要可以确证有足够大量独立理论的存在，其中每个理论都可以导出天然蛋白质的结构，这些结构都能解释天然蛋白质独立分布的分子量、变性能力（在溶液中自发形成高度不溶性的单分子层）等。就我们所知，目前还没有提出新的替代结构。同时，"与环醇理论相关的大量蛋白质的极其简单的独立性质，以及少数相关假设（环醇理论就是根据这些假设通过纯逻辑推理得到的）" [1] 似乎赋予它相当强的后验或然概率。

有人极力反对，认为对四臂单元 >N–CHR–COH< [3] 的假设、甚至对环醇结构本身的假设都缺乏化学基础，因为在有机化学里还没有出现过这种二嗪 – 三嗪类结构 [4] 的先例。蛋白质和其他物质之间的差异如此巨大，令人惊讶的是竟然有人不愿意接受它们作为可能存在的结构类型，仅仅是因为在有机化学中找不到它们的相似物。目前，实验室内还不曾合成球蛋白。因此，多肽 [5] 形成环状结构的可能性尚未被证实这个事实也不足以被视为反对环醇理论的证据。此外，我们也不会将多肽内酰胺 – 内酰亚胺的互变异构现象作为环醇理论的化学基础 [4]。目前我们还不知道在

we do not know whether polypeptide chains constitute an intermediate stage in protein synthesis, nor is it clear that the cyclization of chains, if it occurs, entails the postulate of lactam-lactim tautomerism of peptides.

Further criticisms of the cyclol hypothesis are as follows: (a) the theory is incompatible with the findings of enzyme chemistry[4,6]; (b) it cannot explain certain facts of denaturation[4]; and (c) it has not proved possible to synthesize in the laboratory certain "simple models of cyclol type"[4], or to induce the formation of cyclol links between simple molecules[6].

(a) In accordance with the current ideas in the kinetics of reactions, it was suggested by Langmuir[7] that there is a tautomeric equilibrium in the globular proteins between some of the four-armed units >COH–CHR–N< and the two-armed units –CO–CHR–NH–, by means of which cyclol bonds are continually opening and reforming. Thus at any one time there are some points at which a peptide link, CO–NH, can be attacked directly. The cyclol theory therefore does not, as has been suggested[4], need to make the assumption that proteolytic enzymes open cyclol bonds. We know of no evidence which conflicts with the view that the enzyme can take advantage of the situation arising from the opening of these bonds, so that, if it is a fact that proteolytic enzymes act only on CO–NH bonds, there is no incompatibility with the cyclol structure proposed for the globular proteins.

The objections (b) and (c) again raise the question of the nature of the cyclol bond. This bond in isolation may well be unstable; indeed the marked instability of the globular proteins in general and other considerations[8] require it to be so. Failure to synthesize in the laboratory so-called "simple models of the cyclol type"[4] (a phrase which may ultimately be found to be a contradiction in terms), or to induce the formation of isolated intermolecular cyclol links, is then no evidence against the cyclol hypothesis.

The stability of the globular proteins, under special conditions, in solution and in the crystal, we attribute to definite stabilizing factors[7,9]; namely, (1) hydrogen bonds between the oxygens of certain of the triazine rings, (2) the multiple paths of linkage between atoms in the fabric, (3) the closing of the fabric into a polyhedral surface which eliminates boundaries of the fabric and greatly increases the symmetry, and (4) the coalescence of the hydrophobic groups in the interior of the cage. If these stabilizing factors are withdrawn the cage structure collapses. Denaturation on this theory (apart from the special type due to the dissociation of structures held together by hydroxyl or hydrogen bonds or salt or covalent linkages between R-groups[10,11]), corresponds to any breakdown of the structure due to the opening of cyclol bonds[1,12]. When few bonds are open they may re-form because of the multiple paths of binding holding the parts in position. Reversible denaturation (of either type) is thus not excluded by the cyclol theory. In the case of the fibrous proteins in which some cyclol bonds may be present,[13] the first and second stabilizing factors may operate. The denaturation of myosin (which it is suggested is a difficulty for the cyclol theory[4]) thus seems to be easily interpretable.

570

蛋白质合成过程中多肽链是否会构成一种中间态，也还没有搞清楚多肽链的环化，如果环化发生的话，就意味着多肽的内酰胺－内酰亚胺结构互变异构的假设是必然的。

对于环醇假说进一步的批评如下：(a) 这个理论与酶化学发现的结果不相容 [4,6]；(b) 它无法解释蛋白质变性中的一些事实 [4]；(c) 尚未证明可以在实验室中合成某些"环醇类的简单化合物"[4]，或者诱导简单分子形成环醇连接 [6]。

(a) 与反应动力学目前的观点一致，朗缪尔 [7] 提出：在球蛋白中，有些四臂单元 >COH–CHR–N< 和两臂单元 –CO–CHR–NH– 之间存在着互变异构平衡，因为环醇键不断地打开和再形成。所以在任何时刻，都可以从某些点上直接攻击多肽连接 CO–NH。因此，环醇理论没有必要像人们提出的那样 [4] 去假设蛋白水解酶可以打开环醇键。就我们所知，并没有证据与下述观点相悖，即酶可以在这些键打开的情况下发挥作用，因此，如果蛋白水解酶只作用于 CO–NH 键是事实的话，我们为球蛋白提出的环醇结构就不存在矛盾了。

反对的理由 (b) 和 (c) 再次提出了环醇键本质的问题。环醇键在孤立的情况下很可能是不稳定的；事实上，在通常以及其他一些情况下球蛋白所具有的显著不稳定性正需要它如此 [8]。那么无法在实验室中合成所谓"环醇类的简单化合物"[4]（可能最终会发现这一说法是自相矛盾的）或者不能诱导孤立的分子间形成环醇连接的事实，就都不能作为证据来反对环醇假说。

我们将球蛋白在某些特定状态下（在溶液中或晶体中）的稳定性归因于特定的稳定因素 [7,9]；即 (1) 某些三嗪环上氧原子之间的氢键，(2) 纤维结构中原子之间的多种连接途径，(3) 纤维结构闭合成多面体的表面可以消除纤维结构的边界，并且极大地提高对称性，(4) 疏水性基团在笼状结构内部汇集。如果这些稳定性因素不存在了，笼状结构就会崩塌。在这个理论基础上的变性（不考虑由 R 基团间的羟键、氢键、盐键或共价键紧密维系的结构发生分解 [10,11] 这种特殊情况）对应于环醇键打开造成的任何结构崩溃 [1,12]。当只有少数键打开时，它们可以重新再次生成，因为有多种结合途径使各部分维持原位。因此可逆变性（其中的任何一种类型）并没有被环醇理论排除在外。对于可能含有一些环醇键的纤维蛋白来说 [13]，第一个和第二个稳定性因素可以起到作用。肌球蛋白的变性（这被认为是环醇理论不能解决的一个难题 [4]）由此变得很容易解释。

The first stability factor also, it appears, may explain the fact that it has not proved possible to methylate or acetylate the peptide hydroxyls, which on the present hypothesis should be present in egg albumin and haemoglobin[14].

It may be emphasized that whereas the first three stability factors are uniform for all the globular proteins, the strength of the fourth factor varies with the specific amino-acid composition of the individual protein. This point is demonstrated by the case of insulin, in which the exceptional behaviour (its resistance towards heat and acid, the stability of its crystals in the dry state, etc.) can perhaps be correlated with its abnormally high content of hydrophobic groups. The fact that insulin "cannot be denatured in the usual sense of the word"[4] does not provide evidence against the cyclol theory of denaturation: it illustrates the importance of the fourth stability factor. Incidentally, insulin, like many other globular proteins, spontaneously forms very insoluble monolayers from solution[15], a property which in itself indicates the likelihood of a cage structure[1,10,11]. The spontaneous formation of monolayers from solution represents a very mild type of degradation, presumably involving no hydrolysis. It seems likely that much could be learnt about protein structure by studying the structure of the constituents of these protein monolayers. On the cyclol theory, fragments of fabric and closed polypeptide chains are to be expected when gentle methods of degradation are used which involve no hydrolysis[12]. The theory would not (as has been suggested[4]) make any predictions as to the nature of the products obtained when the usual gross methods of degrading proteins are used.

Other criticisms of the cyclol theory[3] (dealt with in detail in other communications[16,17]) relate to one particular point, namely, the suggestion that the insulin molecule has the cage structure C_2. It was shown at the outset[18] that this structure satisfies the chemical and physico-chemical facts and also those relating to cell molecular weight, space-group and cell dimensions obtained in an X-ray analysis of a dry zinc-insulin crystal[19]. Controversy has, however, arisen as to whether it is consistent with certain vector diagrams of a dry zinc-insulin crystal published later[20]. In view of authoritative opinions as to the inadequacy of the X-ray date[21] (which make it highly uncertain how far the vector diagrams give even an approximately correct picture of the situation in the crystal) and as to the feasibility of making any deductions from such data in the absence of a chemical analysis of the crystal[21,22], it seems necessary at present to abandon the hope of reaching any final conclusion on this special point. Arguments can only revolve round the plausibility of subsidiary hypotheses.

The Geometrical Attack on Protein Structure

It has been pointed out by Neuberger[4] that many of the arguments in favour of the cyclol hypothesis could be used equally well in favour of any "regular geometrical structure which joins peptide chains to form a globular molecule", a theme which has already been developed in considerable detail[23,24]. This remark, in focusing attention on the fundamental problem of protein structure, namely, the existence of megamolecules, puts into correct perspective the general investigations on protein structure of which those

第一个稳定性因素似乎也可以解释至今不能使多肽的羟基实现甲基化或者乙酰化这一事实。在目前的假说下，这种情况应当在卵清白蛋白和血红蛋白中存在[14]。

需要强调的是，尽管前三种稳定性因素对于所有的球蛋白是等同的，但第四种稳定性因素的强度会随着每种蛋白的特定氨基酸组成的变化而变化。这一点可以通过胰岛素的例子得到证明，它的异常行为（耐受热和酸的能力，晶体在干燥状态下的稳定性等）可能与其含有的疏水基团异常多有关。胰岛素"不会发生通常意义上的变性"[4]这一事实并不能作为反驳关于变性的环醇理论的证据：它只是进一步说明第四种稳定性因素的重要性。附带提一下，胰岛素像许多其他的球蛋白一样，可以在溶液中自发形成非常难溶的单分子层[15]，这个特性本身就暗示了它具有笼状结构的可能性[1,10,11]。在溶液中自发形成单分子层代表了一种非常温和的降解类型，据推测，这种类型不涉及水解作用。看来，可以通过研究这些蛋白单分子层组分的结构来获得许多关于蛋白质结构的知识。基于环醇理论，当采用不涉及水解在内的温和方法实现变性时，可以预期将会有笼状纤维片段和闭合的多肽链片段出现[12]。但是当采取降解蛋白惯用的粗糙方法时，这个理论不会（就像人们曾经建议的那样[4]）对获得产物的性质作出任何预测。

针对环醇理论的另外一些批评[3]（在其他通讯中已有详细的阐述[16,17]）是和一个特定的问题相关的，即认为胰岛素分子具有 C_2 笼状结构。我们在一开始就提到[18]，这个结构可以满足已知的化学和物理化学事实，以及通过对干燥的锌－胰岛素晶体[19]进行 X 射线分析所得到的细胞分子量、空间群和晶胞大小相关的诸多性质。然而，争论又出现了，即它是否与随后发表的干燥的锌－胰岛素晶体结构[20]的矢量图相一致。鉴于权威的观点认为 X 射线数据不充分[21]（这使得矢量图究竟能在多大程度上对晶体内真实情况给出即便只是近似正确的图像这一问题带有高度不确定性）以及在缺少对晶体进行化学分析的条件下[21,22]根据这样的数据进行任何推导并不可行，目前似乎必须放弃在这个特定问题上达到任何最终结论的希望。争议只能围绕着辅助性假说的合理性来进行。

对蛋白质结构的几何学上的攻击

纽伯格[4]曾经指出，支持环醇理论的许多论点同样适用于支持任何"能将多肽链连接成球状分子的规则几何结构"，这个主题已在很多细节方面都有了发展[23,24]。这个说法将注意力集中在蛋白质结构的基本问题上，即巨大分子的存在问题，把对蛋白质结构的一般研究纳入了正确的视野，对环醇理论的处理正是这些研究中的一部分。这些研究的范围广阔。如果蛋白质分子是氨基酸的多缩聚产物，由一个氨基

dealing with the cyclol theory form a part. These investigations have a wide scope. Given that protein molecules are polycondensation products of amino acids, interlinked by bonds between the nitrogen of one and the terminal carbon of another, there are only a certain mathematically determinate set of possible structures. The full and exhaustive formulation of these is the objective of this work[11,13,24].

Now the cyclol theory gives precise expression to this general point of view by postulating that these polycondensation products are built on the particular two-dimensional scheme exemplified by the cyclol network. No alternative comprehensive scheme has so far been forthcoming; but on the other hand, it has never been claimed that the cyclol pattern is the only design consistent with the chemical and stereochemical specifications[24]. The characteristic pattern must, of course, satisfy certain conditions; thus it must be such as to allow "the possibility of the regular and orderly arrangement of hundreds of residues"[25] (and herein lies the difficulty of attributing the fine structure of proteins to S–S, CO–S, NH–S or CO–NH–CO links as suggested by Neuberger[4]), and it must be capable of fragmentation into polypeptide chains. The cyclol postulate has been developed in considerable detail, since it was scarcely feasible to show the potentialities of the geometrical method by general statements alone.

It should, however, be recognized that there are broad deductions to be drawn from this point of view, irrespective of the particular form of the atomic pattern. Chief among these is the suggestion that the molecules of the globular proteins are cage-like structures, consisting of a characteristic fabric folded round to form a closed polyhedral surface[10,13,24]. This simple corollary of the idea of a protein fabric, though in point of fact suggested by the cyclol hypothesis, is independent of this or any other postulate. Whether or not the cyclol hypothesis proves to be correct, it certainly establishes the existence theorem in the mathematical sense, proving that there are no intrinsic impossibilities in the cage type of structure, showing how the atomic pattern can determine size and shape, and proving also that the cages may be rendered highly specific by the conditions of linkage imposed on the individual atoms.

The present controversy—wholly concerned with details of the cyclol pattern—makes it clear that the determination of the atomic pattern of proteins is beyond the range of present chemical and physical techniques. It then seems all the more important to direct attention to this general issue as to the general nature of structures of the globular proteins. Whatever the atomic pattern may be, the fact remains that the defining characteristics of the native proteins not only fit in with the idea of a cage, but even seem to demand a structsure of this kind for their molecules. On this point there seems indeed to be a growing consensus of opinion[2,4]. In any case, the central problem is to explain the existence of very large but chemically and physically well-defined molecules. The idea of a cage structure has been offered for consideration, as an explanation of this striking fact. Is it not possible, by means of experimental techniques already available, to recognize a cage when we see one?

(**143**, 482-483; 1939)

酸的氮和另一个氨基酸的末端碳之间形成的化学键相互连接，那么就只有某些特定的通过数学确定的可能结构存在。本项研究的目标就是对这些结构作出全面而详尽的表述 [11,13,24]。

现在环醇理论对上述这个一般性观点给出了准确的表达：它假定这些多缩聚产物是建立在以环醇网络为代表的特定二维系统之上。迄今为止还没有人提出其他可替代的全面方案；但另一方面，也从来没有人宣称过环醇模式是符合化学和立体化学特征的唯一模式 [24]。当然，这种特征模式必须满足某些条件；它必须要满足"数百个氨基酸规则有序地排列的可能" [25]（在这里存在的困难是如何像纽伯格 [4] 曾经建议的那样把蛋白质精细结构归因于 S–S、CO–S、NH–S 或者 CO–NH–CO 之间的连接），而且它还要可以断裂为多肽链。环醇假说在很多细节方面已经有了进一步的发展，因为仅依靠一般性陈述来表明几何学方法的潜能，几乎是不可行的。

然而应该认识到，不管原子排列的特定形式如何，从这个观点出发，都可以得到大量的推论。其中首要的建议是球蛋白分子为笼状结构，由特定的纤维结构折叠环绕构成一个封闭的多面体表面 [10,13,24]。关于蛋白质是纤维结构的观点，其简单的必然结果与环醇假说或任何其他假说无关，尽管事实上正是环醇假说提出了蛋白质的纤维结构。无论环醇假说的正确性是否被证实，它无疑在数学意义上建立了存在性命题法则，证实笼状结构没有内在的本质矛盾，显示了原子排列模式如何可以确定分子的大小和形状，另外也证实了笼状结构可以通过施加在各个原子上的连接条件而被赋予高度的特异性。

目前的争论——完全是关注环醇模式的细节——使人清楚，测定蛋白质内原子排列方式超出了目前化学和物理技术的能力范围。看来现在更为重要的事情是将注意力集中在球蛋白结构的一般性质这个更普遍的议题上。无论原子的排列方式如何，事实仍然是天然蛋白质的定义性特征不仅符合分子笼状结构的理念，甚至似乎还要求蛋白质的分子具有这样的结构。在这一点上，似乎达成共识的意见真的越来越多 [2,4]。无论如何，核心问题就是去解释那些非常大但是化学和物理上定义明确的分子的存在。作为这个引人关注事实的解释，笼状结构的理念已经被提出来供人们考虑。有没有可能在我们看到一个笼状结构的时候通过已经可用的实验技术手段把它识别出来呢？

（刘振明 翻译；顾孝诚 审稿）

References:

1. This lecture was summarized in *Nature*, **143**, 34 (1939): it will be published in full in the *Proceedings of the Physical Society*.

2. Bernal, Royal Institution, Jan. 27, 1939.

3. Bernal, *Nature*, **143**, 74 (1939).

4. Neuberger, *Nature* [this issue P. 473].

5. Neuberger, *Nature*, **142**, 1024 (1938).

6. Bergmann and Niemann, "Annual Reviews of Biochemistry", **7**, 11 (1938).

7. Cold Spring Harbor Symposium on Proteins, **6** (1938).

8. Wrinch, *Nature*, **138**, 241 (1936).

9. Langmuir and Wrinch, *Nature*, **143**, 49 (1939).

10. Wrinch, *Proc. Roy. Soc.*, A, **161**, 505 (1937)

11. Wrinch, *Phil. Mag*, **23**, 313 (1938).

12. Wrinch, *Phil. Mag*, **25**, 705 (1938).

13. Wrinch, *Proc. Roy. Soc.*, A, **160**, 81, 1937.

14. Haurowitz, *Z. physiol. Chem.*, **256**, 28 (1938).

15. Langmuir, Pilgrim Lecture, Royal Society, November 8, 1938.

16. *Nature* [forthcoming].

17. Languir and Wrinch, *Proc. Phys. Soc.* [in course of publication].

18. Wrinch, *Science*, **85**, 568 (1937); *Trans. Faraday Soc.*, **33**, 1368 (1937).

19. Crowfoot, *Nature*, **135**, 591 (1935).

20. Crowfoot, *Proc. Roy. Soc.*, A, **164**, 580 (1938).

21. Robertson, *Nature*, **143**, 75 (1939).

22. Bragg, *Nature*, **143**, 73 (1939).

23. Wrinch, International Congress of Physics, Chemistry and Biology, Paris, 1937.

24. Wrinch, Cold Spring Harbor Symposium on Proteins, **6** (1938).

25. Wrinch, *Nature*, **137**, 411 (1936).

New Products of the Fission of the Thorium Nucleus

L. Meitner

Editor's Note

In 1939, physicists were close to discovering exothermic nuclear fission—the splitting of large nuclei, such as uranium, into smaller parts, with an immense release of energy. Here Austrian physicist Lise Meitner extends recent experiments in which uranium nuclei, bombarded with neutrons, seemed to split into two more or less equal fragments. Meitner describes how similar experiments with thorium showed similar signs of the nucleus splitting into large fragments, and finds that both thorium and uranium fission led to similar end products. Meitner, a Jew, had recently been forced to flee Germany, helped by her German colleague Otto Hahn. Hahn would win the Nobel Prize for the definitive discovery of nuclear fission five years later.

IN a preceding communication[1] it has been shown that the "transuranium" elements are found among the fission products of uranium under neutron bombardment. Consequently they must be lower elements, probably partly somewhere near tellurium[2], partly (the complementary fission fragments) in the region of ruthenium.

It was then natural to carry out similar experiments with thorium in order to see whether the fission of thorium gave rise to elements with chemical properties similar to those of the "transuranium" elements, that is, elements which can be precipitated with hydrogen sulphide from a strong hydrochloric acid solution. No search for such elements had previously been carried out with thorium, since the formation of elements beyond uranium, from thorium, was not to be expected. So far, chemical analysis of the radioactive bodies produced in thorium by neutron bombardment has revealed (apart from a thorium and a protactinium isotope resulting from pure neutron capture) only products which, on the basis of their chemical properties, had originally to be assigned to radium and actinium isotopes[3] and which have more recently been identified with barium and lanthanum isotopes[4].

A "thick" layer of thorium oxide on a glass plate was irradiated by neutrons obtained by bombarding a lithium target with deuterons of 800 kv. from the high-tension equipment of the Institute of Theoretical Physics, Copenhagen. In order to collect the recoil nuclei, a water surface was used in the way previously described[1]. After irradiation (of about one hour) a fraction (2 c.c.) of the water was evaporated without chemical separation; with the rest (9 c.c.) the usual hydrogen sulphide precipitation was carried out in exactly the same way as in the uranium recoil experiments[1].

钍核裂变的新产物

迈特纳

编者按

1939 年，物理学家接近于发现放热核裂变——大原子核（例如铀）分裂为稍小的碎片，并释放出巨大的能量。近期的一些实验用中子轰击铀核，结果似乎使之分裂成了两份大致相等的碎片，本文中奥地利物理学家莉泽·迈特纳对这些实验进行了拓展。迈特纳描述了用钍核进行类似的实验显示，类似的核反应分裂生成了大碎片，并发现钍核和铀核裂变都产生相似的最终产物。迈特纳是犹太人，最近她在德国同事奥托·哈恩帮助下被迫逃离德国。五年后哈恩因为发现核裂变而获得了诺贝尔物理学奖。

在此前的一篇通讯 [1] 中我们曾指出，在中子轰击下产生的铀的裂变产物中，发现了"超铀"元素。因此它们一定是序数较小的元素，可能部分位于碲附近 [2]，部分（互补的裂变碎片）则位于钌的附近区域。

于是很自然地我就使用钍来进行类似的实验，目的是看看钍的裂变是否也能产生与"超铀"元素化学性质类似的元素，所谓的"超铀"元素就是那些可以从浓的盐酸溶液中利用硫化氢沉淀下来的元素。此前从未利用钍对这些元素进行过探寻，因为人们从未期望用钍来制得铀后面的元素。迄今为止，对于那些通过中子轰击在钍中产生的放射性物质所做的化学分析表明（除去由单纯的中子俘获所产生的一种钍的同位素和一种镁的同位素之外），只存在这种产物：根据其化学性质，它们最初曾被归为镭和锕的同位素 [3]，但最近已确认其为是钡和镧的同位素 [4]。

利用哥本哈根理论物理研究所的高压设备，以 800 千电子伏的氘核轰击锂靶，用所得的中子辐照玻璃板上的氧化钍"厚"涂层。按照以前曾描述过的方法 [1]，利用水的表面来收集反冲核。经过辐照（大约 1 个小时）后，一部分（2 立方厘米）水蒸发但不发生化学分离；对剩余部分（9 立方厘米）进行常规的硫化氢沉淀，所用方法与铀反冲实验 [1] 中的完全一致。

沉淀表现出明显的、可测量到的放射性，其衰变显著区别于类似的铀产物的衰变。

The precipitate showed a clearly measurable activity, the decay of which was distinctly different from the decay of the analogous uranium products. After an initial decrease with a half-value period of about 40 minutes, an activity remained which was followed for almost two days and showed a single decay period of 14-15 hours. The evaporated sample showed first a much faster decay which then gradually became slower; after two days, the activity had vanished.

A second experiment with 2.5 hours' irradiation gave the same result, with correspondingly greater intensity, especially of the longer period. In this experiment, after the sulphide precipitation, the filtrate was neutralized and the barium and lanthanum[1] were precipitated as carbonates. The carbonate precipitate decayed first with about 20 minutes and then with 4 hours half-value period, in agreement with the periods already known[3,4]. Analysis of the decay of the sulphide precipitate showed again the presence of a substance of half-period about 40 minutes and of one of 14.5 hours, which was followed for nearly three days and found to decay to zero. The initial intensities of the two periods were about equal, in spite of the short duration of bombardment. The possible existence of very short or very long additional periods can, of course, not be excluded on the basis of this experiment. The two periods observed are quite different from those of the chemically analogous uranium products.

Several check experiments without neutrons showed that there was no contamination of the water by thorium B or C, which might have resulted from radioactive recoil or traces of emanating thoron. As a further protective measure, the thorium layer was sealed, in the second experiment, by a celluloid membrane of 0.3 mm. stopping power.

From the evidence given above, one can conclude that some of the fission products of thorium show a chemical behaviour similar to that of the "transuranium" elements. This is a further indication that essentially the same chemical elements are produced in the fission of uranium and thorium.

In conclusion, I wish to express my thanks to Dr. T. Bjerge, Dr. J. Koch, and K. J. Brostrøm for kind help in the irradiations with the high-tension tube. I am especially grateful to Prof. N. Bohr for the opportunity to carry out these experiments and for the facilities kindly put at my disposal at the Institute of Theoretical Physics, Copenhagen.

(**143**, 637; 1939)

Lise Meitner: Physical Institute, Academy of Sciences, Stockholm, March 26.

References:
1. Meitner, L., and Frisch, O. R. *Nature*, **143**, 471 (1939).
2. Abelson, P., *Phys. Rev.*, **55**, 418 (1939). Feather, N., and Bretscher. E., *Nature*, **143**, 516 (1939).
3. Meitner, L., Hahn, O., and Strassmann, F., *Phys., Z.* **109**, 538 (1938).
4. Hahn, O., and Strassmann, F., *Naturwiss.*, **27**, 89 (1939).

在经历半衰期约 40 分钟的初始衰减后，在随后几乎两天仍保持放射性并且表现出单一的 14~15 小时的半衰期。蒸发的样品最初衰变很快，随后便逐渐减慢；两天后，放射性消失。

第二次实验经过了 2.5 小时的辐射，得到了相同的结果，但相应的强度更大一些，尤其是对于更长的周期。在这次实验中，在硫化物沉淀后滤液呈中性，钡和镧 [1] 以碳酸盐的形式沉淀。这些碳酸盐最初的半衰期为 20 分钟，随后变为 4 小时，这与已知的半衰期 [3,4] 相一致。对硫化物沉淀的衰变进行分析，再次表明一种具有 40 分钟半衰期和一种具有 14.5 小时半衰期的物质存在，后者持续大约三天，然后消失。尽管轰击持续时间很短，然而两种半衰期的初始强度大致上是相等的。当然，根据这个实验并不能排除存在额外的极短或极长半衰期的可能性。不过我观测到的这两个半衰期与化学性质类似的铀的产物的半衰期全然不同。

几次无中子辐照的检查性实验表明，水中不存在钍 B 或钍 C（钍 B 或钍 C 可能由放射性物质反冲或者极少量钍射气的发射而产生）。为了保险起见，在第二次实验中用阻止本领为 0.3 毫米的赛璐珞膜将钍层密封。

根据上面给出的证据可以得出这样的结论，钍的某些裂变产物表现出与"超铀"元素类似的化学特性。这进一步表明在铀和钍的裂变中实质上产生了同样的化学元素。

最后，我要向伯格博士、科赫博士和布罗斯特伦表示感谢，他们对于高压管辐射实验给予了热心帮助。我还要特别感谢玻尔教授，他使我有机会进行这些实验并慷慨地为我提供了哥本哈根理论物理研究所的实验设备。

（王耀杨 翻译；朱永生 审稿）

Structure of Proteins*

J. D. Bernal

Editor's Note

Like several of the authoritative overviews in *Nature* at this time, this one is based on a talk at the Royal Institution in London. J. Desmond Bernal had worked there as a student of William Bragg, and by now he was the world's expert on the study of protein structure through X-ray crystallography. Here he presents the current state of play, in which impressive progress had been made despite the fact that proteins contain very complex structures built of hundreds or thousands of atoms. Bernal was still baffled by the apparent complexity of the process by which the chain-like molecules fold into a compact form (this is still not fully understood), but the important role of "hydrophobic" interactions between insoluble regions was already emerging.

THE structure of proteins is the major unsolved problem on the boundary of chemistry and biology today. We have not yet found the key to the problem, but in recent years a mass of new evidence and new lines of attack have enabled us to see it in a far more concrete and precise form, and to have some hope that we are near to solving it.

The problem of protein structure is twofold: the first is that of the form and properties of the protein molecule, and the second that of its internal structure. Owing to the extreme instability of the protein molecule, only the gentlest physical methods can be used; nevertheless three lines of attack—centrifugal, electrical, and X-ray—have already led to great success. The most fundamental has been the ultra-centrifuge, particularly the work of Svedberg and his school[1]. Protein molecules will sediment in sufficiently high centrifugal fields, and from their sedimentation constant it is possible to arrive at a fairly accurate value for the weight of the molecule, though there is some doubt as to whether what is measured is that of the complete protein molecule, because of its inevitable association with the solution in which it is suspended.

The most striking discovery of Svedberg was that the weights thus obtained seemed to fall into definite classes which were multiples of each other. This suggests very strongly that all proteins are built from some common unit. What that unit is is more difficult to determine. Originally taken as 35,000, proteins are now found of 17,000 and even of 10,000 molecular weight. Critical examination of the data, moreover, shows that there is no exact correspondence to certain weights, but rather a scattering of weights concentrated in certain regions. There is no doubt that in closely related proteins there are simple

---

* From a Friday evening discourse delivered at the Royal Institution on January 27.

蛋白质结构*

贝尔纳

编者按

就像同时期发表在《自然》上的其他几篇权威综述一样，这篇综述基于作者在伦敦皇家研究院的一次演讲。德斯蒙德·贝尔纳曾作为威廉·布拉格的学生在此工作，如今他已成为通过 X 射线晶体学研究蛋白质结构方面的世界知名专家。在此他介绍了这方面研究的现状，尽管蛋白质具有由成百上千个原子构成的非常复杂的结构，但是对其结构的研究仍取得了巨大的进展。链状分子折叠成一种紧密结构这一过程显而易见的复杂性难住了贝尔纳（这个问题到现在依然没有被彻底解决），不过他已经意识到了不溶性区域之间的"疏水性"相互作用在其中所起的重要作用。

时至今日，蛋白质的结构仍然是化学和生物学交叉研究领域尚未解决的一个主要问题。我们还未找到解决这个问题的关键点，但是最近几年大量新的证据和一系列新的研究使我们能够以更为具体和精确的形式去研究和看待它，同时也使我们有望解决这个问题了。

蛋白质结构的问题主要包括两个方面：首先是蛋白质分子的形式和性质，其次是它的内在结构。由于蛋白质分子极不稳定，因此只能采用最温和的物理方法进行研究；目前，三种研究方法——离心法、电化学法和 X 射线法，在对蛋白质的研究上已经取得了极大的成功。其中最为基础的研究工作是应用超速离心机获得的，特别是斯韦德贝里及其学院同事的研究工作 [1]。在足够高的离心场中蛋白质分子会发生沉降，依据它们的沉降系数就有可能推算出分子量相当精确的数值。由于蛋白质悬浮在溶液中时不可避免地与溶液结合，所以目前对于测定的对象是否是真正完整的蛋白质分子还存在一定的疑问。

斯韦德贝里最为著名的发现在于，这样得到的分子量似乎可以分成一些确定的等级，这些等级之间互为倍数。这一点非常强有力地说明，所有的蛋白质都是由一些共同的单元构建而成的。然而要确定这些单元是什么就更困难了。最初认为蛋白质单元的分子量是 35,000，不过现在又发现了分子量是 17,000 甚至 10,000 的蛋白质。此外，对数据的严格分析表明蛋白质的分子量并不是严格对应于某些确定的分子量，而是集中于某一区域内呈散点分布。毫无疑问的是，关系密切的蛋白质的分子量之

---

* 来自 1 月 27 日在英国皇家研究院星期五晚间演讲的内容。

relationships. Both haemoglobins and haemocyanins can, for example, be split reversibly into 2, 4, or 8 parts. But whether these relationships hold for all proteins is more doubtful; particularly as studies of viscosity have shown that proteins belonging to the same weight class such as insulin and gliadin may differ enormously in shape, the first being a flattened sphere and the other an elongated rod, and it is difficult to see what common physical structure they can have.

It has been claimed that this variation of weight of proteins of the same Svedberg class is to be expected on account of the known difference in amino-acid content. On the basis of existing analytical figures, it is as yet impossible to say whether this is or is not sufficient to account for the observed discrepancy. The figure of 288 amino-acid residues in a 35,000 molecular weight class protein cannot be taken at present as more than an inspired guess.

The second approach to protein structure comes from the electric properties of their molecules. The work of Cohn, Tiselius, and others gives us a picture of a protein molecule in solution as a particle covered with positive and negative charges due to the acid and basic nature of the amino-acid side-chains. The number of these groups depends on the condition of the medium. The protein molecule is, therefore, in its external relationship an essentially ionic structure, and probably carries with it an ionic atmosphere stretching out into the water in which it is dissolved.

The third line of attack is that of X-ray study. The beautiful crystalline forms exhibited by proteins, which have been known for at least a hundred years, were always a powerful attraction to X-ray crystallographers, but until the last five years the instability of protein crystals and their small size had defeated their efforts. Since 1934, however, it has been possible to examine a number of typical protein crystals[2]. This has been done by mounting them in small tubes in their mother liquor, for most, if not all, proteins suffer considerable breakdown if examined dry. From the beginning, the results of this examination revealed important new facts. In the first place, the pictures yielded by protein crystals were of exceptional perfection. They showed large unit cells with a great wealth of reflections (see accompanying illustration), and these reflections were found even at comparatively high angles corresponding to such low spacings as 2 A. This indicated that not only were the molecules of the proteins substantially identical in shape and size, but also that they had identical and regular internal structures right down to atomic dimensions.

From the size of the unit cells and their densities it was possible to compute the weight of matter in each repeat unit. This, however, does not immediately give the molecular weight, for two reasons. In the first place, the number of molecules in the cell is not known, and in the second it is difficult to determine how much of the cell weight is due to the protein and how much to the water in the cell. By measuring the loss of water on drying it is, however, possible to arrive at a figure for the—possibly fictitious—dry weight, which can be compared with those obtained by the centrifuge or by chemical means. Here it is found that there is excellent agreement on the assumption that there are only a few, 2, 4, or 8, such molecules per cell[3]. Thus the X-ray method furnishes an extremely accurate measure

584

间具有简单的关系。举例来讲，血红蛋白和血蓝蛋白都可以被可逆地分解为 2、4 或者 8 个部分。但是是否所有的蛋白质都有这种关系还存在着更多的质疑；特别是通过测定物质黏度的研究发现，属于相同分子量量级的蛋白质，例如胰岛素和麦醇溶蛋白，可能在形状上差别非常大；前者是一个扁平球体，而后者是伸长的棒状结构，很难看出它们具有什么共同的物理结构。

曾经有人认为属于同一个斯韦德贝里等级的蛋白质分子量的变化，可以被归结为已知的氨基酸成分之间的差异。然而，在现有分析数据的基础之上，至今都不可能说这是否就能充分地解释观察到的差异。因此，认为分子量在 35,000 这个等级的蛋白质是由 288 个氨基酸残基组成，这在目前只不过是个猜测而已。

研究蛋白质结构的第二类方法是基于这些分子的带电性质。科恩、蒂塞利乌斯以及其他一些研究者的工作给我们展示了由于氨基酸侧链具有酸性和碱性的特性，蛋白质分子作为携带正电荷和负电荷的粒子存在于溶液中的情形。这些带电基团的数目取决于溶液的条件。因而，从外表面观察，蛋白质分子是一个离子结构，进而溶解到水中时可能以一种离子态的形式分散到水中。

第三类方法是应用 X 射线衍射研究蛋白质的结构。至少在一百年前，人们就已经知道蛋白质能形成漂亮的晶体形式，这些晶体一直以来都深深地吸引着 X 射线晶体学家，但是直到最近五年，蛋白质晶体的不稳定性及其小的尺寸仍然一次次地挫伤研究者的信心。然而，自 1934 年起，研究一些典型的蛋白质晶体已经成为可能 [2]。这些研究取得成功的关键是将蛋白质置于装有它自身母液的小试管中，如在其干燥时进行检验，即使不是全部也是大多数的蛋白质晶体会出现相当程度的断裂。从一开始，这些研究结果就揭示了重要的新的事实。首先，蛋白质晶体产生的图像异常完美。通过大量的衍射，它们显示出了大的晶胞结构（参见随后的插图），即使在与 2 Å 这样的小间隔相对应的较大角度上也可以看到这些衍射。这些结果显示，蛋白质分子不仅在形状和大小上具有大体的一致性，而且在原子水平上也具有相同的、规则的内部结构。

从晶胞的尺寸和密度出发，我们有可能可以计算每一个重复单元中物质的质量。但是，这并不能直接给出分子的分子量，主要有两个原因。首先，晶胞中所包含的分子的数目是未知的；其次，很难测算出晶胞质量有多少是源于蛋白质，又有多少是源于晶胞中的水分子。然而，通过测量干燥过程中的失水量，就有可能可以得到（或者假定得到）其干重，这个数据可以与采用离心机或者化学方法得到的结果进行比较。研究结果与先前的假设有着近乎完美的一致，即每个晶胞中只包含少数这类分子，诸如 2、4、8 个 [3]。从而，X 射线方法提供了一种非常精确地测定蛋白质基本分子

for the basic molecular weight of proteins though it cannot determine its multiplicity. It may well be that many proteins are built of sub-units, which though of approximately equal weight are not chemically identical, and are more properly to be called molecular compounds than molecules.

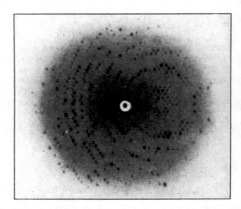

Horse methhaemoglobin, *b* axis, oscillation photograph, the ring coming through central spot showing (*hko*) zone.

The most striking feature of the cell measurements of crystalline proteins is the considerable change which occurs on drying, where in many cases shrinkage of nearly 50 percent occurs. But what is more remarkable is that the shrinkage is often confined to one or two directions in the cell. There are two possible explanations of this fact. First, that the molecules of the protein are linked together in extremely loose aggregates which collapse on the removal of water, leaving the skeleton of molecules in a now more closely packed array. The other explanation is that the molecules are held apart by their ionic atmospheres due to the charges on them, and contain, therefore, sheets of free water. It may be that both explanations hold, one more markedly for some crystals and the other for others. Thus for haemoglobin, where there is a marked shrinkage from 55 A. to 38 A. in one direction, it is difficult to imagine an ionic atmosphere, as the crystals are practically saltfree and at an isoelectric point of *p*H 6.8. On the other hand, it is difficult to explain the remarkable properties of tobacco mosaic virus on any other hypothesis. This virus has long thin particles which have a tendency to set equidistant and parallel, even down to concentrations of 13 percent and probably down to 1.5 percent. It is difficult to imagine what force other than that of ionic atmospheres can preserve this regularity. Quite recently we have shown that the equilibrium distance between the particles depends on *p*H and salt concentrations, varying, for example, between 320 A. at *p*H 7, and 206 at *p*H 3.4. It should be possible to find a quantitative theory to explain these changes and, indeed, the beginning of such a theory has been made by Langmuir[4] and Levine[5].

The general picture of the external character of protein molecules is beginning to be definite. The molecules are spheroidal bodies of dimensions varying from 30 A. to 100 A., are covered with hydrophil groups bearing charges of both signs, and probably carry with them in solution an atmosphere of ions.

量的方法，尽管该方法还不能检测它们的多样性。许多蛋白质都是由分子量近似相等但化学结构并不相同的亚基构成的，因此，更准确的是称其为分子复合物而不是分子。

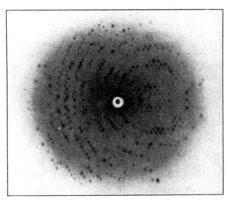

马的甲基血红蛋白，b 轴，振动晶体图相，穿过中心点的圆环显示（hko）区。

结晶蛋白最为明显的一个特点是在逐渐干燥的过程中晶胞的大小会发生非常显著的变化。很多情况下，尺寸收缩可以达到 50% 以上。但是，更值得关注的是，这种收缩通常是被限定在晶胞的某一个或者某两个方向上。对于这种现象有两种可能的解释。其一，组成蛋白质的各个分子连接在一起形成了非常松散的聚集体，当除去水分子时此聚集体便会瓦解，只留下分子骨架，从而形成我们看到的这种更为紧密的堆积状态。另一种解释是将其原因归结为蛋白质分子带电而形成的离子氛对分子的隔离作用，以及由此而包含的大片的自由水。可能这两种解释都成立，其中一种解释非常适用于某些晶体，另一种解释可能适用于另外一些晶体。例如血红蛋白可以在一个方向上从 55 Å 显著地收缩到 38 Å，当晶体处在等电点的 pH 值 6.8 时，晶体几乎不带电，所以很难想象这种收缩是因为离子氛的存在而导致的。另一方面，任何其他假设都很难解释烟草花叶病毒的显著特征。这种病毒具有细长的颗粒，倾向于等距、平行地排列，即使是在浓度降低到 13%，甚至 1.5% 的情况下。我们很难想象除了离子氛之外什么力量能够保持这种规律性。就在最近，我们发现粒子间的平衡距离取决于 pH 值和盐浓度。例如，它可以在 320 Å (pH 为 7 时）和 206 Å (pH 为 3.4 时）之间变动。应当有可能可以找到一种定量的理论来解释这些变化。事实上，朗缪尔 [4] 和莱文 [5] 已经给这样一种理论奠定了基础。

现在人们已经开始确定蛋白质分子外部特征的大致图像。这类分子的形状类似于球体，尺寸从 30 Å~100 Å 不等。分子的表面被亲水性基团覆盖，带有正负两种类型的电荷，并依靠它们溶解在溶液中形成离子氛。

The problem of the internal structure of protein molecules is one of enormously greater difficulty. Any effective picture of protein structure must provide at the same time for the common character of all proteins as exemplified by their many chemical and physical similarities, and for the highly specific nature of each protein type. It is reasonable to believe, though impossible to prove, that the first of these depends on some common arrangement of the amino-acids. The first hint of this comes from a study of the fibrous proteins. Here, owing to their technical importance and their much greater ease of handling, a very considerable advance has been made, due largely to the well-planned and persistent researches of Astbury[6].

The fully extended β-keratin fibre has a strong repeat at every 3.5 A., corresponding to the length of one amino-acid residue, and two other repeats at 10 A. and 4.5 A. respectively, corresponding to periodicities at right angles to the chain length. One of the most significant of Astbury's discoveries was that these two periodicities are also at right angles to each other. In other words, that the repeat unit of the fully extended protein has distinct characters in three dimensions. The significance of these repeats seems also beyond doubt, the 10 A. spacing corresponding to the length of the side-chains of the amino-acid residues, and the 4.5 A. to the so-called backbone spacing between the main chains themselves, which are held together by the CO and NH groups. In the shorter α form, the 10 A. spacing remains, while the 4.5 A. disappears, and this indicates that the chains are folded, but folded definitely in a plane and not as in rubber in two dimensions. What the precise mechanism of this folding is remains obscure, but it is of fundamental importance because it is probably very closely associated with the kind of folding that occurs in the corpuscular proteins.

The significance of these findings for the general protein problem is, first, that all soluble proteins hitherto examined give on denaturation a fibrous material which can be oriented and seems identical in basic structure with β-keratin, and secondly, that the actual change which a crystalline protein undergoes on denaturation must be very slight. This is shown by the close resemblance of powder photographs of crystalline proteins before and after denaturation, and also by the observations of Astbury, Dickinson, and Bailey[7] that a single crystal of excelsin gives on partial denaturation fibres orientated in the direction of the crystal axes. Further, recent work by Perutz[8] has shown by an entirely different method, namely, the study of the absorption spectra in different directions in crystals, that the position of the prosthetic group in haemoglobin is not altered by denaturation.

The evidence that the X-ray study of the crystalline proteins themselves provides for the elucidation of their structure is abundant, but it is extremely difficult to interpret. Photographs of crystalline proteins (see illustration) show hundreds of spots and marked differences of intensities stretching right out to reflections corresponding to interatomic distances. Unfortunately, however, direct analysis of these photographs is rendered impossible by the fact that we can never know the phases of the reflections corresponding to the different spots. The ambiguity introduced in this way can only be removed by some physical artifice, such as the introduction of a heavy atom, or the observation of intensity

解析蛋白质分子内部结构面临更大的困难。任何蛋白质结构的有效图像都必须同时提供对于所有蛋白质而言的共同特性，因为已确证它们不仅具有诸多化学的和物理学的相似性，每一类蛋白质还具有高度的特异性。尽管无法证实，我们仍有理由相信这其中首要一点依赖于氨基酸的某种基本排布。关于这一点的最初线索来自对纤维蛋白的研究。由于这类蛋白在技术上的重要性以及它们具有的便于操作和处理的特性，此方面的研究已经取得了相当大的进展，这主要归功于阿斯特伯里等人的精心设计以及坚持不懈的研究 [6]。

全伸展的 β-角蛋白纤维每隔 3.5 Å 就会有一次重复，这个长度与一个氨基酸残基的长度相一致；另外两种重复的间隔分别是 10 Å 和 4.5 Å，与链长度的直角周期相一致。阿斯特伯里最为重大的发现之一是这两种周期性重复结构之间是彼此垂直的。换句话说，整个完全伸展蛋白的重复单元在三维空间上具有明显的特征。这些重复单元的重要性是毋庸置疑的，其中 10 Å 的间距对应于氨基酸残基侧链的长度；4.5 Å 的间距对应于主链之间我们称之为骨架的空间距离，它们彼此之间通过羧基基团和氨基基团连在一起。在较短的 α 类型结构中，10 Å 的间距仍然存在，4.5 Å 的间距却消失了，这充分说明这种链是折叠的，但折叠肯定发生在同一个平面上，而不像在橡胶中观察到的折叠发生在两个维度上。目前尚不清楚这种折叠的确切机制，但它具有根本的重要性，因为它可能与出现在血球蛋白中的折叠类型是紧密相关的。

这些发现对于蛋白质的基本问题的意义在于，第一，迄今为止观测过的所有可溶性蛋白质在变性后都会得到一种纤维状物质。这些物质能够被定向且似乎与 β-角蛋白的基本结构是一样的。第二，结晶蛋白在变性过程中经历的实际变化一定是非常微小的。结晶蛋白变性前后的粉末照片极度类同证实了这一点，阿斯特伯里、迪金森和贝利等人 [7] 对巴西果蛋白单晶的观测结果也证实了这一点，他们发现部分变性的巴西果蛋白单晶形成的纤维的取向沿着晶体轴的方向。除此之外，佩鲁茨 [8] 近来的研究工作通过一种完全不同的方法，即研究晶体在不同方向上的吸收光谱，证实了血红蛋白中辅基的位置不会因蛋白质的变性而改变。

对结晶蛋白本身进行的 X 射线研究为阐明它们的结构所提供的证据是很丰富的，但数据很难解释。结晶蛋白的图像（参见插图）展示了数百个点并且强度明显不同，这种不同直接反映蛋白质内部原子间的距离。然而，不幸的是，由于事实上我们无法确定不同点所对应的衍射相位，因此对这些图像的直接分析是不可能的。因此而引入的不确定性只能通过一些物理技巧来消除，例如引入重原子，或者通过观测脱水过程中强度的变化，迄今为止后者尚未在实践中得到实施。对于所有被检测过的

changes on dehydration, which have not hitherto been carried out in practice. For all but one of the proteins examined, the task is made still more difficult by the presence of more than one Svedberg unit in the cell.

The resulting X-ray pattern is such cases depends both on the position of the molecules in the cell and on their internal structure. Fortunately the one exception, insulin, has only one molecule per cell. An X-ray study of dry insulin crystals has been made by D. Crowfoot[9] and the intensities of the reflecting planes determined. It is to be regretted that it was not possible to examine the crystals wet because in the dry crystals no planes of spacing less than 8 A. are observed, and consequently no evidence exists as to the fine structure of the molecule. The evidence on the coarse structure is, however, striking enough; it can most easily be seen from a study of the Patterson projections and Patterson-Harker sections which Miss Crowfoot has computed for insulin.

It should be explained that these projections do not represent the distribution of the density of scattering matter in the cell, but merely the product of the densities at points separated by a constant vector. It is not surprising, therefore, that the interpretation of these diagrams has already given rise to acute controversy. It seems natural to assume, though it is in fact an arbitrary simplification, that the peaks in the Patterson projection correspond to distances between a small number of high concentrations of scattering matter. Attempts have been made to reduce the analysis of the pattern to that of finding a pattern of points in space that will give maxima at the places observed. All these attempts have in fact failed. It is easy to find a large number of point patterns which will give the correct basal plane projection, but none of these will at the same time fit the sections. The claims to have done so[10] are based on the arbitrary selection of a certain number of vectors, and the agreement disappears if all the vectors are taken[11]. The failure to find a point solution suggests that we are dealing with groups of size of the same order as their distance apart, and that the appearance of the enhancement of reflections at spacings 10 A. and 4.5 A. corresponds to an arrangement of side-chains or backbone spacings similar to those occurring in the fibrous proteins.

On the basis of present X-ray knowledge, it is clearly impossible to arrive at any detailed picture of protein structure. Indeed, up to now the chief value of the X-ray method has been to disprove such hypothetical structures as have been put forward. It is, however, possible to formulate in a broad way some of the possible modes of arrangement and to suggest working hypotheses as a guide to future work.

The formal problems of structure of the protein molecule are:

(*a*) What is the nature of the link between amino-acid residues?

(*b*) Does the linkage run through the whole of the molecule or only through parts of it? In other words, is the protein one unit held together by primary valence forces, or is it made of sub-units held together in some different way?

蛋白质（除了一个例外）而言，晶胞中存在不止一个斯韦德贝里单元，这使得研究工作依然是非常困难的。

在这些例子中，最终的 X 射线图案取决于晶胞中分子的位置以及它们的内在结构。幸好作为一个例外，胰岛素在每个晶胞中只有一个分子。克劳福特[9]等人对干燥的胰岛素晶体进行了 X 射线研究，测定了反射平面的强度分布情况。遗憾的是，无法对带水晶体进行观测研究，因为在干燥的晶体中没有观测到任何间距小于 8 Å 的平面，因此无法获得关于分子的精细结构的证据。不过，关于粗略结构的证据就足以令人震惊了；这一点可以非常容易地从克劳福特女士对胰岛素计算得到的帕特森投影和帕特森 – 哈克截面中看到。

这里需要解释的是，这些投影并不代表晶胞中散射物质的密度分布情况，而仅仅是由一些被某个常向量分隔的点上的密度形成的。因此，丝毫不用感到奇怪的是，对于这些图像的解释早已经引发了激烈的争论。虽然事实上这是一种主观的简化，但我们会很自然地假设，帕特森投影上的峰对应于少数高浓度散射点之间的距离。目前已经有一些研究工作在试图简化对图案的分析，以发现空间中那些能够给出观测位置上最大值点的特征。事实上所有这些努力最终都宣告失败。虽然可以很容易地找到大量的点特征，它们可以得到正确的基本平面投影，但是它们其中的任何一个都不能同时满足区域的分布。导致这种情况的原因[10]在于对一定数量的向量的主观选定，如果选择所有的向量，则一致性会消失[11]。无法找到解决问题的关键点的事实说明，我们处理的分子基团的大小与它们之间的间距处在同一个数量级上，因此在间距为 10 Å 和 4.5 Å 时反射强度的增加对应的是侧链或者主链间距的排布，就像在纤维蛋白中存在的情况那样。

基于当前的 X 射线知识，非常清楚的是，我们不可能获得关于蛋白质结构的任何细节图像信息。事实上，到目前为止，X 射线方法的主要价值是用于反驳那些已被提出的假设结构。然而，这种方法有可能在更广的范围内阐述可能的排列方式，以及提出有效的假设来指引未来的研究工作。

关于蛋白质分子的结构，真正重要的问题主要有：

(a) 氨基酸残基之间的连接的本质是什么？

(b) 这种连接贯穿于整个分子中还是仅仅存在于分子的某些部分？换句话说，是蛋白质作为一个整体依靠基本的价键力量结合在一起，抑或是它由亚单位构成，以另外的某种方式结合在一起？

(*c*) If such sub-units exist, what is the nature of the link between them?

As to the first question, the difficulty of accounting for the structure of spherical molecules out of a linear peptide chain has led to the idea of an alternate mode of linkage in which each amino-acid residue can be linked to four others and not merely to two. While this hypothesis at first sight has a theoretical attractiveness, it still lacks any chemical support, and has been subjected to serious criticism on chemical grounds[12]. There are enough unknown factors in protein structure already without employing doubtful chemical assumptions.

The question of the unitary nature of the protein molecule arises whether the inter-residue linkage is peptide or not. With a multiple link it is easy to construct models either of the cage or solid type, but as has already been pointed out, it is difficult to reconcile such continuous structures with the definite 10 A. discontinuities revealed by the X-ray analysis. With a peptide chain, however, the unitary solution becomes more difficult. It is difficult to imagine any kind of fold or coil by which a single chain can occupy the observable space and at the same time not be so intricate that its formation by any natural process would be enormously improbable. There is, however, much evidence that at least the larger protein molecules are not unitary in structure. In the first place, some of them can be split in solution down to particles of molecular weight of the order of 10,000, and this is probably not the lower limit, as smaller particles are difficult to isolate or measure.

Two lines of X-ray evidence also point to sub-units, the high symmetry of protein crystals and the 10 A. repetitions. The symmetry of protein crystals is much higher than would be expected statistically from compounds of such great complexity. This would seem to indicate that each molecule is built of sub-units themselves unsymmetrical but arranged in a symmetrical way. The size of the sub-units must lie between that of the smallest protein observed, that is, one with a molecular weight 9,000, and that of a single amino-acid of molecular weight averaging 120, that is, it must contain some sub-multiple of probably 72 amino-acid residues. The uncertainty arises from the fact that it is not necessary for all the sub-units to be the same, though some must be to account for the symmetry. The presence of trigonal symmetry suggests that the asymmetrical unit must be a third or less of this number, that is, it must contain 24, 12, or 8 amino-acid residues.

The question of the structure of the sub-unit would seem to raise at first sight the same difficulties as the structure of the molecule itself. Actually, however, with the smaller number of residues the difficulties and the improbabilities of the coiling become much less, particularly if we postulate—which is not unreasonable—that the sub-units are closed peptide rings. Such rings would necessarily curl up owing to the mutual attraction of the positive and negative charged amino and keto groups in the chain, and models of such coiled chains can be constructed which preserve the distances between such groups that have been found in other compounds. The difficulty is, however, that there is a very large number of such possible models, and as yet nothing to choose between them. The method of folding in the chains in the sub-units may well be similar to that of the contracted form (*c*) 如果这些亚单位存在的话，那么存在于它们之间的连接的本质又是什么？

对于第一个问题，解释由线性多肽链形成球形分子结构所面临的困难引出了交替式连接的概念，其中每一个氨基酸残基都可与其他四个或者不少于两个氨基酸残基连接起来。尽管这种假设初看上去具有理论上的吸引力，但是它仍然缺乏任何化学方面证据的支持，在化学领域 [12] 备受争议。即便不引入不确定的化学假设，在蛋白质结构研究方面也已经存在大量的未知因素了。

关于蛋白质分子整体本质的问题在于其残基之间的连接是否是肽键。通过多重连接的方式，很容易构建出笼状或者立体的模型，但是就像已指出的那样，使这些连续的结构符合于 X 射线分析揭示的确定的 10 Å 长度的不连续性是很困难的。就肽链而言，整体的解决方案变得更为困难。很难想象一条单链能够通过任何类型的折叠或者卷曲而占据整个可观测空间，另外不难理解的是，它也不可能通过自然过程而自发形成。然而，有相当多的证据表明，至少大的蛋白质分子在结构上不是单一的。首先，有一些大的蛋白质在溶液中分解成分子量在 10,000 这个量级上的粒子，而且，这可能还不是下限，只不过是由于更小的粒子难于被分离和测量。

来自 X 射线研究的两条证据同样证明了亚单位结构的存在，即蛋白质晶体的高度对称性以及 10 Å 的重复性。蛋白质晶体的对称性比我们根据同等复杂的化合物而统计推断出的要高得多。这似乎预示着每个分子都是由本身并不对称但却以一种对称的方式进行排布的亚单位构成的。亚单位的大小必然介于所观测到的分子量为 9,000 的最小蛋白质和平均分子量为 120 的单个氨基酸之间，也就是说，它必须包含大约 72 个氨基酸残基。其中的不确定性来自这样一个事实，即所有的亚单位不必完全一样，尽管其中的一些必须保证分子的对称性。三角对称的存在说明非对称单元中的氨基酸残基数必须是这个数的 1/3 或者更小，换句话说，它必须包含 24、12 或者 8 个氨基酸残基。

初看上去亚单位结构的问题与对分子本身结构的研究似乎有相同的困难。事实上，伴随着氨基酸残基数目的减少，其困难和卷曲的不可能性也越来越小，特别是如果我们假定——这不是不切实际的——亚单元是封闭的多肽环。由于链中氨基团和酮基基团之间正负电性的相互吸引，这些环必然会卷曲，并且这类卷曲链模型的构建可以基于从其他化合物中已获得的相似化学基团之间的距离。然而，困难在于，这类可能的模型非常多，无法在它们中间做出选择。亚单位中链的折叠方式可能会非常类似于上面提到的纤维蛋白的收缩模式，事实上，对于这些蛋白质的更细致的

of the fibrous proteins mentioned above, and indeed a more detailed study of these may give us a clue to the whole arrangement.

The postulation of sub-units, however, raises further questions in the molecular structure, for they must be bound together sufficiently tightly to hold the molecule together in aqueous and ionic solutions. For this purpose a limited number of bonds are available. Ionic bonds are plainly out of the question, as they would certainly hydrate. There remains the possibility of amino-carboxy links between the ends of side-chains, but this is somewhat liable to the same criticism. It seems more probable that the links are either or both of two kinds, S–S linkages and association of hydrophobe groups. With the small number of sub-units, the number of S–S linkages needed to hold the molecule together is for all proteins hitherto examined sufficiently provided for by the amount of sulphur present, and the extreme changes in activity that proteins undergo when S–S bonds are broken indicate that they may have this fundamental part to play. Whether this is so or not, however, the behaviour of the hydrophobe groups of the protein must be such as to hold it together. As Danielli[13] and Langmuir[14] have pointed out, on the basis of surface-film work, the protein molecule in solution must have its hydrophobe groups out of contact with water, that is, in contact with each other, whereas on the surface the molecule is broken up into a film of 10 A. thickness in which the hydrophobe groups are driven out of contact with the water. In this way a force of association is provided which is not so much that of attraction between hydrophobe groups, which is always weak, but that of repulsion of the groups out of the water medium.

Langmuir has used this picture as a justification of the cyclol cage hypothesis, but it is strictly quite independent of it, and the model outlined above has the advantage of accounting very satisfactorily for the phenomenon of denaturation, particularly on a surface. Once the sub-units come to the surface, their rings are brought into a plane and different rings can interact according to the familiar ring-chain polymerization process, which will result in the formation of the fibres which Astbury has shown to exist in such films. This polymerization process takes measurable time as Danielli's work has shown.

The picture thus presented is far from being a finished or even a satisfactory one. The crucial fact that requires elucidation is the precise mode of folding or coiling of the peptide chains, and for this we may have to wait for some considerable time, until the technique of X-ray and other methods have been advanced much further than at present. The problem of the protein structure is now a definite and not unattainable goal, but for success it requires a degree of collaboration between research workers which has not yet been reached. Most of the work on proteins at present is uncoordinated; different workers examine different proteins by different techniques, whereas a concentrated and planned attack would probably save much effort which is now wasted, and lead to an immediate clarifying of the problem.

(**143**, 663-667; 1939)

研究可以在整体排列上给我们一些提示。

然而，亚单位假设在分子结构方面提出了另外一些问题，因为如果存在亚单位，它们必然要非常牢固地结合在一起，从而保证分子在水中和离子溶液中聚集在一起。能用于达到这个目的的键是非常有限的。离子键显然要排除在外，因为它们必然与水结合。剩下的可能性是侧链末端的氨基和羰基之间的作用，但是它们在一定程度上也有与水结合的倾向。看上去更有可能的是 S–S 连接和疏水性基团之间的相互作用中的一种或两种。对迄今为止观测过的仅由少数几个亚单位组成的所有蛋白质而言，分子中存在的 S 的数量足以提供使整个分子结合在一起所需的 S–S 键，而且，S–S 键断裂时蛋白质活性所发生的巨大变化显示出这些二硫键有一些基本的功能。然而，无论它是否如此，蛋白质疏水性基团的特性决定了它们必然要结合在一起。就像丹尼利 [13] 和朗缪尔 [14] 基于表面膜工作指出的那样，溶液中的蛋白质分子必然会使其疏水性基团避免与水分子接触，而处于表面的分子则断裂形成厚度为 10 Å 的薄膜，其中的疏水性基团并不与水接触。通过这样一种方式，就提供了一种结合力，与其说这是疏水基团之间的弱的吸引力，不如说是使基团与水介质分离开来的一种排斥力。

朗缪尔曾经用这个图像来证明环醇笼状假设，但是从严格意义上来讲它是独立于这个理论的，上面所提到的模型的优势在于它可以非常好地解释变性现象，特别是在表面上发生的蛋白质变性。一旦亚单位到达分子的表面，它们的环就会破裂成平面，不同的环之间依据普通的环 – 链聚合过程发生相互作用，这会导致纤维的形成，就像阿斯特伯里发现纤维存在于这类薄膜中那样。这个聚合过程持续的时间是可测的，正如丹尼利的研究工作所展示的那样。

目前所得到的图像远不能说是最终的或者是令人满意的。需要阐明的至关重要的问题是肽链折叠或者卷曲的精细模型，为此我们可能不得不等待相当长的时间，直到 X 射线技术以及其他方法获得比现在更进一步的发展。蛋白质结构的问题目前是一个明确而且并非不可实现的目标，但是为了获得成功，它需要研究者之间某种程度的协作，然而现在的协作远未达到所需要的程度。目前绝大多数的蛋白质研究工作之间都是不协调的，不同的研究者采用不同的技术观测不同的蛋白质，也许集中而又有计划的研究可能会节省许多现在这种状态下浪费掉的时间和精力，从而有助于对问题的直接阐明。

（刘振明 翻译；周筠梅 审稿）

References:

1. Svedberg, T., *Proc. Roy. Soc.*, A, **170**, 40 (1939).

2. Bernal, J. D., and Crowfoot, D., *Nature*, **133**, 794 (1934).

3. Bernal, J. D., *et al.*, *Nature*, **141**, 521 (1938).

4. Langmuir, I., *J. Chem. Phys.*, **6**, 873 (1938).

5. Levine, S., *Proc. Roy. Soc.*, A, **170**, 145 (1939).

6. Astbury, W. T., "Fundamentals of Fibre Structure", *Phil. Trans.*, **232**, 333 (1933).

7. *Biochem. J.*, **29**, 2351 (1935).

8. Personal communication.

9. *Proc. Roy. Soc.*, A, **164**, 580 (1938).

10. *J. Amer. Chem. Soc.*, **60**, 2247 (1938).

11. Bernal, J. D., *Nature*, **143**, 74 (1939).

12. Neuberger, A., *Proc. Roy. Soc.*, A, **170**, 64 (1939).

13. Danielli, J. F., *Proc. Roy. Soc.*, A, **170**, 73 (1939).

14. Langmuir, I., and Wrinch, D., *Nature*, **143**, 49 (1939).

Number of Neutrons Liberated in the Nuclear Fission of Uranium

H. von Halban, jun. *et al.*

Editor's Note

Experiments had confirmed that uranium nuclei could be fissioned—induced to split into two large nuclei—when bombarded by a neutron, and that secondary neutrons were given off in the process. But physicists had little idea how many neutrons were produced in such a fission event. This was important to the possibility of a self-sustaining fission chain-reaction. Here physicist Hans von Halban, then working with Frédéric Joliot-Curie and Lew Kowarski in Paris, estimates experimentally how many neutrons are released. The answer—3.5 on average—suggested that a chain reaction might be possible in uranium if the likelihood for a neutron to trigger a fission event were sufficiently high. After the German invasion in 1940, von Halban fled France for England.

RECENT experiments have shown that neutrons are liberated in the nuclear fission of uranium induced by slow neutron bombardment: secondary neutrons have been observed which show spatial[1], energetic[2] or temporal[3] properties different from those which primary neutrons possess or may acquire. Such observations give no information on the mean number of neutrons produced per nucleus split; this number ν may be very small (less than 1) and the result of the experiment will still be positive.

We are now able to give information on the value of ν. Let us consider the curve representing the density distribution of neutrons slowed down in an aqueous solution surrounding a primary neutron source[1]; the area S of this curve is proportional to $Q \cdot \tau$, Q being the number of neutrons per second emitted by the source or formed in the solution, and τ the mean time a neutron spends in the solution before being captured. Assuming that the solution contains only nuclei which absorb neutrons according to the $1/v$ law (the only exception to this rule will presently be dealt with), τ is proportional to $1/\Sigma c_i \sigma_i$, where c_i is the concentration (atom grams per litre) of an absorbing nucleus, σ_i its cross-section for the capture of neutrons of velocity 1 and the index i is extended to all kinds of neutron-absorbing reactions attributable to nuclei present in the solution. Substituting the symbol A_i for $c_i \sigma_i$ and A_{tot} for ΣA_i, we have identically:

$$\frac{\Delta S}{S} = \frac{\Delta Q}{Q} - \frac{\Delta A_{tot}}{A_{tot}}, \tag{1}$$

neglecting all terms of higher orders, such as those containing $(\Delta Q)^2$, $\Delta Q \cdot \Delta A_{tot}$, etc.

Let the symbol Δ stand for the differences observed between the two solutions (uranyl and ammonium) used in our previous experiment[1]. Neglecting ΔA_{tot} before A_{tot} introduces an ambiguity in the definition of A_{tot} (uranyl *vs.* ammonium value) which is numerically

铀核裂变时释放的中子数量

冯·哈尔班等

编者按

实验已证实被中子轰击时铀核可以分裂为两个大核，并且裂变过程中会释放出次级中子。但是关于一个裂变事件中释放出多少中子，物理学家对此了解很少。但是这直接关系到自持裂变链式反应实现的可能性。物理学家汉斯·冯·哈尔班当时与费雷德里克·约里奥－居里及卢·科瓦尔斯基在巴黎一起工作，基于实验他对释放中子数进行了估测。答案是——平均3.5个——这意味着如果一个中子诱发一个裂变事件的可能性足够高，铀就可以发生链式反应。1940年德国入侵后，冯·哈尔班从法国逃亡到英国。

最近的实验表明，慢中子轰击铀核引发核裂变可以释放出中子：次级中子在空间 [1]、能量 [2]、时间 [3] 上的性质都与初级中子所拥有或者可能获得的性质不同。这些实验没有给出每次核分裂所产生的中子的平均数量；虽然这个数量 ν 可能非常小（小于1），但是实验测量仍然可以得出正的结果。

现在我们可以给出 ν 值的一些信息。让我们仔细思考一下在包围着初级中子源 [1] 的水溶液中减速的中子的密度分布曲线；曲线的面积 S 和 $Q \cdot \tau$ 成正比，Q 是每秒由中子源发射出的或在溶液中形成的中子数，τ 是中子被俘获之前在溶液中度过的平均时间。假设溶液中只有依照 $1/v$ 定律吸收中子的原子核（这个法则的唯一例外将在不久后处理），τ 正比于 $1/\Sigma c_i \sigma_i$，其中 c_i 是吸收中子的原子核浓度（克原子每升），σ_i 是所有速度为1的中子的俘获截面，指标 i 遍历溶液中原子核所致的各种中子吸收反应。用 A_i 代替 $c_i \sigma_i$，用 A_{tot} 代替 ΣA_i，我们将得到：

$$\frac{\Delta S}{S} = \frac{\Delta Q}{Q} - \frac{\Delta A_{tot}}{A_{tot}} \tag{1}$$

上式忽略了所有包含诸如 $(\Delta Q)^2$、$\Delta Q \cdot \Delta A_{tot}$ 等的高阶项。

符号 Δ 代表我们在以前实验所使用的两种溶液（硝酸双氧铀和硝酸铵）中观察到的差值 [1]。在 A_{tot} 引入使 A_{tot} 定义不明确的因素之前，ΔA_{tot} 可以忽略不计，这（硝酸双氧铀对硝酸铵的值）在数值上并不重要，并且可以采用算数平均值

unimportant and can be reduced by adopting the arithmetical mean $(A_{tot}$ (amm.) $+\Delta A_{tot}) /2$.

In the quantity ΔA_{tot} the uranium nuclei are represented by several separate terms standing for the different modes of neutron capture (see below); let A_f be the term for the capture leading to fission. Every neutron has the probability A_f/A_{tot} of causing a fission and, since one individual fission process liberates v neutrons on the average, the total number ΔQ of neutrons thus created is $Q \cdot \dfrac{A_f}{A_{tot}} \cdot v$, and the equation (1) can be rewritten as follows:

$$v = \frac{\Delta S}{S} \cdot \frac{A_{tot}}{A_f} + \frac{\Delta A_{tot}}{A_f} \qquad (2)$$

Let us estimate the values of all quantities necessary to calculate v according to this formula. The area variation $\Delta S/S$ can be read from the graph given in our previous letter with an error of less than 20 percent (due to the uncertainties of inter- and extrapolation; in order to facilitate the latter, we added to the curves a further experimental point for $r = 29$ cm.). The value of A_{tot} for the ammonium solution can be easily calculated from the known concentrations and capture cross-sections (hydrogen, nitrogen and oxygen). A_f is equal to c_U (1.6 in our experiment), multiplied by the value of σ_f given in a recent paper by Anderson et al.[4]. ΔA_{tot} contains a term expressing the small difference of the hydrogen content between the two solutions; and three terms relative to uranium, namely, the fission term A_f, already dealt with, the thermal capture term A_{ct} which can be calculated by using a recently found value for σ_{ct}[5] and finally the resonance capture term A_r, which requires some explanation.

Our reasoning assumed that all neutrons introduced into the solution spend practically all their life, and are absorbed, in the thermal state. This is true in so far as the $1/v$ law is valid for absorption of neutrons in all nuclei concerned; and, therefore, not wholly true for uranium, which shows a pronounced resonance capture of neutrons of about 25 volts[6]. A certain proportion of neutrons entering the solution is bound to come within this resonance band and to be absorbed by resonance; therefore, it will never reach the thermal state. This proportion depends on the width of the resonance band and on the concentration c_U; its value in our system of symbols is equal to A_r/A_{tot} and was numerically determined by an experiment reported elsewhere[5].

Putting all numerical values in the formula (2) (with 10^{-24} cm.[2] as the unit of cross-section), that is: $\Delta S/S = 0.05 \pm 0.01$; $A_{tot} = 36 \pm 3$; $A_f = 1.6 \times 2 = 3.2$; $\Delta A_{tot} = 8.7 \pm 1.4$ decomposable into $\Delta A_H = 1.2 \pm 0.1$, $A_{ct} = 1.6 \times (1.3 \pm 0.45) = 2.1 \pm 0.7$, $A_r = 6.4 \pm 1.1$ and $A_f = 3.2$, we find:

$$v = 3.5 \pm 0.7.$$

We were not able to allow for an error in A_f, since the value of σ_f given by Anderson et al. contains no indication of probable error. Any error in σ_f will affect $v - 1$ in an inversely proportional way; in any case v will remain greater than 1.

The interest of the phenomenon discussed here as a means of producing a chain of

(A_{tot}（铵）$+\Delta A_{tot}$）/2 来进行简化。

在 ΔA_{tot} 这个量中，铀原子核由代表不同中子俘获模式的分离项所描述（如下）；设 A_f 为引发裂变的俘获项。每个中子都有 A_f/A_{tot} 的引起裂变的概率，而且因为一次单独的裂变过程平均释放 ν 个中子，这样产生的中子总数 $\Delta Q = Q \cdot \dfrac{A_f}{A_{tot}} \cdot \nu$，则式（1）可以写成如下形式：

$$\nu = \frac{\Delta S}{S} \cdot \frac{A_{tot}}{A_f} + \frac{\Delta A_{tot}}{A_f} \tag{2}$$

让我们估算一下用上式来计算 ν 所必需的量。面积变化量 $\Delta S/S$ 可以从我们以前文章的图中得知，其误差小于 20%（误差是由插值和外推的不确定性造成；为了便于外推，我们在曲线 $r = 29$ 厘米处增加了一个实验点）。利用已知的浓度和俘获截面（氢、氮和氧），可以很容易地计算出铵溶液中的 A_{tot} 值。A_f 等于 c_U（在我们实验中值是 1.6）乘以安德森等人 [4] 在近期文章中给出的 σ_f 值。ΔA_{tot} 中包含了一个表示两种溶液中关于氢含量微小差异的项，以及三个与铀相关的项，即前面已经讨论过的裂变项 A_f，可以用最近得到的 σ_{ct} 值来计算的热俘获项 A_{ct}[5]，还有共振俘获项 A_r，最后这一项需要一些解释。

我们合理地假设：所有进入溶液的中子，几乎全部寿命都处于热态，并且在这个态被吸收。只要保证所涉及的原子核对中子的吸收满足 $1/\nu$ 定律，这个假设就是成立的；然而，对于 25 电子伏的中子有显著中子共振俘获的铀 [6]，这个假设并不完全成立。因为以一定比例进入溶液的中子会被束缚在这种共振带中，并被共振吸收；因此，它们就不会到达热态。这个比例依赖于共振带宽和浓度 c_U；在我们的符号系统中，其数值等于 A_r/A_{tot}，我们已经有实验确定了它的数值并已在别处发表 [5]。

把上述所有的数值都代入公式（2）（以 10^{-24} 平方厘米作为截面的单位），即：$\Delta S/S = 0.05 \pm 0.01$；$A_{tot} = 36 \pm 3$；$A_f = 1.6 \times 2 = 3.2$；$\Delta A_{tot} = 8.7 \pm 1.4$，可以分解为 $\Delta A_H = 1.2 \pm 0.1$；$A_{ct} = 1.6 \times (1.3 \pm 0.45) = 2.1 \pm 0.7$，$A_r = 6.4 \pm 1.1$，$A_f = 3.2$，我们得到：
$$\nu = 3.5 \pm 0.7$$

我们无法推算 A_f 的误差，因为安德森等人给出的 σ_f 值并不包含任何可能的误差值。σ_f 中的任何误差都会对 $\nu - 1$ 产生一个反比例的影响；但无论怎样，ν 都会大于 1。

本文讨论的现象可以作为一种产生链式核反应的方法，我们在以前的文章中

nuclear reactions was already mentioned in our previous letter. Some further conclusions can now be drawn from the results reported here. Let us imagine a medium containing only uranium and nuclei the total neutron absorption of which, as compared to that of uranium, may be neglected (containing, for example, only some hydrogen for slowing down purposes). In such a medium, if $\frac{A_f}{A_{tot}} \cdot v > 1$ (A_{tot} includes now only uranium terms), the fission chain will perpetuate itself and break up only after reaching the walls limiting the medium. Our experimental results show that this condition will most probably be satisfied (the quantity $\frac{A_f}{A_{tot}} \cdot v - 1$, though positive, will be, however, small), especially if one keeps in view that the term A_r, because of the self-reversal of the resonance absorption line, increases much more slowly than the other uranium terms when the uranium content of the medium is increased.

(**143**, 680; 1939)

H.von Halban, jun., F. Joliot and L. Kowarski: Laboratoire de Chimie Nucléaire, College de France, Paris, April 7.

References:

1. von Halban, jun., H., Joliot, F., Kowarski, L., *Nature*, **143**, 470 (1939).

2. Dodé, M., von Halban, jun., H., Joliot, F., Kowarski, L., *C.R.*, **208**, 995 (1939).

3. Roberts, R., Meyer, R., Wang, P, *Phys. Rev.*, **55**, 510 (1939).

4. Anderson, H., Booth, E., Dunning, J., Fermi, E., Glasoe, G., Slack, F., *Phys. Rev.*, **55**, 511 (1939).

5. von Halban, jun., H., Kowarski, L., Savitch, P., *C.R.* (in the Press).

6. Meither, L., Hahn, O., Strassmann, F., *Z. Phys.*, **106**, 249 (1937).

已经提到过它的重要性。这里报道的结果可以得到一些更进一步的结论。设想一种介质中只含有铀和一些与铀相比对中子的吸收可以忽略不计的原子核（比如，只含有一些用于减速的氢）。在这种介质中，如果 $\frac{A_f}{A_{tot}} \cdot v > 1$（$A_{tot}$ 此处只含有铀的项），链式裂变反应将一直继续下去，直到到达介质的边界为止。我们的实验结果表明，这种条件非常有可能实现（$\frac{A_f}{A_{tot}} \cdot v - 1$ 的值虽然为正，但是会非常小），特别是考虑到当介质中的铀含量增加时，由于共振吸收线的自蚀，A_r 要比铀的其他项增加得缓慢得多。

（王静 翻译；夏海鸿 审稿）

Use of Isotopes in Biology

Editor's Note

Here *Nature* reports on developments in the application of radioactive elements and heavy non-radioactive isotopes as tracers in biology and medicine. The possibility of identifying single-atom decays made such methods very sensitive. At a recent meeting of the Chemical Society and the Physiology Society, researchers described the use of radioactive phosphorus in tracing the uptake of phosphorus by bones in the human body. Similar studies were probing the chemical activity of organs, and providing estimates of the timescales for protein formation. Other experiments were probing both human and plant physiology with tracers such as heavy oxygen or radioactive sodium. These experiments were generally safe, as the radioactivity involved was small compared to that naturally produced within the body.

THE discovery both of artificial radioactive elements and heavy non-radioactive isotopes, together with methods of concentration of the latter, has opened up new methods of examining the reactions and movements of substances in the body.

The isotopic indicator most frequently used in biological research is radioactive phosphorus (^{32}P) which may be prepared by the bombardment of carbon disulphide by neutrons from a radium-beryllium source. The sulphur atom takes up a neutron and gives out a proton, forming heavy, unstable, radioactive phosphorus (half-life period 14 days):

$$^{32}_{16}S + ^{1}_{0}n \rightarrow ^{32}_{15}P + ^{1}_{1}H.$$

The phosphorus is then oxidized to phosphate. Stronger preparations may be obtained by bombarding red phosphorus with deuterium ions using a cyclotron:

$$^{31}_{15}S + ^{2}_{1}D \rightarrow ^{32}_{15}P + ^{1}_{1}H.$$

For use, a small amount of the labelled sodium phosphate is added to ordinary sodium phosphate solution, and by this means the path of the phosphorus in the body can be traced. Estimations are carried out by observing the decay, at a given time, using a Geiger counter, and comparing directly with the decay of a similar standard at the same time, thus avoiding corrections for the rate of decay due to lapse of time. Thus if it is desired to determine the radioactive phosphorus content of the bone of an animal to which a labelled phosphate solution has been administered (and hence determine any exchange in the phosphate of the bone), a known weight of bone ash from the animal is placed under the Geiger counter and the strength observed. This is compared directly with the same weight of calcium phosphate, precipitated together with the labelled phosphate from a known weight of solution. This method has placed an extremely delicate method of estimation in the hands of the experimenter and has the great advantage that it is not necessary to purify the substance carefully from non-radioactive elements.

同位素在生物学中的应用

编者按

《自然》的这篇文章报道了在生物学和医学领域应用放射性元素和非放射性元素的重同位素作为示踪剂的进展。对单原子衰变的识别能力使该类方法具有很高的灵敏性。在最近召开的化学学会与生理学学会上，研究者们描述了在追踪人体内骨骼对磷的吸收时放射性磷的应用。类似的研究还有探测器官的化学放射性，评估蛋白质形成的时间。还有一些实验是利用诸如重氧或放射性钠等作为示踪剂研究人体生理及植物生理。与机体内自然产生的放射性相比，实验引入的放射性是较小的，因此这些实验基本上是安全的。

人工放射性同位素和非放射性元素的重同位素的发现，以及后者的浓缩方法的出现，为检测体内物质的反应和运动开辟了新途径。

在生物学研究中最常使用的同位素示踪剂是放射性磷（^{32}P），用来自镭－铍放射源的中子轰击二硫化碳可以得到。硫原子吸收一个中子并释放出一个质子，形成重的、不稳定的、放射性的磷（半衰期为 14 天）：

$$^{32}_{16}S + ^{1}_{0}n \rightarrow ^{32}_{15}P + ^{1}_{1}H$$

接着，磷被氧化成磷酸盐。借助于回旋加速器，用氘离子轰击红磷可以得到更强的制剂：

$$^{31}_{15}S + ^{2}_{1}D \rightarrow ^{32}_{15}P + ^{1}_{1}H$$

使用时，将少量同位素标记的磷酸钠加入普通的磷酸钠溶液中，通过这种方法就能够追踪磷元素在体内的路径。在给定的时刻，使用盖革计数器，通过观测衰变进行估计，并且同时与类似标准物的衰变直接进行比较，这样可以不用再修正因时间流逝而产生的衰变速率。因此，如果想检测已被施用同位素标记的磷酸盐溶液的动物的骨骼中放射性磷的含量（并由此确定骨骼中任何磷酸盐交换），就要将已知重量的该动物的骨灰置于盖革计数器之下并观测其强度。将它立即与同等质量的磷酸钙进行比较，后者是从已知重量的溶液中与同位素标记的磷酸盐共沉淀得到的。这给实验者提供了一种极为巧妙的估计方法，其最大优势在于不必从非放射性元素中提纯物质。

Of the non-radioactive elements, deuterium (^{2}H) has been isolated in a state of purity; while heavy oxygen (^{18}O) and heavy nitrogen (^{15}N) have been concentrated sufficiently to make their use as indicators possible.

Heavy hydrogen and oxygen may be accurately estimated by conversion to water, and, after careful purification, determination of the density of the latter. Heavy nitrogen is determined by the mass-spectrograph. This method may also be used for the determination of heavy oxygen: it has the advantage that very careful purification is unnecessary.

It may be objected that the use of isotopes as indicators in the living body may disturb the normal conditions. Actually, the proportion of radioactive phosphorus which it is necessary to use is extremely small, and the radiation from it may be comparable with that from the potassium which is already present in the body, and on decaying it is converted to a sulphur atom. Heavy non-radioactive isotopes are also already present in small proportions in the body, and the use of a slightly greater concentration as an indicator should not be objectionable. In the case of deuterium, it may be best to avoid the use of concentrated preparations.

A joint meeting of the Chemical Society and the Physiological Society on February 9 last took the form of a discussion on the use of isotopes in biology, which was opened by Prof. G. von Hevesy, of the Institute of Theoretical Physics, Copenhagen.

Among examples of the use of radioactive phosphorus, Prof. Hevesy described the results of experiments in which labelled sodium phosphate was injected intravenously; blood samples of known volume taken at intervals showed a very rapid decrease at first, followed by a slow decrease, in the labelled phosphate. This was found to be taken up by the bones and organs of the body, but chiefly by the former. It can be shown, by shaking up solid calcium phosphate with labelled phosphate solution, that there is a rapid exchange between the phosphate ions and the phosphate in the solid, the rate depending on the concentrations of the ions and the surface area of the solid. In the case of the body, the weight of the solid phosphate in the bones is very great compared with the inorganic phosphate in the blood, and most of the labelled phosphate will exchange with ordinary phosphate on the surface of the bones. As phosphate is lost by excretion through the kidneys and bowels, the uptake of labelled phosphate by the bones will cease, and finally, when the labelled phosphate in the blood is nearly removed, there will be a slow exchange of labelled phosphate back from the bones to the blood. Thus it may be possible to detect labelled phosphate several weeks after administration. Examination of the separate organs of the body enables the passage of the phosphate to be followed, and similarly examination of sections of bone shows that the rate of exchange of phosphate varies with different bones. In the case of growing bone such as the teeth of rats, the greater activity is found in the tooth formed after the addition of the labelled phosphate; the part formed before the addition, however, also shows some activity, indicating that exchange of phosphate takes place at the same time as new growth.

在非放射性元素中,已经分离出了纯净状态的氘 (^{2}H);而重氧 (^{18}O) 和重氮 (^{15}N) 则已被浓缩到足以作为示踪剂的浓度。

将重氢和氧转化成水,经过仔细提纯后,测定后者密度,以对其进行精确的估计。重氮是用质谱仪来测定的。这种方法也可以用来测定重氧:它的优势在于不需要进行极为细致的纯化。

也许有反对意见认为,将同位素作为示踪剂引入活体可能会扰乱正常的生理状态。实际上,必须使用的放射性磷所占比例极小,其放射性可能与体内存在的钾的放射性相当,而且在衰变过程中它会转变成为硫原子。另外,体内原本就存在少量的非放射性元素的重同位素,因而使用浓度稍高一点的重同位素作为示踪剂应当不会引起排斥。对于氘来说,最好还是避免使用浓缩制剂。

2 月 9 日,哥本哈根理论物理研究所的赫维西教授组织召开了化学学会与生理学学会的联席会议,会议最后讨论了同位素在生物学中的应用。

在放射性磷的应用实例中,赫维西教授描述了静脉注射标记磷酸钠的实验结果;间隔性采集的定量血液样品显示,标记磷酸钠先快速减少,接着缓慢减少。机体骨骼及器官均有摄取,但以前者为主。将固态磷酸钙与同位素标记的磷酸盐溶液摇匀,可以看出,磷酸根离子与固态中的磷酸盐之间存在快速交换,交换速率取决于离子的浓度以及固体的表面积。在体内,骨骼中固态磷酸盐的量远大于血液中无机磷酸盐的量,因此大部分同位素标记的磷酸盐与骨骼表面的普通磷酸盐进行交换。随着磷酸盐经由肾和肠被排出体外,骨骼对同位素标记的磷酸盐的吸收也会停止,最后,当血液中同位素标记的磷酸盐被基本清除后,同位素标记的磷酸盐缓慢交换而后从骨骼返回血液中。因此有可能在注药几周后也能检测到同位素标记的磷酸盐。检测机体内的各个器官可以追踪磷酸盐的通路,而对各部分骨骼进行的类似检测表明:不同骨骼中磷酸盐的交换速率也不同。对于诸如鼠齿那样的处在生长中的骨骼,在添加同位素标记的磷酸盐后长出的牙齿中发现了更强的放射性;然而,在添加之前就已经形成的那部分牙齿也表现出一些放射性,这说明伴随着新的生长过程同时也发生着磷酸盐的交换。

Phosphorus atoms in an organic molecule such as lecithin do not exchange with labelled sodium phosphate. Thus, if active lecithin is found, it indicates that the lecithin molecule has been synthesized after the administration of the labelled sodium phosphate (in the presence of suitable enzymes) and thus a distinction can be made between old and new molecules. This method may be used, for example, to find the place of formation of the phosphatides in the yolk of hens' eggs. By killing a hen five hours after an injection of labelled phosphate, it was found that the liver and plasma phosphatide were very active (the former more than the latter) compared with that in the ovary and yolk; thus the phosphatide molecules formed during the last five hours do not originate in the ovary, but are taken by the ovary from the plasma and used in the building up of the yolk. It was also found that after the egg had left the ovary no labelled phosphatide was formed in it. This was shown by examination of eggs laid less than 20 hours after administration of labelled phosphate (the egg, after leaving the ovary, remains in the oviduct about 20 hours).

The use of radioactive sodium phosphate have also been of great help in a study of the formation of (goat) milk. Samples of blood and milk taken at intervals after administration of labelled phosphate were examined for the activity of the phosphate in the blood and the various phosphorus compounds in the milk. It was found that after three to four hours the milk inorganic phosphate was replaced by the active phosphate of the plasma; while if heavy water was injected at the same time as the active phosphate, after one hour water samples prepared from blood and milk had the same density, the difference in the rates being due to the fact that water molecules diffuse through the membranes at a greater rate than phosphate ions. From the rate at which the casein phosphorus becomes active, compared with the active inorganic phosphorus in the milk, it was estimated that the time of formation of casein in the gland cells was about one hour.

The fact that a few hours after addition of the labelled phosphate the milk phosphatides are only slightly active compared with the inorganic phosphate, indicates that the latter cannot be produced from the former, thus contradicting the view that the fats and inorganic phosphate are produced by the breaking up, in the milk gland, of the phosphatides of the blood. The investigation of problems of milk secretion was also referred to by Dr. S. K. Kon.

Labelled sodium phosphate has also been used in a study of the movements of phosphate in plants. Maize and sunflowers grown first in a culture solution were then transferred to a second solution containing labelled phosphate. The leaves which grew while the plant was in the second solution were examined for activity and compared with the leaves which grew in the first (inactive) solution. It was found that, after four days, the lower leaves had 80 percent of the activity of the upper leaves, showing that a rapid replacement of phosphate took place. Similar experiments have been carried out using heavy nitrogen as indicator.

The use of deuterium as an indicator was discussed by Prof H. S. Raper and Dr. W. E. van Heyningen. The former referred to the work of Cavanagh and Raper, in which fats

诸如卵磷脂等有机分子中的磷原子与同位素标记的磷酸钠之间不发生交换。因此，如果发现有放射性的卵磷脂，就意味着该卵磷脂分子是在施用同位素标记的磷酸钠之后合成的（在合适的酶存在的条件下），因此便可以区分以前合成的分子和最新合成的分子。例如，利用这种方法可以找到鸡蛋卵黄中的磷脂的形成部位。给一只母鸡注射同位素标记的磷酸盐，5 小时后将其杀死，发现相对于卵巢和卵黄中的磷脂来说，肝和血浆中的磷脂（前者尤甚于后者）具有更强的放射性；因此在最后 5 小时内合成的磷脂分子并非生成于卵巢，而是由卵巢从血浆中获得并用于制造卵黄。此外还发现离开卵巢的鸡蛋中不会再形成同位素标记的磷脂。这可以通过检测注射标记磷酸盐后 20 小时内（鸡蛋在离开卵巢后，在输卵管中保存约 20 小时）生产的鸡蛋得以证明。

放射性磷酸钠的使用也为研究（山羊）奶的形成提供了很大的帮助。在注射同位素标记的磷酸盐后，间隔性采集血液和奶液样品，检测血液中磷酸盐的放射性以及奶液中的各种含磷化合物。3 到 4 小时之后，发现奶液中的无机磷酸盐被血浆中的放射性磷酸盐取代；然而如果在注射放射性磷酸盐的同时注射重水，那么 1 小时后由血液和奶液制得的水溶液样品就具有相同的放射强度，速率方面的差异可归结为水分子扩散通过膜的速率比磷酸根离子更快这一事实。根据酪蛋白变得具有放射性的速率，对比奶液中的放射性无机磷，可以估算出腺细胞中酪蛋白的形成时间大约为一小时。

在加入同位素标记的磷酸盐几个小时后，与无机磷酸盐相比，奶液中的磷脂仅具有轻微的放射性，这一事实意味着后者不是由前者生成的，从而与认为脂肪和无机磷酸盐是在乳腺中通过血液中磷脂的断裂而生成的观点相矛盾。科恩博士也谈到了关于泌乳问题的研究。

同位素标记的磷酸钠还被用于研究磷酸盐在植物体内的运动。首先将玉米和向日葵在培养液中进行培养，然后再将其转入另一份含同位素标记的磷酸盐溶液中。当植物体处于第二份溶液中时检测其生长叶片的放射性，并与在第一份溶液（无放射性）中生长的叶片进行比较。四天后，发现下部叶片的放射性是上部叶片的 80%，这表明发生了磷酸盐的快速置换。有人将重氮作为示踪剂进行了类似的实验。

雷珀教授和海宁根博士论述了将氘作为一种示踪剂的应用。雷珀教授提到了卡

labelled with deuterium were fed to animals and a study made of the rate of formation of the deuterium labelled lipins in the liver and kidney; the latter gave an account of the work of Schoenheimer and Rittenberg *et al.* on deuterium as an indicator in the study of intermediary metabolism, and referred especially to the uses and limitations of the method.

The use of heavy oxygen as an indicator was discussed by Dr. J. N. E. Day. He referred to the work of Aten and Hevesy, who examined the possibility of exchange of oxygen in sulphate, with other oxygen atoms present in the body, by injecting heavy sodium sulphate into rabbits, and concluded that there was little or no exchange. Reference was also made to the work of Day and Sheel on the use of heavy oxygen in animal respiration, in which the heaviness of the expired carbon dioxide was determined.

Radioactive sodium was dealt with by Dr. B. G. Maegraith, who mentioned experiments in which active sodium chloride had been injected into rabbits, and the distribution of the active sodium investigated. He suggested that this might be used to estimate the extracellular fluid content of the rabbit.

Dr. W. D. Armstrong described experiments dealing with the exchange of phosphorus of the enamel of teeth and the blood using radioactive phosphorus. A very slow exchange was noticed, indicating, not the formation of new molecules, but exchange of phosphate between enamel and blood. Mr. C. H. Collie referred to work of Collie and Morgan showing that radioactive sulphur can be used as an indicator.

Dr. D. Roaf described a method of producing radioactive phosphorus by irradiation of tricresyl phosphate with slow neutrons.

(**143**, 709-711; 1939)

瓦纳和他本人的工作，即给动物喂食用氘标记的脂肪并研究其肝和肾中氘标记脂类的形成速率；海宁根博士描述了舍恩海默与里滕伯格等人所作的将氘作为示踪剂用于研究中间代谢的工作，特别是谈到了方法的使用和限制。

戴博士论述了将重氧作为一种示踪剂的应用。他提到了阿滕和赫维西的工作，他们通过给兔子注射重硫酸钠研究了硫酸盐中的氧与机体内存在的其他氧原子之间发生交换的可能性，其结论是两者之间很少或完全不交换。此外戴博士还提到了他自己和席尔应用重氧研究动物呼吸作用的工作，在此研究中他们测定了呼出二氧化碳的重量。

梅格雷思使用了放射性钠，他提到了对兔子注射放射性氯化钠后研究放射性钠在体内的分布的实验。他暗示该方法可能可以用于估计兔子细胞外液的量。

阿姆斯特朗博士描述了使用放射性磷研究牙齿珐琅质中的磷和血液中的磷交换的实验。实验中可以观察到极为缓慢的交换，这意味着在珐琅质和血液之间发生了磷酸盐的交换，而不是新分子的形成。科利先生提到了他自己和摩根的工作，证明放射性硫可以作为示踪剂。

娄夫博士描述了一种用慢中子激发磷酸三甲苯酯产生放射性磷的方法。

（王耀杨 翻译；杨志 审稿）

Surface Transport in Liquid Helium II

J. G. Daunt and K. Mendelssohn

Editor's Note

Experimenters had recently discovered some strange behaviours in liquid helium—in particular, its seeming ability to flow with no viscosity. Here physicists John Daunt and Kurt Mendelssohn of the Clarendon Laboratory in Oxford report a further odd effect. They had placed a container, open at the top and holding liquid helium, into a bath of the same liquid. Applying heat inside the vessel, they had found that a thin film of liquid flowed up and over the vessel's lip, linking the two otherwise separate fluids. The authors suggest that the phenomenon may be linked to the recently noted "fountain effect", in which the heat from a weak light beam can expel a jet of liquid helium from a container.

IN our previous communications[1] on the "transfer" of liquid helium II by a surface film above the liquid level, we stressed the similarity of this "transfer" with the so-called transport phenomena in the free liquid, and suggested that the latter might be due to a process similar to the transfer above the liquid level. Later experiments on the formation of this film[2] seemed further to strengthen the conception that there existed a similar surface transport below the liquid level, and we have recently made two observations which seem to corroborate this hypothesis:

(*a*) A small Dewar vessel (see Fig. 1) containing a heating coil was suspended by a thread in a bath of liquid helium II. When no heat was supplied, the levels of the liquid both inside and outside the vessel adjusted themselves to the same height L_1, owing to the "transfer" through the film on the interconnecting glass surface. When, however, a current was passed through the heating coil, the level of the liquid inside the vessel *rose* above the outside level and took up an equilibrium position L_2. By increasing the connecting surface between the vessel and bath by a number of wires, differences between inside and outside levels up to 5 mm. could be obtained. This clearly shows that there exists a "transfer" of helium from a colder to a hotter place when a temperature gradient is imposed. On further increasing the heat supplied, however, the evaporation from the vessel became the predominant factor and the inside level fell below that of the bath.

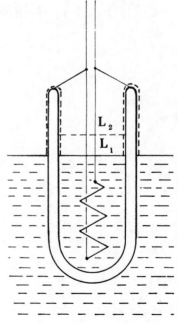

Fig. 1

液氦 II 中的表面传输

当特，门德尔松

编者按

最近的实验研究发现了液氦的一些奇特的行为，特别是它似乎具有完全无黏滞流动的能力。而在这篇文章中，牛津克拉伦登实验室的物理学家约翰·当特和库尔特·门德尔松报道了一个更为古怪的效应。他们将一个盛有液氦的上端开口的容器放置于液氦池中。在容器内加热时，他们发现有一薄层液膜向上流动，越过容器的边缘将两部分分开的液体连接在一起。本文作者认为这个现象可能与当时刚刚为人所知的"喷泉效应"有关，在"喷泉效应"中，微弱的光束产生的热量就可以使液氦从容器中喷射而出。

之前关于液氦 II 通过液面上的表面膜进行"迁移"的讨论中 [1]，我们强调这种"迁移"与所谓自由液体中的传输现象非常相似，并指出后者可能是由一个类似于在液面上迁移的过程引起的。后来关于表面膜形成的一些实验 [2] 似乎进一步证实了这种说法，即在液面下存在着类似的表面传输，而且我们最近做的两项观察实验似乎也证实了这一假设：

（*a*）用一根线系着一个装有加热线圈的小杜瓦瓶（如图 1）浸没在液氦 II 中。当不加热的时候，杜瓦瓶内外的液面通过自我调节达到相同的高度 L_1，这是由于液氦 II 以膜的形式在相互连接的玻璃表面"迁移"造成的。然而，当给加热线圈通以电流的时候，杜瓦瓶内的液面会**上升**到高于瓶外的液面并稳定在高度 L_2。如果用一些金属丝来增加杜瓦瓶与池中液氦的接触面积，瓶内外的液面高度差就可以上升到 5 毫米。这清楚地表明，当存在温度差的时候，氦会从温度较低的地方"迁移"到温度较高的地方。然而，当进一步加热时，瓶内的蒸发就成为主导因素，因此，杜瓦瓶内的液面会下降到低于池中的液面高度。

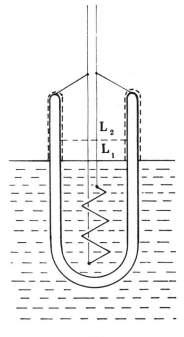

图 1

613

This effect is quite analogous to the "fountain phenomenon" in the bulk liquid, discovered by Allen and Jones[3]. However, in the present case the transfer of liquid must be carried out through the surface film above the liquid level, which shows that there exists a flow of helium against a temperature gradient, even if the two containers are not connected by free liquid. One may conclude therefore that the "fountain phenomenon" in the bulk liquid is probably also due to a surface transfer, though in this case along the surface below the liquid level. This hypothesis is further strengthened by the fact that the "fountain phenomenon" is more pronounced when tubes containing fine powder are used to connect the two volumes of liquid rather than a straight capillary, for which the available surface is comparatively small[4].

(*b*) A Dewar vessel (see Fig. 2) was closed at the top and had a hole at the lower end which was constricted by a plug, *P*, of fine emery powder. It contained a phosphor-bronze thermometer, *T*, and was suspended in a bath of liquid helium II. When the Dewar vessel was lifted out of the bath, the liquid ran rapidly out of the vessel through *P* and fell into the bath, and at the same time the temperature of the inside liquid was noticed to rise by about 0.01°. On lowering the vessel so that now liquid ran from the bath into the vessel, the liquid inside was cooled by a similar amount.

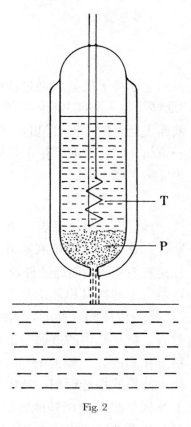

This mechano-caloric effect is evidently the reverse of the "fountain phenomenon", for whereas the latter means that the setting up of a temperature difference results in a flow of liquid helium II, the mechano-caloric effect shows that a flow of liquid helium II is accompanied by a development of heat (or cold). Such a caloric effect has actually been postulated by Tisza[5] for a flow of liquid helium II through capillaries. It seems to us, however, that the anomalous phenomena of liquid helium II are not so much caused by capillary flow as by a transport along solid surfaces;

Fig. 2

and these results seem to indicate that the heat content of those atoms transported by surface flow must be lower than average. The hypothesis that the transport phenomena in the bulk liquid are due (at least primarily) to a surface transport similar to the "transfer" above the liquid level seems also to agree with observations by Allen and Misener[6] and H. London[7], as well as with theoretical considerations of F. London[8].

这一效应与艾伦和琼斯 [3] 在体相液体中发现的"喷泉现象"极为相似。然而，在我们的实验中，液体迁移必须通过液面上的表面膜才能实现，这说明：即使两个容器之间没有自由液体相连通，也会存在与温度梯度方向相反的液氦流。有人也许因此得出结论：瓶内液体中的"喷泉现象"可能也是由于表面迁移而产生的，尽管在这种情况下迁移处于液面之下。下面的事实则进一步证实了这一假设：当用装有细粉的管子连接两个容器中的液体时，产生的"喷泉现象"比用直毛细管时更加明显，因为毛细管可进行迁移的表面积相对较小 [4]。

（*b*）一个顶部封闭的杜瓦瓶（如图 2）底部有一个洞，洞口上方是由细金刚砂粉形成的填塞物 *P*。瓶中还有一个由磷青铜制成的温度计 *T*，它被悬挂在液氦 II 池中。当杜瓦瓶被升高到液氦 II 池面以上时，瓶内的液体很快地通过 *P* 流入液氦 II 池中，同时，瓶内液体的温度升高约 0.01 度。当降低杜瓦瓶使液体得以从液氦 II 池流入瓶中的时候，瓶内液体的温度也降低了大体相同的度数。

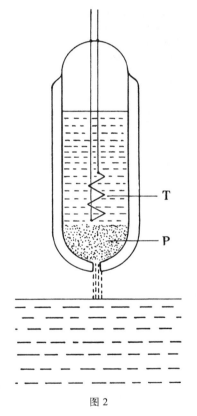

图 2

这一机械 – 热效应显然与"喷泉现象"正好相反，因为后者说明温度差导致了液氦 II 流的形成，而机械 – 热效应则显示液氦 II 流的形成伴随着温度的变化。实际上，蒂萨 [5] 根据通过毛细管的液氦 II 流曾提出过关于这一热效应的假设。不过，在我们看来，与其说液氦 II 流的异常现象是由毛细管流引起的，不如说是由固体表面传输造成的；这些结果似乎表明，那些在表面传输的原子的热容肯定低于平均值。体相液体中的传输现象是（至少主要是）由一种类似于液面上的"迁移"的表面传输而引起的，这一假设似乎与艾伦和麦色纳 [6] 以及伦敦 [7] 的观察结果相一致，同时也与伦敦 [8] 的理论研究相吻合。

A more detailed discussion of this tentative explanation with regard to these and other results will be given elsewhere.

(**143**, 719-720; 1939)

J. G. Daunt and K. Mendelssohn: Clarendon Laboratory, Oxford, March 21.

References:

1. Daunt and Mendelssohn, *Nature*, **141**, 911; and **142**, 475 (1938) and *Proc. Roy. Soc.*, in the Press.

2. To be published shortly.

3. Allen and Jones, *Nature*, **141**, 243 (1938).

4. Allen and Reekie, *Proc. Camb. Phil. Soc.*, **35**, 114 (1939).

5. Tisza, *Nature*, **141**, 913 (1938); *C.R.*, **207**, 1186 (1938).

6. Allen and Misener, *Nature*, **142**, 643 (1938); see also Allen and Jones, *Nature*, **143**, 227 (1939).

7. London, H., *Nature*, **142**, 612 (1938).

8. London, F., *Phys. Rev.*, **54**, 947 (1938).

有关上述以及其他一些研究成果的尝试性解释，我们将在别处进行更为详细地讨论。

(李世媛 翻译；于渌 审稿)

The Living Coelacanthid Fish from South Africa

J. L. B. Smith

Editor's Note

James Smith's announcement of the discovery of the coelacanth on 18 March 1938 caused a sensation. This brief report on the coelacanth's anatomy, less than two months later, was intended to be a stopgap, pending a projected monographic treatment. A problem was that Smith worked in what was then a distant part of the world in which resources were few. Some of the letters he received "contained very harsh criticism about the loss of the carcass of this fish". "Few persons outside South Africa have any knowledge of our conditions", he complained. Without the "energy and determination" of a Miss Latimer of East London, the fish might have gone undescribed. "The genus *Latimeria* stands as my tribute", Smith wrote.

THE recent discovery of the Coelacanthid fish (*Latimeria chalumnoe* J. L. B. Smith) near East London, as described in *Nature* of March 18, p. 455, has aroused great interest. This has partly found expression in numerous requests from all parts of the world for the earliest possible publication of a detailed description. I am able to pursue my investigations only in very limited spare time. The preparation of an adequately illustrated detailed description, under present conditions, will occupy several months. I have therefore decided upon the somewhat unusual procedure of issuing a synopsis of the more important results of my investigations to date. This is in the form of brief outlines without discussion.

Few scientific workers are as fortunate as those who have concentrated upon Coelacanthid remains. The present specimen is a living tribute to the accuracy of their interpretations and reconstructions.

The specimen was somewhat damaged in the trawl, the skin having been broken in several places. Repairs were skilfully executed by the taxidermist.

Skull and head. The skull is unfortunately not quite intact. The basisphenoid and part of the structures around the foramen magnum were removed (and discarded) in mounting. The soft parts of the head appear to have been removed rather roughly. The remaining tissues are in poor condition. Only the structures left intact will be described as fact.

Air-bladder. According to the fairly definite evidence of the taxidermist, this organ was at the very most but feebly ossified.

The scales are cycloid and but little ossified. The proportion of residue after ignition of

在南非发现的现生腔棘鱼

史密斯

编者按

1938 年 3 月 18 日，詹姆斯·史密斯宣布发现了腔棘鱼，这引起了一场轰动。不到两个月后，在一篇精心构思的学术论文完成之前，发表了这篇简短的用作临时补缺的腔棘鱼解剖报告。那时史密斯在非常偏远的地方工作，那里的资源非常稀少。他收到的一些信件"对这个鱼的躯体的缺损进行了非常尖锐的批评"。对此他抱怨道，"南非之外几乎没有人了解我们的条件"。如果没有东伦敦拉蒂迈小姐的"能力和决心"，这个鱼可能根本不会得到记载。史密斯写道，"我以拉蒂迈命名这个属就是为了表达对她的感谢"。

最近，在东伦敦附近发现腔棘鱼（拉蒂迈鱼，史密斯）的消息引起了人们极大的关注，3 月 18 日出版的《自然》第 455 页曾对这一发现进行了描述。从世界各地发来的众多信件希望我们可以尽快发表一篇详尽的报告，人们对此的关注程度由此也可见一斑。但是我只能在十分有限的业余时间里从事研究。在当前条件下，若要准备一份图解充分、描述详细的记载，要花费几个月的时间。因此我决定采用一个不太常用的办法，就是发表一些至今为止较为重要的研究结果的摘要。这些摘要将以简明概要的形式给出，而不作详细讨论。

很少有科学工作者能够像专注于腔棘鱼遗迹研究的科学家那样幸运。当前的标本为他们准确地解释和重构腔棘鱼提供了一个鲜活的参照。

标本在拖网中有所损坏，鱼皮有几个地方已经破损。标本剥制师对此进行了很巧妙的修复。

头骨与头部。遗憾的是头骨并不十分完整。在安装固定过程中，基蝶骨与枕骨大孔周围的部分结构被移除（并且被丢弃了）。头部的软组织部分似乎被粗暴地移除了。保留下来的组织状况不佳。因此，下文将仅对保留完整的组织结构进行如实的描述。

鱼鳔。依照标本剥制师提供的较为确切的证据，这个器官至多只是轻微骨化。

鱼鳞为圆鳞，但轻微骨化。对身体中部无修饰部分的鱼鳞进行灼烧处理，其剩

the unornamented portion of a mid-body scale is very much less than, but qualitatively identical with, that obtained by similar treatment of a teleostean scale. The exposed surface of a scale varies from one fourth to one sixth of the total area. The ornamentation on the caudal scales is in the form of spines, on the rest of the body as tubercles. The tubercles are superficial only; each is set in a thin oval basal plate with corrugated surface. The plates are attached to the scales by tissue which is softened by alkali. The tubercles are of simple structure with a central cavity (see Fig. 1). The lateral line tubes are posteriorly widely bifurcate.

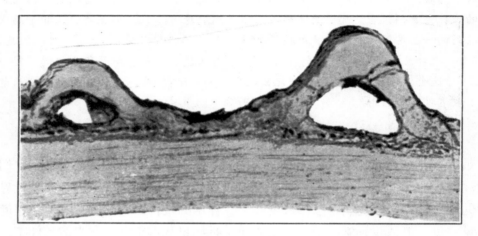

Fig. 1. Section of a scale (×50) of *Latimeria chalumnoe* J. L. B. Smith.

Fins. All the rays of the first dorsal, of the principal and of the supplementary caudal are spinate. A few of the rays of the second dorsal and of the anal are basally feebly spinate. The outer face of the pectoral is spinate. The pelvics only are quite smooth. The bony rays of the dorsal and caudal are articulated. The soft rays are finely articulated to their bases. All rays are composed of two fused lateral segments.

Dermal bones. The cheek-bones are a postorbital, a squamosal, a preopercular and a suborbital (lacrimojugal). On the middle of the lower surface of each cheek is a small bony stud which may be an obsolescent quadratojugal. The opercular is moderate in size. There are two dermal structures in a stage of arrested metamorphosis from scale to dermal bone, which are regarded as subopercular and interopercular respectively.

The intertemporals and the supratemporals appear to be fused. The exposed portion of each frontal is small, oval and flat. These bones are all feebly ornamented. The splenial and angular alone show externally on the lower jaw. The gulars are large and heavy.

Fronto-rostrals. Just beneath the skin there are nineteen bones in this series on each side. One large frontal and a smaller "pre"-frontal; nine "rostro-nasals", including a canal-bearing bone (No. 18) often named "premaxilla" in fossils.

余物远远少于对硬骨鱼类鱼鳞进行类似处理后得到的剩余物，但性质是相同的。每片鱼鳞外露的表面积占总面积的 1/4 到 1/6 不等。尾部鱼鳞上的装饰为皮刺形式，而在身体的其他部分是结节形式。结节仅在表面存在；每一个结节位于一个有波纹的薄的椭圆形基板上。基板通过已被碱软化过的组织固定在鱼鳞表面。结节是带有中央空腔的简单结构（见图 1）。侧线管后端分叉较宽。

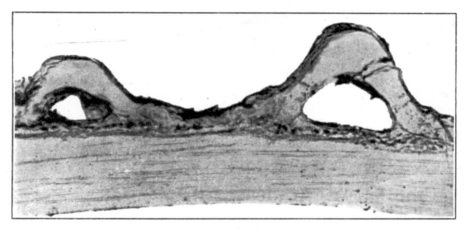

图 1. 拉蒂迈鱼（史密斯）的鳞片截面图（放大 50 倍）。

鳍。第一背鳍、主鳍及副尾鳍的所有辐射线都是棘状的。第二背鳍和臀鳍的一些鳍条基部略微呈棘状。胸鳍的外表面也呈棘状。只有腹鳍完全平滑。背鳍和尾鳍的骨质鳍条是分节的。软鳍条精巧地分节到其基部。所有鳍条都由两个愈合的侧节构成。

真皮骨。颊骨包括眼窝骨、鳞状骨、前鳃盖骨与眶下骨（泪－轭骨）。每个颊的下表面中间是一个小的骨质柱，可能是退化的方轭骨。鳃盖骨中等大小。有两个真皮结构，处于从鳞到真皮骨的停止变形阶段，它们分别被当作是下鳃盖骨和间鳃盖骨。

间颞骨与上颞骨看起来像是愈合了。每个额骨的外露部分很小，呈椭圆扁平状。这些骨全都略有修饰。夹骨和隅骨在下颌上单独外露出来。咽喉板大而厚重。

额部－吻突。位于皮肤之下，这个系列每一边均有 19 块骨头。一块大的额骨与一块较小的"前"额骨；9 块"吻突－鼻"骨，包括一块含有管道的骨（第 18 号），在化石中这块骨通常被命名为"前颌骨"。

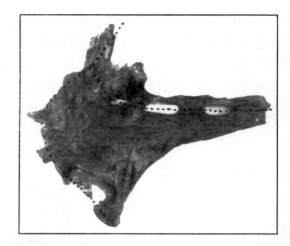

Fig. 2. Rostro-nasal, No. 18. Nat. size. Inner margin to the left. A piece of white paper has been inserted into the canal. The dotted lines show the course of sensory canals. The right-hand limb anastomoses with the suborbital.

There are eight bones in the "parafrontal" series, the anterior expanded bones having been named "antorbitals" in fossils. Besides these nineteen there are the small dentigerous rostral plates. Most of these bones are small and laminate.

Sensory canals. The main canals run much as have been shown in reconstructions. From the lateral line the canal passes through the supratemporals and intertemporals, thence "parafrontal" to the snout. There it has a small superior median branch. Just below that it gives off an inferior branch which is the infraorbital canal (running through the lateral limb of bone No. 18, which anastomoses with the suborbital). Below this junction is a commissure across the snout. The canal then runs downwards and curves outwards to end on the outer edge of the rostrum around the inner face of bone No. 18. Just behind the frontal is the junction of the infraorbital canal running downwards through the postorbital, which continues through the suborbital to the snout. The anterior limb of the squamosal anastomoses with the postorbital-suborbital anastomosis and carries the jugal canal which continues through the preopercular, thence as a tube in the skin obliquely over the lower outer face of the quadrate. It enters the angular very obliquely and thence runs forward on the lower margin just below the surface to the symphysis. There is a posterior branch on the lower surface of the angular.

Olfactory organs. There are on each side three "narial" apertures, two conventionally on the side of the snout before the eye, the third on the front of the rostrum. Each opening is the end of a simple tube which leads from a median capsule situated beneath a thin layer of mesethmoidal cartilage. The tubes and the capsule were apparently lined with fine rugose tissue. The capsule is depressed biconical in shape. There is also on each side of the rostrum an infero-lateral nasal tentacle, apparently imperforate. On each side of the snout, inferior and anterior to the median nasal cavity, lies a sac, typically covered below, laterally, and partly behind, by the prevomer, in front by bone No. 18. That bone lies against the

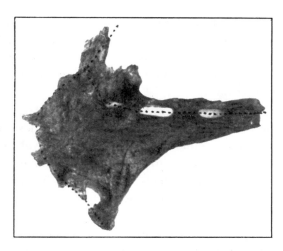

图 2. 吻–鼻，第18号。原始大小。左边为内缘。将一片白纸插入了管道中。
虚线表示感觉管的线路。右侧分支与眶下骨吻合。

"侧额骨"系列有 8 块骨，在化石中前端膨大的骨通常被命名为"眶前骨"。除了这 19 块，还有小的有齿的吻骨板。这些骨多数较小且呈薄片状。

感觉管。如复原图中所示，总管延伸很长。从侧线开始，管道通过上颞骨与间颞骨，然后从"侧额骨"到口鼻部。在那里有一个小的上中分支。就在那之下分出一个下支，即眶下管（贯穿第 18 号骨的侧支，与眶下骨汇合）。在这个连接点下面是一个横过口鼻部的接合处。然后管道下行并向外弯曲至第 18 号骨的内表面周围，于嘴外缘终止。眶下管下行直通后眶骨，穿过眶下骨延伸到口鼻部，眶下管的连接点恰好在额骨后面。鳞状骨前肢与后眶骨–眶下骨连接点吻合，其上的眶下管延伸至前鳃盖骨，继而斜开口于方骨下部外面的皮肤上。其十分倾斜地进入隅骨，然后沿表面下缘向前延伸至联合处。在隅骨下表面上有一后支。

嗅觉器官。在每边均有 3 个"鼻孔"孔隙，照例两个在眼睛前口鼻部的一边，第三个在吻的前端。每个孔都是一个单管的末端，管子从位于中筛软骨薄膜层之下的中囊导出。管子和囊明显与细皱褶组织在一条线上。囊呈扁平双锥形。嘴的每一边也有一条下侧鼻触须，明显无孔。在吻部的每一边，中央鼻腔的下部和前部，都生有一个囊，很有代表性的是，它的下面、侧面甚至部分后面都被前犁骨覆盖着，前面则被第 18 号骨覆盖。那块骨位于前犁骨后柱的外表面。这些囊与普通的"嗅觉

outer surface of the hind column of the prevomer. These sacs correspond with the usual "olfactory capsules", but do not appear to have any external narial opening. The nerve supply to these paired capsules appears to be from the olfactory lobe, and to enter at the upper inner portion of the surface. The nerve supply of the mesethmoidal (pineal?) cavity appears to come from farther back.

Respiratory organs. The branchial arches and appendages were lost. The arches are stated to have been strongly spinate. Remaining is a spinate epihyal and ceratohyal. Also a superficially ossified tuberculate copula ("tongue"), to which appear to have been attached four branchial arches. There is apparently a hyoidean gill-slit behind the free margin of the "preoperculum". The spiracles are small and probably functionless.

The palato-pterygo-quadrate apparatus is massive and typically coelacanthid. There is no hyomandibular. The prevomer is an unexpectedly solid structure, with the anterior edge of the autopalatine bearing against the hind surface of its outer columnar vertical process. The ectopterygoid overlaps the autopalatine and the pterygoid above.

Upper jaw. Maxillae are absent, probably also premaxillae. The upper jaw bears paired dermal plates attached to rostrals, prevomers, palatines and ectopterygoids. These plates are of fused small teeth, and each bears one or two large conical tusks. On the pterygoids and parasphenoid are conical granular teeth. There are two feeble granulate "epi"-pterygoid areas.

Lower jaw. There is a series of small "labial" dentate plates on the outer surface of the dentary. Superiorly are four dentate plates on each dentary. The anterior coronoid is small and bears granular teeth as well as several large tusks. The posterior coronoid is large and feebly granulate at the base. The articular-prearticular plate is very long and is granulate anteriorly only.

Several letters from overseas have contained very harsh criticism about the loss of the carcass of this fish. Few persons outside South Africa have any knowledge of our conditions. In the coastal belt only the South African Museum at Cape Town has a staff of scientific workers among whom is an ichthyologist. The other six small museums serving the coastal area are in extremely poor circumstances, and generally have only a director or curator, who cannot possibly be an expert in all branches of natural history. There are not uncommon fishes in the sea which to any of the latter would appear as strange as, if not stranger than, a coelacanthid. It was the energy and determination of Miss Latimer which saved so much, and scientific workers have good cause to be grateful. The genus *Latimeria* stands as my tribute.

(**143**, 748-750; 1939)

J. L. B. Smith: Rhodes University College, Grahamstown.

囊"相似，但似乎没有任何外部鼻孔开口。这些成对的囊的神经分布似乎来自嗅叶，并于表面的内上部进入。中筛 (松果体 ?) 腔的神经分布似乎来自更后方。

呼吸器官。鳃弓与附肢缺失。鳃弓被描述为强有力的棘状。棘状上舌骨与角舌骨得以保存。另外还有一个表面骨化的有结节的舌联桁（"舌状物"），似乎有 4 个鳃弓附在其上。在"前鳃盖骨"活动缘的后面有一个明显的 U 字形腮裂。呼吸孔小，而且可能已经丧失了功能。

腭骨 – 翼骨 – 方骨系列厚重，属于典型的腔棘鱼结构。没有舌颌骨。出人意料的是，前犁骨为实心结构，原腭骨的前缘靠在其外部柱状垂直突起的后表面。外翼骨重叠在原腭骨和翼骨上面。

上颌。上颌骨缺失，前上颌骨可能也缺失了。上颌有成对的真皮骨板附在吻骨突、前犁骨、腭骨及外翼骨上。这些骨板是小牙齿融合而成的，而且每个骨板都有一个或两个大的圆锥形长牙。在翼骨与副蝶骨上是圆锥形粒状牙齿。有两个略微成粒状的"上"翼骨区域。

下颌。齿骨外表面上有一系列小的"唇"齿状板。每个齿骨上是 4 个齿状板。前冠状骨小，具颗粒状牙齿，并且还有几个大的长牙。后冠状骨大，并在基部略微成粒状。关节 – 前关节骨板很长，并且仅前部呈粒状。

来自国外的一些信件对这个鱼的躯体的缺损进行了非常尖锐的批评。南非之外几乎没有人了解我们的条件。在海岸地带，仅在开普敦的南非博物馆有科学工作者，他们之中只有一位是鱼类学家。海岸区的其他 6 个小博物馆条件非常艰苦，一般只有一个主管或馆员，他们不可能精通博物学所有的分支学科。他们中的任何人对海中比腔棘鱼更加陌生或至少一样陌生的鱼早已见怪不怪。正是拉蒂迈小姐的能力和决心挽回了很多损失，科学工作者有足够的理由对其表示感谢。我以拉蒂迈命名这个属就是为了表达对她的感谢。

（田晓阳 翻译；陈平富 审稿）

Control of the Chain Reaction Involved in Fission of the Uranium Nucleus

F. Adler and H. von Halban, jun.

Editor's Note

Because roughly 3.5 neutrons are typically released in a uranium fission event, physicists now understood that chain reactions were probably possible. There is thus a considerable danger, as Felix Adler and Hans von Halban here note, that a sample of uranium might explode. But they also suggest a means for controlling such reactions. Into a system of highly concentrated uranium one might insert materials known to absorb neutrons efficiently, such as cadmium. In so doing, the number of further fission events triggered by one such event could be tuned close to 1, so that the reaction would grow only slowly. This suggestion ultimately pointed the way to the "moderator rods" used to control reactions in modern nuclear reactors.

IT has recently been shown that the number[1] of neutrons liberated[2] in the nuclear fission of a uranium nucleus is sufficiently high to make the realization of a self-perpetuating reaction chain seem possible. The danger that a system containing uranium in high concentration might explode, once the chain is started, is considerable. It is therefore useful to point out a mechanism which gives the possibility of controlling the development of such a chain.

We form an expression which is characteristic for the behaviour of the chain:

$$\nu'' = \frac{A_f}{A} \nu \left(1 - \alpha\right) \tag{1}$$

A_f being the product of the cross-section for nuclear fission for a thermal neutron of the uranium nucleus with the concentration of the uranium; A_i the product of the absorption cross-section for thermal neutrons of the nucleus of kind i multiplied with its concentration; A the sum of all A_i's, which is to be taken over all kinds of nuclei present in the solution; ν is the average number of neutrons liberated in one fission, α the average probability for a neutron to diffuse out of the system before being absorbed.

The energy liberated by the chain will be

$$E = NF, \tag{2}$$

F being the energy liberated in one fission and N the number of fissions produced by the chain. We have

$$N = \nu'' + \nu''^2 + \nu''^3 + \cdots \tag{3}$$

铀核裂变中链式反应的控制

阿德勒，冯·哈尔班

编者按

由于平均每个铀核裂变事件中大约释放 3.5 个中子，物理学家此时已明白链式反应是可以发生的。正如费利克斯·阿德勒和汉斯·冯·哈尔班在本文中所说的，铀样品可能会爆炸，并且会产生相当大的危险。不过他们也提出了一个控制这种反应的方法。对于包含高浓缩铀的系统，人们可以往里面注入已知的可以有效吸收中子的材料，例如镉。通过这种做法，可以将一个裂变事例触发的次级裂变的数目控制在 1 左右，因此整个反应可以缓慢地进行。这个建议从根本上提供了现代核反应堆中反应的"控制棒"的制作途径。

最近实验表明，一个铀核在核裂变时释放 [2] 出的中子的数目 [1] 似乎高到足以使自持反应链的实现成为可能。一个含有高浓度铀的体系一旦开始链式反应就可能会爆炸，这种危险是不容忽视的。因此，提出一种可能能够控制这种链式反应发展的机制将是有益的。

我们构建了一个描述链式反应行为的特征表达式：

$$v'' = \frac{A_f}{A} v (1 - \alpha) \tag{1}$$

其中 A_f 是热中子铀核裂变截面与铀浓度的乘积；A_i 是 i 类核的热中子吸收截面与该类核的浓度的乘积；A 是所有 A_i 之和，此求和遍及存在于溶液中的所有类型的核；v 是一次裂变中释放出中子的平均数目，α 是一个中子在被吸收前扩散到体系外的平均概率。

链式反应释放的能量为：

$$E = NF \tag{2}$$

其中 F 是一次裂变释放出的能量，N 是由链式反应所产生的裂变数目。我们有：

$$N = v'' + v''^2 + v''^3 + \cdots \tag{3}$$

The chain gives thus a quantity of energy, which is increasing rapidly with time, if ν'' is greater than 1. Let us consider the case of a chain which is due to fission produced by thermal neutrons; that is, a chain propagating itself in a system containing sufficient hydrogen for the slowing down of the neutrons.

If the cross-sections for capture or fission of all nuclei present follow the $1/\upsilon$ law, ν'' will not depend on the velocity of the neutrons and therefore not on the temperature of the system (since α will in practice be small and since it depends in the first place on the distance necessary for slowing down the neutron; the temperature has, of course, an effect, although it will be very small).

Let us, however, introduce an absorbent, such as cadmium, the cross-section of which does not depend on the neutron energy in the thermal region. We will have, instead of (1),

$$\nu'' = \nu \frac{A_f}{A' + A_c}(1 - \alpha), \tag{4}$$

where A' is the sum of all A_i's following the $1/\upsilon$ law and A_c is a constant, the term due to the newly added absorbent. ν'' will now decrease with increasing temperature. At a temperature, which will be characteristic for the composition and the geometrical constants of the system, ν'' will become smaller than unity and the system will stabilize itself somewhere near this temperature; the equilibrium being determined by the fact that the amount of energy given out per unit of time by the system (in the form of heat and nuclear radiation) is equal to the energy produced by the system. Similar questions have been discussed by F. Perrin[3].

Added in proof: In the case of a chain propagating itself by thermal neutrons, the time necessary for the slowing down and for the absorption of a neutron, that is, its mean life, is of the order of 10^{-4} sec. If one makes ν'' as small as 1,007, it needs 100 times the mean life of a neutron or about 10^{-2} sec. to double the number of neutrons, and with that the energy liberated per unit of time. It is therefore possible to control the development of the chain by a periodical interaction of absorbers which break up the chains by entering the system.

(143, 793; 1939)

F. Adler and H. von Halban, jun.: Laboratoire de Chimie Nucléaire, Collège de France, Paris.

References:

1. von Halban, jun., H., Joliot, F., and Kowarski, L., *Nature*, 143, 470 (1939).

2. von Halban, jun., H., Joliot, F., and Kowarski, L., *Nature*, 143, 680 (1939). Roberts, R., Meyer, R., and Wang, P., *Phys. Rev.*, 55, 510 (1939). Haenny, C., and Rosenberg, A., *C.R.*, 208, 898 (1939). Szilard and Zinn (private communication). Huber and Buldinger (private communication).

3. Perrin, F., *C.R.*, in the Press.

于是链式反应给出了能量的值，当 ν'' 大于 1 时，该值随时间的增加快速增加。让我们来考虑由热中子引发的裂变所导致的一个链式反应；即一条在含有足够用来慢化中子的氢的体系中的自持增殖链。

如果所有核的俘获或裂变截面都遵循 $1/\upsilon$ 定律，那么 ν'' 就不会依赖于中子的速度，因此也就不依赖于系统的温度（因为 α 实际上会是很小的，而且它首先取决于慢化中子所必需的距离；当然，温度也会产生一定的影响，尽管这种影响很小）。

不过，我们可以引入一种吸收剂，比如镉，它的截面不依赖于热区的中子的能量。我们将用下面的式子来代替式（1）：

$$\nu'' = \nu \, \frac{A_f}{A' + A_c}(1 - \alpha) \tag{4}$$

其中 A' 是所有遵循 $1/\upsilon$ 定律的 A_i 的和，而 A_c 是一个常数，它取决于新加入的吸收剂。此时的 ν'' 将会随着温度的增加而减小。在系统的组成和几何常数的特征温度下，ν'' 会变得比 1 还小，而系统则会在该温度附近的某个温度下达到自稳定；平衡是由下面的事实所决定的，即单位时间内系统释放出的能量大小（以热或者核辐射的形式）等于系统产生的能量。佩兰曾经讨论过类似的问题 [3]。

附加说明： 在热中子所导致的自持增殖链的情况中，对中子慢化和吸收所需要的时间，即中子的平均寿命，为 10^{-4} 秒的数量级。如果使 ν'' 小到 1,007，就需要 100 倍于中子平均寿命或者说大约 10^{-2} 秒的时间来使中子数量加倍，同时单位时间释放的能量也随之翻倍。于是，有可能通过利用吸收剂周期性的相互作用（它会进入系统破坏链式反应）来控制链式反应的发展。

（王耀杨 翻译；张焕乔 审稿）

Emission of Neutrons Accompanying the Fission of Uranium Nuclei

J. Rotblat

Editor's Note

The Polish physicist Joseph Rotblat here supplies further evidence on the release of neutrons in the fissioning of uranium nuclei, indirect evidence for which had already been reported. Using a new technique, he suggests that the number of secondary neutrons produced in a fission event might be as high as six. Rotblat went on to work on the Manhattan Project which led to the atomic bomb, but after the war became a fierce critic of nuclear weapons and worked tirelessly on international arms control. In 1957, with the philosopher Bertrand Russell, Rotblat founded the highly influential Pugwash Conferences, which bring together scientists and public figures in an effort to reduce the proliferation of nuclear weapons.

THE experiments of Halban, Joliot, and Kowarski described in *Nature*[1] give an indirect proof of the neutron multiplication accompanying the fission of uranium nuclei after neutron capture. It can be deduced from these experiments that the additional neutrons are, on the average, faster than the photo-neutrons from radium C-beryllium used as active primary radiation. This conclusion is confirmed in a subsequent note[2] by the same authors in which they find that the neutrons contributed by uranium are able to produce the endo-energetic reaction $S(n, p)P$.

I have made some experiments on the same problem by a different method. Any increase of neutron effects observed when neutrons are allowed to pass through a given medium may be due: (*a*) to the inelastic scattering of neutrons, (*b*) to the reaction $(n, 2n)$ or, exceptionally $(n, 3n)$; (*c*) to an unknown cause, as in the case of uranium to the fission of its nuclei. In the experiments of Halban, Joliot and Kowarski, effects (*a*) and (*b*) are excluded owing to the integrating method adopted and to the low energy of the primary neutrons. But if these effects are present, it is possible to estimate their importance relatively to effect (*c*) by comparing uranium with substances in which only effect (*a*) or only (*a*) and (*b*) are possible. I have used aluminium and copper as comparison substances of the first and of the second type respectively.

A radon plus beryllium source was placed in the cylindrical axial hole of a cylinder of aluminium, of 2.2 cm. diameter and 5 cm. height, or, alternatively, of a cylindrical double-walled vessel of identical dimensions filled with uranium oxide (U_3O_8) or copper oxide. The mass of aluminium was 40 gm., of uranium oxide 49 gm. and of copper oxide 42 gm., and the thickness of walls could be neglected. The number of absorbing or scattering uranium nuclei was therefore 9.2 times smaller than the corresponding number

伴随铀核裂变的中子发射

罗特布拉特

编者按

波兰物理学家约瑟夫·罗特布拉特在本文中提供了关于铀核裂变过程中中子释放的进一步证据，此前已经报道过相关的间接证据。他使用了一项新技术，并提出一个裂变事件中产生的次级中子数目可能高达 6 个。罗特布拉特持续从事研制原子弹的曼哈顿项目工作，但是战后他成了核武器的强烈批评者，并且坚持不懈地致力于国际核武器控制。1957 年，罗特布拉特和哲学家伯特兰·罗素一起发起了具有极大影响力的帕格沃什会议，这次会议上科学家和社会名人一起努力以实现减少核武器的扩散。

哈尔班、约里奥和科瓦尔斯基在《自然》中所描述的实验 [1] 为在中子俘获之后伴随着铀核裂变的中子倍增提供了间接证据。从这些实验可以推知，一般来说，这些新产生的中子比来自作为放射性初级辐射的镭 C– 铍源的光中子更快。这一结论在这几位作者随后的一篇文章 [2] 中得到证实，他们发现由铀贡献的中子能够产生吸能反应 $S(n, p)P$。

我对同样的问题用不同方法做了一些实验。在令中子通过一种给定介质的实验中，所观察到的中子效应的任何增长都可能是由于以下原因造成的：(a) 中子的非弹性散射；(b) $(n,2n)$ 反应，个别时候是 $(n,3n)$ 反应；(c) 未知原因，就像在铀核裂变的情况中那样。在哈尔班、约里奥和科瓦尔斯基的实验中，由于集成方法的采用和初级中子的能量较低，故可以排除效应 (a) 和 (b)。但是如果这些效应存在的话，就有可能通过将铀与只可能有 (a) 效应或只有 (a) 和 (b) 效应的物质进行比较，进而估计出它们相对于效应 (c) 的重要性。我曾经使用铝和铜分别作为第一类和第二类对比物质。

把氡 – 铍放射源置于一个铝质圆柱体（直径为 2.2 厘米，高为 5.0 厘米）轴向的孔中，或者，也可以采用同样尺寸的装填有氧化铀（U_3O_8）或氧化铜的圆柱形双层壁容器。铝的质量为 40 克，氧化铀质量为 49 克，氧化铜质量为 42 克，器壁厚度是可忽略的。结果吸收或散射的铀核数目是相应的铝核数目的 9.2 分之一，是铜核

of aluminium nuclei and 3.3 times smaller than the number of copper nuclei. One would expect, therefore, that the effect (*a*) due to aluminium, and effects (*a*) and (*b*) due to copper would be at least of the same importance and probably larger than the same effects due to uranium. The number and quality of neutrons issuing from these substances were compared by measuring the activation of a silver foil surrounding the cylinders in two cases: first, when no appreciable scattering of neutrons took place outside the cylinders, and secondly, when the neutrons were scattered back by a cylindrical sheet of paraffin wax of 6 mm. thickness. The results are given below, the figures being the total numbers of counts of a Geiger-Müller counter in corresponding series.

	Aluminium	Uranium	Increase (%)	Copper	Uranium	Increase (%)
No paraffin	9,089	9,325	2.6	4,810	4,869	1.2
With paraffin	10,285	10,775	4.8	10,049	10,292	2.4

It can be inferred from these data that uranium gives off, in fact, more neutrons than aluminium or copper. The increase is larger relatively to aluminium than to copper, which must be attributed to the reaction (*n*, 2*n*) occurring in this last element. In both cases, the increase is larger when the neutrons are slowed down by a small quantity of paraffin, which shows that the additional neutrons from uranium are, on the average, slower than the bulk of primary neutrons emitted by the source. As, from other evidence, they appear to be faster than the radium C-beryllium neutrons, we can estimate that their *average* energy must be of the order of 1 Mev.

Owing to the small number of uranium nuclei acting as absorbers or scatterers, it seems very unlikely that the apparent excess of neutrons given off by these nuclei should be due to some trivial cause like the inelastic scattering or the reaction (*n*, 2*n*). It probably represents the neutron shower' accompanying the fission of an activated uranium nucleus. Assuming the cross-section for this process produced by the neutrons from radon plus beryllium equal to 5×10^{-25} cm.^{2}, I calculate that the number of neutrons emitted in a single fission is equal to 6.

(**143**, 852; 1939)

J. Rotblat: Miroslaw Kernbaum Radiological Laboratory of the Scientific Society of Warsaw, Warsaw, April 8.

References:

1. *Nature*, **143**, 470 (1939).

2. *C.R.* **208**, 995 (1939).

数目的 3.3 分之一。由此我们预期，铝产生的效应（a）与铜产生的效应（a）和（b）至少是同样重要的，甚至可能比铀产生的同种效应更大。我们将这些物质所发出的中子的数目和性质进行比较，比较的方法是分别在下述两种情况下测量包裹在圆柱体周围的银箔的放射性：第一种情况是在圆柱体外部没有发生明显的中子散射时，第二种情况是中子经 6 毫米厚的圆柱形石蜡层散射而返回时。下面数据列出了该实验的结果，数字表示用盖革－米勒计数器在相应的序列中得到的总计数。

	铝	铀	增量（%）	铜	铀	增量（%）
无石蜡	9,089	9,325	2.6	4,810	4,869	1.2
有石蜡	10,285	10,775	4.8	10,049	10,292	2.4

根据这些数据可以推测，事实上铀比铝或者铜发射出更多的中子。相对于铝的增量比相对于铜的增量要大，这必定是因为后一种元素中发生了（$n,2n$）反应。在铝和铜两种情况中，当中子被少量石蜡慢化时这种增量是比较大的，这表明从铀所产生的新的中子平均来说比放射源发射出的大量初级中子慢。由于在其他的证据中，它们似乎比镭 C－铍中子快，因此我们可以估算出它们的**平均**能量必定具有 1 兆电子伏的数量级。

由于作为吸收体或散射体的铀核数目较小，所以由这些核发射出的中子的明显过剩似乎不可能归结为某些细微的原因，比如非弹性散射或（$n,2n$）反应。它可能代表了伴随着一个放射性铀核的裂变而产生的中子簇射。假定由氡－铍源的中子产生这个过程的截面等于 5×10^{-25} 平方厘米，我计算出单独一次裂变发射出的中子数等于 6。

（王耀杨 翻译；张焕乔 审稿）

Fission of Heavy Nuclei: a New Type of Nuclear Disintegration

N. Feather

Editor's Note

Physicist Norman Feather offers a review of advances in the understanding of nuclear fission reactions, and the possibility of a controlled chain reaction. In retrospect, he notes, the first evidence for fission in uranium nuclei came in experiments by Enrico Fermi and colleagues in 1934, though five years passed before the physics could be clarified. It was now clear that each such fission gave off several neutrons on average, and may well suffice to drive a sustained chain reaction. However, experiments also showed that slow "thermal" neutrons are most effective in stimulating fission events. No experiments on chain reactions had at that point been carried out, however.

THE first indication that the transmutation of heavy nuclei could be effected in a laboratory experiment was obtained by Fermi in March 1934. Curie and Joliot had just discovered that short-lived radioactive species are produced as the result of α-particle bombardment of certain light elements, and Fermi, accepting the appearance of such "induced" radioactivity as proof of transmutation, very soon showed that the nuclei of almost all elements, even those of highest atomic weight, undergo transformation when neutrons are used. From his early experiments Fermi concluded that in general the neutron is simply captured by the nucleus, and he went on to show that this process of capture is usually more efficient—and sometimes very much more efficient—when the neutron is moving with a small ("thermal") velocity, before the collision, than when its energy is large. Eventually he found that negative electrons were emitted in the disintegration of the radioactive products obtained in all these capture transformations, and thus the final result of the combined process of neutron capture and β disintegration was in every case shown to be the production of a nucleus having both mass and charge numbers greater by one unit than the mass and charge numbers of the nucleus bombarded.

In June 1934[1], Fermi and his collaborators obtained negative electron activities from thorium and uranium under neutron bombardment, and they quite naturally supposed, on the basis of their previous investigations, that in the latter case a nuclear species of atomic number $Z = 93$ must remain after disintegration of the unstable product first formed. Further examination showed that not one but several distinct radioelements were produced as a result of the bombardment of uranium, and rough chemical tests proved that one of these, at least (half-value period $\tau = 13$ minutes), was not attributable to an element of atomic number $Z = 92, 91, 90, 89, 88, 83$ or 82. It seemed quite clear, then, that after the uranium nucleus had captured a neutron, not less than two β transformations followed, and consequently that a new element, for which Z was not less than 94, was ultimately

重核裂变：一种新型的核蜕变

编者按

物理学家诺曼·费瑟根据他对核裂变以及可控链式反应的可能性的理解写了一篇综述性文章。他指出实验上首次观察到铀核裂变的证据是在 1934 年由恩里科·费米及其同事发现的，然而 5 年后裂变的物理原理才被阐释。现在人们知道每个这样的裂变反应平均释放几个中子，并且有可能驱动持续的链式反应。但实验也表明慢的"热"中子对于激发裂变是非常有效的。不过关于这一点，还没有链式反应实验予以证实。

在实验室所进行的实验中，费米于 1934 年 3 月首次发现影响重核嬗变的迹象。居里和约里奥刚刚发现 α 粒子轰击某些轻元素时会产生短寿命的放射性核素，费米便认识到这种"诱发的"放射性的出现可以作为嬗变的证据，并且很快指出，几乎所有元素的核——即使是那些具有最大原子量的核——在用中子轰击时都会发生转变。费米根据自己的早期实验推断，中子通常只是被核俘获，他接着指出，当撞击前的中子以慢的（"热"）速度运动时，这个俘获过程一般会比它具有高能量时更为有效——而且有时会高效很多。最后他发现，在所有这些俘获转变中生成的放射性产物，它们的分裂都会释放出负电子。因此，在任何情况下，兼有中子俘获与 β 蜕变的组合过程的最终结果都显示出，生成的核的质量和电荷数都比被轰击核大一个单位。

1934 年 6 月 [1]，费米及其合作者通过用中子轰击钍和铀，得到了负电子放射性。于是，基于之前的研究，他们很自然地认为，在后一情况中，最初形成的不稳定产物蜕变之后一定会有一种原子序数 $Z=93$ 的核素保存下来。进一步的检测表明，轰击铀的结果不是生成了一种放射性元素，而是生成了几种截然不同的放射性元素，而粗略的化学检验证明，其中至少有一种（半衰期 $\tau=13$ 分钟）不能归结为原子序数 $Z=92$、91、90、89、88、83 或 82 的元素。于是，看起来非常明确，铀核在俘获了一个中子后至少会接着发生两次 β 转变，因而最终会生成一种 Z 不小于 94 的新

produced. These conclusions at once gave rise to much argument amongst chemists as to what the chief chemical properties of these hypothetical transuranic elements might be, but a great deal of careful research in many physical laboratories throughout the world only served to strengthen the assumption that, apart from any preconceived ideas about chemical behaviour, such elements were certainly formed when uranium was bombarded by neutrons.

By May 1937, Meitner, Hahn and Strassmann[2] had recognized the existence of nine separate species arising from this transformation, and had suggested genetic relations between them which supposed that every element of atomic number between (and including) 92 and 97 was represented, either as intermediate or end product of a series. They identified three of these nine products (τ = 10 sec., 40 sec., 23 min.) as unstable isotopes of uranium, and the remainder, which could all be obtained by precipitation with platinum as sulphide in acid solution, as the transuranic elements already mentioned. The scheme presented certain difficulties, it was admitted, (no evidence for the final return of the unstable nucleus within the ordinary range, Z less than 93, could be found, and awkward questions concerning isomeric forms were raised in an acute form) but it was the best that could be done.

Then, in October 1937, Curie and Savitch[3] discovered a tenth activity of about $3\frac{1}{2}$ hours period, and at once proceeded to investigate the chemical nature of the element to which it belonged. They showed that this radioelement did not separate with the platinum precipitate and soon discovered that it bore a close resemblance to lanthanum in chemical behaviour. At first the most plausible suggestion appeared to be that the new species was an isotope of actinium (Z = 89). Then two very disturbing facts were encountered. First, a body of the same period and almost identical properties was among the active products formed in the disintegration of thorium by neutrons, and, secondly, it was found possible to separate actinium almost completely from the new body by a lanthanum fractionation. In September 1938, Curie and Savitch[4] wrote, "On the whole, the properties of R 3.5 h. are those of lanthanum, from which it appears that until now it has not been separated".

The work of Curie and Savitch immediately prompted a further search for activities belonging to elements of atomic number less than 92 produced in the uranium transformation, and, as a result, Hahn and Strassmann[5] discovered two other lanthanum-like and three barium-like products. These workers believed that they had demonstranted the production of each of the former species from one of the latter, but at that time they still inclined to the view that actinium and radium isotopes were really in question. However, in January of this year, they reported[6] that fractionation of the new bodies with mesothorium and barium (or lanthanum) invariably concentrated the neutron-produced activity with the lighter carrier and resulted in a complete separation of mesothorium 1 (radium), or mesothorium 2 (actinium). The conclusion now appeared inescapable that active isotopes of barium and lanthanum were among the products of the bombardment of uranium with neutrons.

元素。这些结论立刻在化学家中间引起了很多争论，内容是关于这些假想的超铀元素可能具备的主要化学性质是什么的问题。然而除去任何预先的关于化学行为的想法，在全世界多所物理实验室中所进行的大量细致的研究却只能用来支持下面的假设，即这些元素确实是在中子轰击铀时形成的。

到 1937 年 5 月时，迈特纳、哈恩和施特拉斯曼 [2] 已经认识到存在着 9 种由这类转变所产生的独立核素，并且提出了它们之间的亲缘关系，这种关系假定原子序数介于（且包括）92 和 97 之间的每一种元素不是作为某一序列的中间产物就是作为其最终产物而出现。他们鉴别出这 9 种产物中的 3 种（半衰期 τ=10 秒、40 秒、23 分钟）是铀的不稳定同位素，而其余的几种都可以通过在酸溶液中与铂以硫化物的形式沉淀而得到，它们被视为是前面提到的超铀元素。虽然这一方案存在着某些难点，但人们还是接受了，（没有能够找到最终收回的不稳定核处于 Z 小于 93 的常规范围内的证据，这就尖锐地提出了有关异构形式的棘手问题），而这也是当时所能做到的方案中最好的一个。

然后，1937 年 10 月，居里和萨维奇 [3] 发现了半衰期为 3.5 小时的第 10 种放射性，并立即着手研究该放射性所属元素的化学本质。他们指出这种放射性元素不能用铂沉淀来分离，并且很快发现它的化学行为与镧极为相似。最初看来最有道理的观点似乎是，这一新核素是锕（Z=89）的某种同位素。但是后来遇到两个令人极为困扰的事实。第一，在中子轰击所导致的钍的分裂中形成的放射性产物中，存在着某种具有相同周期和几乎同样性质的物质，第二，发现通过镧分级分离的方法，从这种新物质中有可能将镧几乎完全分离出来。1938 年 9 月居里和萨维奇 [4] 写到，"大体上讲，半衰期 3.5 小时就是镧的性质，而到目前为止，似乎仍不能把这种新元素与镧分离开来"。

居里和萨维奇的工作直接促进了在铀转变过程中产生的原子序数小于 92 的元素的放射性的进一步研究。而其结果是，哈恩和施特拉斯曼 [5] 发现了另外两种类镧产物和三种类钡产物。这些研究者相信，他们已经论证了所有类镧产物都是由类钡产物中的一种产生的，但是在那时，他们仍然倾向于这样的观点，即锕和镭的同位素有待研究。不过，今年 1 月他们报道了 [6] 含有新钍和钡（或镧）的新物质的组分，总是可以通过较轻载体聚集由中子引起的放射性，从而导致新钍 1（镭）或新钍 2（锕）的完全分离。这时得到如下结论似乎是顺理成章的，即在铀经中子轰击所得产物之中存在着钡和镧的放射性同位素。

At this stage, Meitner and Frisch[7] discussed the problem on the Bohr theory of heavy nuclei, making particular use of the essentially classical "water-drop model" of the highly condensed system of particles of which such a nucleus is constituted. They concluded, "It seems therefore possible that the uranium nucleus has only small stability of form, and may, after neutron capture, divide itself into two nuclei of roughly equal size. ... These two nuclei ... should gain a total kinetic energy of c. 200 Mev. ... This amount of energy may actually be expected to be available from the difference in packing fraction between uranium and the elements in the middle of the periodic system". Then Frisch[8] obtained direct evidence for the projection of fission fragments with approximately the energy predicted, being able to detect the production of large bursts of ionization in a uranium-lined ionization chamber which was irradiated by neutrons. Similar results were obtained when thorium was substituted for uranium in the chamber, and it was concluded that some of the activities previously ascribed to isotopes of radium and actinium, in this case also resulted from fission of the nucleus under neutron bombardment.

The investigations begun by Meitner and Frisch were rapidly followed by many others in physical laboratories both in Europe and in the United States: the confirmation of the findings of Curie and Savitch by Hahn and Strassmann had indicated quite clearly to many workers that something new was involved. In Paris, in Berkeley, in Washington, New York and Baltimore, direct proof of the fission of uranium and thorium was obtained within the space of a few days. Now, some three and a half months after the original announcement, so much has been published that rigorous selection is necessary in any report on the subject. For the remainder of this survey, therefore, only the most interesting features of the new phenomenon can possibly be included.

Perhaps the first such feature concerns the radioelements of the platinum precipitate, of which the previously supposed transuranic nature was now in question. Before the fission process was discovered, both in Berkeley and in Cambridge projects had already been formed of investigating these elements for natural X-radiations, in the hope of being able to deduce the atomic number from the energy of the radiations (natural L-radiations) as determined by the method of critical absorption. This problem became much simpler once the presence of medium-heavy elements was suspected, since K-radiations could be looked for, instead of the more complex radiations of the L-series. Almost at once, Abelson[9] and Feather and Bretscher[10] found evidence for the natural K-radiations of iodine from the long-lived activities of the platinum precipitate, and, guided by this observation, were able to identify chemically as tellurium and iodine two products previously described as eka-iridium and eka-platinum, respectively. Then several workers found other of the so-called transuranic activities in the products collected by recoil from bombarded uranium. Observations concerning the rates of decay of these recoil activities[11]—and the results of chemical tests[12]—left little doubt that almost all the previous assignments had been seriously in error. At the present time, one might justly say that it cannot definitely be maintained, concerning any of the activities separable from uranium, that it does not arise in a process of fission of the uranium nucleus.

在这个阶段，迈特纳和弗里施 [7] 对玻尔的重核理论中存在的问题进行了讨论，尤其是应用了本质上经典的"液滴模型"来描述构成这种核的粒子所组成的高密度系统。他们得出结论，"由此看来，可能铀核只具有较低稳定性的形式，并且可能在俘获中子之后将自身分裂成两个大小基本相同的核……这两个核……应该获得大约200 兆电子伏的总动能……根据铀和位于周期表中部的元素之间聚集率的差异，实际上这部分能量预计是可以得到的"。接着，弗里施 [8] 获得了裂变碎片基本上是以预计能量发射的直接证据，在用中子照射以铀填衬的电离室时，检测到有强烈的电离脉冲出现。在用钍代替电离室中的铀的情况下，得到了类似的结果，从而得出结论，某些从前被归结为来源于镭和锕的同位素的放射性，在这种情况下也是由中子轰击下发生的核裂变所致。

由迈特纳和弗里施所开创的研究很快便引发了欧洲及美国物理实验室的众多研究人员的追随：哈恩和施特拉斯曼对居里与萨维奇的发现进行的证实已经向很多研究者非常明确地指出，这涉及了某些新的事物。在巴黎、伯克利、华盛顿、纽约和巴尔的摩，短短几天的时间内就得到了有关铀和钍裂变的直接证据。现在，在最初宣布之后大约三个半月的时间内，已经发表了大量的文章，这样就有必要对关于这一主题的报道进行严格的筛选。因此，在这篇综述的其余部分中将只能包括有关新现象的最值得关注的特征。

也许第一个值得关注的特征就是关于铂沉淀物中的放射性元素，以前曾认为其所具有的超铀性质现在遭到了质疑。在发现裂变过程之前，对这些元素的天然 X 辐射研究项目在伯克利和剑桥已经展开，希望能够用通过临界吸收方法测定的辐射能量（天然的 L-辐射）来推断原子序数。一旦假设存在中重元素，这个问题就变得非常简单了，因为这样就可以去寻找 K-辐射，而不再需要寻找较为复杂的 L-序列的辐射。埃布尔森 [9] 以及费瑟和布雷切尔 [10] 几乎立刻从铂沉淀物的长寿命放射性中发现了碘的天然 K-辐射的证据，并且在这一观测结果的指引下，将两种最初分别被描述为类铱和类铂的产物，用化学方法确定为碲和碘。接着，在收集到的被轰击的铀的反冲产物中，几位研究者发现了其他一些所谓的超铀放射性。这些反冲产物放射性衰变速率的观测结果 [11] 及化学检测的结果 [12] 毫无疑问地表明，此前几乎所有的认定结果都是严重错误的。目前，对于任何可以从铀中分离出的放射性，我们都可以公正地说，认为它不是在铀核的裂变过程中产生的这一观点肯定是得不到支持的。

There is, however, one important activity, of 23 minutes half-value period, which is not separable from uranium and for which, in consequence, the fission process cannot be assumed to be responsible. This non-separable activity arises in a process of resonance capture of neutrons of about 25 ev. energy, and the fact that negative electrons are involved must clearly indicate that a species for which $Z = 93$ is formed as the result of the disintegration. Yet, in spite of much careful investigation, no radioactivity of any kind has been discovered which is unquestionably due to the transformation of this species. Furthermore, in respect of the parent species (the uranium isotope for which $\tau = 23$ min.), this is clearly a quasi-stable modification of the body which undergoes fission in the majority of cases, and Meitner and Frisch and Bohr[13] have discussed this aspect of the phenomenon. They have pointed out that there is nothing intrinsically incomprehensible in the occurrence of resonance capture (emission of γ-radiation) rather than fission in certain circumstances. In any event, division of the nucleus into two fragments must be preceded by the concentration of the available energy in a type of nuclear motion of large deformation, and this concentration may be very unlikely if the original state of the system, after capture of the neutron, is one of considerable symmetry. Or if, as Bohr has assumed, the effect of thermal neutrons in producing fission in the case of uranium (such neutrons are quite ineffective when thorium is bombarded) is ascribed to capture by the rare isotope ^{235}U, and the resonance effect and the fission process due to fast neutrons are ascribed to ^{238}U, it may even be that, at the resonance energy, the compound nucleus is not formed with sufficient energy of excitation for the neutralization of the small stability of form which it naturally possesses. As regards the whole of this question, more definite conclusions must clearly await further experiments: Joliot[14] has reported a variation in the relative proportions of the different fission products as the energy of the neutrons is altered—and this might be held to favour the suggestions of Bohr—but Bjerge, Brostrøm and Koch[15] have failed to establish any difference in the decay of the products obtained with high-energy neutrons and thermal neutrons, respectively.

Hitherto, the process of fission has been spoken of without any precise statement regarding the nature of the fragments which result from the primary act of division of the nucleus, and in fact very little exact knowledge is as yet available on this point. Determinations of the range of the fission products provide some information. In the first place, they indicate that (with uranium and fast neutrons) the process occupies less than 5×10^{-13} sec. from the time of capture of the neutron (the forwards range is slightly greater than the backwards range, showing that very little of its original momentum is lost before the compound nucleus divides[16]), and, secondly, they appear to favour a very small number of competing primary processes, rather than a large number of possibilities[17]. On the other hand, chemical investigation reveals such a wealth of active products[18] (with atomic numbers lying between 35 (Br) and 57 (La), if not more widely distributed) that some adequate explanation of their complexity must certainly be found. It would appear that the discovery that very frequently neutrons are emitted almost instantaneously by the original products of fission[19] already provides a basis for such explanation (nuclei, first formed, presumably, in states of high excitation, emit either neutrons or quanta of radiation in passing to longer-lived states). Also, even after these states have decayed with

640

　　但是，存在着一种半衰期为 23 分钟的重要的放射性，它是不能从铀中分离出来的，因此，不能认为它是在裂变过程中产生的。这种不可分离的放射性来源于能量约为 25 电子伏的中子共振俘获的过程，而有负电子参与的事实必然明确表明，一种 Z=93 的核素的形成是由蜕变所导致的。可是，尽管已进行了很多细致的研究，却仍没有发现任何一种无疑是来自于该核素的转变过程的放射性。此外，关于母体核素（相应的铀的同位素半衰期 τ=23 分钟），很明显它是该物质的一种准稳态变体，在大多数情况下会发生裂变，迈特纳、弗里施和玻尔 [13] 已经就这种现象对这个方面的问题进行了讨论。他们已经指出，在某些情况下发生共振俘获（γ 射线的发射）而不是裂变，本质上并不存在任何不可理解的问题。无论如何，核分裂成两块碎片之前，必定要先通过核的巨大形变的运动形式聚集可用的能量，而如果在俘获中子之后，系统的初始状态仍然具有相当大的对称性，那么出现这种聚集的可能性就非常小了。或者如果，就像玻尔假设的那样，热中子对引起铀的裂变的影响（在轰击钍时这样的中子所产生的效果是相当弱的）是由稀有同位素铀–235 的俘获所造成的，而由快中子导致的共振效应和裂变过程是由铀–238 所造成的，那么甚至可以说，由于复合核天然具有形式的低稳定性导致的抵消作用，使得它在共振能量下形成时不会具有足量的激发能。就这个问题整体而言，要得到更为确定的结论显然必须等待进一步的实验研究：约里奥 [14] 曾报道过中子能量发生改变时会发生不同裂变产物相对比例的变化，而这有可能被认为是对玻尔的提议的支持。但是对于分别由高能中子和热中子得到的产物，伯格、布罗斯特伦和科赫 [15] 却没有从它们的衰变过程中发现任何差别。

　　到目前为止，谈及的裂变过程仍未给出任何关于裂变碎片性质的精确陈述，这些碎片是在核分裂第一阶段产生的，而实际上至今对这一点的确切的认识也只是极少量的。对裂变产物范围进行测定可以提供一些信息。首先，它们意味着（利用铀和快中子）该过程从俘获中子时刻（向前的范围略大于向后的，这表明在复合核分裂之前，初始动量几乎没有损失 [16]）算起持续时间不足 5×10^{-13} 秒。其次，它们似乎倾向于极少量的竞争性初级过程，而不具有该过程大量出现的可能 [17]。另一方面，化学研究显示出如此丰富的放射性产物 [18]（如果没有更广泛的分布，其原子序数介于 35（Br）到 57（La）之间），这样就必定可以对它们的复杂性找到一些充分的解释。看来，裂变初始产物经常几乎是瞬间发射出中子 [19]，这一现象的发现，已经为这种解释提供了基础（据推测，最初以高激发态形成的核，在到达寿命较长态的过程中会发射出中子或者量子辐射）。实验也表明，甚至当这些态发生 β 衰变之后，有时产物核仍然具有足够的激发能，为了到达更稳定态，相对于辐射跃迁而言"蒸发"中子

β-emission, experiment shows that occasionally product nuclei result, still with sufficient energy of excitation for the "evaporation" of neutrons to be a possible alternative to radiative transitions leading to more stable states. In this connexion, Roberts, Meyer, and Wang[20] and Booth, Dunning and Slack[21] have reported delayed neutron periods of about 12 sec. and 45 sec., when uranium is bombarded, whilst a similar feature has also been established in the case of thorium.

The frequency of the neutron-evaporation process accompanying fission, and the energies of the neutrons so produced, have been studied by many workers, but so far most exhaustively by Joliot[22] and his colleagues, and by Fermi[23] and others in New York. The general result appears to be that, for each process of fission with uranium, at least two neutrons, having a mean energy of the order of 10^6 ev., eventually evaporate from the residual fragments. Since neutrons of less than this energy are still capable of producing fission on their own account (probably in ^{235}U, as already suggested), the possibility of a cumulative process of exothermic disintegration has to be considered. Clearly, if the probability of removal of neutrons in processes other than those which result in fission is sufficiently reduced, the latter process must eventually build up in any solid substance containing uranium. Direct experiments on this aspect of the matter have not yet been reported in the scientific literature, but at this stage it may be pointed out that, even in pure uranium, it is well known that a non-fission capture process takes place (*v. sup.*), whilst the unlimited generation of energy in the solid material would ultimately increase the energy of the "thermal" neutrons until their efficiency as agents for fission was greatly reduced. Already several attempts have been made[24] to calculate the course of the phenomenon using existing data, but the assumptions upon which they have been based have generally been so severely idealized that no confidence in numerical values is at present likely to result.

(**143**, 877-879; 1939)

N. Feather: Cavendish Laboratory, Cambridge.

References:
1. *Nature*, **133**, 898 (1934).
2. *Z. Phys.*, **108**, 249 (1937).
3. *J. Phys.*, **8**, 385 (1937).
4. *J. Phys.*, **9**, 355 (1938).
5. *Naturwiss.*, **26**, 755 (1938).
6. *Naturwiss.*, **27**, 11 (1939).
7. *Nature*, **143**, 239 (1939).
8. *Nature*, **143**, 276 (1939).
9. *Phys. Rev.*, **55**, 418 (1939).
10. *Nature*, **143**, 516 (1939).
11. Meitner and Frisch, *Nature*, **143,** 471 (1939). Glasoe and Steigman *Bull. Amer. Phys. Soc.*, (2), **14**, 20 (1939).
12. Bretscher and Cook, *Nature*, **143**, 559 (1939).

仍是一个可能的选择。关于这一点，罗伯茨、迈耶和王 [20] 以及布思、邓宁和斯莱克 [21] 都曾报道，在轰击铀时缓发中子的周期约为 12 秒和 45 秒，而对于钍而言，类似的特征也得到了证实。

对于伴随裂变的中子蒸发过程的频率，以及这种过程中产生的中子的能量，已经有很多研究者进行过研究，但是到目前为止最为详尽的当属约里奥 [22] 和他的同事，以及费米 [23] 和另外一些来自纽约的研究者。看来一般性的结论是，对于铀的每一次裂变过程，至少有两个具有 10^6 电子伏数量级的平均能量的中子，最终会从残存碎片中蒸发。由于能量比这还低的中子仍然可以靠自己来产生裂变（如前所述，可能是在铀–235 中），因此必须要对可能出现的放热分裂累积过程加以考虑。很明显，除了中子导致裂变的可能性之外，如果过程中消去中子的可能性充分减小，那么对任何含铀的固体物质，裂变过程最终都一定会逐渐累积。在科学文献中还没有关于该问题的直接实验的报道，但是目前我们可以指出，即使是在纯铀中，众所周知会发生非裂变俘获过程（见上），同时在固体材料中无限制产生的能量最终将会增加"热"中子的能量，直到它们引发裂变的效能大大减弱为止。已经有人利用现有数据进行过几次计算该现象过程的尝试 [24]，但是一般来说他们所依赖的前提过于理想化，因而这些数值目前还不大可能获得认可。

（王耀杨 翻译；夏海鸿 审稿）

13. *Phys. Rev.*, **55**, 418 (1939).

14. *J. Phys.*, **10**, 159 (1939).

15. *Nature*, **143**, 794 (1939).

16. Feather, *Nature*, **143**, 597 (1939).

17. McMillan, *Phys. Rev.*, **55**, 510 (1939).

18. Heyn, Aten and Bakker, *Nature*, **143**, 516 (1939). Abelson, *phys. Rev.*, **55**, 670 (1939).

19. v. Halban, Joliot and Kowarski, *Nature*, **143**, 470 (1939).

20. *Phys. Rev.*, **55**, 510 (1939).

21. *Bull. Amer. Phys. Soc.*, (2), **14**, 19 (1939).

22. v. Halban, Joliot and Kowarski, *Nature*, **143**, 680 (1939). Dodé, v. Halban, Joliot and Kowarski, *C.R.*, **208**, 995 (1939).

23. Anderson, Fermi and Hanstein, *Phys. Rev.*, **55**, 797 (1939). Szilard and Zinn, *Phys. Rev.*, **55**, 799 (1939).

24. For example, Perrin, *C.R.*, **208**, 1394 (1939).

Energy of Neutrons Liberated in the Nuclear Fission of Uranium Induced by Thermal Neutrons

H. von Halban, jun. *et al.*

Editor's Note

The fissioning of a uranium nucleus, physicists now knew, releases further neutrons, which might in principle trigger splitting in other nuclei. But researchers knew little about the energy of the released neutrons. Here Hans von Halban and colleagues in Paris clarify this matter. In a series of experiments, they used an ionization chamber to probe the distribution of energies of "fast" neutrons—that is, those having energy above 1.5 million electronvolts (1.5 MeV). The number of neutrons declines at higher energies, but some neutrons can carry away as much as 11 MeV. Knowledge of the distribution of neutron energies played an important role in the engineering of nuclear reactors, as slow neutrons trigger fission events more effectively than fast ones.

IT has been shown that *fast* neutrons are liberated in the process of nuclear fission induced in uranium by primary *thermal* neutrons. Two different methods of detection have been used: in the first method[1], the primary and (if any) secondary neutrons are absorbed in a medium in which an endo-energetic reaction can take place, leading to the formation of an easily detectable radioactive nucleus. If the energy threshold is situated above the maximum energy of the primary neutrons, any positive results observed must be ascribed to the secondary neutrons. In the second method[2], elastic collisions of fast neutrons with heavier nuclei are observed by means of an ionization chamber filled with a gas at atmospheric pressure and connected to a linear amplifier. In order to study separately the effect due to the primary thermal neutrons, the experiment is performed with, and without, a cadmium shield between the source and the uranium mass.

The first method having shown us that fast secondary neutrons are produced with energies of at least 2 Mev. (sufficient to transform ^{32}S into radioactive ^{32}P in detectable quantities), we sought to ascertain, by the second method, whether neutrons of energy notably higher than 2 Mev. are also present in the secondary radiation. In our experiment, the oxygen-filled ionization chamber was placed in a nearly cubical box (9 cm. × 9 cm. × 8 cm.) containing uranium oxide and surrounded by a thick layer of paraffin wax. The source (300 mgm. RaγY + Be), surrounded by a lead shield (5 cm. in the direction of the chamber) was buried in the wax. In order to absorb thermal neutrons, the uranium box could be screened on all sides with a cadmium foil. The pulses were recorded either in the presence or in the absence of this foil and the part of the effect (projection of oxygen nuclei by fast neutrons liberated in the uranium) due to thermal neutrons could thus be evaluated.

在热中子诱发的铀核裂变中释放出的中子的能量

冯·哈尔班等

编者按

物理学家现在已经知道，原则上铀核裂变释放的中子可以诱发其他核的分裂。但是研究人员关于释放中子的能量知之甚微。这里汉斯·冯·哈尔班和他巴黎的同事阐述清楚了这个问题。他们在一系列的实验中采用电离室来探测"快"中子的能量分布——即那些能量高于 1.5 兆电子伏的中子。中子数目随着能量升高而降低，但是一些中子携带能量多达 11 兆电子伏。中子能量分布的认知在核反应堆工程技术中有重要影响，因为慢中子比快中子能够更有效地诱发裂变。

目前实验已表明，**快**中子是从初级**热**中子诱发的铀核裂变过程中释放出来的。已经使用了两种不同的检测方法：在第一种方法中 [1]，初级中子和次级中子（如果有的话）在一种可以发生吸能反应的介质中被吸收，以致形成了一种易于检测的放射性核。如果能量阈值高于初级中子的最大能量，那么所观测的一切肯定的结果都必定要归结为次级中子。在第二种方法中 [2]，快中子与较重核的弹性碰撞是借助电离室进行观测的，这个电离室充满着一个大气压的气体并与线性放大器相连。为了单独研究由初级热中子所产生的影响，我们在源与铀块之间，分别在加入和没有加入镉屏蔽层的两种情况下进行实验。

第一种方法向我们表明，产生的次级快中子的能量至少为 2 兆电子伏（足以将可检测量的 ^{32}S 转变为放射性的 ^{32}P），我们设法通过第二种方法来确定，能量明显高于 2 兆电子伏的中子是否也会在次级辐射中出现。在我们的实验里，将充满氧气的电离室置于装有氧化铀且四周用厚的固体石蜡层包裹的近似立方（9 厘米 × 9 厘米 × 8 厘米）的盒子中，将用铅屏蔽层包裹（在电离室的方向上的厚度为 5 厘米）的源（300 毫克镭铍源）埋入石蜡之中。为了吸收热中子，我们可以用镉箔将铀盒的所有面都遮挡起来。在镉箔存在或者不存在的两种情况下记录脉冲，并且由此可以估算出受到热中子影响的部分（铀核所释放的快中子导致氧核的反冲）。

647

In view of the large number of of accidental pulses due to the strong γ-radiation emitted by the source, only nuclei recoiling with at least 1.5 Mev. could be taken into consideration. The distribution curve shows that the frequency of pulses observed falls off rapidly between 1.5 Mev. and 2.5 Mev.; between 2.5 Mev. and 3.7 Mev. the frequency decreases much more slowly, pulses observed in this second region being, however, very rare. The total number of pulses recorded is small (with cadmium: 84 pulses in 90 minutes; without cadmium: 161 pulses in 90 minutes); but it appears clearly that recoils with energy of about 2.5 Mev. are notably more frequent in the absence of cadmium and, therefore, that *neutrons possessing an energy of at least* 11 Mev. *are liberated in uranium irradiated with thermal neutrons.*

The high energy of these fast neutrons shows that their parent nuclei are in a highly excited state at the moment of their liberation, which is probably simultaneous with the fission. In this way a non-negligible fraction of the fission energy is disposed of; a further fraction is carried off by the β- and γ-rays afterwards emitted by the nuclei produced in the fission. The remainder available as kinetic energy for these recoiling nuclei is therefore considerably smaller than the total amount of energy liberated in the fission process (about 200 Mev.).

(**143**, 939; 1939)

H. von Halban, jun., F. Joliot and L.Kowarski: Laboratoire de Chimie Nucléaire, Collège de France, Paris, May 20.

References:

1. Dodé, M., von Halban, jun., H., Joliot, F., and Kowarski, L., *C.R.*, **208**, 995 (1939).
2. Szilard, L., and Zinn, W., *Phys. Rev.*, 55, 799 (1939).

鉴于由源发出强 γ 辐射所导致随机脉冲的数目很大，我们只考虑反冲能量至少为 1.5 兆电子伏的核。分布曲线显示，观测到的脉冲频率在能量 1.5 兆电子伏到 2.5 兆电子伏之间快速下降；在能量 2.5 兆电子伏到 3.7 兆电子伏之间，频率的下降减慢了很多，不过，在这第二个能量区域所观测到的脉冲非常稀少。记录到的总的脉冲数很少（使用镉时：90 分钟里有 84 个脉冲；不使用镉时：90 分钟里有 161 个脉冲）；但是似乎很明确的是，在没有镉时能量约为 2.5 兆电子伏的反冲明显出现得更为频繁，因此，**用热中子辐照铀时释放出至少具有 11 兆电子伏能量的中子。**

这些快中子所具有的高能量表明，在它们释出时其母核处于高激发态，释出与裂变可能是同时发生的。这样，裂变能中不容忽视的一部分就被转移走了；更大的一部分则被在裂变中生成的核通过发射 β 射线和 γ 射线带走了。因此，能够作为反冲核的动能的剩余能量就明显少于裂变过程中释放出的能量总量（约为 200 兆电子伏）。

（王耀杨 翻译；夏海鸿 审稿）

New Prospects in Isotope Separation

H. S. Taylor

Editor's Note

The discovery in 1932 by Harold Urey that hydrogen consists of two isotopes—ordinary hydrogen whose nucleus is a single proton and a heavier isotope whose nucleus consists of a proton and a neutron tightly bound together—stimulated interest in the isotopic composition of other elements. This article by Hugh Taylor of Princeton University in New Jersey describes work carried out since the discovery of heavy hydrogen. The thermal diffusion technique referred to in the article was that eventually used for separating the isotopes of uranium as part of the Manhattan Project to build the world's first nuclear explosives. (It is now known that hydrogen has a third isotope, called tritium, which is weakly radioactive.)

THE identification of the heavy hydrogen isotope and its separation gave considerable impetus to the search for methods of bulk separation of the isotopes of other elements. Previous to this time, the experimental man of science had been content to demonstrate that displacements of normal isotope ratios could be secured by one or other method. Aston and Harkins had shown that these ratios could be changed by diffusion processes in the cases of neon and chlorine. Brönsted and Hevesy changed slightly the atomic weight of mercury by distillation methods. It was the separation of the hydrogen isotopes and the demonstration of their extraordinary utility in many problems of chemical, physical and biological interest that re-awakened the interest in more complete separations of other isotopic elements. The simultaneous advances in the study of the nucleus, by bombardment with swift-moving primary particles, enhanced the desire for individual isotopic species of the elements, at the same time that it provided an alternative tool for research in the form of artificially produced radioactive elements.

The successful separation of the hydrogen isotopes by electrolysis has not been extended to other elements. The separation factor is too low in the case of oxygen to make the method practicable, and the same is true for lithium. The use of a series of diffusion pump units, developed by Hertz, has permitted large changes in isotope concentrations to be secured, notably with hydrogen, neon and carbon. The separation was complete in the first two cases, and 50 percent ^{13}C has been secured with methane as the diffusing gas. Minor concentrations of heavy nitrogen and oxygen have also been obtained. The principal objection to the method is the small amount of concentrated products which may thus be secured, since the pumps operate at not more than a few millimetres pressure. Capron and de Hemptinne were enabled to increase the speed of attainment and the yield of 50 percent ^{13}C from methane by incorporating in the pump circuit, at the light end, a reservoir of methane in the form of gas adsorbed on silica gel at liquid air temperatures. For the concentration of oxygen, the most promising method developed hitherto has

同位素分离的新视野

泰勒

编者按

哈罗德·尤里在 1932 年关于氢元素由两种同位素组成（一种是普通氢，其原子核中只有一个质子；另一种较重的同位素，其核由紧密结合在一起的一个质子与一个中子构成）的发现，激起了人们对其他元素同位素组成的研究兴趣。新泽西普林斯顿大学的休·泰勒在本文中描述了自重氢发现以来的各种研究工作。文中提到的热扩散技术最终被用于铀同位素的分离，并成为曼哈顿计划的一部分，被用于制造世界上第一批核炸药。（现在我们知道，氢还有第三种同位素——氚，它具有微弱的放射性。）

对重氢同位素的鉴定及分离极大地促进了大量分离其他元素同位素方法的研究。在此之前，科学实验研究人员一直满足于证实可以通过这样或那样的方法来改变正常的同位素比。阿斯顿和哈金斯曾指出，对于氖和氯来说，可以通过扩散过程来改变其同位素比。布朗斯泰德与赫维西利用蒸馏法轻微地改变了汞的原子量。正是氢的同位素分离及其在化学、物理学和生物学等众多重要问题中的特殊应用价值，重新唤起了科学家们对更彻底地分离其他同位素的兴趣。利用高速运动的初级粒子进行轰击的方法使核领域研究有了很大进展，这不仅使人们更加渴望发现元素的新同位素，同时也为人工制造放射性元素的研究提供了一种可选择的方法。

利用电解法对氢同位素进行的成功分离还没有推广到其他元素上。对于氧和锂来说，其分离系数过低，所以这种方法并不适用。赫兹将一套扩散泵设备应用于这一领域，使得大幅度改变同位素浓度的想法成为现实，尤其是应用到氢、氖和碳上最为显著。氢和氖的分离是非常彻底的，而对于碳来说，使用甲烷作为扩散气体也能得到 50% 的 ^{13}C。另外，人们还得到了低浓度的氮和氧的重同位素。该方法的主要缺点是只能保证得到很少量的富集产物，因为只能在不超过几毫米的大气压下操作这种泵。凯普伦与德昂普蒂纳合并了泵的回路，并在轻同位素一端用处于液态空气温度的硅胶吸收气态甲烷的方式来存储气体，从而提高了分离速度，并从甲烷中得到了 50% 的 ^{13}C。迄今为止，已发展起来的富集氧同位素的最具前景的方法似乎

seemed to be the distillation column method as constructed by Pegram, Huffmann and Urey.

The most encouraging successor to the electrolytic separation of hydrogen proved to be the isotopic exchange reaction method developed by Urey and his colleagues. With this method isotopic ^{15}N has been made available in large amounts of moderate concentrations and smaller amounts of highly concentrated heavy isotope. In this method, ammonia gas is exchanged counter current with ammonium ion in a column, the heavy nitrogen accumulating at the bottom. The success of this process makes 100 percent ^{15}N available at not too great cost, whenever required. The extension to heavy carbon is in progress, involving exchange between hydrogen cyanide gas and sodium cyanide liquors, by which exchange simultaneous separation of both carbon and nitrogen may be secured. The laboratory scale data seem as promising as those of nitrogen. Sulphur can be similarly treated with a greater separation factor than with carbon. Exchanges with zeolitic materials may be employed in the case of the ions of the alkali elements.

The mass spectrographic method can obviously be employed for the separation of charged ions, and this has been put to use in the preparation of the small amounts of the lithium isotopes necessary for nuclear and transmutation reactions. The development of high speed air-driven centrifuges, notably by Beams of the University of Virginia, has led to their use in isotope separation. Units are now in operation on liquids, with continuous feed and bleed. Marked displacements of the isotope ratio of chlorine in carbon tetrachloride have thus been secured. This method is most promising for not too large separations but in marked quantities. The separation depends only on the atomic weight difference and not on the mass ratio, and can thus be applied to liquids containing isotopes of high atomic weight as well as to the lighter isotopes. The method requires, however, expensive equipment and a slowly acquired technique.

From the point of view of general availability in the average laboratory, the newest method of isotope separation developed by Clusius and Dickel[1] is the most interesting, and of great promise for the general solution of the problem of separation of gaseous and liquid isotopic materials in quantity. Clusius combines the well-known thermal diffusion process, suggested by Chapman, with a thermal syphoning process by carrying out the separation in vertical tubes in the axis of which is a hot surface, the outside surface being kept cooled. The original form consisted of a heated wire placed concentrically in a cylindrical tube. In tubes of one metre length with a temperature gradient from centre to outside of 300-600°, it was shown that bromine in helium and carbon dioxide in hydrogen could be practically completely separated, the heavier gas concentrating at the bottom of the vertical column. With a three-metre tube, a four-fold concentration of oxygen in air was secured and a three-fold concentration of the heavy neon isotope. In the same tube a displacement of the chlorine isotopes in hydrogen chloride from 76:24 to 60:40 was secured in one operation. More recently[2] Clusius and Dickel announced the production in a tube of total length 36 metres, of 8 c.c. daily of hydrochloric acid of which more than 99 percent of the chlorine was of mass 37. Simultaneously, at the top of the column two

就是佩格勒姆、胡夫曼和尤里创立的精馏塔方法。

继氢的电解分离之后，最鼓舞人心的成果当数尤里及其同事发明的同位素交换反应法。利用这种方法可以得到大量中等浓度的 ^{15}N 同位素及少量高浓度的重同位素。在该方法中，氨气与精馏塔中的铵根离子逆流相遇并进行交换，重氮便积聚在精馏塔底部。这一过程的成功实现使得我们随时都能以较低的成本获得 100% 浓度的 ^{15}N。使用该方法分离重碳的实验还在进行中，这一过程涉及氰化氢气体和氰化钠溶液之间的交换，在交换的同时也可能会实现碳和氮的可靠分离。实验室范围的数据如同上述氮的实验数据一样令人鼓舞。硫也可以进行类似的处理，并且具有比碳更大的分离系数。在处理碱金属元素的离子时，可以使用沸石类材料进行交换。

很明显，质谱法可用于带电离子的分离，而且该方法已被用于制备核反应和嬗变反应所必需的少量锂同位素。高速气动离心机的进步（这主要归功于弗吉尼亚大学的比姆斯）使这项技术得以应用于同位素的分离。目前使用的设备可以控制液体连续流入和流出，因此可以使四氯化碳中氯的同位素比例发生显著的变化。对于数量显著但又不是非常大的分离情况来说，这种方法是最有前景的。这种分离仅仅取决于原子量的差异而不依赖于质量比，因而既可以应用于具有高原子量的液态同位素，又可应用于较轻的同位素。不过，这种方法需要昂贵的设备，并且技术不易掌握。

从普通实验室的一般利用率来看，由克劳修斯和迪克尔 [1] 开发的最新方法是最吸引人的，它为大量气态和液态同位素原料的分离提供了一般性的解决方案，因而具有广阔的发展前景。克劳修斯将广为人知的热扩散过程（由查普曼提出）与热虹吸过程结合起来，在一根垂直放置的管中进行分离操作，该管的中轴处为热表面，而外壁则保持冷却。最初的装置在其圆柱形管轴心处放置了一根加热导线。实验表明，当管子长度为 1 米，且由内而外的温度梯度为 300~600 度时，氦气中的溴与氢气中的二氧化碳在该装置中可以被完全分离，较重的气体富集于垂直管柱的底部。使用 3 米长的管子可使管中空气的氧气浓度增加到 4 倍，而使空气中的重氖同位素浓度增加到 3 倍。在相同的管子中，经过一次操作，可以使氯化氢中氯的同位素比从 76:24 变为 60:40。克劳修斯与迪克尔最近 [2] 声称，他们使用一根总长 36 米的管子，每天可以得到 8 立方厘米的盐酸，其中 99% 的氯质量数为 37。同时，管子的顶部生成了 2 升盐酸（Cl = 35.147），其中每升又可以产生 25 立方厘米的盐酸

653

litres of hydrochloric acid (Cl=35.147) was produced, from one litre of which 25 c.c. of hydrochloric acid (Cl=35.06) could be produced. Further purification of this should, owing to the packing fraction of the element, give a chlorine of atomic weight just less than 35.

The method has been tested by W. Groth[3] on the separation of xenon isotopes in comparison with a 12-stage Hertz diffusion pump system which gives a displacement of 0.5 units in the atomic weight in 12 hours at 2 mm. pressure. The same displacement can be secured at atmospheric pressure in a 2.5-metre tube, 12 mm. wall diameter, heated down the centre by a tungsten wire at 1,000°. With a 5-mm. tube and a wire temperature of 1,650°, a displacement of 1.6 atomic weight units was secured. In a metre tube with a glass core heated internally, Brewer and Bramley[4] showed that a 27 percent enrichment of ammonia at the bottom of the column with 50:50 methane (16)–ammonia (17) mixtures could be secured in fifteen minutes under favourable pressure and temperature gradient conditions.

The separation of the chlorine isotopes, successfully achieved by Clusius and Dickel, represents one of the most favourable cases for the operation of the thermal diffusion process. For, as Chapman showed, the separation is dependent on the product, C_1C_2, of the two fractions C_1 and C_2 of the mixture, respectively 0.76 and 0.24 in the cases of ^{35}Cl and ^{37}Cl. The separation of the carbon isotopes is much less favourable since the ratio ^{12}C to ^{13}C is 0.99:0.01.

Experiments conducted by G. G. Joris in the Princeton laboratories show, however, that even this mixture is capable of efficient resolution. In a column 1.5 metre long, with wall distance between hot and cold glass surfaces of 7.5 mm., a mean temperature of 400°K. and a temperature gradient of 450°, a separation factor $^{13}C:^{12}C$ (bottom)÷$^{13}C:^{12}C$ (top) of 1.21 is secured in one hour. In three separate three-metre columns with varying dimensions of hot and cold surfaces and wall distances from 7.5 mm. to 10 mm., with the same temperature conditions, the separation factor rose to 2, but in longer time intervals up to 5 hours. The most recent data secured on a 12-metre iron tube, 2 cm. internal diameter, heated axially by a chromel wire, No. 16 gauge, gave a separation factor of 3 in 48 hours with a heating current of 6 amperes, and a separation factor of 20 in 48 hours with a heating current of 9 amperes. This latter represents a concentration of the normal isotopic fraction of 1.1 percent ^{13}C to 2.1 percent at the bottom of the column and a depletion to ~0.1 percent ^{13}C at the top of the column.

It is obvious that the maintenance of this separation factor will result in concentrations of upwards of 20 percent ^{13}C at the bottom of the column when the normal ratio of 1.1 percent ^{13}C is kept at the top of the column. Such experiments are in progress. In the 12-metre tube, 3.76 litres of gas at 20 cm. pressure at ordinary temperatures are employed, methane being the gas used for the separation. Experiments by Prof. T. Ri, in the smaller columns, with carbon dioxide–oxygen and nitrogen–ammonia have shown that the separation factor depends on composition variables, on the pressure (the factor shows, in agreement with a previous finding of Brewer and Bramley, a broad maximum

(Cl = 35.06)。受该元素敛集率的影响，继续对此溶液进行纯化应该可以得到原子量刚好低于 35 的氯。

格罗特[3] 对此方法进行了验证，他将氖同位素的分离与 12 级的赫兹扩散泵系统进行了比较，后者在 2 毫米大气压下于 12 小时内产生了 0.5 个单位的原子量变化。在大气压下实现相同的原子量改变需要使用长 2.5 米、壁厚 12 毫米的管子，管子中心用一根温度达 1,000 K 的钨丝加热。如果使用 5 毫米的管子和温度为 1,650 K 的钨丝，那么原子量可以发生 1.6 个单位的改变。布鲁尔和布拉姆利[4] 指出，使用 1 米长的管子和从内部加热的玻璃芯，在合适的压强与温度梯度条件下，15 分钟内就能在管底部得到浓度为 27% 的氨气以及 50:50 的甲烷 (分子量 16) – 氨气 (分子量 17) 混合物。

由克劳修斯与迪克尔成功实现的氯同位素的分离是热扩散过程操作最为成功的实例之一。正如查普曼指出的那样，因为分离结果取决于同位素产物 C_1C_2 混合物中 C_1 和 C_2 分别所占的百分数，例如，^{35}Cl 和 ^{37}Cl 所占的百分数分别为 0.76 和 0.24。碳同位素的分离不太顺利，就是因为 ^{12}C 与 ^{13}C 的比例为 0.99:0.01。

不过，普林斯顿实验室的约里斯所做的实验显示，即使是碳同位素的混合物也可以实现有效的分离。在一根 1.5 米长的管子里，冷热玻璃表面之间的距离为 7.5 毫米，平均温度为 400 K，温度梯度为 450 K，在一小时内就可以得到 $^{13}C:^{12}C$ (底部) $\div$ $^{13}C:^{12}C$ (顶部) = 1.21 的分离系数。在 3 个冷热表面大小不同的 3 米长的管子中分别进行分离实验，冷热表面之间的距离从 7.5 毫米到 10 毫米不等，温度条件不变，得到的分离系数提高到 2，但间隔时间要延长至 5 小时。最新数据表明，在一根长 12 米、内径 2 厘米的铁管中，用 16 号镍铬合金导线进行径向加热，加热电流为 6 A 时在 48 小时内分离系数为 3，加热电流为 9 A 时在 48 小时内分离系数为 20。后一结果表明，在管底部，^{13}C 同位素的比例从正常的 1.1% 提高到 2.1%，而管顶部的 ^{13}C 的比例则减少到 0.1% 左右。

显而易见，维持这一分离系数就会使管底部的 ^{13}C 浓度达到 20% 以上，同时管顶部的 ^{13}C 比例保持为正常的 1.1%。这样的实验还在进行之中。在 12 米长的管中，通入常温 20 厘米气压下的气体 3.76 升，待分离的气体为甲烷。李教授在较小的管子中分别用二氧化碳 – 氧气和氮气 – 氨气进行了实验，结果显示，分离系数取决于成分百分比的变化和压强（与之前布鲁尔和布拉姆利的发现一致，分离系数在压强处于 20~30 厘米范围内时达到最大值），而影响最为显著的因素则是温度梯度。之前

in the region of 20-30 cm.) and most pronouncedly on the temperature gradient. This is obvious from the preceding data in the 12-metre column and also from data obtained with nitrogen–ammonia mixtures in the 1.5-metre column.

The theory of the thermal diffusion–thermal syphon process is complex. Two contributions are now available, one by Waldmann[5] and a paper by Furry, Jones and Onsager[6]. From Waldmann's paper the superiority of the process over straight thermal diffusion is measured by the ratio $0.67\ h/d^*$ where h is the height of the column and d^* is of the order of magnitude of the distance between hot and cold surfaces. The convection therefore multiplies the thermal diffusion effect enormously in tall columns. The temperature gradient also plays a determining role in the same theory. That the process is also applicable to liquid separations is evident from data of Clusius and Dickel[2] with sodium chloride solutions, acetone–water mixtures, and light and heavy water. The same conclusion is reached from the data of H. Korsching and K. Wirtz[7] with n-hexane–carbon tetrachloride and benzene–chlorobenzene mixtures.

(**144**, 8-9; 1939)

H. S. Taylor: F.R.S., Princeton University.

References:
1. *Naturwiss.*, **26**, 546 (1938).
2. *Naturwiss.*, **27**, 148 (1939).
3. *Naturwiss.*, **27**. 260 (1939).
4. *Phys. Rev.*, **55A**, 590 (1939); *Amer. Chem. Soc. Abstracts*, Baltimore Meeting, April 1939.
5. *Naturwiss.*, **27**, 230 (1939).
6. *Phys. Rev.*, in the press.
7. *Naturwiss.*, **27**, 110 (1939).

12 米长的管子中得到的实验数据和 1.5 米长的管子中氮气 – 氨气混合气体得到的实验数据，都能明显地证明这一点。

关于热扩散 – 热虹吸过程的理论是很复杂的。目前有两篇很有价值的文献，其中一篇的作者是瓦尔德曼 [5]，另一篇则是弗里、琼斯和翁萨格 [6] 合作的论文。根据瓦尔德曼的论文，热扩散 – 热虹吸过程相对于直接热扩散所具有的优势可以用比值 $0.67\ h/d^*$ 来表示，其中 h 为管子高度，d^* 为冷热表面之间距离的数量级。因此，高柱子中的对流大大增强了热扩散的效果。温度梯度在该理论中也具有决定性的作用。克劳修斯和迪克尔 [2] 从氯化钠溶液、丙酮 – 水混合物、轻水与重水中得到的实验数据证明，这一过程同样适用于液体的分离。科兴和沃茨 [7] 从正己烷 – 四氯化碳和苯 – 氯苯混合物中得到的实验数据也可推出同样的结论。

（王耀杨 翻译；汪长征 审稿）

Nuclear Reactions in the Continuous Energy Region

N. Bohr *et al.*

Editor's Note

The chief interest of this Letter to *Nature* is its authors: Niels Bohr at Copenhagen was the acknowledged father of quantum mechanics, Rudolf Peierls was a graduate research worker at Copenhagen who eventually migrated to Britain and was the designer of the thermal diffusion process for separating isotopes, and George Placzek was a close colleague of the other two. The point of their letter was to emphasise the utility of an idea due to Bohr that when nuclei collide with each other they first form a " compound nucleus" which can then split up in several different ways.

IT is typical for nuclear reactions initiated by collisions or radiation that they may, to a large extent, be considered as taking place in two steps: the formation of a highly excited compound system and its subsequent disintegration or radiative transition to a less excited state. We denote by A, B, ... the possible alternative products of the reaction, specified by the nature, internal quantum state, and spin direction both of the emitted particle or photon and of the residual nucleus and the orbital momentum. Further, we call P_A, P_B ... the probabilities, per unit time, of transitions to A, B, ... respectively, from the compound state.

The cross-section of the reaction $A \rightarrow B$ is then evidently

$$\sigma_B^A = \sigma^A \frac{P_B}{P_A + P_B + \cdots},$$

(1)

where σ^A is the cross-section for a collision in which, starting from the state A, a compound nucleus is produced. This formula implies, of course, that we are dealing with energies for which the compound nucleus can actually exist, that is, that we are either in a region of continuous energy values or, if the levels are discrete, that we are at optimum resonance. Moreover, it is assumed that all possible reactions, including scattering, proceed by way of the compound state, neglecting, in particular, the influence of the so-called "potential scattering", where the particle is deflected without actually getting into close interaction with the individual constituents of the original nucleus.

On these assumptions a very general conservation theorem of wave mechanics[1] yields the relation

$$\sigma^A = \frac{\lambda^2}{\pi}(2l + 1)\frac{P_A}{P_A + P_B + \cdots},$$

(2)

连续能量区域的核反应

玻尔等

编者按

这篇寄给《自然》的通讯最令人感兴趣的是他的作者：哥本哈根的尼尔斯·玻尔，他是众所周知的量子力学之父，鲁道夫·佩尔斯为哥本哈根的研究生，最后移居英国，是应用热扩散过程来分离同位素方法的设计者，乔治·普拉切克是上述两位作者的亲密同事。他们的这篇文章的要点是强调玻尔的关于核碰撞的观点，他们认为，原子核在发生碰撞时首先形成"复合核"，这种复合核可以通过多种方式分裂。

通常认为，由碰撞或者辐射引发的核反应在很大程度上分为两步发生：首先形成一个处于较高激发态的复合体系，然后通过衰变或辐射跃迁到较低的激发态。我们用 A，B，……表示反应中可能出现的两类不同的产物，并通过发射出的粒子或光子及残余核的性质、内在量子态、自旋方向及轨道角动量来决定。此外，我们定义 P_A，P_B，……为单位时间内由复合态分别跃迁到 A，B，……态上的概率。

显然，$A \rightarrow B$ 反应的有效截面为：

$$\sigma_B^A = \sigma^A \frac{P_B}{P_A + P_B + \cdots} \tag{1}$$

式中 σ^A 为从 A 状态发生碰撞产生一个复合核的有效截面。这个公式表示，我们讨论的能量是这个复合核能够真正存在的能量，也就是说，我们或者有一个能量连续的区域，或者如果能级是分立的，我们将得到最适合的共振态。而且，假定所有可能发生的反应，包括散射，都是通过复合状态进行的，特别忽略了被称作"势散射"的影响，在"势散射"中，粒子的轨迹发生偏斜，因而未能与原始原子核中的某个粒子发生近距离的相互作用。

基于这些假定，根据波动力学 [1] 普适的守恒定理给出以下关系式：

$$\sigma^A = \frac{\lambda^2}{\pi}(2l + 1)\frac{P_A}{P_A + P_B + \cdots} \tag{2}$$

where λ is the wave-length of the incident particle and l is the angular momentum.

In the case of discrete levels, (1) and (2) give the same cross-section as the usual dispersion formula, if one applies it to the centre of a resonance level and neglects the influence of all other levels. In this case we have for each resonance level a well-defined quantum state of the compound nucleus, and its properties, in particular the probabilities P_A, P_B, ... then cannot depend on the kind of collision by which it has been formed, that is, they would be the same if we had started from the fragments B, or C, ... instead of A.

In the case of the continuum, however, where there are many quantum states with energies that are indistinguishable within the life-time of the compound nucleus, the actual state of the system is a superposition of several quantum states and its properties depend on their phase relations, and hence on the process by which the compound nucleus has been produced.

This dependence is made particularly obvious if we consider the formula

$$\overline{\sigma^A} = \frac{\hbar}{2}\rho\lambda^2(2l+1)P_A^0 , \tag{3}$$

for the mean value of the cross-section over an interval containing many levels, which follows from the well-known considerations of detailed balancing. Here ρ is the density per unit energy of levels (of suitable angular momentum and symmetry) of the compound nucleus. P_A^0 is the probability for process A in statistical equilibrium and thus refers to a micro-canonical ensemble of compound states built up from the fragments A, B ... respectively, with proper statistical weights.

In the case of discrete levels, where formula (3) can also be derived directly from the dispersion formula, P_A^0 is simply an average over the individual levels of the probability P_A, which in this case is well defined.

In the continuum, (3) must be identical with (2), since the cross-section does not vary appreciably over an energy interval containing many levels, and hence, comparing (2) and (3)

$$\frac{P_A^{(A)}}{P_A^0} = \frac{\pi}{2}\,\hbar\rho\,(P_A^{(A)} + P_B^{(A)} + \cdots) = \frac{\pi}{2}\frac{\Gamma^{(A)}}{d}, \tag{4}$$

where the superscript A has been added to the probabilities occurring in (1) in order to show explicitly the dependence on the mode of formation, and where $\Gamma^{(A)}$ is the total energy width of the compound state concerned and $d = \frac{1}{\rho}$ the average level distance. In the continuum, where $\Gamma^{(A)} \gg d$, the probability $P_A^{(A)}$ of re-emitting the incident particle without change of state of the nucleus will thus be much larger than the probability of the same process in a compound nucleus produced in other ways.

式中 λ 为入射粒子的波长，l 为其角动量。

假如人们应用色散公式于一个共振能级的中心而且忽略了所有其他能级的影响的话，对于分立的能级，由式 (1) 和式 (2) 给出的有效截面与通常色散公式得到的结果相同。在这种情况下，我们将为复合核中的每一个共振能级确定一个明确的量子态，同时它的特性，尤其是概率 P_A，P_B，……并不依赖于通过什么类型的碰撞而形成，也就是说反应从阶段 B 或者 C 及其他碎片开始与从 A 开始得到的结果是一样的。

然而，对于能量连续的情况来说，在复合核的寿命期内存在着很多不易区分能量的量子态，系统的实际状态就是多个量子态的叠加，系统的性质取决于它们的相位关系，因此取决于复合核的形成过程。

如果我们考虑以下的公式，这种相关性就会变得非常明显：

$$\overline{\sigma^A} = \frac{\hbar}{2}\rho\lambda^2(2l+1)P_A^0 \tag{3}$$

对于在一个包含若干能级的区间中截面的平均值，它服从著名的细致平衡原理。式中 ρ 在这里表示复合核中能级（具有适当的角动量和对称性）的每单位能量上的密度，P_A^0 为 A 过程的统计平衡概率，因此引出一个由各自具有特有的统计权重的碎片 A，B，……构成的复合状态的微正则系综。

对于分立能级的情况，式 (3) 也可以直接由色散公式导出，在这种情况下我们可很容易的定义 P_A^0 为对概率 P_A 的单个能级上的简单的平均值。

对于能量连续的情况，式 (3) 和式 (2) 必须一致，因为有效截面在一个包含多个能级的能量区间中的变化并不明显。因此，比较式 (2) 和式 (3)，我们会得出：

$$\frac{P_A^{(A)}}{P_A^0} = \frac{\pi}{2}\hbar\rho\left(P_A^{(A)} + P_B^{(A)} + \cdots\right) = \frac{\pi}{2}\frac{\Gamma^{(A)}}{d} \tag{4}$$

其中，在式 (1) 中的概率上添加上标 A 是为了明确地表示其与形成模式的相关性，$\Gamma^{(A)}$ 是对应复合态的总能级宽度，$d = \frac{1}{\rho}$ 表示能级的平均间距。在能量连续的体系中，当 $\Gamma^{(A)} \gg d$ 时，在不改变原子核状态的条件下再次发射入射粒子的概率 $P_A^{(A)}$ 会比在以其他方式形成的复合核中发生同样过程的概率大得多。

While the arguments used so far are of a very general character, more detailed considerations of the mechanism of nuclear excitation are required for a discussion of the dependence $P_B^{(A)}$ of the mode A of the compound nucleus provided $A=B$.

One can think of cases in which such a dependence must obviously be expected; in fact, if a large system be hit by a fast particle, the energy of excitation might be localized in the neighbourhood of the point of impact, and the escape of fast particles from this neighbourhood may be more probable than in statistical equilibrium. Further, if the system had modes of vibration very loosely coupled, the excitation of one of them, for example by radiation, would be unlikely to lead to the excitation of a state of vibration made up of very different normal modes, even though the state may be quite strongly represented in statistical equilibrium.

In actual nuclei, however, the motion cannot be described in terms of loosely coupled vibrations, nor would one expect localization of the excitation energy to be of importance in nuclear reactions of moderate energy. If we suppose that there are no other special circumstances which would lead to a dependence of $P_B^{(A)}$ on A, it is thus a reasonable idealization to assume that, even in the continuum, all $P_A^{(A)}$ are equal to P_B^0, except, of course, for $A=B$, where we have seen in (4) that the phases are necessarily such as to favour the re-emission of the incident particle.

A typical case of a reaction in the continuum is the nuclear photo-effect in heavy elements, produced by γ-rays of about 17 mv. In the first experiments of Bothe and Gentner, there seemed to be marked differences between the cross-sections of different elements, but the continuation of their investigations[2] indicated that these differences can be accounted for by the different radioactive properties of the residual nuclei, and that the cross-sections of all heavy nuclei for photo-effect are of the order of 5×10^{-26} cm.[2].

In previous discussions, based on formulae (1) and (2), where the distinction between $P_A^{(A)}$ and P_A^0 was not clearly recognized, it was found difficult, however, to account for photo-effect cross-sections of this magnitude. In fact, if one estimates the probability of neutron escape P_B at about 10^{17} sec.$^{-1}$, one should have for P_A 10^{15} sec.$^{-1}$ and as long as this was taken as P_A^0 it seemed much too large, since it evidently must be much smaller then the total radiation probability, estimated at about 10^{15}, which included transitions to many more final levels besides the ground state.

We see now, however, that $P^{(A)}$ is here considerably larger than P_A^0, since the level distance at the high excitations concerned is probably of the order of 1 volt, whereas the level width corresponding to the above value of P_B is about 100 volts. From (4), or more directly from (3), P_A^0 is thus seen to be only about 10^{13} sec.$^{-1}$, which would appear quite reasonable.

(**144**, 200-201; 1939)

前面的论述针对的都是总体上的特征，要进一步考量核激发机制需要讨论当 $A=B$ 时，$P_B^{(A)}$ 对复合核中模式 A 的依赖性。

人们可以设想一些这种依赖性肯定存在的情况，实际上，如果一个很大的系统被一个快速粒子撞击，激发的能量也许只局限于碰撞点附近，快速粒子逃离该区域的可能性比到达统计平衡时的概率大。而且，如果这个系统具有松散耦合的振动模式，它们当中一个被激发，比如通过辐射，很难导致一个差异很大的普通模式组成的振动态被激发，即使这种状态在统计平衡中占有很大的优势。

然而，在实际的原子核中，我们不能用松散耦合的振动模式来描述运动，也不能期望激发能的局域化对中等能量的核反应的重要性。如果我们假定没有其他的特殊情况可以导致 $P_B^{(A)}$ 对 A 的依赖性，那么除去 $A=B$ 的情况以外，理想化地假定所有 $P_A^{(A)}$ 都等于 P_B^0 是合理的，即使是在能量连续的体系中，正如我们在式 (4) 看到的那样，该状态必然更有利于产生入射粒子的再发射过程。

在能量连续体系中的一个典型反应是重元素原子的光电效应，由 17 毫伏的 γ 射线引发。博特和根特纳在最初的实验中发现，不同元素的有效截面明显不同，但是他们后来的研究 [2] 又表明这种不同可以用残余核子的放射性差异来解释，而且所有重元素在光电效应中的有效截面均为 5×10^{-26} 平方厘米的量级。

在前面基于式 (1) 和 (2) 的讨论中，由于没有清楚地认识到 $P_A^{(A)}$ 和 P_A^0 之间的差别，我们发现要解析这种大小的光电效应的有效截面是有困难的。事实上，如果人们估算中子逃逸的概率 P_B 约为每秒 10^{17}，那么 P_A 应为每秒 10^{15}，但如果认为 P_A^0 也具有同样的数值，那就太大了，因为它显然必须远远小于整个辐射的概率，整个辐射的概率约为 10^{15}，其中包括向基态以及更多其他最终能级的跃迁过程。

然而，我们现在得出，在本文 $P^{(A)}$ 要远大于 P_A^0，因为在高激发态中能级间距的数量级大约为 1 电子伏，但是对于上面的 P_B 值得到的能级宽度大约为 100 电子伏。从式 (4)，或者更直接地从式 (3) 中看出，P_A^0 的合理值只有每秒 10^{13} 左右。

（胡雪兰 翻译；王乃彦 审稿）

N. Bohr, R. Peierls and G. Placzek: Institute of Theoretical Physics, Copenhagen, July 4.

References:
1. The details of this and of the other arguments of this note will be published in the *Proceedings of the Copenhagen Academy*.
2. Bothe, W., and Gentner, W., *Z. Phys.*, **106**, 236 (1937); **112**, 45 (1939).

The Scattering by Uranium Nuclei of Fast Neutrons and the Possible Neutron Emission Resulting from Fission

L. Goldstein *et al.*

Editor's Note

Here Goldstein, Rogazinski and Walen describe experiments measuring how neutrons interact with uranium nuclei. They used neutrons from a polonium-beryllium source to irradiate samples of lead oxide and uranium oxide, and detected neutrons with an ionization chamber. They are able to estimate the "cross-section"—the "size" of the nuclei as seen by the neutrons—for neutrons that are scattered with or without a change in energy. As they noted, their cross-section was somewhat higher than previous estimates, implying that neutrons can travel a little less far than thought in uranium. This suggested, in turn, that a critical mass for a chain reaction might also be smaller than previously suspected.

THE work to be described concerns only fast neutrons, and its object is the study of their scattering by uranium and the possible neutron emission which accompanies the fission of the nucleus.

The experiments were performed with a polonium plus beryllium source equivalent to 3 mC. of radon plus beryllium. An ionization chamber surrounded with 2.5 cm. lead, filled with hydrogen at a pressure of 35 atm., was used as a neutron detector. The insulated electrode was connected to a compensated electrometer valve[1], the grid leak being 10^{11} ohms and the sensitivity 1.2×10^{-15} amp./div. on the scale.

We have employed two experimental arrangements in which the source was placed (1) between the chamber and the substance used as scatterer, the nature and the thickness of which were variable; (2) in the centre of a cube of 16 cm. side, alternately filled with uranium oxide (specific gravity, $d=4.0$) and lead oxide (compressed to $d=3.8$).

The first type of experiment gave us the total scattering cross-section, which is, as can be shown, $\sigma_t = \sigma_e + k_i \sigma_i$; for uranium oxide $\sigma_t = \sigma_e + k_i \sigma_i + k_r v_r \sigma_r$, where $\sigma_e, \sigma_i, \sigma_r$ are respectively the average cross-sections of elastic and inelastic scattering and of fission; v_r is the average number of neutrons produced per fission; k_i and k_r are the average efficiency factors of the chamber for the neutrons having undergone an inelastic collision or for the neutrons resulting from fission. The efficiency for the direct neutrons was taken to be unity, $k=1$. For neutrons elastically scattered by nuclei of sufficiently high mass, $k_e=k=1$. We have calculated k, taking into account the size of the chamber, the cross-section for proton

铀核的快中子散射与可能源于裂变的中子发射

戈尔德施泰因等

编者按

本文戈尔德施泰因、罗格兹尼斯基和瓦伦描述了测量中子与铀核如何相互作用的实验。他们使用钋－铍源的中子辐照氧化铅和氧化铀的样品，并用电离室探测中子。他们可以估算出有能量变化和无能量变化两种实验情况下散射中子的"截面"，即中子与核碰撞的"尺寸"。正如他们所说的，他们计算得出的截面比先前估算的稍高，这意味着中子在铀中的行程比想象的稍小。反过来说，这也表明了链式反应的临界质量值也可能小于原先估算的值。

本文所描述的内容仅涉及快中子，目标是研究铀的快中子散射以及核裂变过程中可能伴随的中子发射。

实验是用一个钋－铍源（相当于 3 毫居氡－铍源）完成的。我们用 2.5 厘米厚的铅板包围电离室来作为中子探测器，室内充满了 35 个大气压的氢气。绝缘电极与补偿静电计电子管相连接[1]，栅漏电阻为 10^{11} 欧姆，标度灵敏度为每分度 1.2×10^{-15} 安培。

我们使用了两套实验装置：（1）实验源位于电离室和作为散射体的物质之间，其中散射体物质的性质和厚度是可变的；（2）实验源位于边长为 16 厘米的立方体中心，其中交替填充氧化铀（比重 $d = 4.0$）和氧化铅（压缩后比重 $d = 3.8$）。

第一种实验给出了总的散射截面，可以表示为 $\sigma_t = \sigma_e + k_i \sigma_i$；对于氧化铀，散射截面为 $\sigma_t = \sigma_e + k_i \sigma_i + k_r v_r \sigma_r$，其中，$\sigma_e$、$\sigma_i$、$\sigma_r$ 分别是弹性散射、非弹性散射及裂变的平均截面；v_r 是每次裂变产生的平均中子数；k_i 和 k_r 分别是电离室对发生非弹性碰撞的中子和裂变产生的中子的平均效率因子；直接入射中子的效率因子取为 1，即 $k = 1$。对于由质量足够高的原子核弹性散射的中子，$k_e = k = 1$。我们在考虑了电离室的尺寸、质子投射截面等值后计算了 k 的值。现在认为[2]，钋－铍源的中子能谱

projection, etc. The spectrum of polonium plus beryllium neutrons has been considered[2] to contain 50 percent of neutrons of W_n less than 10^5 ev. We thus obtain:

$10^{-6}W_n$	0.1	0.5	3	5	10	ev.
k	0.3	1	1.9	1.7	1.2	

In view of a possible extrapolation that would give $\sigma_e + k_i \sigma_i$ for uranium, we have in the same way experimented with scattering by lead oxide, lead, copper and zinc.

The results of the first experiment were as follows:

Substance	Cu	Zn	Pb	PbO_2	UO_2	$(O)_{calc.}$	$(U)_{calc.}$
$\sigma_t \times 10^{-24}$ cm.^{2} ($\pm 10\%$)	2.2	2.3	5.4	9.5	14.4	2	10.3

The values for uranium and oxygen are calculated on the assumption of the additivity of the cross-sections in lead oxide and uranium oxide.

The second experiment gives us, in the first approximation, the absorption coefficient $(1 - k_i)\sigma_i + (1 - k_r v_r)\sigma_r$, the value of σ_e being only as a correction term in the determination of the mean free path λ and the average distance L travelled by the neutrons before they escape from the whole mass, which is supposed spherical, the radius being r and $L = r(1 + \frac{1}{2}\frac{r}{\lambda})$. This experiment, taking into account the results of the previous experiments, gives for lead, $(1 - k_i)\sigma_i \simeq 2 \times 10^{-24}$ cm.^{2}. Assuming that σ_i can reach 30 percent of σ_e[3], this gives $k_i (\simeq) 0$.

With the exception of uranium, for which one must consider not only σ_i, but also $v_r \sigma_r$, it is probable that σ_t is not very different from σ_e because of the small value of k_i.

In the case of uranium, however, we have,

$$(1 - k_i)\sigma_i + (1 - k_r v_r)\sigma_r \simeq 0.9 \times 10^{-24} \text{ cm.}^2 \tag{1},$$

or, by adding to σ_t, thus eliminating k_i and k_r,

$$\sigma_e + \sigma_i + \sigma_r \simeq 11.2 \times 10^{-24} \text{ cm.}^2. \tag{2}.$$

If it is supposed that each fission produces radioelements, the cross-section measured by Joliot, and by Anderson et al.[4] would be identical with σ_r, which they found to be $\sigma_r \simeq 10^{-25}$ cm.^{2}. In this case we see that $(\sigma_e + \sigma_i)$ is much greater ($\simeq 11.1 \times 10^{-24}$ cm.^{2}) than that given by an extrapolation ($\simeq 6 \times 10^{-24}$ cm.^{2})

包含了 W_n 小于 10^5 电子伏的中子的 50%。因此，我们得到：

$10^{-6}W_n$	0.1	0.5	3	5	10	电子伏
k	0.3	1	1.9	1.7	1.2	

鉴于一种可行的外推法可以给出铀的 $\sigma_e + k_i\sigma_i$ 值，我们以相同的方法用氧化铅、铅、铜和锌与中子发生散射进行实验。

第一种实验结果如下：

物质	Cu	Zn	Pb	PbO_2	UO_2	(O) 计算值	(U) 计算值
$\sigma_t \times 10^{-24}$ 平方厘米 (±10%)	2.2	2.3	5.4	9.5	14.4	2	10.3

假定氧化铅和氧化铀截面具有可加性的前提下，我们计算了铀和氧的截面值。

第二种实验我们在一阶近似下给出了吸收系数 $(1 - k_i)\sigma_i + (1 - k_r v_r)\sigma_r$ 的值，σ_e 的值只是作为中子从假设为球形的块状物体逃逸前的测定平均自由程 λ 和中子穿行平均距离 L 的修正项，球块的半径是 r，且 $L = r(1 + \frac{1}{2}\frac{r}{\lambda})$。考虑到以前实验的结果，这个实验给出了铅的 $(1 - k_i)\sigma_i \simeq 2 \times 10^{-24}$ 平方厘米。假定 σ_i 的值能达到 σ_e 值 [3] 的 30%，则有 $k_i(\simeq)0$。

对于铀我们不仅要考虑 σ_i，还要考虑 $v_r\sigma_r$，而对于其他物质很有可能由于 k_i 的值很小，σ_t 与 σ_e 的值相差并不大。

对于铀的情况，我们有

$$(1 - k_i)\sigma_i + (1 - k_r v_r)\sigma_r \simeq 0.9 \times 10^{-24} \text{平方厘米} \tag{1}$$

或者，在式子两边加上 σ_t 将消掉 k_i 和 k_r，得到

$$\sigma_e + \sigma_i + \sigma_r \simeq 11.2 \times 10^{-24} \text{平方厘米} \tag{2}$$

如果假定每次裂变都产生放射性元素，约里奥和安德森等人 [4] 测得的截面值则与 σ_r 一致，他们测得的结果是 $\sigma_r \simeq 10^{-25}$ 平方厘米。在这种情况下，我们看到，$(\sigma_e + \sigma_i)$ 的值 $(\simeq 11.1 \times 10^{-24}$ 平方厘米) 远大于外推法所给出的值 $(\simeq 6 \times 10^{-24}$ 平方厘米)。

On the other hand, it results from (1) that, if the value of σ_i is comparable to that of the next elements (1 to 2×10^{-24} cm.²), v_r can, with plausible assumptions as to the coefficients k_i and k_r, take variable values, for example, from 1 to 5, or even more.

One can see that, so long as σ_i is not determined separately, the experiments of the type described do not allow us to determine v_r and σ_r (characteristics of the fission), or to conclude that neutrons are liberated; or *a fortiori*, to form a conclusion as to the possibility of chain reactions, contrary to the results of similar experiments[5].

The only suitable case for showing with certainty, by means of an ionization chamber, the production of neutrons, would be that in which, by the use of a sufficient quantity of uranium, the chain mechanism would give multiplication of neutrons, if such chain is realizable[6].

In conclusion, it results from these experiments with neutrons of polonium plus beryllium that the sum of the cross-sections $\sigma_e + \sigma_i + \sigma_r$ for the uranium nucleus is $(11.2 \pm 1.5)10^{-24}$ cm.². This value implies a mean path in uranium much shorter than that usually admitted; this suggests that smaller masses than those hitherto expected might be used to show chain fission.

(**144**, 201-202; 1939)

La. Goldstein, A. Rogozinski and R. J. Walen: Laboratoire Curie, Institut du Radium, Paris, 5, July 13.

References:

1. Rogozinski, A., *C.R.*, **208**, 427 (1939).

2. Auger, P., *J. Phys. Radium*, **4**, 719 (1933).

3. Seaborg, G. F., Gibson, G. E., and Graham, D. C., *Phys. Rev.*, **52**, 408 (1937).

4. Joliot, F., *J. Phys. Radium*, **10**, 159 (1939). Anderson, H. L., Booth, E. T., Dunning, J. R., Fermi, E., Glasoe, G. N., and Slack, F. G., *Phys. Rev.*, **55**, 511 (1939).

5. Haenny, C., and Rosenberg, A., *C.R.*, **208**, 898 (1939).

6. v. Halban, H., Joliot, F., and Kowarski, L., *Nature*, **143**, 680 (1939). Perrin, F., *C.R.*, **208**, 1394, 1573 (1939).

另一方面，根据（1）式的结果可知，如果 σ_i 的值与接下来 σ_r 的值（1×10^{-24}～2×10^{-24} 平方厘米）相近的话，在 k_i 和 k_r 系数运用合理的假定下，ν_r 的值是可变的，例如可以从 1 取到 5 甚至更大的值。

可以看到，只要不能独立地测定 σ_i 值，在这类实验中我们就不能测定 ν_r 和 σ_r（分裂的特征）的值，也就不能断定是否释放了中子；更不用说得到可能发生链式反应的结论了，这与类似实验的结果 [5] 相反。

通过使用电离室，唯一可以确定的合理情况是，对于中子的产生，如果链式反应可以实现的话 [6]，通过使用足量的铀，链式反应就可以产生出中子的倍增效应。

综上所述，通过运用钋－铍中子源的这些实验可知，对铀核截面求和，即 $\sigma_e + \sigma_i + \sigma_r = (11.2 \pm 1.5)\times10^{-24}$ 平方厘米。这个值表明铀中的平均自由程远小于通常公认的值；而这也意味着可以用比现在预期的更小的质量来实现链式核裂变。

（沈乃澂 翻译；张焕乔 审稿）

Recent Experimental Results in Nuclear Isomerism

B. Pontecorvo

Editor's Note

The idea that two atomic nuclei might be identical in their physical composition and mass but nevertheless might differ in their radioactive properties goes back to 1917 and to Frederick Soddy, one of the pioneers of radioactive studies. It is equivalent to saying that isomeric nuclei are capable of decaying by more than one route. With the discovery of artificial radioactivity, pairs of isomeric nuclei became more common. Bruno Pontecorvo, who migrated from France to Britain in 1940, had made a special study of isomeric nuclei and published this account of their properties a few months before the Second World War began.

THE hypothesis that two atomic nuclei indistinguishable in respect of atomic and mass number could nevertheless have different radioactive properties (the hypothesis of nuclear isomerism) was put forward for the first time by Soddy[1] in 1917. In 1921 uranium Z was discovered by Hahn[2]; by studying the chemical and radioactive properties of this element, Hahn deduced that uranium Z and uranium X_2 are isomeric nuclei. The problem of uranium Z has been taken up recently by Feather and Bretscher (*Proc. Roy. Soc.*, **165**, 542; 1938). It should be noted that, for many years, uranium Z and uranium X_2 were the only known example of an isomeric pair.

After the discovery of artificial radioactivity, the study of isomerism received considerable impetus on account of the experimental material assembled in the course of research on artificial radio-elements. The first *certain* example of an isomeric pair to which it has been possible to attribute a mass number ($A=80$) in the domain of the artificial radio-elements was furnished[3] by the study of the radioactivity produced in bromine by neutrons (slow and fast) and by γ-rays of great energy.

Then, as the experimental material on artificial radio-elements has increased, the number of pairs of nuclei which are undoubtedly isomeric has grown to such an extent that it is not possible to quote here all the investigations which have been published on the question. More than thirty such pairs are known and there is no doubt that the number still unknown is much greater. We can say, now, *that nuclear isomerism is by no means an exceptional phenomenon.*

It is natural to think that the physical difference between two isomeric nuclei is connected with two states of different excitation of the same nucleus (let us say ground state and first excited state). But in this case, how could the upper state be metastable, that is,

核同质异能性的最新实验结果

庞蒂科夫

编者按

两个原子核可以具有相同的物理组成和质量但却有不同的放射性质，这一想法最初是由放射性研究的开拓者之一——弗雷德里克·索迪于 1917 年提出的。这一观点还可以理解为，同质异能核衰变的方式不止一种。随着人工放射性的发现，同质异能核对变得更为普遍。布鲁诺·庞蒂科夫对同质异能核进行了一番专门研究，并在第二次世界大战前几个月发表了这篇关于同质异能核性质的文章，1940 年他从法国移居英国。

原子序数和质量数都相同的两个原子核却可能具有不同的放射性质（即核同质异能性的假说），这一假说最早是由索迪 [1] 于 1917 年提出的。1921 年，哈恩 [2] 发现了铀 Z；通过对该元素化学性质和放射性质的研究，哈恩推测铀 Z 与铀 X_2 是同质异能核。最近，费瑟和布雷切尔重新提出了铀 Z 的问题（《皇家学会会刊》，第 165 卷，第 542 页，1938 年）。值得人们注意的是，很多年以来铀 Z 和铀 X_2 是仅有的已经知道的同质异能核对。

发现人工放射性以后，科研工作者在对人工放射性元素的研究过程中积累的大量实验材料为同质异能现象的研究起到了相当大的推动作用。通过研究（慢和快）中子和高能 γ 射线轰击溴所产生的放射性可为人工放射性元素的领域中增添一个质量数为 80 的新元素，该元素也是首次得到的**确定的**同质异能对 [3]。

于是，随着关于人工放射性元素实验材料的增加，已确定为同质异能核对的数目大量增加，以至于我在此处不能一一引述所有关于这一问题的已发表的研究结果。目前已知道超过 30 对这样的核，并且毫无疑问的是，尚未发现的同质异能核对比这数目要多得多。现在我们可以说，**核的同质异能性绝对不是一种个别现象**。

我们可以很自然地想到，两个同质异能核之间的物理差异与相同原子核的两个不同激发态有关（比如说基态和第一激发态）。但是，在这种情况下，高能态是如何成为亚稳态的，或者说，它怎么能维持这么长时间（在某些情况下甚至超过一天）呢？

how could it live for any length of time (greater than one day, in some cases)? By what mechanism would it be preserved from destruction in a very short time by the emission of an electromagnetic radiation? Weiszäcker has answered this question[4].

According to Weiszäcker's *hypothesis*, nuclear isomerism may be explained by assuming that *the lowest excited state of the nucleus has an angular momentum differing by several units from that of the ground state*. Selection rules may then be invoked to weaken considerably the probability per unit of time of the transition from the upper to the ground state of the nucleus. Of course, experiments which make it possible to test the truth of Weiszäcker's hypothesis are of great interest.

One of the most important points is the study of the γ-radiation eventually emitted in the transition from one isomeric state to another: I say "eventually emitted" because, the nucleus being radioactive, the upper state corresponding to one of the isomeric forms may be destroyed by an ordinary β transition. The γ-ray−β-ray branching ratio will depend on the relative life-times for the two modes of decay. The first researches made to observe this γ-radiation failed. But it should be noted[5] that the considerable difficulty in detecting this radiation might be due to the fact that transitions between isomeric nuclei can be strongly converted: in this case electrons of small energy would be emitted and not γ-rays.

The very complete theory of the internal conversion of radiations emitted in the transitions between isomeric states[6], given by Hebb and Uhlenbeck, Dancoff and Morrison, has shown that these radiations must have internal conversion coefficients of approximately 1. Since these calculations are based on Weiszäcker's hypothesis, it can be concluded that *experiments which prove that the conversion coefficient in question is very high would indicate, to a certain extent, that Weiszäcker's hypothesis is correct*.

Indeed, in the case of the isomerism of radio-rhodium, Pontecorvo[7] has observed a radiation of low-energy electrons, which he interpreted as an electron line emitted in the transition from the metastable state to the ground state of the nucleus.*

At the present time, after a number of recent experiments, *there is no longer any doubt as to the fact that these transitions are generally strongly converted*. In particular, in the cases of isomeric nuclei of radio-bromine[8] and of element 43[9], strong lines of conversion electrons have been photographed in the Wilson chamber or in the magnetic spectrograph. Of course, the internal conversion is accompanied by emission of X-rays: as a rule, the analysis of these rays is an invaluable test in the interpretation of these phenomena[9,10].

It is interesting to find possible genetic relations between isomeric states of the same nucleus (β-radioactive): in this direction an extremely brilliant method has been described

---

* Note added in proof. A similar conclusion was independently obtained by Roussinow and Yusephovitch [*C. R. Acad. Sci. U.R.S.S.*, **20**, 9 (1938)] who observed a soft electron radiation in the case of isomeric forms of radio-bromine.

是什么机制使它们免于在很短时间内通过发射电磁辐射而崩溃呢？魏茨克回答了上述问题 [4]。

根据魏茨克的**假说**，核的同质异能现象可以这样解释：即假定**核的最低激发态具有与基态相差若干单位的角动量**。这样，根据选择规则，原子核在单位时间内从上述激发态跃迁到基态的概率就会明显减少。当然，能够检验魏茨克假说真实性的实验才是最令人感兴趣的。

最重要的问题之一是，对于在从一种同质异能态到另一种同质异能态的跃迁过程中最终发射出的 γ 辐射的研究。我之所以要说"最终发射"，是因为原子核具有放射性，相应于同质异能形式之一的较高能态可能会被一次普通的 β 跃迁破坏。γ 射线–β 射线分支比将取决于两种衰变方式的相对寿命。虽然最初观测这种 γ 辐射的研究未能成功，不过值得注意的是 [5]，探测这种辐射时所遇到的相当大的困难可能是因为同质异能核之间的跃迁可以发生强烈的转换，即在这种情况下，发射出来的是低能电子而不是 γ 射线。

关于在同质异能态之间的跃迁过程中发射出的辐射的内转换问题，赫布与乌伦贝克，以及丹克夫与莫里森给出了非常完整的理论 [6]，该理论指出，这些辐射必须具有接近于 1 的内转换系数。这些计算都是基于魏茨克的假说，因此可以得出下面的结论：**如果能够找到证明其所涉及的内转换系数的确很高的实验，就在一定程度上意味着魏茨克的假说是正确的。**

确实，庞蒂科夫 [7] 在研究放射性铑时曾观测到低能电子辐射，他将其解释为原子核从亚稳态跃迁到基态时发射出来的电子线。*

在近期的大量实验之后，**人们目前对于这些跃迁普遍发生强烈转换这一事实再没有任何怀疑**。特别是在放射性溴 [8] 和 43 号元素 [9] 的同质异能核的实验研究中，人们已经在威尔逊云室和磁谱仪中拍下了转换电子的强线的照片。当然，内转换伴随着 X 射线的发射，因此，通常情况下在解释上述现象时 [9,10]，对 X 射线的分析就是极其重要的检验标准。

寻找同种原子核（β 放射性）的同质异能态之间可能具有的遗传关系是很有意思的：在这个研究方向上，塞格雷、哈尔福德和西博格曾描述过一种极为出色的方

---

* 附加说明：卢西诺和约瑟夫维奇独立地得到了一个类似的结论 [《苏联科学院院刊》**20**, 9(1938)]，他们在研究放射性溴的同质异能现象时观测到了软性电子辐射。

by Segré, Halford and Seaborg[11], who have succeeded in *separating*, one from the other, the two isomeric forms of radio-bromine. The principle of their method is as follows. Suppose the element, of which the isomeric states are being studied, can give compounds suitable for the application of the Szilard-Chalmers method of concentration. When the isomer in the upper state decays to the lower state, there is a γ-ray emission: corresponding recoil may be sufficient to knock the decayed atom out of the compound. The daughter activity can then be separated, as in the Szilard-Chalmers method.

This method, which has been successfully applied in several cases[12], can then be used (*a*) to separate known isomers in some cases; (*b*) to discover the existence of isomeric pairs, still unknown, in the study of artificial radioactivity.

Moreover, it has given a striking new proof that the transitions between isomeric states are strongly converted: in effect, the recoil due to the γ-emission is not sufficient to knock the decayed atom out of the compound, while the recoil of a conversion electron *can* be sufficient.

So far we have discussed radioactive isomers: the isomerism in this case, implies a difference in the life-times of the isomers. It has been noticed by Pontecorvo[5] that β-stable nuclei with a metastable excited state ought not to be very rare and should be revealed by the study of the radiation emitted by this metastable state. These nuclei are interesting for the understanding of nuclear isomerism, because the radiation corresponding to the transition from one isomeric state to the other is not troubled by the presence of β- or γ-rays. It should be possible to obtain a β-stable nucleus in a metastable state, after a nuclear transmutation or a radioactive disintegration.

Dodé and Pontecorvo[13], by bombardment of cadmium with fast neutrons, have obtained an activity ($T=50$ min.) which chemical proofs have shown to be due to an isotope of cadmium. On the other hand, there is no question of a reaction of simple neutron capture or of an $n,2n$ reaction. They interpreted the soft radiation emitted by cadmium (50 min.) as proceeding from a metastable state of an isotope of cadmium; the reaction of excitation without capture by fast neutrons (reaction n,n), having a considerable cross-section (some 10^{-24} cm.²), it is not impossible, indeed, that part of the nuclei so excited might fall into a metastable state.

Segré and Seaborg[9] have observed a metastable state of element 43, decaying (only a line spectrum of electrons) with a 6-hour period into the ground state, which is stable or perhaps radioactive with a long life: the 6-hour activity is daughter of a β-radioactive molybdenum.

A very interesting case has been observed and studied thoroughly by Goldhaber, Szilard and Hill[14]. They have obtained by the n,n reaction already quoted, a metastable state (^{115}In*) of ^{115}In, decaying with a period of 4.1 hours; moreover, the same state can be obtained after the disintegration of a radio-cadmium ($T=2.5$ days). The radiation emitted

法 [11]，他们成功地将放射性溴的两种同质异能形式彼此分离开来。他们所用方法的原理是，假定所要研究其同质异能状态的元素能够形成某些适用于齐拉特－查默斯富集方法的化合物。当处在较高能态的同质异能核衰变到较低能态时，就会放射出 γ 射线，而由此引起的反冲作用可能足以将衰变后的原子撞出化合物。于是就可以分离出子体放射性，如同在齐拉特－查默斯方法所描述的那样。

于是，这种已经成功应用于若干实例 [12] 的方法就可以用于：(a) 分离某些研究中的已知同质异能核；(b) 在人工放射性研究中，发现未知的同质异能核对的存在。

此外，这种方法对于同质异能态之间的跃迁发生强烈转换这一事实给出了一个令人惊奇的新证据：实际上，由于 γ 辐射而产生的反冲是不足以将衰变后的原子撞出化合物的，但是转换电子引起的反冲却**能够**做到这一点。

到目前为止我们讨论了放射性的同质异能素：在这些情况下出现的同质异能现象意味着同质异能素寿命之间的差异。庞蒂科夫 [5] 已经注意到，具有亚稳激发态的 β 稳定核应该不是很稀有，并且，对这种亚稳态所发射的辐射进行研究应该会有助于对它的了解。这些核对于理解核的同质异能现象是有帮助的，因为对应于从一个同质异能态到另一个同质异能态的跃迁的辐射并没有受到 β 射线或 γ 射线的干扰。在经过一次核嬗变或者一次放射性衰变之后，可能会得到一个处于亚稳态的 β 稳定核。

多德和庞蒂科夫 [13] 通过用快中子轰击镉的方法获得了一种放射性（$T = 50$ 分钟），化学证据表明这种放射性源自镉的一种同位素。另外，无疑同时发生了单纯的中子俘获反应或者 ($n,2n$) 反应。他们将镉（50 分钟）发射的软辐射解释为镉的一种同位素的某一亚稳态的辐射；事实上，对具有相当可观截面（大约为 10^{-24} 平方厘米）的不伴随快中子俘获的 (n,n) 激发反应，激发的那部分核落入亚稳态是可能的。

塞格雷和西博格 [9] 曾观测到 43 号元素的亚稳态，它以 6 小时的周期衰变（只有电子的线型能谱）到基态，基态是稳定的，或者可能具有长寿命的放射性。因此，周期为 6 小时的放射性是一种 β 放射性钼的子体。

戈德哈伯、齐拉特和希尔 [14] 曾观测到一种非常有趣的情况，并对其进行了充分的研究。他们通过上面提到的 (n,n) 反应得到了 ^{115}In 的一个半衰期为 4.1 小时的亚稳态（^{115}In*），此外，一种放射性镉（$T = 2.5$ 天）衰变后也能得到同样的态。^{115}In*

by [115]In* has not yet been sufficiently studied; its properties are of the greatest interest both for the understanding of the nuclear isomerism and for that of isobaric pairs. In effect, [115]In and [115]Sn are one of the rare cases of stable neighbouring isobaric nuclei: [115]In* might then decay into [115]Sn (β-emission) or into [115]In, or into both together.

The same metastable state of [115]In has been obtained also by irradiating indium with 5.8 Mev. protons (reaction p,p), by Barnes and Aradine[15]. Nevertheless, it is not yet clear whether the mechanism of nuclear excitation is that discussed by Weisskopf, that is, excitation by the action of the electric field of the proton[16].

In all these cases and in others studied more recently[17], the metastable states of stable isotopes are obtained from *nuclear transmutations*.

Lazard and Pontecorvo[18] have tried a new method, by which *it would be impossible to transmute the nucleus* and, consequently, to obtain artificial radio-elements, the presence of which may interfere with the investigation.

This method consists of irradiating the target with a continuous spectrum of X-rays, the energy of which is less than the dissociation energy of the nuclei. Suppose the radiated nuclei have a metastable state; the X-rays may excite higher levels of the nuclei; a part of the nuclei thus excited can fall into the metastable state, and it is the radiation from this state which can be observed. The maximum energy of the continuous spectrum utilized was 1,850 kilovolts: indium gives an activity of approximately 4 hours period, which is obviously due to the same metastable state [115]In*, of which we have already spoken. Similar results on the stable nuclear fluorescence of indium were obtained by Collins and others[19].

There is no doubt that new isomers of β-stable nuclei will be discovered, in the course of research undertaken in different laboratories; systematic research on the radiations emitted by metastable states will certainly be very useful for the understanding of nuclear isomerism.

In conclusion, we may remark that it is very probable, on account of the great number of known isomers, that the radiative transitions of life-times between, say, 10^{-7} sec. and 1 sec. are much more frequent than is generally supposed. These transitions, on the other hand, are strongly converted[6]. We would expect[20], consequently, that *transitions of this kind, with conversion coefficients approximately* 1, *may be found frequently.*

Indeed, in the radiation emitted in the capture of slow neutrons by gadolinium, a strong component of soft electrons has been observed by Amaldi and Rasetti[21] (life-time less than 10^{-3} sec.). Soft electronic components have also been observed in the capture of slow neutrons by other nuclei[22]. On the other hand, these strongly converted transitions may play a considerable part in the interpretation of γ- and X-spectra emitted by certain natural radio-elements[20].

发射出的辐射还没被充分的研究；它的性质对理解核的同质异能现象与同量异位对来说都是非常重要的。实际上，^{115}In 与 ^{115}Sn 是稳定的相邻同量异位核的罕见实例之一：^{115}In* 可以衰变成 ^{115}Sn（β 辐射），或者衰变成 ^{115}In，或者同时衰变成这两种元素。

巴恩斯与阿拉丁 [15] 通过用 5.8 兆电子伏的质子照射铟元素（反应 p,p），也得到了 ^{115}In 的同一亚稳态。不过，我们目前仍不清楚，核激发机制是否如魏斯科普夫所讨论的那样，是由质子电场的作用而导致的激发 [16]。

在上述各情况以及一些更为近期的研究 [17] 中，稳定同位素的亚稳态都是通过**核嬗变**得到的。

拉扎德和庞蒂科夫 [18] 尝试了一种新方法，该方法使**核嬗变不可能发生**从而获得人工放射性元素，而人工放射性元素的出现有可能干扰实验研究。

这种方法要使用具有连续谱的 X 射线照射靶子，所用 X 射线的能量低于核的离解能。假定被照射的核具有一个亚稳态；X 射线可以激发核的较高能级；由此而被激发的一部分核就可能落入亚稳态，可以观测到的正是来自这个态的辐射。所用连续谱的最大能量为 1,850 千电子伏，铟原子产生了周期约为 4 小时的放射性，这一放射性显然是来自我们曾提到过的 ^{115}In* 亚稳态。柯林斯与其他一些研究人员 [19] 从铟的稳定核荧光现象上得到了类似结果。

毫无疑问，在不同实验室所进行的研究工作中，一定会发现 β 稳定核的新同质异能素；关于亚稳态发射辐射的系统性研究对于理解核同质异能现象无疑是大有助益的。

总而言之，根据大量已知的同质异能素，我们可以说，具有介于诸如寿命在 10^{-7} 秒到 1 秒之间的放射性跃迁,很有可能比我们一般所认为的更为频繁。另一方面，这些跃迁发生了强烈的转换 [6]。由此，我们预期 [20] **会频繁地发现这种转换系数近乎1 的跃迁**。

实际上，在钆俘获慢中子的过程所发出的辐射中，阿马尔迪和拉塞蒂 [21] 已经观测到了强的软电子成分（寿命不足 10^{-3} 秒）。在其他核的慢中子俘获过程中也观测到了软电子成分 [22]。此外，这些强烈转换的跃迁对于解释某些天然放射性元素发射的 γ 光谱和 X 光谱可能也会起到相当重要的作用。

(**144**, 212-213; 1939)

B. Pontecorvo: Laboratory of Nuclear Chemistry, College de France, Paris.

References:

1. Soddy, *Proc. Roy. Inst.*, **22**, 117 (1917).

2. Hahn, *Ber. dtsch. Chem. Ges.*, B, **54**, 1131 (1921).

3. Kourtchatow, Myssowsky, Roussinow, *C.R.*, **200**, 1201 (1935). Amaldi, d'Agostino, Fermi, Pontecorvo, Segré, *Ric. Scient.*, **6**, 581 (1935). Amaldi and Fermi, *Phys. Rev.*, **50**, 899 (1936). Bothe and Gentner, *Z. Phys.*, **106**, 236 (1937).

4. Weiszäcker, *Naturwiss.*, **24**, 813(1936).

5. Pontecorvo, *Congrès du Palais de la Decouverte*, Paris, 1937, p. 118.

6. Hebb and Uhlenbeck, *Physica*, 5, 605 (1938). Dancoff and Morrison, *Phys. Rev.*, 55, 122 (1939).

7. Pontecorvo, *Phys. Rev.*, 54, 542 (1938).

8. Valley and McCreary, *Phys. Rev.*, 55, 666 (1939). Siday, *Nature*, **143**, 681 (1939).

9. Seaborg and Segré, *Phys. Rev.*, 55, 808 (1939). Kalbfell, *Phys. Rev.*, 54, 543 (1938).

10. Alvarez, *Phys. Rev.*, 54, 486 (1938). Roussinow, Yusephovitch, *Phys. Rev.*, 55, 979 (1939). Siday, ref. 8. Walke, Williams and Evans, *Proc. Roy. Soc.*, A, **171**, 360 (1939).

11. Segré, Halford and Seaborg, *Phys. Rev.*, 55, 321 (1939).

12. De Vault and Libby, *Phys. Rev.*, 55, 322 (1939). Le Roux, Lu and Sugden, *Nature*, **143**, 517 (1939). Seaborg and Kennedy, *Phys. Rev.*, 55, 410 (1939).

13. Dodé and Pontecorvo, *C.R.*, **207**, 287 (1938).

14. Goldhaber, Hill and Szilard, *Phys. Rev.*, 55, 46 (1939).

15. Barnes and Aradine, *Phys. Rev.*, 55, 50(1939).

16. Weisskopf, *Phys. Rev.*, **53**, 1018 (1938).

17. Delsasso, Ridenour, Sherr and White, *Phys. Rev.*, 55, 113.

18. Pontecorvo and Lazard, *C.R.*, **208**, 99(1939).

19. Collins, Waldman, Stubblefield and Goldhaber, *Phys. Rev.*, 55, 507 (1939).

20. Pontecorvo, *C.R.*, **207**, 230 (1938).

21. Amaldi and Rasetti, *Ric. Scient.*, **10**, 115 (1939).

22. Hoffman and Bacher, *Phys. Rev.*, 54, 644 (1938). Pontecorvo, *C.R.*, **207**, 856 (1938).

（王耀杨 翻译；厉光烈 审稿）

Heavy Cosmic Ray Particles at Jungfraujoch and Sea-Level

W. Heitler *et al.*

Editor's Note

Most cosmic-ray observations in the 1930s were made using the instrument called a cloud chamber, in which the tracks of electrification left by cosmic-ray particles are rendered visible (and capable of being photographed) by a change of pressure. This paper is one of the first employing a new technique in which cosmic rays were identified as the tracks left in photographic emulsions by the movement through them of cosmic-ray particles. Cecil Frank Powell was trained as a physicist at the Cavendish Laboratory in Cambridge, but had moved to Bristol in 1939, where he pioneered the technique for using photographic emulsions as a means of tracking cosmic rays. He was awarded a Nobel Prize in 1950 for precisely this work.

THE heavy ionizing particles in the cosmic rays are so rare that it seems unlikely that much information can be obtained from experiments with cloud chambers. The only method at present available which can yield quantitative results is the method of direct photography, which has been used recently by several investigators mainly for investigating the nuclear disintegrations which the cosmic rays produce[1,2]. On a plate which has been exposed for a sufficiently long time is observed, in addition to a great wealth of phenomena associated with disintegration effects, a large number of single tracks probably due to protons or slow mesotrons.

In approaching the problem of elucidating the various processes taking place, the first question which presents itself is that of the nature of the primary radiation responsible for the heavy tracks, and we have therefore made absorption measurements in lead and air. A set of Ilford half-tone plates (emulsion 70 μ thick and sensitive to α-particles and protons), covered with different thicknesses of lead, have been exposed to cosmic rays on the Jungfraujoch and in Bristol for a period of 230 days. We divide the observed tracks into two classes according to their length (that is, the length of the part of the track appearing in the emulsion): (i) tracks less than 10 cm. air equivalent and (ii) tracks greater than 10 cm. air. A large fraction of (i) is due to radioactive contamination, whereas all the tracks (ii) are of cosmic ray origin. The results are given in the following table:

	No. of tracks greater than 10 cm. air per mm.^{2}	No. of tracks less than 10 cm. air per mm.^{2}
Jungfraujoch, no lead	6.2 ± 1.0	20 ± 1.4
5 cm. ,,	8.4 ± 1.0	27 ± 2.0
13 cm. ,,	4.5 ± 1.0	16 ± 1.5
Bristol, no lead	0.6 ± 0.2	11 ± 1.5
13 cm. ,,	0.25 ± 0.2	14 ± 2.0

少女峰和海平面处的重宇宙射线粒子

海特勒 等

编者按

20世纪30年代，对大多数宇宙射线的观测都是借助一种叫作"云室"的仪器进行的，通过改变云室中的气体压力可以使宇宙射线粒子穿过时留下的电离径迹变得可见（并能被拍照）。本文的研究首次采用了一种新的技术，即通过进入感光乳胶中的宇宙射线粒子的运动径迹来确认宇宙线。塞西尔·弗兰克·鲍威尔曾在剑桥大学卡文迪什实验室工作并成为一名物理学家，但于1939年迁往布里斯托尔，在那里他研发了一种应用照相乳胶标记宇宙射线的技术。正是因为这项工作他获得了1950年的诺贝尔奖。

宇宙射线中重电离粒子非常稀少，以至于从云室的实验中获得关于这些粒子较多的信息是不大可能的。为了得到定量的结果，目前唯一可采用的方法是直接照相法。最近，几位研究人员已经使用该方法对宇宙射线产生的核裂变进行了研究[1,2]。对已经曝光了足够长时间的照相底片进行观测，我们发现除了与裂变效应相伴随的大量现象外，还有大量可能由质子或慢介子引起的单根径迹存在。

在对发生的各种过程进行解释时，首先遇到的问题是相应于那些重电离粒子径迹的原初射线的性质；因此我们分别测量了其在铅和空气中被吸收的情况。用不同厚度的铅覆盖一组半色调的伊尔福底片（感光乳胶厚度为70微米，对 α 粒子和质子敏感），分别放置在少女峰和布里斯托尔，并让其在宇宙射线中曝光230天。我们把观测到的径迹按照其长度（即出现在乳胶上的那部分径迹的长度）分作两类：（i）长度小于 10 cm air（即10厘米等效空气长度）的径迹，（ii）长度大于 10 cm air 的径迹。第一类径迹大部分是由放射性污染引起的，而第二类径迹全部是由宇宙射线产生。具体的实验结果如下表所示：

	每平方毫米的径迹数（> 10 cm air）	每平方毫米的径迹数（< 10 cm air）
少女峰，无铅	6.2 ± 1.0	20 ± 1.4
5 cm 铅	8.4 ± 1.0	27 ± 2.0
13 cm 铅	4.5 ± 1.0	16 ± 1.5
布里斯托尔，无铅	0.6 ± 0.2	11 ± 1.5
13 cm 铅	0.25 ± 0.2	14 ± 2.0

It will be seen that radiation primarily responsible for the long tracks suffers practically no absorption in lead but is strongly absorbed in air. The short tracks also indicate that the primary radiation giving rise to them is strongly absorbed in air but not in lead. (Probably most of the short tracks on the Bristol plates are of radioactive origin, and we must expect an equal number of this origin in the Jungfrau plates.)

The results show that the *long tracks are neither produced by the electron nor by the mesotron component*. Electrons would be strongly absorbed in lead, whereas the mesotron intensity increases only by a factor 1.7 between Bristol and Jungfraujoch. *The heavy tracks are therefore produced by a third component*. It seems likely that this third component consists of *neutrons*. Further support for this view is given by the experiments of Schopper[3]. Experiments with paraffin as absorber are in progress.

The grain spacing of the tracks is in agreement with that of artificially produced protons. Most of the long tracks are probably protons; but it cannot be excluded that some of the shorter tracks due to cosmic rays are also α-particles, since on the half-tone plates there is little difference between the grain spacing of α-particles and protons. The distribution of tracks was found to be more or less isotropic. The plates were placed in a horizontal position, but no appreciable preponderance of vertical tracks was observed.

We have also observed numerous disintegration stars which will be the subject of a later investigation. Here we only wish to mention one particular case, similar to a heavy particle in a disintegration star observed by Schopper and Schopper[2], which is of interest in connexion with the question of nuclear fission. The star in question has five tracks: four of them are comparatively short (5-11 cm. air) proton or α-ray tracks. The fifth track is 14 cm. long and has an average grain density of about *three times* that of α-rays of 8 cm. range. Considering that there is very little difference between the grain density produced by protons and α-particles of the same range, we must ascribe this track to a heavy particle with a *very high effective charge*. Moreover, the grain density does not increase steadily towards the end of the range, as is the case for α-particles, but has a maximum at the beginning of its path and then decreases slowly, until at the end of its range it approaches that of an α-particle (see accompanying diagram). This effect is presumably due to capture of extra nuclear electrons.

由上表可见，相应于长程径迹的原初射线实际上在铅中并没有被吸收，但在空气中却被强烈地吸收。短程径迹也表明，其相应的原初射线在空气中被强烈吸收，但在铅中却没有被吸收。（布里斯托尔实验的底片上的大多数短程径迹可能都是放射性射线造成的，因此我们也肯定地预期在少女峰实验的底片上也有相同数量的源于放射性射线的径迹。）

结果表明，**长程径迹既不是由电子产生也不是由介子产生的**。因为电子可以被铅强烈地吸收，而介子的强度从布里斯托尔到少女峰只增加了 1.7 倍。**因此，重径迹是由第三种射线组分产生的**；这第三种组分可能是由**中子**组成。朔佩尔 [3] 的实验进一步证实了这一观点。目前正在进行以石蜡作为吸收体的实验。

这些径迹的颗粒间距与人工产生的质子的间距是一致的。所以大多数的长程径迹可能由质子形成，但是也不排除一些由宇宙射线造成的短程径迹可能是由 α 粒子产生的，因为在半色调的底片上，分别由 α 粒子和质子形成的颗粒间距差异很小。实验中，径迹的分布在各个方向上大体相同。虽然乳胶底片是水平放置的，但在垂直方向上观测到径迹数没有明显的优势。

同时，我们也观测了大量的星型裂变情况，这将是下一阶段研究的内容。这里我们只提及一个特殊案例，类似于朔佩尔等 [2] 观测到的一个星型裂变中的重粒子，有意思的是这个案例与核裂变问题密切相关。这里提到的这颗裂变星有五条径迹：其中四条是比较短（5~11 cm air）的质子或 α 射线的径迹；第五条径迹长 14 cm air，其平均颗粒密度大约是射程为 8 cm air 的 α 粒子的**三倍**。考虑到在相同的射程内质子和 α 粒子产生的颗粒密度没有多大区别，我们必须将该径迹归为一个具有**很高有效电荷**的重粒子。此外，该粒子的颗粒密度并不像 α 粒子那样沿着射程方向连续增加，而是在径迹开始处具有最大值，然后缓慢减小，直至射程末端才接近 α 粒子的颗粒密度（参见附图）。这种效应可能是由于俘获了额外的核电子形成的。

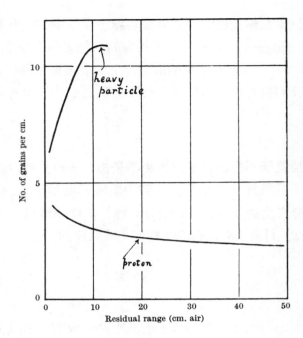

We do not think it very likely that this track represents the mere recoil from the original cosmic ray particle. The recoil tracks in even very energetic disintegrations are very short, and besides, there is no reason why the recoil nucleus should have such a high effective charge. In all probability we are dealing here with a heavy, highly charged splinter, released by a highly excited heavy nucleus, a process which bears some similarity to the fission of the uranium nucleus.

(**144**, 283-284; 1939)

W. Heitler: At present at Royal Society Mond Laboratory, Cambridge.

C. F. Powell and G. E. F. Fertel: H. H. Wills Physical Laboratory, University, Bristol.

References:
1. Blau and Wambacher, *Sitz. Akad. Wien*, **146**, 623 (1937).

2. Schopper and Schopper, *Phys. Z.*, **40**, 22 (1939).

3. Schopper, *Naturwiss.*, **25**, 557(1937).

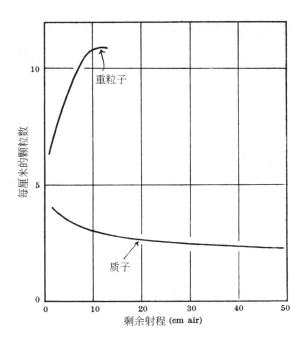

我们并不认为这条径迹是来自于原始宇宙射线粒子的反冲径迹。因为即使是很高能的粒子裂变，其反冲轨迹也都是非常短的。此外，反冲核也没有理由具有这么高的有效电荷。总之情况很可能是，这种粒子是高激发态的重原子核释放出的一个高电荷、重粒子碎片，该过程类似于铀原子核的裂变。

（金世超 翻译；马宇蒨 审稿）

Interpretation of the Red-Shifts of the Light from Extra-Galactic Nebulae

M. E. J. G. de Bray

Editor's Note

Edwin Hubble, the distinguished American astronomer, was the first to point out that the galaxies identified in the sky as groups of stars held together by their mutual gravitational attraction also appeared to be receding from the Earth (or our own galaxy) with velocities that may be a substantial fraction of the velocity of light. This letter shows that the new facts did not disconcert those who believed in a secular decline of the velocity of light with the mere passage of time.

IN his most recent contribution on this subject[1] Hubble mentions a red-shift of +0.231 A. This corresponds to a velocity of recession of approximately 43,000 miles per second, nearly a quarter of the velocity of light! The conviction grows upon one that these fantastic velocities are not real.

Alternative interpretations of the red-shift have been proposed, but have failed to provide an acceptable explanation. No one has taken account of the fact that a list of the available determinations of the velocity of light shows a steady decrease of velocity with time, following a linear law, $c = 299,900 - 3.855\ T$, for the epoch 1900[2] (see Table 1).

Table 1

T	c
1902.4	299,901 ± 84 km./sec.
1924.6	299,802 ± 30
1926.0	299,796 ± 4
1928.5	299,778 ± 20
1932.1	299,774 ± 11
1937.7	299,764 ± 15
1938.5	299,761 ± ?

This may be due to a "fatigue" phenomenon: there are in Nature no inexhaustible stores of energy, no examples of perpetual motion. There are tremendous stores of energy and the ensuing motion may continue without perceptible alteration for periods almost beyond reckoning, but neither lasts indefinitely. The energy of a photon is not considerable and an explanation of the slowing-down may be sought in a decrease of frequency as the light journeys through space. It may be sought in the fact that the velocity of propagation of a vibration depends on the physical properties (gravitational, electrical, magnetic, atomic, thermal and probably others) of the space through which it is propagated, and that these properties are gradually altering. Whatever its explanation, the slowing-down is an observed fact.

河外星云光谱红移的解释

德布雷

编者按

美国著名天文学家埃德温·哈勃第一个指出，星系——那些在太空中由于恒星自身之间的引力作用而聚集在一起的星群——似乎也在以与光速相比相当可观的速度渐渐远离地球（或者说是银河系）。本文表明，对于那些相信仅仅随着时间的消逝光速就会持续减少的人们，新得到的观测事实并没有使他们感到惶恐不安。

哈勃在其红移课题[1]的最新研究中提到了河外星云光谱存在 +0.231 埃的红移量。这意味着该河外星云的退行速度大约为每秒 43,000 英里，这几乎是光速的 1/4！但是人们逐渐相信，如此巨大的速度并不是真实的。

人们已经提出若干种对红移的解释，但都没有达到令人满意的程度。因为这些解释中都没有考虑以下事实，即：一系列对光速的测量表明，光速随着时间流逝而持续减小，在 1900 年之后，其满足线性关系，$c=299,900-3.855T$ [2]（参见表 1）。

表 1

T	c
1902.4	299,901 ± 84 千米 / 秒
1924.6	299,802 ± 30
1926.0	299,796 ± 4
1928.5	299,778 ± 20
1932.1	299,774 ± 11
1937.7	299,764 ± 15
1938.5	299,761 ± ?

这可能是一种"疲劳"现象，即：自然界中存储的能量并不是无穷无尽的，也没有永恒运动的实例存在。尽管目前自然界中存在着巨大的能量，并且在我们无法想象的很长的时间内运动会不断持续，这段时间内并不会发生任何可以察觉的变化，但这些运动并不会无限地持续。尽管一个光子的能量微不足道，但根据光在空间的传播过程中频率的减小，或许可以找到光速减慢的原因。我们借助以下事实加以理解，即：光振动的传播速度取决于它所通过空间的物理属性（包括引力、电、磁、原子、热和其他可能的作用），而这些属性是在逐渐变化的。但无论哪一种解释是正确的，光速变慢都是不争的事实。

Besides this, a satisfactory interpretation of the red-shifts must conform to the following further observed facts:

(1) Strömberg, by measuring the aberration of light from nebulae of the Ursa Major I cluster, has shown that the velocity of the light from this cluster is the same as that of light from laboratory sources[3]. Light from all sources, near and far, reach therefore the eye with the same velocity, c.

(2) Planck's constant h is constant, for Adams and Humason[3] have shown that the relation $E\lambda=ch$ (1) holds good for sources of light near and far, by comparing a grating and a prism spectrogram of the emission spectrum of the nucleus of $N.G.C.$ 4151.

(3) The wave-length is constant during the light's journey: this assumption is accepted as correct when measuring radial velocities.

(4) The frequency n of a newly generated photon of energy E is the same for all sources of light near and far, since (1) may be written $E=hn$, and it is admitted that the energy of a photon generated by an atom of the same element under the same conditions is the same in all sources near and far. For example, the energy of the photon giving the K line of Ca^+ has the same energy whether generated in a remote nebula or on the Earth.

It follows from the above that light leaves a remote nebula with a velocity $c_0>c$, and a wave-length λ_0 given by the relation $c_0=n\lambda_0$ (2). During the light's journey, both c_0 and n decrease until, when the light reaches the Earth, they have become c and n' respectively, with $c=n'\lambda_0$ (3) and n' is less than n. Since $c_0>c$, from (2), $\lambda_0>\lambda$, the corresponding wave-length of light from laboratory sources, and $\lambda_0=\lambda+d\lambda$, which is the observed red-shift.

In Table 2, m_c is the luminosity of the fifth brightest nebula in each cluster (the clusters are so similar that this gives a precise measurement of distance) and $d\lambda/\lambda$ is the observed red-shift[1]. R is the distance in light years, from the relation $\log r =0.2\ m_c+4.803$; λ_0 is the initial wave-length of the K line of Ca^+, calculated from the red-shift, taking its Earth value as $\lambda=3933$ A.—it is the wave-length at both ends of the light's journey; n' is the frequency of the light from the nebula when it reaches the Earth, and c_0 is the initial velocity of the light. The nebulae are in order of increasing distances. The data relating to Ursa Major II are inconclusive: they have been derived from a single spectrogram of a single nebula only.

此外，一种令人满意的关于红移的解释还需要与以下几条进一步的观测事实相吻合：

（1）斯特伦贝里测量了大熊座 I 星团中星云的光行差，结果表明来自该星团的光速与实验室光速相同 [3]。因此，可以认为远近不同的所有光源发出的光到达人眼时的速度是一样的，均为 c。

（2）亚当斯和赫马森 [3] 分别用光栅和棱镜测量了 N.G.C.4151 核心区域的光谱，对比结果表明，无论光源远近，关系式 $E\lambda=ch$（1）都可以很好地满足。这说明普朗克常数 h 确实是一个常数。

（3）在测量视向速度时，我们认为此假设是正确的，即：光在传播过程中波长保持恒定。

（4）由于（1）式也可以写为 $E=hn$，那么无论光源远近，新产生的能量为 E 的光子的频率 n 都是相同的。这相当于承认，无论远近，同种元素的原子在相同条件下产生的光子能量都是相同的。例如，Ca^+ 的 K 线对应的光子，无论产生于地球还是遥远的星云中，能量都是一样的。

根据上述可以得出以下推论：光离开遥远星云时的速度 $c_0>c$，其波长 λ_0 可以由关系式 $c_0=n\lambda_0$（2）得到。光在传播的过程中，光速 c_0 和频率 n 都不断减小，直至到达地球，此时二者分别变为 c 和 n'，但是它们仍然满足关系 $c=n'\lambda_0$（3），其中 $n'<n$。由于 $c_0>c$，根据（2）式可得 $\lambda_0>\lambda$，其中，λ 为实验室光源的波长。该不等式也可以写为 $\lambda_0=\lambda+d\lambda$，这就是我们观测到的红移现象。

在表 2 中，m_c 表示每个星团中亮度排名第五的星云的光度（这些星团非常相似，所以可以用于精确的距离测量），$d\lambda/\lambda$ 表示观测到的红移 [1]。R 表示以光年为单位的距离，由下面的关系式可确定 R：$\log r = 0.2\, m_c+4.803$。λ_0 是 Ca^+ 的 K 线的初始波长，可以由观测到的红移量计算得到，地球上的光源发出的相应谱线的波长取为 $\lambda=3,933$ 埃，我们认为光发出时和被接收到时波长都是该值。n' 表示来自星云的光到达地球时的频率，而 c_0 表示光的初始速度。表 2 中的星云按距离由近及远排列。大熊座 II 的数据是由单个星云的单一光谱推出来的，所以是不确定的。

Table 2

Cluster	m_c	$d\lambda/\lambda$	r light-years	λ_0 of K line of Ca^+	n'	c_0
—	—	—	—	(λ=3,933 A.)	(n=762.2×10^{12})	(c=299,774 km./sec.)
Virgo	10.49	0.0041A.	8×10^6	3,949 A.	759.1×10^{12}	300,990
Pegasus	12.88	0.0127	24	3,983	752.6	303,585
Perseus	13.48	0.0174	31.6	4,001	749.1	305,030
Coma	14.23	0.0245	44.6	4,029	744.0	307,090
U. Ma. I	16.12	0.0517	106.4	4,137	724.6	315,320
Leo	16.33	0.0653	117	4,190	715.5	319,360
Cor. Bor.	16.54	0.0707	129	4,211	711.9	320,960
(U. Ma. II	17.73	0.1403	223.4	4,485	668.4	341,850)
Boötes	17.89	0.1307	210.4	4,447	674.1	338,950

The slowing down of the frequency and of the velocity both follow linear laws: $n'(\times 10^{12})=$ 762.2$-$0.4T; and c_0(Km./sec.)=299,774$-$173T, where T is in millions of years.

Accordingly, 240 millions years ago, light travelled with a velocity approximately 13 percent greater than now, and the wave-length of the K line of Ca^+ was 4,447 A.

Should the above be confirmed, our measurements of stellar radial velocities will require a correction depending on the distance.

(**144**, 285; 1939)

M. E. J. Gheury de Bray: First Avenue House, High Holborn, London, W. C. 1, June 29.

References:

1. Hubble, "The Observational Approach to Cosmology".

2. *Nature*, **120**, 602 (1927). A later list of observations appears in *Isis*, **25** (2), No. 70 (Sept. 1927).

3. Reports Mount Wilson Obs., 1935–1936.

表 2

星云	m_c	$d\lambda/\lambda$	r 光年	λ_0 为 Ca^+ 的 K 线的初始波长	n'	c_0
—	—	—	—	(λ=3,933 埃)	(n=762.2×10¹²)	(c=299,774 千米/秒)
室女座	10.49	0.0041 埃	8×10⁶	3,949 埃	759.1×10¹²	300,990
飞马座	12.88	0.0127	24	3,983	752.6	303,585
英仙座	13.48	0.0174	31.6	4,001	749.1	305,030
后发座	14.23	0.0245	44.6	4,029	744.0	307,090
大熊座 I	16.12	0.0517	106.4	4,137	724.6	315,320
狮子座	16.33	0.0653	117	4,190	715.5	319,360
北冕座	16.54	0.0707	129	4,211	711.9	320,960
(大熊座 II	17.73	0.1403	223.4	4,485	668.4	341,850)
牧夫座	17.89	0.1307	210.4	4,447	674.1	338,950

由表可知，频率和速度的减小都遵循以下的线性规律：$n'(\times 10^{12})$=762.2−0.4T；c_0（千米/秒）=299,774−173T，其中 T 的单位为百万年。

因此，2.4 亿年前，光传播的速度比现在的值大约高 13%，那时 Ca^+ 的 K 线的波长为 4,447 埃。

如果以上理论得到证实的话，那么我们测量的恒星视向速度都需要根据距离的大小予以修正。

（金世超 翻译；何香涛 审稿）

Cosmic Ray Ionization Bursts

H. Carmichael and C. N. Chou

Editor's Note

Since the beginning of the twentieth century, the study of cosmic rays had preoccupied a great many physicists for a number of reasons. First, they appeared to consist of fast-moving particles whose identity was for a long time unknown. The energy of these particles was much higher than could be created artificially in the laboratory, and they seemed to offer clues to the nature of phenomena and matter at great distances in the Universe. This paper is based on observations carried out under 30 metres of London clay on the disused part of a platform in Holborn Station on London's Underground railway network. The object of the experiment was to measure the numbers of showers of cosmic-ray particles created within electrically sensitive ionization chambers. Curve C represents the results of an experiment at the surface of the Earth, A an experiment running for 150 hours at the Underground station itself and B an experiment lasting 350 hours. The bends in the experimental curves A and C are taken to indicate a change in the mechanism of the production of showers of cosmic-ray particles.

COSMIC ray ionization bursts produced by showers of ten or more particles in a small ionization chamber (volume 1 litre) have been recorded at sea-level in Cambridge and, thanks to the hospitality of Prof. P. M. S. Blackett and Dr. H. J. J. Braddick, under 30 m. of clay in London. The data discussed here, curves A (150 hours) and B (350 hours), are from runs with no lead or other dense shower-producing material above the chamber (the wall of the chamber was of duralumin, 1.2 cm. thick, so as to avoid as much as possible showers produced by cascade multiplication in the chamber itself). Curve C (500 hours) is the result of similar observations at sea-level with a large ionization chamber (volume 175 litres, wall-thickness 0.3 cm. of steel), most of which were published by one of us[1] in 1936, when the method of recording was also described. The curves show the number of showers per hour in which N or more particles intersected the ionization chamber; the number of shower particles N was estimated on the basis of a specific ionization in normal argon of 90 ion-pairs per cm.

The ionization bursts obtained at sea-level with the big ionization chamber (curve C) involve much larger numbers of shower particles than those obtained with the small chamber (curve A), and also each curve has a remarkable change of slope at a rate of occurrence about 0.16 per hour. The curves, however, can be superposed fairly closely if the size of the showers in the small chamber is multiplied by 10. We deduce from this approximate proportionality of the *size* of these showers (as distinct from their rate of occurrence) to the areas of the thin-walled chambers used to observe them that they are mostly *extensive showers*, originating in the atmosphere, of the same type as those found by

宇宙射线的"电离暴"

卡迈克尔，周长宁

编者按

从 20 世纪初开始，由于各种原因，很多物理学家都对宇宙射线的研究给予了关注。首先，它们似乎是由快速运动的粒子组成，但究竟是什么粒子，这在很长一段时间里都是未知的。这些粒子的能量大大地超过了在实验室里人工所能产生出来的能量，并且它们似乎能够为宇宙中远距离的现象和物质性质的研究提供线索。本论文是基于伦敦地面以下 30 米处的观察结果，该地是伦敦地铁网络霍尔本车站一个废弃不用的站台。实验的目的是采用对电荷灵敏的电离室测量宇宙射线粒子簇射的数目。C 曲线代表地球表面的实验结果，A 曲线代表一个在地下车站为时 150 个小时的实验结果，B 曲线代表为时 350 小时的实验。A 和 C 实验结果曲线的弯曲则用来显示宇宙射线粒子簇射产生机制的变化。

把一个小电离室（容量为 1 升）放在剑桥的海平面上，对其中 10 个或更多粒子的簇射产生的宇宙射线电离暴进行了记录，并且多亏了布莱克特教授和布拉迪克博士的热心帮助，我们在伦敦地面以下 30 米的地方也完成了同样的实验。在本文要讨论的数据中，A 曲线（150 小时）和 B 曲线（350 小时）是在小电离室上部没有覆盖铅或者其他密度较大的引发簇射的物质时得到的（电离室内壁由硬铝制造，厚 1.2 厘米，以尽可能避免在电离室内由连续倍增效应产生的簇射）。C 曲线（500 小时）是我们在海平面上用大电离室（容量为 175 升，壁厚 0.3 厘米，钢制）重复类似实验得到的结果，我们中的一人 [1] 已于 1936 年发表了大部分数据，当时他也描述了记录的方法。从这些曲线中可以得到每小时的簇射数量，即有 N 个或是更多的粒子横穿电离室；簇射粒子数 N 是在每厘米 90 个离子对的普通氩气的特定离子化过程中得到的。

在海平面上的大电离室观察到的离子爆发过程（C 曲线）所产生的簇射粒子数量要比在小电离室里（A 曲线）看到的数量多很多，而这两条曲线的斜率都在每小时观测到的簇射线为 0.16 处出现明显变化。如果将小电离室里的簇射量大小乘以 10，那么 A 曲线和 C 曲线会很好地重叠在一起。我们根据簇射量（这一点可以从发生率中很明显地看到）与所用薄壁电离室的横截面面积大致成正比这一现象可以推断出，所发生的簇射多半是**广延簇射**，它们产生于空气中并且与俄歇及其同事 [2] 用

695

Auger and his co-workers[2] with counters. We should not expect to find exactly the ratio of the areas (approximately 1:30) because narrow showers or condensations of rays of cross-section smaller than the area of the large chamber tend to increase disproportionately the bursts in the small chamber.

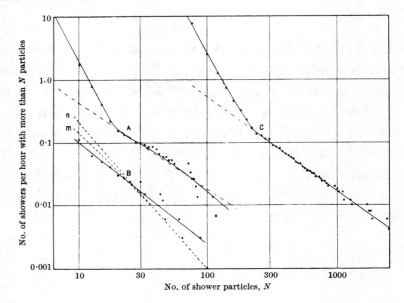

The bursts which are found underground (curve B) must be produced by the penetrating component of the cosmic rays. We have calculated the distribution curve to be expected in the tube station for cascade showers produced by electrons "knocked on" by mesons using the data given in the paper by Bhabha[4] in which, however, the meson was assumed to have spin $\frac{1}{2}$. We adopted, following Euler and Heisenberg[3], an exponent 1.87 for the integral energy distribution of the mesons originating in the atmosphere. The calculation shows (curve m) that the showers resulting from this process alone are nearly sufficient to account for the bursts recorded underground, if we assume that the cross-sectional area of the showers underground is not much greater than the area of the chamber (actually more of the larger bursts are found than are given by this calculation, but the theoretical implications of this discrepancy will be discussed later).

At sea-level a similar calculation (curve n) gives much fewer bursts than are observed even if we suppose that the showers are so narrow that all the shower particles in any one burst can intersect the small chamber: but we already know that most of the showers observed at sea-level are at least wider than the large chamber. We therefore conclude that a negligible number of the extensive showers observed at sea-level is produced by electrons knocked-on by mesons. It would seem also that an insufficient number of such showers can be produced by the spontaneous decay of the meson, a process which might be invoked to explain the steeper parts of the sea-level curves.

计数器测量到的簇射属于同一类型。我们不能指望由此得到精确的面积之比（大约是 1:30），因为当窄簇射或射线凝聚效应的横截面比大电离室的面积小时更容易引起非均匀的离子爆发。

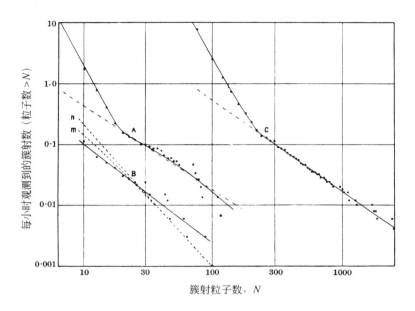

在地面以下测量到的爆发（B 曲线）肯定是由穿越了的宇宙射线产生的。利用霍米·巴巴[4] 在其论文里给出的数据，假设介子的自旋为 $\frac{1}{2}$，我们已经计算出由电子被介子撞击而产生的级联簇射在地铁站里的预期曲线分布。根据欧拉和海森堡[3] 的方法，我们认为大气中介子累积能量分布曲线的指数为 1.87。如果我们假设在地面以下的实验中，簇射区域的横截面不比电离室大多少，那么从计算结果中可以看到（m 曲线）：仅由介子和电子的碰撞过程所产生的簇射就足以解释在地面以下记录的爆发了（实际上测量到的大型爆发数值要多于计算值，对这种差异的理论解释将在以后讨论）。

在海平面上用上述方法得到的计算值（n 曲线）比观察到爆发的数值低很多，即使我们假设簇射范围非常窄，以至于每次爆发中的所有簇射粒子都能够横穿小电离室，但事实上我们已经知道，在海平面上所观察到的大部分簇射范围至少都比大电离室的范围大。因此，我们得出结论：在海平面上所观察到的少量爆发簇射是由介子撞击电子产生的。这种簇射的量不够大，可能是由介子的自发衰退造成的，这也许可以作为由海平面上的观测数据得到的 n 曲线有一个斜率较大的部分的原因。

We think, therefore, that nearly all the showers which produce bursts at sea-level in our thin-walled ionization chambers originate very high in the atmosphere, and that the dual nature of the distribution curve at sea-level (as indicated by the change of slope) is due, not to the existence of showers of two kinds, but to the fact (already noted by Auger[2]) that each extensive shower has a core of closely spaced particles surrounded by a relatively wide fringe of much more thinly spaced particles able to produce bursts of small size.

(144, 325-326; 1939)

Hugh Carmichael: St. John's College, Cambridge.

Chang-Ning Chou: Cavendish Laboratory, Cambridge.

References:

1. Carmichael, *Proc. Roy. Soc.*, A, **154**, 223 (1936).

2. Auger, Maze, Ehrenfest and Freon, *J. Phys. et Rad.*, **10**, 39(1939).

3. Euler and Heisenberg, *Er. exak. Naturwiss.*, **17**, 1 (1938).

4. Bhabha, *Proc. Roy. Soc.*, A, **164**, 257 (1938).

因此，我们认为，几乎所有能在位于海平面上的薄壁电离室内产生爆发的簇射都来自于大气层中非常高的地方，而海平面上分布曲线所表现出的双重特性（由斜率的变化可以看出）并不是由于存在两类簇射，而是由于以下原因（这一点俄歇[2]也注意到了），即每次爆发簇射都有一个由密排粒子组成的核心，其周围是由排列非常松散的粒子组成的广大边界地区，而在这些边界地区就会产生规模较小的爆发。

（李忠伟 翻译；马宇蒨 审稿）

Social Biology and Population Improvement

F. A. E. Crew *et al.*

Editor's Note

This document is remarkable in many ways, not least the auspicious timing. It is a response from many leading biologists to a question posed in the United States of how the world's population might be improved genetically. In the 1930s this question, seemingly anachronistic today, was generally viewed through a Darwinian lens, and the response in the US and Nazi Germany had tended to favour eugenics, partly through enforced sterilizations. That solution might have been expected to find favour with some of these signatories, such as Julian Huxley. But in fact the note is remarkably progressive, placing emphasis on the need for equality of opportunity before comparisons can be made, and challenging the notion that dominant classes are genetically superior.

IN response to a request from Science Service, of Washington, D.C., for a reply to the question "How could the world's population be improved most effectively genetically?", addressed to a number of scientific workers, the subjoined statement was prepared, and signed by those whose names appear at the end.

The question "How could the world's population be improved most effectively genetically?" raises far broader problems than the purely biological ones, problems which the biologist unavoidably encounters as soon as he tries to get the principles of his own special field put into practice. For the effective genetic improvement of mankind is dependent upon major changes in social conditions, and correlative changes in human attitudes. In the first place, there can be no valid basis for estimating and comparing the intrinsic worth of different individuals, without economic and social conditions which provide approximately equal opportunities for all members of society instead of stratifying them from birth into classes with widely different privileges.

The second major hindrance to genetic improvement lies in the economic and political conditions which foster antagonism between different peoples, nations and "races". The removal of race prejudices and of the unscientific doctrine that good or bad genes are the monopoly of particular peoples or of persons with features of a given kind will not be possible, however, before the conditions which make for war and economic exploitation have been eliminated. This requires some effective sort of federation of the whole world, based on the common interests of all its peoples.

Thirdly, it cannot be expected that the raising of children will be influenced actively by considerations of the worth of future generations unless parents in general have a very

社会生物学与人种改良

克鲁等

编者按

这篇文章从许多方面来说都是值得注意的，特别是本文发表的良好时机。它是许多杰出的生物学家对美国提出的关于世界人种的遗传改良问题的回应。尽管如今看来这个问题似乎已经过时，但是在 20 世纪 30 年代，科学家们从达尔文理论的视角出发对这个问题进行了综合的考虑，美国和纳粹德国的倾向于支持部分地通过强制性绝育来实现优生。原先预期这一解决方案可能会得到本文的部分签署者的支持，比如朱利安·赫胥黎，然而事实并非如此。实际上这篇短文是非常进步的，它强调了在作出比较之前首先需要均等的机会，并且质疑了统治阶层具有优等遗传基因的观点。

"怎样可以使世界人种得到最有效的遗传改良？"，华盛顿特区科学服务社希望科学工作者能够就这一问题给予回应，于是我们起草了这份补充声明，并在文章末尾联合署名。

与单纯的生物学问题相比，"怎样可以使世界人种得到最有效的遗传改良？"这一问题会引出更加宽泛的难题，一旦生物学家试图将自己专业领域的法则付诸实践，他就不得不面对这些问题。人类有效的遗传改良依赖于社会条件的重大变化，以及在人类态度方面与此相关的变化。首先，如果经济和社会条件不能为所有的社会成员提供大致均等的机会来取代社会成员从出生时就被划分为权力相差非常大的不同阶级，那就不存在可以用于估计和比较不同个体的内在价值的有效依据。

遗传改良的第二个主要障碍在于经济和政治条件，它催生了不同国家、不同民族和不同"种族"间的对立。然而，在消除导致战争和经济剥削的条件之前，要消除种族偏见以及认为优良或劣质基因专属于某一民族或具有特定特征的人这种不科学的信条是不可能的。这需要在全世界人民的共同利益的基础上，建立全世界的某种有效的联合。

第三，通常来说，除非父母有可观的经济保障，而且在生育和抚养每个孩子的过程中都能为他们提供充分的经济、医疗、教育和其他方面的帮助，从而保证拥有

considerable economic security and unless they are extended such adequate economic, medical, educational and other aids in the bearing and rearing of each additional child that the having of more children does not overburden either of them. As the woman is more especially affected by childbearing and rearing, she must be given special protection to ensure that her reproductive duties do not interfere too greatly with her opportunities to participate in the life and work of the community at large. These objects cannot be achieved unless there is an organization of production primarily for the benefit of consumer and worker, unless the conditions of employment are adapted to the needs of parents and especially of mothers, and unless dwellings, towns and community services generally are reshaped with the good of children as one of their main objectives.

A fourth prerequisite for effective genetic improvement is the legalization, the universal dissemination, and the further development through scientific investigation, of ever more efficacious means of birth control, both negative and positive, that can be put into effect at all stages of the reproductive process—as by voluntary temporary or permanent sterilization, contraception, abortion (as a third line of defence), control of fertility and of the sexual cycle, artificial insemination, etc. Along with all this the development of social consciousness and responsibility in regard to the production of children is required, and this cannot be expected to be operative unless the above-mentioned economic and social conditions for its fulfilment are present, and unless the superstitious attitude towards sex and reproduction now prevalent has been replaced by a scientific and social attitude. This will result in its being regarded as an honour and a privilege, if not a duty, for a mother, married or unmarried, or for a couple, to have the best children possible, both in respect of their upbringing and of their genetic endowment, even where the latter would mean an artificial—though always voluntary—control over the process of parenthood.

Before people in general, or the State which is supposed to represent them, can be relied upon to adopt rational policies for the guidance of their reproduction, there will have to be, fifthly, a far wider spread of knowledge of biological principles and of recognition of the truth that both environment and heredity constitute dominating and inescapable complementary factors in human wellbeing, but factors both of which are under the potential control of man and admit of unlimited but interdependent progress. Betterment of environmental conditions enhances the opportunities for genetic betterment in the ways above indicated. But it must also be understood that the effect of the bettered environment is not a direct one on the germ cells and that the Lamarckian doctrine is fallacious, according to which the children of parents who have had better opportunities for physical and mental development inherit these improvements biologically, and according to which, in consequence, the dominant classes and peoples would have become genetically superior to the underprivileged ones. The intrinsic (genetic) characteristics of any generation can be better than those of the preceding generation only as a result of some kind of *selection*, that is, by those persons of the preceding generation who had a better genetic equipment having produced more offspring, on the whole, than the rest, either through conscious choice, or as an automatic result of the way in which they lived. Under modern civilized conditions such selection is far less likely to be automatic than under primitive conditions,

更多的孩子不会成为他们过重的负担，否则考虑到抚养后代的代价，就不要指望生养小孩能带来积极主动的影响。因为女性会更多地受到分娩和养育孩子的影响，所以必须给予特别的保护以确保她的生育责任不会过分地干扰其参与一般的社会生活和工作的机会。除非有生产机构来保证消费者和工人的利益，工作条件适合父母尤其是母亲的需要，而且住宅、城镇及社区服务都基本上被改造成把对孩子有益作为它们的主要目标之一，这些目标才有可能实现。

有效遗传改良的第四个必要条件就是曾经奏效的生育控制手段的合法化、广泛传播以及通过科学研究使其进一步发展，不论消极的还是积极的，这些措施都能在生育过程的所有阶段实施——如自愿进行的暂时性或永久性绝育、避孕、流产（作为第三道防线）、控制生育力和生殖周期、人工授精等。与此同时，还需要与生育孩子相关的社会意识和社会责任的发展，并且只有上述所需的经济和社会条件都具备，以及现在盛行的关于性别和生育的迷信态度都已被科学的社会态度所取代的时候，这一发展才可能是切实有效的。对一位无论是已婚还是未婚的母亲或者一对夫妻而言，这将使得即便不会视生育为一项责任，也会视其为使拥有最好的孩子成为可能的一项荣誉和权利，这包括对他们的养育和遗传赋予，后者甚至意味着一种人为的——虽然通常是自愿的——对亲子关系的控制。

第五，在依靠广大民众或者代表他们的国家采取合理的政策来指导人们的生育之前，必须要广泛普及有关生物学原理的知识，广泛普及环境和遗传是共同构成人类福祉的主要的、不可或缺的互补因素的认识，但这两个因素都受到人类潜能的控制并且允许无限的但相互依存的进步。环境条件的改善能以上面提到的方式增加遗传改良的机会。但是也必须明白改善的环境并非直接影响生殖细胞，必须明白拉马克学说是错误的，根据该学说，拥有更好的身体和智力发育机会的父母生育的孩子能遗传这些生物学改良，而且按照这个学说可以得出，处于统治阶层的人比下层穷苦的人具有遗传上的优越性。仅仅作为某种**选择**的结果，任何一代的内在（遗传）特征就会比上一代的更好，即，总体而言，上一代中具有较好遗传资质的人可以通过有意识的选择或者作为其生活方式的无意识的结果从而产生比其他人更多的后代。与原始条件下相比，现代文明条件下的这种选择已经远不可能是无意识的了，因此要求对选择进行某些有意识的指导。然而，要想使这种选择成为可能，人们必

hence some kind of conscious guidance of selection is called for. To make this possible, however, the population must first appreciate the force of the above principles, and the social value which a wisely guided selection would have.

Sixthly, conscious selection requires, in addition, an agreed direction or directions for selection to take, and these directions cannot be social ones, that is, for the good of mankind at large, unless social motives predominate in society. This in turn implies its socialized organization. The most important genetic objectives, from a social point of view, are the improvement of those genetic characteristics which make (*a*) for health, (*b*) for the complex called intelligence, and (*c*) for those temperamental qualities which favour fellow-feeling and social behaviour rather than those (today most esteemed by many) which make for personal "success", as success is usually understood at present.

A more widespread understanding of biological principles will bring with it the realization that much more than the prevention of genetic deterioration is to be sought for, and that the raising of the level of the average of the population nearly to that of the highest now existing in isolated individuals, in regard to physical wellbeing, intelligence and temperamental qualities, is an achievement that would—so far as purely genetic considerations are concerned—be physically possible within a comparatively small number of generations. Thus everyone might look upon "genius", combined of course with stability, as his birthright. As the course of evolution shows, this would represent no final stage at all, but only an earnest of still further progress in the future.

The effectiveness of such progress, however, would demand increasingly extensive and intensive research in human genetics and in the numerous fields of investigation correlated therewith. This would involve the co-operation of specialists in various branches of medicine, psychology, chemistry and, not least, the social sciences, with the improvement of the inner constitution of man himself as their central theme. The organization of the human body is marvellously intricate, and the study of its genetics is beset with special difficulties which require the prosecution of research in this field to be on a much vaster scale, as well as more exact and analytical, than hitherto contemplated. This can, however, come about when men's minds are turned from war and hate and the struggle for the elementary means of subsistence to larger aims, pursued in common.

The day when economic reconstruction will reach the stage where such human forces will be released is not yet, but it is the task of this generation to prepare for it, and all steps along the way will represent a gain, not only for the possibilities of the ultimate genetic improvement of man, to a degree seldom dreamed of hitherto, but at the same time, more directly, for human mastery over those more immediate evils which are so threatening our modern civilization.

须首先意识到上述法则的重要性以及一种具有明智的指导性的选择所拥有的社会价值。

第六，有意识的选择还要求一个一致的方向或者多个可供选择的方向，并且这些方向不能是社会方面的，即，为了尽可能对人类有益，除非社会动机成为社会的主流。反过来看，这也暗示着它的社会化组织。从社会观点来看，最重要的遗传目标是使有助于（a）健康、（b）智力和（c）建立促成同情心和社会行为的性情素质的那些遗传特征得到改良，而非那些（如今被许多人最为看重的）有助于个人"成功"的素质，正如当前大家通常所理解的成功一样。

对生物学原理更广泛的理解将会使人们认识到有更多方面比预防遗传退化更值得被追求，另外就是关于身体健康程度、智力和性情素质的人种平均水平提高至接近现存的单独个体的最高水平，仅从遗传因素考虑，这在数量相对少的一代中是可能达到的。因而，当然与稳定性相结合，每个人都可以把"天赋"看作自己生来就有的权利。正如进化过程所显示的，这根本不代表最终阶段，而只是预示着将来还会进一步发展。

然而，这种进展的有效性要求对人类遗传学和其他与之相关的多个领域进行更加广泛和深入的研究。这将需要医学、心理学、化学和社会科学等多个学科的专家们以改善人类自身的内在构成作为中心主题而进行合作。人体组织的精细程度令人称奇，对其遗传特征的研究一直被特殊的困难所困扰，这些困难要求该领域的研究具有比迄今所预期的更大的规模以及更强的准确性和可分析性。然而，当人类的思想从战争、仇恨和为基本的生存方式而斗争转向共同追求更大目标的时候，它就能实现。

经济重建达到能够释放人类力量的阶段的那一天尚未来临，但是我们这一代人要随时为这一天做好准备并以此为己任。在沿着这条路奋进的途中，我们所经历的每一步都代表着收获，这种收获不仅是迄今为止还很难想象的人类最终遗传改良的可能性，而且同时，更直接的是，使人类能够更好地制服那些随时出现的威胁我们现代文明的邪恶力量。

F. A. E. Crew

C. D. Darlington

J. B. S. Haldane

S. C. Harland

L. T. Hogben

J. S. Huxley

H. J. Muller

J. Needham

G. P. Child

P. R. David

G. Dahlberg

Th. Dobzhansky

R. A. Emerson

C. Gordon

J. Hammond

C. L. Huskins

P. C. Koller

W. Landauer

H. H. Plough

B. Price

J. Schultz

A. G. Steinberg

C. H. Waddington

(**144**, 521-522; 1939)

克鲁　　　　蔡尔德　　　　科勒
达林顿　　　戴维　　　　　兰道尔
霍尔丹　　　达尔伯格　　　普劳
哈兰德　　　多布赞斯基　　普赖斯
霍格本　　　爱默生　　　　舒尔茨
赫胥黎　　　戈登　　　　　斯坦伯格
马勒　　　　哈蒙德　　　　沃丁顿
尼达姆　　　赫斯金斯

（刘皓芳 翻译；刘京国 审稿）

707

Myosine and Adenosinetriphosphatase

W. A. Engelhardt and M. N. Ljubimowa

Editor's Note

Here biochemist Wladimir Engelhardt and his wife and former postgraduate student Militza Ljubimowa, both from Moscow's Academy of Sciences, show that myosine (now myosin), one of the contractile proteins of muscle, catalyses the breakdown of adenosinetriphosphate (ATP), and that ATP provides the energy for muscular contraction. Myosine, they suggest, splits ATP into adenosinediphosphate (ADP) and free phosphate ions, liberating energy along the way that can be used in muscle action. This led to the concept of ATP as a universal biochemical energy source that can be used by cells for many different functions. The molecule's breakdown liberates energy which enzymes harness to drive other chemical reactions.

ORDINARY aqueous or potassium chloride extracts of muscle exhibit but a slight capacity to mineralize adenosinetriphosphate. Even this slight liberation of phosphate is mainly due, not to direct hydrolysis of adenosinetriphosphate, but to a process of secondary, indirect mineralization, accompanying the transfer of phosphate from the adenylic system to creatine, the corresponding enzymes (for which the name "phosphopherases" is suggested) being readily soluble.

In contrast to this lack of adenosinetriphosphatase in the soluble fraction, a high adenosinetriphosphatase activity is associated with the water-insoluble proteins of muscle. This enzymatic activity is easily brought into solution by all the buffer and concentrated salt solutions usually employed for the extraction of myosine. On precipitation of myosine from such extracts, the adenosinetriphosphatase activity is always found in the myosine fraction, whichever mode of precipitation be used: dialysis, dilution, cautious acidification, salting out. On repeated reprecipitations of myosine, the activity per mgm. nitrogen attains a fairly constant level, unless denaturation of myosine takes place. Under the conditions of our experiments (optimal conditions have not been determined) the activity of myosine preparations ranged in different experiments from 350 to 600 microgram phosphorus liberated per mgm. nitrogen in 5 min. at 37°. Expressed as

$$Q_p \left(= \frac{\mu\text{gm. P}/31 \times 22.4}{\text{mgm. N} \times 6.25 \times \text{hour}} \right),$$

this gives values of 500-850.

Acidification to pH below 4, which is known to bring about the denaturation of myosine[1], rapidly destroys the adenosinetriphosphatase activity. Most remarkable is the extreme thermolability of the adenosinetriphosphatase of muscle: the enzymatic activity shown

肌球蛋白与三磷酸腺苷酶

恩格尔哈特，卢比莫娃

编者按

在这篇文章中，生物化学家弗拉基米尔·恩格尔哈特和他的妻子米丽莎·卢比莫娃（卢比莫娃之前是恩格尔哈特的研究生，他们都来自莫斯科科学院）指出，肌肉中一种可以收缩的蛋白——肌球蛋白（myosine，现在的拼法是myosin）催化了三磷酸腺苷（ATP）的分解，而ATP提供了肌肉收缩所需的能量。他们认为肌球蛋白将ATP分解为二磷酸腺苷（ADP）和自由的磷酸根阴离子，这一过程中释放的能量可被用于肌肉的运动。这引出了这样一种观点，即：ATP作为一种生化能源可以被细胞广泛地用在许多功能的实现中。这种分子断裂释放出来的能量可以被酶利用以驱动其他的化学反应。

通常肌肉中的水或氯化钾提取物仅具有微弱的矿化三磷酸腺苷的能力。即便是这种磷酸盐轻微的析出也不是主要由三磷酸腺苷（ATP）的直接水解引起的，而是由一个间接的矿化作用过程造成。这个过程通常伴随着磷酸盐从腺苷酸系统到肌氨酸的转移，并且会引起相应的酶（有人建议命名为"磷酸水解酶"）的可溶性增强。

三磷酸腺苷酶在肌肉可溶性组分中含量很少，而相比之下，很高的三磷酸腺苷酶活性却与肌肉中的水不溶性蛋白质相结合。所有用来提取肌球蛋白的缓冲液及高浓度盐溶液，都可以很容易地使这种酶的活性溶于其中。这使得人们在从肌肉抽提物中分离肌球蛋白时，无论是采用透析、稀释、谨慎酸化还是盐析的方法，往往都可以在分离得到的肌球蛋白组分中检测到三磷酸腺苷酶的活性。除非肌球蛋白在纯化过程中发生变性，否则即使反复析出肌球蛋白，以每毫克含氮量表示的比活性几乎都维持在一个恒定水平上。在我们的实验中（尚未确定最佳反应条件），37℃下5分钟内肌球蛋白抽提物的三磷酸腺苷酶活性在不同的实验中介于 350~600 微克磷 / 毫克氮。用下式表示得到的结果在 500~850 之间：

$$酶比活力 = \frac{每微克磷含量 \div 31 \times 22.4}{每毫克样品含氮量 \times 6.25 \times 小时}$$

人们已经知道，把溶液酸化到 pH 值在 4 以下会引起肌球蛋白的变性 [1]，也会迅速地破坏三磷酸腺苷酶的活性。然而最值得注意的是肌肉中的三磷酸腺苷酶的极

by myosine solutions is completely lost after 10 min. exposure to 37°. This corresponds with the well-known thermolability of myosine[2]. In respect of its high thermolability adenosinetriphosphatase resembles the protein of the yellow enzyme, which when separated from its prosthetic group is also rapidly inactivated at 38° (Theorell[3]). Evidently in the intact tissue of the warm-blooded animal (all experiments were performed on rabbit muscles), some conditions must exist which stabilize the myosine against the action of temperature. A marked stabilizing effect on the adenosinetriphosphatase activity seems to be produced by the adenylic nucleotide itself. As can be seen from the accompanying graph, in the presence of adenosinetriphosphate the liberation of phosphate proceeds at 37° over a considerable period (Curves I, Ia and Ib), whereas the same myosine solution warmed alone to 37° for 10-15 min. shows on subsequent addition of adenosinetriphosphate an insignificant or no mineralization whatever.

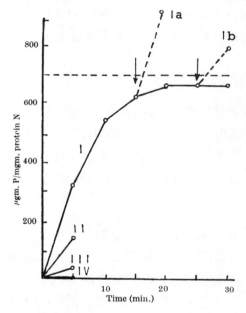

Crude buffer extracts accomplish a quantitative hydrolysis of the labile phosphate groups of adenosinetriphosphate; myosine, reprecipitated three times, liberates but 50 percent of the theoretical amount of phosphorus (see figure). It acts as true adenosine-*tri*-phosphatase and yields adenosinediphosphate, which is not further dephosphorylated and has been isolated in substance. This may serve as a convenient way of preparing adenosinediphosphate, instead of using crayfish muscle[4]. The adenosinediphosphatase is thus associated with the more soluble proteins, occupying an intermediate position between adenosinetriphosphatase and the most readily soluble phosphopherases.

Under no conditions tested could we obtain a separation of adenosinetriphosphatase from myosine. Either the activity was found in the myosine precipitate or else it was absent from the precipitates and from the remaining solution. This disappearance of the enzymatic activity we regard as the result of the start of denaturation of the very unstable myosine.

端不耐热性：肌球蛋白溶液在 37℃ 下放置 10 分钟，其中的酶的活性就会被完全破坏。这与公认的肌球蛋白的不耐热性是一致的 [2]。三磷酸腺苷酶的这种不耐热性与黄酶的蛋白质类似，黄酶与其辅基分离后在 38℃ 下也会很快失活（特奥雷尔 [3]）。显然，在温血动物（所有实验均在兔肌肉中进行）的完整组织中必定存在某种条件可以使肌球蛋白在温度作用下保持稳定。似乎腺苷酸自身就可以显著地使三磷酸腺苷酶活性保持稳定。从附图中可以看出，ATP 存在的情况下，在 37℃ 下相当长的时间内都有磷酸盐的生成（曲线 I、Ia 及 Ib），但单独加热同样的肌球蛋白溶液，使其在 37℃ 保持 10~15 分钟，再加入 ATP，无论如何其作用都是微乎其微的，或者根本就不存在矿化作用。

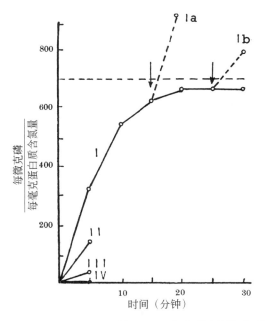

缓冲液原始提取物可以实现不稳定的 ATP 磷酸基团的定量水解。经过 3 次反复沉淀后，肌球蛋白析出的磷只有理论量的一半（见图）。它以纯的三磷酸腺苷形式存在并又生成二磷酸腺苷（ADP）。ADP 没有进一步脱去磷酸，并已从本体中分离出来。这也为制备 ADP 提供了一条新的途径，替代了使用小龙虾肌肉组织的方法 [4]。这也表明二磷酸腺苷酶结合可溶性更高的蛋白质，其溶解性介于三磷酸腺苷酶和那些极易溶解的磷酸水解酶之间。

在我们所尝试过的实验条件中，没有一种可以将三磷酸腺苷酶从肌球蛋白中分离出来。这种酶活性要么出现在肌球蛋白沉淀中，要么在沉淀及剩余溶液中都不出现。我们认为这种酶活性的消失可能是由于非常不稳定的肌球蛋白发生了变性。

We are led to conclude that the adenosinetriphosphatase activity is to be ascribed to myosine or, at least, to a protein very closely related to and at present not distinguishable from myosine. Thus the mineralization of adenosinetriphosphate, often regarded as the primary exothermic reaction in muscle contraction, proceeds under the influence and with the direct participation of the protein considered to form the main basis of the contractile mechanism of the muscle fibre.

(**144**, 668-669; 1939)

W. A. Engelhardt and M. N. Ljubimowa: Institute of Biochemistry, Academy of Sciences of the U.S.S.R., Moscow, August 7.

References:
1. v. Muralt, A., and Edsall, J. T., *J. Biol. Chem.*, **89**, 351 (1930).
2. Bate Smith, E. C., *Proc. Roy. Soc.*, B, **124**, 136 (1937).
3. Theorell, H., *Biochem. Z.*, **272**, 155 (1934); **278**, 263 (1935).
4. Lohmann, K., *Biochem. Z.*, **282**, 109 (1935).

总之，我们认为三磷酸腺苷酶活性应该来自于肌球蛋白，或者，至少来自于一个与肌球蛋白密切相关而目前我们尚不能将其分离出来的蛋白。因此，通常看作是肌肉收缩的主要放热反应的 ATP 矿化，在蛋白质的影响及直接参与下，可以认为是肌肉纤维收缩机理的主要基础。

（张锦彬 翻译；刘京国 审稿）

Action Potentials Recorded from Inside a Nerve Fibre

A. L. Hodgkin and A. F. Huxley

Editor's Note

Before this paper, no one had ever managed to record the electrical impulse, or "action potential", inside a nerve fibre. Here physiologists Alan Lloyd Hodgkin and Andrew Fielding Huxley (grandson of Thomas Henry Huxley) from the Laboratory of the Marine Biological Association, Plymouth, do just that, taking advantage of the considerable size of the nerve fibres (axon) of the giant squid. Their study proved that action potentials—self-propagating waves of electrochemical activity—arise at the cell surface, and for the first time measured their strength. The two scientists later won the 1963 Nobel Prize in Physiology or Medicine for their work on how action potentials arise and spread in nerve cells.

NERVOUS messages are invariably associated with an electrical change known as the action potential. This potential is generally believed to arise at a membrane which is situated between the axoplasm and the external medium. If this theory is correct, it should be possible to record the action potential between an electrode inside a nerve fibre and the conducting fluid outside it. Most nerve fibres are too small for this to be tested directly, but we have recently succeeded in inserting micro-electrodes into the giant axons of squids (*Loligo forbesi*)[1].

The following method was used. A 500 μ axon was partially dissected from the first stellar nerve and cut half through with sharp scissors. A fine cannula was pushed through the cut and tied into the axon with a thread of silk. The cannula was mounted with the axon hanging from it in sea water. The upper part of the axon was illuminated from behind and could be observed from the front and side by means of a system of mirrors and a microscope; the lower part was insulated by oil and could be stimulated electrically. Action potentials were recorded by connecting one amplifier lead to the sea water outside the axon and the other to a micro-electrode which was lowered through the cannula into the intact nerve beneath it. The micro-electrode consisted of a glass tube about 100 μ in diameter and 10-20 mm. in length; the end of the tube was filled with sea water, and electrical contact with this was made by a 20 μ silver wire which was coated with sliver chloride at the tip. Fig. 1 is a photograph of an electrode inside the living axon. The giant axon shows as a clear space and is surrounded by the small fibres and connective tissue which make up the rest of the nerve trunk. The silver wire can be seen inside the electrode and about 1 mm. from its tip. A small action potential was recorded from the upper end of the axon and this gradually increased as the electrode was lowered, until it reached

从神经纤维内记录到的动作电位

霍奇金，赫胥黎

编者按

在这篇论文之前，从未有人成功地测得神经纤维内的电脉冲或者"动作电位"。在此，来自普利茅斯英国海洋生物协会实验室的生理学家艾伦·劳埃德·霍奇金与安德鲁·菲尔丁·赫胥黎（托马斯·亨利·赫胥黎的孙子）利用巨型乌贼相当大的神经纤维（轴突）完成了这一壮举。他们的研究证明了动作电位——可自行传导的电化学波——产生于细胞表面，并且第一次测量了它们的强度。后来，这两位科学家因为他们在神经细胞中动作电位的产生和传播方面的研究工作而获得了 1963 年诺贝尔生理学或医学奖。

神经信号常与被称为动作电位的电学变化相联系。人们普遍认为，这种电位出现在位于轴突细胞质与外部介质之间的隔膜处。如果这一理论是正确的，那么我们就应该可以记录到置于神经纤维内部的电极与外部导电液之间的动作电位。由于大多数神经纤维都太小了，所以一直以来都难以直接测定这一电位，不过，最近我们成功地将微电极植入到了乌贼（福布斯式枪乌贼）的巨轴突中[1]。

电极植入的方法记述如下。从第一星状神经中部分地剥离出一根 500 微米的神经轴突，并用锋利的剪刀划开一半。将一根微型套管植入开口，并用一根丝线将其缚于轴突内。套管和悬挂于其上的轴突被安置在海水中。利用一组镜面和显微镜从后面将轴突上部照亮，从而可以从前面和侧面对其进行观测；用油将轴突下部隔离，使其可以接受电刺激。把微电极穿过微型套管下放到套管下方没有触动过的神经上。把两个放大器分别通向轴突外部的海水和神经纤维内的微电极，通过这两个相连接的放大器即可记录动作电位。微电极由一个直径约 100 微米，长约 10~20 毫米的玻璃管构成；管的末端充入海水，用顶部覆盖有氯化银的一根 20 微米长的银导线与其进行电接触。图 1 是活体轴突内部的电极的照片。巨轴突呈现为明显的空白区，四周包围着小纤维和构成神经干其余部分的结缔组织。可以看到电极内部的银导线及其顶部约 1 毫米的部分。在轴突上端可以记录到小的动作电位，随着电极下降动作电位逐渐增大，到距离套管约 10 毫米时达到恒定数值，80~95 毫伏。在这个范围内，

a constant amplitude of 80-95 mv. at a distance of about 10 mm. from the cannula. In this region the axon appeared to be in a completely normal condition, for it survived and transmitted impulses for several hours. Experiments with external electrodes showed that the action potential was conducted for at least a centimetre past the tip of the micro-electrode.

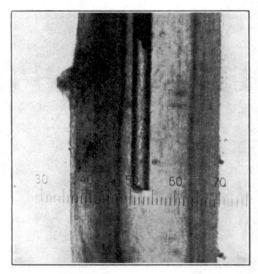

Fig. 1. Photomicrograph of electrode inside giant axon. 1 scale division = 33 μ.

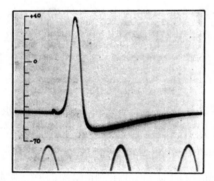

Fig. 2. Action potential recorded between inside and outside of axon. Time marker, 500 cycles/sec. The vertical scale indicates the potential of the internal electrode in millivolts, the sea water outside being taken at zero potential.

These results are important for two reasons. In the first place they prove that the action potential arises at the surface, and in the second, they give the absolute magnitude of the action potential as about 90 mv. at 20°C. Previous measurements have always been made with external electrodes and give values which are reduced by the short-circuiting effect of the fluid outside the nerve fibre.

The potential difference recorded between the interior and exterior of the resting fibre is about 50 mv. The potential difference across the membrane may be greater than this, because there may be a junction potential between the axoplasm and the sea water in

轴突看起来处于完全正常的状态，因为它可以存活并传输脉冲达几小时之久。外部电极实验表明，动作电位的传导至少越过微电极顶端 1 厘米。

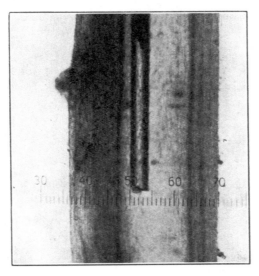

图 1. 植入巨轴突的电极的照片。1 刻度 = 33 微米。

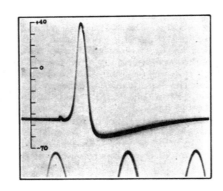

图 2. 记录到的轴突内部与外部之间的动作电位。计时器，500 周 / 秒。纵坐标以毫伏为单位显示内部电极的电势，以外部海水作为电势零点。

这些结果是很重要的，原因有两点。首先，它们证明动作电位出现于表面，其次，它们给出了动作电位的绝对数值，在 20℃ 时约为 90 毫伏。以前的观测都是用外部电极进行的，所以得到的数值由于神经纤维外部流体的短路效应而减小。

我们记录到的静息纤维内部与外部之间的电势差约为 50 毫伏。膜两边的电势差可能比这个数值更大些，因为在轴突细胞质与电极顶部的海水之间可能存在接界电

the tip of the electrode. This potential cannot be estimated, because the anions inside the nerve fibre have not been identified.

We wish to express our indebtedness to Mr. J. Z. Young, whose discovery of the giant axon in *Loligo* made this work possible.

(**144**, 710-711; 1939)

A. L. Hodgkin and A. F. Huxley: Laboratory of the Marine Biological Association, Plymouth, August 26.

Reference:
1. Young, J. Z., *Proc. Roy. Soc.*, B, **121**, 319 (1936).

势。由于尚未确定神经纤维内的负电荷，所以无法估计这一电势。

我们向扬先生表示感谢，正是他发现了枪乌贼的巨轴突才使得本项研究成为可能。

（王耀杨 翻译；金侠 审稿）

Solar and Terrestrial Relationships*

Editor's Note

The onset of war prevented a scheduled discussion at the British Association meeting of the relationships between events on the Earth and on the Sun. But this report summarizes what the intended contributions had to say. Sunspot activity had been shown to correlate with aurorae, and with "magnetic storms" in the upper atmosphere that could disrupt radio telecommunications. These effects were also linked to eruptions in the Sun's chromosphere, now called solar flares. Such links, the report says, may be due to changes in the flux of charged subatomic particles from the Sun—the solar wind—during active periods. The associations are now well established, but remain controversial in terms of their implications for solar effects on climate change.

MANY attempts have been made in the past to correlate solar and terrestrial phenomena. Until quite recently, the only one that was found to show a clearly measurable relationship was that between sunspot activity, auroras and magnetic activity. There is no direct meteorological effect of any serious importance, although in some climates tree-rings suggest a connexion of a complex type with the sunspot cycle not shown up by ordinary data. The recent study of the ionosphere has shown a new relation, involving an increase in ionization in the upper atmosphere accompanying increased magnetic activity at times of maximum sunspot activity; this relation appears in a peculiarly clear-cut fashion at times of chromospheric eruptions which closely coincide with short-wave radio fade-outs. The correlations so far found can all be attributed either to a stream of corpuscles ejected radially from the Sun's surface or to an increase in ultra-violet solar radiation.

Nearly every type of solar activity is capable of emitting a stream of particles or high-frequency radiation which may ultimately strike the Earth's upper atmosphere. In the lowest levels of the Sun's atmosphere, direct observation reveals sunspots, faculae and granulation; with the spectroscope, high-level flocculi and prominences are detected (chiefly in hydrogen or ionized calcium light); still higher, coronal streamers suggest a permanent outward flow of particles. Eruptive prominences, which may ultimately attain velocities

---

*A discussion on solar and terrestrial relationships had been arranged to take place on September 5 as part of the programme of Section A (Mathematical and Physical Sciences) of the British Association meeting at Dundee. The meeting was not held, owing to the international situation, and the following account contains the subject-matter of contributions from Dr. E. V. Appleton (radio effects), Mr. H. W. Newton (solar phenomena and terrestrial magnetism), Dr. A. D. Thackeray (solar phenomena), Prof. L. Vegard (auroral phenomena and the physics of the upper atmosphere), Prof. W. M. H. Greaves (the 27-day recurrence tendency of magnetic storms) and Prof. F. J. M. Stratton (general summary).

日地关系[*]

编者按

战争的爆发使英国科学促进会原计划举行的关于日地关系的学术讨论会被迫取消。但是这篇报告总结了此次会议的意向来稿的主要内容。报告指出，太阳黑子活动与极光有关，而且还与大气层上部能扰动无线电通讯的磁暴有关。这些效应也与现在被称为太阳耀斑的色球内爆发有关。报告指出这些联系可能是由于在活跃期带电亚原子粒子的流动即太阳风的变化所引起的。这些联系现在都已被充分证实，但是这些联系能否显示太阳影响气候变化目前还存在争议。

过去，人们对日地现象的联系已经做了各种探究。直到最近，仅发现太阳黑子活动、极光与地磁活动之间具有明确的可测关系。虽然在某些气候条件下，树木年轮显示出与太阳黑子周期具有一种一般数据无法显示的复杂关系，但这并没有显示出任何重要的与气象直接相关的效应。人们对于电离层的最新研究揭示了一个新的关系，即在太阳黑子最活跃的时期，伴随着高层大气层电离作用的增加，电磁活动也相应增强。这种关系在与无线电短波衰落密切相关的色球爆发时期表现得尤为明显。迄今为止，人们发现的这些对应关系可以全部归因于太阳表面的粒子喷射流，或归因于太阳紫外线辐射的增强。

几乎每种太阳活动都能发射一束粒子流或高频辐射，它们最终会冲击地球较高层处的大气。在太阳大气层的最低层，我们可以直接观察到太阳黑子、光斑和米粒组织；在高一些的大气层中，借助分光镜可以观测到（主要在氢谱线或电离钙谱线中）谱斑和日珥现象；在更高的大气层中，会观测到冕流，这表明存在不断向外的粒子流。由于辐射压力，物质从太阳中突然喷发而出形成壮观的日珥，其速度最终可达

---

* 关于日地关系的讨论原本定于 9 月 5 号作为科学促进会 A 分会（数学物理分会）的主题在邓迪进行。由于国际形势的原因，该会没能举行，于是下面的报道包括了来自不同人士关于这一主题各个方面的内容：阿普尔顿博士的无线电效应，牛顿先生的太阳现象和地磁场，撒克里博士的太阳现象，韦加德教授的极光现象和高层大气物理，格里夫斯教授的磁暴 27 天的重现性和斯特拉顿教授最后的概括总结。

of the order of 600 km./sec., form a spectacular example of the sudden expulsion of matter from the Sun, presumably through radiation pressure; the motions of prominences, however, as revealed by cinematography, show many characteristics which are difficult to explain even in terms of a complex interaction of radiation pressure, gravitation and electrical forces.

Radiation pressure is insufficient to support the whole mass of chromospheric gases, but the dynamical concept of turbulence has partially solved this difficulty. A turbulent velocity of 15 km./sec. in the chromosphere is indicated; in the lower layers it is on a much smaller scale. The short-lived granules, with a life-time of only three minutes, represent permanent activity all over the Sun's surface, *independent of the 11-year sunspot cycle*, while chromospheric eruptions represent temporary localized activity on a large scale. These eruptions consist of intense brightenings in hydrogen and calcium light which sometimes last only a few minutes. Thanks to the spectrohelioscope, perfected in 1924 by Hale, a practically continuous watch for these short-lived phenomena is now kept throughout all longitudes by international cooperation. It has been found that 50 percent of the brightest eruptions are associated with *simultaneous* radio fade-outs; with the fainter eruptions the association is much less direct.

The statistical relationship between sunspots and magnetic storms may be summarized as follows: (*a*) there is a general similarity in the frequency curves of the two phenomena in the 11-year cycle; (*b*) the largest sunspots, at the time of their passage across the central solar meridian, are often associated with large magnetic storms; (*c*) the most favoured position of the associated sunspot at the time of the magnetic storm is about one day past the central meridian. The time-lag suggests the time of travel of a stream of particles from Sun to Earth. The relationship becomes progressively more obscure when smaller spots are studied.

It is natural to inquire whether this relationship is due to the presence of chromospheric eruptions, which are most commonly observed in or near large active sunspots. A distinct relationship has been established between eruptions and magnetic storms, similar to that with sunspots. Of the twenty-nine greatest eruptions observed since 1892, twenty-one were found to be followed within 4.0 days by a magnetic storm, and half of these storms were classified as "great". Magnetic storms do in fact appear to be more closely associated with chromospheric eruptions than with sunspots.

The association of chromospheric eruptions with ionospheric disturbances is of a different character: (*a*) there is no time-lag; (*b*) the eruption can be effective wherever it occurs on the solar disk; (*c*) the ionospheric disturbance is practically confined to the Earth's sunlit hemisphere; (*d*) there is an accompanying small perturbation of the Earth's magnetic field. These four facts are consistent with the suggestion that the solar agency is ultra-violet radiation emitted from active regions of the solar surface. The agency responsible for magnetic storms, however, is to be looked for in a radially ejected stream of high-velocity particles. The observations favour a common origin of radiation and particles in an active

600 千米 / 秒。然而，由摄影机拍摄到的日珥运动过程具有许多复杂的特性，即使考虑了辐射压力、地球引力和电动力之间的这些复杂相互作用，也很难对这些特性给出解释。

辐射压力不足以支持色球气体的全部质量，但湍流动力学理论已部分解决了这个难题。色球中湍流的速度为 15 千米 / 秒，在较低层速度要更小。米粒组织寿命短暂，仅为 3 分钟，其代表了整个太阳表面的持续活动，**且不受 11 年太阳黑子周期的影响**。太阳耀斑以短周期、大规模、局域性的方式进行活动。这些耀斑由高亮度的氢和钙谱线组成，它们有时仅持续几分钟。海耳于 1924 年发明了太阳分光镜，使得通过国际合作在全球范围内可对这些短暂的喷流现象进行长期持续的观测。科学家们发现，最亮喷发现象中的 50% 与**同时发生**的无线电波衰落紧密相关，喷发越弱，其相关性越小。

太阳黑子和磁暴之间的统计关系可总结如下：(a) 在 11 年的周期中，这两种现象的频率曲线大致是相似的；(b) 当最大的太阳黑子穿过太阳中心子午线时通常与大磁暴相关；(c) 发生磁暴时，太阳黑子最有可能位于其通过太阳中心子午线一天后的地方。延迟的时间恰好是一束粒子从太阳到地球的时间。当所研究的太阳黑子较小时，这种关系会变得越来越不明确。

在活跃的大的太阳黑子里面或者附近可经常见到太阳耀斑，那么人们不禁要问，这种关系是否是由太阳耀斑引起的呢？类似于与太阳黑子之间的关系，耀斑和磁暴间也存在一种明显的关系。自 1892 年以来，已经观测到了 29 种大耀斑现象，其中有 21 个在 4 天后发生磁暴，这些磁暴中有一半的量级都到了"大"磁暴的程度。事实上，相对于磁暴与太阳黑子来说，磁暴与太阳耀斑有着更为紧密的联系。

太阳耀斑与电离层扰动的关系具有不同的特征：(a) 没有时间延迟；(b) 只要出现在日面上，耀斑都是有效的；(c) 电离层扰动仅发生在面日半球上；(d) 伴随发生小的地磁场扰动。上述四个特点与太阳能从太阳表面活跃区域发射紫外线辐射的观点是一致的。然而，引起磁暴的原因应该从喷射出的高速粒子流中寻找。这些观察表明普通粒子和辐射都来源于太阳表面的活跃区域，该区域通常但并不一定以大的

portion of the Sun's surface, which may also but not necessarily be marked by a large sunspot. The association of terrestrial phenomena with sunspots must be regarded as an indirect one; it is only because they are so easily observed that sunspots have been taken as a convenient index of solar activity.

A further relationship between sunspots and terrestrial magnetism is shown by the fact, known for many years, that magnetic storms tend to recur at intervals of one synodic solar rotation (about 27 days). A catalogue of 403 storms based on Greenwich records for the years 1874-1927 has been used to study this relationship in detail. These were divided into five groups according to intensity, represented by the mean of the three components D, H and V. The history of storm-days following each storm was followed up and the tendency to recur after 27 days was found to be confined to the less intense storms (less than 180 γ); in the weakest storms (less than 150 γ), there is a definite additional tendency to recur at intervals of 54 days.

This result can be expressed in another way: if attention is confined to storms which tend to recur after 27 days, it is found that the ratio "sequence storms" to all storms decreases progressively from 0.25 to 0.05 as one passes from weak to great storms. This result does not contradict the conclusion that magnetic storms are due to radial streams of corpuscles from active regions of the Sun; it merely suggests that the most intense solar disturbances which eject such streams are comparatively short-lived and will not survive a solar rotation. The 27-day recurrence has been found to persist throughout spotless periods of minimum activity; thus, as implied previously, the spots themselves must not be regarded as the origin of the corpuscular streams.

The frequency of auroras has long been known to follow the cycle of solar activity; there is also a slight tendency for intense auroras to occur near the times of the equinoxes, when the Earth lies in the plane of the equatorial belt of the Sun where activity is greatest. The spectrum of auroras consists of bands (chiefly due to nitrogen) and lines (due to atomic oxygen and nitrogen, neutral and ionized). The wave-lengths of the strong green and red lines have been measured with great accuracy, and, with the help of knowledge of atomic energy levels, attributed to "forbidden" transitions of neutral oxygen.

The presence of ionized oxygen and nitrogen indicates the action of particles of high energy. The work of Störmer has shown how the streamers may be identified with the paths of electrified particles entering the Earth's magnetic field. Analysis of the intensity distribution within auroral bands yields a mean temperature determination of $-44\,°C$. There is no evidence of any increase in temperature with height either from band analysis or from measures of interferometer fringes of atomic lines. Further, the observed light intensity along auroral streamers suggests that the density of atmospheric gases diminishes but slowly within the auroral region from 100 km. to 800 km. It is suggested that matter is driven to these heights by electric forces in an ionized or partially electrified atmosphere.

A theory proposed by Vegard in 1923 accounts for the main facts on the assumption of

太阳黑子的出现为标志。地球上的各种现象和太阳黑子的联系是间接的，这只是由于太阳黑子较容易被观察到，因而可以方便地作为太阳活动的标志。

根据一个已知多年的事实可以说明太阳黑子和地磁场之间存在更进一步的关系，即磁暴现象往往发生在一个太阳自转朔望月（大约27天）的时间间隔内。根据1874~1927年格林尼治对403次磁暴的记录，人们已经对此关系进行了详细的研究。磁暴根据强烈程度不同可分为5组，其划分标准是地磁三分量D、H和V的平均值。通常的情况是每个磁暴后都会有几天磁暴日，且只有强度较小的磁暴（小于180γ）才有27天周期性出现的趋势；在一些更小的磁暴（小于150γ）中，这种周期需要54天。

这个结果可以用另一种方式来表述：如果仅关注27天周期性出现的磁暴，会发现随着磁暴从微弱到剧烈的变化过程，"连续磁暴"在所有磁暴中所占的比率会从0.25逐渐降为0.05。这个结果与磁暴是由太阳活跃区域辐射粒子束引起的结论并不矛盾；它仅仅表明了导致出现这些粒子束的太阳最大强度紊乱相对短暂，并不能持续一个太阳自转周期。27天的周期性现象在太阳整体最不活跃的无黑子阶段都会发生，所以正如上面所说，太阳黑子本身不应是粒子束的来源。

人们早已认识到，极光出现的频次随太阳活动周期变化；并且当地球位于受太阳活动影响最剧烈的太阳赤道平面时，即在春分或者秋分时存在产生强极光的一个微弱趋势。极光的光谱由光谱带（主要由氮引起）和光谱线（主要由呈中性和电离化的氧和氮原子引起）组成。人们已经精确测定了强绿线和红线的波长，并且基于原子能级理论将其归因于中性氧的"禁戒"跃迁。

氧离子和氮离子的出现表明了高能粒子的作用。斯托末的工作显示了如何用进入地磁场的带电粒子路径来识别极光。对极光区域强度分布的研究得出的平均温度为－44℃。根据对波段和原子谱线干涉条纹的分析，没有发现任何有关温度随高度的增加而升高的证据。另外，沿着极光流所观察到的光线强度表明，大气的气体密度在100~800千米的极光区缓慢减弱。这种现象表明，离子化或部分电离化大气中的电力驱使物质达到该高度。

韦加德1923年提出的理论可解释其中主要的现象，但该理论建立在下面的假

a stream of photon radiation, the wave-length of which corresponds to soft X-rays, in addition to the ordinary temperature radiation and corpuscular rays emitted by the Sun. The incidence of this radiation on the extreme upper atmosphere produces a sort of terrestrial corona. The theory has been very successful in explaining the chief layers of ionization in the upper atmosphere. The soft X-rays will produce two ionization maxima; the first, formed at a high altitude by high-speed photo-electrons, is identified with the F_2 layer, which surrounds the whole Earth, but is higher by night than by day; the second, at a low altitude where the absorption per unit length is a maximum, is identified with the E layer, which is confined to the sunlit hemisphere. The energy of the photons must be about 1,000 volts to account for the observed heights of the E and F_2 layers. Finally, the absorption coefficient for rays in a large range of wave-length (100-1,000 A.) is a maximum, so that these rays will produce an ionization maximum at about the same height—calculated to be 200 km.—which will be confined to the sunlit hemisphere. This maximum is identified by Vegard with the F_1 layer.

The variations in ionization in these three layers may be very efficiently studied by means of the radio sounding method, developed by Appleton and others. The ionosphere may, in fact, be regarded as a solar laboratory in which the effects of high-frequency radiation and particles emitted by the Sun may be analysed. By timing echoes of vertically transmitted waves, a relation is obtained between equivalent height of reflection and radio-wave frequency. At a critical frequency, echoes from the ionosphere are lost, and this gives a clue to the maximum electron density in any layer. Layers E and F_1 show comparatively smooth diurnal, seasonal and sunspot-cycle variations, all of which confirm the supposition that these layers are produced by high-frequency solar radiation. The long-scale variations in ionospheric reflectivity do, in fact, give a very perfect reproduction of the 11-year cycle of solar activity. The ionization in layer F_2, however, suffers remarkable irregularities, particularly during magnetic storms, when the ionization maximum is less than normal. The most striking type of ionospheric irregularity is that known as an irruption or fade-out, which is usually associated with a chromospheric eruption. Here the absorption is so great that the echo may be entirely lost, but the height of reflection is not usually greatly affected.

The question of the ultimate character of the short-wave solar radiation associated with these disturbances (for example, its frequency and whether it consists of continuous or line-emission) is still quite unsettled. The spectrum of chromospheric eruptions in the observable range has been found to consist of lines due to H, He and Ca$^+$. Photometric measures show that during an eruption, the total Hα radiation from the sun increases by only a few tenths of one percent; it is quite clear that what the spectrohelioscope observer sees is a secondary effect, and that the primary disturbance consists in the leakage of unobservable ultra-violet radiation. As Milne has pointed out, given an increase of radiation, the ejection of a stream of high-speed particles is easily accounted for by radiation pressure. Lyman emission of hydrogen is insufficient to account for all the observed effects, and it is probable that we have to deal with a mixture of line and continuous radiation. Continuous emission is not normally observed in the visible region, although a small increase at wave-length 3,220 A. has been

设之上：除了常温辐射和来自太阳的微粒射线，还存在波长对应于软 X 射线的光子辐射流。该射线对极高大气产生影响而形成一种地冕。该理论成功地解释了高层大气中主要电离层的形成。软 X 射线将产生两个电离最大值：第一个是由高速光电子在高纬度形成的 F_2 层，它包围整个地球，但其位置在夜晚要比白天高；第二个是指在低纬度地区每单位长度的吸收量为最大值的 E 层，并仅限于面日半球。光子的能量必须达到 1,000 电子伏才能用来解释所观察到的 E 层和 F_2 层高度。光线在很大波长（100~1,000 埃）范围内吸收系数最大，因此这些射线在大致相同的高度（经计算为 200 千米）产生最大的电离，这仅限于面日半球。韦加德将这个最大值定义为 F_1 层。

阿普尔顿及其相关研究人员发明了一种无线电探测方法，利用这一方法或许可以有效地研究电离层三个区域中电离度的变化。电离层实际上可以作为一个太阳实验室，在那里可以对高频辐射和太阳喷流粒子效应进行分析。通过对垂直运动波的反射运动计时，我们可以得到等效反射高度与无线电波频率的关系。在某个特定频率下，来自电离层的反射会消失，这暗示各个层都存在一个最大的电子密度。E 层和 F_1 层显示出昼夜、季节和黑子各个不同周期上相对平稳的变化，这验证了这些层都是由高频太阳辐射产生的假设。电离反射的长期变化实际上是太阳活动 11 年周期的一个完美的再现。然而，在 F_2 层中的电离活动非常不规律，特别是在磁暴期间，其最大电离值小于正常值。我们所知的最不规律的一类电离是通常与太阳耀斑有关的突发和渐隐现象。由于此时吸收特别强烈，所以反射现象可能完全消失，但反射的高度通常不会受到很大影响。

关于与扰动相关（例如，它的频率以及它是否存在连续发射谱或者线发射谱）的太阳短波辐射的基本特性问题仍然没有解决。在可观测范围内，我们发现太阳耀斑光谱中含有 H、He 和 Ca^+ 的谱线。光度测量结果显示，在整个爆发期间来自太阳的全部 Hα 射线仅仅增加了千分之几；显然，太阳分光仪观察到的是次级效应，而初级扰动存在于漏掉的观察不到的紫外辐射之中。正如米耳恩指出，假定辐射增加，那么辐射压力可以很好地解释高速粒子流的喷射。但氢的莱曼射线不足以解释观察到的所有效应，因此也许我们需要研究谱线和连续辐射同时存在的情况。尽管在一次意外的爆发中观测到波长 3,220 埃处有小量增加，但在可见区域内一般观测不到连续发射。

detected in one exceptional eruption.

Further analysis of ionospheric disturbances by radio sounding probably holds out greater hopes for the ultimate solution of the problem than the observation of secondary solar effects in the visible spectrum. Finally, the spectra of "sunlit auroras" recently observed by Störmer promises a fruitful field for research into the uppermost regions, where the solar rays first strike the Earth's atmosphere.

(**144**, 808-810; 1939)

利用无线电探测对电离层扰动做进一步的分析可能比在可见波段中观察太阳的次级效应更有希望从根本上解决问题。最后，斯托末近来观测得到的"日耀极光"光谱似乎预示了对大气最高层区域的研究具有广阔的前景，而这一区域也正是太阳辐射最初冲击到地球的大气部分。

（刘霞 翻译；孟庆任 审稿）

Gene and Chromosome Theory*

H. J. Muller

Editor's Note

Hermann Joseph Muller, an American geneticist, here reports on a recent meeting to discuss the current understanding of genes and chromosomes. Clearly the outbreak of war had severely disrupted proceedings, forcing Muller to rely in some cases on written abstracts. As his comments reveal, it was then still unclear whether the critical component of chromosomes, on which genes reside, was protein or nucleic acid—the genetic role of DNA was still unknown. That question was further complicated by studies on viruses, which, like chromosomes, are intimate mixtures of both substances. Much of the work Muller discusses examines gene mutation caused by ionizing radiation such as X-rays—the topic for which Muller himself was awarded a Nobel Prize seven years later.

THE treatment of gene and chromosome theory was on a far more analytical plane than ever before. Thus, the multiform variations of behaviour of chromosomes at meiosis, and the rules governing these variations, were shown by Darlington to trace back to variations in two primary factors: the region (centric or telic) in which pairing begins, and the time limit set to the pairing process; normally, these must be adapted to each other, so that a mixing of two systems tends to disturb the balance.

Regarding the mechanism whereby structural changes in chromosomes come about, a series of experiments by the present author and co-workers was reported, substantiating and extending, for Drosophila, the earlier conclusions of Stadler, of McClintock and of Sax on plant material, and of Muller and Belgovsky on Drosophila, to the effect that the manifold kinds of structural changes capable of surviving indefinitely are all caused by two distinct primary processes, succeeding one another. These are: (1) breakage of the chromonema at two or more points, followed (2) (though not until after the spermatozoon stage is passed) by two-by-two junction between the adhesive broken ends, giving a new linear order. Distant breakages, giving gross changes, were shown to result from separate individual ionizations, but nearby ones, giving minute rearrangements, to result from one and the same ionization by a spreading of its effect. The reports and demonstrations of a large series of separate investigators—Bauer, Fabergé, Demerec, Camara, Catcheside, Oliver and Belgovsky—in one way or another agreed with or led to one or more of the

---

* Although the Russian geneticists had withdrawn and most of the Germans had left before the time for their addresses, their abstracts had already been submitted, and in this Section the policy was followed of reading all such papers *in absentia*. They are accordingly included in this report, although only the papers of official members will be printed in the *Proceedings*. Also included here are papers given in joint meetings of this and the next Section.

基因与染色体理论*

马勒

编者按

美国遗传学家赫尔曼·约瑟夫·马勒在此对最近一次有关基因和染色体现状的会议进行了综述。很显然，战争的爆发严重阻碍了会议进程，这使得马勒有些时候不得不依赖于一些书面的摘要。就像他的文章揭示的那样，当时仍然不清楚携带基因的染色体主要是由蛋白质组成还是由核酸组成——DNA的遗传角色仍然是未知的。对病毒的研究使该问题更加复杂，和染色体类似，病毒也是由蛋白质和核酸混合组成的。马勒探讨的大部分工作都与电离辐射（例如X射线）诱导的基因突变有关，他自己也因在该领域的研究成果而在7年后获得了诺贝尔奖。

在对待基因与染色体理论方面现在正处于一个比以往任何时候都更具分析性的平台之上。因此，达林顿指出，在减数分裂阶段染色体行为多种形式的变化以及控制这些变化的规则，可以回溯到两个主要因素的变化：配对开始时的区域（着丝点区域或目的区域），以及配对过程受到的时间限制；通常情况下，这些都是必须彼此适应的，以至于混合两个体系便会倾向于扰乱平衡。

关于染色体中产生结构变化的机制，笔者与合作者们报道了用果蝇进行的一系列实验，证实并推广了斯塔德勒、麦克林托克和萨克斯之前基于植物材料得出的结论以及马勒和别利戈夫斯基之前基于果蝇得出的结论，大意是，能够保存下来的多种类型的结构变化可能是由两个截然不同的相继发生的重要过程引起的。它们是：（1）染色丝在两个或更多个位点断裂，接着（2）黏性的断裂末端之间通过两两接合形成新的线性序列（不过要等精子阶段过去之后）。导致总体改变的远距离断裂看来是由个别独立的电离作用造成的，而导致微小重排的邻近距离的断裂则是由同一次电离及其效果的传播造成的。许多彼此独立的研究者——鲍尔、法贝热、德梅雷茨、卡马拉、卡奇赛德、奥利弗和别利戈夫斯基——的报道和论述以不同的方式同意或得到了一条或几条相同的结论，尽管有些研究者直到那时仍持有相反的观点。

---

*尽管俄国遗传学家已经撤离，而且大多数德国学者在他们的演讲时间之前就已离去，但由于他们都已经提交了论文摘要，依会议条例，所有这类的论文也给予缺席宣读。因此它们也包含于这份报道之中，但只有正式与会成员的论文将会印在《会刊》中。此外，这里还包括在本部分和下一部分的联席会议中提交的论文。

same conclusions, although some investigators had until then held contrary views. Further light was thrown on chromosome structure and on the changes to which it is subject, in a special evening lecture by Metz, recounting his notable findings in Sciara.

A considerable group of papers analysed the special, though not absolutely distinctive, properties of heterochromatic regions of chromosomes. In this connexion, further illustrations were given of the high breakability of these regions by Kaufmann, Camara, Prokofyeva and Sidorov, and of their somatic variability (correlated in related cells) in respect to manner of chromatin staining, manner of aggregation of chromonemata and gene functioning. It was noted that all these properties extend, although to a degree diminishing with distance, beyond the originally heterochromatic regions into regions lying near to them in the chromonema, by a kind of "position effect" (Schultz, Prokofyeva, Panshin, Khvostova), and the important new point was brought out that the variations in staining—which, as proved by Caspersson and Schultz's studies of ultra-violet absorption spectra, fairly represent nucleic acid distribution—and the variations in gene activity are correlated with one another. Evidence was also adduced, by Prokofyeva and by Kaufmann, that small interstitial regions having some degree of heterochromaticity are scattered rather widely throughout the chromatin, and often coincide with regions that apparently originated relatively recently as duplications (which suggests that genes may become heterochromatic by a kind of denaturizing degeneration).

Analysing the mechanism of gene mutation on the basis of a great series of experiments, Timoféeff-Ressovsky brought out its causation (1) by individual atomic activations, apparently resulting from the accidental peaks of kinetic energy of thermal origin, as well as (2) by individual ionizations, resulting from radiation. The dependence on single ionizations was further strengthened by Rai-Choudhuri's finding that even radiation of intensities so low as 0.01 r./min. (a hundred times lower than the lowest previously used in such work) is so effective, ion for ion, as radiation of higher intensities. At the same time, the generality of the gene mutation effect of radiation was strengthened in another important way, by its definite extension to mammals (mice), in experiments of P. Hertwig.

In earlier work, no dependence of the frequency of the gene mutations upon the closeness of spacing of the ions within the radiation-paths could be detected, but newer work by Timoféeff-Ressovsky and his collaborators, reported at the meeting, suggested that a perceptible influence of this kind might be found by the use of the extremely closely spaced ions resulting from some neutron radiation. If so, it should be possible to estimate the "sensitive volume" for a gene mutation, that is, the amount of contiguous space occupied by material so constituted that one ionization, occurring anywhere within it, is capable of producing some one or more of a given series of alleles. Similar work, utilizing the frequency of chromosome breakage instead of that of gene mutations, was reported by Marshak. In this connexion, however, it should be noted that if, as seems likely, only a small proportion of the ionizations occurring within the region in question actually resulted in the effect looked for, this method would tend to lose its efficacy. Moreover, we have no basis for identifying the volume or area in question with that of the gene or

梅茨在一次特殊的晚间演讲中进一步阐述了染色体结构及其发生的变化，详细说明了他研究蕈蚊时取得的重要发现。

有相当数量的论文分析了染色体异染色质区域的一些虽非绝对独有但十分特殊的性质。关于这一点，考夫曼、卡马拉、普罗科菲耶娃和西多罗夫对这些区域的高度易断裂性及与染色质着色方式和染色丝凝聚及基因作用方式有关的细胞体易变性（在相关细胞中）进行了更深入的阐释。值得注意的是，所有这些性质都通过一种"位置效应"（舒尔茨、普罗科菲耶娃、潘申、赫沃斯托娃）延伸到最初的异染质区域之外——尽管在一定程度上随着距离而减少——进入染色丝中与其邻近的区域中。因而有人提出下面这一重要的新观点，着色的变化与基因活性的变化彼此关联——这已被卡斯帕森和舒尔茨通过紫外吸收光谱研究证明。紫外吸收光谱可以清楚地反映出核酸的分布。普罗科菲耶娃和考夫曼还发现，具有某种程度异染色质性的小间隙区域相当广泛地分散于染色质中并且经常与那些显然是新生成的重复段区域相一致（这意味着基因可以通过裂解方式而表现出异染色质性）。

在大量实验的基础上，季莫费耶夫–列索夫斯基对基因突变的机制进行了分析并提出其起因：（1）通过孤立的原子活化作用，它们显然是来自于热动能的突然增值；（2）通过来自于辐射的单一电离化作用。拉伊–乔杜里发现，在单一离子水平，即使是强度低达 0.01 r/min（比以前进行的这类研究中所用的最低强度还低 100 倍）的辐射也能像较高强度的辐射一样有效，这进一步证实了对单一电离化作用的依赖性。同时，赫特维希在哺乳动物（老鼠）中的实验通过另一种重要的方式证实了辐射对于基因突变的影响的普遍性。

在早期研究中，没能检测到基因突变频率是否依赖于放射线的离子间隔密度，但是在这次会议上报道的季莫费耶夫–列索夫斯基及其同事的近期研究表明，利用某种中子辐射产生的高密度离子，可以观测到这类影响。如果确实如此，就应该有可能估计出基因突变的"灵敏范围"，即这样形成的物质所占据的毗邻空间的总和，其中任何位置发生的一次电离化都可以产生一个或多个等位基因的特定序列。马沙克报道了利用染色体断裂频率而非基因突变频率进行的类似研究。不过就此而言，应该注意的是，若在可疑区域中仅仅发生小频率的电离化就导致预期结果的话，这种方法就会丧失有效性。此外，我们尚无法将可疑范围或区域与基因或染色丝自身的范围或区域对应起来。

chromonema itself.

In addition to the seemingly simple thermal effect of van't Hoff type, above-mentioned, there were shown—by Plough, Timoféeff-Ressovsky, Kerkis and Zuitin—to be decided increases in mutation frequency attending the abnormal physiological states of organisms subjected to temperature changes too rapid or too extreme for the organisms to adjust to them. This makes the search for special chemical influences affecting gene mutations seem more promising, despite certain negative results reported by Auerbach with carcinogenic substances. The sensitivity, as well as the intricacy, of the chemical complexes conditioning mutation was further evidenced by the strong dependence of the general mutation frequency upon the genetic complex present, as reported by Plough and by Tiniakov, and more especially by observations of Rhoades and of Harland showing certain enormous and highly specific mutational effects on particular genes, not previously known as "mutable genes", by other particular genes and genecombinations.

The series of papers dealing with the production of mutations by ultra-violet light showed the notable progress made in this field since the last congress. It was shown by Stadler that the curve representing the effectiveness of different wave-lengths in producing gene mutations and deficiencies in maize pollen begins at about 313 mμ and rises to a peak at 254 mμ, declining thereafter. This is suggestively similar to the absorption spectrum of nucleic acid and quite different from that of protein. Both Hollaender, working on fungus spores, and Knapp and Schreiber, on spermatozoids of Sphaerocarpus, reported results substantially similar to this, although their peaks of mutational effect (as well as of directly lethal effect) were at 265 mμ, which corresponds more exactly to the absorption peak for thymonucleic acid. In Hollaender's work, however, there was also a secondary peak, at 238 mμ; and another peculiarity in his results (one suggesting differential sensitivity of different spore stages) was a falling off in the mutation frequency of surviving individuals at very high doses.

In Stadler's work, a basis was found for drawing qualitative distinctions between several different classes of radiation effects. Thus, the frequency of abortive embryos at different wave-lengths, unlike that of gene mutations and deficiencies, failed to follow the nucleic acid curve, as it showed too high frequencies for the shorter wave-lengths. While these abortive embryos may after all represent some kind of non-genetic effect, the same cannot be said of sectional rearrangements of chromosomes (translocations). Stadler found that the latter were not produced by ultra-violet light, or were produced with a markedly lower frequency than by X-rays of the same gene mutation-producing strength.

This result, which was corroborated for Drosophila sperm by experiments carried out by Muller and Mackenzie, gives some ground for supposing that ultra-violet does not act by breaking the chromosomes, and that therefore gene mutations may not consist merely of linear rearrangements of ultra-small size, involving "intragenic" breakage and reunion. The latter idea, which is not yet actually refuted, would have tended to make the concept of the segmentation of the chromosomes into discrete "genes" a mere matter of verbal

除以上提到的范特霍夫类型的看似简单的热效应之外，普劳、季莫费耶夫–列索夫斯基、克尔基斯和祖伊京等人还指出，由于温度变化过快或过于极端以至于有机体无法适应而处于异常生理状态时，突变频率明显增加。这使得对于影响基因突变的特殊化学效应的研究看来更具前景，尽管奥尔巴赫在关于致癌物质的报道中存在某些阴性结果。普劳和京亚科夫的报道显示，基因突变的频率依赖于遗传体系，这进一步证实了化学复合物诱导突变发生的敏感性和复杂性。罗兹和哈兰德的观测也提供了进一步的证据。他们发现，某些特定的基因或基因组能够诱发另外的某些特定基因（之前并不知道这些特定基因就是"易突变基因"）发生大规模的高度特异性的突变。

一系列探讨因紫外线作用而产生突变的论文，展示了自上次会议以来该领域取得的重要进展。斯塔德勒展示了不同波长的光线引起玉米花粉的基因发生突变和缺陷的效果随波长变化的曲线。它始于约 313 纳米，于 254 纳米处达到峰值，此后逐渐下落。发人深省的是，这与核酸的吸收光谱类似，而与蛋白质的截然不同。研究真菌孢子的霍兰德和研究球蒴苔属的游动精子的纳普与施赖伯都报道了在本质上与此类似的结果，只不过他们的结果中突变效应峰值（以及直接致死效应）出现在265 纳米处，这与胸腺核酸的吸收峰对应得更为精确。不过，在霍兰德的研究中还出现了 238 纳米处的次级峰；他的结果中的另一个特异之处（暗示不同孢子时期的灵敏度不同）是在极高剂量时存活个体的突变频率下降。

斯塔德勒在研究中发现了定量区分不同类型辐射效应的基础。例如，不同波长下败育胚的频率——与基因突变和缺陷的频率不同——与核酸曲线并不一致，因为在较短波长处败育胚出现的频率非常高。虽然这些败育胚终究有可能代表某种非遗传效应，染色体的部分重排（易位）则不同。斯塔德勒发现后者不是由紫外线引发的，或者说相对于 X 射线而言，由紫外线引发相同的基因突变强度的概率极低。

被马勒和麦肯齐用果蝇精子进行的实验所确认的这一结果为下列假定提供了某种基础，即紫外线并不是通过使染色体断裂而起作用，因而基因突变可能不仅仅是由诸如"基因内"断裂和重接等极小尺度的线性重排组成的。后一观点——目前还没有被实质性地驳倒——将会倾向于将染色体区段的概念简称为离散的"基因"。斯

convenience. Possibly connected with the same series of problems was Stadler's further finding that the gene mutations produced by ultra-violet are far oftener "fractionals"—that is, confined to one of the chromatids derived from a given treated chromosome—than are those produced by X-rays.

For the first time in the history of genetics congresses a session was included on virus and protein studies in relation to the problem of the gene. A peculiar case of non-chromosomal, probably virus, "inheritance" in Drosophila, was reported by L'Héritier and Teissier. As was brought out by Mckinney, by Gowen and by Kausche, viruses, now known to be crystallizable nucleoproteins, have the distinctive combination of properties characteristic of genes, namely, mutation and (despite mutation) self-duplication, thus substantiating the concept (Muller, 1921, 1926) that viruses represent relatively free genes, and that the gene constitutes the basis of life.

An illuminating account was given by Astbury of his and other modern studies of the chemical structure of viruses and other proteins, with especial consideration of those features which might help to explain the gene's property of mutable self-duplication. He, as well as Caspersson and Schultz (who reported an increase of nucleic acid during periods of growth, both for chromosomes and for cytoplasm), directed attention to the role which nucleic acid may have in this process. The significant fact was reported by Astbury that the nucleic acid spacings are of the same magnitude as those within the protein (polypeptide) chain, a feature which would allow the nucleic acid to unite in parallel with the protein and so perhaps to serve as an intermediary in its synthesis. The paper of Mazia also was of interest in this connexion, since it showed that in salivary chromosomes the framework is not disintegrated by digestion either by pepsin or by nuclease, though it is by trypsin; hence it probably consists of protamine or histone chains, bound together laterally in some other way than by nucleic acid cross-connexions. Other chemical studies of nuclear material were reported by Gulick, which among other things cast doubt on the presence of iron in chromosomes, thus bringing their composition closer to that of the virus.

Our present knowledge of the internal structure of the tobacco mosaic virus particles, as disclosed by the pioneer X-ray diffraction studies of Bernal, Crowfoot et al., was described by D. Crowfoot as well as by Astbury. It was shown that in these rods, which are 15 mμ thick and at least ten times as long, the smallest possible chemical unit—that associated with one nucleotide—must contain about fifty-four amino-acid radicals, although there may be a geometrical sub-unit as small as one eighth of this volume (that is, about 1 mμ each way). But these units (or sub-units) are grouped according to a regular pattern into larger aggregates, about 7 mμ long, and the latter in turn are grouped in a regular way to form the aggregate of high order—the virus rod itself. The globular protein insulin, as well as the fibrous proteins, all show elementary units of about the same size, but the mode of aggregation varies both with the protein and with the conditions (pH, amount of water, etc.) under which it is being kept. Thus this type of analysis is already bridging the gap between the structures of the chemist and those of the microbiologist and geneticist.

736

塔德勒的进一步发现可能与同样的一系列问题有关联，即由紫外线产生的基因突变比由 X 射线产生的基因突变更为频繁地"断片化"——即突变局限于经过特定处理的染色体中的一条染色单体上。

在遗传学会议的历史上，这是第一次举办关于与基因问题相关的病毒和蛋白质研究的分会。莱里捷和泰西耶报道了果蝇中一种特殊的非染色体式的"遗传"，可能是病毒。如同麦金尼、高恩和考施所提出的那样，病毒，现在已经知道就是结晶核蛋白，具有基因性状性质的独特组合，即突变和（不考虑是否突变）自我复制，从而证实了病毒代表相对自由的基因以及基因构成生命基础的观点（马勒，1921 年，1926 年）。

阿斯特伯里就其本人的研究和另外一些关于病毒及其他蛋白质化学结构的现代研究进行了精彩的描述，并对那些可能会有助于解释基因的可突变自我复制的特征给予了特别的考虑。他，还有卡斯帕森和舒尔茨（他们报道了处于生长期时染色体和细胞质中核酸的增加），将注意力集中于核酸在这一过程中担当的角色。阿斯特伯里报道的一个重要事实是核酸间隔与蛋白质（多肽）链内的间隔具有同等的数量级，此特点将核酸和蛋白质联系起来，因此有可能在其合成过程中充当媒介。就此而言梅齐亚的论文也是值得注意的，因为该论文指出用胃蛋白酶或核酸酶消化并不能使唾液染色体的骨架分解，但用胰酶消化则能使其分解；因此它可能是由精蛋白或组蛋白链构成的，以核酸交叉连接以外的某种方式横向连接在一起。古利克报道了关于核物质的另外一些化学研究，这些研究和其他一些研究都对染色体中是否存在铁提出了疑问，从而使其组成与病毒的组成又接近了一些。

如同贝尔纳和克劳福特等人进行的先驱性的 X 射线衍射研究所提示的那样，克劳福特和阿斯特伯里阐述了现在我们关于烟草花叶病毒颗粒内部结构的知识。在这种粗为 15 纳米、长则至少 10 倍于此的杆状物中，最小的可能的化学单元——与一种核酸有关——必定包含约 54 个氨基酸残基，尽管也可能还存在一种大小仅为该体积 1/8（即每个维度方向上约 1 纳米）的几何亚单元，但是这些单元（或亚单元）依据一个规则模式聚合形成长约 7 纳米的较大的团聚体，后者再以某种规则方式聚合形成高级团聚体——那就是杆状病毒。球状蛋白胰岛素和纤维蛋白都呈现出同等尺寸的基本单元，但是在蛋白质的团聚方式以及保存所需条件（pH、水量等）方面却各不相同。于是，这类分析在化学家得到的结构与微生物学家和遗传学家得到的结构之间的裂谷上架起了桥梁。

A series of special conferences were held on problems of the gene, presided over chiefly by J. B. S. Haldane. These were very well attended. At these "gene conferences" many of the reports of those unable to attend were read, and many of the above and related questions concerning gene and virus structure and gene mutation were subjected to animated and searching discussion.

(**144**, 814-816; 1939)

近来召开了一系列关于基因问题的专门会议，主要是由霍尔丹主持的。这些会议举办得都很成功。在这些"基因会议"上宣读了很多无法亲自与会人员的报告，并且对上述关于基因、病毒结构和基因突变的很多相关问题都进行了活跃而深入的讨论。

（王耀杨 翻译；金侠 审稿）

Physiological Genetics

C. H. Waddington

Editor's Note

The English biologist Conrad Hal Waddington was one of the pioneers of modern developmental biology, in particular in building links between embryology and development. In this report he gives an overview of the developmental genetics of his time, describing how researchers were then seeking to understand how genes, cellular process and the external environment combine to determine the development and form of the organism. The advent of techniques for sequencing and manipulating DNA has now revolutionized the understanding of development, yet these questions are still at the heart of developmental biology and its interplay with evolution (called "evo-devo"). In particular, the relative importance of genes and environment in development is still hotly debated.

ONE of the most active branches of genetics at the present time is the study of the ways in which genes affect developmental processes, and the section devoted to physiological genetics had a full and interesting programme. The problem of genic action is so complex and many sided that very many different methods of approach are possible, and examples of most of these can be found in the papers presented at the Congress.

The embryological approach was well exemplified in a paper by Landauer, in which he reviewed the correlated effects on different organs which are found both in fortuitous teratological specimens and also in abnormalities which are known to be dependent on genes. He suggested that many of these phenomena can be explained by the hypothesis of a general deleterious effect, often on the growth-rate, acting at a period which is critical for a certain set of developmental processes. A general embryological approach of a rather different kind was presented by Waddington, who discussed the relation of genes to developmental processes of the kind exemplified by the organizer reaction.

The importance of nuclear factors in particular steps of differentiation was analysed in more detail by Baltzer, who gave a summary of his well-known and important work on bastard merogons, in which an enucleated egg of one species of newt is fertilized by a sperm of a different species. He showed that some tissues are able to develop to late embryonic stages, while others die presumably owing to disharmonies of nucleus and cytoplasm during particular processes of differentiation; still other tissues, such as some of the anterior mesoderm, while able to live, lose their normal power of inducing other organs—in this instance the balancers and gills. Similar studies of the importance of particular elements in the nucleus were reported by Poulson in his studies of the abnormalities produced by total absence of certain genes (homozygous deficiencies) on the

发育遗传学

沃丁顿

编者按

英国生物学家康拉德·哈尔·沃丁顿是现代发育生物学的先驱之一，特别是在建立胚胎学和发育学之间的联系方面有着重要的贡献。在这份报告中他对其所处时代的发育遗传学进行了综述，描述了当时研究者不断探索试图弄清楚基因、细胞过程以及外部环境是如何共同决定生物的发育和类型的。如今 DNA 测序技术和操纵技术的进步已彻底改变了对发育的理解，然而这些问题仍然是发育生物学及其与进化的相互作用（即"进化发育生物学"）的核心部分。特别地，基因与环境在发育中的相对重要性仍然被热烈地讨论着。

目前遗传学最活跃的分支之一就是研究基因影响发育过程的方式，而且发育遗传学这一部分有一项完整又有意义的计划。基因行为的问题如此的复杂和多面，以至于可能有多种不同的研究途径，其中大部分的实例都可以在大会上提交的论文中找到。

兰道尔的论文从胚胎学途径进行了很好的例证。在论文中他综述了在偶发的畸形生物和与基因有关的异常物种中发现的不同器官的相关效应。他指出这些现象中的许多都能用一般有害效应假说来解释，它作用于某一发育过程至关重要的阶段，常常影响生长速率。沃丁顿则提出了另一种完全不同的胚胎学途径，他讨论了基因与由组织者效应例证的一类发育过程之间的关系。

巴尔策更加详细地分析了细胞核因素在分化的特定步骤中的重要性，他对自己著名且重要的关于无核卵杂交的工作进行了总结，实验中用不同物种的精子来使一种蝾螈的去除了细胞核的卵子受精。他的研究显示一些组织能够发育到晚期胚胎阶段，而其他的组织则死亡了，可能是由于在分化的特定过程中细胞核与细胞质的不协调造成的；还有一些其他的组织，例如一些前中胚层组织，能够生存，但是丧失了诱导其他器官——在这个例子中主要是平衡器和鳃——的正常功能。波尔森在他的关于果蝇的早期发育阶段由于某些基因的完全缺失（纯合缺失）而产生变异的研究中报道了证实细胞核内特定成分重要性的类似研究。

early development of Drosophila.

Several reports dealt with gene effects on processes which are chemically more or less defined. Thus we had further chapters in the important and rapidly developing researches of Price, Lawrence and others on flower pigments, and Beadle, Ephrussi and others on Drosophila eye colours. Perhaps the most important new contribution in this field was a fresh study by Sewall Wright of guinea pig coat colours, which he dealt with in a preliminary way many years ago. He was now able to suggest a scheme for the relations of the numerous genes which are known, and to present a mathematical theory of their quantitative interactions.

Quite a different method of approach to the same problem was reported by Schultz and Caspersson, who, by studying the chromosome itself, obtained data which allow of some speculation as to the chemical changes occurring under the immediate influence of genes. Owing to their strong absorption in the middle ultra-violet, the distribution and changes of the substances belonging to the nucleotide group can be followed in the living cell by spectrophotometric methods elaborated by Caspersson. It is found that in the nucleus the nucleic acids seem to the indispensable for the development of chromosomes, and that they are synthesized mainly in earliest prophase just before the chromosomes split. Schultz studied translocations of parts of the heterochromatic regions of the chromosomes, which are rich in nucleic acid, into normal euchromatic regions in Drosophila. In certain of these translocations the adult flies show variegation for characters affected by genes near the position of the break in the chromosome, as though frequent mutations of the genes had occurred in late stages of development. Schultz showed that this variegation is correlated with cytological effects in the salivary chromosome bands corresponding to the variegated genes; these effects ranged from appearance of excess nucleic acid to the assumption of a heterochromatic character and finally apparent disappearance. It is suggested that the appearance of excess nucleic acid is correlated with an inactivation of the gene as a developmental agent. The nucleic acid metabolism can be followed somewhat further, since it is found that the presence of extra heterochromatic material (for example, supernumerary Y-chromosomes) affects both the degree of variegation, the cytological correlates of variegation mentioned above, and also the nucleic acid content of the cytoplasm. The different types of nucleic acid occurring in chromosomes, nucleolus and cytoplasm can be determined spectroscopically and suggestions made as to their functional relations with the fundamental processes of gene action and gene reduplication.

It is possible, as Schultz suggests, that we may in this way obtain some insight into the changes of gene activity in different chromosome regions in the different tissues, which may provide a mechanism for the primary differentiation of the nuclei in development.

(**144**, 817-818; 1939)

一些报告讨论了基因对某些生物学过程的作用，从化学角度来看，这些生物学过程基本上是明确的。因此，我们还用另外的章节讨论了某些重要且迅速发展的研究方向，其中包括普赖斯、劳伦斯等对花色素的研究以及比德尔、伊弗鲁西等对果蝇眼睛颜色的研究。在这个领域中最重要的新发现可能是休厄尔·赖特对豚鼠皮毛颜色的新研究，数年前他就进行过初步的实验。现在他已经能够给出已知的为数众多的基因之间关系的结构图，并且提出它们之间定量关系的数学理论。

针对相同的问题，舒尔茨和卡斯帕森提出了一种截然不同的研究途径，他们通过研究染色体本身获得了一些数据，这些数据引发了人们对受基因直接影响而发生的化学改变的思考。由于其在中紫外区有强烈的吸收，卡斯帕森提出用分光光度计法检测活细胞内核苷酸类物质的分布和变化。他们发现，在细胞核中核酸对于染色体的发育似乎是必不可少的，而且它们主要是在染色体分离之前的最早期合成的。舒尔茨对果蝇中富含核酸的染色体上异染色质区域的一部分转移到正常常染色质区域的易位现象进行了研究。一些发生易位的成体果蝇由于受到染色体中断裂位点附近基因的影响而表现出性状的多样性，犹如发育后期这些基因发生的频繁突变。舒尔茨发现这种多样性与对应于唾液腺染色体条带中多样化的基因的细胞学效应有关；这些效应的作用从过量核苷酸的出现一直延伸到异染色质特征的假设，以及最终明显的消失。研究表明，过量核苷酸的出现与发育相关基因的失活有关。对核苷酸代谢的研究可以进一步深入，因为人们发现额外异染质物质的存在（例如超数 Y 染色体）能够影响多样性的程度、上述多样性的细胞学相关性以及细胞质中的核酸含量。可以借助分光光度计检测染色体、核仁和细胞质中不同类型的核酸，进而就能提出它们与基因行为和基因复制的基本过程之间的功能关系。

正如舒尔茨所提出的，我们很有可能能够通过这种方法深刻了解不同组织的不同染色体区域中基因行为的变化，从而了解发育过程中核初始分化的机制。

（毛晨晖 翻译；王晓晨 审稿）

The Crab Nebula: a Probable Super-Nova

Editor's Note

In 1932, Subrahmanyan Chandrasekhar had proposed that massive stars which had exhausted their energy source would collapse and then, if sufficiently massive, would explode in a thermonuclear explosion called a supernova. The Crab Nebula has been recognised as an unusual object in the sky—a ring of light—and by the beginning of the twentieth century it was known to be expanding. By a remarkable sequence of inferences in which ancient Chinese records played an important part, the object has now been recognised to be the remnant of a supernova, as defined by Chandrasekhar, that exploded in 1054.

THE Crab Nebula in Taurus, which has the distinction of being No. 1 in Messier's Catalogue, is of peculiar interest, as is shown by articles published respectively in *L'Astronomie* (August 1939) and in the *Telescope* (September 1939). These articles summarize the results of several technical papers published on this subject during the past few years. It seems likely that the Crab Nebula was first recorded by John Bevis, an English physician, in 1731. It was rediscovered in 1758 by the French astronomer, Charles Messier, and was later the subject of careful scrutiny by Sir William Herschel. It was observed with the great reflector at Parsonstown, Ireland, by Lord Rosse, whose drawing of the nebula, published in 1844, probably suggested its name. It remained, however, for astronomical photography to show, first in 1892 by Isaac Roberts and later by the American astronomers (Keeler, Curtis and Ritchey), its peculiar filamentary structure and afterwards to provide data for measuring its linear rate of expansion of about 0.18″ per annum.

Using this value and the present angular dimensions of the nebula and extrapolating backwards, an interval of about 800 years is obtained for the nebula to expand from a point of origin. A similar time interval (900 years) was obtained by Hubble. Spectra of the Crab Nebula, first obtained in 1913-1915 at the Lowell Observatory, showed a bowing of the emission lines, when the slit of the spectrograph crossed the whole extent of the nebula (major axis 6′). Interpreting this feature as a differential Doppler effect due to the approaching nearer side of a shell of gas and the receding further side, Mayall in 1937 derived a velocity of expansion of about 1,300 km./sec. from Lick spectrograms. Assuming a constant rate of expansion, he concluded from the available data that the epoch of the outburst was about A.D. 1100. Meanwhile, Lundmark had pointed out that the Crab Nebula was near the position of the bright object recorded in Chinese and Japanese annals as having been seen for six months in A.D. 1054. In 1934, a translation by Y. Iba of the Japanese records gave the position of the object as near the star ζ Tauri and

蟹状星云可能是一颗超新星

编者按

1932 年，苏布拉马尼扬·钱德拉塞卡提出，已耗尽能量的大质量恒星会发生塌缩，而且如果质量足够大，塌缩的恒星将会发生热核爆炸，从而形成所谓的超新星。人们已经认识到蟹状星云是太空中一个独特的天体——一个光环，并且早在 20 世纪初就知道它在不断地膨胀。通过一系列惊人的推断（其中中国古代的相关记载起了很大的作用）表明该天体是超新星爆发后留下的遗迹。按照钱德拉塞卡的观点，这颗超新星爆发于 1054 年。

在梅西耶星云表中金牛座的蟹状星云编号为 No.1，人们对它特别感兴趣。关于这一星云的介绍可以分别参考《天文学》（1939 年 8 月）和《望远镜》（1939 年 9 月）中的文章。这些文章总结了在过去的几年中人们对这一天体的研究成果。1731 年，英国内科医生约翰·贝维斯记载了蟹状星云，这很可能是关于该星云的最早记录。后来，法国天文学家夏尔·梅西耶于 1758 年再次发现该星云。紧接着，威廉·赫歇尔爵士对这一星云又进行了仔细的研究。罗斯勋爵在爱尔兰的帕森斯城也使用大反射望远镜对这一星云进行了观测，他所绘制的蟹状星云发表于 1844 年，这很可能就是其星名的由来。然而，直到 1892 年艾萨克·罗伯茨对该星云进行了拍摄，以及后来美国天文学家（基勒、柯蒂斯和里奇）所进行的类似工作，人们才发现该星云具有独特的细丝状结构，之后从这些相关的数据中人们还测出了其膨胀的线速度为每年 0.18″。

根据蟹状星云这一膨胀速度和目前观测到的张角大小，通过反推可以求得蟹状星云从原点向外膨胀至今约有 800 年。哈勃也曾得到类似的结果（为 900 年）。洛威尔天文台于 1913~1915 年首次测量了蟹状星云的光谱；当摄谱仪的狭缝横跨整个星云（长轴为 6′）时，观测到了许多弓状的发射谱线。这些特征被解释为由于靠近观测者一侧的星云气体壳的逼近和远端气体壳的远离造成的差分多普勒效应，梅奥尔于 1937 年根据利克天文台的光谱图推导出该星云的膨胀速度约为 1,300 千米/秒。他假定该膨胀速率一直不变，从而由现有的数据计算出该星云大约爆发于公元 1100 年。同时，伦德马克指出，中国和日本的史书中记载，公元 1054 年曾观测到持续了 6 个月（编者注：北宋至和元年）的特亮的客星（超新星），其位置与蟹伏星云的位置相近。1934 年，伊巴翻译了日本古书中的相关记录，发现这一天体的位置靠近金

its brightness as equalling that of Jupiter. By combining the apparent linear expansion in seconds of arc per annum with the absolute expansion in km./sec., the order of distance was derived as 1,500 parsecs, equivalent to nearly 5,000 light years. Using this distance and the apparent magnitude of Jupiter (−2.2 m.), the absolute magnitude of −13.1 is obtained for the nova, which must have been at least one hundred times as bright as an ordinary nova.

In *Contributions* from the Mount Wilson Observatory No. 600, W. Baade assembles the evidence for the existence of two classes of novae, common novae and super-novae, which differ in luminosity by a factor of about 10,000. Typical of the former class is the nova which appeared in the Andromeda nebula in 1885 and reached a maximum apparent visual magnitude of 7.2, equivalent to an absolute magnitude of −15.0. To this recently recognized class of super-novae, so the evidence suggests, the nova of 1054 may have belonged, and the expanding shell of gas originating with the cosmic explosion is still visible as the Crab Nebula.

(**144**, 874; 1939)

牛座 ζ 星，其亮度相当于木星的亮度。综合上面已经得到蟹状星云的视膨胀角速度（单位：角秒 / 年）和绝对膨胀线速度（单位：千米 / 秒），我们可以计算出蟹状星云与地球的距离为 1,500 秒差距，约等于 5,000 光年。利用这一距离和木星的视星等（-2.2 等），我们可以得到这颗新星的绝对星等为 -13.1，该亮度至少是普通新星的 100 倍。

在第 600 期的《威尔逊山天文台研究通讯》上，巴德根据收集到的观测数据将新星分为两类：普通新星和超新星，后者的光度大约是前者的 10,000 倍。1885 年出现在仙女座星云中的新星就属于典型的普通新星，其最大视目视星等为 7.2，相当于绝对星等 -15.0。至于最近才发现的这类新星，即超新星，有关证据表明公元 1054 年观测到的那颗新星就属于这一类，并且这类新星中源于宇宙爆炸时期的气体壳层膨胀现象，至今仍然可以在蟹状星云中看到。

（金世超 翻译；何香涛 审稿）

The Relationship between Pithecanthropus and Sinanthropus

Editor's Note

In 1931, not long after his discovery of "Peking Man" (*Sinanthropus*), Davidson Black—perhaps inevitably—remarked on the similarity between this form and that of *Pithecanthropus* from Java. Relatively little cranial material of *Pithecanthropus* was available at the time. However, by the end of the 1930s, enough had been discovered to allow Gustav von Koenigswald and Franz Weidenreich to attempt this comparison. Their conclusion was that the two forms were no more different than people from two different modern human races. Indeed, both forms are now referred to *Homo erectus*. Neither scientist was to know it, but this was the last occasion any direct comparison could be made—the original Peking Man fossils disappeared during World War II.

DAVIDSON Black had remarked on the great similarity between the first skull of Sinanthropus to be found and the Pithecanthropus skull of Trinil, a condition which induced him to see in Pithecanthropus a Hominid form closely related to Sinanthropus (1931). The additional finds of the latter, unearthed in the interval, have confirmed Black's interpretation in every respect. But on the other hand, since the Pithecanthropus finds remained restricted to that rather incomplete specimen of Trinil, absolute evidence for his true Hominid character was lacking. In such circumstances, there was no other way open but to await the discovery of additional Pithecanthropus material before definitely solving this problem.

These discoveries materialized. Following the recovery of a rather primitive infantile skull (*Homo modjokertensis*) in 1936 and of a lower jaw of an adult individual, one of us (G. H. R. von K.), during 1937, discovered a skull in the undoubted Trinil deposits of Sangiran. This skull, preserved up to the basal region, conforms in every respect as to size, shape, and details to Dubois's Trinil specimen. Dubois, however, opposed the attribution of this skull to Pithecanthropus. Nevertheless, the details of the interior, as well as exterior surfaces of the skull, and also the skiagrams, delineating the otherwise indistinct sutures and breakage lines, show not the slightest trace of irregularity or deformation, such as would be unavoidable if the assembly of the fragments had been artificially adapted to a particular form. To this skull of Sangiran was added another skull fragment derived from the same deposits and of the same site during the summer of 1938, briefly described in *Nature* of October 15, 1938, p. 715, by us. We are now in a position to report on an additional Pithecanthropus find made this year. It concerns the lower part of an upper jaw of unusually large dimensions, comprising the processus alveolares of both sides with completely preserved nasal floor and palate, the complete left dental arch with all the teeth leading from the canine backward, and a part of the right dental arch up to the first molar.

爪哇猿人与中国猿人的关系

编者按

1931 年，戴维森·布莱克（步达生）在发现"北京人"（中国猿人）后不久，又对中国猿人与在爪哇发现的爪哇猿人之间的相似性进行了探讨，这项工作似乎是自然而然顺理成章的。当时爪哇猿人的头骨材料相对匮乏。然而到了 20 世纪 30 年代末，已经有了充足的材料，这使得古斯塔夫·冯·柯尼希斯瓦尔德（孔尼华）和弗朗茨·魏登赖希（魏登瑞）可以尝试进行比较研究。他们认为这两类猿人之间的差别并不比两个现代人种之间的差别大。确实，现在这两个类型都被归为直立人。然而两位科学家都没有预料到，这是他们最后一次有机会对这两类猿人进行直接的比较——北京人化石的原件在第二次世界大战期间遗失了。

步达生对已发现的第一件中国猿人头骨和特里尼尔爪哇猿人头骨之间极大的相似性进行了探讨，基于对比结果，他认为爪哇猿人是一种与中国猿人关系紧密的原始人类的新类型（1931 年）。后来发掘出的中国猿人的其他化石在各个方面都证实了步达生的观点。但另一方面，对于爪哇猿人化石的研究仅限于一件取自于特里尼尔的相当不完整的标本，因此缺乏有关其真正人类形态的确实证据。在此情形下，彻底解决这个问题之前除了继续等待发现其他爪哇猿人化石资料之外，别无他法。

化石标本终于被发现了。1936 年在修复了一件相当原始的婴儿头骨（莫佐托克人）和一件成年个体的下颌之后，笔者之一（孔尼华博士）于 1937 年在桑吉兰无疑属于特里尼尔层的沉积中发现了一件头骨。这件头骨位于基底区上方，其大小、形状及细节等各方面都与杜布瓦的特里尼尔标本一致。然而，杜布瓦反对把这件头骨归为爪哇猿人。不过，这块头骨的内部细节与外部表面，以及能从中看出不同的模糊骨缝线与破裂线的 X 射线照片，都没有显示出丝毫不规则或变形的迹象。如果把这些碎片按照某种特别形式人为地拼接组装起来，就难免会造成一些不规则或变形迹象。我们在 1938 夏天于同一遗址的同一沉积层又发现了桑吉兰头骨的一件碎片，1938 年 10 月 15 日的《自然》第 715 页曾对其进行过简要的描述。现在我们要报道在这一年里所得到的有关爪哇猿人的另外一个发现。这是一件尺寸非常大的上颌的下部，它包括两侧的齿槽突，保存有完整的鼻腔底和腭骨；有从犬齿向后的全部牙齿的齐全左齿弓以及到第一臼齿的部分右齿弓。门齿缺失，但是它们的齿槽被保存

The incisors were lost, but their alveoli are preserved (see accompanying reproductions, *a* and *c*). Afterwards the skull belonging to this jaw was also found. It comprises the posterior third of the brain case, including the entire basis.

Morphologically and geologically, we believe we are justified in attributing all these finds to Pithecanthropus. This type is thus represented by the following finds:

(1) Skull of Trinil (Dubois, 1891): Pithecanthropus skull I.

(2) Mandible of Kedung Brubus (Dubois, 1891): Pithecanthropus mandible A.

(3) Juvenile skull of *Homo modjokertensis* (Geol. Survey 1936)*.

(4) Mandible of Sangiran (v. Koenigswald, 1936): Pithecanthropus mandible B.

(5) Skull of Sangiran (v. Koenigswald, 1937): Pithecanthropus skull II.

(6) Skull fragment of Sangiran (v. Koenigswald, 1938): Pithecanthropus skull III.

(7) (*a*) Maxilla of Sangiran (v. Koenigswald, 1939); (*b*) Skull fragment of Sangiran (v. Koenigswald, 1939): Pithecanthropus skull IV.

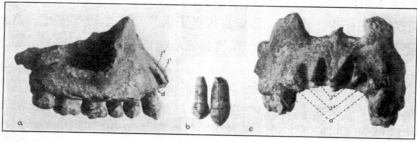

(*a*) Upper jaw of a male Pithecanthropus (Sangiran, January 1939), viewed from the right side. *d*, diastema; J^1, alveolus of J^1; J^2, alveolus of J^2. $\frac{2}{3}$ nat. size.

(*b*) Upper right canine and first premolar of a male individual of Sinanthropus (*FIV*), so as to demonstrate the protrusion of the canine. $\frac{2}{3}$ nat. size.

(*c*) The same as (*a*) but viewed from in front. $\frac{2}{3}$ nat. size.

The Sangiran skull (Pithecanthropus skull II) resembles the Trinil skull as closely as one egg another. The former (skull II) is only slightly smaller than skull I—its capacity being 835 c.c. as compared with 914 c.c. of the Trinil skull—but its parietal and occipital parts are relatively broader. The Sangiran fragment (Pithecanthropus skull III) is, in its preserved

---

* On the basis of my study of the original, I have now come to the conclusion that this infantile skull really represents a Pithecanthropus child. I shall report on this elsewhere.—F. W.

了下来（见所附的复制品，a 与 c）。后来这个下颌所属的头骨也被发现了。这件头骨包括脑壳的后 1/3，其中包含整个颅底部。

从形态学与地质学的角度分析，我们相信将所有这些化石归为爪哇猿人是合理的。因而爪哇猿人类型由以下化石来代表：

（1）特里尼尔头骨（杜布瓦，1891 年）：爪哇猿人头骨 I。

（2）凯登布鲁伯斯下颌骨（杜布瓦，1891 年）：爪哇猿人下颌骨 A。

（3）莫佐托克托人少年头骨，（《地质调查》，1936 年）[*]。

（4）桑吉兰下颌骨（孔尼华，1936 年）：爪哇猿人下颌骨 B。

（5）桑吉兰头骨（孔尼华，1937 年）：爪哇猿人头骨 II。

（6）桑吉兰头骨碎片（孔尼华，1938 年）：爪哇猿人头骨 III。

（7）（a）桑吉兰颌骨（孔尼华，1939 年）；（b）桑吉兰头骨碎片（孔尼华，1939 年）：爪哇猿人头骨 IV。

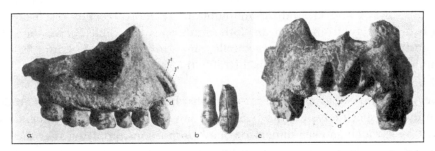

（a）男性爪哇猿人（桑吉兰，1939 年 1 月）上颌，右侧观察。$d=$ 齿隙；$J^1=J^1$ 齿槽；$J^2=J^2$ 齿槽。实际尺寸的 $\frac{2}{3}$。

（b）中国猿人男性个体的右上犬齿和第一前臼齿（FIV），以此来显示凸出的犬齿。实际尺寸的 $\frac{2}{3}$。

（c）与（a）一样，但是是从前面观察。实际尺寸的 $\frac{2}{3}$。

桑吉兰头骨（爪哇猿人头骨 II）与特里尼尔头骨极为相似。只是前者（头骨 II）稍小于头骨 I（其颅容量为 835 毫升，特里尼尔头骨颅容量为 914 毫升），但其顶骨与枕骨相对较宽。桑吉兰头骨碎片（爪哇猿人头骨 III）的保存部分，不像其他两个（头骨 I 和 II）那样扁，但是在其他方面均与它们相似。另外，它的矢状

---

[*] 这篇文章是基于我最初的研究成果，现在我得出的结论是：这件婴儿头骨确实属于一个幼年爪哇猿人。我将在别处对此进行报道。——魏登瑞

part, not so flat as the other two (skulls I and II), but otherwise resembles them in every detail. In addition, it bears a distinctly pronounced crista sagittalis.

Of the Sinanthropus cranial material, skulls E and II of Locus L are most suitable for a comparison, having capacities of approximately 915 c.c. and 1,015 c.c., respectively. These skulls are slightly larger than the Pithecanthropus skulls, but they are the same in general form and particularly in height.

The main differences so far as the skull cap is concerned consist in that in Pithecanthropus (skulls I and II) the supraorbital tori pass directly over to the extraordinarily flattened forehead, whereas in Sinanthropus the supraorbital ridges are much more demarcated from the tuber-like vaulted but otherwise also strongly receding forehead. On the other hand, the obelion region in Sinanthropus is flat, while in Pithecanthropus it is rounded off. The greatest similarity is seen in the general form and structure of the temporal and occipital bones, and there is absolute conformity in some special details of these bones. The Pithecanthropus fragment III and Sinanthropus skull E show identical features even in apparently unessential structures. Beside the first mentioned sagittal crest, there is in the obelion region on each side of the sagittal suture a short groove which Black described and illustrated in Sinanthropus skull E.

With regard to the lower jaws, that from Kedung Brubus is characterized as representing Pithecanthropus by the exclusively basal location of a broad digastric fossa—the only usable criterion. This mandible corresponds in size and proportions to the small female Sinanthropus jaws A and H, and the mandible M II, more recently discovered, and not yet described. The jaw from Sangiran (Pithecanthropus mandible B), on the other hand, is large, and corresponds to the large male Sinanthropus jaws G I and K I, with the exception that the frontal section is considerably thicker than in the latter.

The upper jaw from Sangiran (see reproductions) has as yet nothing comparable among the Sinanthropus specimens, for the two upper jaw fragments of the latter known up to the present have much smaller dimensions and proportions, implying that they belong to female individuals, while the upper jaw from Sangiran must be ascribed to a male.

The differences in size and proportions of the upper and lower jaws of both Pithecanthropus and Sinanthropus, apparently chiefly due to sexual differences, also serve as a criterion of the cranial conditions in this respect. The lower and upper jaws from Sangiran are much too large for the small Pithecanthropus skulls I and II, whereas the lower jaw fragment of Kedung Brubus would seem to fit them better. It may be concluded, therefore, that the two Pithecanthropus skulls, regardless of their minor differences in size and thickness, must have belonged to female individuals, whereas the rather heavy Pithecanthropus skull IV represents undoubtedly an old male individual.

With respect to the dentition, the Pithecanthropus molars are larger than those of Sinanthropus available so far. But the lower incisors—so far as the size of the crowns can be estimated from that of the alveoli—and especially the lower canines of

脊非常明显。

在中国猿人头盖骨化石中，头骨 E 和发现于 L 地点的 II 号头骨最适于进行比较研究，其颅容量分别约为 915 毫升和 1,015 毫升。这些头骨稍大于爪哇猿人头骨，但它们的形状大体一样，特别是高度。

头盖骨的主要差别在于：爪哇猿人（头骨 I 和 II）的眶上圆枕直接过渡到非常扁平的前额，而中国猿人的眶上脊（眉脊）与拱状隆起且同样呈低平状的前额之间的界限更为明显。另一方面，中国猿人的顶孔区扁平，而爪哇猿人的顶孔区圆隆。最大的相似性在于颞骨和枕骨的一般形式和结构，而且这些骨头的某些特别的细节也完全相似。爪哇猿人 III 号头骨碎片与中国猿人头骨 E 呈现出完全相似的特征，即便在一些非重要的结构上也是如此。除首次提到的矢状脊外，在矢状缝每一边的顶孔点区都有一条短沟，步达生在中国猿人头骨 E 中对此作了描述与图示。

凯登·布鲁伯斯发现的下颌骨因其宽阔的二腹肌窝位置靠近底部——这是唯一可用的判断标准——被视为爪哇猿人的代表。在大小和比例上，这件下颌骨与尺寸较小的女性中国猿人下颌骨 A 与 H 以及最近发现的尚未被描述过的下颌骨 M II 皆相似。另一方面，桑吉兰下颌骨（爪哇猿人下颌骨 B）尺寸较大，相当于大型中国猿人男性下颌骨 G I 和 K I。只是桑吉兰下颌骨的前部切面明显厚于中国猿人颌骨。

发现于桑吉兰的上颌骨（见复制品）与中国猿人标本没有任何可比性，因为迄今发现的两件中国猿人上颌骨碎片的尺寸和比例都很小，这表明它属于女性个体，而出自桑吉兰的上颌骨应该属于男性。

对于爪哇猿人和中国猿人，其上下颌骨在大小和比例上的差异主要是由于性别差异引起的，这也是判定头骨情况的一个标准。与尺寸较小的爪哇猿人 I 号和 II 号头骨相比，发现于桑吉兰的下颌骨和上颌骨要大得多，而凯登·布鲁伯斯下颌碎片似乎与它们更加符合。因此，尽管这两件爪哇猿人头骨在大小和头骨厚度方面存在微小差异，我们仍然可以推断，它们一定是属于女性个体，而粗重的爪哇猿人 IV 号头骨则无疑应属于老年男性个体。

牙齿方面，爪哇猿人的臼齿大于迄今为止发现的所有中国猿人的臼齿。但是爪哇猿人的下门齿（目前可根据齿槽大小估测出齿冠大小）尤其是下犬齿，无疑都比

Pithecanthropus, are decidedly smaller than those of Sinanthropus. The canines of the Pithecanthropus upper jaw (see reproduction *a*) protrude considerably beyond the premolars, despite the fact that both are much worn. They conform in this respect to the Sinanthropus canines (see *b*) so far as male individuals are concerned. The pattern of the Pithecanthropus canine resembles that of Sinanthropus, but is less complicated by lacking the cingulum so characteristic of the latter. These differences are also true for the premolars and molars, in so far as no one of these teeth in Pithecanthropus shows such primitive characteristics as are found in Sinanthropus. Pithecanthropus, therefore, undoubtedly stands in this respect at the upper limit of the range of variation approaching the Neanderthal types. On the other hand, in respect to other features, Pithecanthropus is of a more primitive nature than Sinanthropus: for example, the second molar of both upper and lower jaw of Pithecanthropus is distinctly larger than the first, and the third lower molar the longest of all three. In addition, it is evident that—the first example of a fossil Hominid known hitherto—the upper canines of both sides are separated from the lateral incisors by a broad diastema, the width of which amounts to 6.2 mm. on the right side (*d*, in reproductions *a* and *c*). This width comes close to the average width known for male gorillas and corresponds to that of the male orang (average width, according to Remane, 6.8 mm. and 6.2 mm. respectively).

The dental arch of the Pithecanthropus upper jaw is long and relatively narrow. The front teeth, according to the alveoli, were ranged within a curved line and directed forward, whereas the molars form two straight and backwardly diverging rows. Thus, all the skeletal remains and teeth of Pithecanthropus and Sinanthropus so far available prove the close general relationship between the two types.

With respect to the affinity of the Pithecanthropus femora—that is to say, the so-called Trinil femur, and the five femora afterwards recovered by Dubois and also attributed to Pithecanthropus—it must be taken into consideration that the seven femora of Sinanthropus, most of them represented only by shafts, show significant differences when compared with those femora. All of the Sinanthropus femora display, among other characteristics, a marked degree of platymeria, and at the same time a very low pilaster index; while the supposed Pithecanthropus femora show no indication of this kind, and are in all respects identical with those of modern man. All this points against the probability of their belonging to Pithecanthropus.

Pithecanthropus and Sinanthropus undoubtedly represent the most primitive Hominid forms known hitherto, which, according to Boule, may be ranged collectively under the name Prehominids. Which of the two types must be taken as the more primitive cannot be decided with absolute certainty for the present. Fragments of Sinanthropus skulls suggest that this type includes also specimens the capacities of which did not exceed that of Pithecanthropus II—as, for example, Sinanthropus skull J—and, on the other hand, those with a very long and rather low cranium, as the Sinanthropus skull fragment H III. Nevertheless, it is certain that Pithecanthropus shows some significant characteristics which must be considered more primitive than those evident in Sinanthropus, especially

中国猿人的小。爪哇猿人上颌（见复制品 *a*）犬齿明显突出于前臼齿，尽管它们二者都磨损严重。就男性个体而言，在这方面它们与中国猿人的犬齿（见 *b*）一致。虽然爪哇猿人犬齿与中国猿人犬齿有相似之处，但由于缺少中国猿人特有的齿带，因而并不怎么复杂。前臼齿与臼齿也有这样的差异，也就是说，没有一个爪哇猿人的牙齿能够显示出在中国猿人中发现的这种原始的特征。因此，毋庸置疑，爪哇猿人在这方面是处在变化范围的上限，接近尼安德特人。另一方面，就其他特征而论，爪哇猿人比中国猿人更为原始：例如爪哇猿人上颌与下颌的第二臼齿均明显大于第一臼齿，而下颌第三臼齿是所有三个下颌臼齿中最长的。另外，两侧上犬齿明显与侧门齿分开，其间裂隙很宽，在右侧（*d*，见复制品 *a* 与 *c*）其宽度达 6.2 毫米，而这一特征在迄今为止发现的化石人类中还是第一次出现。这个宽度与雄性大猩猩的已知平均宽度接近，并与雄性猩猩的平均宽度一致（根据雷马内的测量，平均宽度分别为 6.8 毫米和 6.2 毫米）。

爪哇猿人上颌的齿弓较长且相对较窄。从齿槽来看，前齿沿曲线排列且朝向前方，然而臼齿形成直线向后分叉的两排。这样，迄今为止所有可供研究的爪哇猿人与中国猿人的骨骼遗迹和牙齿都证明这两种类型之间总体接近。

至于爪哇猿人股骨（即所谓的特里尼尔股骨，以及后来杜布瓦发现的同样属于爪哇猿人的 5 根股骨）的亲缘性，一定要考虑到，中国猿人 7 件股骨（其中大部分仅保留骨干部分）与这些股骨进行比较时呈现出了重大差别。其他特征还包括，所有的中国猿人股骨扁平程度明显，而且同时股骨的脊指数十分低；推测属于爪哇猿人的股骨没有显示出这种迹象，并且在各个方面都与现代人类的相同。所有这些特点都不支持将它们归为爪哇猿人。

毫无疑问，爪哇猿人与中国猿人代表了迄今为止所知道的最原始的化石人类类型，按照布勒的意见，它们可以一并划归为前人。目前还不能确定这两个类型中哪个类型更为原始。中国猿人头骨碎片表明这个类型也包括脑量不超过爪哇猿人 II 号头骨的标本（例如中国猿人头骨 J），此外还包括具有很长且相当低平的头盖骨的标本，如中国猿人 H III 号头骨碎片。不过，可以肯定爪哇猿人显示出的某些重要特征明显比中国猿人的更原始，特别是具有上颌齿隙。

the presence of a diastema in the upper jaw.

Considered from the general point of view of human evolution, Pithecanthropus and Sinanthropus, the two representatives of the Prehominid stage, are related to each other in the same way as two different races of present mankind, which may also display certain variations in the degree of their advancement.

The Prehominids are separated from the Neanderthal group by a considerable gap. On the other hand, an apparently close relationship exists between Pithecanthropus and *Homo soloensis*, the skulls of the latter appearing like an enlarged form of the former. Certain peculiarities of Pithecanthropus reappear in exactly the same form in *Homo soloensis*. Those traits which suggest an already more advanced type, like the greater cranial capacity, and several other structural features, can be derived directly from Pithecanthropus, and correspond to the condition in the Neanderthal stage already attained by *Homo soloensis*. The two available fragments of the tibia of *Homo soloensis* show no special peculiarities, with the exception of a pronounced platymeria, exhibiting only recent human characters in their general form and in details.

The finds reported herein show that Java has become the most important centre for the study of Prehominid forms. Not only Prehominids, but also the following evolutionary stage, *Homo soloensis*, are represented there. Furthermore, we know that the Wadjak man of Java represents another early form of recent man, whose upper jaw (Wadjak II) displays in some respects a most surprising resemblance to the Pithecanthropus upper jaw.

In conclusion, we wish to express our gratitude to the officers of the Government of the Netherlands East Indies, and the Carnegie Institution in Washington for their generous support, which made possible not only the more recent investigations in Java itself, but also our joint study, conducted in the Cenozoic Research Laboratory, Peiping Union Medical College, Peking, of recently obtained Pithecanthropus material.

G.H.R. von Koenigswald and Franz Weidenreich

(**144**, 926-929; 1939)

*   *   *

The article by Dr. G. H. R. von Koenigswald and Prof. F. Weidenreich on the relationship between Pithecanthropus and Sinanthropus in *Nature* of December 2 is eminently satisfactory to those anatomists who have not been able to understand why these two hominids should ever have been separated generically. Probably my colleague, Dr. S. Zuckerman, was the first to express doubt on the justification for this distinction, in an essay on Sinanthropus[1], and I have on more than one occasion urged that the Peking hominid is but a Chinese variant of Pithecanthropus[2].

从人类进化的一般观点来考虑，爪哇猿人和中国猿人，作为前人阶段的两个典型代表，就如同现代人类的两个不同人种一样，它们可能在进化程度上显示出某些差异，但彼此仍然是密切关联的。

前人与尼安德特人之间存在着相当大的时间间隔。另外，爪哇猿人与梭罗人明显存在着密切的关系，梭罗人头骨似乎是爪哇猿人头骨的放大版。爪哇猿人的某些特征在梭罗人化石上以完全一样的形式再现。那些象征着相对进步的特征，如较大的颅容量以及其他一些结构特征，可能是直接从爪哇猿人演化而来，并且与梭罗人已达到的尼安德特人阶段的情况相符合。现有的两件梭罗人胫骨碎片除呈现明显的扁平外，在一般形状和细节上没有显示出特别现代人类的特点。

在这里所报道的发现表明，爪哇已经成为最重要的研究前人类型的中心。因为那里不仅有被归为前人的爪哇猿人，还有作为其后续进化阶段的梭罗人。此外，我们还知道爪哇的瓦贾克代表着现代人类的另一种早期类型，其上颌（瓦贾克 II）在某些方面与爪哇猿人的上颌惊人地相似。

最后，我们对荷属东印度群岛政府的官员和华盛顿卡内基研究院表示感谢，感谢他们慷慨的支持，他们的支持不仅使得近期在爪哇当地的研究得以进行，也使得我们在北平协和医学院新生代研究室对最近获得的爪哇猿人材料进行共同研究成为可能。

孔尼华，魏登瑞

（田晓阳 翻译；刘武 审稿）

*　　*　　*

孔尼华博士和魏登瑞教授在 12 月 2 日《自然》杂志上发表的有关爪哇猿人和中国猿人之间关系的文章，为那些不能理解为什么这两种原始人类群体属于不同的种属的解剖学家提供了非常令人满意的解释。我的同事朱克曼博士可能是第一位对这一区分的合理性表示怀疑的人，他在一篇关于中国猿人的文章 [1] 中表达了这一观点，我也曾多次极力主张北京人只是爪哇猿人的一个中国变种而已 [2]。

While for some years Prof. Weidenreich, with his first-hand knowledge of the Chinese fossils, has been insisting on their supposed distinctive characters, and has put forward the thesis that they represent an early type of man still more primitive than Pithecanthropus, he now agrees not only that Pithecanthropus and Sinanthropus "are related to each other in the same way as two different races of present mankind", but also that in some significant characteristics Pithecanthropus is the more primitive of the two. If these conclusions are accepted (as they certainly should be) it now becomes necessary finally to discard the generic term Sinanthropus. The Chinese fossils should logically be referred to the species *Pithecanthropus erectus*, or, if it should be thought more desirable as a temporary convenience for purposes of reference, they might be conceded a specific distinction with the name *Pithecanthropus pekinensis*.

The article of Dr. von Koenigswald and Prof. Weidenreich raises again the whole question of the validity of the morphological evidence upon which physical anthropologists often seem to depend for their taxonomic conclusions. For example, the authors use the remarkable argument that, because the femora ascribed to Pithecanthropus of Java show a marked degree of platymeria such as is not found in the femora of "Sinanthropus", therefore they probably do not belong to Pithecanthropus. This statement would provide a pretty exercise in logical analysis. A similar process of reasoning would also lead to the conclusion that, because a femur excavated from a Neolithic barrow shows more platymeria than the femur of a modern Englishman, therefore it cannot belong to *Homo sapiens*! In any event, an acquaintance with recent literature might have informed the authors of a short, but not unimportant, paper by the late Dr. Dudley Buxton on platymeria and platycnemia[3] in which evidence is adduced in support of the thesis that these characters may have a nutritional basis, and no racial significance.

W. E. Le Gros Clark

(**145**, 70-71; 1940)

G. H. R. von Koenigswald: Bandoeng.

Franz Weidenreich: Peking Cenozoic Research Laboratory, Peiping Union Medical College, Peking.

W. E. Le Gros Clark: Department of Human Anatomy, University Museum, Oxford, Dec. 17.

References:

1. *Eugenics Rev.*, **24** (1931).

2. *Man*, **60** (April 1937); *Modern Quarterly*, 115 (April 1939); Presidential Address, Section H, British Association, 1939.

3. *J. Anat.*, **73**, 31 (1938-1939).

　　然而魏登瑞教授凭借自己多年来对中国化石的第一手了解，一直都坚持认为中国化石人类具有不同的特征，并且进一步提出中国猿人可以作为比爪哇猿人更原始的早期人类型的代表的观点。现在他不仅认可爪哇猿人和中国猿人"就如同现代人类的两个不同人种一样"，而且同意在某些主要特征上，二者相比，爪哇猿人要更原始一些。如果这些结论被认可了（事实上理应如此），那么现在就有必要废弃中国猿人这个属名。逻辑上应该将中国化石归为爪哇猿人直立种，或者，如果希望它更便于被临时引用，那么可以给它一个具有鲜明特征的名字，北京直立猿人。

　　孔尼华博士和魏登瑞教授的文章再次提出了形态学证据的有效性的问题，人类学家似乎常常将这些形态学证据作为分类学结论的依据。例如，作者下述值得注意的论证，即由于爪哇猿人的股骨具有显著的股骨扁平特点，而"中国猿人"的股骨却非如此，因此中国猿人很可能不属于爪哇猿人属。这样的阐述非常漂亮地应用了逻辑分析。那么同理也可得出如下结论：因为从新石器时代的古墓中发掘到的股骨显示出比现代英国人股骨更扁平的特点，所以不能将其归属于智人！但不管怎样，已故的达德利·巴克斯顿博士关于股骨和胫骨扁平度的文章[3]虽然短小却很重要，它可能使作者们对最近的文献有所认识，在这篇论文中，他举出了相关证据来支持如下观点：这些特征可能是由于营养问题造成的，而并不能反映种族的特征。

勒格罗·克拉克

（刘皓芳 翻译；刘武 审稿）

Measurements of the Velocity of Light

Editor's Note

Commenting on the earlier proposal of M. E. J. Gheury de Bray, Lord Kitchener asserted that observations suggesting a very slight slowing of the speed of light over time were probably due to error. Here Gheury de Bray responds. Although some techniques for measuring the speed of light could be criticized, he says, this cannot be said of his toothed-wheel method. He also notes that Simon Newcomb and Albert Michelson had independently reported similar results, which differed by just the amount expected if the speed of light were slowly changing. All the same, there seems now no evidence of such an effect, although the possibility of changes in physical constants over time is still debated.

M E. J. Gheury de Bray suggests[1] that measurements of the velocity of light show that it is changing according to a formula:

$$c = 299,900 - 3.855\, T, \tag{1}$$

T being measured in years from 1900.

Assuming that Planck's constant and the energy E given out by an excited atom remain unchanged, the relation

$$E\lambda = ch \tag{2}$$

shows that a change in c must be accompanied by a proportional change in λ. But the wave-length of the red calcium line has remained constant to within one part in five million for thirty years, only 0.5 percent of the change required by (1).

It is probable that there are unsuspected systematic errors in the determinations of c.

Kitchener

*   *   *

The decrease of velocity of light deduced from the red-shifts is of the order of 1 km./sec. in 6,000 years, or 1 in 600,000,000 for thirty years, which is quite consistent with the apparent constancy of the wave-length mentioned by Lord Kitchener. Our observations, being affected by unsuspected systematic errors, and covering only a third of a century, give what is probably a greatly exaggerated rate of slowing down. The remarkable fact is that *all* the determinations are unanimous in indicating the existence of such a variation, and the red-shifts, if interpreted so as to escape from fantastic results, confirm it.

光速的测定

编者按

基奇纳勋爵在评论谷瑞·德布雷早前的猜想时断言，观测结果所显示的光速随时间的轻微变慢很可能是由于误差造成的。谷瑞·德布雷在这篇文章中予以回应。他说，尽管测量光速所用的一些技术值得怀疑，但他所使用的齿轮方法不在此列。他也指出西蒙·纽科姆和阿尔伯特·迈克尔逊都曾独立地报道过类似的结果，区别仅仅在于光速减慢的变化速率不同。尽管如此现在看来似乎仍没有证据支持这个效应的存在，虽然对物理常数随时间变化的可能性仍然在探讨之中。

谷瑞·德布雷指出 [1]，光速的测定结果表明它依照如下公式而变化：

$$c = 299{,}900 - 3.855\,T, \tag{1}$$

式中的 T 是自 1900 年以来的年份。

假定普朗克常数和受激发原子释放出的能量 E 保持恒定，则关系

$$E\lambda = ch \tag{2}$$

表明光速 c 变化的同时必定伴随着 λ 与之成比例的变化。但是我们观测到红色钙谱线的波长在 30 年中的变化小于五百万分之一，而这只有公式（1）中变化量的 0.5%。

这可能是在光速 c 的测量过程中存在的未知的系统误差。

基奇纳

*　　*　　*

根据红移推断，光速在 6,000 年中降低了 1 千米 / 秒的数量级，或者说在 30 年中降低了 1/600,000,000，这与基奇纳勋爵所谈到的波长的表观不变性颇为一致。由于受未知的系统误差的影响，以及观测仅持续了 1/3 个世纪，所以我们观测到的结果很可能远远夸大了光速减慢的速率。不过显而易见的是，**所有**测量结果都一致地表明这种变化的存在，而且，如果不对红移进行荒诞怪异的解释的话，那么红移就证实了这一点。

The Table 1 of the communication referred to cannot be dismissed on the ground of "unsuspected systematic errors". It is admitted that the method of the revolving mirror may suffer from physical bias, but no such reproach can be levelled against the toothed wheel method, which is only open to objections of a physiological nature. These can be readily overcome by substituting for the observer's eye a photo-electric sensitive device. While France and the United States share between them practically the whole initiative in the measurement of c, Great Britain has only to her credit a conspicuous failure. Is there in this country no one who can redeem it from this position and settle this question, which lies at the basis of physical science, considered in its broadest aspect?

Two observations, of Newcomb (1882.7 : 299,860) and of Michelson (1882.8 : 299,853) agree so closely that, if we consider that they were made by different observers, working independently with different instruments and different techniques, in different places, they must be extremely accurate, despite their large probable errors. It is significant that the second in date gives a lesser value of c.

M. E. J. Gheury de Bray

(**144**, 945; 1939)

Kitchener: Trinity College, Cambridge.

M. E. J. Gheury de Bray: 49, Great Thrift, Petts Wood, Nov. 2.

Reference:
1. *Nature*, 144, 285 (1939).

不能由于存在"未知的系统误差"而把我之前提到的表 1（见本书第 689 页）排除在考虑的范围之外。我们知道，旋转镜方法可能会受到物理偏置的影响，但是齿轮方法就没有受到这类影响，这种齿轮方法存在的唯一问题是研究者的生理特征的影响。不过通过用光电敏感装置代替观测者的眼睛，我们就可以很容易地克服这些困难。实际上，当法国和美国共同占据了测定光速 c 值的全部主动性时，留给英国的只是赤裸裸的失败。难道这个国家就没有人能挽回这种局面并且从最广泛的视角来解决这个物理科学的基础问题吗？

纽科姆（1882.7：299,860）和迈克尔逊（1882.8：299,853）的观测结果惊人一致，如果考虑到它们是由不同的观测者用不同的装置和技术方法在不同的地点各自独立地得到的，我们甚至可以断言这些结果是极为精确的，哪怕存在着较大的或然误差。重要的是，观测日期靠后的迈克尔逊给出了较小的 c 值。

谷瑞·德布雷

（王耀杨 翻译；张元仲 审稿）

The Evolution of the Stars

F. Hoyle and R. A. Lyttleton

Editor's Note

Astronomers Fred Hoyle and Raymond Lyttleton review how recent advances in nuclear theory were fundamentally changing astronomers' understanding of stellar evolution. It was now possible, as George Gamow had recently argued, to probe the nuclear chemistry likely to be important at the densities and temperatures prevailing in stars. But Hoyle and Lyttleton think Gamow went rather too far in suggesting most problems of stellar evolution were now solved. In Gamow's view, for example, all red giant stars must be of very recent origin, which seemed most unlikely. Hoyle and Lyttleton were correct: physicists then understood only the rudiments of nuclear chemistry, and knew nothing of nuclear fusion, a key process driving all stellar activity and evolution.

PROF. G. Gamow has recently discussed in *Nature*[1] the consequences of recent developments in nuclear theory on the problem of stellar evolution. In the light of the exact knowledge that is now available of a large number of nuclear reactions, it is possible to decide which processes rise to importance at the densities and temperatures prevailing in the stars, and on this basis trustworthy estimates have been given for the rate of liberation of subatomic energy. These results, which are the outcome of laboratory investigations, furnish the mathematical theory of internal constitution of the stars with a new equation that enables the luminosity of a star to be calculated by direct methods. The information so obtained has been utilized to attempt to resolve the many paradoxes and discrepancies encountered in discussing the general problem of stellar evolution. All this recent work has been authoritatively summarized by Gamow with great clarity and understanding in the article referred to above. It is therefore with some surprise that we find that Prof. Gamow concludes his article with the impression that these new developments practically solve the problems of stellar evolution. This seems to us to be so far from being the case that some further discussion of the claims of nuclear theory as the main factor in stellar evolution would be desirable.

In the first place, it should be noticed that the application of nuclear theory in its present state inevitably leads to a result at least as embarrassing as any of the questions that it might possibly resolve. For the theory maintains that no synthesis of atomic nuclei from hydrogen is possible within the stars except for the very light elements. This would imply that the stars can no longer be regarded as the building place of the heavy elements, which must have formed before they became part of the star—if indeed they ever were formed. Now although such a conclusion does not itself constitute a logical contradiction, it seems to us to present such overwhelming difficulty that it is much more reasonable to conclude that the basis of nuclear theory is in need of revision rather than that the heavy

恒星的演化

霍伊尔，利特尔顿

编者按

天文学家弗雷德·霍伊尔和雷蒙德·利特尔顿回顾了核物理理论的近期进展是如何从根本上改变天文学家对恒星演化的理解的。如乔治·伽莫夫近期所指出的，现在有可能证明核化学在恒星当时的密度和温度下是有重要作用的。伽莫夫认为恒星演化的大多数问题现在都已经解决了，但霍伊尔和利特尔顿对此并不认同。例如，伽莫夫认为所有红巨星一定是在新近才产生的，但这似乎是最不可能的事情。霍伊尔和利特尔顿是对的：那时的大多数物理学家只知道核化学方面的初级知识，但对核聚变这一驱动恒星活动和演化的关键过程却一无所知。

乔治·伽莫夫教授最近在《自然》[1]杂志上讨论了核物理理论的最新进展在恒星演化问题上所取得的结果。根据现有可用大量核反应得到的准确知识，人们有可能确定在恒星当时密度和温度下哪些过程具有重要的作用，并且在此基础上，人们得到了对亚原子能量释放率的可靠估计。这些实验研究得到的结果为计算恒星内部结构的数学理论提供了一个新的方程，由此可以采用直接的方法计算恒星的光度。我们利用所获得的信息尝试解决恒星演化的普遍问题中遇到的许多矛盾和差异。在上面所引用的那篇文章中，伽莫夫以十分清晰易懂的方式对近来的所有工作进行了权威性的总结。令人有些惊讶的是伽莫夫教授在他的文章中得出的结论给人这样的印象：这些新的进展从实际上解决了恒星演化的多种问题。而在我们看来情况远非如此，核物理理论在恒星演化中作为主要因素的论断还需要进一步讨论。

首先，我们应该注意到目前核物理理论的应用和它有可能解决的任何问题一样，会不可避免地导致一种同样令人为难的结果。因为该理论认为，在恒星内部氢仅能合成一些非常轻的元素，而不能合成其他的原子核。这意味着恒星不能再被当成是重元素产生的地方，如果这些重元素确实曾经产生过，那么它们必须在变成恒星的一部分之前就已经产生了。现在尽管这个结论自身在逻辑上并不矛盾，但是目前在我们看来它却造成了非常巨大的困难，所以更为合理的结论是：核物理理论的基础所需要的是修正而非重元素不是由合成产生的。另一方面，许多研究者似乎已经认

elements were not formed by synthesis. On the other hand, many investigators seem to have accepted the former result as satisfactory, and in particular Gamow has proceeded to make it the basis of a theory of the red giant stars.

Secondly, Prof. Gamow apparently regards the conclusion that various classes of stars should be of totally different ages as a natural one. Thus the fact that the present theory leads to a life-time for certain massive stars of order 10^{-3} the life-time of the Sun is not regarded as a difficulty at all; indeed it is merely supposed that this is the case and the theory remains unquestioned. In point of fact, it is an essential part of the theory as proposed by Gamow that all red giant stars are considered as of very recent formation, since the presence of lithium, etc., is required to enable them to radiate with their supposed low internal temperatures.

Now if all the stars could be regarded as single autonomous bodies, it would be difficult to dispute the validity of these views by direct means. But it so happens that the frequent occurrence of binary systems enables a simple test of the theory to be made, for in the case of binary stars both components must be of comparable age. It is immediately clear that the well-known difficulty concerning the relative emission per unit mass of the components of doublestars must remain in any theory that appeals only to the internal properties of the stars, although by making very artificial assumptions in Gamow's theory some of these discrepancies might be avoided. For example, it would require as a general result that the less massive components of binary systems form with a hydrogen content differing systematically from that of their companions. In certain cases this would lead to even more dubious initial conditions: thus, whilst Sirius must have formed with high hydrogen content, it would have to be assumed (according to the more generally accepted theory of degenerate matter) that the companion formed almost solely from heavy elements for it to have been practically exhausted during the whole of its existence. Such a solution of this difficulty could scarcely be regarded as satisfactory even if there were no other objection to the theory described by Gamow.

It should be particularly noticed that the foregoing suggestion assumes that the components have not evolved by fission, for this latter process (even if it were dynamically satisfactory) would clearly lead to two stars of closely similar compositions. We have been able to show, however, that to produce close binary systems, periods of order 5×10^{10} years are necessary[2]. Thus the existence of spectroscopic binary systems in which one component is a red giant or any highly luminous star presents an immediate contradiction of the theory given by Gamow. Moreover, there seems to be a general tendency for the mass of binary systems to increase with decreasing separation.

While on the subject of fission, it is perhaps only proper to point out here that although the mathematical investigations of the development of rotating fluid masses clearly demonstrate that binary stars cannot be generated by fission[3], many astronomers do not yet seem to have realized the physical significance of the mathematical results. As a consequence of this there are still many who "believe" in the fission theory. But as will

同前一个结论是令人满意的,特别是伽莫夫,他已着手把它作为了红巨星理论的基础。

其次,伽莫夫教授显然认为各种类型的恒星有完全不同的年龄是很自然的事情。因此,由现有理论得出的某些大质量恒星的寿命仅仅是太阳寿命的 10^{-3} 倍的结论完全没有被认为是一件困难的事情;事实上大家认为这就是事实且现有理论是毋庸置疑的。其实正如伽莫夫所提出的,所有红巨星形成于最近这样一个观点是现有理论里必不可少的一部分,这是因为需要锂等元素的存在,以使其可以在假定的内部低温中发出辐射。

现在,如果所有恒星都可以被看作是独立的天体,那么可能很难用直接的方法对这些观点的正确性提出质疑。但幸亏多次发现的双星系统使我们可以对该理论进行简单的检验,因为在此情况下,两颗成员星应该有同等的年龄。尽管伽莫夫理论中人为的假设避免了某些矛盾,但很显然,对于任何单纯只研究恒星内部性质的理论来说,著名的关于双星中成员星的单位质量相对辐射的困难仍然存在。例如,作为一个一般性结果人们可能会假设双星系统中质量较小的成员星在形成的时候氢含量系统性地和它们另外的成员星不同。在某些情况下,这可能会让初始条件变得更加可疑;所以,虽然天狼星在形成时氢含量可能很高,但我们不得不假设(考虑到简并态物质的理论已被更为广泛地接受了)其成员星几乎只由重元素组成,以使其在存在的整个期间耗尽主要的核燃料。即使对于伽莫夫提出的理论没有其他反对的理由,但是对于上述困难,这样的解决方案也是绝不可能令人满意的。

应该特别注意,上述理论假设了成员星不是通过分裂演化而来的,因为分裂演化(尽管在动力学上是合理的)会产生两颗组分相似的恒星。然而,我们已经能够证明,必须有 5×10^{10} 年量级的时间 [2] 才能产生密近双星系统。于是分光双星中,若其中一颗成员星是红巨星或者任一颗高亮度的星,就必然同伽莫夫所提出的理论相矛盾。另外,似乎存在一个普遍趋势,即双星系统的质量随间距的减小而增加。

在恒星分裂的问题上,或许在这里指出最为合适,即尽管转动流体演化的数学研究结果清楚地证明了双星不可能由分裂产生 [3],但是许多天文学家似乎还并没有意识到这些数学结果在物理方面上的重要性。因此仍然还有很多人"相信"分裂理论。但是正如人们将要看到的,即使求助于分裂理论也不能挽救伽莫夫的红巨星理论,

be seen, even an appeal to fission could not save Gamow's theory of the red giant stars, in addition to which it would raise afresh the difficulty of the relative emissions of the components in binary stars. Even if some process of break-up of a single star led to a binary system, it is evident that the components must have similar chemical compositions, while in close binary systems consisting of a red giant star and a class B star, Gamow's theory would require the red star to be the less massive component on account of the mass luminosity relation. But observation shows that in such pairs the giant star tends to be the more massive component. This is the case, for example, in the three stars υ Sagittarius, $V\ V$ Cephei and ζ Aurigae. Thus it seems that no matter from what angle we approach the questions raised by the observed properties of binary systems, the paradoxes already recognized by astronomers must remain in one form or another.

However, quite apart from the foregoing objections to the constructive portion of Gamow's article, it is very noticeable that no reference is made to the wide class of dynamical features that is associated with the stars. This, of course, is the direct result of attending only to the internal physical properties of the stars; but the dynamical features we have in mind are altogether too marked to remain unaccounted for in a satisfactory theory. Thus such questions as the formation of individual stars, and of binary and multiple systems, together with the general increase of mass with decreasing separation, and the observed approximation to equipartition of energy among the stars seem to present the real key to any theory of stellar evolution. An internal theory can give no explanation for the correlation between peculiar velocity and spectral class or the observed tendency for massive stars to lie in the galactic plane, features that must be related to the previous history of the stars.

It has been customary during recent years for investigators on stellar evolution to devote attention to internal constitution with little or no regard for the dynamical features. It appears that Prof. Gamow has followed essentially in this tradition and therefore confined his article to the modifications effected by the introduction of modern nuclear theory. Thus, in dealing with the properties of variable stars, no attempt is made to account for the three distinct periodicity groups comprised by stars of periods of order half a day, four days and 300 days. These variables also show a marked preference as regards spectral class, the first being largely of classes B and A, the second of F and G and the third of class M. Moreover, the two short-period groups exhibit a most remarkable property in that none of them, out of more than two hundred available examples, possesses a close companion, whereas about one star in five of normal stars of similar spectral classes does possess a close companion. On the other hand, long-period variables appear to possess a normal complement of companions. The first and third types are stars of moderate luminosity and show no pronounced galactic concentration, whereas the variables of intermediate period, the Cepheids, are strongly concentrated to the galactic plane and are among the most luminous known stars. Thus it is clear that very remarkable dynamical properties are intimately connected with even the different types of variability, and therefore that purely internal considerations are most unlikely to prove capable of elucidating the nature of the connexion.

768

此外双星成员星的相对辐射问题将再次出现。就算单星分裂的某一阶段会产生双星系统，但可以肯定的是成员星之间仍应该有相似的化学组成，对于一个由一颗红巨星和一颗 B 型星组成的密近双星系统，伽莫夫的理论认为基于质光关系，红巨星的质量相对较小。但观测结果表明在这种双星系统中，红巨星的质量往往相对较大。例如在人马座 υ、仙王座 VV、御夫座 ζ 这三个双星系统中，情况均是如此。这样看来，似乎无论我们从什么角度来处理双星系统观测性质上的问题，这个已被天文学家意识到的矛盾总会以某种形式存在。

然而，除了前面对伽莫夫文章理论构建部分提出的异议外，很明显，还没有文献提到与恒星相关的广泛动力学特征。当然，这是只关注恒星内部物理性质的直接结果；但是，总的来说我们考虑的动力学性质是个很重要的问题，为此任何一个理论要令人信服都应该对此给出说明。于是，诸如单个恒星、双星以及聚星系统的形成，双星质量普遍随间距的减小而增加，以及观测到类似在恒星之间近似均分能量，类似这样的问题似乎是所有恒星演化理论的真正关键。一个恒星内部结构的理论不能解释本动速度和光谱类型之间的关系，也不能解释为什么观测到的大质量恒星都倾向位于银道面上，而这些特征必然和恒星早先的历史有关。

近年来，致力于恒星演化研究的科学家们都习惯性地只关注恒星内部组成而很少或者不关心其动力学特征。伽莫夫教授似乎也基本上遵循了这个传统，因此他的文章局限于引入现代核物理理论加以改进。因此，在处理变星性质的时候，他没有试图解释由周期为半天、四天和 300 天量级的恒星组成的三个不同的周期组。这些不同周期的变星也明确显示出了与光谱型相关的顺序，第一类主要是 B 和 A 型星，第二类是 F 型星和 G 型星，而第三类是 M 型星。此外，两个短周期的组还显示出一个最显著的特性：在已有的两百多个例子中，没有一个有密近的伴星。而在具有类似光谱型的一般双星中，每 5 对就有一个具有密近的伴星。另一方面，长周期的变星有正常的伴星。第一类和第三类中等亮度的恒星并没有显著的向银道面聚拢，而中等周期的变星，如造父变星，却都位于已知最明亮的恒星之中并且都高度聚集在银道面上。这清晰地表示，明显的动力学性质甚至与不同类型的光变有着紧密的联系，因此只考虑恒星的内部结构是不大可能诠释这些联系的本质的。

From these and many other dynamical qualities associated with various types of stars, it appears to us that Prof. Gamow has over-estimated the importance of nuclear theory in the problem of stellar evolution. Indeed, in our opinion nuclear physics has very little to add to the results already conjectured by astrophysicists, and can merely serve to confirm these conjectures, a typical instance being the mass-luminosity relation itself. Finally, we wish to point out that although the present article consists largely of criticism, we have discussed elsewhere a number of the questions raised[2], and it has been found that purely dynamical considerations may be sufficient to provide a natural explanation of many of the difficulties mentioned in this article.

(**144**, 1019-1020; 1939)

F. Hoyle and R. A. Lyttleton: St. John's College, Cambridge.

References:
1. *Nature*, 144, 575, 620 (Sept. 30 and Oct. 7, 1939).
2. *Proc. Camb. Phil. Soc.*, (4), 35 (1939).
3. *Mon. Not. Roy. Astr. Soc.*, 98, 646 (1938).

　　考虑到上述这些情况以及其他与各种类型恒星相联系的动力学性质，在我们看来伽莫夫教授高估了核物理理论在恒星演化问题中的重要性。事实上，我们认为核物理对天体物理学家所推测出的结果几乎没有什么补充，只能用其来验证这些推断，一个典型的例子是质光关系本身。最后，我们想指出，尽管本文主要是批评，但是我们已经在另外一篇文章中对所提出的许多问题 [2] 进行了讨论，并且我们发现从纯粹的动力学角度考虑可能足以为本文中提到的这些困难提供一个合理的解释。

（钱磊 翻译；何香涛 审稿）

Radioactive Gases Evolved in Uranium Fission

L. Wertenstein

Editor's Note

The discovery of nuclear fission and its release of enormous energy posed the possibility of putting that energy to use, either in weapons or in industry. But scientists still knew very little of many fundamental processes which might influence its successful engineering. Here physicist Ludwik Wertenstein, writing from a Poland recently occupied by Nazi Germany, reports that the fission process produces radioactive gases. He had detected the radioactivity induced into several gases circulating about a sample of uranium bombarded by neutrons, and found traces of essentially two distinct radioactive components, with half-lives of about 30 seconds and four minutes. This was merely the beginning of detailed investigation required to bring nuclear energy into engineering practice.

IN this letter, a brief account is given of the preliminary results of an investigation of the radioactive gases evolved in the fission of uranium nuclei. This investigation was commenced this summer but was interrupted by the outbreak of the War. Even if the results so far obtained are not more complete than those obtained in the meantime by other investigators[1], it may still be of interest to describe the method employed, which follows somewhat different lines.

The radioactive gases evolved in the fission process were carried by a circulating stream of an inactive gas through two Geiger-Müller counters placed in succession. The time lag of the arrival of the gas in the two counters could be varied within wide limits by means of a system of capillary glass tubes of various bores placed in parallel and fitted with stopcocks. The magnitude of the lag was ascertained by separate experiments in which actinon or thoron was circulated. As a carrier gas, acetone vapour at a pressure of 10 mm. mercury was used because of its favourable properties for the working of the counters. The circulation was kept up by means of a Vollmer glass pump.

The uranium vessel, containing about 30 gm. of uranium oxide (U_2O_3), was surrounded by paraffin and provided with a well to allow introduction or removal of the neutron source, which consisted of about 30 mgm. of radon + beryllium. In the experiments, the counting rate of both counters was recorded for a period of time immediately following the commencement or cessation of irradiation. Typical results, using a time lag between the counters of 15 sec., are shown in the accompanying figure, from which it may be seen that the curves obtained for increase and for decay are almost complementary, and indicate several periods, of which some are of the order of a minute, while others are evidently much longer, giving rise to a residual activity almost constant within the time of the experiment.

铀核裂变时放出的放射性气体

维腾斯坦

编者按

核裂变的发现及其释放的巨大能量显示了将这种能量用于武器和工业的可能性。但是科学家对它的许多基本的过程仍了解很少，这可能影响到对它的成功工程化。物理学家卢德维克·维腾斯坦从最近被纳粹德国占领的波兰写出的信中指出，裂变过程产生放射性气体。他探测到在中子轰击铀样品周围几种气体循环引入的放射性，并发现两种截然不同的放射性组分的踪迹，它们的半衰期分别为 30 秒钟和 4 分钟。这仅仅是将核能引入工程应用详细研究的必要开端。

这封信对铀核裂变中放出放射性气体研究的初步结果进行了简要地说明。这项工作原计划于今年夏天开始着手，但是因二战的爆发而中断。尽管到目前为止我们所得到的结果并不比其他研究者在此期间所得到的结果 [1] 更为完善，但我们采用了一种稍为不同的研究方法，而描述该方法可能也是很有趣的。

裂变过程中放出的放射性气体依次流经放置好的两套盖革 – 米勒计数器，被其中无放射性气体环流携带出来。利用一套平行放置且装有活栓的不同孔径的毛细玻璃管构成的系统，可以对两套计数器内气体到达的时间延迟在很宽的限度内进行调节。时间延迟的长短可以通过锕射气或钍射气循环的分立实验来确定。实验中我们使用 10 毫米汞柱压强的丙酮作为载气，因为它具有有利于计数器正常运转的性质。气体循环是通过瓦尔莫玻璃泵来维持的。

将盛有大约 30 克氧化铀（U_2O_3）的容器用石蜡包围起来，并提供一个很容易引入和取走中子源的井，中子源由大约 30 毫克氡和铍组成。实验过程中，在照射开始或停止之后的一段时间，记录两台计数器的计数率。附图中显示了两计数器间的时间延迟为 15 秒钟时得到的典型结果，从图中我们可以看到，所得到的增长和衰减曲线几乎是互补的，并且展现出若干个周期（其中一些的数量级为分钟，另外一些则明显要长很多），这些在实验期间引起了几乎恒定的剩余放射性。

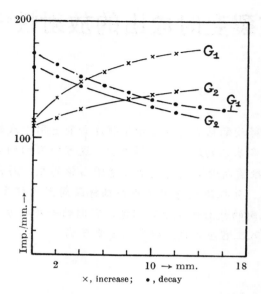

×, increase; •, decay

The shorter periods were estimated from a decay curve obtained in a separate experiment, in which the flow of gas was stopped at the same time that the source was removed, and the records of the two counters at any subsequent time simply added. This gave two periods of about 30 sec. and 4 min., the ratio between the rates of production of the corresponding gases being estimated as 1.82. (Glasoe and Steigman (*loc. cit.*) find two gaseous products of uranium fission of periods 30 sec. and 5 min., of which the first transforms into a product of 3 min. period. It is possible that the period of 4 min. found in our experiments results from a combination of the periods 3 min. and 5 min.)

A test of these estimates was further obtained by calculating from them the values of the ratio between the counting rates of the two counters for steady flow with the various circulating periods obtained by inserting different capillary tubes in the circuit, and comparing the calculated values with the values measured 12 min. after the beginning of the irradiation. This interval of time is not quite sufficient for complete equilibrium to be established, but, on the other hand, it is sufficiently short compared to the periods of the long-lived transformation products to ensure that the values obtained do not depend on the formation of these products to any appreciable extent.

Assuming that the radioactive gas consists only of the two short-period components of decay constants λ_1, λ_2 produced at the rate of n_1, n_2 atoms per sec., the counting rate in any of the counters can readily be shown to be given by

$$G = n_1 e^{-\lambda_1 \tau} \frac{1 - e^{-\lambda_1 \theta}}{1 - e^{-\lambda_1 T}} + n_2 e^{-\lambda_2 \tau} \frac{1 - e^{-\lambda_2 \theta}}{1 - e^{-\lambda_2 T}},$$

where τ is the time taken by the circulating gas to travel from the uranium container to the counter in question, θ the time taken by the gas to flow through the counter, and T the period of the whole circulation process.

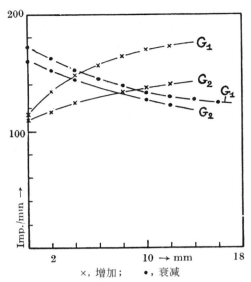

×,增加; ●,衰减

我们根据分立实验中得到的衰减曲线估算了较短的周期。实验中，气体的流动随着移开中子源而同时停止，在此之后对两台计数器的记录结果简单相加。这给出了约为 30 秒钟和 4 分钟的两个周期，产生相应气体的速率的比值的估算值为 1.82。（格拉索和斯泰格曼（见上述参考文献）发现铀裂变的两种气体产物周期分别为 30 秒钟和 5 分钟，其中第一种转变为一种周期为 3 分钟的产物。我们在实验中发现的周期为 4 分钟的产物有可能是 3 分钟和 5 分钟周期结合的结果。）

对上述估算的检验可以通过如下方式获得：通过在环路中插入不同的毛细管，获得各种环流周期，对具有这些周期的稳定流动计算两台计数器计数率的比值，并将计算所得的数值与辐射开始 12 分钟后测得的数值相比较。这一时间间隔对于完全建立平衡来说不是很充足，不过从另一方面来说，它与长寿命衰变产物的周期相比却已足够短，这足以确定所获得的值在任何可观程度上都不依赖于这些产物的形成。

假设放射性气体仅由衰变常数分别为 λ_1 和 λ_2、生成速率分别为每秒 n_1 和 n_2 个原子的两种短周期成分组成，其任一台计数器中的计数率都可以很容易由下列式子给出：

$$G = n_1 e^{-\lambda_1 \tau} \frac{1 - e^{-\lambda_1 \theta}}{1 - e^{-\lambda_1 T}} + n_2 e^{-\lambda_2 \tau} \frac{1 - e^{-\lambda_2 \theta}}{1 - e^{-\lambda_2 T}}$$

式中，τ 表示循环气体从盛铀容器到达我们正在讨论的计数器所需的时间，θ 表示气体流过计数器所需的时间，T 表示整个循环过程的周期。

In the table are recorded the counting rates, G_1, G_2, for the two counters measured 12 min. after the beginning of the irradiation for four capillary tubes corresponding to values of the time lag $\tau_2-\tau_1$ between the counters stated in the first column.

$\tau_2-\tau_1$	G_1	G_2	$G_1 : G_2$	$(G_1 : G_2)$ calc.
15 sec.	108	63	1.72	1.31
50 sec.	94	45	2.09	2.01
2 min.	52	24	2.15	2.10
3 min.	42	21	2.00	2.01

The agreement between the experimental and calculated values for the ratio $G_1 : G_2$ is seen to be very good except for the fastest circulation, for which the calculated value depends mostly on the shorter period and on the short time-lag, the determinations of which are the least precise.

(**144**, 1045-1046; 1939)

L. Wertenstein: Miroslaw Kernbaum Radiological Laboratory, Warsaw Society of Sciences, At Turczynck, near Warsaw, Sept. 24.

Reference:
1. Hahn, O., Strassmann, F., *Naturwiss.*, **27**, 163 (1939). Heyn F., Aten, A., and Bakker, C., *Nature*, **143**, 516 and **679** (1939). Glasoe and Steigman, *Phys. Rev.*, **55**, 982 (1939).

下面的表格中记录了两台计数器的计数率 G_1 和 G_2，其中，G_1 和 G_2 是在辐照开始 12 分钟后，两台计数器对相应于表中第一栏所列出的两个计数器之间的时间延迟 $\tau_2 - \tau_1$ 的四个毛细管进行计数所得结果。

$\tau_2 - \tau_1$	G_1	G_2	$G_1 : G_2$	$(G_1 : G_2)$ 计算值
15 秒钟	108	63	1.72	1.31
50 秒钟	94	45	2.09	2.01
2 分钟	52	24	2.15	2.10
3 分钟	42	21	2.00	2.01

我们可以看到，除了对于最快的循环之外，实验值和计算值之比 $G_1 : G_2$ 符合得相当好，这是因为对于最快的循环计算值主要依赖于较短的周期和短时间延迟，所以由此确定的结果精确性最差。

（王耀杨 翻译；张焕乔 审稿）

Scattering of Mesons and the Magnetic Moments of Proton and Neutron

W. Heitler

Editor's Note

Walter Heinrich Heitler was a German scientist who had emigrated to Britain in the 1930s. The particles of matter called mesons had not been observed in practice but only their existence inferred; their role was supposed to mediate the forces between particles of nuclear matter, neutrons and protons for example. This highly technical note suggests that other properties of the nuclear particles such as their magnetic moment could be calculated from their functions as mediators of the nuclear force.

THE meson theory in its present form exhibits a number of difficulties which are connected with the particular way in which the conservation of charge and the spin enter the interaction between mesons and the nuclear particles. The expression for the anomalous magnetic moment of the proton and neutron[1], for example, diverges as $\int_0^\infty dk$. The cross-section for the scattering of mesons by a nucleus is found to be very much larger than experiments permit and increases rapidly with increasing energy. This would be incompatible with the high penetrating power of cosmic ray mesons. The cross-section for scattering of a longitudinal meson (rest mass μ) with energy ε (momentum p/c) is, according to the present theory, given by[2]

$$\varphi = 4\pi\left(\frac{g^2}{\mu c^2}\right)^2 \frac{p^4}{\varepsilon^2(\mu c^2)^2} \tag{1}$$

From the analogy of mesons with light quanta, one would expect a cross-section of the order $(g^2/Mc^2)^2$, where M is the mass of the proton, and no increase with energy for $\varepsilon > \mu c^2$. The experiments by J. G. Wilson[3] have shown that the scattering cross-section even for an energy so low as a few times μc^2 (10^8 ev.) is smaller than (1) by an order of magnitude and does not increase with energy.

As can be seen from the computation of (1), both difficulties are due to the fact that the conservation of charge forbids a number of transitions which could occur if mesons were neutral particles[2]. A neutral meson could, for example, be *emitted and absorbed* by a proton. A positive meson can *only be emitted by a proton but not absorbed*. The cross-section for scattering would be of the right order of magnitude if we allow a positive meson also to be absorbed and a negative one to be emitted by a proton, etc., or, in other words, if "proton states" with charges $-e$ and $+2e$ existed[4]. The introduction of those particles meets, however, with the following difficulties. First, particles of this nature are not observed and are unlikely to have escaped observation if they occur in heavy nuclei. Secondly, if a proton were capable

介子散射与质子和中子的磁矩

瓦尔特·海因里希·海特勒是一位德国科学家，他于 20 世纪 30 年代移居英国。名
为介子的物质粒子实际上并没有观察到，它们的存在只是推测；其作用被认为是核
物质的粒子（比如中子和质子）之间作用力的媒介。这篇专业性很强的短文指出核
内粒子的其他一些性质，如磁矩，也能被视为核力的介质，我们可以通过它们的功
能函数计算得到它们的值。

现有形式的介子理论呈现若干困难，这是与电荷守恒和自旋引入介子与核粒子
之间相互作用的特殊方式相联系的。例如，质子和中子的反常磁矩表达式[1]作为
$\int_0^\infty dk$ 是发散的。我们发现介子被核散射的截面比实验允许值大很多，而且其随着能
量的增加而迅速增加。这种现象与宇宙线介子具有高穿透本领是相矛盾的。根据
现有的理论，能量为 ε（动量为 p/c）的纵向介子（静止质量为 μ）的散射截面为[2]

$$\varphi = 4\pi \left(\frac{g^2}{\mu c^2} \right)^2 \frac{p^4}{\varepsilon^2 (\mu c^2)^2} \tag{1}$$

通过将介子与光量子类比，我们可以预计散射截面的量级为 $(g^2/Mc^2)^2$，其中 M
为质子的质量，并且当能量 ε>μc² 时不再增加。由威尔逊[3]的实验表明，即使在能
量低至几倍 μc²（10⁸ 电子伏）时散射截面的量级比表达式（1）的值小，而且其值不
随能量的增加而增加。

从对表达式（1）的计算我们可以看出，前面所述的两种困难都源于电荷守恒禁
止了一些跃迁这个事实，而如果介子是中性粒子这些跃迁就会发生[2]。例如，一个
中性介子可以被一个质子**发射和吸收**。而一个正介子**只能被一个质子发射却不能被
其吸收**。如果我们允许一个正介子也可以被一个质子吸收且一个负介子可以被一个
质子发射等等，或者换句话讲，如果带有 −e 和 +2e 电荷的"质子态"存在[4]，那么
将得出数量级正确的散射截面。但是这些粒子的引入会遇到下面的困难。首先，具
有这些性质的粒子并没有被观测到，而如果它们在重核中出现时它们是不太可能不

of emitting also a negative meson, the negative meson would give a contribution to the anomalous magnetic moment of the proton of opposite sign and—all other quantities being equal—of the same value as the contribution from the positive meson. Thus, there would be no anomalous magnetic moment at all.

These difficulties can be overcome if we assume that the rest mass of the new particles is considerably *higher* than that of the proton, say, by 25-50 electron masses (see below). The particles would then be extremely unstable and would not play any part in the structure of heavy nuclei. Denoting the mass difference between the new particles and the proton by ΔM, the cross-section for the scattering of a longitudinal meson becomes, for $\varepsilon < Mc^2$, assuming $\Delta M \ll \mu$,

$$\varphi = 4\pi \left(\frac{g^2}{\mu c^2} \right)^2 \left\{ \frac{1}{3} \left(\frac{\mu}{M} \right)^2 \left(\frac{\mu c^2}{\varepsilon} \right)^4 + \left(\frac{\Delta M}{\mu} \right)^2 \frac{p^4}{\varepsilon^4} \right\} \tag{2}$$

This expression does *not* increase with energy for $\varepsilon > \mu c^2$. If p is approximately μc^2, (2) is smaller by a factor $(\Delta M / \mu)^2$ than (1). A value $\Delta M / \mu$ of approximately 1/5 would be sufficient to bring (2) into harmony with the experimental requirements. For ε greater than Mc^2, φ will probably decrease owing to the relativistic features of the proton.

Similar considerations must be applied to the spin. The spin contributes also to the high scattering cross-section (for transverse mesons). This can be avoided if we introduce also "higher spin states", for example, heavy particles with spin s of 3/2. Transitions from the normal proton state, s equal to 1/2, to these higher states under the influence of a meson field can be included in the theory in a very simple manner. In the present theory the spin-dependent interaction between a meson field φ and a nuclear particle is f/λ (σ curl φ), where σ is the spin matrix and has only matrix elements for $\Delta s = 0$. σ has to be extended in such a way as to include transitions $\Delta s = 1$. This can be done if we replace σ by the matrix of a dipole moment r/r. For transitions $\Delta s = 0$, the matrix elements of r/r and of σ are identical. If this is done, the cross-section for the scattering of transverse mesons also is small and of the order of magnitude (2). The physical significance of r/r is that of the *intrinsic* magnetic dipole moment of the proton, which is a characteristic feature of the meson theory (r is not, of course, the spacial position of the proton).

As a further result of our new assumptions, the anomalous magnetic moments diverge only *logarithmically*. Such a divergence can, at the present stage of the theory of the meson, scarcely be considered as a very serious difficulty. The relativistic features of the proton have so far been neglected, and it may well be that the logarithmic divergence would disappear if they are taken into account properly. As an upper limit for the validity of the meson theory in the form proposed above, we therefore take the rest energy of the proton. The anomalous magnetic moment of the proton then becomes (in units of the nuclear magneton μ_0)

$$\frac{\mu}{\mu_0} = \frac{16}{3\pi} \frac{M \Delta M}{\mu^2} \frac{f^2}{\hbar c} \left(\log \frac{2E_m}{\mu c^2} - \frac{4}{3} \right), \quad E_m \sim Mc^2 \tag{3}$$

被观测到的。其次，如果一个质子也能够发射一个负介子，那么负介子会对异号质子的反常磁矩有一定的贡献，并且其他所有的量都是相同的话，这些贡献与来自于正介子的贡献有相同的值，因此，根本就不会存在反常磁矩。

如果假定这些新粒子的静止质量远远**大于**质子的质量，比如说为电子质量的25~50 倍（见下文），我们就能够克服这些困难。那么，这些粒子将会极其不稳定，并且在重核结构中不会起任何作用。用 ΔM 表示新粒子与质子之间的质量差，当能量满足 $\varepsilon < Mc^2$ 时，假定 $\Delta M \ll \mu$，纵向介子的散射截面可以表示为：

$$\varphi = 4\pi \left(\frac{g^2}{\mu c^2}\right)^2 \left\{\frac{1}{3}\left(\frac{\mu}{M}\right)^2 \left(\frac{\mu c^2}{\varepsilon}\right)^4 + \left(\frac{\Delta M}{\mu}\right)^2 \frac{p^4}{\varepsilon^4}\right\} \tag{2}$$

然而当能量满足 $\varepsilon > \mu c^2$ 时，这个表达式的值**不会**随能量增加。如果 p 趋近于 μc^2，表达式（2）比表达式（1）小 $(\Delta M/\mu)^2$ 倍。一个趋于 1/5 的 $\Delta M/\mu$ 值，足以使表达式（2）与实验要求相吻合。如果能量 ε 大于 Mc^2，φ 可能会因为质子的相对论特征而减小。

对于自旋问题必须采取相似的分析思路。自旋同样会对高散射截面（对于横向介子）有贡献。如果我们同样引入"较高自旋态"，比如，具有自旋 s 为 3/2 的重粒子，就可以避开这个问题。在介子场的影响下，自旋 s 为 1/2 的正常质子态跃迁到较高能态，可以以非常简单的方式包含于理论中。在现有的理论中，介子场 φ 与核粒子之间与自旋相关的相互作用为 f/λ（σ 与 φ 做旋度计算），其中 σ 为自旋矩阵，且仅当 $\Delta s = 0$ 时才有矩阵元。必须对 σ 矩阵进行扩展，这样才能够包含 $\Delta s = 1$ 的跃迁。如果我们用偶极矩 $\bar{r}/r$ 矩阵来替代 σ，那么就可以满足上面的要求。对于 $\Delta s = 0$ 的跃迁，$\bar{r}/r$ 的矩阵元和 σ 的相同。假若这些得以实现，在 $\bar{r}/r$ 替代 σ 后，横向介子的散射截面仍然很小，同表达式（2）中的散射截面具有一样的数量级。$\bar{r}/r$ 的物理意义为质子的**内禀**磁偶极矩，这是介子理论的显著特点（当然，$\bar{r}$ 并不是质子的空间位置）。

作为新的假定所得到的进一步的结果是，反常磁矩仅仅是**对数**上的发散。从现阶段的介子理论看来，这种发散几乎可以不被当作一个很严重的困难。到目前为止，质子的相对论效应都被忽略了，如果对此进行适当的考虑的话，目前存在的对数发散也会消失。作为上述形式的介子理论有效性的上限，我们采用了质子的静止能量。因此质子的反常磁矩表示为（以核子的磁矩 μ_0 为单位）：

$$\frac{\mu}{\mu_0} = \frac{16}{3\pi} \frac{M\Delta M}{\mu^2} \frac{f^2}{\hbar c}\left(\log \frac{2E_m}{\mu c^2} - \frac{4}{3}\right), \; E_m \sim Mc^2 \tag{3}$$

This is of the right order of magnitude when $\Delta M/\mu$ is approximately 1/5, which is the value assumed above.

(**145**, 29-30; 1940)

W. Heitler: H. H. Wills Physical Laboratory, University, Bristol, 8, Nov. 28.

———————————————————

References:

1. Fröhlich, Heitler and Kemmer, *Proc. Roy. Soc.*, A, **166**, 154 (1938). Yukawa, Sakata and Taketani, *Proc. Math. Phys. Soc. Japan*, **20**, 319 (1938).

2. Heitler, *Proc. Roy. Soc.*, A, **166**, 529 (1938), and Report of the Eighth Solvay Conference, Brussels, in the press, where the reasons for the high cross-section are analysed.

3. Wilson, *Proc. Roy. Soc.*, in the press. I am very much indebted to Dr. Wilson for having sent me his MS. before publication.

4. This possibility was first mentioned to me by Bhabha in a private discussion in connexion with his classical theory for neutral mesons. The whole problem was very much clarified in discussions with Bhabha, Fröhlich and Kemmer.

当 $\Delta M/\mu$ 趋于 1/5 时这是正确的数量级，而 1/5 正是上面所假定的值。

（胡雪兰 翻译；张焕乔 审稿）

Interpretation of Nebular Red-Shifts

K. R. Popper

Editor's Note

The chief interest of this paper is the name of the author—Karl R. Popper. He was born in New Zealand, trained as a physicist and in the 1940s took a lively interest in controversies about the expansion of the Universe. Popper eventually became a philosopher, based at the London School of Economics, and introduced into science the idea that the only valuable scientific theories are those that can be falsified.

IN a recent communication[1], M. E. J. Gheury de Bray discusses the possibility of explaining the red-shifts by assuming that the velocity of light (c_T) is constant throughout the universe at any given time but decreases with time (T).

This hypothesis implies the assumption (*a*) that the atomic frequencies remain constant throughout space and time and may therefore be used as clocks (atomic clock "AC") for time measurements; (*b*) that measuring rods, other than light years (which contract with a decrease of c_T), can be found. For such measuring rods we may now choose the distances of *the material points* (for example, the nebulae) in the universe, as according to the hypothesis the universe neither expands nor contracts. Such measuring rods we call "material rods" ("MR").

It shall be shown here that the proffered hypothesis, based on the measuring system $AC + MR$, is one of three alternative ways of formulating the hypothesis of the expanding universe.

The following clocks and measuring rods can be taken as basis of a measuring system for cosmological purposes:

(*a*) Clocks	(*b*) Measuring rods
AC (atomic clocks); *or*	MR (material rods); *or*
LC (light-clocks: the time taken by light over a given distance— c is here assumed as constant).	LR (light-rods, for example, light years: the distance covered by light in a given time—c is here assumed as constant)

Only the following three combinations of these clocks and measuring rods can be taken as basis of a measuring system: $AC + MR$, which is the basis of Mr. Gheury de Bray's hypothesis; $AC + LR$, a basis which leads to the expansion theory of the red-shifts, and $LC + MR$, which leads to what Milne[2] calls "dynamical time scale", and to the "speeding up" theory of the red-shifts.

对星云红移的解释

波普尔

编者按

这篇文章最有意思的是作者本人——卡尔·波普尔。他出生于新西兰并被培养成为一名物理学家，20世纪40年代他对有关宇宙膨胀的争论产生了极大的兴趣。但波普尔最终成为了伦敦经济学院的一名哲学家，并把只有有价值的科学理论才是可证伪的这一理念引入到科学中。

在最近的通信文章中[1]，谷瑞·德布雷讨论了一种对引力红移的解释，该解释假设：对于一个给定的时刻，宇宙中各处光速（c_T）都是常数，但会随时间（T）的流逝而减小。

该假说包含以下假设：(a) 原子的频率保持恒定，不随空间和时间变化，因此可以作为测量时间的钟（即原子钟，缩写为"AC"）；(b) 除了随着 c_T 减小而缩短的光年外，还存在其他的测量标尺。根据宇宙既不扩张也不收缩的假说，我们可以选择宇宙中**物质点**（比如星云）之间的距离作为这种测量标尺。我们称这种测量标尺为"物质标尺"（缩写为"MR"）。

我们将在本文中证明，基于 $AC+MR$ 测量系统提出的假设是构建宇宙膨胀假说的三种可选方法之一。

下文中的钟和测量标尺可以作为宇宙学测量的基准：

(a) 钟	(b) 测量标尺
AC（原子钟）：**或者**	MR（物质标尺）：**或者**
LC（光钟：光传播一段给定距离所需的时间——c 在这里被假设为常数）。	LR（光标尺，例如光年：光在一段给定时间内传播的距离——c 在这里被假设为常数）。

只有以下三种钟和测量标尺的组合才能作为测量系统的基准：$AC+MR$，这是谷瑞·德布雷先生假说的基础；$AC+LR$，这是红移膨胀理论的基础；$LC+MR$，这构成了米耳恩[2]的"动力学时标"理论以及红移"加速"理论的基础。

(AC + LR). The theory of the expanding universe states that the distances between material points, measured in LR, increase; in other words, it maintains an increase of MR against LR. This leads to the recession of distant nebulae and to the Doppler effect. The identity of the frequencies of characteristic spectral lines throughout the universe (atomic clocks) is thereby assumed; the measuring system of the theory is thus the AC + LR -system. In tracing back the recessive movements it is found that 1.86×10^9 years ago the size of the universe was zero. Thus an absolute scale of time T (based on the atomic clock) is assumed in which the unit is the (atomic) year and the *present value* of T is $T_P = 1.86 \times 10^9$. (This "age of the world" is confirmed by other measurements based on atomic radioactivity clocks.)

(AC + MR). The above statement that MR increases if measured in LR is equivalent to saying that LR decreases if measured in MR. If MR is chosen and the clocks are not changed, the system AC + MR is adopted. The decrease of LR means a decrease of the velocity of light (measured in MR). This permits an explanation of the red-shift of old light, since c_T was greater at the time $T - \Delta T$ when it was emitted and therefore $\lambda_{T - \Delta T}$ is longer than λ_T.

(LC + MR). There is a third way to express the same facts. If we allow the light a longer time for its voyage, by defining our clocks in such a manner that they are slowing down as compared with the atomic clocks, then the decrease of c can be made to disappear. In other words, we adopt a new time scale τ in which the atomic frequencies throughout the universe are speeding up; this explains the red-shift of old light.

The three alternative ways of expressing things agree in regard to the observable effects they describe. All predict the red-shift of old (distant) light. All therefore also predict a violet shift of characteristic spectral lines in the course of time to come (in AC + LR, that is, in the expansion theory, this has to be explained by an expansion of the spectroscope's grating). The three theories are logically equivalent, and therefore do not describe alternative *facts*, but the same facts in alternative *languages*. (To ask whether "in reality" the universe expands, or c decreases, or the frequencies speed up, is not more legitimate than, when prices of goods fall throughout the economic system, to ask whether "in reality" the value of money has increased or the value of the goods has decreased.) Nevertheless, the AC + MR-language seems to offer a particularly simple mathematical treatment and, furthermore, an *observational approach* to Milne's "dynamical" time scale. It shall therefore be briefly examined.

In AC + MR, where characteristic atomic frequencies are assumed constant and c_T depends in some way upon T,

$$(d\lambda/\lambda)_{T+\Delta T} = (\Delta c_T/T)_{T+\Delta T}; \tag{1}$$

on the other hand, the observational law of red-shifts (velocity-distance relation) can be written:

$$(d\lambda/\lambda)_{T_P - \Delta T} = (\Delta T/T)_P, \tag{2}$$

（$AC+LR$）。宇宙膨胀理论认为，用 LR 测量得到的物质点之间距离是不断增加的；换言之，相对于 LR 测量结果，MR 测量结果有所增加。这种膨胀将导致远距离星云的退行以及多普勒效应。因此假设宇宙各处的特征谱线频率（即原子钟）是相同的；则对应的测量系自然是 $AC+LR$ 系。根据反演退行运动可知，1.86×10^9 年前宇宙的尺寸为 0。因此，我们假定时间 T（基于原子钟）的绝对标度以（原子）年为单位，T 的**当时值**为 $T_P=1.86\times10^9$。（基于原子放射钟的其他测量方法也可证实这一"世界年龄"。）

（$AC+MR$）。上文中提到，如果用 LR 测量会发现 MR 值增加了，这相当于说如果用 MR 测量会发现 LR 值减小。如果保持原子钟 AC 不变，而用 MR 代替 LR，那么就构成了另一种测量系统 $AC+MR$。LR 的减小意味着光速的减小（用 MR 测量）。这就可解释远距离光的红移现象了，因为光速 c_T 在光发出的时刻 $T-\Delta T$ 时较大，所以 $\lambda_{T-\Delta T}$ 大于 λ_T。

（$LC+MR$）。本文中第三种描述相同的物理事实的方式。如果我们定义一种新的相对原子钟变慢的钟，这样就可以使光传播一段相同的距离但时间变长，于是光速 c 就不会减少了。换言之，我们采用一种新的时间标度 τ，在这种时标中，宇宙各处的原子频率都会加速；这同时也解释了远距离光的红移现象。

以上三种可选的描述方式与观测到的效应相符。三者均预言了远距离光的红移以及特征谱线随着时间到来的过程中的紫移现象（在 $AC+LR$ 系统中，即宇宙膨胀理论中，这必须用分光镜光栅的膨胀来解释）。这三种理论在逻辑上是等价的，因此它们并不是用于描述不同的物理**事实**，而是用不同的**语言**描述相同的事实。（若要问"实际上"是宇宙在膨胀，还是光速 c 在减小，还是频率在增加，这无异于在经济系统中物价下降时询问"实际上"是钱的价值在增加还是商品的价值在降低，疑问本身就缺乏合理性。）然而，$AC+MR$ 方法似乎可以提供一种十分简单的数学处理办法，并且可以为米耳恩的"动力学"时标提供**观测方法**。下面我们就对这方法进行简要的检验。

在 $AC+MR$ 系统中，假定原子的特征频率为常数，而 c_T 以某种规律随着 T 的变化而变化，

$$(d\lambda/\lambda)_{T+\Delta T}=(\Delta c_T/T)_{T+\Delta T} \tag{1}$$

另一方面，红移的观测定律（速度 – 距离关系）可以用下式表达：

$$(d\lambda/\lambda)_{T_P-\Delta T}=(\Delta T/T)_P \tag{2}$$

if the "apparent distance" in light years, calculated on observed luminosities, is identified with ΔT. From (1) and (2) we get

$$(\Delta c_T/\Delta T)_P = (dc_T/dT)_P = - (c_T/T)_P, \tag{3}$$

Generalizing this and integrating we get the law of the decrease of c:

$$c_T = c_P T_P/T. \tag{4}$$

If we proceed from $AC + MR$, to $LC + MR$, we have to introduce a time scale τ so that $c_\tau = c_P = $ constant. In order to get the general formula for $d\tau/dT$, we make use of (4), which can now be written as

$$d\tau/dT = c_T/c_\tau = c_T \, / \, c_P = T_P/T; \tag{5}$$

integrating and choosing $\tau_P = 0$ (Milne chooses $\tau_P = T_P$), we arrive at

$$\tau = T_P \log \left(T_\tau /T_P \right), \tag{6}$$

which is essentially Milne's formula $(A)^2$; the index "τ" in "T_τ" indicates the value of T at the instant τ of the τ-scale. Equivalent to (6) is $T_\tau = T_P e^{\tau/T_P}$. From this and (5) we get the law of the "speeding up" of characteristic frequencies when measured in $LC+MR$; that is, on the τ-scale:

$$v_\tau = v_P dT_\tau/d\tau = v_P e^{\tau/T_P}, \tag{7}$$

and from this and $c_\tau = c_P$ we get, corresponding to (2), the law of red and violet shifts in the form

$$(d\lambda/\lambda)_{\tau+\Delta\tau} = - \Delta e^{\tau/T_P}/e^{\tau/T_P} = -\Delta T_\tau/T_\tau. \tag{8}$$

In the above deduction we have identified the "apparent distance" (calculated on observed luminosities, that is, energy densities ρ, and not corrected for departures) with ΔT. Thus our assumption regarding ρ is that it measures the square of the *time* ΔT the light travels, which in $AC+MR$ cannot be identified with the ("real") *distance* r; for as the light was quicker when it was emitted, $r>\Delta T$. If the usual assumption that ρ measures not $(\Delta T)^2$ but r^2 is upheld, our deductions would have to be altered and we would neither get (4) nor its equivalent (6), that is, Milne's scale of τ. Vice versa, if our assumption regarding ρ is upheld and if we consequently arrive in $LC + MR$ at Milne's τ-scale, in which $r = \Delta\tau$, then neither r^2 nor $(\Delta\tau)^2$ can be taken as being measured by ρ. Whether this behaviour of ρ in τ can be deduced *a priori* in Milne's theory I do not know. But available *empirical* data seem to speak at least not against our assumption that $(\Delta T)^2$— which is smaller than r^2 —is a measure of ρ, for "present evidence points to observed luminosities (ρ) decreasing

如果根据观测的光度计算出"视距离"(以光年为单位)等同于 ΔT,那么根据公式(1)和(2),我们可以得到:

$$(\Delta c_T/\Delta T)_P = (dc_T/dT)_P = -(c_T/T)_P \tag{3}$$

将上式进行推广并积分,我们可以得出 c 的递减定律,公式如下:

$$c_T = c_P T_P/T \tag{4}$$

为了将 $AC+MR$ 系统转化为 $LC+MR$ 系统,我们必须引入时标 τ,这样可得 $c_\tau = c_P =$ 常数。为了得到 $d\tau/dT$ 的一般公式,我们可以将(4)式变形如下:

$$d\tau/dT = c_T/c_\tau = c_T / c_P = T_P/T \tag{5}$$

对上式积分并取 $\tau_P = 0$(米耳恩选取 $\tau_P = T_P$),我们可以得到下式:

$$\tau = T_P \log (T_\tau/T_P) \tag{6}$$

该式本质上就是米耳恩的公式 (A)[2];其中,T_τ 的下标 τ 表示在 τ 时标下 τ 时刻的 T 值。(6)式可以变形为 $T_\tau = T_P e^{\tau/T_P}$。根据此式和(5)式,我们可以用 $LC+MR$ 测量得到特征频率的"加速"定律;在 τ 时标中,可以表达为:

$$v_\tau = v_P dT_\tau/d\tau = v_P e^{\tau/T_P} \tag{7}$$

根据此式和 $c_\tau = c_P$,并结合(2)式,红移和紫移规律可以表达为以下形式:

$$(d\lambda/\lambda)_{\tau+\Delta\tau} = -\Delta e^{\tau/T_P}/e^{\tau/T_P} = -\Delta T_\tau/T_\tau \tag{8}$$

在上述推导中,我们假定"视距离"(视距离是根据观测光度,即能量密度 ρ 计算得到的,而且没有经过偏差校正)等同于 ΔT。因此,我们假设密度 ρ 与光传播一段距离所用的**时间** ΔT 的平方是相关的,在 $AC+MR$ 的测量系统中这种视距离与("真实")**距离** r 是不能等同的。因为这个系统中光刚发射时的速度要更大些,所以 $r > \Delta T$。如果采用通常的假设,即密度 ρ 并不符合 $(\Delta T)^2$ 的规律,而符合 r^2 的规律,那么我们就不得不修改我们的推导,这样的话,我们既不会得到(4)式也不会得到(6)式(即米耳恩 τ 时标)。反之亦然,如果我们关于密度 ρ 的假设成立,而且在 $LC+MR$ 系统中米耳恩时标 τ,即 $r = \Delta\tau$ 成立的话,那么 r^2 和 $(\Delta\tau)^2$ 便都不能用密度 ρ 来测量。我尚不清楚在米耳恩的理论中是否可以**先验地**推导出时标 τ 中 ρ 的规律。但是目前的**经验数据**至少没有与我们的假设相矛盾,在我们的假设中 ΔT^2(小

with distance *not even quite as rapidly* as we should expect. ..."[3].

(**145**, 69-70; 1940)

K. R. Popper: Canterbury University College, Christchurch, New Zealand, Nov. 27.

References:
1. *Nature*, **144**, 285 (1939).
2. Milne, E. A., *Proc. Roy. Soc.*, A, **158**, 327.
3. Schroedinger, E., *Nature*, **144**. 593(1939).

于 r^2）是 ρ 的一种量度，因为"目前的证据显示，尽管观测到的光度（ρ）随距离减小，但**并没有预期的那样迅速**……"[3]。

（金世超 翻译；何香涛 审稿）

Evidence for Transformation of Mesotrons into Electrons

E. J. Williams and G. E. Roberts

Editor's Note

If seeing is believing, then Figure 2*b* of this paper is a complete demonstration that mesons, thought to mediate nuclear forces between particles such as neutrons and protons, themselves decay into electrons. The tracks exhibited in this paper were made in a cloud chamber, a device filled with nearly super-saturated water vapour and air which can be expanded quickly, thus forming droplets of water wherever there are free electric charges in the chamber. The first author of this paper, Evan J. Williams, was one of the most talented British physicists of his generation. He died at the age of 43. (Since 1940, several different kinds of mesons have been discovered; that described in this paper is now called a π-meson.)

ONE of the outstanding questions regarding the mesotron is that of its ultimate fate. Certain properties of this particle are remarkably like those of the hypothetical particle assumed by Yukawa in his theory of nuclear forces and β-disintegration, and this has led to the view that the two may be identical. Within a rather large experimental error they have the same mass, and both are unstable in the free state, having an average life of the order of 10^{-6} seconds. The disappearance of the particle of Yukawa's theory at the end of its life takes place through its transformation into an electron and a neutrino, and it is regarding this that hitherto there has been no evidence of a parallel between it and the mesotron of cosmic rays. In fact, existing experimental evidence has rather gone to show that mesotrons suffer at the end of their life some other fate than befalls the Yukawa particle.

With the object of obtaining information on this crucial point we constructed a large cloud-chamber (24 in. diameter, 20 in. deep) which, with its large sensitive period and volume, might catch a cosmic ray mesotron coming to the end of its range in the gas of the chamber. A recent photograph taken with this shows a mesotron track terminating in the gas as desired. From its end there emerges a fast electron track, the kinetic energy of which is very much greater than the kinetic energy of the mesotron, but is comparable with its mass energy. This indicates that the mesotron transforms into an electron, in which case the remarkable parallel between the mesotron and the Yukawa particle is taken one stage further. In terms of Yukawa's theory, the phenomenon observed may be described as a disintegration of the mesotron with the emission of an electron, thus constituting the most elementary form of β-disintegration.

Fig. 1 is a reproduction of one of the photographs of the stereoscopic pair. The dense

792

介子向电子转化的证明

威廉姆斯，罗伯茨

编者按

如果说眼见为实，那么本文图 2b 就是作为诸如中子和质子这样的粒子之间核力媒介的介子衰变成电子的实证。本文所展现的径迹是在云室中获得的，那是一个充满近乎过饱和水蒸气和空气并且其中的气体可迅速扩张的装置，这样在云室中只要是存在自由电荷的地方就会形成很多小水滴。本文的第一作者埃文·威廉姆斯是同时代人中最有才华的英国物理学家之一，享年 43 岁。（自 1940 年以来，已经发现了几种不同类型的介子，本文中描述的介子现在被称为 π 介子。）

关于介子的一个最突出的问题是它的最终命运。这种粒子的某些性质与汤川秀树在他的核力和 β 衰变理论中假设的粒子的性质是明显一致的，这使得人们认为这两种粒子是同一种粒子。在相当大的实验误差范围内，它们具有相同的质量，而且在自由态时都是不稳定的，平均寿命的数量级为 10^{-6} 秒。汤川秀树理论中的粒子在其寿命结束时转化成电子和中微子，但至今都没有发现在这一点上它与宇宙线中的介子有相似之处的证据。事实上，有实验证据表明这种粒子在其寿命终结时会遭受另一种命运——一种不同于汤川秀树粒子的命运。

为了得到与这个至关重要的问题有关的信息，我们构建了一个大云室（直径为 24 英寸，深度为 20 英寸），由于其具有高灵敏周期和庞大的体积，因此可以在云室气体中捕捉到即将到达其行程尽头的宇宙线介子。最近拍摄的相关照片中显示出了那些我们所期望得到的在气体中终结的介子径迹。其终结处出现快电子的径迹，快电子的动能明显大于介子的动能，但是质量和能量则与介子的相当。这表明，介子会转化成为电子。在这种情况下介子与汤川秀树粒子之间的相同之处又更近了一步。根据汤川秀树的理论，观察到的这种现象可以这样描述，介子在衰变中发射了一个电子，从而构成了 β 衰变的一种最基本的形式。

图 1 为其中一张立体像对照片的复制片。密集的径迹 AF 是介子的，而从其终

track AF is that of the mesotron, and the faint track FG leaving its end, near the bottom of the chamber, is that of the fast electron. It will be noticed that the latter is comparable in density with the tracks of other fast particles which happened to traverse the chamber in the same region. Fig. 2 is a larger reproduction of the stereoscopic pair, showing only the end portion of the mesotron track and the emergent electron ($2a$ is not in as good focus as $2b$). Fig. 3 is a heavily exposed reproduction of the last few millimetres of the mesotron track to bring out its shape though the electron track is thereby nearly lost, and Fig. 4 is an enlargement of the δ-track at E to show more clearly its initial direction. The tracks in the present reproductions are much less distinct than in the original negatives and photographic prints, and this particularly applies to the fast tracks (including FG) and the short δ-tracks, of which there are at least six obvious ones to be seen between C and F on the original negative.

20 cm.

Fig. 1

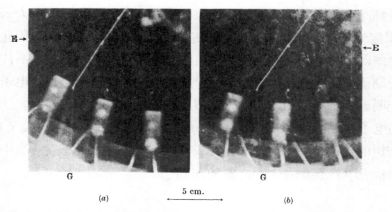

5 cm.

(a)   (b)

Fig. 2. a and b are arranged for stereoscopic observation with the naked eye, when usually the left eye sees the right-hand picture.

端远去的那条模糊的、靠近云室底部的径迹 FG 则是快电子的。我们将会注意到，后者与碰巧在同一区域穿过云室的其他快速粒子的径迹在密度上是相当的。图 2 是立体像对照片的一个更大的复制片，仅仅显示了介子径迹的末端部分和出射的电子（$2a$ 不如 $2b$ 的聚焦效果好）。图 3 为介子径迹最后几毫米的一个严重曝光的复制片，以此来显示介子的径迹形状，尽管这样基本上会看不到电子的径迹。图 4 是对 E 处 δ 径迹的放大，是为了更清楚地显示出其初始方向。在这里给出的复制片中的径迹不如原底片和用底片冲洗出来的照片中那么清晰，尤其是对于快电子的径迹（包括 FG）和短的 δ 径迹，在原始底片中的 C 和 F 之间至少能够看到 6 条它们这样的清晰径迹。

20 cm

图 1

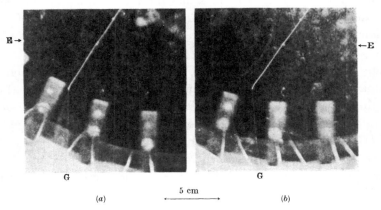

5 cm

(a)   (b)

图 2. a 和 b 是为用肉眼进行立体观察所准备的，通常用左眼看着右手边的图片。

That the dense track is that of a mesotron follows from its range and curvature, and from the δ-tracks. An accurate estimate of the mass from the curvature is not possible because the scattering which the particle suffers interferes appreciably with the curvature due to the magnetic field. The straightness of *FG* and of neighbouring fast tracks shows that there was no appreciable distortion from air motion. The radius of curvature, ρ, at *B*, measured over *AC* (~20 cm.), is 70 cm., giving $H\rho = 1{,}180 \times 70 = 8.3 \times 10^4$. The range beyond *B* is 33 cm. in the chamber, corresponding to 41 cm. of normal air. These data give a mass, μ, of $(250\pm70)\ m$, where *m* represents electronic mass. This is of the same order as previous estimates of the mass of the mesotron, and is sufficiently far removed from the mass of the proton $(1{,}840\ m)$ to establish the particle as a mesotron. The number and range of the δ-tracks also indicate mesotronic mass, and rule out a proton. In particular the long δ-track at *E*, which in the reproduction in Fig. 3 is seen to be directed nearly forward, has a path-range, *R'*, equal to 0.06 ± 0.03 times the remaining range, *R*, of the heavy particle. This is roughly the range that would be expected for a secondary electron knocked nearly forward by a mesotron with the observed remaining range. It is, however, at least five times greater than the range of the longest δ-track that could be produced by a proton. The latter is approximately $(2^{3.4}/1{,}840)\ R = 0.006\ R$.

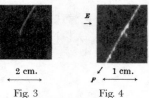

2 cm. 1 cm.

Fig. 3   Fig. 4

Regarding the "scattering" of the track, while it is more pronounced than the *average* effect expected for a mesotron, it is more compatible with the latter than with a proton or any other known particle. The natural "curvature" of cloud-tracks due to multiple and single scattering is discussed by one of us in a paper now in the press (*Physical Review*). It is there shown that towards the end of its range—last 5 cm. or so—the natural curvature of a mesotron track may well exceed its magnetic curvature in a field of 1,200 gauss. (The "kink" at *D* contributes little to the average curvature and is possibly more a thinning of the track on one side than a true deflection. The "single" scattering at *C* appreciably reduces the overall curvature.) The bending of the track in the last 5 mm. or so (Fig. 3) is of interest. It indicates that the mesotron has come to the end of its range, thus discounting the possibility that the photograph represents the production of a mesotron and an electron by a neutral particle. Against this supposition are also the facts that the long δ-track at *E* is initially directed forward, and that the δ-tracks are more numerous in the lower half of the track. Both indicate motion of the mesotron towards *F*.

The curvature of the electron track, *FG*, is very small. Actually there is detectable (Fig. 2*b*), a small curvature in a direction indicating a positive charge, which is also the direction of the curvature of the mesotron. The photograph thus represents a positive mesotron transforming into a positive electron. So far as it can be estimated, the radius of curvature of *FG* is 200 cm. ± 50 percent, which in the field of 1,180 gauss (neglecting any distortion due to air-motion) indicates an energy of 70 Mev. ± 50 percent. Taking $\mu = 200\ m$, and assuming that a neutrino takes half the energy, the energy of the electron would be $100\ mc^2 = 50$ Mev.

The large energy of the electron shows, quite apart from Yukawa's theory, that mass

密集的径迹是介子的，这是根据该径迹的范围和曲率，以及 δ 径迹分析得出的。根据曲率是不可能精确估算出粒子质量的，因为粒子受到的散射对由磁场引起的曲率有明显的干扰。FG 和近邻的快电子径迹的平直度表明，不存在明显的由空气运动而导致的畸变。在 AC 段（约 20 厘米）上测量到的 B 处的曲率半径 ρ 为 70 厘米，它使得 $H\rho=1{,}180\times70=8.3\times10^4$。在云室中 B 以后的行程范围为 33 厘米，对应于普通空气中的 41 厘米。这些数据可以给出质量 μ 为 (250±70) m，其中 m 为电子的质量。这同先前估算的介子质量具有相同的量级，而且与质子质量（1,840 m）相差甚远，进而可以确定这一粒子为介子。δ 径迹的数量和范围同样也表明了介子的质量，从而排除了质子的可能。特别是图 3 的复制片中 E 处的长 δ 轨迹看上去几乎一直向前，这个直的径迹的行程长度 R'，为普通重粒子的残留径迹 R 的 0.06±0.03 倍。这就是介子在观测到的持续范围内被近似向前敲出的次级电子的粗略范围。然而，这至少比质子可以产生的最长 δ 轨迹范围大五倍，后者大约是 $(2^{3.4}/1{,}840)R = 0.006R$。

至于径迹的"散开"，虽然它比对介子预期的**平均**效应要更为明显，但是与质子或其他任何已知粒子相比，它同介子的更为符合。由多重和单个散射引起的云迹的自身"曲率"已被我们中的一位在一篇即将出版的文章中进行了讨论（《物理学评论》）。该文章指出，对于介子行程末端，大约是最后 5 厘米，其径迹自身的曲率会超过它在 1,200

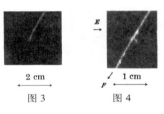

2 cm
图 3

1 cm
图 4

高斯的磁场中的磁曲率。（D 处的"纽结"对平均曲率几乎没有作用，与真正的偏转相比更有可能的情况是径迹一边的稀疏。C 处的"单"散射明显使整个曲率减小了。）径迹的最后大约 5 毫米处的弯曲（图 3）是非常有价值的。它表明了介子已经到达了其行程的末端，这就使照片表示由一个中性粒子产生一个介子和一个电子的可能性不可置信。E 处的长 δ 径迹最初是一直向前的事实，以及在径迹下半段 δ 轨迹的数量更多的事实，也驳斥了这一假说。这两者均表明介子是朝向 F 方向运动的。

电子径迹 FG 的曲率是很小的。实际上可以发现（图 2b）在一个表明是正电荷的方向上有一个较小的曲率，这个方向也就是介子曲率的方向。因此，照片所表示的是一个正介子正在向一个正电子转化的过程。到目前为止可以估算得出，FG 的曲率半径为 200 厘米 ±50%，这表明在 1,180 高斯的磁场中（忽略所有由空气运动造成的扭曲）能量为 70 兆电子伏 ±50%。设 μ=200 m，并且假定一个中微子具有一半的能量，那么电子的能量将会是 100 mc^2 =50 兆电子伏。

完全抛开汤川秀树理论，高的电子能量表明，质量已经湮没了。对于介子，即

has been annihilated—for the mesotron, even if we suppose it has disintegrated before "stopping", has certainly less than 4 Mev. of kinetic energy. Actually, the large bending of the end of the mesotron track indicates (as already pointed out) that E is the normal end of its range, where it has reached too low a velocity to ionize further. In this connexion it is of interest that an upper limit to the lifetime, τ, of this mesotron, since its entry into the chamber, can be set from the fact that the electron track starts from a point certainly not more than 0.4 mm. from the end of the mesotron track. Assuming the mesotron, after it ceases to ionize, to diffuse with gas-kinetic free path (10^{-5} cm.) and thermal velocity (10^6 cm./sec.) this gives an upper limit to τ of $(0.04^2/10^{-5} \times 10^6) \sim 2 \times 10^{-4}$ seconds. Actually it is likely that a mesotron, when it stops ionizing, has a velocity of at least 10^7 cm./sec., and a free path considerably greater than gas-kinetic values, so that τ must be much less than the above limit. The average value of τ deduced from the anomalous absorption of cosmic ray mesotrons is of the order of 10^{-6} seconds.

(**145**, 102-103; 1940)

E. J. Williams and G. E. Roberts: University College of Wales, Aberystwyth, Dec. 21.

使我们假定它在"停止"之前已经衰变，它所具有的动能也小于 4 兆电子伏。实际上，介子径迹末端的大弯曲表明（正如以前所指出的）E 是它的行程范围的常规终点，到达此处时它所具有的速度太小，以致不能发生进一步的电离。关于这个问题值得注意的是，可以根据电子径迹从介子径迹末端不超过 0.4 毫米处算起这一事实判断出介子进入云室后的寿命上限 τ。假定介子不再电离后，沿着气体分子运动自由程（10^{-5} 厘米）以热速度（每秒 10^6 厘米）扩散，这就给定了寿命的上限 τ 为 $(0.04^2/10^{-5} \times 10^6) \sim 2 \times 10^{-4}$ 秒。事实上，很有可能的是介子在停止电离后，其速度至少为每秒 10^7 厘米，而其自由程比气体分子运动的值要大很多，因此寿命上限 τ 肯定会远小于上述的值。由宇宙射线介子的反常吸收推断出 τ 平均值的量级为 10^{-6} 秒。

（胡雪兰 翻译；厉光烈 审稿）

Some Biological Applications of Neutrons and Artificial Radioactivity*

J. H. Lawrence

Editor's Note

The discovery of nuclear transmutation and artificial means for inducing it stimulated a new era of fundamental physics. But as John Lawrence of the University of California here reports, it also triggered a revolution in biology and medicine. The use of radioactive tracers had already led to many new discoveries about the movement of sodium, potassium, calcium, iodine and other elements in the human body and in plants. Iodine, for example, quickly became concentrated in the thyroid gland. This effect also suggested the potential use of radioactive agents in the treatment of cancers. These studies were racing forward, in part because the new 220-ton cyclotron at Berkeley produced copious amounts of various radioactive elements, as well as powerful neutron beams.

THE biological and medical sciences are being stimulated and benefited by the recent discoveries of the nuclear physicist in a manner similar to that following the discovery of the naturally occurring radioactive elements and the production of X-rays. The nuclear physicist can now induce radioactivity in practically all of the elements, and he can harness a beam of neutrons of intense biological activity. This new wonderland for the biologist has been brought about by such events as the first successful experiments of Joliot and Curie in artificial radioactivity, the discovery of the neutron by Chadwick, the discovery of heavy hydrogen by Urey, and the development of the cyclotron by E. O. Lawrence and his associates.

During the past four years, workers at the University of California have been intensely interested in the biological applications of these products of the physicist, and recently a new medical-biological laboratory dedicated to this study and housing the new 220-ton cyclotron—the William H. Crocker Radiation Laboratory—has been completed in Berkeley. Because of its ability to produce large quantities of the various radio-elements and neutron rays, the cyclotron is the nucleus of this unit. The Laboratory is, however, staffed not only by physicists, but also by chemists, biologists, cytologists, bacteriologists, physicians and radiologists—all of whom are interested in both the fundamental and practical problems concerned with the interaction of radiation and matter. My purpose here is to discuss briefly some of the investigations carried on in this laboratory or in conjunction with it. Unfortunately, there is not sufficient space to discuss the extensive and

---

* Based in part on a paper given before Section A (Mathematical and Physical Sciences) of the British Association, given on August 31 and September 1, 1939, at Dundee.

中子与人工放射性的若干生物学应用[*]

劳伦斯

编者按

核嬗变以及用于诱导核嬗变的人工方法的发现开创了基础物理学的一个新纪元。但是正如加利福尼亚大学的约翰·劳伦斯在这篇报告中所指出的，上述成果还引发了一场生物学和医学的革命。放射性示踪剂的使用使人们对钠、钾、钙、碘和其他元素在人体和植物体内的运动有了新认识。例如，钠在甲状腺中很快富集。这种效应也表明了放射剂在治疗癌症中的潜在用途。这些研究得到了飞速发展，这在一定程度上是因为伯克利的新的220吨回旋加速器可以产生大量不同的放射性元素和强中子束。

生物学和医学正在从核物理学家最近的发现中得到启发并且受益，在某种程度上类似于发现天然存在放射性元素与X射线的产生之后所带来的影响。现在，核物理学家几乎可以诱发所有元素的放射性，并且能对一束具有强烈生物活性的中子进行操控。生物学家涉足这一新奇领域是因为受到了下列事件的直接影响，这包括约里奥和居里第一次成功地进行了人工放射性实验，查德威克发现了中子，尤里发现了重氢，以及劳伦斯及其合作者研制出了回旋加速器。

在过去的四年中，加利福尼亚大学的研究人员一直对物理学家取得的这些成果在生物学中的应用具有强烈的兴趣，而且最近一座致力于这项研究的新医学－生物学实验室已经在伯克利建成，即威廉·克罗克辐射实验室，这个实验室拥有一台新的220吨回旋加速器。由于这台回旋加速器能够产生大量不同的放射性元素和中子射线，因此它是这个单位的核心。不过该实验室配备的工作人员并非只包括物理学家，此外还有化学家、生物学家、细胞学家、细菌学家、医师和放射学家，所有这些人都非常关注与辐射和物质之间相互作用有关的基础性和实用性问题。这里，我的目的是简要地讨论在这个实验室进行的或与其相关联的一些研究工作。遗憾的是，

---

[*] 部分依据1939年8月31日及9月1日在邓迪举行的英国科学促进会A分会（数学和物理科学）上宣读的一篇论文。

important work being done in this field in other laboratories.

When Hevesy first used radium D, an isotope of lead, as a "tracer" of lead movement in plants, the potential value of similar isotopes of elements which are important in physiological processes, such as phosphorus, sodium, iron and iodine, became apparent. These and other radioactive isotopes are now available; and, since they are chemically like their inactive relatives, their radiations simply label or tag them and enable the investigator (with the aid of a Geiger counter) to study their average exchange and distribution in biological and chemical processes, in health and disease. The effect of irradiation on the reaction is avoided by the use of sufficiently small "tracer" amounts. On the other hand, many of these isotopes may be used as potent sources of radiation if the metabolism of the element in question is not being studied. In Table 1 are listed some of the isotopes that are used in this University. A brief discussion of studies in which these isotopes are employed follows.

Table 1

Atomic number	Radio-element	Radiation	Half-life
1	Hydrogen (3)	Beta	150-170 days
6	Carbon (11)	Positron and gamma	20.5 minutes
11	Sodium (24)	Beta and gamma	14.8 hours
15	Phosphorus (32)	Beta	14.3 days
16	Sulphur (35)	Beta	88 days
17	Chlorine (34)	Positron and gamma	33 minutes
19	Potassium (42)	Beta and gamma	12.4 hours
20	Calcium (45)	Beta and gamma	180 days
26	Iron (59)	Beta and gamma	47 days
35	Bromine (82)	Beta and gamma	34 hours
53	Iodine (126)	Beta and gamma	13 days

Radioactive hydrogen is written ^3_1H, in contrast to ordinary hydrogen (^1_1H) and heavy hydrogen (^2_1H), and has only recently been discovered by Alvarez and Cornog of this Laboratory. This newly labelled form is used in biological work and promises to become a valuable adjunct to heavy hydrogen, which has been so extensively used in "tracer" studies. Although radio-carbon has a very short half-life (20.5 minutes), Ruben, Hassid and Kamen are successfully using it in the study of photosynthesis. Leaves of barley plants grown in an atmosphere of C^*O_2 form radioactive carbohydrates*, even when the plants are kept in darkness prior to exposure to C^*O_2. The bulk of the radioactive material found in the plant is water-soluble and does not contain carbohydrate, carbonate, keto acids or pigments. Jenny and Overstreet of the College of Agriculture grew barley in the presence of K^* and showed that the intake of ions is not a uni-directional process, but that ions of the same species may move into the root and out of the root at the same time. Stout and Hoagland of the same department, using the radioactive isotopes of potassium, sodium, phosphorus, and bromine, studied their upward movement after absorption by

---

* The radioactive form of an element is denoted by an asterisk.

没有足够的篇幅来讨论其他实验室在这一领域中所做的广泛而重要的工作。

当赫维西最早使用镭 D（铅的一种同位素）作为铅在植物体内运动的"示踪剂"时，那些在生理过程中十分重要的元素，例如磷、钠、铁和碘，它们的类似同位素的潜在价值变得明朗起来。这些以及其他一些放射性同位素现在都可以得到了；而且，既然它们的化学性质与它们相对应的非放射性元素的类似，那么它们的放射性只是给其加上标记或将其标示出来，并且使研究者（借助于盖革计数器）得以研究其在生物学和化学过程中、在健康和疾病状态间的平均交换和分布情况。通过使用剂量足够小的"示踪剂"，可以防止辐射对反应造成影响。另一方面，如果不研究涉及到的元素的代谢，那么很多这样的同位素也许可以作为潜在的放射源使用。表 1 列出了加利福尼亚大学使用的一些同位素。下面会对利用这些同位素进行的研究作简要论述。

表 1

原子序数	放射性元素	辐射	半衰期
1	氢（3）	β辐射	150～170天
6	碳（11）	正电子和γ辐射	20.5分钟
11	钠（24）	β和γ辐射	14.8小时
15	磷（32）	β辐射	14.3天
16	硫（35）	β辐射	88天
17	氯（34）	正电子和γ辐射	33分钟
19	钾（42）	β和γ辐射	12.4小时
20	钙（45）	β和γ辐射	180天
26	铁（59）	β和γ辐射	47天
35	溴（82）	β和γ辐射	34小时
53	碘（126）	β和γ辐射	13天

为了与普通氢（^1_1H）和重氢（^2_1H）相对照，放射性氢被写作 ^3_1H，直到前不久它才被本实验室的阿尔瓦雷茨和考诺格发现。这种新的被标记的形式在生物学研究中得到了应用，并且有望成为重氢的一个有价值的补充，而重氢已被极为广泛地应用于"示踪剂"的研究。尽管放射性碳的半衰期很短（20.5 分钟），鲁宾、哈西德和卡门还是成功地将其用于对光合作用的研究之中。在 C*O$_2$ 环境中生长的大麦类植物的叶子*，会形成放射性的碳水化合物，即使这种植物在暴露于 C*O$_2$ 之前保存在黑暗中，结果也会如此。在植物中发现的大量放射性物质是水溶性的，而且并不包含碳水化合物、碳酸盐、酮酸或色素。农学院的珍妮和奥弗斯特里特使大麦生长在有 K* 存在的条件下，结果发现离子的摄入并不是一个单向过程，实际上相同种类的离子也可能在移入根部的同时移出根部。同一院系的斯托特和霍格兰研究了钾、钠、磷和溴的放射性同位素被生长旺盛的柳树和天竺葵植物的根部吸收后的向上运动。他

---

* 某一元素的放射性形式用星号（*）标记。

the roots in actively growing willow and geranium plants. They found that when salts are absorbed by roots, some portion enters the xylem within very short periods of time, and is carried rapidly towards the leaves under the influence of transpiration. That the content of radioactivity in the bark as compared with the root is slight indicates that movement of salts in the former is very slow.

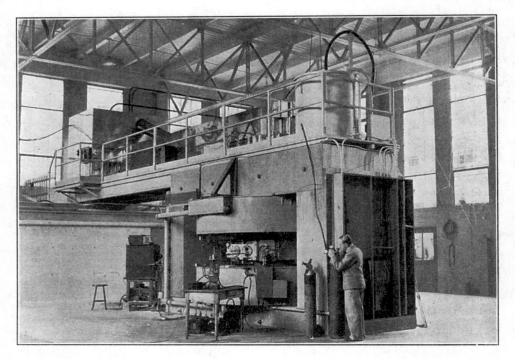

Fig. 1. The 200-ton 60-inch cyclotron in the Crocker Radiation Laboratory on the Berkeley campus of the University of California.

Standing by the corner of the magnet and adjusting the helium flow to the target chamber is the late Dr. Harold Walke, of the University of Liverpool. On the table in the foreground is an experimental deuterium generator. The target chamber is behind, marked by the two port holes. Above and to the rear is seen the aluminium oscillator house or radio-frequency power supply. Photograph taken by Dr. Donald Cooksey, assistant director of the Radiation Laboratory.

Mullins, of the Department of Zoology, has investigated the effect of increasing activities of radio-sodium on the penetration of Na^+ into the single-celled alga Nitella. His results show that, below certain activity concentrations, there is no "radiation" effect, and point out the importance of using low activities in "tracer" work. Hamilton is making an extensive study of the physiology of the isotopes of sodium, potassium, iodine and other elements, in health and disease. Their rapid absorption and distribution is evidenced by their appearance in the hand a few minutes after oral administration of small amounts. The isotope of iodine is proving to be valuable in the study of thyroid physiology. Hamilton has demonstrated the marked concentration of ingested iodine in

们发现，当盐类被根吸收后，其中一部分会在很短的时间周期内进入木质部，并在蒸腾作用的影响下被迅速运往叶片。树皮中放射性成分的含量比根部的少，这意味着盐类在树皮中的运动是非常缓慢的。

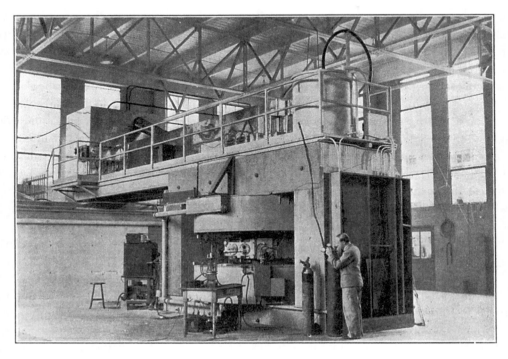

图 1. 位于加利福尼亚大学伯克利校区克罗克辐射实验室中的 200 吨重 60 英寸高的回旋加速器。

站在磁铁边缘部、正调节通往靶室的氘气流的是利物浦大学已故的哈罗德·沃克博士。前部的桌子上放置的就是用于实验的氘发生器。靶室在其后面，以两个通道孔作为标志标示出来。上方向后的地方可以看到铝振荡器柜或射频电源。照片由辐射实验室助理主管唐纳德·库克西博士拍摄。

动物学系的马林斯曾研究过放射性钠的活性的增加对 Na^+ 穿透单细胞丽藻的能力的影响。他的研究结果表明，在一定的放射性浓度下不存在"辐射"效应，并且指出在"示踪剂"研究中使用低活性的重要性。汉密尔顿对健康状态和疾病状态下钠、钾、碘及其他元素的同位素进行了广泛的生理学研究。在口服少量试剂几分钟后它们就在手上出现，这证明了它们是被快速吸收并传播出去的。事实证明碘的同位素在甲状腺生理学的研究中是很有价值的。汉密尔顿已说明了被摄取的碘明显聚集在甲状腺中，并且已经能够通过将切除的腺体置于感光胶片上而对碘的分布进行拍照。

the thyroid gland and has been able to photograph the distribution of iodine by placing the excised gland on a photographic film. Anderson and her associates of the Institute of Experimental Biology have found that in adrenalectomized rats a single dose of "tagged" sodium is rapidly lost, while potassium tends to be retained.

Radio-phosphorus (P^{32}) has been the most extensively used radioactive isotope. The ease of manufacture in the cyclotron and its relatively long half-life (14.3 days) make it ideal for biological studies. Chaikoff and his associates in their studies of phospholipid metabolism have shown that various kinds of neoplasms in animals have individual rates of phospholipid turnover, and that cell type does not seem to be the determining factor. In association with Scott and Tuttle, the metabolism of labelled phosphorus in leukaemia in both animals and man is being investigated. The finding that in leukaemic mice the phosphorus turnover is apparently proportional to the degree of leukaemic infiltration suggested the use of radiophosphorus as a source of radiation in the treatment of leukaemia in humans. The concentration of the radio-phosphorus in the areas infiltrated with leukaemic cells tends to localize the therapeutic irradiation (beta-rays). Given by mouth in the form of sodium phosphate, phosphorus is well absorbed (75 percent) and slowly excreted (2 percent per day). The turnover of phosphorus in red cells is rapid, whereas the white cells retain it for longer periods of time. Numerous patients suffering from chronic leukaemia are being treated with this material, and in many instances remissions in the disease are obtained.

Tarver and Schmidt, of the Department of Biochemistry, have synthesized methionine from radio-sulphur and, after feeding it to rats, have shown that the radio-sulphur may later appear as cystine extracted from the tissues. Finally, Whipple and his associates at the University of Rochester, in their studies on normal and anaemic dogs, report the following: radio-iron is poorly absorbed by normal animals; anaemic animals absorb iron in proportion to their need for it; plasma is the medium for the transport of iron; the rapid appearance of iron in the red blood cells is spectacular.

The intense beam of neutrons produced by the cyclotron has made it possible to investigate their biological effects on various objects such as bacteria, plants, Drosophila eggs, animal tumours and normal mammals. This new penetrating form of radiation has intense biological effects, even greater than X-rays or gamma rays, on normal and tumour tissue, but when compared with X-rays, selectively affects some tissues more than others. Experiments on animals indicating that neutrons are more destructive to neoplastic tissue than to normal tissue suggested their trial in cancer therapy. In association with R. S. Stone, of the Department of Roentgenology, patients suffering from cancer are now regularly being treated with neutrons from the new 60-inch medical cyclotron. The recent experiments of Kruger in this Laboratory have opened up another possible application of neutrons to cancer therapy. He has demonstrated that cancers from mice placed in non-toxic concentrations of boric acid and irradiated with slow neutrons can be killed with doses of irradiation harmless to tissues not in contact with boron. The slow neutron is

安德森和她在实验生物学研究所的同事们曾发现，在肾上腺被切除的老鼠体内，单一剂量的"被标示"的钠迅速流失，而钾则往往得以保留。

放射性磷（^{32}P）已经成为应用最为广泛的放射性同位素。在回旋加速器中易于被制备且相对较长的半衰期（14.3 天）使它十分适用于生物学研究。柴可夫和他的同事们在他们对磷脂代谢的研究中已经表明，动物体内各种类型的肿瘤都有各自的磷脂转换率，而且细胞类型似乎并不是决定因素。在与斯科特和塔特尔的合作中，被标记的磷元素在患白血病的动物和人的体内的代谢正在被研究。结果发现，在患白血病的老鼠体内，磷的转换与白血病的浸润程度明显成正比，这一发现使人们想到在人类白血病治疗中把放射性磷作为辐射源来使用。放射性磷聚集在白血病细胞浸润的区域，这使得局部的放射治疗（β 射线）得以实现。将磷以磷酸钠的形式通过口服摄取，磷会被很好地吸收（75%）并被缓慢地排出（每天 2%）。磷在红细胞中的转换是很快的，而在白细胞中则会保持相对较长的一段时间。利用这种物质对患有慢性白血病的大量患者进行了治疗，并且在很多病例中病症都有所缓解。

生物化学系的塔弗和施密特用放射性硫合成了蛋氨酸，并且在把它喂给老鼠之后发现放射性硫随后可能作为从组织中提取出的胱氨酸而出现。最终，惠普尔及其在罗切斯特大学的合作者们在对正常的和患贫血症的狗进行了研究之后，给出了下面的结论：正常动物对于放射性铁的吸收效果很差；患贫血症的动物吸收的铁与它们所需铁元素的量成正比；血浆是输送铁的媒介；铁在红血球中的迅速出现是非常惊人的。

回旋加速器产生的强中子束使得研究其对各种不同对象的生物学效应成为可能，这些对象包括细菌、植物、果蝇卵、动物肿瘤和正常的哺乳动物等。这种新的贯穿辐射具有强烈的生物学效应，对于正常组织和肿瘤组织，它甚至比 X 射线或 γ 射线还要强，但是在与 X 射线进行比较时，它对某些组织的选择性影响要超过其他组织。动物实验表明，中子对肿瘤组织的破坏性比对正常组织的大，这就启发人们开始尝试将其用于癌症治疗。在与伦琴射线学系的斯通的合作研究中，癌症患者目前正在有规律地接受新的 60 英寸医用回旋加速器发出的中子的治疗。该实验室的克鲁格进行的最新实验研发出了另一种利用中子治疗癌症的可行性方法。他已经证实，将老鼠置于不会导致中毒浓度的硼酸之中并用慢中子进行辐射，在辐射剂量对未与硼接触的组织不构成伤害的条件下，便能杀死它体内的肿瘤。慢中子被硼核捕获。该结

captured by the boron nucleus. The combination emits two heavy ionizing particles in opposite directions—an alpha particle and a lithium nucleus—which traverse a distance of about 7 μ in tissue and thus approximate an explosion within the cell.

Fig. 2. The path of a 16-million electron volt deuteron beam traversing the air for a distance of nearly five feet.

These particles emerge from the vacuum of the target chamber with a velocity of approximately 18,000 miles per second. In slowing down over the course of their path, they give up their energy to the air molecules, causing them to glow with a violet light. However, in practice, a target to be made radioactive is placed at the emergent point of the beam and thus bombarded. Where neutrons are desired the target used is beryllium. Photograph taken by Dr. Donald Cooksey, assistant director of the Radiation Laboratory.

Although the great contribution of the new nuclear physics to the problems of biology and medicine is certainly the "labelled" or "tagged" isotope, nevertheless it seems important to pursue the possibilities of artificial radioactivity and neutron rays in cancer therapy until a more satisfactory answer to this problem has been reached.

(**145**, 125-127; 1940)

John H. Lawrence: Radiation Laboratory, University of California, Berkeley.

合会在相反方向上释放出两个重离子，一个 α 粒子和一个锂核，它们在组织中的穿透距离约 7 微米，这近似于细胞内部的一个爆炸。

图 2. 一束16兆电子伏特的氘核束在空气中穿行约5英尺距离产生的轨迹。

这些粒子以近似每秒18,000英里的速度从靶室的真空中发出。在沿其轨迹行进的过程中它们不断减速，将能量转移给空气分子，使它们发出紫色的光。然而实际上，是因为将一个具有放射性的靶置于粒子束出现的位置上，所以受到了轰击。在希望得到中子的地方用铍来作靶。照片由辐射实验室的助理主管唐纳德·库克西博士拍摄。

毫无疑问"标记的"或"标示的"同位素是新核物理学对于生物学和医学问题所作出的一个巨大贡献，但是在我们对于癌症治疗问题得到更为令人满意的答案之前，继续探寻人工放射性和中子射线在癌症治疗中的可能似乎仍然是十分重要的。

（王耀杨 翻译；王乃彦 审稿）

Radium Treatment

Editor's Note

Here two scientists write to defend cancer radiotherapy using radium in the face of criticisms expressed in *Nature* by Leonard Hill. Sidney Russ, a renowned English physician, rejects Hill's accusation that radium therapy served the vested interests of the medical community, and argues that the risks are already understood and responsibly observed. Arthur Eve, a former collaborator with Rutherford in nuclear chemistry, also accuses Hill of using gossip and anecdote to attack a strategy that is used in general with care and caution, even if some mistakes have been made through ignorance. Radiotherapy to combat cancer is uncontroversial today, its debilitating side-effects accepted as a necessary evil. It serves a reminder of Paracelsus's famous dictum that the poison is in the dose.

REFERENCE is made in *Nature* of December 9, 1939, p. 973, to a paper (*J. Roy. Soc. Arts*, Dec. 8, 1939) entitled "The Penetration of Rays through the Skin, and Radiant Energy for the Treatment of Wounds", in which I express the view that we would be little the worse off if all the radium now buried in deep holes for security from bombing remained there, and states that the Cancer Act is Great Britain's reply to the question whether monetary influence determines the practice of radium therapy in Great Britain.

Radium, a destroyer of living cells in active division, cannot be used to attack cancer without also damaging living normal cells of the circulating blood, etc. It can only be used for accessible cancers in the skin or surfaces of the body, which can be removed in nearly all cases by the knife or the diathermy needle of the surgeon; and these last do not cause necrosis and incurable neuralgias, which have often followed the use of radium. Deaths due to leucopaenia have resulted from vain attempts to cure deep cancers by the use of radium in bombs. I can instance the damage done by radium by a case now attending the St. John Clinic and Institute of Physical Medicine; radium treatment of a small epithelioma in the skin on the side of the skull resulted in necrosis of the bone, probably incurable, in an area the size of the top of a sherry glass.

Loss of well-being and an incurable neuralgia were recorded by Mr. Furnival, the late distinguished surgeon, who died not long after radium treatment, in his case of cancer of the throat. Such an intolerable neuralgia was suffered by a relative of mine through treatment of a cancer of the root of the tongue, and he also died of a recurrence; and I have heard of many other such cases. There are good clinicians who hold the view that the use of radium favours the spread of metastases. Radium is popular because it can be used instead of the knife, which people dread, and therefore doctors use it.

镭疗

编者按

针对伦纳德·希尔在《自然》上的批评，两位科学家写了这篇文章为使用镭对癌症进行放射治疗作了辩护。悉尼·拉斯是英国著名医师，他反对希尔提出的关于镭疗法为医疗界提供既得利益的指责，并认为人们已经了解并负责任地注意到了镭疗法的危险。阿瑟·伊夫是卢瑟福在核化学领域的早期合作者，他也指责希尔用流言和奇闻来攻击一个总体来说被小心谨慎使用的方法，尽管曾经因为知识不够全面而犯过一些错误。现如今用放射疗法治疗癌症是没有争议的，其使人虚弱的副作用也被公认为是不可避免的。它使人想起了帕拉切尔苏斯著名的格言——毒药在于剂量。

1939 年 12 月 9 日《自然》杂志第 973 页提到了我的一篇题为《射线对皮肤的穿透性，以及用于伤口治疗的辐射能》的文章（《皇家艺术学会会刊》，1939 年 12 月 8 日），其中我表达了如下观点：如果我们基于防爆安全考虑而让储藏于深洞之中的镭继续待在那里，就可以使局面不再继续恶化。我认为，肿瘤法案就是英国对于是否由金融势力决定镭疗法在英国的应用这一问题的答复。

镭可以破坏分裂旺盛的活细胞，但是在攻击癌细胞的同时，必然也会攻击血液循环中的正常活细胞等。它只能被用于杀死那些位于皮肤或体表的易接近的肿瘤，但是所有这些病例几乎都可以用切除或透热治疗针的外科方法来治疗，而且后面这两种治疗方法还不会引起镭疗后的患者经常出现的组织坏死和难以治愈的神经痛。由于白血球减少症而导致的死亡，都是徒劳地试图用炸弹中的镭来治愈深部肿瘤而造成的。我能举出一个使用镭而造成伤害的实例，该患者目前正在圣约翰物理医学研究与治疗中心接受治疗；正是由于用镭治疗头颅侧面皮肤上的一小块上皮瘤，结果导致了可能终身无法治愈的颅骨坏死，其面积足有一个高脚酒杯的杯口那么大。

已故的杰出外科医生弗尔尼沃先生罹患喉癌，在使用镭疗后不久即去世。他在自己的病历中留下了健康状况下降和不可治愈的神经痛的记录。我的一位亲戚因舌根部癌症而接受镭疗后，也遭受到这种无法忍受的神经痛，并且死于癌症复发；我还听到过许多类似的病例。很多优秀的临床医师都认为，镭的使用容易导致肿瘤转移。镭之所以流行，是因为它可以代替人们畏惧的手术刀，因此医生们才使用它。

X-ray apparatus is now available which operates at a million volts or more, so that radiations approaching those of radium are produced. The dosage of radium is controlled by time and filtration; that of X-rays can be further controlled in wave-length and intensity. Radium may be chosen as more convenient for application in such a place as the larynx.

Both radium and X-rays can produce, not only necrosis, but also cancer, and Sir Norman Walker considers that the use of X-rays for lupus should be abandoned. I know of an excellent laboratory servant who, only by continued observation and treatment, is kept, so far, free from cancer resulting from scars due to X-ray treatment of lupus of the face.

We know that death has resulted in several workers who licked the paint off brushes when applying luminous, radioactive paint to watch dials, and cancer has resulted from a radium tube being left in the body. Those who mine radium-bearing ore die generally from cancer of the lung.

The *Lancet* (Dec. 23, 1939) says, "to ensure that radiation treatment is in charge of really competent workers, and to give opportunities for training therapists, a high degree of centralisation will be more effective than the creation of individual treatments units". "To use both radium and X-rays to the best advantage some surgical training and a good grasp of radiation physics are needed, and for the purpose of the Act clinical knowledge of cancer in all its manifestations as well".

While vast sums have been spent on radium, numbers of poor people have to die, unrelieved, of cancer, in their homes. The pressing needs are to spread knowledge, secure prevention where possible, and every early diagnosis, allowing a hopeful removal by the knife or diathermy needle, which can be used by surgeons everywhere, the use of radium or X-rays being reserved for one or two places in the body where surgical operation is very difficult, and to be used by specialists as the *Lancet* suggests. There is no trustworthy evidence that radium in weak doses has any beneficial action.

Leonard Hill

(145, 151; 1940)

*   *   *

Sir Leonard Hill returns in *Nature* of January 27, p. 151, to his statement "that we would be little the worse off if all the radium now buried in deep holes for security from bombing remained there", and seeks to make good this assertion by reminding us of some of the casualties of radiological practice. He has allowed these examples to stay in the forefront of his mind, instead of fitting them into the groundwork of experience, which every practising radiologist must do.

现在有了在一百万伏特或者更高电压下操作的 X 射线装置，因此可以产生出与镭接近的射线。镭的剂量可以通过时间和滤光作用得到控制，而 X 射线的剂量则可以通过波长和强度进一步控制。对于像咽喉这样的部位来说，选用镭疗似乎更为便利。

镭和 X 射线不仅会导致组织坏死，还可能会诱发癌症。诺曼·沃克先生甚至认为，应该放弃使用 X 射线来治疗狼疮的方法。我知道有一位优秀的实验室工作人员，仅仅依靠持续观察和治疗，到目前为止，避免了由于使用 X 射线治疗面部狼疮留下的伤疤而引发的癌症。

我们知道，有几个工人在使用发光放射性涂料涂抹表盘时因为舔食了刷子上的涂料而致死，另外还有因镭管遗留在体内而诱发癌症的病例。那些开采含镭矿石的工人通常会死于肺癌。

1939 年 12 月 23 日的《柳叶刀》杂志中提到，"要保证放射治疗由真正能够胜任的人来负责，并且要为放射治疗工作者提供培训的机会，高度的集中化治疗要比创建个体治疗单位更为有效"。"要想最出色地使用镭和 X 射线，需要一些专门的外科训练，并充分掌握辐射物理学，此外，按照肿瘤法案的要求，还需要掌握肿瘤的临床知识及其所有表现形式"。

虽然已经有大量资金投入镭疗，但仍有大批穷人得不到救治，只能在家中死于癌症。当前最紧迫的是传播相关知识、尽可能地保障预防以及力争对所有癌症都能做到早期诊断，以便增加通过手术或透热针将其切除的希望，这是任何地方的外科医生都能使用的方法，应该将镭或者 X 射线的使用限制在外科手术难以治疗的一两个身体部位，并且如《柳叶刀》杂志所建议的那样由专家们来施用。还没有可靠的证据证明小剂量的镭能带来什么好的效果。

伦纳德·希尔

*　　*　　*

伦纳德·希尔爵士在 1 月 27 日的《自然》杂志第 151 页中重申了他的观点，"如果我们基于防爆安全考虑而让储藏于深洞之中的镭继续待在那里，就可以使局面不再继续恶化"，他还试图通过提醒我们有一些放射治疗导致伤亡的事例来证实他的论断。他过于强调这些事例，却没有将它们与经验的基础结合起来考虑，而这一点恰恰是每一个放射科医生必须要做的。

The dangers attending the use of radium and X-rays have been the concern of the X-ray and Radium Protection Committee for many years. No Committee can possibly safeguard a patient against an unskilful application of rays, but radiologists have striven to limit such dangers by making a real specialty of their subject; and there are at present five universities or kindred bodies in Great Britain which grant medical diplomas in this subject. The subject has, indeed, reached a status where its exponents can afford to ignore the rather baser charges in question, but the dis-service of Sir Leonard is to the public, who pay undue attention to his *ex cathedra* statements.

It is not true that the 15,000 patients (mostly cancer patients) who received radium treatment in Great Britain during the year 1938 had such treatment because of the vested interests of the medical public; the vast majority had radium treatment because it was considered the best available for them. It should be remembered that more than 90 percent of the country's radium is held by big organizations, such as the Radium Commission, the King's Fund and the Medical Research Council; this is some guarantee that it is used by people of responsibility.

Sir Leonard would like to see "the use of radium or X-rays being reserved for one or two places in the body where surgical operation is very difficult". The publication "Medical Uses of Radium" has been issued yearly since 1922 by the Medical Research Council, and the Radium Commission has in recent years made annual reports on the results of treatment; from them the pertinent fact emerges that the medical profession continues year by year to treat various forms of cancer at many sites of the body, and there is a disposition to widen rather than restrict the field. As for radium in the boreholes, it is only right that the public should know that much of the radium put away for safety has now been brought into use for their treatment.

Sidney Russ

(**145**, 347; 1940)

*　　*　　*

Sir Leonard Hill writes, in *Nature* of January 27, with reference to radium treatment and expresses a belief that "we would be little the worse off if all the radium now buried in deep holes for security from bombing remained there. ..." This pessimism contrasts notably with the enlightened optimism of the article, in the same issue, written by Dr. John H. Lawrence, of the University of California, who is working with great opportunities at present lacking in Great Britain. Lawrence and his co-workers are pursuing "the possibilities of artificial radioactivity and neutron rays in cancer therapy until a more satisfactory answer to this problem has been reached". What we require in Great Britain is a well-organized radiological institute where the various possibilities of radiation can be developed and extended. It had always been my hope and ambition that such an institute

使用镭和 X 射线治疗的危险，多年以来一直受到 X 射线与镭防护委员会的关注。没有委员会能够向病人保证对射线的不熟练的应用不会导致事故，但是，放射科医生一直在努力打造真正的学科专长，从而降低射线治疗产生危险的概率；到目前为止，英国已经有五所大学和科研机构获得了该学科领域的医学许可证。实际上，该学科领域已经发展到了相当的程度，其倡导者完全可以忽视那些没有价值的质疑，但是伦纳德爵士的论述是对公众有害的，他对他的那些**权威**陈述过于关注了。

1938 年，英国有 15,000 位患者（大多数是癌症患者）接受了镭疗。但是他们接受镭疗的原因并不是由于医疗界的既得利益；绝大多数人接受镭疗是因为他们相信这是他们能选择的最好的治疗方法。必须指出的是，我们国家超过 90% 的镭是由大型团体组织掌控的，例如镭管理委员会、国王基金和医学研究理事会；这在一定程度上保证了镭是由负责任的人使用的。

伦纳德爵士希望看到"将镭或者 X 射线的使用限制在外科手术难以治疗的一两个身体部位"。自 1922 年以来，医学研究理事会每年都会出版发行《镭的医学应用》，近年来镭管理委员会也有发布关于镭疗效果的年度报告；报告中的有关事实表明，医学界每年都在使用镭治疗身体各个部位各种形式的癌症，镭疗使用的范围在扩大，而不是受到限制。至于矿井中的镭，公众应该知道大量基于安全考虑而被储存起来的镭现已被用于医疗才是对的。

悉尼·拉斯

*　　*　　*

伦纳德·希尔爵士在 1 月 27 日的《自然》杂志中谈到了镭疗，并表达了如下信念，"如果我们基于防爆安全考虑而让储藏于深洞之中的镭继续待在那里，就可以使局面不再继续恶化……"。这种悲观论调与同一期杂志中另一篇由约翰·劳伦斯博士撰写的文章中对该问题的开明乐观态度，形成了鲜明的对比；劳伦斯博士来自加州大学，他在极好的便利条件下工作，而这些条件正是目前英国所缺乏的。劳伦斯和他的同事们正在研究"癌症治疗中应用人工放射性与中子射线的可能性，直至对该问题得到一个更令人满意的答案"。现在英国急需的，就是一个组织良好并能使射线的各种可能应用得以开发和扩展的放射学中心。一直以来，我的期望和理想就是建立这样

would be founded as a memorial to Lord Rutherford, who was always wide awake as to the possibilities of radiotherapy and the proper means by which they could be furthered or achieved.

Sir Leonard Hill has collected a certain amount of gossip about radium and narrates a few cases of failure due to the misuse of radium which have come to his personal notice. To counterbalance his citation of deplorable failure, I could quote instances in my own experience where men with cancer of the throat, and elsewhere, have been treated by radium and returned in full health and happiness to their useful work and daily life.

It is admitted by all that the cause, prevention and cure of cancer have not yet been attained. In some cases, when early treatment has been given, there has been cure or palliation by three chief means, surgery, radium, X-rays. All three methods can be and have been grossly abused in some cases, but wisely applied in a vast number of instances. It is not proposed to abolish railway signals because a signalman has wrecked a train by pulling the wrong switch; the effort is made to improve the arrangement, to make if foolproof, to have an efficient block system. Surgery is not condemned wholesale because of occasional deaths by incapacity, ignorance or carelessness. There have been deaths from dressings or swabs left in the wound. The wrong gas has been administered as anaesthetic. Overdoses of morphia have been given. A man can cut his throat with a safety razor. All such mistakes are no justification for complete disuse of the means employed.

It is, however, necessary to answer Sir Leonard Hill's ill-timed statement in a more positive sense, always remembering that while surgery has been under the guidance of men of high skill and intelligence for centuries—of men provided with every facility—on the other hand, both radium and X-rays are recent discoveries and naturally their applications to therapy are yet in their infancy.

A system of properly controlled and measured dosage, which can be repeated at will with exactitude, has scarcely yet been fully evolved. Certainly, in the past haphazard applications have produced deplorable results, but these are new avoidable in consequence of the research work already done on the proper direction of the radiation and on the determination of the magnitude of the dosage delivered to the growth and to the surrounding tissues.

Sir Leonard raises the question of the relative merits of radium and of X-rays and settles the matter to his own satisfaction with a positive assertion in favour of X-rays. In no part of the world has this difficult question yet been answered with sufficient scientific evidence to admit of certainty. The same uncertainty prevails as to the rival merits of X-rays of various voltages and wave-lengths. We may conjecture, but we cannot assert. Indeed these two important questions are forming part of an investigation by the Radium Beam Therapy Research under the Medical Research Council, and it is a matter for deep regret that this important work should be temporarily suspended by the exigencies of war.

一个中心来纪念卢瑟福勋爵，他对于放射治疗的可能性以及促使其进一步发展和完善的正确方法一直有着非常清醒的认识。

伦纳德·希尔爵士收集了一些关于镭的流言，又讲述了几个引起他关注的由于错误使用镭而导致失败的病例。为了与他所引用的悲惨的失败例证相对比，我也可以引用我亲身经历过的患喉癌或其他部位癌症的患者实例，他们接受了镭疗并完全康复，快乐地回到了正常的工作和生活中。

众所周知，人们对癌症的起因、预防和治疗还知之甚少。在癌症的早期治疗中，主要有三种方法来治愈或缓解病情：手术、镭和 X 射线。这三种方法都有可能并且已经在某些情况下被粗暴地滥用，但这只是极少数情况。没有人会因为曾有一个信号工人按错开关毁掉了一辆火车就提议废除铁路信号；人们会努力改进管理，确保系统万无一失，建立更高效的闭锁系统。外科手术并没有因为由无能、无知或疏忽导致的偶然死亡事故而遭到广泛的禁止。曾经出现过将敷料或棉签遗留在伤口中而导致死亡的事故，还曾发生过使用错误的气体作为麻醉剂以及施用了过量吗啡的事故。即使使用安全的剃须刀也有可能会割伤自己的喉咙。所有这些失误，并不能作为完全禁用相应方法和手段的正当理由。

不过，有必要对于伦纳德·希尔爵士不合时宜的陈述给予更积极的回应，我们必须始终记得，几个世纪以来，外科手术治疗一直是在具有高超技能和智慧且能获得各种所需设备的专业人士的指导下进行的，相比之下，镭和 X 射线都是最近发现的，很自然地，它们在治疗中的应用还处于初始阶段。

目前还没有完全开发出一个可随意并精确重复操作的、能合理控制和测量剂量的系统。无疑，过去对射线的肆意滥用已经造成了恶果，但在今天，这些恶果都是可以避免的，因为我们已经就实施辐射的正确操作和施用于肿瘤及周围组织的放射物剂量大小的确定进行了研究。

伦纳德爵士提出了关于镭与 X 射线相对价值的问题，他积极主张并赞成使用 X 射线从而得到令自己满意的答案。世界上还没有任何一个地方对这个难题给出过足以令人信服的科学解答。就像不同电压和波长的 X 射线哪种效果更好依然没有被确定一样。我们可以猜测，却无法断言。实际上，这两个问题是医学研究理事会下属的镭射线治疗研究所正在进行的研究中的一部分，而令人深感遗憾的是，这一重要的研究将会由于紧急的战事而暂时中断。

Some of my well-informed friends point out to me that, in the case of cancer of the uterus, Wertheim's operation for the removal of the whole organ has been given up by surgeons throughout the world and replaced by the use of radium and subsequent wider irradiation with X-rays. This change was largely due to the influence of pioneer work done at the Curie Institute in Paris and Radiumhemmet of Stockholm. In fact, no sooner was the radium placed underground in September than gynaecologists implored that some of it should be made immediately available to save life and relieve distress.

In the case of cancer of the breast, both surgery and radiation are available, and it is a matter of expert advice to decide which is the better in a given case; always insisting on the importance of early and *correct* diagnosis. In carcinoma of the throat, treatment by the radium beam can be used without mutilation or loss of speech, and in cases too advanced for surgery. While surgery may be of some avail with cancer of the rectum and prostate, we have to admit with regret that all methods fail when the oesophagus or stomach is concerned. In less serious cases—such as skin and lip cancer—either surgery or radiation is effective, but most patients would prefer to avoid mutilation and scar by the simple and perfectly safe application of a few milligrams of radium, or its equivalent, for a few hours.

It is scarcely necessary to reply to Sir Leonard Hill's reference to those unfortunate girls, who licking radium paint from their brushes, accumulated radium in their system. Is it suggested that this is in the remotest degree connected with radium therapy? As to the miners' phthisis in the Joachimthal mines, it can unfortunately be matched with closely similar results in the gold mines of South Africa—a matter requiring the closest attention and medical research with a view to prevention and cure.

A. S. Eve

(**145**, 347-348; 1940)

Leonard Hill: St. John Clinic and Institute of Physical Medicine, Ranelagh Road, London, S. W. 1, Jan. 5.

Sidney Russ: Barnato Joel Laboratories, Middlesex Hospital, London, W. 1, Feb. 6.

A. S. Eve: Overponds Cottage, Shackleford, Surrey, Feb. 5.

一些博学的朋友告诉我，在治疗子宫癌时，全世界的外科医生们都已经放弃了韦特海姆提出的切除整个器官的手术，而代之以镭疗和随后的大范围 X 射线照射治疗。这一转变，很大程度上是受到巴黎的居里研究所以及斯德哥尔摩镭治疗医院所做的开创性研究的影响。事实上，那些镭刚刚于九月被置于地下后不久，就立即有妇科医生请求使用其中一部分来拯救生命和缓解病痛。

对于乳腺癌来说，手术和放射疗法都是可行的，在具体病例中哪种方法更好，是由专家建议来决定的事情；但早期发现和**正确**诊断总是很重要的。对于喉癌来说，使用镭射线照射可以避免残疾或者语言功能的丧失，比手术治疗更好。手术治疗对于直肠癌和前列腺癌可能会有帮助，但我们不得不遗憾地承认，所有的方法对于食道癌和胃癌都无效。在不是很严重的病例中——例如皮肤癌和唇癌——手术或者放射疗法都是有效的，但是大多数患者为了避免躯体受损或留下疤痕而更倾向于用几毫克镭（或者其等效物）进行几小时的简单而又绝对安全的放射治疗。

对于伦纳德·希尔爵士提到的那些因为舔食了刷子上的含镭涂料而在体内积累了镭的不幸的女孩们，则根本没有必要作出回答。这是与镭疗法毫不相干的事情，难道不是吗？至于约阿希姆斯塔尔矿场工人的肺结核，与南非金矿中发生的不幸事件非常类似——这是一件需要给予密切关注并从预防和治疗的角度进行医学研究的事情。

伊夫

（王耀杨 翻译；杨志 审稿）

Cancer-Producing Chemical Compounds

J. W. Cook

Editor's Note

That some substances are carcinogenic was recognized at least since the eighteenth century, when some component of soot was deemed responsible for the high incidence of scrotal cancer in chimney sweeps. This led to a recognition that so-called aromatic hydrocarbons, common in tars and oils, are often carcinogens. Such compounds were also widely used in the dyestuffs industry, where they also posed a threat to industrial workers. By the time of this review by eminent chemist James Cook at Glasgow, the notion that carcinogenic compounds might feature not just in specialized petrochemical products but in human foodstuffs was starting to appear. Cook confesses that the variety of cancer-inducing agents made it hard to identify any generic chemical features among them.

IN the last resort, the degree of importance which is attached to the carcinogenic substances depends upon whether such compounds are concerned in the etiology of "spontaneous" human cancer. Perhaps closely bound up with this question is another unsolved problem of outstanding importance, namely, the manner in which these compounds bring about a transformation of normal cells into malignant cells. At least until answers are forthcoming to these questions, the carcinogenic compounds will continue to furnish useful material for the experimental study of cancer. Industrial cancer, in its various forms, has stimulated the researches which have brought to light the cancer-producing properties of the various carcinogenic agents, and in the preparation of the present brief survey of these agents regard has been paid to the correlation of the various forms of industrial cancer with their causative compounds.

In the earlier work on the carcinogenic properties of substances the skin of the mouse was usually employed as the test object. This was due to a number of reasons. Results could be expected comparatively rapidly; the ear of the rabbit, which had been first used, was less satisfactory in this respect. Moreover, the modes of application of the substances under examination were considerably restricted by the toxic and inflammatory properties of the crude mixtures which it was necessary to use. Many of these difficulties have been resolved by the availability of pure chemical compounds of high carcinogenic potency, and in recent years new techniques of administration have been developed, so that malignant tumours have been induced in a large number of different tissues, and in several different species. One outcome of these and other studies has been the revelation that, in certain strains of animal, tumours of a particular organ are apt to occur spontaneously. Thus, some strains of mice show a high incidence of mammary carcinoma; other strains show a high incidence of lung cancer; and there is at least one strain of mice in which liver-cell cancer (hepatoma) is apt to arise spontaneously. These findings indicate the caution

诱发癌症的化合物

库克

编者按

早在 18 世纪，人们便认识到有些物质具有致癌性，当时发现煤烟中的某种组分与烟囱清洁工人的阴囊癌的高发病率有关，这使人们注意到在焦油和石油中普遍存在的芳香烃物质是致癌的。这类物质也广泛应用于染料工业，因而它们也会威胁产业工人的健康。当格拉斯哥的著名化学家詹姆斯·库克撰写这篇论文的时候，人们就开始认识到，致癌化合物可能不仅存在于特殊的石化产品中，也存在于人类的饮食中。库克坦言，引发癌症的物质种类繁多，以至于难以确定它们在化学特征上的共性。

判定化合物致癌程度最重要的依据是看这种化合物是否与人类"自发"癌症的发病原因有关。与此紧密相关的另一个十分重要但尚未解决的问题是这些化合物将正常细胞转变为恶性细胞的作用方式。至少在这些问题得到解决之前，致癌化合物将一直是癌症实验研究的有用材料。工业化引发的各种癌症促使人们对此展开研究，从而带来了揭示出致癌物质诱发癌症机制的希望。此外，在当前对这些物质进行简要描述的准备阶段，人们已经注意到工业引发的癌症与相应致癌物之间存在关联。

早期研究致癌物的特性时，经常用小鼠的皮肤作为测试对象。这是有多种原因的。首先，这样可以较快地得到结果，而最早使用兔子耳朵作为测试对象时这方面就不太令人满意。另外，因为研究中必须使用的天然混合物有毒性并能引起炎症反应，因此在实验中待检物质的给药方式受到很大程度的制约。现在，人们已经可以提纯出具有高致癌性的单一化合物，许多这样的问题已经得到了解决。近几年来，一些新的给药技术已经得到了发展，因而已经可以在好几种动物的多种组织中诱导出恶性肿瘤。这些以及其他一些相关研究的结果表明，对于某些品系的动物，肿瘤容易在某些特定器官中自发产生。因而，一些品系的小鼠表现出很高的乳腺癌发生率；另外一些品系表现出很高的肺癌发生率；此外，至少有一个品系的小鼠容易自发产生肝细胞癌（肝细胞瘤）。这些结果提示我们，当实验动物的一些器官发生了癌

that must be used in interpreting the results when cancers of such organs are found in experimental animals, especially when the tumours arise at sites other than that of application of the carcinogenic agent. Yet even so, tumours clearly attributable to the treatment have been found, usually at the site of application, in a variety of tissues of animals treated with carcinogenic compounds. In this respect the most versatile substances so far found are contained in the group of polycyclic hydrocarbons, mostly related to 1:2-benzanthracene (I), in which substituents are present at certain well-defined positions in the molecule. With these compounds malignant tumours have been obtained, usually in mice and rats, in such tissues as the skin, the subcutaneous tissues, the peritoneal cavity, the liver, the prostate, the forestomach, the brain, and the spleen; and this list is not exhaustive. Less widespread in their effect are members of other classes of compounds, where usually carcinogenic action has not been shown except in a single organ. In this connexion it needs to be borne in mind that these substances have not usually been so widely investigated as the polycyclic hydrocarbon class.

(I)   (II)

The earliest form of industrial cancer, recognized as such in the latter part of the eighteenth century, was the cancer of the scrotum to which chimney sweeps were specially liable. This was caused by soot, and the pursuit of the clue so provided culminated eventually in the isolation from coal tar of the individual compound responsible. This is 3:4-benzpyrene (II), an aromatic hydrocarbon, the relationship of which to 1:2-benzanthracene (I) is apparent from the formulae. 3:4-Benzpyrene is undoubtedly the principal cancer-producing constituent of coal tar. It has a high boiling point, and hence is present to an appreciable extent only in the highest boiling fractions of the tar. There are grounds for inferring that this or a similar compound is responsible for the carcinogenic properties shown to varying degrees by some of the mineral lubricating oils. Prolonged contact with industrial products of these types is now recognized as being fraught with danger, and the use of suitable precautions should lead to diminution if not to eradication of the form of industrial cancer which they are liable to cause.

The widespread use of tar in road surfaces, and the publication of statistics which appear to show that cancer of the lung is increasing at an alarming rate, have led to the suggestion that tarred road dust may be partly responsible for this increase. This suggestion has been tested experimentally; but although an increase in lung cancer was found in mice breathing air impregnated with road dust, this increase was not wholly related to the presence of tar in the dust, and the results of the experiments do not directly implicate such an agent in the increase of the human disease. Furthermore, it is considered by many

变，特别是肿瘤并不是发生在施用致癌剂的部位时，对结果的解释一定要小心谨慎。尽管如此，在用致癌物处理的动物的各种组织中，还是经常能观察到肿瘤出现在给药部位。迄今为止，人们发现的最常见的致癌物都属于多环烃类，其中大多数与1,2-苯并蒽（I）有关，一般是在该分子的某些特定位置上发生取代而形成的。通过施用这些化合物，可以在小鼠或大鼠的某些组织中成功诱导出恶性肿瘤，如皮肤、皮下组织、腹腔、肝脏、前列腺、前胃、脑、脾脏等等。还有一些其他类型的致癌物，其作用效果不是很广泛，一般只在单一的器官中显示出致癌活性。所以，这些物质并不像多环烃类那样受到广泛的关注。

(I)　　　　　　　　(II)

最早发现的由工业引发的癌症是烟囱清洁工们特别易患的阴囊癌，这种癌症在18世纪后半叶才被人们认识到。它是由煤烟引起的，对其发病原因的追踪使人们最终从煤焦油中分离出了单一的致癌化合物。这就是3,4-苯并芘（II），它是一种芳香烃，从分子式可以很容易地看出它与1,2-苯并蒽（I）的关系。3,4-苯并芘的确是煤焦油中主要的致癌组分。它有很高的沸点，因此只有在焦油最高沸点的馏分中，它的含量才能达到可测量的程度。有理由推断，某些矿物润滑油表现出的不同程度的致癌特性正是由于含有这种化合物或类似化合物。现在人们已经认识到，长时间接触这类工业产品是危险的，进行适当的防范即使不能完全消除至少也能够降低由这些物质诱发癌症的概率。

焦油被广泛应用于公路表面，而公布的统计数据也显示肺癌的发病率正在以惊人的速度增长，据此我们推测，导致肺癌发病率升高的部分原因可能是焦油路面的粉尘。人们已经通过实验检验了这种推测；让小鼠呼吸充满公路尘埃的空气，人们发现其肺癌发病率会升高，但是尽管如此，这种升高并不完全是由尘埃中存在焦油引起的，并且实验结果没有直接证明焦油就是导致人类肺癌病例增加的原因。许多

authorities that the recorded increase in lung cancer is largely accounted for by improved methods of diagnosis. Unconvincing attempts have also been made to implicate pollution of town air by soot, exhaust fumes, etc., and also tobacco smoking in the increase of lung cancer. However, the knowledge that the agencies in question may be, and sometimes are, associated with carcinogenic substances, does not allow such speculations to be too lightly dismissed.

The carcinogenic activity of 3:4-benzpyrene is of a high order, inasmuch as tumours arise in a large proportion of the treated animals, in a relatively short time. A somewhat greater potency is shown by 20-methylcholanthrene (III), a hydrocarbon first obtained by chemical transformation of the bile acids, and later indirectly from cholesterol. Other hydrocarbons of similar structure have similar high activity. An altogether higher order of activity, judged by the criterion of shortness of the latent period in the induction of skin tumours in mice, has recently been found in a small group of hydrocarbons typified by 9:10-dimethyl-1:2-benzanthracene (IV). These compounds, which are characterized by the presence of methyl groups in the positions shown, have in mice skin given tumours which frequently made their appearance within a month of the first application.

CH$_3$

(III)

CH$_3$

CH$_3$

(IV)

It will be observed that the carcinogenic hydrocarbons thus far mentioned are all derived from 1:2-benzanthracene (I). A very considerable number of other carcinogenic derivatives of 1:2-benzanthracene is now known. These are purely synthetic compounds, not known to be associated with either industrial or naturally occurring products. Their chief interest lies in the large number of closely related compounds which have been shown to have such biological activity, and in the generalizations which it has been possible to arrive at regarding the correlation of carcinogenic activity with molecular structure and with other properties.

The benzanthracene group is not the only group of polycyclic hydrocarbons with carcinogenic properties. Feeble activity is shown by 3:4-benzphenanthrene (V), and systematic examination of homologues and derivatives now in progress is pointing to the conclusion that much enhanced activity is shown when suitable substituents are introduced into positions 1 and 2, but not into other positions of the molecule. Before 3:4-benzpyrene had been isolated from coal tar, it had been claimed erroneously that chrysene, also a coal tar constituent, had carcinogenic properties. This error appeared to be due to the

824

专家甚至认为有记录的肺癌病例的增加主要是因为诊断方法的进步。还有一些其他的实验尝试证明肺癌病例的增加与煤烟、废气等对城市空气的污染以及吸烟有关，但结果都不令人信服。尽管如此，以上这些物质还是有可能（或者是在某些情况下）与致癌作用有关，因此前面的推测不能完全被舍弃。

3,4-苯并芘的致癌活性非常高，因为用它处理过的动物很大一部分在相对较短的时间内就产生了肿瘤。20-甲基胆蒽（III）的致癌能力还要更强一点，这种烃类物质最先由胆汁酸通过化学转化得到，后来也可以通过胆固醇间接得到。其他一些具有类似结构的烃类也具有相似的高致癌活性。通过以小鼠皮肤癌诱导过程中潜伏期的长短作为判断标准，研究人员最近发现以 9,10-二甲基-1,2苯并蒽（IV）为代表的一小类烃具有更高的致癌活性。这些化合物的特点是在附图所示位置上存在甲基，它们可以诱发小鼠皮肤产生肿瘤。往往在首次施药后一个月内肿瘤就会出现。

(III) (IV)

我们可以看到，迄今为止有记载的致癌烃类都是由 1,2-苯并蒽（I）衍生而来的。现在已经知道了相当多的其他 1,2-苯并蒽的致癌衍生物。这些化合物完全都是人工合成的，与工业产物或纯天然生成的物质无关。这些化合物在研究领域的主要意义在于：这些结构类似并具有致癌活性的化合物种类非常多；通过研究其共性人们可能可以揭示致癌物活性与致癌物分子结构及其他特性之间的关系。

多环烃类化合物中并非只有苯并蒽家族才具有致癌活性。3,4-苯并菲（V）也具有微弱的致癌活性，根据目前正在进行的对其同系物及相应衍生物的系统检测，可以初步断定当在 1 位和 2 位上引入合适的取代基后其致癌活性会大大增加，而在分子结构中其他位置上引入取代基则无此作用。在从煤焦油中分离纯化出 3,4-苯并芘之前，人们一直错误地认为煤焦油中的另一种成分䓛具有致癌活性。出现这种错误的原因应该是最初从煤焦油中获得的的䓛由于提纯不彻底而含有杂质。诸如此类

incomplete purification of chrysene of coal tar origin. These and other circumstances have caused some attention to be devoted to chrysene derivatives, and a number of chrysene homologues, selected in a haphazard way, have been synthesized and found inactive when tested biologically. More recently a consideration of the structural relationship among the carcinogenic derivatives of 1:2-benzanthracene and 3:4-benzphenanthrene led C. L. Hewett (*J. Chem. Soc.*, in the press) to synthesize 1:2-dimethylchrysene (VI), and this hydrocarbon has been found to have definite carcinogenic activity when tested by application to the skin of mice.

(v)   (VI)

For many years it has been recognized that the operatives engaged in certain sections of the chemical industry, and especially in the manufacture of dyestuffs, are more liable to cancer of the urinary bladder than is the general population. This form of cancer was long known as "aniline cancer", and the prevailing opinion for many years has been that it is due to absorption of nitrogenous bases such as benzidine and the naphthylamines, especially β-naphthylamine. Until recently the evidence was purely circumstantial, and many unsuccessful attempts have been made to induce experimental tumours with these bases. Some two years ago, however, the production of bladder tumours in dogs given, subcutaneously and orally, large daily doses of a high grade of commercial β-naphthylamine was reported by American workers. It was doubtless the prevalence of this dye-workers' cancer, coupled with the known cell-proliferating properties of Biebrich Scarlet *R*, which led to Japanese researches which have shown that a number of relatively simple azo compounds have carcinogenic properties. The principal active compounds which have been revealed by this work are 4'-amino-2:3'-azotoluene (VII), which gives liver-cell tumours when fed to rats and mice, 2:3'-azotoluene (VIII), which gave malignant tumours of the urinary bladder in rats, and *p*-dimethylaminoazobenzene (IX), which is mainly carcinogenic towards the liver.

的相关情况使一些研究者将注意力投向了菧的衍生物。人们以随机选择的方式合成了大量菧的同系物，但通过生物学检测发现这些化合物并无致癌活性。最近，基于对 1,2–苯并蒽的各种致癌衍生物与 3,4–苯并菲的结构关系的考察，休伊特合成了（《英国化学会志》，即将出版）1,2–二甲基菧（VI），并且通过施用于小鼠皮肤进行测试发现这种烃类确实具有致癌活性。

(v)

(VI)

多年来人们一直认为，在化学工业的某些部门特别是染料制造部门工作的工人比普通人群更容易患膀胱癌。长期以来，这种癌症被认为是"苯胺癌"，人们一直认为该病的起因是人体吸收了含氮碱基，例如联苯胺和萘胺，特别是 β–萘胺。但是直到最近仍然缺乏直接证据。人们进行了大量研究，试图通过实验的方法用这些碱基诱导肿瘤，但都没有成功。不过，美国的研究人员在两年多以前曾报道，每天给狗大剂量皮下注射和口服商品化的超纯 β–萘胺能够诱导出膀胱癌。毫无疑问，染料工人中膀胱癌的盛行与人们熟知的偶氮染料 R 所具有的使细胞增殖的特性有关。在此基础上，日本研究人员进一步研究发现许多相对比较简单的偶氮化合物也具有致癌活性。这项研究发现的具有致癌活性的化合物主要是 4′–氨基 –2,3′–偶氮甲苯（VII），2,3′–偶氮甲苯（VIII）和对二甲氨基偶氮苯（IX）。4′–氨基 –2,3′–偶氮甲苯能使大鼠和小鼠产生肝细胞瘤，2,3′–偶氮甲苯（VIII）能在大鼠中诱导出膀胱恶性肿瘤，对二甲氨基偶氮苯（IX）则主要对肝脏产生致癌作用。

(VII)   (VIII)   (IX)

In view of the possibility that contaminants of the naphthylamines might be responsible for the dye-workers' cancer, a number of possible transformation products have been administered to rats and mice in the research laboratories of the Royal Cancer Hospital, London. Mice treated with 2:2′-azonaphthalene (X) by application to the skin, or by subcutaneous injection, or by feeding, have developed many liver growths, some of them liver-cell carcinomas, but most were of a cholangiomatous type. Similar tumours were obtained with 2:2′-diamino-1:1′-dinaphthyl (XI), a product which arises easily by intramolecular change of the dihydride of (X), and also with 3:4:5:6-dibenzcarbazole (XII), which is formed by deamination of (XI). There is thus the possibility that the biological effects of this series of compounds are due to a common metabolite, and it is worth noting that the final product of the series (XII) has a structural resemblance to the carcinogenic polycyclic hydrocarbons.

(X)   (XI)

(XII)

One of the azo dyes found to be carcinogenic to the liver by the Japanese workers, namely, *p*-dimethylaminoazobenzene (IX), was formerly used as a food colouring matter under the name of "butter yellow" and has also been used in dyeing leather. Fortunately, its use in these respects appears now to be obsolete. In Great Britain the range of permitted food colouring matter is now very limited. With the co-operation of the Government

(VII) (VIII) (IX)

考虑到也有可能是萘胺中的杂质使染料工人患上癌症，因此，在伦敦皇家肿瘤医院的许多实验室中，研究人员对大鼠和小鼠施用了萘胺的多种可能的转化产物以进行研究。不管是通过皮肤表面用药，还是进行皮下注射，抑或通过饲喂给药，用2,2′-偶氮萘（X）处理过的小鼠中都出现了肝脏增生，其中有一些小鼠出现了肝细胞癌，但大多数是胆管瘤类型的。对小鼠施用2,2′-二氨基-1,1′-二萘（XI）或3,4,5,6-二苯咔唑（XII）也可以得到相似的肿瘤。当2,2′-偶氮萘（X）分子内发生二氢化可以很容易地得到2,2′-二氨基-1,1′-二萘（XI）；而后者去氨基就能得到3,4,5,6-二苯咔唑（XII）。因此，这一生物学效应有可能是由同一代谢产物引起的，而且值得注意的是，这一系列化合物的代谢终产物（XII）具有与致癌多环烃类相似的分子结构。

(x) (XI)

(XII)

日本的研究人员发现，有一种偶氮染料对二甲氨基偶氮苯（IX）对肝脏有致癌作用。这种先前被称为"甲基黄"的物质被用作食物色素，同时也用于皮革制品染色。幸运的是，现在这些行业已经很少使用这种物质了。如今在英国被允许用作食物色素的物质是非常有限的。在政府化学家的协助下，相关部门选取了一批被允许

Chemist, tests have been carried out in which relatively large amounts of a selection of these permitted dyes were regularly administered with the food to rats and mice. The compounds chosen were azo compounds bearing some structural resemblance to the azo compounds discussed in the present article. They are mostly water-soluble sulphonates, a circumstance which facilitates rapid elimination. In a few of the mice stomach tumours were obtained; but it is by no means certain that these were due to the dyes.

Existing knowledge of the structures of the various carcinogenic compounds and of the conditions under which they may be formed has led to various speculations regarding the possibility of such substances being present in human food. Some workers have recorded the production of skin tumours by heated fats and by tars prepared by heating coffee. It has been claimed also that wheat-germ oil prepared by a special extraction process produces sarcomatous tumours in rats. This claim has not thus far received independent confirmation, and at the present time there is no evidence that cancer of the internal organs is due to specific dietary constituents. However, it is evident that such lines of inquiry should be pursued.

A puzzling and in some ways disconcerting feature of the carcinogenic agents now known is their variety and their apparent lack of correlation. It may be recalled that cancer may be induced not only by the classes of compound reviewed in this article, but also by several other agencies. The malignant tumours which arise in consequence of exposure to ultra-violet light, X-rays, and radioactive substances may well be due to the production of carcinogenic compounds from normal constituents of the tissues.

There is, however, no evidence that the radiations exert their influence in this indirect manner. Cancer of the skin occurs in persons taking arsenic by mouth over long periods, and has also been found in workmen engaged in handling arsenical sheep dips. Teratoma of the testis in fowls can be induced by injection of zinc salts at the season of the year when the testis is actively secreting androgenic hormone. At other times also this type of growth may be produced if gonadotropic hormone is simultaneously administered, so that at least two factors seem to be involved.

Thus, in carcinogenesis we have a biological phenomenon which may be attributed to a variety of different substances and agencies. This is by no means unique, for the same is true of other biological phenomena; but it is a circumstance which adds to the difficulty of interpreting the biological properties of the carcinogenic compounds and in estimation their ultimate significance.

(**145**, 335-338; 1940)

J. W. Cook: University of Glasgow.

使用的染料，并通过定期地让小鼠和大鼠在进食时大量服用这些染料的方法对它们进行了测试。测试中选取的化合物都是与本文中讨论的化合物有一些类似结构的偶氮化合物。它们主要以水溶性的磺酸盐形式存在，这使得它们容易快速降解。实验中，部分小鼠出现了胃癌，但是不能完全肯定这就是由染料引起的。

目前，通过依据现有的对各种致癌化合物的结构以及产生条件的认识，人们提出了各种推测，这些推测都提到了这些致癌物质存在于人类食物中的可能性。一些研究者发现热油脂和加热咖啡时产生的焦油都可以诱发皮肤癌。还有研究表明，经某种特殊提取方法制备的麦胚油可以诱发大鼠产生肉瘤样肿瘤。这一报道迄今还没有得到确切的证实，而且目前也没有证据表明体内器官的肿瘤是由特殊的饮食成分造成的。不过，很明显这类研究还需要进一步深入。

目前已知的致癌物质有一个令人困惑的、在某些方面甚至是令人担忧的特点，这就是它们的多样性以及彼此之间缺乏明显关联。值得一提的是，不仅是本文所提到的这一系列化合物能够诱发癌症，很多其他物质也能诱发癌症。暴露于紫外线、X 射线或放射性物质后诱发的恶性肿瘤，也可能是由于组织中正常成分产生的致癌物质引起的。

然而，还没有证据证明放射物以这种间接的方式发挥作用。长期口服含砷物质的人容易患皮肤癌，另外还发现那些处理含砷的羊用防腐浸液的工人也容易患皮肤癌。在家禽睾丸活跃分泌雄性激素期间给它们注射锌盐会诱导其产生睾丸畸胎瘤。在其他时间，如果同时施用促性腺激素也会诱发家禽产生这类肿瘤。这样看来，在肿瘤诱发过程中至少涉及到这两个因素。

综上所述，在癌症发生过程中，我们看到了一种可能由多种不同的物质或因素引发的生物学现象。无独有偶，其他一些生物现象也是如此。但是，这种情况为阐明致癌化合物的生物学特性以及评价它们的最终意义增加了不少难度。

（吴彦 翻译；秦志海 审稿）

Molecular Structure of the Collagen Fibres

W. T. Astbury and F. O. Bell

Editor's Note

Collagen is the fibrous protein that constitutes connective tissue—tendons and such structures in living things. William T. Astbury from the University of Leeds had built a reputation for himself during the 1930s by attempting the X-ray analysis of long polymer molecules, even including DNA. Here he describes the atomic structure of the collagen molecule. Unfortunately, Astbury had no means of knowing that collagen consists of a triple helix formed by protein polymer molecules. The problem that Astbury set himself was solved only in the 1980s.

X-RAY studies of the fibrous proteins indicate that they fall almost exclusively into one or other of two main configurational groups, the keratinmyosin group and the collagen group[1]. The interpretation of the structure and properties of the former group is now well advanced and has frequently been reported on in *Nature* and elsewhere, but the structure of the latter, in spite of many investigations, has hitherto remained unexplained. It was suggested several years ago that the amino-acid residues in gelatin (which also gives the typical collagen diffraction pattern) are somehow grouped in threes with probably every third a glycine residue and every ninth a hydroxyproline residue, that the strong meridian arc of spacing about 2.86 A. is associated with the average length of a residue in the direction of the fire axis, and that such an average length could very well arise from an alternate *cis*- and *trans*-configuration[2]; but further progress was not possible for lack of experimental data. More recent chemical and X-ray evidence points now to a solution that is both simple and convincing.

(1) Bergmann[3] concludes that the average residue weight in gelatin is about 94, and that the chief residues are present in the proportions set out in the accompanying table:

Amino-acid Frequencies in Gelatin

Amino-acid		Wt.%	Mol. Wt.	Gm. Mol.	Frequency
Glycine	..	25.5	75	0.34	$3 \ (2^0 \cdot 3^1)$
Proline	..	19.7	115	0.17	$6 \ (2^1 \cdot 3^1)$
Hydroxyproline	..	14.4	131	0.11	$9 \ (2^0 \cdot 3^2)$
Alanine	..	8.7	89	0.098	$9 \ (2^0 \cdot 3^2)$
Arginine	..	9.1	174	0.052	$18 \ (2^1 \cdot 3^2)$
Leucine-*iso*leucine	..	7.1	131	0.054	$18 \ (2^1 \cdot 3^2)$
Lysine	..	5.9	146	0.040	$24 \ (2^3 \cdot 3^1)$

胶原纤维的分子结构

阿斯特伯里，贝尔

编者按

胶原纤维是构成生物体内肌腱等结缔组织的纤维状蛋白质。在20世纪30年代，利兹大学的威廉·阿斯特伯里对包括DNA在内的多种长形聚合物分子进行了X射线分析并由此闻名于世。他在这篇文章中描述了胶原纤维分子的原子结构。遗憾的是，阿斯特伯里当时还无法了解到胶原纤维是由三股蛋白质聚合物分子形成的螺旋构成的。他提出的问题直到20世纪80年代才得到解决。

对纤维状蛋白质的 X 射线研究表明，它们几乎可以毫无例外地被归入两种主要构型族中的任意一种，即角蛋白 – 肌球蛋白族和胶原蛋白族[1]。对于第一种构型族的结构和性质的解析目前进展顺利，其相关报道常在《自然》或其他一些杂志上发表。对于第二种构型族的结构，尽管已进行了很多研究，但迄今为止仍没有得到解析。几年前有人提出，在结构上，明胶（它也能产生典型的胶原蛋白衍射图样）中的氨基酸残基以三个为一组，并且每到第三个就很可能是一个甘氨酸残基，而第九个则很可能是羟基脯氨酸残基，这样就把弧长约为 2.86 Å 的强子午线与沿纤维轴方向上一个残基的平均长度关联起来了，而这样的平均长度又正好可以由顺式与反式构型[2]相互交替产生；不过，由于缺乏实验数据一直无法取得进一步的进展。如今，最新的化学证据与 X 射线数据都指向了一个更为简单和令人信服的结果。

（1）伯格曼[3] 得到的结论是，明胶中氨基酸残基的平均分子量约为 94，其中最主要的几种氨基酸残基出现的比例如下表所示：

明胶中氨基酸出现的频率

氨基酸	质量百分比	分子量	摩尔质量	频率
甘氨酸	25.5	75	0.34	3 $(2^0 \cdot 3^1)$
脯氨酸	19.7	115	0.17	6 $(2^1 \cdot 3^1)$
羟基脯氨酸	14.4	131	0.11	9 $(2^0 \cdot 3^2)$
丙氨酸	8.7	89	0.098	9 $(2^0 \cdot 3^2)$
精氨酸	9.1	174	0.052	18 $(2^1 \cdot 3^2)$
亮氨酸和异亮氨酸	7.1	131	0.054	18 $(2^1 \cdot 3^2)$
赖氨酸	5.9	146	0.040	24 $(2^3 \cdot 3^1)$

Thus not only are one third of the residues glycine residues, but also, except for one residue in eighteen, another third are either proline or hydroxyproline residues; that is to say, are of the form:

The table shows too that there cannot be fewer than 72 residues in the gelatin "molecule" (there will not be any definite molecule of gelatin itself, but only large, and possibly somewhat modified, fragments of the original collagen pattern): the true number must be a fairly high multiple of this, possibly 576, to judge by the histidine content for example.

(2) The side-chain and backbone spacings in dry gelatin are about 10.4 A. and 4.4 A., respectively, while the density is about 1.32 gm./c.c. Suppose these two spacings to be inclined at an angle β, and the average length of a residue in the direction of the fibre axis to be L A., then

$$94 \times 1.65 = \frac{10.4 \times 4.4 \times L \times 1.32}{\sin\beta}$$

that is,
$$L = 2.6 \sin\beta \text{ (approx.)}$$

and therefore L cannot be greater than about 2.6 A. This is only an approximate calculation, but it is sufficiently accurate to confirm that the strong meridian arc of spacing 2.86 A. is almost certainly associated with the average length of a residue.

(3) If it is actually equal to it, as seems most probable, and the residues follow one another in a row, then from the table the minimum length of the intramolecular pattern along the fibre axis is about 72×2.86 A. This length is not only too small to include the residues of other acids, such as histidine, omitted from the table, but also it is too small to account for the meridian spacings reported by Wyckoff and Corey[4] and by Clark and co-workers[5]. Their data are best explained by a sequence of 4×72 residues in a row, grouped in approximate sets of 12, 24 and 36. This gives a molecular weight of about 27,000, or a multiple thereof, corresponding to Svedberg's gliadin class[6].

(4) The proposed partial *cis*-configuration[2] is readily accounted for by the preponderance of imino residues. When we allow for this and the glycine content, there seems to be only one reasonable solution, represented by the scale model shown in the accompanying illustration. The basic sequence is –P–G–R–, where (with the exception of one residue

这样看来，不仅有 1/3 的残基是甘氨酸残基，而且，另外 1/3 的残基基本上不是脯氨酸残基就是羟脯氨酸残基（每 18 个氨基酸残基中有 1 个例外）；也就是说，它具有如下结构：

表中数据还显示，明胶"分子"（这里并非指明胶本身的某种确切分子，而仅仅是指那些大的并且可能受到某些修饰的具有胶原蛋白特性的片段）中的氨基酸残基数不可能少于 72 个，真实的残基数必定是 72 的很多倍，比如，根据组氨酸的含量推断出的残基数可能是 576。

（2）在干明胶中，氨基酸的侧链与主干的长度分别约为 10.4 Å 和 4.4 Å，而密度则约为 1.32 g/c.c.。假定侧链与主干之间的倾角为 β，而一个氨基酸残基沿纤维轴方向的平均长度为 L Å，那么：

$$94 \times 1.65 = \frac{10.4 \times 4.4 \times L \times 1.32}{\sin\beta}$$

即：
$$L = 2.6 \sin\beta \text{（近似值）}$$

因此 L 大约不会超过 2.6 Å。虽然只是粗略估算，不过这已经足够准确地证实弧长约为 2.86 Å 的强子午线与一个残基的平均长度是有关联的。

（3）如果实际长度确实如此（目前看来这是很有可能的），并且残基一个接一个地连成一行，那么根据表中的数据，分子内模块在沿着纤维轴方向上的最小长度约为 72×2.86 Å。这个长度太小了，不但根本无法包括上述表格中被忽略的其他氨基酸残基，如组氨酸，而且也不足以解释威科夫与科里 [4]、克拉克及其合作者们 [5] 所报道的子午线长度。对他们的数据所能作出的最佳解释是一条由 4×72 个氨基酸残基排成一行的序列，其中大约 12、24 或 36 个组成一组。这样得到的分子量大约是 27,000 或其若干倍，这与斯韦德贝里的醇溶蛋白类 [6] 是一致的。

（4）亚氨基残基 [2] 在数量上占优势地位的事实能很好地解释之前有人提出过的部分顺式构型。当我们考虑到这一点和甘氨酸的含量之后，看来似乎就只有一个合理的答案了，即如附图中展示的比例模型所代表的结构。基本序列是 –P–G–R–，其

in eighteen) *P* stands for either proline or hydroxyproline, *G* for glycine, and *R* for one or other of the remaining residues. The full-length pattern, and also variations within the collagen group as a whole, must arise by suitably modifying this simple theme.

Using the interatomic distances found in silk fibroin, the average length per residue in the pattern shown in the illustration works out to be 2.85 A., almost exactly the spacing of the strong meridian arc. Other points in favour of the model are: (*a*) there is no steric interference between the side-chains, the longer side-chains all lying on the side of the main-chain remote from the rings, leaving only the unobtrusive glycine side-chain (–*H*) on the same side as the rings; and (*b*) the polypeptide chain proceeds in a straight line, and any attempt to stretch it results in the side-chain (–*R*) swinging over towards the rings and the system coiling back upon itself: thus we have an explanation of the paradox that though the collagen configuration is shorter than that of the β-proteins, it is nevertheless practically inextensible.

The above solution of the collagen problem permits now of the broad generalization that all the extended forms of the fibrous proteins fall into either of two classes: they are built from polypeptide chains in either the *cis*- or the *trans*-configuration.

A fuller account of this investigation may be found in the first Procter Memorial Lecture[7], and a more detailed discussion still will be published elsewhere.

(**145**, 421-422; 1940)

中 P 代表脯氨酸或羟基脯氨酸（除去每 18 个中的一个例外），G 代表甘氨酸，R 则代表其他残基中的某一个。明胶分子内模块的全长以及明胶与胶原纤维组这个整体的差异，应该可以通过适当调整这个简单序列的形式而得到。

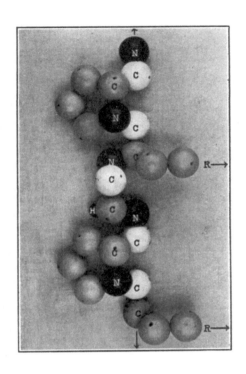

利用研究丝素蛋白时得到的原子间距离，可以推算出插图所示的模块中每个氨基酸残基的平均长度为 2.85 Å，基本上完全等同于强子午线弧长。还有一些支持这种模型的证据：(a) 侧链之间不存在位阻影响，较长的侧链全都位于主链上远离环的一侧，只有小得不起眼的甘氨酸侧链（$-H$）位于环的同一侧；(b) 多肽链沿着直线延伸，任何拉伸链的尝试都会使侧链（$-R$）转向环，从而使整个体系转个弯折回来。因而，我们便可以对胶原蛋白的构型比 β–蛋白短但几乎不能伸展这一看似矛盾的现象作出解释了。

上述关于胶原纤维问题的解决经过推广可以得到如下结论：纤维状蛋白质的所有伸展形式都可以归入两类中的一种，要么是由顺式构型的多肽链构成，要么是由反式构型的多肽链构成。

关于这项研究的更为完整的叙述可以在第一届普罗克特纪念讲演 [7] 中找到，我们还将在其他地方发表一份更详细的论述。

（王耀杨 翻译；刘京国 审稿）

W. T. Astbury and Florence O. Bell: Textile Physics Laboratory, University of Leeds, Jan. 31.

References:

1. Astbury, W. T., *C.R. Lab. Carlsberg*, **22**, 45 (1938) (Sørensen Jubilee Vol.); *Trans. Faraday Soc.*, **34**, 377 (1938); *Ann. Rev. Biochem.*, **8**,113(1939); *Ann. Rep. Chem. Soic.*, **35**, 198 (1939).

2. Astbury, W. T., *Trans. Faraday Soc.*, **29**, 193 (1933); *Cold Spring Harbor Symposia on Quantitative Biology*, **2**, 15 (1934); *Chem. Weekbl.*, **33**, 778 (1936). Astbury, W. T., and Atkin, W. R., *Nature*, **132**, 348 (1933).

3. Bergmann M., *J. Biol. Chem.*, **110**, 471 (1935). Bergmann, M., and Niemann, C., *ibid.*, **115**, 77 (1936).

4. Wyckoff, R. W. G., Corey, R. B., and Biscoe, J., *Science*, **82**, 175 (1935). Corey, R. B., and Wyckoff, R. W. G., *J. Biol, Chem.*, **114**, 407 (1936). Wyckoff, R. W. G., and Corey, R. B., *Proc. Soc. Expt. Biol. and Med.*, **34**, 285 (1936).

5. Clark, G. L., Parker, E. A., Schaad, J. A., and Warren, W. J., *J. Amer. Chem. Soc.*, **57**, 1509 (1935).

6. Svedberg, T., *Proc. Roy. Soc.*, B, **127**, 1 (1939).

7. Astbury, W. T., *J. Int. Soc. Leather Trades' Chemists* (in the press).

Capture Cross-Sections for Thermal Neutrons in Thorium, Lead and Uranium 238

L. Meitner

Editor's Note

Physicists had not yet measured the "capture cross-section"—the tendency to become captured—of thermal neutrons in the nuclei of ^{238}U, an important parameter for the possibility of a nuclear chain reaction. A small capture cross-section—fewer neutrons captured—would make the process more likely, as this leaves others to trigger fission events. Here Lise Meitner measures this cross-section in thorium and then uses it to estimate the corresponding value for uranium. Using a relationship derived by Niels Bohr linking the ratio of beta decay events in thorium and uranium, she reports a value very close to that reported independently by Enrico Fermi and Carl Anderson.

EXPERIMENTS on the processes arising in thorium under neutron bombardment have shown that nuclear fission is induced only by fast neutrons of energies of about 2 Mev. or more. There exists also a radiative capture process producing an isotope of thorium (Th 233) of 26 min. half-life; this process has a resonance character with a large contribution from thermal neutrons[1]. So far, the capture cross-section of thermal neutrons in thorium has not been measured. The following experiments were carried out in order to determine this cross-section.

As the neutron source available was not very strong (100 mgm. Ra+Be), all dimensions had to be kept as small as possible. On the other hand, in order to obtain high accuracy of measurement, one had to use an absorbing thorium layer of reasonable thickness. By the kindness of Prof. Coster, I obtained a sample of metallic thorium of more than 99 percent purity. Dysprosium of the highest purity, also kindly given me by Prof. Coster, was used as detector. The thorium was almost exactly prismatic in form (1.2 cm. × 1.2 cm. × 2.96 cm.). The dysprosium was a thin layer (15.7 mgm./cm.^{2} Dy) of rectangular form, 1.0 cm. × 2.7 cm., and its upper face was covered with 2 μ "Cellophane". For the absorption measurement the thorium was placed directly on the dysprosium with or without a cadmium screen, so that the neutrons impinging normally had to go through 1.2 cm. thickness corresponding to 13.4 gm. thorium.

The experimental arrangement was as follows. In a plate of paraffin wax of 3.8 cm. thickness, there was cut out a rectangular cavity of 1.3 cm. depth, the bottom and sides of which were covered with cadmium of 0.5 mm. thickness so that thermal neutrons could not enter except from above. This plate was put between two other plates of paraffin wax, forming in this way a block of 11.5 cm. height and about 25 cm. × 25 cm. area. The dysprosium was placed on the cadmium-shielded bottom of the cavity. The upper paraffin plate contained the neutron source 3.3 cm. below the surface in such a way that the source just touched the upper edges of the cadmium screened cavity.

840

钍、铅和铀–238中热中子的俘获截面

迈特纳

编者按

物理学家还没有测量出铀–238 对热中子的"俘获截面"，该截面表征热中子被俘获的倾向，它是核链式反应可能性的一个重要参数。小的俘获截面表明有很少中子被俘获，这使得更有可能发生剩下的中子引发裂变的事件。本文中莉泽·迈特纳测量了钍的热中子俘获截面，然后用它估算铀中的相应值。根据尼尔斯·玻尔导出的钍核和铀核 β 衰变事例比值之间的关系，她宣称这个值与恩里科·费米和卡尔·安德森所报道的值非常接近。

在用中子轰击钍的实验过程中，我们发现，只有能量大于或等于大约 2 兆电子伏的快中子才能诱发核裂变。这里也存在一个辐射俘获过程，产生了一个半衰期为 26 分钟的钍的同位素钍–233；而且这一过程具有源自热中子[1]贡献的共振特征。迄今为止，热中子在钍元素中的俘获截面还没能被成功测量。为了测量出这个截面，我们做了下面的实验。

由于可利用的中子源并不是特别的强（100 毫克的镭和铍），所以全部实验材料的尺寸都要保持尽量的小。另一方面，为了得到高精度的测量结果，我们必须使用厚度合适的吸收钍片。在科斯特教授的慷慨帮助下，我得到了一个纯度高于 99% 的金属钍的样品。科斯特教授还提供了纯度最高的镝，我们把它用作探测器。钍样品的形状是一个规则的棱柱形（1.2 厘米 × 1.2 厘米 ×2.96 厘米）。镝为一个矩形（1.0 厘米 ×2.7 厘米）的薄层（15.7 毫克每平方厘米镝），上表面覆盖了一层 2 微米的"玻璃纸"。为了进行吸收测量，我们把钍直接放在带镉屏或者不带镉屏的镝片上，这样中子轰击时一般就必须通过厚度为 1.2 厘米的钍片，其相当于 13.4 克的钍。

具体的实验做法如下。在一个 3.8 厘米厚的石蜡平板上，挖出一个 1.3 厘米深的矩形空腔，底部和侧面都覆盖有 0.5 毫米厚的镉，这样使得热中子只能从上面进入。把这个石蜡板放在另外两个石蜡板的中间，用这种方法组成一个高 11.5 厘米、底面为 25 厘米 ×25 厘米的长方体。镝放在被镉屏蔽了的空腔的底部。最上面的石蜡平板里含有一个中子源，中子源距离上表面 3.3 厘米，这样放置后，中子源就刚好接触到了被镉屏蔽的空腔的上边界。

The activity of the dysprosium detector was measured with a Geiger-Müller counter with 0.1 mm. aluminium walls connected to an amplifier. The dysprosium, the half-life of which was carefully determined and found to be 156 ± 3 min., was in all experiments irradiated up to saturation, and the decay of the activity was followed for several hours in order to increase the accuracy of measurements. All measurements were referred to a uranium standard. The contribution from thermal neutrons was determined by carrying out the irradiation with and without 0.5 mm. cadmium directly over the exposed face of the detector. With cadmium screens on all faces of the detector, the observed activity is due to neutrons faster than thermal neutrons. Under the experimental conditions used here, it amounted to 9 percent of the activity obtained without cadmium on the exposed face.

For the determination of the capture cross-section for thermal neutrons in thorium, one has to consider the different kinds of interaction of neutrons with the thorium nucleus. The fission cross-section of fast neutrons is so small as to be negligible. The same holds for the radiative capture cross-section of fast neutrons. Therefore for fast neutrons one has to take into account the scattering cross-section only. Because of the arrangement used—the absorber being put directly on a detector of nearly equal size—one would expect that practically all the scattered neutrons would be efficient in the irradiation, that is, the scattering cross-section would not enter into these measurements. Experiment confirmed this expectation. When the detector was screened on both faces by cadmium, the measurements of the activity with and without thorium (or with and without lead) gave the same values within the experimental error of 2-3 percent. Further, in order to test the influence of inelastic scattering, the cadmium was placed by turns either directly on the exposed face of the detector (with the thorium put upon that), or between the neutron source and the thorium absorber. No difference could be detected. Thus the inelastic scattering does not give rise to thermal neutrons in any observable quantity, a result to be expected.

These results suggest that, under the conditions actually used, the scattering of thermal neutrons too will be negligible, and thus the decrease in activity (of about 28 percent) caused by the thorium absorber is due to radiative capture processes only. To obtain a direct proof the absorption in metallic lead was measured. The lead absorber had practically the same dimensions as the thorium absorber, but the thickness of the cast lead prism of density 10.6 was kept a little smaller (1.10 cm.) in order to have the same number of absorbing nuclei per cm.^{2}.

Of course, in determining the cross-sections, the angular distribution of the thermal neutrons was taken into account and obliquity corrections (angles up to nearly 70° were involved) were made according to the data given by Frisch[2].

The total cross-section for thermal neutrons in lead was found to be $\sigma_{Pb}^{th} = 2.5 \pm 0.2 \times 10^{-24}$ cm.^{2}. This value is in very good agreement with the value of 2.3×10^{-24} cm.^{2} obtained by Fleischmann[3] from γ-ray measurements. Thus one can be sure that for thorium too the radiative capture cross-section alone enters into the measurements. The value obtained is $\sigma_{Pb}^{th} = 6.0 \pm 0.3 \times 10^{-24}$ cm.^{2}. This cross-section can be used to evaluate the capture cross-

镝探测器的放射性是由盖革－米勒计数器进行测量的，计数器的壁是厚度为 0.1 毫米的铝箔，并与一个放大器相连。镝的半衰期被精确地测定为 156±3 分钟，在所有的实验中，镝都会被强烈照射达到饱和，为了提高测量的精度，对镝放射性强度的衰减要跟踪数个小时。所有的测量都参照着铀的标准进行。对于探测器的被照表面直接覆盖和不覆盖 0.5 毫米镉这两种情形分别进行辐照测量，可以测定热中子的贡献。在探测器的所有面都有镉层屏蔽的时候，探测到的放射性来源于比热中子快的中子。在这里所使用的实验条件下，其放射性仅为无镉片屏蔽探测器被照表面情形下的 9%。

为了测定钍的热中子俘获截面，我们必须考虑到中子与钍核之间各种各样的相互作用。快中子的裂变截面很小几乎可以忽略。快中子的辐射俘获截面同样如此。因此，对于快中子来说，我们只需要考虑它的散射截面。由于实验安排中吸收体直接放在尺寸几乎相等的探测器的上面，可以认为实际上所有的散射中子在辐照中均是有效的，也就是说，这个散射截面在测量中不起作用。实验证实了这一推测。当探测器的两个面全被镉遮盖时，在实验误差 2%~3% 允许的范围内，实验中测得的有钍和没有钍时（或者有铅和没有铅）的放射性是一样的。为了进一步测定非弹性散射的影响，我们把镉先后放在探测器的被照表面（钍放在该表面之上）和中子源与钍吸收器的中间，分别对它进行了研究。结果显示没有任何的差别，因此，正如人们预测的那样，非弹性散射并不产生可观测到的热中子。

这些研究结果表明，在实际使用的条件下，热中子的散射也是可以忽略的，因此由钍吸收体导致的放射性的减少（28% 左右）仅仅是由辐射俘获过程引起的。为了得到更直接的证明，我们对在金属铅中的吸收进行了测量。铅吸收体的大小实际上和钍吸收体相同，但是为了使单位面积上吸收体原子核的数量相同，密度为 10.6 的棱柱形铅铸件的厚度要小一些（1.10 厘米）。

当然，在测量截面的过程中，热中子的角分布也被考虑在内，而且根据弗里施[2] 提供的数据进行了倾斜度校正（最大角度接近 70°）。

经计算，铅的热中子总截面为 $\sigma_{Pb}^{th}=$（2.5±0.2）×10^{-24} 平方厘米。这与弗莱施曼[3] 在 γ 射线测量中得到的结果 2.3×10^{-24} 平方厘米是非常吻合的。因此我们可以肯定，对于钍来说，在测量中也仅仅是辐射俘获截面起了作用。所测得的结果为 $\sigma_{Th}^{th}=$（6.0±0.3）×10^{-24} 平方厘米，这个值可以用来估算铀-238 的俘获截面。在这种

section of ^{238}U. In this isotope, as Bohr[4] has emphasized, thermal neutrons do not produce fission processes. Thus when equal small quantities of uranium and thorium are subjected to neutron bombardment under identical conditions, ^{239}U and ^{233}Th respectively being produced, it is clear that if on account of their nearly equal half-life the efficiency of the β-rays is assumed to be approximately the same, the β-ray activities due to thermal neutrons (corrected for equal numbers of nuclei) must be proportional to the respective cross-sections:

$$\frac{T^{th}_{U(239)}}{T^{th}_{Th(233)}} = \frac{\sigma^{th}_{U(238)} \cdot \frac{1}{238}}{\sigma^{th}_{Th} \cdot \frac{1}{232}}$$

From earlier measurements carried out in Dahlem, I find for this ratio the value 1/4.15. Using the above value for the cross-section of thorium, the cross-section for uranium 238 is

$$\sigma^{th}_{U(238)} = 1.5 \pm 0.2 \times 10^{-24} \text{ cm.}^2.$$

Anderson and Fermi[5], measuring directly the β-ray intensity of ^{239}U due to a known number of thermal neutrons, found

$$\sigma^{th}_{U(238)} = 1.2 \times 10^{-24} \text{ cm.}^2.$$

Considering the possibility of fairly large errors in this type of measurement, the agreement is very good.

I wish to express my gratitude to the Academy of Sciences for a grant and in particular to Prof. Siegbahn for the facilities kindly put at my disposal.

(**145**, 422-423; 1940)

Lise Meitner: Forskningsinstitutet för Fysik, Stockholm, Feb.1.

References:

1. Meitner, L., Hahn, O., and Strassmann, F., *Z. Phys.*, **109**, 538 (1938).

2. Frisch, O. R., *Kgl. Dansk Vid. Selskab. Math. Phys. Medd.*, **14**, No. 5 (1936).

3. Fleischmann, R., and Bothe, W., *Ergeb. exact. Naturwiss.*, **16**, 37 (1937).

4. Bohr, N., *Phys. Rev.*, **55**, 418 (1939).

5. Anderson, H. L., and Fermi, E., *Phys. Rev.*, **55**, 1106 (1939).

同位素中，正如玻尔 [4] 强调的，热中子不会诱发裂变。因此，当同样少量的铀和钍在相同的条件下受到中子的轰击时，结果就会相应地产生铀-239 和钍-233。显然，考虑到它们的半衰期几乎都是相同的，如果假设产生 β 射线的效率也近似相等，那么由热中子（修正为相同数量的原子核）引起的 β 射线的放射性一定正比于相应的截面：

$$\frac{T^{th}_{U(239)}}{T^{th}_{Th(233)}} = \frac{\sigma^{th}_{U(238)} \cdot \frac{1}{238}}{\sigma^{th}_{Th} \cdot \frac{1}{232}}$$

在达勒姆早期的测量中，我找到了这个比值为 1/4.15。应用上面钍俘获截面的值，得出铀-238 的俘获截面应为：

$$\sigma^{th}_{U(238)} = （1.5 \pm 0.2）\times 10^{-24} \text{ 平方厘米}$$

安德森和费米 [5] 通过直接测量由已知数量的热中子引起的铀-239 的 β 射线强度，得出：

$$\sigma^{th}_{U(238)} = 1.2 \times 10^{-24} \text{ 平方厘米}$$

考虑到这种类型的测量存在较大的误差，我们认为结果的一致性还是很好的。

在此对科学院的资金支持表示衷心的感谢，尤其要感谢西格巴恩教授，他慷慨地为我提供了实验设备。

（胡雪兰 翻译；朱永生 审稿）

The Mass Centre in Relativity

M. Born and K. Fuchs

Editor's Note

Part of the interest of this paper is its authorship. Max Born was a German émigré to Britain, awarded a Nobel Prize in 1954 for his work on quantum mechanics, while Klaus Fuchs was also a German exile working as a physicist in Britain. Fuchs afterwards joined the Manhattan Project at Los Alamos, New Mexico, and was later convicted by the British government of espionage on behalf of the Soviet Union; he working in Berlin after serving a prison sentence. The point of their paper was to show that, despite appearances, relativity can deal well with the centre of mass of a collection of particles.

THE question whether there exists in relativity mechanics a theorem analogous to the classical law for the motion of the mass centre (conservation of total momentum) has, as far as we can see, never found a satisfactory answer. Eddington[1] has taken this fact as the starting point for a general attack against the usual application of wave mechanics to fast-moving particles without contributing himself anything positive to the question. The reason why this problem has never been seriously treated seems to be this.

In classical mechanics the internal potential energy depends on the simultaneous relative positions of the particles; therefore one can separate the relative motion from the translatory motion of the centre. In relativity, however, all forces are retarded, the interaction does not depend on simultaneous relative positions and the separation of the relative motion from the translation of the whole system loses its meaning.

Quantum mechanics circumvents this problem by considering interactions as produced by emission and reabsorption of other particles. We were induced to reconsider this problem by its bearing on a relativistic and "reciprocal" formulation of second quantization. Without touching this question, we shall state here some simple results concerning free particles. It is clear that in this case there must exist a "rest system" Σ°, that is, a Lorentz frame in which the total momentum vanishes. The problem is to describe the relative motion in an invariant way.

We start by bringing the classical derivation into a form permitting generalization. If $\mathbf{r}_1$, $\mathbf{r}_2$ are the position vectors, $\mathbf{P}_1$, $\mathbf{P}_2$ the momenta of two particles, we form the vector of relative position and that of total momentum

$$\rho = \mathbf{r}_1 - \mathbf{r}_2, \qquad \mathbf{P} = \mathbf{P}_1 + \mathbf{P}_2 \tag{1}$$

and determine their canonical conjugate variables' components of the vectors π and $\mathbf{R}$. A simple calculation shows that these are not uniquely determined but have the form

相对论中的质心

玻恩，富克斯

编者按

本文作者是这篇文章令人感兴趣的原因之一。马克斯·玻恩是流亡到英国的德国人，1954 年因为他在量子力学方面的工作获得了诺贝尔奖，而克劳斯·富克斯也是从德国流亡至英国并在英国工作的物理学家。后来富克斯加入了在美国新墨西哥州洛斯阿拉莫斯实施的"曼哈顿计划"，之后被英国政府以苏联间谍的名义定罪；刑满之后他回到柏林工作。他们这篇文章的观点认为，相对论并不像表现的那样，实际上它可以很好地处理一个粒子集合的质心问题。

在相对论力学中是否存在一个类似于经典质心运动定律（总动量守恒）的定理，关于这个问题，就我们所知尚未找到一个满意的答案。爱丁顿[1]以这个事实作为出发点，对通常将波动力学应用到快速运动粒子的作法进行了一般性的抨击，而他自己却没有对此问题做出任何积极的贡献。这似乎就是此问题从未被认真对待的原因。

在经典力学中，内部势能取决于粒子的瞬时相对位置；因此，我们可以将相对运动从质心的平移运动中分离出来。然而在相对论中，所有的力都是迟滞的，相互作用并不取决于瞬时相对位置，所以把相对运动从整个系统的平移运动中分离出来是没有意义的。

量子力学把相互作用当作是由其他粒子的发射和重吸收所引起的，以此来规避这个问题。这使得我们需要通过一个相对论的和"倒易的"二次量子化公式来重新考虑这个问题。暂不考虑这个问题，我们在此将给出一些关于自由粒子的简单结果。显然，在这种情况下，必然存在一个"静止系统"Σ^0，即一个总动量等于零的洛伦兹参考系。具体来说，这个问题就是要以一种不变量的形式对相对运动进行描述。

我们先把经典推导变为允许进行推广的形式。如果 $\vec{r_1}$、$\vec{r_2}$ 是两个粒子的位置矢量，$\vec{P_1}$、$\vec{P_2}$ 是它们的动量，我们可以得出相对位置的矢量和总动量的矢量为：

$$\vec{\rho} = \vec{r_1} - \vec{r_2}, \qquad \vec{P} = \vec{P_1} + \vec{P_2} \tag{1}$$

我们还可以确定其正则共轭变量，即矢量 $\vec{\pi}$ 和 $\vec{R}$。经简单的计算表明，它们并不是唯一确定的，而是具有下列形式：

$$\pi = (1 - a)\,\mathbf{p}_1 - a\mathbf{p}_2, \qquad \mathbf{R} = a\mathbf{r}_1 + (1 - a)\,\mathbf{r}_2, \tag{2}$$

where a is an arbitrary constant. Hence another condition must be added.

We postulate that the kinetic energy $p_1^2/2m_1 + p_2^2/2m_2$ assumes the form $P^2/2m + \pi^2/2\mu$. This condition leads to a determination of the three constants a, m, μ, namely,

$$a = \frac{m_1}{m_1 + m_2}, \quad m = m_1 + m_2, \quad \mu = \frac{m_1 m_2}{m_1 + m_2},$$

which introduced into (2) give the usual expressions for relative momentum and centre of mass.

In relativity, the energies E_1, E_2 of two free particles are given by

$$E_1^2 = m_1^2 + p_1^2, \quad E_2^2 = m_2^2 + p_2^2. \tag{3}$$

We consider now the 4-vectors $\mathbf{P}_+ = \mathbf{P}_1 + \mathbf{P}_2$, $E_+ = E_1 + E_2$ and $\mathbf{P}_- = \mathbf{P}_1 - \mathbf{P}_2$, $E_- = E_1 - E_2$. A simple calculation leads to

$$E^2_+ = m^2_+ + p^2_+ + \pi^2, \quad E^2_- = m^2_- + p^2_- - \pi^2; \tag{4}$$

here $m_+ = m_1 + m_2$, $m_- = m_1 - m_2$

and
$$\pi = 2m_1 m_2 \sinh \Gamma/2, \tag{5}$$

where Γ is the "angular distance" of the two 4-vectors, given by

$$m_1 m_2 \cosh \Gamma = E_1 E_2 - \mathbf{P}_1\mathbf{P}_2. \tag{6}$$

Γ is invariant, hence π is invariant also. π has a simple meaning in the case of equal masses. In the rest system Σ°, where $\mathring{p} = \mathring{p}_+ = \mathring{p}_1 + \mathring{p}_2 = 0$, we have $m_1 - m_2 = m_- = 0$, and $\mathring{E}_1 - \mathring{E}_2 = \mathring{E}_- = 0$; hence $\pi^2 = (\mathring{p})^2$. This shows that π is the length of the vector $\boldsymbol{\pi}$ representing relative momentum.

For different masses π can be described as the relative momentum in that Lorentz frame (which always exists) in which

$$E_1 - E_2 = \pm\,(m_1 - m_2).$$

The first equation (4) can now be written

$$E^2 = M^2 + P^2, \quad M^2 = \mu^2 + \pi^2, \tag{7}$$

Where $\mu = m_1 + m_2$ is the sum of the rest masses, M the total internal energy, which represents also the rest mass of the whole system, and $\mathbf{P} = \mathbf{P}_+ = \mathbf{P}_1 + \mathbf{P}_2$ the total momentum.

$$\vec{\pi} = (1-a)\vec{P_1} - a\vec{P_2}, \qquad \vec{R} = a\vec{r_1} + (1-a)\vec{r_2} \qquad (2)$$

式中 a 是一个任意常数。因此，必须加入另一个条件。

我们假定，动能 $p_1^2/2m_1 + p_2^2/2m_2$ 满足 $P^2/2m + \pi^2/2\mu$ 的形式。根据这个条件可以确定三个常数 a、m 和 μ，即

$$a = \frac{m_1}{m_1 + m_2}, \quad m = m_1 + m_2, \quad \mu = \frac{m_1 m_2}{m_1 + m_2},$$

将它们代入式 (2) 可得相对动量和质心的通常表达式。

在相对论中，两个自由粒子的能量 E_1、E_2 如下式：

$$E_1^2 = m_1^2 + p_1^2, \quad E_2^2 = m_2^2 + p_2^2 \qquad (3)$$

我们现在考虑 4 矢量 $\vec{P_+} = \vec{P_1} + \vec{P_2}$，$E_+ = E_1 + E_2$ 以及 $\vec{P_-} = \vec{P_1} - \vec{P_2}$，$E_- = E_1 - E_2$。简单的计算可导出：

$$E_+^2 = m_+^2 + p_+^2 + \pi^2, \quad E_-^2 = m_-^2 + p_-^2 - \pi^2 \qquad (4)$$

式中，$m_+ = m_1 + m_2$，$m_- = m_1 - m_2$

且

$$\pi = 2m_1 m_2 \sinh \Gamma/2 \qquad (5)$$

其中 Γ 是这两个 4 矢量的"角距离"，如下式：

$$m_1 m_2 \cosh \Gamma = E_1 E_2 - \vec{P_1}\vec{P_2} \qquad (6)$$

Γ 是不变量，因此 π 也是不变量。在两个自由粒子的质量相等的情况下，π 的含义是简单的。在静止系 Σ° 中，$\overset{\circ}{P} = \overset{\circ}{p}_+ = \overset{\circ}{p}_1 + \overset{\circ}{p}_2 = 0$，我们已知 $m_1 - m_2 = m_- = 0$，及 $\overset{\circ}{E}_1 - \overset{\circ}{E}_2 = \overset{\circ}{E}_- = 0$；因此 $\pi^2 = (\overset{\circ}{p}_-)^2$。这表明 π 是表示相对动量的矢量 $\vec{\pi}$ 的长度。

对于两个自由粒子的质量不相同的情况，在使下式成立的洛伦兹系（它总是存在的）中，π 是相对动量。

$$E_1 - E_2 = \pm (m_1 - m_2)$$

(4) 中的第一个方程现可写为：

$$E^2 = M^2 + P^2, \quad M^2 = \mu^2 + \pi^2, \qquad (7)$$

式中，$\mu = m_1 + m_2$ 是静止质量之和，M 是总内能，它也代表整个系统的静止质量，$\vec{P} = \vec{P_+} = \vec{P_1} + \vec{P_2}$ 是总动量。

Taking the components of $\mathbf{P}$ and π as new canonical momenta, one can determine the conjugate coordinates, $\mathbf{R}$ and ρ. They are linear in $\mathbf{r}_1$, $\mathbf{r}_2$; the coefficients are, however, not constants but functions of $\mathbf{P}_1$, $\mathbf{P}_2$.

For small $\mathbf{P}_1$, $\mathbf{P}_2$ the formulae reduce to the classical ones.

It is interesting to remark that in relativity there exists a "reciprocal"[2] theorem obtained by interchanging coordinates and momenta.

(**145**, 587; 1940)

Max Born and Klaus Fuchs: Department of Applied Mathematics, University of Edinburgh.

References:
1. Eddington, A., *Proc. Camb. Phil. Soc.*, 35, 186 (1939).
2. Born, M., *Proc. Roy. Soc. Edinburgh*, (ii), 59, 219(1939).

取 $\vec{P}$ 和 $\vec{\pi}$ 的分量为新的正则动量，我们可以确定共轭坐标 $\vec{R}$ 和 $\vec{\rho}$。它们对于 $\vec{r_1}$，$\vec{r_2}$ 是线性的；然而系数不是常数，而是 $\vec{P_1}$、$\vec{P_2}$ 的函数。

当 $\vec{P_1}$、$\vec{P_2}$ 很小时，该公式可简化为经典形式。

值得注意的是，在相对论中存在着"倒易"[2] 定理，它是通过交换坐标和动量得到的。

（沈乃澂 翻译；张元仲 审稿）

The Theory of Nuclear Forces*

R. Peierls

Editor's Note

Rudolph Peierls offers a summary of the emerging theory of nuclear forces. These forces could be most easily probed in two-particle interactions involving neutrons and protons. Scattering experiments had established the range of the force as about 1.2×10^{-13} cm, and supported the notion that the nuclear forces between neutrons and protons were identical, ignoring electrostatic differences. Nuclear forces could also depend strongly on direction in relation to the orientation of quantum-mechanical spins of the particles. The best theory proposed so far was that of Japanese physicist Hideki Yukawa, which viewed the nuclear force as originating from a nuclear field associated with a new quantum particle having mass of around 300 electron masses—later identified with the pion.

THE forces between the constituents of a nucleus are "short-range" forces, which have no appreciable effect over distances of more than a few times 10^{-13} cm. Hence it is impossible to find the laws of force by extrapolation from large-scale observations (as in the case of Coulomb's law) and the only possible lines of attack are either, to deduce the law of force from direct observations on the properties of nuclei, or to derive them from some simpler, and more general, laws.

Using the direct experimental approach, it is best to start from phenomena which involve only two particles, since only these permit an unambiguous theoretical interpretation. This group consists of the properties of the deuteron, including its disintegration, and the scattering of protons and neutrons by hydrogen.

Practically all experiments are carried out in conditions in which the de Broglie wavelength of the particles is greater than the range of the forces, and this has the effect that one need consider only those states of motion in which the motion of one particle with respect to the other has no angular momentum. (In all other states of motion the centrifugal force prevents the particles from approaching sufficiently close for any interaction to take place.) Moreover, so long as the wave-length is greater than the range of the force, the effect of the field of force is largely independent of the exact variation of force with distance within the range, and depends approximately only on one constant, which may be called the "strength" of the field of force. (In the case of a potential of the type of a potential well, this strength is approximately proportional to the depth times the square of the width.)[1]

---

* Based on lectures given at the Royal Institution on January 17, 24 and 31.

核力的理论[*]

佩尔斯

编者按

鲁道夫·佩尔斯概述了现有的关于核力的理论。这种力可以很容易地在含有质子和中子的两粒子相互作用中被探测到。散射实验确定这种力的作用距离大约为 1.2×10^{-13} 厘米，同时在忽略静电力差别的前提下，实验也支持了作用于中子之间、质子之间和中子－质子之间的核力是相同的这一观点。核力在很大程度上还由方向决定，该方向与粒子的量子力学自旋取向有关。目前关于核力的最好理论是由日本物理学家汤川秀树提出的，这一理论认为核力源于一种新的质量约为 300 个电子质量的量子粒子所产生的核场，这一粒子后来被定义为 π 介子。

核的各组分之间的力是"短程力"，当各组分之间的距离超过几个 10^{-13} 厘米时，这个力的作用效果就不明显了。因此，利用大尺度的观测结果（如库仑定律适用的情况）进行推导来得到力的定律是不可能的，因此仅有的两种处理方法是，要么对核的性质进行直接观测来推导微观尺度下力的定律，要么从一些更简单、更一般的定律去导出它们。

利用直接的实验方法，最好从只包含两个粒子的现象出发，因为只有这类情况才有可能作出清晰的理论解释。这样的组合具有氘核的性质，包括氘核的蜕变，以及质子和中子在氢核上的散射。

实际上，所有的相关实验都是在粒子的德布罗意波长大于力程的条件下进行的，在这种情况下，我们只需要考虑相对于另一个粒子而言角动量为 0 的粒子的运动状态。（在所有其他运动状态下，离心力使粒子间保持一定的距离从而不能产生相互作用。）此外，只要波长大于力程，在力程的距离范围内，力场的影响在很大程度上与力的精确变化无关，而几乎仅仅取决于一个常数，我们称之为力场的"强度"。（对于具有势阱形式的势能来说，这种强度近似正比于势阱深度与势阱宽度平方的乘积。）[1]

---

[*] 基于 1 月 17 日、24 日和 31 日在英国皇家研究院所做的演讲。

In the experiments on proton-neutron interaction two possible cases are discussed, according to whether the spins of the two colliding particles are parallel or opposite (in the case of like particles, Pauli's principle ensures that, so long as there is no orbital angular momentum, the spins are necessarily opposite) and the strength of the interaction may be different for these two cases. For the case of a proton and a neutron with parallel spin; the strength constant can be obtained from the binding energy of the deuteron; for those with opposite spin, it follows from the scattering of neutrons by protons, since in this scattering the effect of the neutrons with parallel spin can be allowed for once their strength constant is known. The very high cross-section for slow neutrons is an indication that the strength constant of the interaction for neutrons with opposite spin is either just sufficient or just insufficient to give rise to a bound state of the deuteron with no resultant spin[2]. The choice between these alternatives can be made by means of the scattering of neutrons in *para-* and *ortho*-hydrogen where, because of interference, the results depend on the phase of the wave scattered by each proton. The result is that the force is just insufficient to give a bound state[3].

For the proton-proton force, the strength can be derived from measurements of the scattering of protons in hydrogen.

Once these strength constants are known it is possible to calculate all other observable quantities, namely, the energy variation of the proton-proton and neutron-proton scattering, the photo-effect of the deuteron, etc., to the degree of approximation in which the ratio between the range of the forces and the de Broglie wave-length is negligible. The fact that these calculations give approximate agreement with observations serves as a check on the initial hypothesis of short-range forces.

Actually, all results of this simple theory have to be supplemented by correction terms involving the range. If the experimental data were accurate enough, it should thus be possible to estimate the range of the forces. The use of these correction terms requires greater accuracy than is at present available in the data on neutron-proton scattering, and the determination can only be carried out in the case of the proton-proton scattering, in which more accurate data have been obtained. The result of this is that the "range" for this interaction is about 1.2×10^{-13} cm. The experimental data are even accurate enough to yield a certain amount of information on the actual dependence of the force on distance[4].

More information on these points would be obtained by measuring the neutron-proton scattering at medium energies with higher accuracy, or by observations at higher energies including, in particular, the angular distribution of the scattered particles.

An important contribution to the problem was the discovery by Rabi and others of a quadripole moment of the deuteron[5]. This proves that the neutron and proton have a tendency to have their spins in the direction of the line joining them, rather than at right angles to it. This implies obviously that the forces are not central, but that the potential energy depends on the angle between the spin direction and the line joining

在质子－中子相互作用的实验中，对两个碰撞粒子的自旋呈平行和反平行这两种可能的情况分别进行了讨论（对于同类粒子，只要轨道角动量为 0，泡利不相容原理将确保两个粒子的自旋方向必然是相反的），这两种情况中质子－中子相互作用的强度有可能不同。对于自旋方向相同的质子和中子，强度常数可以由氘核的结合能得到；而对于那些自旋方向相反的质子和中子，强度常数可以通过中子对质子的散射来确定，在这种散射中，一旦获知它们的强度常数，我们就可以考虑自旋平行的中子的效应了。慢中子的截面非常高，这表明与自旋相反的中子间相互作用的强度常数或者刚好能够又或者刚好不够形成总自旋为 0 的氘核束缚态 [2]。我们可以通过**仲氢**和**正氢**中的中子散射对以上两种可能的结果做出判断，由于中子散射中干涉现象的存在，这个结果取决于每一个质子的散射波的相位。结果是这个力刚好不足以形成束缚态 [3]。

对于质子－质子之间的作用力，可以通过测量氢核上的质子散射来导出该作用力的强度。

一旦知道这些强度常数，在力程与德布罗意波长之比可以忽略不计的近似程度下，我们就有可能计算得到所有其他的可观测量，即质子－质子散射和中子－质子散射的能量变化量、氘核的光效应等。这些计算结果与观测结果近似一致，这一点可用来检验与短程力有关的最初假设。

实际上，所有这些简单理论的结果都必须加上与力程有关的修正项。只有实验数据足够准确，才有可能对力程进行估计。考虑这些修正项时所需数据的精确度要比目前在中子－质子散射中获得的数据的精确度更高，因此只有在质子－质子散射情况下，得到了更加精确的数据以后，我们才能确定力程的值。结果是，这种相互作用的"力程"约为 1.2×10^{-13} 厘米。在实验数据更加准确的情况下，我们将可得到一些关于力与距离的明确关系的信息 [4]。

以更加精确的方式对中等能量的中子－质子散射进行测量，或者通过在更高能量情况下的观测，特别是对散射粒子的角分布的观测，我们都将获得更多关于这些问题的信息。

拉比及其他研究人员发现的氘核的四极矩对此问题有重要的贡献 [5]。这证明了中子和质子的自旋方向倾向于与它们的连线方向一致，而不是与连线方向垂直。这显然意味着，中子与质子之间的力并不是中心力，而且它们之间的势能与自旋方向和两个粒子的连线方向之间的夹角有关。尽管上面提到的所有计算都是在中心力的

the two particles. Although all the calculations referred to above were carried out on the assumptions of central forces, the results remain practically unchanged. For opposite spins, which is the only case of interest for proton-proton interaction at low energies, the force must still be central, since the resultant spin is zero and hence does not set up a preferential direction; for parallel spin, the fact that the force is not central means that the angular momentum due to the motion of the particles is no longer constant but fluctuates. Hence the motion in the state of lowest energy is no longer one with zero orbital angular momentum; it can be shown that the state of motion is a mixture of a state with zero angular momentum and one with two units (S and D states in spectroscopic notation). From the electrical quadripole moment one can estimate that the contribution of the D state amounts to only a few percent[6].

However, an appreciable non-central force is required to produce even this small effect, since in the D state a very strong centrifugal force has to be overcome. It seems probable, therefore, that the non-central forces must represent an appreciable fraction of the total force. Yet, again owing to the effect of the centrifugal force, no appreciable influence of this D state should be expected on the other observable phenomena, except possibly on some finer features which have not yet been thoroughly investigated. Thus the approximate agreement with the experimental evidence, and the estimate of the range remain practically unaffected by the correction terms.

The data on the strength and the estimate of the range give the same answer, within the experimental error, for the proton-proton and proton-neutron interactions for opposite spins, and the suggestion has therefore been made that these two forces are exactly the same, except for the electrostatic interaction between the protons ("charge-independence hypothesis")[7].

From the fact that the charge of stable light nuclei is about half their mass, and that only a small change is produced in the energy of a light nucleus if in its constituents the number of neutrons and the number of protons are interchanged, has further led to the belief that the nuclear forces are symmetric in proton and neutron, that is, the neutron-neutron interaction is exactly the same as the proton-proton interaction, except for the effect of the electric forces[1].

Turning now to the evidence from nuclei containing more than two particles, this is usually discussed on the basis of the assumption that the forces are additive; that is, that the interaction force between two particles is not affected by the simultaneous presence of a third particle. Beyond its simplicity and the fact that it holds in the atom, this assumption is not founded on any evidence, and, in fact, there are certain theoretical arguments against it[8]. However, without this assumption the available evidence is insufficient to draw any conclusions at all, and one must therefore use the assumption of additivity as a working hypothesis, which may at a later stage be disproved. Moreover, most of the theoretical work on the nuclei of weight 3 and 4 was done before the discovery of the quadripole moment of the deuteron, and hence central forces were used. It is likely that

假设前提下进行的，但实际上结果并没有因为该假设成立与否而发生变化。在低能量的质子－质子相互作用中，我们唯一感兴趣的是自旋相反的情况，其中的作用力一定仍是中心力，这是因为该情况下的合自旋为零，没有产生任何的偏向；对于自旋平行的情况，作用力不是中心力意味着由粒子运动产生的角动量不再是常数，而是有涨落的。因此，粒子在最低能态中的运动不再是轨道角动量为 0 的状态，研究发现此运动状态是一个包含角动量等于 0 和 2 两种情况（用光谱学符号表示为 S 态和 D 态）的混合态，根据电四极矩我们能估计出 D 态的贡献只占几个百分点 [6]。

然而，即使 D 态产生的效应很小，我们仍需要一个可观的非中心力来产生这个效应，因为 D 态中需要克服一个很强的离心力。因此，非中心力在合力中占有相当大的比重是很有可能的。然而，也是由于离心力的作用，除了一些可能尚未彻底研究过的某些较细微的特性外，预计 D 态不会对其他可观测的现象产生明显的影响。因此，修正项并不会影响理论与实验现象的近似吻合以及力程的估计结果。

在实验误差范围内，对于自旋相反的质子－质子相互作用和质子－中子相互作用，作用强度数据和力程的估算结果给出了同样的答案。由此可知，除了质子间的静电相互作用外，这两种相互作用力是完全相同的（"电荷独立性假说"）[7]。

稳定轻核的电荷数约为其质量数的一半，并且核组分中的中子数与质子数相互交换时，轻核的能量只会发生微小的变化，上述两个事实使我们更加相信质子和中子间的核力是对称的，也就是说，除了电场力的影响以外，中子－中子相互作用与质子－质子相互作用是完全相同的 [1]。

下面来讨论含有两个以上粒子的核的相关证据，这些研究通常是以力具有可加性这一假设为基础的，即两个粒子之间的相互作用力不受同时存在的第三个粒子的影响。除了假设的简单性及其在原子中成立的事实以外，这个假设的建立没有任何根据，实际上，甚至存在某些理论论据认为该假设是不成立的 [8]。然而，如果没有这个假设，现有证据是根本不足以得出任何结论的。因此，我们必须把可加性的假设作为有效的假说来使用，当然后面的研究有可能会证明该假设是不正确的。此外，在发现氘核的四极矩以前，人们就已经完成了大部分质量数为 3 和 4 的核的理论工作，因此当时的相关工作都采用了中心力的假设。实际上，这些问题中力对方向的依赖

the directional dependence of the force will not be negligible in these problems, but its precise effect has yet to be investigated.

So far as the calculations go, they show that the mass defects of the nuclei of mass 3 and 4 are very sensitive to the range of the force, and that the range required to give the right values is roughly of the same order of magnitude as that obtained from scattering experiments[1,9]. Quantitative agreement, however, was not obtained. The laws of force used in these calculations were usually restricted by adopting the charge-independence hypothesis, and also by assuming that the range of the force was the same for parallel and for opposite spins. Whether the remaining discrepancy is due to these restrictions, or to the assumption of central forces, or whether it represents a failure of the additivity, remains to be seen.

For nuclei beyond ^{4}He, the observed binding energy ceases to rise rapidly with the number of particles. This fact, often briefly referred to as "saturation", obviously means that the constituent particles of a large nucleus do not *all* attract each other with the same forces with which the constituents of a helium nucleus attract each other. This may be due to several reasons. For one thing, the additivity of the force might fail, and the attractive force between two particles may depend on the number of other particles in the immediate neighbourhood. This dependence might be such as to ensure that the total potential energy per particle always remained below a certain saturation value. A possible description on these lines has been put forward by Teller, Critchfield and Wigner[10], but the idea has not yet been pursued very far.

Another possibility is that the attraction may turn into repulsion at very close approach, in analogy with the forces between the atoms of a liquefied inert gas. In this case the repulsion might ensure that any one particle can, within the range of its forces, be surrounded only by a small number of others, and hence the binding energy per particle is again limited. This possibility has not been fully explored, but it has the disadvantage that, owing to the wave mechanical penetrability of potential barriers, an extremely strong repulsion would have to be assumed to make this explanation possible.

The most attractive explanation is no doubt that the forces are "exchange forces" which depend on the symmetry of the wave function describing the motion of the particles, like the valency forces between the constituents of organic molecules. On this idea the neutron is trivalent, capable of forming a "bond" with one other neutron and two protons, and correspondingly for the proton. This would give a very natural explanation of the helium nucleus as a saturated structure[1].

The directional properties of the forces, which must be inferred from the existence of the quadripole moment of the deuteron, may have a bearing on this question, since in a large nucleus different particles must necessarily be arranged in different directions relative to a given particle, and the forces may quite well be attractive for some pairs of particles and repulsive for others, if the directional dependence of the forces is strong[6]. This effect will

性很有可能是不可忽略的，但是它的确切的效应还有待研究。

现在的计算结果表明质量数为 3 和 4 的核的质量亏损与力程密切相关，得出正确结果所需的力程与散射实验得到的力程在量级上大致相等 [1,9]。然而，在定量结果上并没有取得一致。上述计算中用到的作用力的相关定律通常受到以下两个条件的限定，即电荷独立性假说以及自旋平行和自旋反平行两种情况中力程相同的假设。至于定量结果的不一致是由这些限制引起的，还是由中心力的假设引起的，或者它是否代表了可加性的失效，这些还有待研究。

对于质量数超过 ⁴He 的核，观测到的结合能不再随着粒子数的增加而快速增长。我们通常把这种现象简单称之为"饱和"，这显然意味着，大核内粒子之间彼此吸引的力，并不**都**与氦核内粒子间相互吸引的力相同。这可能是由多种原因造成的。一方面，力的可加性可能失效，两个粒子之间的吸引力可能与邻近的其他粒子的数目有关。这种关系可能使每个粒子的总势能始终保持在一定的饱和值以下。特勒、克里奇菲尔德和维格纳 [10] 已对此提出了一种可能的描述，但该想法还没有得到深入研究。

另一种可能性是两个粒子在非常接近的情况下吸引力有可能转变为排斥力，这与液化惰性气体中原子之间的力相类似。在这种情况下，斥力可以确保任何一个粒子在其力程范围内，只被少量的几个粒子所包围，因而每个粒子的结合能仍是有限的。这种可能性还没有得到充分的研究，但是根据势垒在波动力学下的穿透原理，这种可能性的缺点是，为了确保这种解释可能是正确的，必须假定斥力的强度非常大。

而最具吸引力的解释无疑是，这些力是与描述粒子运动的波函数的对称性有关的"交换力"，类似于有机分子组分之间的化合价力。按照这种观点，中子是三价的，它能够与另外一个中子及两个质子形成一个"键"，相应地，质子也具有类似的性质。这将为具有饱和结构的氦核给出一个很自然的解释 [1]。

必须从氘核中四极矩的存在推出粒子间作用力的方向性，这或许与以上论述的问题有关，因为在一个大原子核内，不同的粒子相对于某个给定粒子的排列方向必定都不一样，而如果这些粒子间作用力的方向依赖性很强的话 [6]，那么这些作用力很有可能对某些粒子对而言是吸引力，而对其他粒子对而言则是排斥力。这种效应

give rise to some kind of saturation; whether this saturation is of the right kind, and in particular whether it leads naturally to the α-particle as a stable structure, remains to be seen.

Of the attempts to derive the nuclear forces from a more elementary phenomenon, the most interesting is the meson theory, which is based on an idea of Yukawa[11]. Yukawa supposes that the nuclear forces are due to a "nuclear field" in the same manner in which the electromagnetic forces are caused by the electromagnetic field. This field must, however, satisfy different field equations in order to produce short-range forces, and if this requirement is coupled with that of the principle of relativity, there is only one possible type of wave equation, and the law of interaction is limited to laws of a particular type, of which the simplest has the potential:

$$V = g \cdot e^{-kr}/r, \tag{1}$$

where k and g are constants, and r is the distance between the particles. (Coulomb's law is a special case of this with $k = 0$). In quantum theory, just as the electromagnetic field is associated with light quanta, the "nuclear field" will be associated with a new type of particle; the fact that the wave equation differs from that of light indicates that the rest mass of these particles is not zero, like that of light quanta, but has the finite value $hk/2\pi c$, where k is the same constant as in (1). In order to obtain a range of the right order of magnitude this mass has to be assumed to be a few hundred times that of the electron. The subsequent discovery of "mesons" of just such a mass in cosmic rays has very much increased our confidence in the "meson theory" of nuclear forces.

If we try to fit a law of the form of (1) to the observations on proton-proton scattering, we obtain very good agreement, but we have to choose a value of k which corresponds to a meson mass of about 300 electron masses. This is almost certainly higher than the mass of the mesons found in cosmic rays. The origin of this discrepancy is not clear.

On the meson theory of nuclear forces, mesons are capable of being absorbed and emitted in nuclear reactions provided sufficient energy is available for their creation, and they may be exchanged (that is, temporarily created by one particle and absorbed by another) even if the available energy is insufficient to liberate them. If this view is taken, conservation of angular momentum in the process requires the mesons, like light quanta, to have integral spins. (The electron, which has a half-integral spin, can only be absorbed or produced in pairs.) Zero spin would make the nuclear forces repulsive when they should be attractive, and the most likely assumption seems that of a spin of one unit, as for the photon[12].

This assumption fixes the equations of the meson field completely, but not its interaction with the proton and neutron. This interaction is governed by two terms which, by analogy with the electric charge and magnetic moment, one may term the "meson charge" and the "meson moment" of the heavy particles. The law (1), in particular, is obtained if the heavy

将导致某种饱和；但这种饱和是否是上述的那种饱和现象，特别是，能否自然地解释 α 粒子是一种稳定的结构，这些还有待观察。

在所有尝试从更加基本的现象出发来推导核力的理论中，最令人关注的是基于汤川秀树 [11] 关于介子理论的一个构想。汤川秀树认为，核力是由"核场"引起的，这与电磁力是由电磁场引起的相类似。但是，为了产生短程力，这个场必须满足不同的场方程，而如果这个要求与相对性原理相结合，则只可能存在一种形式的波动方程，相互作用的定律也被限制在某种特定类型的定律之中，其中最简单的势能表达形式如下所示：

$$V = g \cdot e^{kr}/r \tag{1}$$

式中 k 和 g 是常数，r 是粒子之间的距离。（库仑定律是上式中 $k=0$ 时的一种特殊情况。）在量子理论中，正如电磁场是与光量子相联系的，"核场"也将与一种新型的粒子相关联；其波动方程与光的波动方程不同，这一事实表明，与光量子不一样，这些粒子的静止质量不为 0，而具有有限值 $hk/2\pi c$，其中 k 是式 (1) 中的常数。为了得到合适的数量级范围，必须假设这个粒子的质量是电子质量的几百倍。随后在宇宙射线中发现的"介子"正好具有这样的质量，这大大增强了我们对核力的"介子理论"的信心。

假如我们试图用一个具有式 (1) 形式的定律来拟合观测到的质子 – 质子散射，将会获得吻合得很好的结果，但为此我们必须选取一个 k 值，该值对应的介子质量约为电子质量的 300 倍。几乎可以肯定的是，这比在宇宙射线中发现的介子质量要高。而这种差异的根源尚不清楚。

在核力的介子理论中，当系统提供形成介子所需的足够能量时，介子将能够在核反应中被吸收和发射，但即使系统提供的能量并不足以释放出介子时，介子仍可以发生交换现象（即在极短的时间内介子由一个粒子产生后马上被另一个粒子吸收）。如果采用这种观点，该过程中角动量守恒要求介子如光量子一样，具有整数自旋。（具有半整数自旋的电子只能成对地被吸收或发射。）假设自旋为 0 的话将使原本应该为引力的核力表现为斥力，因此最有可能的假设似乎应该是，介子如同光子一样，具有一个单位的自旋 [12]。

这个假设使介子场方程完全确定下来了，但介子场与质子和中子的相互作用还不确定。这类相互作用是由类似于电荷和磁矩的两个因素决定的，我们称之为重粒子的"介子电荷"和"介子矩"。特别地，假设重粒子只具有介子电荷 g，而不具有介子矩时可得到定律 (1)。这个定律在细节上与实验结果并不一致，因为它既没

particles have only a meson charge g, but no meson moment. This law does not agree with experiment in detail, since it gives neither a spin dependence of the force (as required to explain the properties of the neutron-proton scattering) nor a directional dependence that would account for the quadripole moment of the deuteron. The introduction of a "meson moment" would help to give the right dependence[12], but the force would then increase so rapidly at short distances that the proton and the neutron would fall into another, producing an infinite binding energy. Probably this result should not be taken too seriously, since the methods of quantum theory are likely to fail for too close approach, but it would mean in any event that the quantitative study of nuclear forces would have to be abandoned until an exact description of this failure of quantum theory is available.

It has also been suggested that two kinds of mesons might exist, of which one has the spin one, the other zero spin, and with such properties that the singular terms in the interaction energy just cancel. In the crude approximation to which such calculations are usually carried out, the directional dependence of the forces would then also just cancel, together with the infinities, but it is possible that finer effects would give a sufficiently large directional variation[13].

Lastly, there arises the question as to the electric charge of the meson. The mesons observed in cosmic rays are charged, and if one of them is emitted by one nuclear particle and absorbed by another, this will involve an exchange of charge, thus ensuring that the forces are of the exchange type, as required by the most widely accepted explanation of the saturation of nuclear forces. Such an exchange will, however, be possible only if one of the heavy particles is a proton and the other a neutron, but not for two like particles. In order to account for the equally strong forces between like particles, one has to assume the existence of neutral mesons in addition to the charged ones[14]. There is certain independent evidence for the existence of neutral mesons in cosmic rays[15]. If we take the view that the saturation of the nuclear forces is due to their directional dependence and not to their exchange character, it is, in fact, possible to attribute *all* nuclear forces to neutral mesons[6]. This would have the advantage of removing the discrepancy between the mass of the charged mesons from cosmic rays, and the range of the forces as determined from proton-proton scattering. It would mean, on the other hand, that the particles, the discovery of which was hailed as a confirmation of Yukawa's theory, had actually no connexion with the particles postulated by Yukawa.

This summary of the present state of the theory[16] closes with a number of questions to which the answer is not known. But the fact that it is possible to ask these questions at all is a sign of the rapid progress that has been made in this field in the last few years.

(145, 687-690; 1940)

Rudolph Peierls: University of Birmingham.

有给出自旋与力的关系（在解释中子－质子散射的性质时需要用到），也没有给出可用来解释氘核四极矩的方向依赖关系式。引入"介子矩"将有助于给出正确的依赖关系[12]，但在距离很近时，作用力将会迅速增大，使质子和中子落入到另一个核子之中，形成一个无限大的结合能。也许我们不该过于认真地看待这个结果，因为在粒子距离非常接近的情况下量子理论的方法可能是失效的，但这也可能意味着，在对量子理论失效的原因进行准确的说明以前，在任何情况下都不得不放弃对核力做定量研究的努力。

也有人提出，可能存在两类介子，其中一类自旋为 1，而另一类自旋为 0，在这种假设性质下，相互作用能中的奇异项恰好得以消除。在粗略的近似下，通常会进行这类计算，从而表示力的方向依赖性的项连同无限大的项一起，也刚好得以消除，但可能出现的情况却是，更加细微的效应将会使力在方向上出现足够大的变化[13]。

最后，出现了与介子电荷有关的问题。在宇宙射线中观测到的介子是带电的，而如果其中的一个介子是由一个核粒子发射并被另一个核粒子吸收，那么这就将涉及电荷的交换，因此，如同最为广泛接受的关于核力饱和的解释所要求的那样，这些力应该保证是交换型的力。然而，这样的一个交换仅可能在重粒子中的质子和中子之间发生，而不可能出现在两个相同类型的粒子之间。为了解释同类粒子间大小相同的力，就必须假定除带电介子外，还存在中性介子[14]。而宇宙射线中存在着中性介子，这是有独立可靠的证据的[15]。如果我们接受这样的观点，即认为核力的饱和是由核力对方向的依赖性所致而不是由其交换特性所致，那么实际上就可以认为所有的核力**都**是由中性介子引起的[6]。这将会带来的好处是，消除了宇宙射线中带电介子的质量与质子－质子散射过程所确定的力程之间的不一致。另一方面，它也将意味着，这个被认为确证了汤川秀树理论的粒子的发现，实际上与汤川秀树假设的粒子无关。

这篇有关核力理论现况[16]的综述，以许多尚未解决的难题作为结尾。但是，能提出这些问题本身就标志着最近几年这一领域取得了迅速的进展。

（沈乃澂 翻译；厉光烈 审稿）

References:

1. Bethe and Bacher, *Rev. Mod. Phys.*, **8**, 82 (1936).

2. Simons, *Phys. Rev.*, **55**, 793 (1939).

3. Brickwedde, Dunning, Hoge and Manley, *Phys. Rev.*, **54**. 266 (1938).

4. Hoisington, Share and Breit, *Phys. Rev.*, **56**, 884 (1939).

5. Kellogg, Rabi, Ramsay and Zacharias, *Phys. Rev.*, **55**, 318 (1939).

6. Bethe, *Phys. Rev.*, **55**, 1261 (1939).

7. Breit, Condon and Present, *Phys. Rev.*, **50**, 825 (1936).

8. Primakoff and Holstein, *Phys. Rev.*, **55**, 1218 (1939).

9. Rarita and Present, *Phys. Rev.*, **51**, 788 (1937); Rarita and Slawsky, *Phys. Rev.*, **54**, 1053 (1938).

10. Wigner, Critchfield and Teller, *Phys. Rev.*, **56**, 530 (1939).

11. Yukawa, *Proc. Phys. Math. Soc. Japan*, **17**, 48 (1935).

12. Fröhlich, Heitler and Kemmer, *Proc. Roy. Soc.*, A, **166**, 154 (1938).

13. Möller and Rosenfeld, *Nature*, **144**, 241 (1939); **144**, 476 (1939).

14. Kemmer, *Proc. Cam. Phil. Soc.*, **34**, 354 (1938).

15. Arley and Heitler, *Nature*, **142**, 158 (1938).

16. Cf. also Peierls, R., *Ann. Rep. Chem. Soc.*, in the press.

True and False Teleology

C. H. Waddington

Editor's Note

Teleology is the notion that a change is induced not solely by the action of physical forces but because it is being drawn toward some ultimate goal. While it normally has no place in physical science, the embryologist Conrad Waddington here argues, the notion does find a sensible use in biology. The existence of separate sexes in many organisms, he points out, allows for cross-breeding and rapid natural selection. Given this context, it then becomes natural to say that developmental mechanisms lead to the differentiation of the sexes for precisely this purpose: a teleological explanation. Today evolutionary biologists tend to be much more wary of invoking teleology, given how it has been abused by religious groups to distort evolutionary theory.

THERE has recently been a considerable revival of interest, largely due to the work of Darlington[1], in the teleology of different systems of reproduction. The logical status of teleological arguments is very different in this connexion from that in other spheres, since the "purpose" which is brought forward is the fulfilment of the conditions for rapid evolutionary advance under the influence of natural selection. That is to say, a genetic system which achieves its "purpose" provides in so doing the mechanism for its survival. The considerations which have led to the rejection of teleological arguments in other connexions therefore do not apply; though one might still question whether the teleological phraseology is the most convincing in which the arguments can be framed.

There is, however, a danger that the teleological method of argument will be carried over, by association, into regions in which it cannot be sustained. This seems to have occurred, to some extent, in the valuable article by Mather[2] in which he discusses the evolutionary significance of the formation of two different sexes in the diploid phase. He is not content to point out that the separation of the sexes is a mechanism for encouraging cross-breeding, but he contrasts this statement with some sentences, taken from a recent work of mine[3], on the developmental mechanisms involved, from which he deduces that "the sexes are separated supposedly in order to ensure that the gametes are differentiated". Such a view, he states later, must be rejected.

But such teleological statements should never arise in a discussion of developmental mechanisms. It is not sufficient to recognize that the development of two distinct sexes may be an evolutionary advantage; we have still to find out how it is done, and the "developmental-genetical idea" cannot be "dismissed". At the same time, this does not invalidate the arguments which Mather brings forward as to the evolutionary consequences of such a differentiation; in fact, he will find a statement of his main point, that the evolutionary advantage of having two distinct sexes is that it ensures cross-breeding, in the

正确的和错误的目的论

沃丁顿

编者按

目的论认为：任何变化都不完全是由物理力的作用引起的，它还取决于这种变化的某种终极目标。虽然这一观点在物理科学中没有得到认可，但是胚胎学家康拉德·沃丁顿在这篇文章中指出，这一观点在生物学中确实能得到合理的应用。他指出，很多有机体存在两性分离的状况，从而允许了杂交育种和快速的自然选择。在这种背景下，可以很自然地说，发育机制正是出于这种目的而导致了性别的分化：这是一种目的论的解释。考虑到一些宗教团体利用目的论来歪曲进化论，现在的进化生物学家往往更加谨慎地引述目的论。

最近，人们对许多不同繁殖体系的目的论重新燃起了相当大的兴趣，这在很大程度上是由达林顿 [1] 的工作引起的。目的论论点的逻辑状态在这种关联性上与其他领域是有很大区别的，因为，在自然选择的影响下，为了加快进化，被提出的"目的"就是条件的满足。也就是说，一个达到其"目的"的遗传体系就为自身的存活提供了途径。这些分析在其他的一些关联上会导致有悖于目的论的论点，因此不能被应用；尽管有人仍然存在疑问：在已有的各种观点中，目的论的表述是否是最令人信服的？

然而，这里存在一个危险：由于与一些它在其中不能成立的领域有着某种联系，目的论的论证方法将无法继续进行下去。从某种程度上来说，这种情况在马瑟 [2] 撰写的那篇极有价值的论文中似乎已经出现过，在文章中，他讨论了在二倍期中两性形成的进化意义。他指出，两性的分离是激发杂交育种的一个机制，他对这一结论并不满意，但是他将这种表述同我 [3] 最近的一篇论文中的一些有关发育机制的句子进行了比较，并推断出，"两性的分离也许是为了有意地确保配子的独特性"。他后来又说，这样的观点一定会被否定。

但是，在关于发育机制的讨论中，这种目的论的陈述应该不会出现。因为目前还不足以确认，发育出两个不同的性别就具有了进化优势；我们仍然不得不去找出它是怎么进行的，并且"发育–遗传的思想"也不能被"抛弃"。同时，这并没有使马瑟提出的关于这种性别分化的进化后果的观点失效；实际上，他将会在所引句子紧挨着的前面找到一句其主要观点的陈述，即拥有两种不同性别的进化优势在于它

867

sentence immediately preceding the ones he chooses to quote. But if the new teleology is to be received with the respect which is its due, it is of the greatest importance that it should not stray outside its own legitimate fields.

(**145**, 705; 1940)

C. H. Waddington: Department of Zoology, Cambridge, April 1.

References:

1. Darlington, C. D., "The Evolution of Genetic Systems". (Cambridge: University Press, 1939.)

2. Mather, K., *Nature*, **145**, 484 (1940).

3. Waddinton, C. H., "An Introduction to Modern Genetics". (London: Allen & Unwin, 1939.)

确保了杂交育种。但是如果这种新的目的论将被人们怀着它应得的尊重加以接受，那么最重要的就是，它不应该游离在自己的合理范围之外。

（刘霞 翻译；赵见高 审稿）

True and False Teleology

K. Mather

Editor's Note

The geneticist Kenneth Mather responds to Waddington's criticisms (in the previous paper) of his views on teleology. While he was taken to task for using teleological expressions, he says he had only quoted from Waddington's own work. In any event, their difference on this point is trivial, as both would agree that evolution by natural selection is not in a true sense purposeful, even if it is often simpler to speak that way. However, Mather points to a true disagreement between himself and Waddington regarding the link between sexual separation in development and cross-fertilization in a species. Mather thus highlights the nub of a persistent problem: evolution indeed has no "goal", but it is often hard not to speak as though it does.

DR. Waddington's criticisms seem to be two. In the first place, I am taken to task for the unwarrantable use of teleological expressions, particularly in the specific case of my paraphrase of his own discussion of sex separation. Inasmuch, however, as the discussion was originally Waddington's and not mine, I can scarcely be called to account for its nature, whether teleological or otherwise. In any event, the point is trivial, as I feel confident that Darlington and Waddington would agree with me in regarding adaptation as the outcome of selection and in denying that it was purposeful, whether the discussion concerned genetical or morphological questions.

Secondly, I am criticized for wishing to "dismiss" the "developmental-genetical idea". This I have no desire to do in general as, clearly, developmental studies can contribute much to our understanding of genetics. But I do disagree with the specific idea, apparently held by Waddington in common with many others, that separation of the sexes in the diploid phase is essentially a reflection of gametic differentiation. They may be related developmentally in dioecious organisms, but this should not blind us to their wholly dissimilar genetical consequences. Gametic differentiation cannot of itself lead to regular outbreeding, as is well shown by Triticum and Pisum, where the two kinds of gametes are strikingly different but where self-fertilization is the rule. On the other hand, crossing between different individuals must always follow from dioecism. As Waddington, in the section of his book which I quoted, and in the previous sentence which I did not quote, relates outbreeding primarily to gametic differentiation and thence secondarily to separation of the sexes, I must disagree with him. Differentiation of the gametes has no place in the genetical relation between outbreeding and unisexuality.

(**145**, 705-706; 1940)

K. Mather: John Innes Horticultural Institution, Mostyn Road, Merton Park, London, S.W.19.

正确的和错误的目的论

马瑟

编者按

遗传学家肯尼思·马瑟回应了沃丁顿对于他的目的论观点的批评（见前一篇论文）。他说当他在工作中使用目的论的表述时，他只是援引了沃丁顿本人的工作。实际上，他们在这一观点上的区别是微小的，例如他们都同意通过自然选择的进化并不是真正意义上有目的的，尽管人们常常采用这种简单的表述。不过，马瑟指出他和沃丁顿的观点之间一个真正的区别在于物种发育中的两性分离和异体受精之间的关联。因此马瑟点明了一个长期存在的问题的症结所在：进化本身的确没有"目的"，但也不能否认，它看起来的确像是有目的的。

沃丁顿博士的批评似乎有两点。第一，我在工作中使用的目的论表述是没有依据的，尤其是我在解释他本人关于两性分离的讨论中使用了这种表达。然而，因为这个讨论最初是沃丁顿引发的，而不是我，所以很少有人来找我证明其性质是目的论的还是其他的。实际上，这一点是微不足道的，因为我相信，不管涉及的讨论是关于遗传学的还是关于形态学的，达林顿先生和沃丁顿先生都会和我一样认同适应是选择的结果，并且也和我一样否认它是有目的的。

第二，我想"抛弃""发育－遗传的思想"的想法受到了批评。一般情况下，我并不希望这样，因为很明显发育学的研究非常有助于我们理解遗传学。尽管如此，我确实不同意这个特殊的观点，即在二倍期中，两性的分离实际上是配子分化的结果，显然，沃丁顿和其他很多人都很认同这一观点。在雌雄异体的生物体内，两性的分离和配子的分化在发育上可能是相关的，但是，这不应该使我们忽视它们完全不同的遗传结果。配子的分化自身不能形成正常的杂交繁殖，这一点已经在小麦和豌豆的例子中得到了证实，这两种植物的配子极为不同，但是它们都是进行自体受精的。另一方面，雌雄异体的生物间都会伴随着不同个体之间的杂交。正如沃丁顿在我引用的他书中的句子中以及我没有引用的他以前的一些句子中所表述的那样，他首先将杂交繁殖与配子的分化相关联，继而与两性的分离相关联，我肯定不同意这一点。配子的分化与杂交繁殖和雌雄异体之间毫无遗传联系。

（刘霞 翻译；赵见高 审稿）

Separation of Uranium Isotopes

W. Krasny-Ergen

Editor's Note

Despite the existence of a panel during the Second World War to censor scientific reports sensitive to the war effort, *Nature* continued to publish work on the fission of uranium. This brief note from the Wenner-Grens Institute in Stockholm, Sweden, suggests that the author, Wilhelm Krasny-Ergen had worked out a way of separating uranium hexafluoride (the only volatile compound of uranium) by means of thermal diffusion, essentially the method devised by Rudolf Peierls and used in the Manhattan Project.

THE separation of the uranium isotopes is of interest because only one of the isotopes, ^{235}U, is believed to undergo fission when bombarded by slow neutrons. The best way to check this theory would be to change the relative particle density of ^{235}U and to see if that has any influence on the number of fissions caused by a certain number of neutrons. If the theory proves correct, one might be able to cause a nuclear chain reaction by concentrating ^{235}U and removing the other isotopes, which only catch neutrons without producing new ones.

To begin with, the most suitable method for concentrating ^{235}U seems to the thermal-diffusion method of Clusius and Dickel[1] or Brewer and Bramley[2], this method being a universal one, applicable to all elements. Of course, other methods, specifically suitable for uranium, may be found later on. The thermal diffusion method can be used both for liquids and for gases, but it works extremely slowly when applied to liquids. It is much better to use gases. The only volatile compound of uranium is uranium fluoride (UF_6). The dimensions of a thermal-diffusion tube system, using this compound, can be calculated from the formulae of Furry, Jones and Onsager[3]. We shall use the same notation as these authors.

The molecular weight of uranium fluoride being 352, the factor α is about 1.5×10^{-3}. The temperature of the colder outer tube must be about $T_1 = 333°K. = 60°C.$, if the apparatus is run at ordinary pressure, as uranium fluoride is a solid below 59°C. at a pressure of 760 mm. mercury. The temperature T_2 of the hot tube can be about $2T_1 = 666°K. = 393°C.$, as experiments have been made with uranium fluoride at 440°C. without decomposition of the gas. Too high a temperature would increase the difficulties of getting materials resistant to uranium fluoride and the loss of energy caused by radiation of the hot tube. For the length of the tubes we take $2l = 10$ m.; for the outer diameter of the inner tube 4 cm. and for the pressure 1 atmosphere. The natural abundance of ^{235}U is 1/139, and if we demand a tenfold increase of the relative particle density of ^{235}U in the equilibrium state of discontinuous operation, we must put $A_d = 1.49 \times 10^{-3}$ cm.$^{-1}$. For uranium fluoride

铀同位素的分离

尽管在第二次世界大战期间存在一个专家小组专门审查与战争有关的敏感的科学报道，但是《自然》还是继续发表关于铀裂变的研究工作。这篇来自瑞典斯德哥尔摩文纳－格伦斯研究所的简报表明，作者威谦·克拉斯尼－埃尔根已经找到一种通过热扩散来分离六氟化铀（唯一一种具有挥发性的铀化合物）的方法，这实质上正是后来由鲁道夫·佩尔斯设计并用于曼哈顿计划中的方法。

铀同位素的分离是个引人关注的问题，这是因为在受到慢中子轰击时，只有 ^{235}U 这一种铀的同位素能够发生裂变。检验这一理论最好的方法是改变 ^{235}U 的相对粒子密度，然后用确定数目的中子轰击 ^{235}U，观察 ^{235}U 相对粒子密度的改变对裂变发生的次数是否有影响。如果该理论得到证实，那么就可以通过富集 ^{235}U 并去除其他那些只俘获中子却不能产生新中子的同位素来引发链式核反应。

首先，富集 ^{235}U 最合适的方法可能就是由克劳修斯与迪克尔 [1] 或者布鲁尔与布拉姆利 [2] 提出的热扩散方法，这是一种对所有元素都适用的普适性方法。当然，以后有可能会找到其他特别适用于铀的方法。热扩散方法对于液体和气体都可以使用，但是在应用于液体时速度非常慢，应用于气体时则要好得多。唯一一种具有挥发性的铀化合物是氟化铀（UF_6）。根据弗里、琼斯和翁萨格 [3] 提出的公式，可以计算出将热扩散方法用于该化合物时所需的管道系统的规模。我们将使用上述作者们采用的符号。

氟化铀的分子量为 352，α 系数约为 1.5×10^{-3}。由于在 760 mm 汞柱的压力条件下温度低于 59℃时氟化铀会变为固体，因此，当装置在常压下运行时，外层较冷管道的温度必须大约是 $T_1 = 333K$（即 60℃）。较热管道的温度 T_2 可以大约是 $2T_1 = 666K$（即 393℃），因为在 440℃ 条件下对氟化铀进行实验时，气体也没有发生分解。而过高的温度下要得到耐氟化铀的物质会更加困难，且较热管道辐射导致的能量损失会更大。我们取管道长度为 $2l = 10\,m$，内管的外直径为 4 cm，压力为一个大气压。^{235}U 的天然丰度为 1/139，如果要让非连续操作达到平衡态时 ^{235}U 的相对粒子密度增加十倍，我们就必须使得 $A_d = 1.49 \times 10^{-3}\ cm^{-1}$。对于氟化铀来说，还没有测定过其热扩散系数 D 和黏度 η 的数值，不过我们可以假定 D 大约是 $0.05\ cm^2/s$， no value has been measured for D, the coefficient of thermal diffusion, and η, the viscosity, but we may assume $D\sim0.05$ cm^2/sec. and $1.4\ \eta/\rho=D$ (ρ=density). This assumption gives us for $2w$, the distance between the tubes, $2w=1.34$ mm.

If the top reservoir contains 5 gm. uranium fluoride, the relaxation time would be 80 days. After this time, the concentration of ^{235}U would have increased to 6.7 times of its original value, or to about 4.8 percent. If we remove the fluoride after this time from the top of the apparatus, we should get about 62.5 mgm./day of uranium fluoride, or 42.5 mgm./day of uranium, 4.8 percent of the uranium removed being ^{235}U. In continuous operation we should get only 41.7 mgm./day of uranium fluoride or 28.3 mgm./day of uranium, if 4.8 percent of the uranium removed be ^{235}U.

Thus a considerable quantity of uranium fluoride with the abundance of ^{235}U several times greater than its natural value can be produced by an apparatus which would not be too difficult to construct and to run. I began to construct such an apparatus together with B. Grabe, in August 1939, but the work had to be discontinued because of the political situation.

(**145**, 742-743; 1940)

W. Krasny-Ergen: Wenner-Grens Institute, University of Stockholm.

References:
1. *Naturwiss.*, **26**, 546 (1938).
2. *Phys. Rev.*, **55**, 590A (1939).
3. *Phys. Rev.*, **55**, 1083 (1939).

另外知道 $1.4\,\eta/\rho = D$（ρ 代表密度）。根据上述假定，我们可以计算出管道间距 $2w = 1.34$ mm。

如果顶部储存装置中有 5 g 氟化铀，弛豫时间将会是 80 天。80 天后，^{235}U 的浓度将会增加到初始数值的 6.7 倍，也就是大约为 4.8%。如果 80 天后将氟化铀从顶部储存装置中移走，我们应该能以大约每天 62.5 mg 的速度得到氟化铀，或者说以每天 42.5 mg 的速度得到铀，取走的铀中有 4.8% 为 ^{235}U。而在连续操作过程中，如果取走的铀中 ^{235}U 占 4.8% 的话，我们则只能以大约每天 41.7 mg 的速度得到氟化铀，或者说以每天 28.3 mg 的速度得到铀。

由此，利用一定的设备就可以生产出数量可观的氟化铀，其中 ^{235}U 的丰度比其天然丰度要大好几倍，而这种设备的建造和运行并不会很难。1939 年 8 月，我和格拉布一起开始建造这样的设备，但是由于政治形势的原因这项工作被迫中断了。

（王耀杨 翻译；汪长征 审稿）

Chemical Estimation of Vitamin B₆ in Foods by Means of the Diazo Reaction and the Phenol Reagent

M. Swaminathan

Editor's Note

The 1930s were years in which academic chemists were urgently seeking to identify the vitamins that function as essential supplements to the ordinary diet. The particular interest of this paper is its author, M. S. Swaminathan, who was a government scientist in India and who developed a rapid means of estimating vitamin B₆ in foodstuffs. He afterwards became the director of the All-India Institute for Agricultural Research, which in the 1960s and 1970s was the driving force behind India's green revolution. He is now president of the M. S. Swaminathan Foundation at Chennai (previously Madras).

THE recent investigations of Kuhn and his coworkers[1] and Harris and Folkers[2] have shown that vitamin B₆ is 2-methyl-3 hydroxy-4:5 di(hydroxymethyl)-pyridine. It contains a hydroxy group in the β-position of the pyridine ring, which gives the characteristic red coloration of true aromatic phenols with ferric chloride. The vitamin also gives colour reactions with diazotized aromatic amines and the phenol reagent of Folin and Ciocalteu[3].

A method has been developed for the estimation of the vitamin in biological materials using diazotized sulphanilic acid or the phenol reagent. Since these reagents are not specific for vitamin B₆, it is necessary to remove all interfering substances before colorimetric estimations can be carried out. By the procedure outlined below it has been found possible to obtain values for the vitamin B₆ content of various foods which appear to correspond approximately to those obtained by other workers using biological methods.

A suitable quantity (2-50 gm. containing 10-20 rat units of vitamin B₆[4]) of the finely minced or powdered test material was digested with pepsin for twenty-four hours. Protein and its derivatives were removed by tungstic acid. Purine, pyrimidine and imidazole bases were precipitated with silver nitrate and barium hydroxide and the excess silver removed. The solution was adjusted to pH 1-2 and the vitamin B₆ present was adsorbed on clarite (2 gm.). The vitamin was eluted from the clarite with hot barium hydroxide and the silver precipitation was repeated. The solution was then adjusted to pH 6, concentrated to 25 ml., and treated with sodium nitrite and acetic acid for 15 minutes to destroy any amino group that might be present. After bringing the pH to 7, the solution was filtered and made up to 50 ml. 10 ml. aliquots were treated with diazotized sulphanilic acid and the azo colour formed estimated colorimetrically by comparison against a standard of 20 µgm. of pure vitamin B₆ treated in the same way. The method is highly sensitive.

利用重氮化反应和酚试剂对食物中的维生素 B6 进行化学测定

斯瓦米纳坦

编者按

20 世纪 30 年代，理论化学家迫切地寻找着能够鉴定那些对普通膳食具有必要补充功能的维生素的方法。这篇文章特别引人注目的是它的作者斯瓦米纳坦，他是一位印度的政府科学家，研究出了一种能够快速测定食物中维生素 B6 含量的方法。后来，他成为了印度农业研究所的主管，在 20 世纪 60 年代和 70 年代，该研究所是印度绿色革命的主要推动力量。现在，他在钦奈市（原马德拉斯市）的斯瓦米纳坦基金会担任会长。

库恩与其合作者 [1] 以及哈里斯与福克斯 [2] 最近的研究都表明，维生素 B6 是 2–甲基–3–羟基–4,5–二羟甲基–吡啶。其吡啶环的 β 位上有一个羟基基团，这一结构使它像芳香酚一样能与氯化铁反应而显示出特征性的红色。此外，这种维生素还能与重氮化的芳香胺以及福林酚试剂 [3] 发生显色反应。

此前，已经有人研究出了一种利用对氨基苯磺酸重氮盐或者酚试剂来测定生物样品中维生素含量的方法。由于这些试剂并不是特异性地与维生素 B6 发生反应，因此必须先除去各种干扰物之后才能进行比色测定。我们发现，按照下面所描述的步骤可以测定各种食物中维生素 B6 的含量，所得数值与其他研究人员使用生物方法获得的数值基本一致。

将适量（2~50 克，其中含 10~20 个大鼠单位的维生素 B6[4]）切碎的或磨成粉末的待测样品用胃蛋白酶消化 24 小时。然后用钨酸除去蛋白质及其衍生物。再用硝酸银和氢氧化钡将嘌呤、嘧啶和咪唑沉淀，之后除去过量的银。将溶液的 pH 调到 1~2，此时维生素 B6 被吸附在微亮煤（2 克）表面。然后，用热的氢氧化钡溶液将维生素从微亮煤上洗脱下来，再重复一次银沉淀的过程。接着将所得溶液的 pH 调到 6 并浓缩至 25 毫升，用亚硝酸钠和醋酸处理 15 分钟以破坏所有可能存在的氨基基团。然后将 pH 调到 7，接着对溶液进行过滤并将其体积补足至 50 毫升。取 10 毫升溶液，用对氨基苯磺酸重氮盐处理，最后通过比色法对生成的偶氮染料进行测定，对照品是将 20 微克纯的维生素 B6 以同样方式处理后得到的标准样品。这种方法是

10 μgm. of vitamin B$_6$ is easily estimated and the colour obtained is proportional in intensity to the amount of vitamin present. The values for fifteen foodstuffs are given in the accompanying table.

Vitamin B$_6$ content of various foodstuffs

Foodstuff	Vitamin B$_6$ μgm./gm.
Yeast, dried (brewer's)	54.0
Yeast, dried (brewer's) (autoclaved at pH 9.4)	53.0
Rice polishings	13.4
Liver, sheep	13.4
Muscle, sheep	4.5
Milk, cow's	1.7
Maize, yellow, whole	7.1
Wheat, whole	7.6
Cholam (*Sorghum vulgare*)	8.0
Rice, husked	6.6
Rice, highly milled, raw	3.0
Soya bean	8.0
Beetroot	1.3
Cabbage	3.1
Plantain, ripe	1.3

Known amounts of vitamin B$_6$ were added to weighed quantities of foodstuffs and the recovery was good in all cases, ranging from 70 to 100 percent.

The method described is applicable to all types of foodstuffs. It is probable that in some cases it may be abbreviated. For example, treatment with nitrous acid has been found to be unnecessary in the case of yeast. Possibly the second silver precipitation is not always necessary. A variety of different phenolic reagents may be used and many modifications in detail are possible. For example, with yeast and potatoes, comparable values have been obtained using diazotized sulphanilic acid and p-nitroaniline and the phenol reagent, nitrous acid treatment being omitted.

A fuller account of these investigations will be published in the *Indian Journal of Medical Research*.

(**145**, 780; 1940)

M. Swaminathan: Nutrition Research Laboratories, Indian Research Fund Association, Coonoor, S. India, March 27.

References:

1. Kuhn, Westphal, Wendt, and Westphal, *Naturwiss.*, 27, 469 (1939). Cited in *Nut. Abstr. Rev.*, 9, 606 (1940).

2. Harris and Folkers, *J. Amer. Chem. Soc.*, 61, 1245 (1939).

3. Folin and Ciocalteu, *J. Biol. Chem.*, 73, 627 (1927).

4. Birch, György and Harris, *Biochem. J.*, 29, 2830 (1935).

非常灵敏的。甚至 10 微克的维生素 B₆ 也可以很容易地被测定出来，反应产生的颜色的强度与样品中维生素的含量成比例。15 种食物的测定结果列在下面的表格中。

各种食物中维生素 B₆ 的含量

食物种类	维生素 B₆ 微克／克
（啤酒）酵母干粉	54.0
（啤酒）酵母干粉（pH 9.4，高温灭菌）	53.0
米糠	13.4
羊肝	13.4
羊肉	4.5
牛奶	1.7
整粒的黄玉米	7.1
整粒的小麦	7.6
高粱	8.0
脱壳的米	6.6
碾成碎末的生米	3.0
大豆	8.0
甜菜根	1.3
卷心菜	3.1
成熟的大蕉	1.3

分别向称重过的各种食物中添加已知量的维生素 B₆，对各组进行重新测定得到的结果都很好，分布在预期值的 70% ～ 100% 之间。

这里介绍的方法对于所有类型的食物都是适用的。在某些情况下这一方法可能还可以简化。例如，对于酵母来说不必用亚硝酸处理。可能有些情况下第二次银沉淀也不是必需的。操作中应该可以使用其他的酚试剂，一些具体的细节也可能略有不同。比如，对于酵母和马铃薯，在省略了亚硝酸处理这一步骤时，不管是用对氨基苯磺酸重氮盐还是对硝基苯胺或者酚试剂，所得到的测定结果是类似的。

这些研究更完整的报道将发表在《印度医学研究杂志》上。

（王耀杨 翻译；汪长征 审稿）

The Hydrogen Bond

C. E. H. Bawn

Editor's Note

One of the distinctive developments in the molecular sciences in the 1930s was the recognition of the importance of the hydrogen bond: a relatively weak interaction between a slightly positively charged hydrogen atom on one molecular group and a region of high electron density on another. This interaction is central to the way proteins and nucleic acids attain their structures, and is the reason for the anomalous properties of liquid water. This report of a meeting held by the Faraday Society in London on 17 May 1940 perceptively refers to the potential importance of hydrogen bonds in the structure of protein molecules and complexes.

IT has been recognized for many years that under certain conditions a hydrogen atom can form a connecting link between two other atoms. It may be considered as forming a bond between them, known as the hydrogen bond. Although the hydrogen bond is not strong, recent investigations have shown it to be of very wide occurrence. The concept has been extremely useful in explaining the association of polar liquids like water, the association of carboxylic acids, alcohols, amides, etc., the closure of rings within the molecule, and in interpreting many measurements of structure by X-ray and electron diffraction methods and of the frequency shifts of the infra-red absorption bands of certain known groupings. It was investigations of this type that not only established the existence of this form of bond but also provided information regarding the conditions in which its formation is to be expected, and, in many cases, of the actual energy of the bond. In spite of the enormous amount of experimental data now available, there is still much information which is lacking; the exact mechanism of the bonding power of the hydrogen is not clear, and there are many difficulties with questions of terminology.

With the object of clarifying the situation, a general discussion on "The Hydrogen Bond" was held by the Faraday Society on May 17 at the Imperial College of Science and Technology, London. A number of subjects was discussed in the six papers presented to the meeting, but briefly, the discussion can be considered under two headings: (1) the methods of studying hydrogen bonds by infra-red absorption, X-ray diffraction, and magnetic susceptibility measurements, and a survey of the results obtained; and (2) the occurrence of hydrogen bonds in molecules of biological importance, such as the proteins and carbohydrates.

It follows from the quantum-mechanical theories of valency that hydrogen cannot form more than one covalent bond and that the attraction of two atoms as found in hydrogen bond formation must be due to ionic forces. The positive hydrogen ion with no electronic shell around it attracts one anion to its normal internuclear separation, and this could then

氢键

鲍尔

编者按

20 世纪 30 年代分子科学中最有特色的进展之一便是对氢键的重要性的认识：氢键是指一个基团中包含的一个带轻微正电荷的氢原子与另一个含有高电子度的基团之间相对较弱的相互作用。这种相互作用对蛋白质和核酸结构的形成非常重要，同时也是造成液态水的一些异常性质的原因。1940 年 5 月 17 日伦敦法拉第学会的这份会议报告，敏锐地提到了氢键在蛋白质分子及其在复合物结构中的潜在重要性。

多年前人们就已知道，在某些条件下，一个氢原子可以在另外两个原子之间形成一种接合性的连接。这可以理解成氢原子在这两个原子之间形成了一个键，也就是我们通常所说的氢键。尽管氢键并不是很强，但是最近的研究显示，它是广泛存在的。氢键这个概念非常有助于解释极性液体（如水）的缔合，羧酸、醇、胺等分子的缔合以及分子中环的闭合，此外还有助于解释通过 X 射线与电子衍射方法得到的结构测量结果以及某些已知聚集体红外吸收谱带频移的测量结果。这些科学研究不仅确认了氢键的存在，还为氢键的形成条件及其在多数情况下的实际键能提供了信息。虽然现在已经掌握了大量的实验数据，但是还缺乏很多信息；氢原子具有黏合力的具体机制仍不清楚，而且很多命名问题还存在困难。

为了厘清这种局面，法拉第学会于 5 月 17 日在伦敦帝国理工学院召开了一次会议全面讨论"氢键"。呈交大会的 6 篇论文讨论了大量关于氢键的主题，但是简要地说，讨论是在两大方向上进行的：（1）红外吸收、X 射线衍射和观测磁化率等研究氢键的方法，以及对所得结果的总览；（2）具有生物学重要性的分子（如蛋白质和碳水化合物）中存在氢键。

根据化合价的量子力学理论，氢原子无法形成一个以上的共价键，在氢键形成过程中发现两个原子对它吸引，这必定是源于离子力。没有电子层围绕的正氢离子将一个阴离子吸引到其正常核距处，接着吸引第二个阴离子，即：$X^- H^+ Y^-$。如同预

attract a second anion, namely, $X^-H^+Y^-$. As might be expected, the strength of the bond formed should increase with increase in the effective negative charge of the bonded atoms. Thus fluorine, oxygen, nitrogen, and chlorine should form hydrogen bonds of strength decreasing in this order. Perhaps the best example of this type of ionic bonding is the HF_2^- ion; Pauling considers that this ion resonates among three structures:

$$\text{F H F}^- \qquad (A)$$
$$\text{F}^-\text{H}^+\text{F}^- \qquad (B)$$
$$\text{F}^-\text{H F} \qquad (C)$$

When we come to consider more complex structures involving intermolecular hydrogen bonds, steric requirements must also be satisfied, that is, the interacting groups must be capable of sufficiently close approach to enable the attractive forces to come into play. When we review the conditions of formation of the hydrogen bond, it is not at all surprising that one meets examples of bonds covering a wide range of interaction, from strong bonds to weak bonds, finally emerging into groups of interaction which we know as due to van der Waals forces. It seems at present that the only means of characterizing the hydrogen bond in the molecule is the energy required to break it.

The most important and useful method for the discovery of hydrogen bonding is infra-red spectroscopy. The main results obtained up to the present time were discussed by Dr. G. B. B. M. Sutherland. Every molecule containing an XH group gives rise to well-marked absorption bands in the near infra-red, which are characteristic of the stretching and contraction of the XH bond. If the hydrogen atom of the XH group becomes subject to the influence of a force other than that which binds it to the X atom, then the frequency of vibration will be altered and the characteristic band will be shifted. The presence of hydrogen bonds in the molecule can therefore be inferred from the perturbation it produces in the normal XH bond. In this way both intermolecular and intramolecular bonds have been determined. As an illustration of the method we may select one of the best-known examples of the hydrogen bond, namely, the dimeric form of the carboxylic acids,

$$X\text{—C}\begin{matrix}\text{O—H}\cdots\text{O}\\ \\ \text{O}\cdots\text{H—O}\end{matrix}\text{C—X.}$$

The effect of association is shown by the shift of the OH fundamental frequency at 2.83 μ to 3.25 μ in the acid, and the change in intensity of the band with temperature can be used as a measure of the degree of dissociation of the dimeric molecule, and hence of the heat of dissociation. The method is equally applicable for the study of hydrogen bonds in solids, solutions and liquids. Thus, the association of the alcohols in carbon tetrachloride is characterized by a band at 2.84 μ-2.88 μ, in contrast to the sharp monomeric band at 2.75 μ. Dr. J. J. Fox and Dr. A. E. Martin find that the monomeric O—H bond of benzyl alcohol in carbon tetrachloride has two components, 2.750 μ and 2.765 μ, which seems to

期的那样，所形成的键的强度将随着键合原子有效负电荷的增加而增加。因此，氟原子、氧原子、氮原子和氯原子形成的氢键强度应该依次减弱。这种离子键合的最好例子可能是 HF_2^- 离子；鲍林认为该离子在下面三种结构之间共振：

$$F \ H \ F^- \qquad (A)$$
$$F^- H^+ F^- \qquad (B)$$
$$F^- H \ F \qquad (C)$$

当我们开始考虑涉及分子间氢键更为复杂的构造时，空间条件也必须得到满足，也就是说，相互作用的基团必须足够近以确保能够产生吸引力。在我们回顾形成氢键的条件时，会遇到各种各样的相互作用的键，从强键到弱键，直至两个基团间的相互作用也就是我们所说的范德华力，这些都不足为奇。目前来看，似乎描述分子中氢键特征的唯一方法就是打开该键所需的能量。

红外光谱是发现氢键作用的最重要和最有用的方法。萨瑟兰博士对目前为止已获得的主要结果进行了讨论。所有含一个 XH 基团的分子都会在近红外区域出现明显的吸收带，这是 XH 键拉伸和收缩的特征吸收带。如果 XH 基团中的氢原子受到别的力的影响（这个力并非是连接它与 X 原子的力），那么其振动频率就会改变，该特征吸收带也会移动。因此，氢键在分子中的存在可以通过它对正常 XH 键产生的微扰推断出来。分子内和分子间的氢键都可以通过这种方式加以确定。为了阐明该方法，我们选取了一个著名的氢键的例子，即羧酸分子的二聚形式：

$$X-C \overset{\displaystyle O-H\cdots O}{\underset{\displaystyle O\cdots H-O}{}} C-X$$

该酸分子中 OH 基频从 2.83 μ 移动到 3.25 μ，这说明存在缔合效应，而谱带强度随温度的变化则可以用来度量二聚体分子的离解度，并进而测得离解热。同理，该方法还可以用来研究固体、溶液和液体中的氢键。乙醇在四氯化碳中的缔合可以通过位于 2.84 μ ~ 2.88 μ 的谱带体现出来，与之相对应的则是位于 2.75 μ 处的尖锐的单体谱带。福克斯博士和马丁博士发现，四氯化碳中苯甲醇的单体 O–H 键谱带有两处，2.750 μ 和 2.765 μ，这似乎意味着该醇有两种分子类型。在低浓度时，这种醇发生二

indicate two molecular species of the alcohol. At low concentrations this alcohol dimerizes (2.865 μ) and an equilibrium

$$2C_6H_5CH_2OH \leftrightarrows (C_6H_5CH_2OH)_2$$

is set up, but it is not possible to decide whether the dimer has the structure,

At higher concentrations polymeric association becomes predominant, and this they conclude is in accordance with an equilibrium between dimer and quadruple molecule.

Numerous infra-red investigations have shown the presence of intramolecular hydrogen bonds. The classic example of this group is the two forms of *o*-chlor-phenol,

and

the possibility of *cis-trans* isomerism giving rise to two absorption peaks, one at about 7,050 cm.[-1] (*trans-* form) and the other at about 6,890 cm.[-1] (*cis-* form). Many other examples were given in Fox and Martin's paper.

The results obtained by the other powerful method of studying hydrogen bonds was reviewed in a paper by Dr. J. M. Robertson. By this method the distance between the bridged atom or groups forming the hydrogen bond can be directly measured. In this way the presence of hydrogen bonds has been demonstrated in many inorganic and organic structures. Perhaps the most interesting example is that of ice, in which each oxygen is surrounded tetrahedrally by four other oxygen atoms at a distance of 2.76 A. The structure is pictured to be of the type

In the crystalline alcohols a similar sort of structure exists, the molecules combining through hydrogen bonds to form indefinitely large structures,

聚 (2.865 μ) 并建立如下平衡：

$$2C_6H_5CH_2OH \leftrightharpoons (C_6H_5CH_2OH)_2$$

但是仍然无法确定二聚体究竟是下面哪种结构：

他们从二聚体与四聚体分子之间的平衡中推断出，在较高浓度时主要发生多聚缩合。

大量红外研究结果表明存在分子内氢键。这类情况的一个典型例子就是邻氯苯酚的两种形式：

顺反异构现象导致其产生两个吸收峰，一个位于约 7,050 cm^{-1} 处 (**反式**)，另一个位于约 6,890 cm^{-1} 处 (**顺式**)。福克斯和马丁的论文中还给出了很多其他的例子。

罗伯逊在一篇论文中回顾了用另外一种有效研究氢键的方法所得到的结果。通过该方法能够直接测得形成氢键的桥原子或桥基团之间的距离，从而证明了在很多种无机和有机结构中存在氢键。可能最有趣的例子就是冰中的氢键，其中每个氧原子被 2.76 Å 处的另外四个氧原子以四面体形式包围。该结构类型图示如下：

在结晶醇中存在一种类似的结构，分子通过氢键缔和形成无限大的结构：

Bernal has suggested that on the basis of results obtained by X-ray analysis, two types of bonds should be distinguished, for which he proposes the names hydrogen and hydroxyl bonds. In the former, hydrogen is attached by equal firmness to two oxygens, O---H---O, the energy being about 8,000 cal. and the distance between the oxygens being 2.5-2.65 A. In the latter, the hydrogen remains unsymmetrically attached to one of the oxygens, O---H—O, giving a bond energy of 5,000 cal. and an oxygen–oxygen distance of 2.7-2.9 A. Since the experimental evidence seems to indicate an almost continuous transition between these two extremes, the necessity for this distinction is not accepted by all.

In a short paper Dr. W. Rogie Angus and W. K. Hill described some preliminary results on a general investigation of diamagnetism and hydrogen bonding. There seems to be every indication that hydrogen bonding should be detectable by susceptibility measurements.

The hydrogen bond may be of great importance biologically, and two papers of the discussion were concerned with the role of hydrogen in determining the structure of the proteins and starch. Our knowledge of the detailed structure of these molecules is still far from complete, and consequently it was not possible to do more than to survey the possible part which hydrogen bonds might take in determining the structure of these substances. In this short summary, one can only restate the conclusion reached by Dr. W. T. Astbury after a critical discussion of the way in which hydrogen bonds may intervene in protein structures, "that whichever way we turn it is impossible to reach a verdict that is really satisfying". However, X-ray analysis of crystalline diketo-piperazine, a substance related to the proteins, shows that the molecules are linked together by hydrogen bonds between their respective oxygen atoms and =NH groups, to form flat continuous chains throughout the structure.

It may be expected that the formation of hydrogen bonds may be important in determining the behaviour of complex molecules containing multiple active hydrogen bond-forming groups, for example, polysaccharides. A critical consideration of this possibility for starch by Prof. E. L. Hirst, Dr. G. T. Young and the present writer shows that the properties of this molecule are inconsistent with those of a structure held together

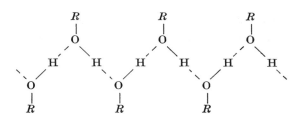

贝尔纳曾基于 X 射线分析结果提出，应该区分这两种类型的键，他提议将其分别命名为氢键和羟基键。在前者中，氢原子以同样的紧密程度被两个氧原子束缚，即 O---H---O，键能约为 8,000 cal，两个氧原子之间距离为 2.5~2.65 Å。在后者中，氢原子不对称地被两个氧原子中的一个束缚，即 O---H—O，键能为 5,000 cal，氧－氧距离为 2.7~2.9 Å。由于实验证据似乎显示出介于这两种极端情况之间存在一个几乎连续的过渡，因此这种区分的必要性没有得到所有人的认可。

罗盖·安格斯和希尔在一篇短文中描述了关于反磁性与氢键作用的一般性研究所取得的一些初步结果。似乎所有迹象都显示，氢键作用应该可以通过测量磁化率而检测到。

氢键可能具有重要的生物学意义，有两篇关于这方面的论文，其关注的是氢键对于确定蛋白质和淀粉结构的作用。目前我们还远没有彻底了解这些分子的具体结构，因此，除了概括一下氢键对于确定上述物质结构可能具有的作用之外，暂时无法进行更进一步的工作。在这篇简短的概述中，我们批判性地讨论了氢键对蛋白质结构的影响方式，然而最终也只是重述了阿斯特伯里博士的结论："无论我们倾向于哪种方式，都不可能得到一个令人十分满意的定论"。不过，二酮哌嗪（一种与蛋白质有关的物质）晶体的 X 射线分析显示，分子通过各自的氧原子和 ═NH 基团之间的氢键缔合在一起，形成了贯穿于整个结构的平滑连续的链。

可以推测，对含有多个活泼的可以形成氢键的基团的复杂分子（比如多糖）来说，氢键的形成对于确定这些分子的行为可能是很重要的。赫斯特教授、扬博士和笔者以淀粉为例对上述推测作了批判性的思考，一致认为该分子的性质与通过氢键连接在一起的结构的性质不同。对物理化学数据的分析表明，淀粉中的重复单元

by hydrogen bonds. Analysis of physico-chemical data indicates that the repeating units in starch are held together by normal glucosidic linkages. It is pointed out, however, that the macro-molecules may be associated by hydrogen bonds in native starch.

(**145**, 846-848; 1940)

C. E. H. Bawn: University of Bristol.

是通过正常的糖苷键连接在一起的。不过还要指出的是，天然淀粉可以通过氢键缔合成大分子。

（王耀杨 翻译；郝项 审稿）

Excited States of Stable Nuclei

C. F. Powell *et al.*

Editor's Note

The idea that the stable nuclei of many atoms could exist in excited energetic states was first canvassed by a group of scientists who had used the newly built cyclotron at the University of Liverpool to bombard atomic nuclei such as neon. This paper shows that neon does indeed have an excited state lying some 2.5 million electron volts above that of the ground state, but that oxygen appears not to have an excited state within the range explored. Of the authors, Cecil Frank Powell and James Chadwick won Nobel Prizes for their work. Alan Nunn May, a lecturer at King's College London, was compromised by his association with Klaus Fuchs, afterwards shown to be a Soviet spy.

WE have recently carried out some experiments on the scattering of protons by light elements, using the proton beam provided by the Liverpool cyclotron and detecting the scattered particles by the photographic method.

A proton beam of about 10^{-8} amperes, with a divergence of one degree, is defined by a system of stops, and emerges from an attachment to the vacuum tank of the cyclotron into the "camera" through a mica window covering a hole $\frac{1}{8}$ in. in diameter. In the camera this narrow proton beam passes down the axis of a tube, which is interrupted for a length of 3 mm. to allow the scattered particles to emerge. A flat photographic plate is placed so that its surface is parallel to the axis of the beam and at a distance of 1 cm. from it. The protons scattered by the gas with which the camera is filled emerge through the interruption and enter the plate at a small glancing angle. This arrangement has the advantage that a single plate can contain the information for determining the probability of scattering from about 15° to 150°, providing for each angle regions containing a suitable number of tracks for counting purposes. At the same time, the energy of the scattered particle can be determined from the length of its track in the photographic emulsion.

Once the difficulties of defining the beam in the stray field of the magnet had been overcome, we found that suitable exposures could be obtained for some six to eight different scattering gases per day.

We have taken plates of the scattering from eleven elements which could be obtained either as elementary gases or in the form of suitable gaseous compounds. The energy of the incident particles at the point of scattering was about 4 million volts. The plates for hydrogen, deuterium and helium are satisfactory, and work is proceeding on these; but we wish to direct attention here to the inelastic scattering which accompanies the elastic

890

稳定核的激发态

鲍威尔等

编者按

一些科学家利用利物浦大学新建的回旋加速器轰击原子核（如氖），从而首次对激发能态下多种原子的稳定核能够存在的观点进行了探讨。这篇论文表明，氖确实存在一个激发态，且该激发态能量比基态能量大约高 2.5 兆电子伏，但是在实验研究范围内氧似乎没有激发态。本文作者中的塞西尔·弗兰克·鲍威尔和詹姆斯·查德威克凭借他们的研究成果获得了诺贝尔奖。另一位作者艾伦·农·梅是伦敦国王学院的一位讲师，他因与克劳斯·富克斯（后被发现是苏联间谍）有交往而受到了牵连。

最近，我们利用一些轻元素进行了质子散射的实验，实验使用利物浦的回旋加速器来产生质子束，并用照相的方法来检测散射粒子。

我们把一束强度为 10^{-8} 安培、分散度为 1° 的质子束，约束于一个静止的系统中，然后将其从回旋加速器的真空罐的附加装置中射出，穿过覆盖了云母窗的直径为 1/8 英寸的小洞后进入"照相机"。在照相机中，这条狭窄的质子束沿着一个长管轴向穿行，这一长管有个 3 毫米长的断口，散射粒子能从这个断口中逃逸出来。在与质子束的轴向相平行的方向上放置一块扁平的照相底板，底板与质子束的轴相距 1 厘米。被充满于照相机中的气体所散射的质子能够穿过长管的断口，并以很小的掠射角射到底板上。这样安置的好处是，假如每个角度区域中都包括适当数量的能用于计数的轨迹的话，那么只用一块底板就能获得用以确定 15° 到 150° 范围内散射概率的相关信息。与此同时，我们还能通过照相乳胶中轨迹的长度来确定散射粒子的能量。

如果能够克服在磁体的杂散场中约束质子束的困难，那么我们一天就能得到大约 6~8 种不同气体散射质子的合适的曝光照片。

我们已经得到了 11 种元素散射质子的底板，实验中采用的这些元素有的是单质气体的形式，有的是适当的气态化合物的形式。入射粒子在散射点的能量约为 4 兆电子伏。由氢、氖和氦得到的底板是令人满意的，后续处理的工作还在进行中；但是在这里，我们想把注意力放在较重元素中与弹性散射伴随出现的非弹性散射上，

scattering from the heavier elements, and gives information about the excited states of the stable nuclei in a particularly direct way.

The distributions in energy of the protons scattered through 90° from the gases oxygen and neon are shown in Fig. 1. In oxygen a single peak appears, corresponding in energy to protons elastically scattered through 90°. With neon, in addition to the elastically scattered group, there is a peak at lower energy which we attribute to inelastic scattering from ^{20}Ne. This view is supported by the fact, deduced from the analysis of the neutron spectrum of fluorine under deuteron bombardment, that ^{20}Ne has an excited state of 1.4 Mev., for the difference in energy of the two groups of scattered particles is just of this amount.

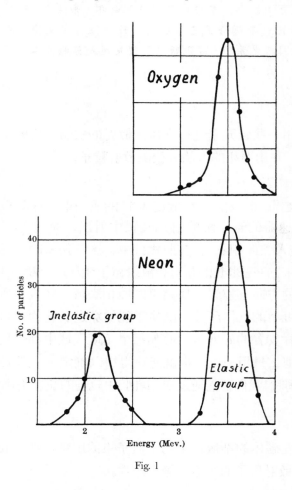

Fig. 1

We have examined the variation of the probability of scattering with angle for elastic and inelastic scattering in neon, and the results are shown in Fig. 2. It will be seen that in the range from 40° to 80° the elastic scattering follows very closely that expected from pure Coulomb scattering. In contrast with this, the inelastically scattered particles are distributed spherically symmetrically about the centre of mass of the system, to within the present accuracy of the measurements. This suggests that the inelastically scattered protons have

这种非弹性散射以特别直接的方式给出了关于稳定核激发态的信息。

图 1 显示了在氧气和氖气中散射后偏转了 90° 的质子的能量分布。在氧气中散射的结果是，只有一个单峰，其对应着发生弹性散射后偏转了 90° 的质子的能量。而在氖气中散射的结果是，除了弹性散射组之外，在能量较低的位置上还有一个峰，我们将其解释为由 ^{20}Ne 导致的非弹性散射。这一观点是有事实依据的，因为，对氟在氘核轰击下得到的中子能谱进行的分析表明 ^{20}Ne 具有一个能量为 1.4 兆电子伏的激发态，而我们的实验结果中两组散射粒子的能量差刚好就是这个数值。

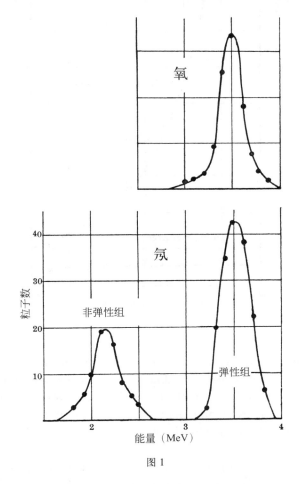

图 1

我们还研究了氖实验中弹性散射和非弹性散射的散射概率随角度的变化，结果如图 2 所示。从图中我们可以看到，在角度为 40°~80° 的范围内，弹性散射的结果与完全由库仑散射而得到的预期结果几乎完全吻合。但与此相反的是，在目前观测所能达到的精度范围内，非弹性散射粒子是以系统质心为中心呈球对称分布的。这

been "evaporated" from the compound nucleus formed in a close collision of an incident proton and a ^{20}Ne nucleus.

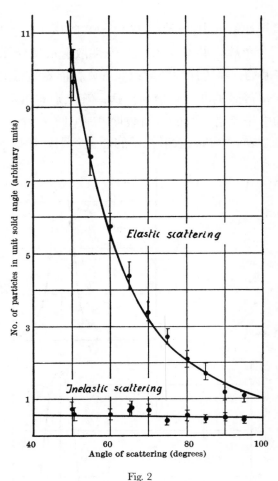

Fig. 2

The absence of inelastically scattered protons in oxygen in the conditions of our experiments is evidently due to the fact that there is no excited state of oxygen below 4 Mev. The variation of scattering with angle shows, however, strong anomalies from Rutherford scattering at angles greater than about 45°, the number of scattered particles per unit solid angle varying only slowly with angle. This point will be investigated further.

With the elements of atomic number greater than that of neon which we have examined, such as chlorine and argon, the ratio of the number of inelastically to elastically scattered particles is very much smaller than in the case of neon, corresponding to the decreasing probability of the protons entering the nucleus with increasing nuclear charge. It is therefore evident that it will be desirable to continue the experiments with protons of higher energy in order that the higher excited states of the light elements may become accessible to investigation, and to obtain results for elements of higher atomic number. It

意味着，一个入射质子与一个 ^{20}Ne 核发生近程碰撞后形成了复合核，其中非弹性散射质子就是从这个复合核中"蒸发"出来的。

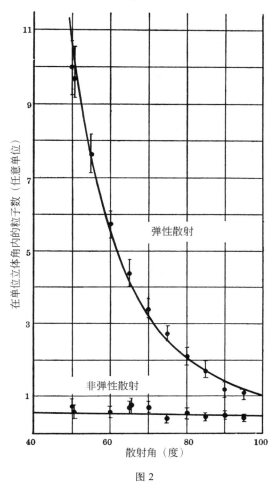

图 2

在我们的实验条件下，氧的实验中没有出现非弹性散射质子，这显然是因为氧不存在比基态能量高出 4 兆电子伏以内的激发态。不过，依据散射随角度的变化关系显示，在大于 45° 时散射结果严重背离了卢瑟福散射，且随着角度的变化，单位立体角中散射粒子的数目只发生缓慢的变化。在后面的工作中我们将对此进行深入的研究。

对于我们研究过的原子序数比氖大的元素，比如氯和氩，非弹性散射粒子数与弹性散射粒子数的比值远远小于氖实验中得到的结果，这与核电荷增大导致质子入核概率减小是相一致的。因此，要研究轻元素的更高能激发态，或者要得到较大原子序数元素的质子散射结果，就必须用更高能量的质子来进行实验。不过，从我们

is clear from our experience, however, that the method is very powerful, the plates being obtained with an exposure of a few minutes and the analysis of the energy distribution of the scattered protons being complete within a few hours. Also the use of what are essentially gas targets gives the advantage of purity control and absence of effects associated with energy loss in the target. We may expect these advantages in experiments of a similar character with high-energy deuterons, where the scattered primary particles may be accompanied by disintegration products.

In general, we may conclude that, using the photographic method of detection, it becomes possible to take advantage of the high-energy particles provided by the cyclotron to make experiments of the kind which have hitherto only been undertaken with direct current generators at relatively low energies.

(**145**, 893-894; 1940)

C. F. Powell: Wills Physical Laboratory, University of Bristol.

A. N. May: King's College, London.

J. Chadwick and T. G. Pickavance: George Holt Physics Laboratory, University of Liverpool.

的实验中可以清楚地看出，我们用的这种方法是非常强大的，短短的几分钟就可以得到曝光底板，而对散射质子能量分布的分析结果也能在短短的几个小时之内完成。另外，至关重要的是，气体靶标的使用有利于纯度控制以及与靶标中的能量损失相关的各种效应的消除。我们可以预期，在使用高能氘核进行的类似实验中这些优点也将会得以体现，只是在这些实验中被散射的入射粒子可能会与衰变产物混在一起。

总之，我们可以确定的是，如果使用照相法来进行检测，那么此前那些只能依靠直流发生器在相对较低的能量水平上进行的实验，现在就可以利用由回旋加速器产生的高能粒子来进行了。

（王耀杨 翻译；汪长征 审稿）

Considerations Concerning the Fundaments of Theoretical Physics[*]

A. Einstein

Editor's Note

Five years before his death, Einstein had been driven to the view that quantum mechanics was a valid description of quantum phenomena but that as a consequence physics had been robbed of its explicit and deterministic foundations. He concluded that "it is open to every man to choose the direction of his striving; and also every man may draw comfort from Lessing's fine saying that the search for truth is more precious than its possession".

WHAT we call physics comprises that group of natural sciences which base their concepts on measurements; and the concepts and propositions of which lend themselves to mathematical formulation. Its realm is accordingly defined as that part of the sum total of our knowledge which is capable of being expressed in mathematical terms. With the progress of science, the realm of physics has so expanded that it seems to be limited only by the limitations of the method itself. The larger part of physical research is devoted to the development of the various branches of physics, in each of which the object is the theoretical understanding of more or less restricted fields of experience, and in each of which the laws and concepts remain as closely as possible related to experience. It is this department of science with its ever-growing specialization, which has revolutionized practical life in the last centuries.

On the other hand, from the very beginning there has always been present the attempt to find a unifying theoretical basis for all these single sciences, consisting of a minimum of concepts and fundamental relationships, from which all the concepts and relationships of the single disciplines might be derived by logical process. This is what we mean by the search for a foundation of the whole of physics.

It is clear that the word foundation in this connexion does not mean something analogous in all respects to the foundations of a building. Logically considered, of course, the various single laws of physics rest upon this foundation. But whereas a building may be seriously damaged by a heavy storm or spring flood, and yet its foundations remain intact, in science the logical foundation is always in greater peril from new experiences or new knowledge than are the branch disciplines with their closer experimental contacts.

The first attempt to lay a uniform theoretical foundation in physics was the work of

---

[*] An address, slightly abridged, delivered at the Eighth American Scientific Congress at Washington on May 15.

关于理论物理基础的思考[*]

爱因斯坦

编者按

爱因斯坦在他生命最后的五年中坚持认为，虽然量子力学对量子现象的描述是合理的，但却摒弃了物理学的明确性和确定性的基础。他做出了如下的结论："世事无绝对，每个人都可以选择自己奋斗的方向；而每个人也都可以从莱辛的一句精辟的名言中得到安慰：追求真理比拥有真理更为可贵。"

我们所说的物理学由这样一类自然科学组成，它们的概念的定义是以测量为依据，而且其中的概念和命题也都可用数学公式表示出来。因此可以说，所有能用数学语言来表达的那部分知识，都可划归为物理学的范畴。因此随着科学的进步，物理学的范畴似乎已经扩展到只受研究方法自身所限制的程度。物理学研究的大部分工作是致力于发展物理学的各个分支，目标是对一定领域内的实践经验给予理论解释，而且其中的定律和概念都要尽可能与实践经验紧密联系。正是这样一门科学，随着它研究发展的不断专业细化，在过去的几个世纪里彻底改变了人们的现实生活方式。

另一方面，人们从一开始就一直尝试寻找一个能把所有独立的科学统一起来的理论基础，这个统一的理论由最少的概念和基本关系组成，在此基础之上各个独立分支的所有概念和关系都可以通过逻辑推导产生。这就是我们探求整个物理学基础的用意所在。

显而易见这个基础并不完全类似于一座建筑的基础。当然，从逻辑上讲，各条物理定律确实都是建立在这一基础之上的。然而建筑物可能在风暴或洪水过后被严重毁坏，而其基础却完好无损；但在科学领域中，相比于与实验联系较为紧密的各个具体学科而言，这一逻辑基础总是由于新经验或新知识而处于危险的境地。

建立物理学统一理论基础的第一次尝试是牛顿的工作。在他的理论中，所有的

---

[*] 这是一篇经过删节的演讲，发表于 5 月 15 日在华盛顿举行的第八届美国科学大会。

Newton. In his system everything is reduced to the following concepts:

(1) Mass points with invariable mass;
(2) action at a distance between any pair of mass points;
(3) law of motion for the mass point.

There was not, strictly speaking, any all-embracing foundation, because an explicit law was formulated only for the actions-at-a-distance of gravitation; while for other actions-at-a-distance nothing was established *a priori* except the law of equality of *actio* and *reactio*. Moreover, Newton himself fully realized that time and space were essential elements as physically effective factors of his system, if only by implication.

This Newtonian basis proved eminently fruitful and was regarded as final up to the end of the nineteenth century. It not only gave results for the movements of the heavenly bodies down to the most minute details, but also furnished a theory of the mechanics of discrete and continuous masses, a simple explanation of the principle of the conservation of energy, and a complete and brilliant theory of heat. The explanation of the facts of electrodynamics within the Newtonian system was more forced; least convincing of all, from the very beginning, was the theory of light.

It is not surprising that Newton would not listen to a wave theory of light; for such a theory was most unsuited to his theoretical foundation. The assumption that space was filled with a medium consisting of material points that propagated light waves without exhibiting any other mechanical properties must have seemed to him quite artificial. The strongest empirical arguments for the wave nature of light, fixed speeds of propagation, interference, diffraction, polarization, were either unknown or else not known in any well-ordered synthesis. He was justified in sticking to his corpuscular theory of light. During the nineteenth century the dispute was settled in favour of the wave theory. Yet no serious doubt of the mechanical foundation of physics arose, in the first place because nobody knew where to find a foundation of another sort. Only slowly, under the irresistible pressure of facts, there developed a new foundation of field-physics.

From Newton's time on, the theory of action-at-a-distance was constantly found artificial. Efforts were not lacking to explain gravitation by a kinetic theory, that is, on the basis of collision forces of hypothetical mass particles. But the attempts were superficial and bore no fruit. The strange part played by space (or the inertial system) within the mechanical foundation was also clearly recognized, and criticized with especial clarity by Ernst Mach.

The great change was brought about by Faraday, Maxwell and Hertz—as a matter of fact half-unconsciously and against their will. All three of them, throughout their lives, considered themselves adherents of the mechanical theory. Hertz had found the simplest form for the equations of the electromagnetic field, and declared that any theory leading to these equations was Maxwellian theory. Yet towards the end of his short life he wrote a paper in which he presented as the foundation of physics a mechanical theory freed from

内容都可归结为如下的几个概念：

（1）具有恒定质量的质点；
（2）任何两个质点之间存在超距作用；
（3）质点的运动定律。

严格说来，这里并没有什么绝对的基础，因为这些明确的定律只有在引力的超距作用下才成立；而对于别的超距作用，除了**作用力**和**反作用力**相等这条定律以外，我们不能**先验**地得到其他任何定律。此外，牛顿自己也充分地意识到，空间和时间是他的理论体系中的根本有效因子，不过他并未明说。

牛顿的基本理论被证明是卓有成效的，并且直到 19 世纪末，它一直被视为是物理学的终极理论。它不但解释了天体运动以及其中最详细的细节，而且也建立了描述离散物质和连续物质的力学理论，对能量守恒原理给予了简单的解释且给出了一套完整而天才的热学理论。在牛顿的理论体系中，对电动力学的事实规律的解释是比较牵强的；而到目前为止，用牛顿的理论体系进行解释的所有理论中，最令人难以信服的是对光的理论的解释。

牛顿不相信光的波动论，这不足为奇；因为这个理论与他的理论基础最不相容。假定空间里充满着一种由质点组成的媒质，这些质点传递着光波但却不显示出任何力学性质，牛顿认为这个假定人为的痕迹很明显。光具有波动性的最有力的经验论据，如不变的传播速度、干涉、衍射、偏振等，这些在当时要么还不清楚，要么就是还没有被整理总结出来。牛顿坚持认为他的光的粒子论是有道理的。到了 19 世纪，这场争论才以波动论的胜利而告终。但是当时人们并没有严重质疑物理学建立的力学基础，这主要是因为没有找到另一种更好的基础。在不可抗拒的事实的压力之下，一种新的场物理学基础才慢慢发展起来。

从牛顿时代起，所谓的超距作用的理论就一直是难以令人信服的。试图根据假想质点发生碰撞的动力学理论来解释引力而做的努力并不少。但是所做的这些尝试都流于表面，没有得出满意的结果。另外，人们显然意识到了空间（或者惯性系）在以力学为基础的理论中有奇特的作用，而恩斯特·马赫也对此做了清楚详细的论述。

法拉第、麦克斯韦和赫兹带来了物理学的伟大变革，事实上这一变革是他们在半无意的情况下做出的，并且同他们最初的意愿相悖。自始至终，这三位物理学家都认为自己是力学理论的拥护者。赫兹发现了电磁场方程最简单的形式，并且宣称任何能够导出这些方程的理论都是麦克斯韦理论。可是就在他短暂的一生结束之前，他写了一篇论文，其中他提出了一种摆脱了力这个概念的力学理论并将其作为物理

the force-concept.

For us, who took in Faraday's ideas so to speak with our mother's milk, it is hard to appreciate their greatness and audacity. Faraday must have grasped with unerring instinct the artificial nature of all attempts to refer electromagnetic phenomena to actions-at-a-distance between electric particles reacting on each other. All these electric particles together seemed to create in the surrounding space spatial states, today called fields, which he conceived as states of mechanical stress in a space-filling medium, similar to the states of stress in an elastically distended body. For at that time this was the only way one could conceive of states that were apparently continuously distributed in space. The peculiar type of mechanical interpretation of these fields remained in the background—a sort of placation of the scientific conscience in view of the mechanical tradition of Faraday's time.

With the help of these new field concepts, Faraday succeeded in forming a qualitative concept of the whole complex of electromagnetic effects discovered by him and his predecessors. The precise formulation of the time-space laws of those fields was the work of Maxwell. Imagine his feelings when the differential equations he had formulated proved to him that electromagnetic fields spread in the form of polarized waves and with the speed of light! At that thrilling moment he surely never guessed that the nature of light, apparently so completely solved, would continue to baffle succeeding generations. Meantime, it took physicists some decades to grasp the full significance of Maxwell's discovery, so bold was the leap that his genius forced upon the conceptions of his fellow-workers. Only after Hertz had demonstrated experimentally the existence of Maxwell's electromagnetic waves did resistance to the new theory break down.

But if the electromagnetic field could exist as a wave independent of the material source, then the electrostatic interaction could no longer be explained as action-at-a-distance; and what was true for electrical action could not be denied for gravitation. Everywhere Newton's actions-at-a-distance gave way to fields spreading with finite velocity.

Of Newton's foundation there now remained only the material mass points subject to the law of motion. But J. J. Thomson pointed out that an electrically charged body in motion must, according to Maxwell's theory, possess a magnetic field the energy of which acted precisely as does an increase of kinetic energy to the body. If, then, a part of kinetic energy consists of field energy, might that not then be true of the whole of the kinetic energy? Perhaps the basic property of matter, its inertia, could be explained within the field theory? The question led to the problem of an interpretation of matter in terms of field theory, the solution of which would furnish an explanation of the atomic structure of matter. It was soon realized that Maxwell's theory could not accomplish such a programme. Since then many men of science have zealously sought to complete the field theory by some generalization that should comprise a theory of matter; but so far such efforts have not been crowned with success.

学的基础。

对于我们来说，接受法拉第的理论如同我们吸吮母亲的乳汁一样自然，我们很难体会到这些物理学家们的伟大和过人的胆识。对于一切试图把电磁现象归结为相互作用的带电粒子之间存在超距作用的做法，法拉第以准确无误的直觉看出了这些做法是人为不客观的。所有这些带电粒子似乎共同在其周围空间中产生了一些空间态，现在我们称之为场，法拉第设想这些空间态是当机械协强作用于充满空间的介质时出现的状态，类似于弹性膨胀体受到协强作用时的状态。因为在那个时候，为了想象这些在空间中明显是连续分布的状态，这是唯一可行的方法。这种对场的特殊的力学解释只属于那个特定的历史背景——从法拉第时代传统的力学理论的角度来看，这是对当时科学意识的一种妥协和退让。

借助这些新的场的概念，法拉第成功地为他和他的先辈们所发现的复杂的电磁效应提出了一整套定性的理论概念。麦克斯韦的工作则是为这些场的时空律推导出严密的公式。当麦克斯韦建立的微分方程证明了电磁场是以偏振波的形式，并且以光速在传播着的时候，想象当时的他该有怎样的感觉呀！在那激动人心的时刻，他肯定不会想到，光的本质这个表面看来已经被完美解决了的问题，仍会继续困惑以后的好几代人。同时，物理学家们也花了几十年的时间才完全领会了麦克斯韦伟大发现的全部意义，由此可见，他的同事们要在观念上作出多么勇敢的飞跃才能接受其天才般的智慧啊。直到赫兹在实验中证实了麦克斯韦电磁波的存在以后，对这个新理论的抵制才彻底消除。

如果电磁场可以独立于介质源而以波的形式存在，那么，静电相互作用就不能再解释成超距作用了；而在电的相互作用情况中是正确的东西，在引力中就也可能是正确的。渐渐地，在物理学的各个方面，牛顿的超距作用都被以有限速度传播的场所替代了。

牛顿的基础理论中，只有质点的运动定律这个概念直到现在仍然保留着。但是汤姆森指出：依照麦克斯韦的理论，运动着的带电体必定具有磁场，磁场的能量正好是带电体增加的那部分动能。那么如果动能的一部分是由场能组成的，那么全部动能不也可能是这样的吗？或许作为物质基本性质的惯性，是否也能在场论中得到解释？这个问题导致了利用场论对物质进行解释的困难，该困难的解决应该会给物质原子结构提供一种解释。人们很快意识到，麦克斯韦理论不能完成这个任务。从那时起，许多科学工作者就充满热情地试图完成将包含物质的理论推广到场论当中；但是到目前为止，这种努力并没有取得圆满成功。

For several decades most physicists clung to the conviction that a mechanical substructure would be found for Maxwell's theory. But the unsatisfactory results of their efforts led to gradual acceptance of the new field concepts as irreducible fundamentals—in other words, physicists resigned themselves to giving up the idea of a mechanical foundation.

Thus physicists held to a field-theory programme. But it could not be called a foundation, since nobody could tell whether a consistent field theory could ever explain on one hand gravitation, on the other hand the elementary components of matter. In this state of affairs it was necessary to think of material particles as mass points subject to Newton's laws of motion. This was the procedure of Lorentz in creating his electron theory and the theory of the electromagnetic phenomena of moving bodies.

Such was the point at which fundamental conceptions had arrived at the turn of the century. Immense progress was made in the theoretical penetration and understanding of whole groups of new phenomena; but the establishment of a unified foundation for physics seemed remote indeed; and this state of things has even been aggravated by subsequent developments.

The development during the present century is characterized by two theoretical systems essentially independent of each other: the theory of relativity and the quantum theory. The two systems do not directly contradict each other; but they seem little adapted to fusion into one unified theory.

The theory of relativity arose out of efforts to improve, with reference to logical economy, the foundation of physics as it existed at the turn of the century. The so-called special or restricted relativity theory is based on the fact that Maxwell's equations (and thus the law of propagation of light in empty space) are converted into equations of the same form, when they undergo Lorentz transformation. This formal property of the Maxwell equations is supplemented by our fairly secure empirical knowledge that the laws of physics are the same with respect to all inertial systems. This leads to the result that the Lorentz transformation—applied to space and time coordinates—must govern the transition from one inertial system to any other. The content of the restricted relativity theory can accordingly be summarized in one sentence: all natural laws must be so conditioned that they are co-variant with respect to Lorentz transformations. From this it follows that the simultaneity of two distant events is not an invariant concept and that the dimensions of rigid bodies and the speed of clocks depend upon their state of motion.

A further consequence was a modification of Newton's law of motion in cases where the speed of a given body was not small compared with the speed of light. There followed also the principle of the equivalence of mass and energy, with the laws of conservation of mass and energy becoming one and the same. Once it was shown that simultaneity was relative and depended on the frame of reference, every possibility of retaining actions-at-a-distance within the foundation of physics disappeared, since that concept presupposed the absolute character of simultaneity (it must be possible to state the location of the two

904

　　几十年以来，大多数物理学家都坚信能为麦克斯韦理论找到更基本的力学基础。但是由于他们的努力没有得到令人满意的结果，人们逐渐将场这个新的概念作为物理学不可约化的基础——换句话说，物理学家不得已放弃了力学是物理学基础的想法。

　　因此，后来物理学家都转而支持场论的研究体系。但是并不能把场论称为基础，因为尚不确定是否有一个统一的场论，既能解释引力，又能解释物质的基本组成成分。在这种情况下，就有必要把物质粒子看作是服从牛顿运动定律的质点。这是洛伦兹在创立其电子论的过程以及研究与运动物体电磁行为有关的理论中都采用了的假设。

　　以上这些就是我们在世纪之交物理学基本概念的由来。当时对所有新奇现象的理解和理论方面的突破都有了极大的进展；但是建立物理学统一的基础的希望似乎仍然很渺茫；而随后的进展更是加重了这一困难。

　　二十世纪科学发展的标志是本质上各自独立的两个理论体系：相对论和量子论。这两个体系彼此没有直接的矛盾；但是它们似乎很难融合成一个统一的理论。

　　考虑到逻辑上的便利，科学家们对物理学基础的探究导致了相对论在世纪之交的诞生。所谓狭义的或者有限制的相对论所根据的事实是：在洛伦兹变换下，麦克斯韦方程在形式上没有变化（因而光在真空中传播的定律也一样是保持不变的）。另外，这一麦克斯韦方程组的形式上的特征可以用我们已知的十分可靠的经验来进行补充，该经验就是：在所有惯性系中，物理定律都是相同的。这导致了一个惯性系到其他任何惯性系的变换必须满足应用于时空坐标的洛伦兹变换。因此，狭义相对论的内容可以总结成一句话：一切自然规律都是有条件限制的，即它们都得具有洛伦兹协变性。由此得知，两个异地事件发生的同时性并非是绝对的，刚体的尺寸和时钟的快慢都同它们的运动状态有关。

　　相对论的另一个结果是，在物体的速率并非远小于光速的情况下，牛顿运动定律必须做相应的修正。我们还得到了质能相当性原理，即质量守恒定律和能量守恒定律可以合并成同一个定律。注意，一旦指明了同时性是相对的，并且同参照系有关，在物理学的基础中保留超距作用的任何可能性都没有了，因为这一概念是以同时性的绝对性作为前提的（即必须能够指明"在同一时刻"两个相互作用的质点

interacting mass points "at the same time").

The general theory of relativity owes its origin to the attempt to explain a fact known since Galileo's and Newton's time but hitherto eluding all theoretical interpretation: the inertia and the weight of a body, in themselves two entirely distinct things, are measured by one and the same constant, the mass. From this correspondence follows that it is impossible to discover by experiment whether a given system of co-ordinates is accelerated, or whether its motion is straight and uniform, and the observed effects are due to a gravitational field (this is the equivalence principle of the general relativity theory). It shatters the concepts of the inertial system, as soon as gravitation enters in. It may be remarked here that the inertial system is a weak point of the Galilean-Newtonian mechanics. For there is presupposed a mysterious property of physical space, conditioning the kind of co-ordination systems for which the law of inertia and the Newtonian law of motion hold good.

These difficulties can be avoided by the following postulate: natural laws are to be formulated in such a way that their form is identical for co-ordinate systems of any kind of states of motion. To accomplish this is the task of the general theory of relativity. On the other hand, we deduce from the restricted theory the existence of a Riemannian metric within the time-space continuum, which, according to the equivalence principle, describes both the gravitational field and the metric properties of space. Assuming that the field equations of gravitation are of the second differential order, the field law is clearly determined.

Aside from this result, the theory frees field physics from the disability it suffered from, in common with the Newtonian mechanics, of ascribing to space those independent physical properties which heretofore had been concealed by the use of an inertial system. But it cannot be claimed that those parts of the general relativity theory which can today be regarded as final have furnished physics with a complete and satisfactory foundation. In the first place, the total field appears in it to be composed of two logically unconnected parts, the gravitational and the electromagnetic. In the second place, this theory, like the earlier field theories, has not yet supplied an explanation of the atomistic structure of matter. This failure has probably some connexion with the fact that so far it has contributed nothing to the understanding of quantum phenomena.

In 1900, in the course of a purely theoretical investigation, Max Planck made a remarkable discovery: the law of radiation of bodies as a function of temperature could not be derived solely from the laws of Maxwellian electrodynamics. To arrive at results consistent with the relevant experiments, radiation of a given frequency had to be treated as though it consisted of energy atoms of the individual energy $h\nu$, where h is Planck's universal constant. During the years following it was shown that light was everywhere produced and absorbed in such energy quanta. In particular, Niels Bohr was able largely to understand the structure of the atom, on the assumption that atoms can have only discrete energy values, and that the discontinuous transitions between them are connected

所处的位置）。

广义相对论源自于对一个从伽利略和牛顿时代起就已经出现的问题进行解释的尝试，迄今为止这个问题也无法用现有的任何理论进行解释：物体的惯性和重量本身是两种完全不同的概念，但却用同一个物理量（质量）进行量度。由此可以推论，我们不可能通过实验判断给定的坐标系是否在加速，或是否在做匀速直线运动，而观察到的结果最终是由引力场所决定的（这就是广义相对论的等效原理）。一旦引入了引力场，惯性系的概念就失效了。这里我们注意到，惯性系是伽利略–牛顿力学的弱点。因为引入惯性系即相当于我们预先假定物理空间具有一种神秘的性质，使得惯性定律和牛顿的运动定律在这种坐标系中仍然有效。

为了避免出现上面的困难，我们可以做以下假设：在处于任何一种运动状态的坐标系中，自然规律的表达形式都是完全一样的。完善这一假设正是广义相对论的任务。另一方面，我们从狭义相对论推出时空连续区中存在黎曼度规，依照等效原理，它既描述了引力场，也描述了空间的度规性质。假定引力的场方程是二阶的微分方程，则我们可以明确地得到与场有关的定律。

除了以上的结果，相对论还使场物理学摆脱了牛顿力学中把独立的物理性质归咎于空间而出现的问题，而这个问题在相对论出现之前一直是通过引入惯性系而被隐藏起来的。但是现在我们还不能断言，当今广义相对论中被视作终极理论的那些部分是否为物理学提供了完整且令人满意的物理学基础。因为首先，相对论中所有的场都由逻辑上毫无关系的两个部分，即引力部分和电磁部分所组成。其次，跟以前的场论一样，相对论直到现在还未能对物质的原子结构给予解释。相对论的这种局限性也许同它至今对理解量子现象尚无贡献这一事实有一定的关系。

1900 年，在纯理论研究的过程中，马克斯·普朗克得到了一个不同寻常的发现：仅从麦克斯韦电动力学定律出发，不能推导出作为温度的函数的物体辐射定律。为了得到同相关实验一致的结果，必须把那些具有一定频率的辐射看作是由一些单个能量为 hv 的能量子所组成，此处 h 是普朗克普适常数。随后几年，事实证明光始终都是以这样的能量子的形式产生或被吸收的。特别是尼尔斯·玻尔假定原子只能具有分立的能量值，而它们之间不连续的跃迁都同这种能量子的发射或者吸收有关，据此他能够基本上推测出原子的结构。这有助于人们理解气体状态下的元素及其化

with the emission or absorption of such an energy quantum. This threw some light on the fact that in their gaseous state elements and their compounds radiate and absorb only light of certain sharply defined frequencies. All this was quite inexplicable within the frame of the theories hitherto existing. It was clear that, at least in the field of atomistic phenomena, the character of everything that happens is determined by discrete states and by apparently discontinuous transitions between them, Planck's constant h having a decisive role.

The next step was taken by de Broglie. He asked himself how the discrete states could be understood by the aid of the current concepts, and hit on a parallel with stationary waves, as for example in the case of the fundamental frequencies of organ pipes and strings in acoustics. True, wave actions of the kind here required were unknown; but they could be constructed, and their mathematical laws formulated, employing Planck's constant h. De Broglie conceived an electron revolving about the atomic nucleus as being connected with such a hypothetical wave train, and made intelligible to some extent the discrete character of Bohr's "permitted" paths by the stationary character of the corresponding waves.

Now in mechanics the motion of material points is determined by the forces or fields of force acting upon them. Hence it was to be expected that those fields of force would also influence de Broglie's wave fields in an analogous way. Erwin Schrödinger showed how this influence was to be taken into account, re-interpreting by an ingenious method certain formulations of classical mechanics. He even succeeded in expanding the wave mechanical theory to a point where, without the introduction of any additional hypotheses, it became applicable to any mechanical system consisting of an arbitrary number of mass points, that is to say, possessing an arbitrary number of degrees of freedom. This was possible because a mechanical system consisting of n mass points is mathematically equivalent, to a considerable degree, to one single mass point moving in a space of $3n$ dimensions.

On the basis of this theory there was obtained a surprisingly good representation of an immense variety of facts which otherwise appeared entirely incomprehensible. But on one point, curiously enough, there was failure: it proved impossible to associate with these Schrödinger waves definite motions of the mass points—and that, after all, had been the original purpose of the whole construction.

The difficulty appeared insurmountable, until it was overcome by Born in a way as simple as it was unexpected. The de Broglie-Schrödinger wave fields were not to be interpreted as a mathematical description of how an event actually takes place in time and space, though, of course, they have reference to such an event. Rather they are a mathematical description of what we can actually know about the system. They serve only to make statistical statements and predictions of the results of all measurements which we can carry out upon the system.

Let me illustrate these general features of quantum mechanics by means of a simple example: we shall consider a mass point kept inside a restricted region G by forces of finite

合物只能辐射和吸收具有某些特定频率的光这一事实。然而所有这些在现存的理论框架内都还无法解释。显然，至少在原子现象的领域里，所发生的每件事情的特征均由分立的状态以及分立的状态之间的不连续的跃迁决定，普朗克常数 h 在这里起着决定性的作用。

进一步的工作是由德布罗意完成的。他向自己提出这样一个问题：如何借助现有的物理概念来理解这些分立的状态呢？他突然想到可以类比驻波，把分立的状态理解为如声学中管风琴和弦的基频一样的情况。虽然这里需要的这样一种波动行为还是未知的；但是用上述普朗克常数 h 应该可以构造出这种波动作用并且写出相应的数学表达式。德布罗意设想电子绕原子核的旋转是同某种有待证实的波列有关的，并且认为通过相应波的驻波特征能在一定程度上理解玻尔的"允许"轨道的分立特征。

既然力学中质点的运动是由作用在质点上的力或力场所决定的，那么我们可以预测，那些力场也以类似的方式影响着德布罗意所谓的波场。欧文·薛定谔向我们展示了如何考虑以上力场对波场的影响，并用巧妙的方法重新解释了经典力学中的某些公式。薛定谔甚至不需要引入任何额外的假设就成功地将波动力学理论拓展至含有任意个质点（换句话说就是具有任意个自由度）的任何力学体系。这是可能的，因为从数学的角度来看，由 n 个质点所组成的力学系统在一定程度上可以看作是在 $3n$ 维空间里运动着的单个质点。

根据以上由薛定谔建立的波动力学的理论，许多用别的理论好像完全无法理解的事实都意外地得到了完美的解释。但奇怪的是，以上理论有一个缺点：它无法将薛定谔波与质点确定的运动联系起来，而毕竟这是当初构造这整个理论的最初目的。

上面提到的困难似乎是不可克服的，直到玻恩用一个意想不到的简单的方法解决了该困难。德布罗意－薛定谔波场不能被理解为时空中确实发生的事件的数学描述形式，尽管该形式肯定是同这样的事件有关系的。说得恰当些，它们实际上是我们能够从体系中获知的事物的一种数学描述。它们只能用来对这个体系所进行的一切测量结果进行统计上的说明和预测。

让我举个简单的例子来说明量子力学这些普遍的特点：我们考查一个质点，它

strength. If the kinetic energy of the mass point is below a certain limit, then the mass point, according to classical mechanics, can never leave the region G. But according to quantum mechanics, the mass point, after a period not immediately predictable, is able to leave the region G, in an unpredictable direction, and escape into surrounding space. This case, according to Gamow, is a simplified model of radioactive disintegration.

The quantum theoretical treatment of this case is as follows: at the time t_0 we have a Schrödinger wave system entirely inside G. But from the time t_0 onwards, the waves leave the interior of G in all directions, in such a way that the amplitude of the outgoing wave is small compared to the initial amplitude of the wave system inside G. The farther these outside waves spread, the more the amplitude of the waves inside G diminishes, and correspondingly the intensity of the later waves issuing from G. Only after infinite time has passed is the wave supply inside G exhausted, while the outside wave has spread over an ever-increasing space.

But what has this wave process to do with the first object of our interest, the particle originally enclosed in G? To answer this question, we must imagine some arrangement which will permit us to carry out measurements on the particle. For example, let us imagine somewhere in the surrounding space a screen so made that the particle sticks to it on coming into contact with it. Then from the intensity of the waves hitting the screen at some point, we draw conclusions as to the probability of the particle hitting the screen there at that time. As soon as the particle has hit any particular point of the screen, the whole wave field loses all its physical meaning; its only purpose was to make probability predictions as to the place and time of the particle hitting the screen (or, for example, its momentum at the time when it hits the screen).

All other cases are analogous. The aim of the theory is to determine the probability of the results of measurement upon a system at a given time. On the other hand, it makes no attempt to give a mathematical representation of what is actually present or goes on in space and time. On this point the quantum theory of today differs fundamentally from all previous theories of physics, mechanistic as well as field theories. Instead of a model description of actual space-time events, it gives the probability distributions for possible measurements as functions of time.

The new theoretical conception owes its origin not to any flight of fancy but to the compelling force of the facts of experience. All attempts to represent the particle and wave features displayed in the phenomena of light and matter, by direct recourse to a space-time model, have so far ended in failure; and Heisenberg has convincingly shown, from an empirical point of view, that any decision as to a rigorously deterministic structure of Nature is definitely ruled out, because of the atomistic structure of our experimental apparatus. Thus it is probably out of the question that any future knowledge can compel physics again to relinquish our present statistical theoretical foundation in favour of a deterministic one which would deal directly with physical reality. Logically, the problem seems to offer two possibilities, between which we are in principle given a choice. In the

被有限大小的力束缚在一个有限的区域 G 内。如果质点的动能小于某一极限，那么根据经典力学，质点就永远不可能离开 G 这个区域。可是根据量子力学，经过一段无法直接预测的时间之后，质点却可能沿某个不确定的方向离开区域 G 而跑到周围的空间里去。按照伽莫夫的观点，这就是放射性蜕变的一个简化模型。

用量子理论处理以上情况如下所示：在 t_0 时刻，薛定谔波系统完全处于 G 的区域内。但是从时间 t_0 以后，这些波沿着所有可能的方向离开 G 的内部区域，在这个过程中，往外传播的波的振幅要小于 G 区域内波系统最初的振幅。往外传播的波扩散得越远，由 G 发出的处于 G 区域内的波的振幅就越小，相应地，其强度也越小。因而只有经过无限长的时间之后由 G 发出的波才会耗尽，与此同时传播到 G 区域外的波则已持续不断地扩散到了更大的空间。

但是这种波动过程同我们刚才提到的最初的对象，即原来被包围在 G 内的粒子有什么关系呢？要回答这个问题，我们必须设想能对粒子进行测量的某种装置。例如，想象周围空间的某个位置上有这样一个屏幕，粒子一旦与它接触就会被粘住。于是，根据波射到屏上某个点的强度，我们就可断定粒子在那时射到屏上这一点的概率。但是一旦粒子被射到屏上的点都是特定的点时，则整个波场立即失去了所有的物理意义；这种做法唯一的目的就是对粒子射到屏上的位置和时间（又或者如，粒子射到屏上时的动量）的概率做出相应的预测。

所有其他的例子也都是类似的。量子理论的目的就是要确定某一时刻体系测量结果的概率。但是另一方面，它并没有试图对时空中真实存在或正在进行的事物作出相应的数学描述。在这一点上，今天的量子理论同以前所有的物理学理论，不管是力学还是场论，都有本质的区别。量子理论不是就真实时空中的事件进行模型化的描述，而是对可能的测量结果给出概率分布随时间的变化。

必须承认，这个新理论的概念并不是来源于任何异想天开的想法，而是在经验事实的强制下产生的。光和物质在现象中都显示出了粒子性和波动性，所有试图借助时空模型来融合这两种性质的做法到目前为止都以失败告终。而且海森堡也给出了令人信服的观点：从经验的角度来看，由于我们的实验仪器的结构是由原子组成的，所以一定不可能出现任何与自然界严格的决定论理论结构有关的结果。因此，虽然决定论可以直接处理物理实在，但是即使是未来进一步发展的知识也不太可能使物理学放弃现在统计性的理论基础而以决定论取而代之。从逻辑上来看，这个问题似乎给出了两种可能性，原则上我们可以在这两种可能性中做出选择。最终，作

end, the choice will be made according to which kind of description yields the formulation of the simplest foundation, logically speaking. At the present, we are quite without any deterministic theory directly describing the events themselves and in consonance with the facts.

For the time being, we have to admit that we do not possess any general theoretical basis for physics which can be regarded as its logical foundation. The field theory, so far, has failed in the molecular sphere. It is agreed on all sides that the only principle which could serve as the basis of quantum theory would be one that constituted a translation of the field theory into the scheme of quantum statistics. Whether this will actually come about in a satisfactory manner, nobody can venture to say.

Some physicists, among them myself, cannot believe that we must abandon, actually and for ever, the idea of direct representation of physical reality in space and time; or that we must accept the view that events in Nature are analogous to a game of chance. It is open to every man to choose the direction of his striving; and also every man may draw comfort from Lessing's fine saying, that the search for truth is more precious than its possession.

(**145**, 920-924; 1940)

Albert Einstein: For. Mem. R. S., Institute of Advanced Study, Princeton University.

为选择依据的是，所选择的描述方式要尽可能得到逻辑上最简单的物理学基础所对应的公式。目前，还完全没有任何一种决定论性的理论既能直接描述事件本身又能同事实相符合。

目前我们还不得不承认，暂时还没有任何全面的物理学的基本理论可被作为物理学的逻辑基础。到现在为止，场论已经被证明不适用于分子领域。人们从各个方面进行考虑，都认为唯一可能作为量子力学根基的原理应是一种能够把场论和量子统计学体系对应统一起来的理论。至于实际上这个原理能否以一种令人满意的方式出现，现在谁也不敢断言。

有些物理学家，包括我自己在内，都不能相信：我们现在甚至将来都必须永远放弃在时空中直接表示物理实在的想法；或者我们必须接受这样的观点，即自然界中发生的事件就像碰运气的赌博一样。每个人都可以自由选择自己奋斗的方向；而每个人也都可以从莱辛的一句精辟的名言中得到安慰：追求真理比拥有真理更为可贵。

（沈乃澂 翻译；葛墨林 审稿）

Dextran as a Substitute for Plasma

A. Grönwall and B. Ingelman

Editor's Note

The First World War prompted searches for artificial blood substitutes, and various colloids (liquid suspensions) were tested. Here two chemists in Sweden revisit the question towards the end of the Second World War. The qualifications for blood substitutes are stringent, in particular the need to evade the body's immune response and tendency to break down foreign substances. The paper reports some promise in the use of solutions of dextran, a sugar made by bacterial fermentation, as blood plasma (a carrier fluid for blood cells). Today's candidates are more sophisticated, mimicking the oxygen-carrying action of real blood—but such blood substitutes are still highly imperfect, and still urgently needed.

AS is well known, we have in blood, plasma and serum adequate media for the treatment of shock, for example, in cases of serious loss of blood or contusions. During the present War, however, it has proved impossible completely to supply the large requirements of these materials. It is therefore natural that physiologists and chemists are seeking for substances the aqueous solutions of which can replace the expensive and delicate blood or plasma.

In the course of the War of 1914-18, Bayliss[1] attempted to employ solutions of gum arabic for purposes of infusion. Later, other substances such as gelatin, polyvinyl alcohol, pectin, polyvinylpyrrolidone and others were tested to this end. The infusion of these colloids has, however, been attended by certain difficulties. Some of the substances tested have antigenic properties, whereas others cannot be broken down by the organism, for which reason they are stored in the organs, especially in the liver.

The conditions to be fulfilled by a foreign colloid in order that it may exercise a therapeutic effect in cases of shock are, in brief, as follows:

In all cases of shock, both in bleeding and in contusions and burns, it is essential to increase the volume of the circulating blood by the infusion of a liquid. This cannot be done satisfactorily with solutions of crystalloids. The infused liquids must instead contain colloids that exert the same colloidal osmotic pressure as the plasma proteins, or 300-400 mm. water. A condition for the exertion of this pressure by the colloids is that they must be of such a molecular size that they cannot pass through the walls of the capillaries.

The colloid must be suited to repeated intravenous injection in large quantities. It must also be completely atoxic and devoid of antigenic properties.

914

作为血浆替代物的葡聚糖

格伦瓦尔，英厄尔曼

编者按

第一次世界大战促使人们展开了对人工血液替代物的探寻，并且检验了各种胶体悬浮液。这篇文章中两位瑞典的化学家在第二次世界大战接近尾声的时候重提了这一课题。血液替代物应满足严格的条件限制，特别是能够避免引发身体的免疫反应以及分解外源物质的倾向。这篇文章报道了使用细菌发酵制得的葡聚糖溶液作为血浆（血细胞的液体环境）的可能性。现如今的血浆替代物要复杂得多，能够模拟真实血液的携氧功能，但是这样的血液替代物仍然很不完善，需求依然迫切。

众所周知，构成血液的血浆和血清可以用来治疗由严重失血或挫伤等原因造成的休克。然而，事实证明在当前战争期间对这些原料的大量需求完全不可能得到满足。因此很自然地，生理学家和化学家开始寻找其水溶液可以替代价格高昂且难以保存的血液或血浆的物质。

1914~1918 年战争期间，贝利斯[1] 为达到输注的目的曾尝试使用阿拉伯树胶溶液。之后，为此目的还测试了其他物质，例如明胶、聚乙烯醇、果胶和聚乙烯吡咯烷酮等。不过，注射上述胶体总会伴随某些特定的困难。有些测试物质具有抗原性，而另一些则无法被机体降解，因而会在某些器官中累积，尤其是肝脏。

下面简要列出使异源性胶体发挥治疗休克的效果所应满足的条件：

在所有发生休克的情况下，包括失血、挫伤和烧伤，通过液体灌输的方式增加循环血量是必要的。用晶体溶液是不能令人满意地实现这一点的。输入的液体必须含有胶体，且能产生与血浆蛋白一样的、相当于 300~400 毫米水的胶体渗透压。使胶体产生渗透压的一个条件是它们必须具有不能透过毛细管壁的分子尺寸。

这种胶体必须适合进行重复的大剂量静脉注射。它还必须是完全无毒的，并且没有抗原性。

The solutions must not have a high viscosity. The viscosity should preferably be of the same order as that of the blood.

Finally, the substance should be of such a nature that the body can gradually rid itself thereof, so that it does not remain long in the blood and is not stored in the organs.

A substance not previously tested for this purpose and apparently fulfilling the requirements listed above is the neutral polysaccharide dextran. Dextran is a water-soluble high-molecular carbohydrate which is formed in solutions of sugar infected with the bacterium *Leuconostoc mesenteroides*. It has been possible to show that the dextran molecule is built up of glucose units, linked together in long, more or less branched chains[2]. The molecular weight of dextran may be very high, of the order of magnitude of many millions[3,4,5]. By partial hydrolysis dextran preparations of lower molecular weight, for example, of the order of 100,000-200,000, can be made[6]. The partially hydrolysed dextran, like the original substance, is inhomogeneous with respect to molecular weight.

By well-controlled partial hydrolysis it is possible to prepare dextran solutions for purposes of infusion in which the solute has a suitable molecular weight and which do not give rise to injuries or reactions even after repeated large infusions. The sedimentation reaction, however, is increased after infusion (which has also been observed after infusion of, for example, gum arabic). The viscosity and colloidal osmotic pressure of the 6 percent solutions employed (with 1-3 percent sodium chloride) are of the same order as those of blood[6,7].

The solutions can be autoclaved and the preparation distributed in concentrated solutions or in the form of dry powder.

If a normal infusion dose is injected intravenously into a dog, the dextran concentration in the blood falls to zero in the course of three to four days. During the whole of this period dextran can be detected in the urine. The dextran ejected with the urine has a lower molecular weight than that originally injected. Even after repeated large infusions, no storage in the organs can be demonstrated histologically[6,7].

As dextran is broken down by the organism, glucose and relatively low-molecular fragments of dextran are presumably formed, which can pass the kidney filter and be expelled with the urine.

The therapeutic effect was investigated experimentally in cases of shock from bleeding, histamine shock and contusion shock developed artificially in rabbits and cats. Rapid and lasting effects on the blood pressure, heart action and respiration were always registered[6].

The experiments on animals giving favourable results, a clinical investigation was therefore commenced, at first on a limited scale. As the first clinical tests also gave promising results, and as there is reason for supposing that dextran is better suited as a plasma substitute

这种胶体溶液的黏度绝对不能太高，最好与血液在同一水平。

最后，该物质还应该具有能被机体自身逐渐清除的特性，这样它才不会长期停留在血液中，也就不会在器官中累积。

有一种物质，之前并未出于这种目的进行检验，但是明显可以满足以上列出的条件，它就是中性的多糖，葡聚糖。葡聚糖是一种水溶性的高分子碳水化合物，可在肠系膜明串珠菌感染的蔗糖水溶液中形成。已经有可能表明葡聚糖分子是由葡萄糖单元构成的，它们彼此连接成长链，并具有或多或少的支链 [2]。葡聚糖的分子量可以非常高，达到百万以上的数量级 [3,4,5]。通过部分水解可以制备出较低分子量的葡聚糖 [6]，例如分子量数量级为 100,000~200,000 的葡聚糖。与初始的葡聚糖一样，部分水解的葡聚糖的分子量也是不均一的。

通过精确控制部分水解，有可能可以制备出满足注射要求的葡聚糖溶液，其溶质具有适当的分子量，并且即使在重复的大剂量注射之后也不会引起损伤或不良反应。不过，注射后沉降反应有所增加（在注射诸如阿拉伯树胶等物质后也观测到这种情况）。所使用的 6% 溶液（含有 1%~3% 的氯化钠）的黏度和胶体溶液渗透压 [6,7] 水平与血液一致。

这种葡聚糖溶液可以进行高压灭菌，产品以浓缩溶液或者干粉的形式进行保存分装。

如果给一只狗进行一次常规剂量的静脉注射，那么其血液中的葡聚糖浓度在三四天之内就会下降到零。整个周期中可以在尿液中检测到葡聚糖。通过尿液排出的葡聚糖比初始注入的葡聚糖的分子量低。组织学检验证实，即使经过重复的大剂量注射，葡聚糖在器官中也不发生累积 [6,7]。

随着葡聚糖被机体降解，估计会有葡萄糖和分子量相对较低的葡聚糖片段形成，它们可以通过肾过滤，并随着尿液排出。

通过人为引发兔子和猫的失血休克、组胺休克和挫伤休克，人们对葡聚糖的疗效进行了实验研究。已有报道表明葡聚糖对血压、心搏和呼吸都有快速且持续的影响 [6]。

动物实验给出了有利的结果，于是一项临床研究随之开始，一开始规模很小。由于最初的临床实验也给出了前景乐观的结果，并且有理由推测葡聚糖作为血浆替

than, for example, gum arabic, polyvinylpyrrolidone or pectin, it was considered justified to set in train a more thorough clinical investigation. An account of this will be submitted at a later stage.

We wish to thank Prof. Arne Tiselius for helpful advice and Profs. T. Svedberg and A. Westerlund for the provision of laboratory facilities. The research has been carried out with grants from A. B. Pharmacia, Stockholm, and Svenska Sockerfabriks A. B., Malmö.

(**155**, 45; 1945)

Anders Grönwall and Björn Ingelman: Institute of Physical Chemistry, University of Uppsala.

References:
1. Bayliss, W. M., *J. Pharm. Exp. Therap.*, 15, 29 (1920).
2. Levi, J., Hawkins, L., and Hibbert, H., *J. Amer, Chem. Soc.*, 64, 1959 (1942).
3. Grönwall, A., and Ingelman, B., *Acta Physiol. Scand.*, 7, 97 (1944).
4. Ingelman, B., and Siegbahn, K., *Ark. Kem. Min. Geol.*, 18B, No.1 (1944).
5. Ingelman, B., and Siegbahn, K., *Nature*, 154, 237 (1944).
6. Grönwall, A., and Ingelman, B., *Acta Physiol. Scand.*, in the press.
7. Grönwall, A., and Ingelman, B., *Nordisk Medicin*, 21, 247 (1944).

代物会比诸如阿拉伯树胶、聚乙烯吡咯烷酮或果胶更合适，因此着手实施一项更加彻底的临床研究是合理的。一份关于这方面的报告将于下一阶段提交。

我们要感谢阿尔内·蒂塞利乌斯教授提供了有益的建议，感谢斯韦德贝里和韦斯特隆德两位教授提供了实验设备。这项研究是在斯德哥尔摩法玛西亚公司和马尔摩斯文斯卡·索克法布里克斯公司的资助下进行的。

（王耀杨 翻译；莫韫 审稿）

A Labour-saving Method of Sampling

J. B. S. Haldane

Editor's Note

Some of the most important advances in statistical analysis during the early twentieth century came from geneticists and population biologists. Here J. B. S. Haldane describes a method for extracting statistical estimates from small samples. The problem he addresses is how to estimate what fraction of a population p have an attribute A—without knowing roughly how big p is, one can't be sure how big a representative sample must be. He shows that one can estimate p with a fixed standard error by counting up just the number of items in the sample that have the minority attribute A, which takes less time and labour.

IF a fraction p of a population have the attribute A, then it is well known that if m members out of a sample of N have this attribute, the best estimate of p is $\frac{m}{N}$, and its standard error is $\sqrt{\dfrac{m(N-m)}{N^3}}$ or $p\sqrt{\dfrac{1-p}{m}}$. Supposing, therefore, that we want our estimate of p to be correct within a standard error of 10 percent of its value, we must count a sample containing $100(1-p)$ members with the attribute A. If we do not know p roughly beforehand we do not know how large to take our sample. For example, if we wish to estimate the frequency of a type of blood corpuscle, and count 1,000 blood corpuscles in all, we should get such values as 20 ± 1.3 percent, or 1 ± 0.31 percent. The former value would be needlessly precise for many purposes. The latter would not differ significantly from an estimate of 2 percent.

The standard error is almost proportional to the estimated frequency if we continue sampling until a fixed number m of the minority with attribute A have been counted, and then stop. Supposing the total number in the sample is now N, we cannot use $\frac{m}{N}$ as an estimate of p. It can, however, be shown that $\frac{m-1}{N-1}$ is an unbiased estimate of p, with standard error very approximately $\frac{1}{N}\sqrt{\dfrac{m(N-m)}{N-1}}$, or $p\sqrt{\dfrac{1-p}{m-2}}$, which is nearly proportional to p when this is small. Thus to get a standard error of about 10 percent of the estimate we should have to count until we had observed a number m of the rarer type A, which only varies from 102 when p is very small, to 72 when it reaches 30 percent. If we were content with a standard error of $0.2p$ we could take a quarter of this value, and so on.

一种省力的抽样方法

霍尔丹

编者按

20 世纪初，统计分析方面的一些重要进展均来自于遗传学家和种群生物学家。这篇文章中霍尔丹描述了一种从少量样本中取样进行统计估算的方法。他将这个问题归结为如何估计一个种群 p 中有多少比例具有 A 特性——如果不知道 p 大概有多大，我们就不能预知需要多大的代表性样本。他指出，可以通过只对样本中少数具有 A 特性的样本的数目进行计数来得到具有固定标准误差的 p 的估计值，这么做既省时又省力。

如果种群中的一个部分 p 具有 A 特性，那么很明显在 N 个样本中有 m 个具有这种特性时，对 p 的最佳估计值为 $\frac{m}{N}$，且其标准误差是 $\sqrt{\frac{m(N-m)}{N^3}}$ 或 $p\sqrt{\frac{1-p}{m}}$。因此，假设我们希望对 p 的估计值的标准误差在 10% 的范围内，那么我们要计数的样本中就必须有 $100(1-p)$ 个具有 A 特性。如果预先不知道 p 的大概数值，我们就不知道该选取多大的样本。例如，如果我们在估计某种血细胞的出现频率时总共计数了 1,000 个血细胞，我们会得到像 20%±1.3% 或 1%±0.31% 这样的数值。多数情况下不必像前一个数那么精确，而后一个数值与 2% 的估计值相比并没有显著差别。

如果我们持续抽样，直到少数具有 A 特性的数量达到固定数字 m 后停止，那么标准误差几乎是与出现频率的估计值成比例。假如样本总量为 N，我们不能用 $\frac{m}{N}$ 作为对 p 的估计值。但是可以将 $\frac{m-1}{N-1}$ 作为对 p 的无偏估计，而且其标准误差非常近似于 $\frac{1}{N}\sqrt{\frac{m(N-m)}{N-1}}$ 或 $p\sqrt{\frac{1-p}{m-2}}$，在数值较小的情况下，这个标准误差值就几乎与 p 成比例。这样，为了使估计值的标准误差是 10% 左右，我们就应该连续计数样品直到具有 A 特性的数量达到 m，m 只在一定范围内变化，当 p 很小时 m 是 102，当 p 接近 30% 时 m 是 72。如果我们可以接受 $0.2p$ 的标准误差，那么 m 取这个值的 1/4 即可，以此类推。

My friend, Dr. R. A. M. Case, has for some time employed a method substantially equivalent to the above in his haematological work, and found it to result in a considerable saving of labour.

Full details will be published elsewhere.

(**155**, 49-50; 1945)

J. B. S. Haldane: Department of Biometry, University College, London, Dec. 7.

一段时间以来，我的好友凯斯博士在他的血液病学工作中使用了一种与此非常类似的方法，他发现这种方法确实省力。

全部细节将在别处发表。

（吴彦 翻译；赵见高 审稿）

A Quantum Theory of the Origin of the Solar System

J. B. S. Haldane

Editor's Note

The British biologist J. B. S. Haldane here proposes a provocative hypothesis for the origin of the Solar System. The belief that it formed out of a rotating nebular disk has, he suggests, fallen into difficulty. Perhaps instead the planets were ejected from the Sun sometime in the distant past by the impact of photons of extraordinarily high energy. The energy required would (via $E = mc^2$) be equivalent to a mass of roughly 10^{19} tons. Haldane argues that such energies could have arisen in the early universe. Nearby stars may also have been hit with photons, and may thus also have planets. Haldane's speculations were soon forgotten, but inspired others to ponder the nature of the very early universe.

THE hypothesis of Kant and Laplace that the solar system originated by a gradual process from the contraction of a rotating nebula has become more and more improbable as the theory of such a process was investigated (cf. Jeans[1]). As a consequence, catastrophic theories of its origin have been put forward. In these theories another star, or even two stars, passed close to the Sun, or collided with it. In this article, which lays no claim to do more than open the discussion of possibilities, I suggest a quite different catastrophic origin, namely, a quantum transaction or perhaps a series of such transactions. I shall try to show that on Milne's[2] cosmological theory, this is a plausible hypothesis, and further that certain other cosmological problems are made less difficult if it is accepted.

According to Milne's cosmology, the universe can be represented in two distinct ways. On the kinematical representation, time t has a finite past t_0 of about 2×10^9 years or 6.3×10^{16} sec. Space is Euclidean, but every observer on a "fundamental particle" has his own private space. The infinite assemblage of fundamental particles, identified with the nuclei of galaxies, is contained in a finite sphere of radius ct, expanding with the velocity of light. An observer on any particle judges himself to be at the centre of this sphere, with the others receding from him. The different private spaces are related by the Lorentz-Larmor transformation. On the dynamical representation the time $\tau = t_0(\log t - \log t_0 + 1)$ has an infinite past, and the fundamental particles are at rest in a public hyperbolic space. The radii of planetary and atomic orbits are constant, as are the periods of planets and electrons, whereas in kinematic time and space the orbital radii and angular momentum increase with t.

太阳系起源的量子理论

霍尔丹

编者按

本文中，英国生物学家霍尔丹就太阳系的起源提出了一个富有争议的假设。他认为，太阳系是由一个旋转的星云盘形成的理论已经陷入了困境。真实的情况可能是在很久以前的某个时期，极端高能光子的冲撞导致行星被太阳喷射出来，所需的能量（根据 $E=mc^2$）相当于约 10^{19} 吨的质量。霍尔丹证明这样高的能量在宇宙早期是有可能存在的。近邻的恒星也会被光子所碰撞过，因而也可能有行星。霍尔丹的猜想很快就被人们遗忘了，但却引起了其他研究者们更深入地思考早期宇宙的性质。

康德和拉普拉斯的假说认为太阳系起源于旋转星云收缩的渐变过程，人们在对这个过程的理论进行研究之后，发现其越来越不可能（参见金斯的书[1]）。结果有人提出了太阳系起源的灾变理论。这些理论认为，另外一颗恒星，甚至两颗恒星，近距离地经过太阳，或者与其相撞。在本文里，我将集中对各种可能性展开讨论，并提出一种完全不同的灾变起源，即量子转换或者一系列类似的转换。我将尝试根据米耳恩[2]的宇宙学理论对此进行证明，这是一个合理的假说，而且如果它被接受的话，某些宇宙学问题就会变得不那么难以理解。

根据米耳恩的宇宙论，宇宙可以以两种截然不同的方式来表示。从运动学角度来看，时间 t 存在有限的过去，大约为 2×10^9 年或者 6.3×10^{16} 秒，用 t_0 表示。空间是欧几里得空间，但是每个处在"基本粒子"上的观察者都有其自己的专有空间。无限个这种被认为是星系核的基本粒子的集合，被包容在一个半径为 ct、以光速膨胀的有限体积的球内。处在任何粒子上的观察者均认为自己就处于这个球的中心，其他粒子则在不断远离他退行。不同的专有空间可由洛伦兹－拉莫尔变换联系起来。而在动力学表象中，时间 $\tau=t_0(\log t-\log t_0+1)$ 有无限长的过去，基本粒子在一个公共的双曲空间中处于静止。行星和原子的轨道半径都是一定的，行星和电子的周期也是恒定的，然而在运动学表象的时间和空间中，行星和原子的轨道半径及角动量都随着时间 t 的增加而增加。

One difficulty of the collision or encounter theory is the extreme rarity of such events. On some versions of the expanding universe theory such encounters were more probable in the remote past, when the stars were densely packed. But in Milne's cosmology an encounter was never more probable in a given stretch of dynamical time than it is now. It could be argued that as the dynamical past is infinite, an encounter is certain. However, it is no part of Milne's hypothesis that the stars have always existed.

Milne has not yet succeeded in deducing quantum mechanics from his few and simple postulates. His mechanics are in fact mainly classical. However, he has considered the behaviour of photons. The quantum parameter h, defined as E/v, where E is the energy radiated in a transition, and v its frequency, is invariant on the kinematical time-scale, for the red-shift of the distant galaxies is explained by the Doppler effect due to their recession; and the energy radiated in an atomic transition is invariant on either scale.

The main difficulty to be overcome in any theory of the origin of the solar system is this. The total angular momentum of the system is about 3.3×10^{50} erg-seconds. This is conserved on the dynamical scale. Unless most of the mass of the Sun is concentrated in a very dense core, all this angular momentum could be present in the Sun, due to its rotation, without its showing any more tendency to burst than does Jupiter at the present time. Hence some external source of energy must be postulated before it could emit the matter which condensed into the planets. The source of this energy has usually been supposed to be a star. I suggest that it may have been a photon.

The mass of the Sun is about 2.0×10^{33} gm., that of the planets about 0.00134 of this value; the solar radius 7×10^{10} cm.; and the gravitational constant 6.66×10^{-8}. The mechanical energy of the solar system is almost wholly given by the work required to lift the planets to their present orbits against solar gravitation. This again is almost equal to the work required to lift them to infinity, namely, $\gamma mM/R$, where γ is the gravitational constant, m and M the masses of the planets and Sun, and R the solar radius. The kinetic energy and the energy of the fall from infinity to the present orbits involve corrections of the order of $\gamma mM/r$, where r is the radius of a planetary orbit. Since for Jupiter $r = 1,100R$, these can be neglected.

$$\frac{\gamma mM}{R} = 5 \times 10^{45} \text{ ergs.}$$

Now at first sight a photon of this energy (and therefore of mass 6×10^{19} tons) appears a ridiculous conception. It would have, on the kinematical scale, a frequency of 8×10^{71} sec.$^{-1}$, and a wave-length of 4×10^{-62} cm. But now consider the conditions at time t, when t was very small. The radius of the universe was ct. It could not accommodate radiation of a wave-length greater than ct, and the past would be too short for such radiation to have accomplished even a single oscillation. At any time t there is a minimal possible size of photon, the frequency of which is of the order of t^{-1}. Probably it is a good deal less. This is borne out by the following consideration.

926

碰撞理论遇到的一个困难是发生这样的事件的概率极端稀少。根据某些膨胀宇宙理论，这种碰撞更有可能发生在非常久远的过去，因为当时恒星非常密集。但是在米耳恩的宇宙论里，在给定的过去某段动力学时间里发生一次碰撞的概率绝不比现在同样的一段时间内发生的概率大。也许可以争辩说，由于动力学的过去是无限的，所以碰撞肯定会发生。但是，米耳恩的假说中并没有假设恒星总是存在的。

米耳恩还没有成功地从其少数而简单的假设中推导出量子力学。实际上他的力学理论主要还是经典力学。然而，他还是考虑到了光子的行为。量子参数 h 被定义为 E/v，其在运动学时标下是不变的，E 是一次跃迁过程中辐射出的光子能量，v 是光子的频率，这是因为遥远星系的红移现象被解释为星系退行产生的多普勒效应，而一次原子跃迁所辐射出的能量在任何一种尺度下都是不变的。

所有太阳系起源的理论中都要克服一个主要困难。太阳系的总角动量大约为 3.3×10^{50} 尔格·秒。这在动力学时标内是守恒的，由于太阳在转动而且并没有比今天的木星有更明显的爆发倾向，所以除非太阳的大部分质量集中在极其致密的核心上，否则太阳系总的角动量将主要是太阳的角动量。因此，必须假设存在某些外在的能量来源，由此太阳才能抛射出之后凝聚成行星的物质。这个外在能量的来源通常被假定为一个恒星。而我认为它可能是一个光子。

太阳质量大约是 2.0×10^{33} 克，而行星质量大约是它的 0.134%；太阳的半径是 7×10^{10} 厘米；引力常数是 6.66×10^{-8}。太阳系的机械能几乎完全等于克服太阳的引力从而将太阳系中的行星送到它们现有的轨道所需做的功。也几乎等于将太阳系中的这些行星送到无穷远所做的功，即 $\gamma mM/R$，其中 γ 是引力常数，m 和 M 分别是行星和太阳的质量，而 R 是太阳的半径。对于行星的动能以及行星从无限远运动到现在的轨道上的能量，我们需要量级为 $\gamma mM/r$ 的修正，其中 r 是行星轨道的半径。由于对木星来说，$r = 1,100R$，因此这个修正项可以忽略不计。

$$\frac{\gamma mM}{R} = 5 \times 10^{45} \text{ 尔格}$$

尽管乍看起来一个光子具有这个能量（质量为 6×10^{19} 吨）是非常荒唐的想法。从运动学的尺度来看，其频率将会是 8×10^{71} 次每秒，其波长仅有 4×10^{-62} 厘米。但是，如果我们考虑时间 t 很小的情况。当时宇宙的半径为 ct，因此它容不下一个波长比 ct 更长的辐射，而由于过去的时间过短以至于这种辐射无法完成哪怕一次振荡。在任何一个时间 t 都有一个最小的光子的可能尺度，其频率为 t^{-1} 的量级。或许还要小得多。这可由下述考虑来证明。

The mean lives of excited atoms liable to radiate light of visible frequency always appear to exceed 10^{-8} sec., though shorter lives are associated with higher frequencies. Thus out of a group of excited atoms existing from the beginning of kinematic time, only a minority would have radiated before $t = 10^{-8}$ sec., when the universe had a radius of 3 metres, or about 10^7 wave-lengths. At a time of the order of $t = 10^{-15}$ sec. there could, on any hypothesis, have been extremely little visible radiation, as it could not have been produced by the ordinary radiation processes. This argument suggests that radiation of frequency less than t^{-1} is impossible, while radiation with a frequency less than about $10^6 t^{-1}$ is produced, if at all, with some difficulty.

We can conclude, then, that at $t = 10^{-72}$ sec. the minimum photon corresponding to a completed oscillation would have had an energy of about 6.5×10^{45} ergs. So if there was any radiation at all at this time, it was sufficiently hard to lift the planets out of the Sun, if the Sun absorbed it. Its contribution of momentum would of course have been negligible. If some planetary matter was shot out of the solar system, and if some hydrogen was lost even from the major planets, the energy required must be multiplied by a small factor. If the radius of the Sun was larger it must be divided by a small factor. But we can conclude that the earliest date for the formation of the solar system is about $t = 10^{-72}$, or $\tau = -4.1 \times 10^{11}$ years, that is to say, the Earth cannot have revolved round the Sun much more than 4×10^{11} times. An error of 5 in the exponent of t would alter τ by about 5 percent.

At a time about $t = 10^{-75}$ sec. the minimal photon, which on the dynamical scale had a period of 2×10^9 years at any date, would have had an energy and frequency about 1,000 times greater than a planet-generating photon. If absorbed by a star of solar dimensions it would have been sufficient to split it into a pair the distance of which was large compared with their radii. In such a case the parent star could not have contained enough angular momentum to allow its progeny to move in circular orbits. Otherwise it would previously have broken up by centrifugal action. Hence the orbits of distant binaries would be expected to be very eccentric, as in fact they generally are. On this hypothesis the more widely separated binary stars were formed about $1\text{-}2 \times 10^{10}$ years earlier than the solar system, on the dynamical scale, in agreement with the arguments based on gravitation, which ascribe to them an age of the order of 10^{11} years.

To return to the solar system, it may be asked whether it was formed by the absorption of a single photon, or of several in succession. The analogy with an atom, now less striking than at the time of Bohr's original theory, suggests the former hypothesis, but the latter must also be considered. The formation of the solar system would appear to have been in principle unobservable, since any radiation with which it could have been observed would either have passed through it unaltered or destroyed it. However, the correspondence principle can be applied to events of this character. The primitive Sun, containing the angular momentum of the whole solar system, had a period of rotation of the order of a day on the dynamical scale, or somewhat more if it was larger than at present on this scale, while Jupiter has a period of revolution of about twelve years. When the correspondence principle is applied to an atom, we find that the frequency of the absorbed radiation lies

发射可见光的受激原子的平均寿命大致都超过 10^{-8} 秒，不过发射更高频率辐射的受激原子寿命则相对较短。因此，在运动学时间一开始就存在的一组受激发原子中，只有少数会在 $t = 10^{-8}$ 秒之前辐射，这时宇宙的半径是 3 米，即相当于原子波长的 10^7 倍。由于可见辐射不能由通常的辐射过程产生，所以在 $t = 10^{-15}$ 秒量级的时间内，无论如何都只可能有极少的可见辐射。这个论证说明频率小于 t^{-1} 的辐射是不可能产生的，而如果真的能发生频率小于 $10^6 t^{-1}$ 的辐射，那也是相当困难的。

由此我们可以得出结论，在 $t = 10^{-72}$ 秒时，一个完整振荡的最小光子能量大约为 6.5×10^{45} 尔格。因此，如果这个时间内真的存在任何辐射，且被太阳吸收那么这个能量就足以使行星从太阳中爆发出来。当然，其动量的贡献在此已被忽略。如果某些行星物质被抛射出太阳系，并且甚至连某些大行星也丢失掉一些氢时，所需能量就必须乘以一个小的因子了。如果太阳的半径再大些的话，那么它就必须再除以一个小的因子。但是我们可以得出结论，太阳系最初形成的时间大约是 $t = 10^{-72}$，或者 $\tau = -4.1 \times 10^{11}$ 年，这也就是说，地球围绕太阳旋转的圈数不可能超过 4×10^{11}。t 的指数上 5 的误差将会使 τ 变化约 5%。

时间约为 $t = 10^{-75}$ 秒时，在任何日期动力学标度上一个周期为 2×10^9 年的最小光子，其质量和频率都比可产生行星的光子高大约 1,000 倍。如果被一个太阳尺度的恒星吸收，它将足以将这颗恒星分裂成一对相距大于各自半径的星体。在这种情况下，母星将没有足够的角动量使其子量沿圆轨道运动。否则，它之前就会由于离心作用而分裂开来了。因此可预期，远距离的双星轨道将是有很大偏心率的，正如它们通常那样。由这个假说可得，距离较大的双星的形成比太阳系早了约 $1 \times 10^{10} \sim 2 \times 10^{10}$ 年，在动力学标度下，这与基于引力的考虑而得到的结果 10^{11} 年相符合。

再回到太阳系，人们或许会问，它是由于单个光子的吸收，还是由于几个连续光子的吸收而形成的。由于现在已经远没有在玻尔理论诞生之初时那么惊人了，所以与原子的相似显示了前一个可能是正确的，但是后一种可能性也必须予以考虑。太阳系的形成原则上似乎是不可观测的，因为任何能够对之进行观测的辐射要么是通过它后没有变化，要么就会毁坏它。然而，对应原理却能够被应用到具有这种特征的事件上。在动力学标度上，包含整个太阳系角动量的原初太阳，其自转周期是一天的量级，而如果它比现在大点的话，这个周期还会稍长点，相对应的木星公转的周期大概是 12 年。当对应原则被应用于一个原子时，我们发现被吸收辐射的频率处于该原子的初态和终态的频率之间。如果行星的形成也是如此的话，那么，在动力

between those of the atom in its initial and final states. If this was so for the formation of planets, the period of the photon required to produce the solar system (or Jupiter alone) is of the order of a year on the dynamical scale, so its frequency was about 2×10^9 times that of the minimum photon, and the epoch of origin was, on the t scale, about 2×10^9 times that calculated above as a minimum. Alternatively, we might argue as follows, The planet-making photon was a train of electro-magnetic waves. A train with a suitable period would set up electro-magnetic oscillations in the Sun, which might lead to the ejection of one or more planets. Given the size and physical state of the Sun, the period would be calculable. It would probably be rather shorter than that calculated above on the correspondence principle. In either case a photon would be most likely to be absorbed if it approached in the direction of the solar axis.

Since $v = 10^{72}$, and if T be the corresponding period on the dynamical scale, while t is the epoch of formation of the solar system, $v = t_0/tT$; hence if T is about a year, $t = 2\times10^{-63}$ sec. roughly, whence $\tau = -3.7\times10^{11}$ years. If, on the other hand, the Sun absorbed a number of photons (say 9 in all, in order to form the major planets with Pluto and the parent of the asteroids) the value of v for Jupiter would be only slightly less, but that for Mercury would be about 10^{66}, while the values of T would not differ among themselves so much. In this case the origins of the various planets were strung out over a period of about 4×10^{10} years of dynamical time, while the larger satellites of the outer planets (but probably not those of the Earth and Mars) could have been generated by photons absorbed by these planets at a still later date.

We must now consider the probable state of matter at this time. There could, of course, have been no radiation from atoms, nuclei, or electrons; and it is fairly clear that all matter was fully ionized, since any atomic systems would be ionized by thermal collisions, and free electrons would be unable to enter quantized orbits by emitting radiation. Thus stars formed by gravitational condensation could only lose the energy liberated in this process by emitting matter. Their radii would be those at which protons and electrons were just lost. Thus the solar radius on the dynamical scale might well have been ten times its present value. If so, the energy of the postulated photon must be diminished by a factor of 10, which would only decrease the dynamical date—τ by 4.6×10^9 years. The planets would, however, lose a good deal of matter immediately on formation, so that their original mass was greater than at present. This would give a correction in the opposite direction, while tidal friction would give a smaller correction.

The planets remained gaseous for a very long stretch of dynamical time. About $t = 10^{-10}$ sec., loss of energy by radiation became appreciable, and by $t = 10^{-4}$ sec., or $\tau = -10^{11}$ years it was in full swing. By about $t = 10^{10}$ sec. or earlier, the planets had liquefied, and by $t = 10^{13}$ sec. or $\tau = -1.5\times10^{10}$ years, the stars had contracted to normal stellar dimensions. These contractions were probably responsible for the origin of many close binary systems, of the Moon, and perhaps of the asteroids. During more than 3×10^{11} dynamical years the planets were gaseous. I suggest that during this period most of them acquired days equal to their years, while the Sun rotated in a period which was some sort of average

学尺度上，产生太阳系（或者仅仅是木星）所需的光子周期具有一年的量级，因此它的频率大概是最小光子的 2×10^9 倍，而在 t 尺度上，其起源的年代大约是上面计算所得到的最小值的 2×10^9 倍。或者也可以这么论证，产生行星的光子是一系列电磁波。具有合适周期的一系列电磁波会在太阳中产生电磁振荡，并由此导致一个或者多个行星的喷射。给定太阳的大小和物理状态，是可以计算出周期的。结果有可能比上面根据对应原则所计算出的结果略短。在任何一种情况下，如果光子沿太阳轴方向接近的话，它将很可能被吸收掉。

当频率 $v = 10^{72}$，如果 T 是动力学标度上相应的周期，而 t 是太阳系形成的时间，则 $v = t_0 / t\mathrm{T}$；因此，如果 T 大约是 1 年，大致取 $t = 2 \times 10^{-63}$ 秒，则 $\tau = -3.7 \times 10^{11}$ 年。另一方面，如果太阳吸收了一些光子（例如说，为了产生包括冥王星在内的大行星以及小行星的母星，总共吸收了 9 个光子），木星的 v 值将只会稍小一点，但水星的 v 值将是 10^{66}，虽然它们各自的 T 值将不会有很大的差别。在这个情况下，各个行星大约是在动力学时标的 4×10^{10} 年时间里接连产生的，而外行星的较大卫星（很可能不包含地球和火星的卫星）可能是在此后的时期内由这些行星吸收光子所产生的。

我们现在必须考虑此时物质的可能状态。当然，原子、原子核和电子已经不再发出辐射了；并且很显然，所有物质都被完全电离了，这是因为任何原子系统都会通过热碰撞而被电离，而自由电子又不能够通过发出辐射而进入量子轨道。因此引力坍缩形成的恒星在这一过程中产生的能量只能通过抛射物质来释放。它们的半径恰好就是质子和电子会被丢失的半径大小。因此，在动力学标度上，太阳系的半径将正好是现在半径的 10 倍。 如果是这样的话，假设的光子的能量必须除以一个因子 10，而这只会使动力学表象的时间 τ 减少 4.6×10^9 年。然而，这会使行星在形成时立即丢失大量物质，因此它们原初的质量比现在的更大。这将会导出与潮汐摩擦力修正相反作用的一个修正，而潮汐摩擦力给出的是一个更小的修正值。

行星在一段很长的动力学时间里都为气态，大约到 $t = 10^{-10}$ 秒时，其辐射所损失的能量开始变得可观，而到 $t = 10^{-4}$ 秒或者 $\tau = -10^{11}$ 年为止其达到最活跃的状态。大约到 $t = 10^{10}$ 秒或者更早，行星已经液化，到 $t = 10^{13}$ 秒或者 $\tau = -1.5 \times 10^{14}$ 年时，恒星就已收缩到通常的恒星尺度了。在这个收缩过程中很可能导致很多密近双星系统、月球、可能还包括小行星的形成。在多于 3×10^{11} 的动力学年里，行星是气态的。我认为，在这个时期中，其中大多数行星的自转周期等于公转周期，而太阳的自转周期则相当于行星公转周期的某种平均值。行星收缩时，动力学标度下的角动量是

of the planetary years. On contraction, angular momentum on the dynamical scale was conserved, and the days therefore shortened to their present lengths on the dynamical scale, except in so far as they were lengthened by the ejection of satellites and by later tidal friction. This would involve contractions of the radii by factors varying between about 20 and 100. The exceptions may be said to prove the rule. Uranus has a retrograde relation. Its satellites revolve at a high inclination to the ecliptic, and that of Neptune has a retrograde motion. It would seem that tidal friction did not complete its work on the outer planets. The other cases of retrograde satellites are probably better explained by capture.

Energy is generally thought to be liberated in stars by the breakdown of unstable nuclei generated by thermal nuclear collisions. At present the rate of liberation is limited by the number of effective collisions, and is thus roughly constant in dynamical time. In the remote past nuclear breakdown was the limiting factor; so the Sun's radiation per dynamical year gradually rose to its present level, and has been fairly steady through geological time. Since through most of the history of the stars and planets in dynamical time nuclei of all kinds were effectively stable, but thermal collisions occurred, and moreover through a long dynamical period the minimum photons were capable of providing the energy for nuclear synthesis, it is suggested that the heavy elements, including the radioactive ones, were built up from hydrogen between the formation of the stars and the effective beginning of their thermal radiation.

If the solar system was generated by nine or more photon absorptions, most of the stars in our neighbourhood must have absorbed several photons, and produced planets. If it only absorbed one, the frequency of long-period binaries suggests that events of this type were not rare, so that our galaxy may include some hundreds of millions of planetary systems. If so, the field of biology is probably wider than has been suggested.

The galaxies have masses of the order of 10^{45} gm. This is the mass of a photon of period 10^{-92} sec., that is, of the minimum photon at $t = 10^{-92}$ sec. Even if the galaxies were originally particles of matter as closely packed as atomic nuclei, and therefore of rather less than the size of the Sun, the energies needed to disrupt them into gas were considerably less than that of such a photon. Hence if the galaxies originated by the absorption of radiation, in which case some of Milne's "fundamental particles" may still exist in a compact form, or even if their whole mass arose from radiation, they cannot date from before $t = 10^{-92}$ sec., or $\tau = -5 \times 10^{11}$ years. Thus the long time-scale of about 10^{12} years deduced from a study of gravitational interactions of stars, which are naturally measured in dynamical time, appears as a consequence of Milne's theory.

The above arguments must be regarded as the attempt of a layman to deduce some of the consequences implicit in Milne's cosmology, consequences which he had partly envisaged when he wrote in 1936 that "all dynamical theories of the origin of the solar system may require drastic revision". I have doubtless missed other consequences as important as any which I may have elicited. Even if my hypothesis is found to be logically coherent, it may well prove, when fully developed, to be as untenable as Laplace's nebular theory. In

守恒的，因此它们的昼夜长度就这样缩短到动力学标度下现在的长度，只是在一定程度上受到抛射出卫星和后来的潮汐摩擦影响而使行星周期略微有所加长。这涉及到的半径收缩因子大约在 20~100 之间。例外的情况也可以证明这个规律。天王星存在一个逆行的关系，其卫星转动轨道与黄道平面存在很大的倾角，而海王星的卫星也有逆行。看来，潮汐摩擦在外行星上并没有完成其作用。而将其他逆行的卫星解释或是被俘获而来的似乎更好一些。

人们通常认为，恒星中释放的能量的来源是热核碰撞产生的不稳定核的分裂。现阶段的能量释放率受有效碰撞数所限制，因此在动力学时间上几乎是常量。在遥远的过去，核碎裂的确是限制因素；所以太阳辐射在一个个动力学年后逐渐上升直到现在的水平，并在整个地质时间上都保持相当稳定。因为从动力学时标上看，在大部分恒星和行星的演化历史中，各种核子实际上都是稳定的，但由于热碰撞的发生，加之经过动力学时标下很长的一段时间后最小光子已能够提供核合成的能量，因此可以认为，包括放射性元素在内的比较重的元素，是在恒星形成之后和它们热辐射真正开始之前的这段时间中由氢所形成的。

如果太阳系是通过吸收九个或者更多的光子而产生的，那么我们周围的大部分恒星也必定吸收了一些光子并由此产生了行星。如果恒星只吸收一个光子，长周期双星的发现频次表明这种情况并不罕见，因此，我们的星系可能包括上亿个行星系统。如果真是这样的话，生物学的领域很可能比一般认为的要更为广阔。

星系质量的数量级为 10^{45} 克，相当于一个周期为 10^{-92} 秒的光子的质量，这也就是在 $t = 10^{-92}$ 秒时极小光子的质量。即使星系最初是像原子核内粒子那样紧密地聚在一起的物质粒子，因此其大小远小于太阳，要使它们瓦解变成气体所需的能量要比这样一个光子的能量小很多。因此如果星系起源于吸收辐射，在这种情况下米耳恩的某些"基本粒子"仍然可能以致密的形式存在，或者即使它们所有的质量都是由辐射产生，它们也不可能起源于 $t = 10^{-92}$ 秒或者 $\tau = -5 \times 10^{11}$ 年以前。因此，从恒星之间的引力相互作用研究中可以导出星系起源这个漫长的时间尺度是 10^{12} 年，基于动力学时间可以很自然地得到这一测量结果，而且似乎也是米耳恩理论的一个结论。

上面的论证应该被看作是一个外行人为了导出暗含于米耳恩宇宙论中某些结果所做的尝试，米耳恩在 1936 年写道，"所有关于太阳系起源的动力学理论都将需要做彻底的修改"，由此可见当时他就已经在一定程度上预见到了这些结果。我一定还忽略了某些和我所提到的结论同样重要的结论。即便我的假设在逻辑上被证明是通顺的，但当相关的理论完全发展起来后，可能事实会证明我的理论就如拉普拉斯的

particular, the secular stability of non-radiating ionized gaseous spheres and the relation of the uncertainty principle to the scale of time will require investigation. Above all, the details of the postulated process were in principle unobservable, and it will therefore be hard to test the proposed theory as rigorously as others have been tested in the past. This is a serious defect, since the value of a scientific theory increases with the number of ways in which it can be tested. But much of current physical theory has the same defect.

I have not suggested an origin for the postulated photon or photons. To do so would involve either a further step in a possibly infinite regress or the assumption that they were primordial constituents of the universe. They might, for example, have been generated by the acceleration of large charges during the origin of the galaxies. It may be asked what is their present state, if any of them have not been wholly or mainly converted into kinetic energy. The energy of a photon is invariant on the kinematic scale appropriate to the particle emitting it; but since a particle absorbing it is moving away from its source, its frequency and energy are lowered by the Doppler effect, and on the kinematical scale appropriate to such a particle, both vary as t^{-1}, where t is the epoch of absorption. Thus the postulated planet-making photons are now trains of electromagnetic waves of a period of the order of a year, and much too small to be observable in practice. The mass of matter at any time is thus the fraction of the mass at an earlier time which has not been degraded by the Doppler effect, and at a sufficiently early date most of the mass of the universe, or all of it, may have been radiation rather than matter.

In conclusion, I wish to thank Prof. Milne for his encouragement, and for elucidating several details of his cosmology in letters; and to emphasize that if the theory here sketched has any value at all, it will only prove its value by serving as a basis for exact calculations by persons better versed than myself in physics and astronomy.

(**155**, 133-135; 1945)

J. B. S. Haldane: F.R.S., University College, London.

References:

1. "Problems of Cosmogony and Stellar Dynamics" (Cambridge, 1919). "Astronomy and Cosmogony" (Cambridge, 1928).

2. "Relativity, Gravitation, and World Structure" (Oxford, 1935). *Proc. Roy. Soc.*, A, 154, 22 (1936); 156, 62 (1936); 158, 324 (1937); 159, 171, 526 (1937); 160, 1, 24(1937); 165, 313, 333 (1937). *Phil. Mag.*, 34, 73 (1943).

星云理论那样站不住脚。特别是，对无辐射的电离气态球的长期稳定性以及不确定性原理与时间标度的关系还需进一步的研究。最重要的是，所假设过程中的细节在原则上是不可观测的，因此，对所提出的理论难以像过去的理论那样进行严格的检验。这是一个致命的缺陷，因为科学理论的价值随着可检验方式的数量的增加而增加。不过，当今很多物理理论都有同样的缺陷。

我并未给出所假设的一个或多个光子的起源。如果这样做的话势必要倒退到无限远的时间之初，或者是假定它们是宇宙的原初组成物。例如，它们可能产生自星系起源之初的大量电荷的加速运动。可能有人会问，如果它们中的任何一种还没有完全或者大部分转化成动能的话，它们现在是什么状态。在粒子发射出光子的情况下，光子的能量在运动学标度下是不变的；但是由于一个吸收光子的粒子远离发出光子的源，根据多普勒效应，其频率和能量都降低了，而在适合此粒子的运动学标度下，则都与 t^{-1} 成正比，其中 t 是吸收发生的时期。因此假设产生行星的光子这时就是一系列周期在年的数量级上的电磁波，这对实际观测来说太小了因而不能被观测。因此，任何时刻物质质量都是早先还没有因多普勒效应而减少时的物质质量的一部分，并且在足够早期时，宇宙的大部分质量，甚至全部质量都可能是辐射而非物质。

最后，我想对米耳恩教授的鼓励，以及他在来信中对他宇宙论的一些具体内容所做的解释表示感谢；我还想强调，如果本文所概述的理论有任何价值的话，它的价值仅限于作为比我更精通物理学和天文学的人进行严格计算时的一个基础。

（李忠伟 翻译；邓祖淦 审稿）

A Quantum Theory of the Origin of the Solar System

E. A. Milne

Editor's Note

Edward Arthur Milne here responds to a highly speculative idea by J. B. S. Haldane about the origin of the Solar System. Haldane noted that, owing to the expansion of the universe, photons in the remote past may have had extremely high energies. Some may have been so energetic that their absorption by matter of any sort may have been sufficient to create planets and perhaps even entire galaxies. Milne supports and adds to this notion. These speculations are in themselves of little interest today. But Milne does recognize that physical conditions in the early universe would be extreme, involving enormous energy densities utterly beyond those observable today—and that quantum theory might be needed to describe that situation.

PROF. Haldane's idea as developed in the foregoing article seems to me to be fundamentally important. As all may not be familiar with the details of kinematic cosmology, and as readers may have difficulty in keeping pace with the rapier-like speed of Prof. Haldane's mind, I beg to be allowed to traverse some of the same ground in more pedestrian fashion.

To begin with, a word of explanation: I first announced my ideas on the two time-scales at the Blackpool meeting of the British Association, in a discussion on the origin of the solar system; but the consequences of the ideas were so bizarre that I felt it to be absolutely necessary to develop the formal and philosophical aspects of the theory in full detail before proceeding to the more speculative consequences. This programme I carried out in a series of papers published by the Royal Society during 1936-38, and, though hindered by war-work, in *Philosophy* (1941), in addresses before the London Mathematical Society (1939), the Royal Society of Edinburgh (1943), the Royal Astronomical Society (1944) and in a series of papers in the *Phil. Mag.*(1943). I am at present wrestling with the difficult problem of the conservation of linear momentum for gravitating bodies in the expanding universe, and I do not wish to be hustled. However, in *Proc. Roy. Soc.*, A, **165**, 354(1938), discussing the role of the correspondence principle on the two time-scales, I wrote: "It is not a fanciful speculation to see in the interplay of radiation keeping t-time with matter obeying the classical laws of mechanics on the τ-scale a phenomenon giving rise to the possibility of change in the universe *in time*, and so an origin for the action of evolution in both the inorganic and organic universes". A possible mode of that interplay has now been pointed out by Haldane.

I have long been aware that all theories of the origin of the solar system require drastic

太阳系起源的量子理论

米耳恩

编者按

爱德华·阿瑟·米耳恩在这篇文章中回应了霍尔丹提出的关于太阳系起源的纯粹猜测性的想法。霍尔丹认为，由于宇宙的膨胀，光子在遥远的过去可能具有极高的能量。有的光子可能已经有非常高的能量，以至于无论何种物质对它们的吸收都足以创造出行星，甚至可能是整个星系。米耳恩支持这个想法，并丰富了该内容。在今天看来，这些推测本身几乎没有价值。但是米耳恩确实认识到宇宙早期的物理条件应该是极端的——包含着巨大的完全超出今天能观测到的能量密度，而要描述那种情况可能需要用到量子理论。

在我看来，霍尔丹教授在前面的文章中提出的观念非常重要。考虑到可能并不是所有人都熟悉运动宇宙学的细节，而且有些读者可能也很难跟上霍尔丹教授灵敏的思维，因此，请允许我在这里以更加通俗的方式对某些相同的话题加以讨论。

首先需要说明一点：事实上，在英国科学促进会的布莱克浦会议上，在讨论太阳系的起源时，我首次提出对于两种时间标度的观点；但是这一观点所导致的结论过于奇异，因而我觉得在进一步得出更加奇怪的结论之前，绝对有必要详细推导出这一理论的具体形式及其哲学内涵。在进行这项计划的过程中，我于1936~1938年间完成并由皇家学会发表了一系列文章，尽管由于战争工作受到阻碍，但我的文章仍然在《哲学》（1941年）上发表了，我在伦敦数学学会（1939年）、爱丁堡皇家学会（1943年）、皇家天文学会（1944年）都进行过这方面的讲演，此外我也在《哲学杂志》上发表过一系列文章（1943年）。目前，我正在努力解决膨胀宇宙中受引力作用天体线动量守恒的难题，但我不希望被人催促。然而，在1938年《皇家学会学报》（A辑，第165卷，第354页）的一篇文章中，当探讨相应原理对于两种时间标度所起的作用时，我写道："对于遵循经典力学定律下时间标度为 τ 的物质与持续时间 t 的辐射，它们之间的相互作用并不是异想天开的猜测；这种现象使得宇宙**及时**演化成为可能，也是无机与有机宇宙世界演化活动的根源。"现在霍尔丹指出了这种相互作用的一种可能的模式。

很久之前我就意识到，由于在时间接近 $t=0$，即太阳系刚刚诞生时，动力学和

re-consideration in the light of the fact that at times of the order of $t = 0$, when the solar system was born, dynamical and optical conditions were very different. Haldane works with equal facility in either time-scale; but it must be remembered that the τ-scale is a concession to our Newtonian predilections, that it has in its description a constant t_0 (the present age of the system on the t-scale) which has nothing to do with *phenomena*; it has to do only with the language by which we describe the phenomena. Phenomena themselves are best studied through the t-scale, and in this scale the precise value of t at the epoch studied is all-important.

In Haldane's calculation of the order of magnitude of the energy required to be communicated to the Sun to form the solar system of planets, he uses the formula $\gamma mM/R$, with the present values of γ and R. It might be objected that on my theory $\gamma \propto t$, and that therefore the required energy was then much smaller. The answer is that $R \propto t$ also, that energy is a "time-invariant", and that Haldane's calculation is accordingly correct. On his data, the value of $\gamma mM/R$ is 5×10^{45} ergs, as he says.

Previous speculators on the early history of the universe had always argued that since the universe is expanding, collisions must have been then more frequent, forgetting that lengths of material objects (that is, radii) would have then been much smaller. By translating to the τ-scale (stationary universe) we see that collisions would be just as frequent, or as infrequent, as now. The new contribution which Haldane makes is that the optical situation would be entirely different. At epoch t, when the radius of the expanding universe was ct, there cannot well have been photons of wave-length exceeding ct. The inequality $l < ct$ implies for the frequency n the relation $n = c/l > 1/t$. (Here l and n are measured on the t-scale.) Working again on the t-scale, the inequality $\Delta E = h_0 n > h_0/t$ gives the minimum permissible photon energy. Taking $h_0 = 6.55 \times 10^{-27}$, at epoch $t = 10^{-72}$ sec., we get $\Delta E > 6.5 \times 10^{45}$ ergs, so that such photons as were then possible would have sufficient energy to disrupt the Sun and form a solar system.

There is no difficulty as to where the photons could come from. For according to kinematic relativity the mass (actual) and energy of the universe are infinite; and light must be present. Hence it must be, at small t, of enormous frequency and energy. The state of material atoms would be one of complete ionization; and the history of any photon would be one of successive degradations of frequency by interaction with matter, until at the present epoch light is *mostly* as we know it. This degradation of the individual photons due to interacting with matter must be distinguished from their constancy of frequency in time (t-scale) as they are propagated through empty space.

The epoch at which a photon ΔE was not less than 6.5×10^{45} ergs was, on the t-scale, 10^{-72} sec. The τ-measure of this epoch was $\tau = t_0 \log(t/t_0) + t_0$. The "time ago" at which it occurred is $\tau_0 - t$, where τ_0, the present epoch on the τ-scale, is equal to t_0. This gives

光学条件与现在非常不同，所以关于太阳系起源的所有理论都需要进行全盘地重新考虑。霍尔丹对于这两种时间标度采用了相同的处理方法；但必须记住的是，这里的时间标度 τ 是对牛顿学说的偏好做出了一定的妥协，因为在它的描述中含有常数 t_0（时间标度 t 中系统的当前年龄），该常数与**现象**本身并无任何关联，只与我们用来描述现象的语言有关。现象本身最好是通过时间标度 t 来加以研究，因为在这样的时标下，研究时期内 t 的精确值是十分重要的。

霍尔丹在计算形成由行星组成的太阳系所需要传送给太阳的能量大小的量级时，采用了公式 $\gamma mM/R$，其中 γ 和 R 均采用了当前值。可能有人反对在我的理论中所采用的 $\gamma \propto t$，因为这样需要的能量就会小得多。对于这一疑问的解答是，也存在 $R \propto t$，这样能量就是一个"不随时间变化的量"，所以霍尔丹的计算是正确的。根据他的数据，如他所说 $\gamma mM/R$ 值为 5×10^{45} 尔格。

以前探讨宇宙早期历史的研究者们总是认为，既然宇宙在膨胀，碰撞在早期的宇宙中一定更加频繁，然而他们忘记了物质实体在那时的尺度（即半径）也比现在小很多。转换到 τ 时间标度中（定态宇宙），我们就会发现碰撞的频繁程度与现在大体相同。霍尔丹的新贡献在于，他认为宇宙早期与现在的光学环境应当完全不同。在时间 t，当膨胀的宇宙的半径为 ct 时，不可能存在波长超过 ct 的光子。根据不等式 $l < ct$ 可知，对于频率 n 而言，存在 $n = c/l > 1/t$。（这里的 l 和 n 均在时间标度 t 中测量。）仍然在时间标度 t 中，不等式 $\Delta E = h_0 n > h_0/t$ 给出了许可的最小光子能量。取 $h_0 = 6.55 \times 10^{-27}$，时间 $t = 10^{-72}$ 秒，我们可以得到 $\Delta E > 6.5 \times 10^{45}$ 尔格，因此这样的光子可以提供足够的能量使最初的太阳瓦解，从而形成太阳系。

解释这些光子的来源并不困难。根据相对论运动学，宇宙的（实际）质量和能量是无限的，而光是肯定存在的。因此在 t 很小时，光子必然具有极高的频率和能量。物质原子应处于一种完全电离状态，任何光子的演化史都将是通过与物质不断作用，频率持续降低的过程，直至现在，光就成为了我们**通常**所了解的样子。但我们必须区分出单个光子由于与物质作用而导致的能量衰减以及这些光子在真空中传播过程中它们的频率对于时间（时间标度 t）的恒定性。

当一个光子的能量 ΔE 不小于 6.5×10^{45} 尔格时，在时间标度 t 中是 10^{-72} 秒。这一时间在时间标度 τ 中的测量为 $\tau = t_0 \log(t/t_0) + t_0$。它在"时间以前"发生是用 $\tau_0 - t$ 表示，其中 τ_0 是现在的时间标度 τ，它就等于 t_0。由此，我们得到

$$\tau_0 - \tau = t_0 - \tau = t_0 \log_e(t_0/t)$$
$$= 6.3 \times 10^{16} \times 2.3 \times \log_{10}(6.3 \times 10^{16}/10^{-72}) \, \text{sec.}$$
$$= 6.3 \times 10^{16} \times 2.3 \times 88.8 \, \text{sec.} = 4.1 \times 10^{11} \, \text{yr.,}$$

in agreement with Haldane. This is of the order of the "long" time-scale estimated by gravitational methods, that is, on the τ-scale.

Haldane's fundamental idea (pressing it to its limit) may be stated in the form that, just as the epoch $t = 0$ is a singularity in the mechanical t-history of the universe—an epoch at which the density was infinite—so the epoch $t = 0$ is a singularity in the optical history of the universe, namely, an epoch at which the frequency of radiation was infinite, because the wave-length had to be zero. Actually we can only make significant statements about the radiation for *small* epochs t, when the frequency would on the whole be very large. A spectrum would soon come into existence, by the absorption and backward emission (or backward scattering) of radiation by the naturally receding particles, with resulting degradation of frequencies by the cumulative Doppler effects. But some of the original high-frequency radiation would traverse space unscathed, and, in spite of the inevitable Doppler effect at the terrestrial receiving end, a small fraction of this would retain a still very high frequency, and might be the origin of the undulatory component of the present cosmic rays.

I think it would be wise, in this preliminary discussion of Haldane's idea, not to go into details as to how a primordial photon of huge energy could disrupt a star. It is sufficient to dwell on the remarkable result that Haldane has deduced from kinematic relativity, namely, that at very early epochs in the history of the universe, such photons as there were must have possessed enormous energies.

(**155**, 135-136; 1945)

E. A. Milne: F.R.S., Wadham College, Oxford.

$$\tau_0 - \tau = t_0 - \tau = t_0 \log_e(t_0/t)$$
$$= 6.3 \times 10^{16} \times 2.3 \times \log_{10}(6.3 \times 10^{16}/10^{-72}) \text{ 秒}$$
$$= 6.3 \times 10^{16} \times 2.3 \times 88.8\text{秒} = 4.1 \times 10^{11} \text{ 年}$$

该值与霍尔丹的计算结果相一致。这正好是由引力方法估算出的"长"时标（即时间标度 τ）的量级。

霍尔丹的基本思想（推到其极致）可以通过以下形式说明：正如时刻 $t = 0$ 是宇宙力学 t 历史中的奇点（那时密度为无穷大）一样，时刻 $t = 0$ 也是宇宙光学史中的奇点，即在该时刻辐射频率无穷大，因为波长必须为 0。实际上，我们只能对那些小的时间 t 中的辐射进行有意义的阐述，此时频率总的说来会非常高。随后由于处于自然退行的粒子对辐射的吸收和逆向发射（或逆向散射），很快就会形成一个光谱，同时，逐渐积累的多普勒效应会导致频率的降低。然而，一些原始的高频辐射将不受干扰地在空间传播，尽管到达地球时不可避免的会存在多普勒效应，但是仍然会有一小部分辐射仍保留着很高的频率，这可能正是现在的宇宙线中波动组分的来源。

我认为在对霍尔丹想法进行的这一初步探讨中，未对有极高能量的原始光子是如何瓦解一颗恒星的问题进行细节的讨论是非常明智的。详细地论述霍尔丹通过运动相对论推导出的非凡的结果，即在宇宙演化早期存在的光子一定具有极高的能量就已经足够了。

（金世超 翻译；邓祖淦 审稿）

Plant Viruses and Virus Diseases*

F. C. Bawden

Editor's Note

Towards the end of the Second World War, the scientific community's knowledge of the nature and mechanism of viruses was only rudimentary. This article by the director of the Rothamsted Experimental Station, Frederick C. Bawden, is a succinct summary of the state of knowledge at the time. The reality of viral infections was adequately supported by experimental work with plant viruses. Little was known of animal viruses such as those responsible for infectious diseases of humans. This naivety was removed by two imminent steps—the development of electron microscopes that made viruses visible for the first time and the discovery of the role of nucleic acids in biology by Watson and Crick in 1953.

THE existence of viruses was first deduced from work done in 1892 on tobacco plants suffering from mosaic, and much of what we now know of these elusive entities has come from further work on this and a few other plant diseases. It is far from certain that this knowledge can safely be applied to the causes of the many diseases, affecting all kinds of animals, higher plants and bacteria, that are now attributed to viruses. These cover a wide range of clinical conditions, and we know for certain of only two features that they have in common; their causes have neither been seen nor cultivated *in vitro*. If we wish, we can turn these negative features into what looks like a positive statement, by defining viruses as obligately parasitic pathogens too small to be resolved by microscopes using visible light. Indefinite as this is, it may still prove to be more precise than the facts warrant, for obligate parasitism is always postulated rather than proved, and serious attempts at cultivation have actually been made with very few viruses. Thus, when we speak of a virus disease, we usually mean merely an infectious disease with an invisible cause. Unless the resolving power of the microscope has some unsuspected significance in defining biological types, this obviously tells us nothing specific about the nature of viruses and might well cover a range of different entities.

This possibility seems increasingly likely when we try to generalize about plant virus diseases, for we find that no statements can be made about such features as symptoms, methods of infection, or distribution of virus in the host, to which there are no exception. This is far from conclusive, however, for what a virus does to a plant is as much a property of the plant as of the virus, and the same virus may produce very different effects in different plants. Also, although complete generalizations are impossible, there are some features shared by a number of different virus diseases, especially those met commonly in Nature.

---

* Substance of two lectures at the Royal Institution delivered on November 21 and 28.

植物病毒和病毒性疾病[*]

鲍登

编者按

第二次世界大战快结束的时候，科学界对病毒本质和机理的认识还非常初步。罗森斯得实验站的主任弗雷德里克·鲍登先生撰写的这篇文章对当时的认识状况进行了精炼的概括。病毒感染的事实得到了利用植物病毒所做的实验工作的充分支持，但是对于诸如引发人类感染性疾病的动物病毒，当时人们仍是知之甚少。这种无知被两种即将获得的重要进展——使得病毒首次能被直接观察到的电子显微镜技术的发展以及 1953 年沃森和克里克对核酸生物学功能的发现——所消除。

早在 1892 年，人们便通过对患有花叶病的烟草的研究而推断出了病毒的存在，我们今天对这些难以捉摸的实体的认识大多是通过对这种病毒以及其它几种植物病毒的进一步研究而获得的。这些知识能否被可靠地用于理解许多疾病的起因还不能确定，这些疾病影响着各类动物、高等植物以及细菌，现在我们把它们都归因于病毒的侵染。这些疾病涵盖了广泛的临床症状。我们只确切地知道它们具有两个相同的特点：这些致病因子既没有被观察到，也没有在体外条件下被成功培养过。如果愿意的话，我们可以将这些否定的特征转换成一种看上去像是肯定性的陈述：病毒可以被定义为一种小到利用光学显微镜无法分辨的专性寄生的病原体。尽管这样的定义很模糊，但它可能仍然比事实所表现出来的更加精确，因为专性寄生状态一直都只是被假设而从未得到证实，而且实际上只对少数几种病毒进行过体外培养的真正尝试。所以，当我们提到一种病毒性疾病的时候，我们通常仅仅指由一种不明病因导致的感染性疾病。除非显微镜的分辨率在定义生物类型方面的某种重要性不容置疑，否则这样的定义显然并没有告诉我们任何关于病毒本质的内容，这样的不明病因可能涵盖的是一个相当范围的不同实体。

当我们试图概括植物病毒性疾病的时候，这种可能性似乎更为明显，因为我们发现无法针对症状、感染方式或者病毒在寄主中的分布等特征作出任何不存在例外情形的论断。但这样的说法也远非结论性的，因为一种病毒对一种植株所作的，与病毒的特性和植株的特性都同样地相关，同一种病毒对不同的植株会产生完全不同的效应。另外，尽管目前还不可能提出一种全面的概括，但很多不同的病毒性疾病也存在一些共同的特征，特别是对那些自然界中常见的病毒性疾病而言。

---

[*] 11 月 21 日和 28 日在皇家研究院所作的两场报告的内容。

The effects most frequently caused by viruses are a dwarfing of the host plants and an alteration of the colour and shape of the leaves. Instead of being uniformly dark green, the leaves may bear spots, rings or patches of light green, yellow or white, or they may be generally chlorotic without definite mottling. Deformation may show only as an alteration in the leaf outline, or the laminae may be so reduced that the leaves consist of little but the main veins; it may take the form of local hyperplasia, to give unusual outgrowths from the leaves or gall-like proliferations in stems. Symptoms tend to occur more generally over a whole plant than with most fungal or bacterial diseases, for in natural infections it is usual for viruses to spread through the vegetative parts of affected plants. In plants infected experimentally, however, symptoms are often restricted to local lesions, produced by the death of tissues around the entry point. Diagnosis from symptoms is by no means easy, for different viruses may cause almost identical symptoms in the same host, whereas the same virus may produce totally different clinical conditions in different hosts. A further complication is that many viruses are unstable and frequently change to give forms that produce different symptoms from those produced by the parent virus. To be recognized, a virus must cause changes in the appearance of some plants; but it need not necessarily cause changes in all susceptible hosts. Indeed, the phenomenon of the carrier—an infected individual showing no symptoms—is common in plants, and such carriers can be of considerable importance as unsuspected sources of infection for intolerant species.

In many virus diseases, three distinct phases can be identified. As a result of virus multiplication at sites of infection, lesions first appear on inoculated leaves. After a few days, the virus passes to the phloem, through which it travels rapidly to distant parts of the plant. It seems to have no autonomous movement, but to travel along with the translocation stream of elaborated food materials, away from tissues actively engaged in photosynthesis and towards regions of active growth. It is because of this, and not because they resist infection, that leaves already fully developed at the time the plant becomes infected rarely show symptoms. Thus results of systemic infection appear on the young, actively growing leaves; the later symptoms of this systemic phase often differ from those first produced, as the disease passes from an acute to a chronic stage. Often both stages are serious diseases; in many potato varieties, for example, leaf-drop-streak is succeeded by severe mosaic. Occasionally, however, the chronic stage is extremely mild, such as in tobacco plants with ring-spot, which recover from an acute necrotic disease and afterwards show few or no symptoms. The virus is present in such plants, but in smaller quantities than during the acute stage. The sequence of three phases is common, but by no means general, and the same virus may give different sequences in different hosts. Potato virus Y, for example, gives local lesions only in one host, local lesions followed by systemic symptoms of two kinds in a second host, whereas in a third it gives no local lesions and systemic symptoms of only one kind.

In addition to altering the external appearance of plants, viruses also produce internal changes. Some of these are simply modifications of normal structures or tissues, such as reduction of the chloroplasts or necrosis of the phloem; but the most characteristic involve the production of new kinds of intracellular inclusion bodies. These are not found in all

　　由病毒引起的最常见的影响包括：宿主植株的矮化、叶子颜色和形状的改变等。原本呈均匀暗绿色的叶片可能出现浅绿色、黄色或白色的斑点、斑环或斑块，或者叶片上虽没有明显的花斑但却普遍萎黄。变形可能只表示叶片外形的一种变化，或者叶片纹层减少只剩下少量的主要叶脉；变形可能以局部增生的形式展现，导致叶片异常地往外生长或者树干上产生类似瘿瘤那样的肿起。与大多数真菌性或细菌性疾病相比，这些症状往往更多发生于整棵植株，因为在自然的感染过程中，病毒通常扩散于植株正在生长的部分。然而，在用实验方法感染的植株中，由于进入点附近组织的死亡，损伤症状通常被限定在局部位置。通过症状来做出诊断并不容易，因为不同的病毒在同一种宿主中可能产生几乎相同的症状，而同一种病毒在不同的宿主中可能产生完全不同的症状。另一个使事情复杂化的因素是，许多病毒不稳定，频繁地变化成能引发与亲代病毒不同的病症的形式。如果要被识别的话，一种病毒必须要引起某些植株的外形上的改变，但问题是，病毒并不一定在所有易感宿主中都会引起这种改变。的确，携带现象——被感染的个体不表现出任何症状的情形——在植物中很常见。这种携带者作为敏感型植物的不被觉察的感染源具有相当重要的意义。

　　许多病毒性疾病的发病过程都可以分成三个明显不同的阶段。由于病毒在侵染部位的增殖，被接种的叶片上首先出现损伤。几天后，病毒会传递到韧皮部，通过韧皮部它就会迅速移动到植株的远端。病毒似乎并不存在自主运动，而只是随着精细营养物质的运输流而移动，避开光合作用活跃的组织，移向活跃生长的区域。那些在植株被病毒感染时已经完全发育的叶片很少表现出症状，正是因为这个原因，而不是因为它们可以抵御病毒感染。因此，全身性感染的结果大多出现在早期还处于活跃生长的叶片中；这种全身性感染的晚期症状经常与最初产生的症状不同，因为此时疾病从急性阶段进入到慢性阶段。这两个阶段经常都会产生严重的病症，例如，在多个马铃薯品种中，条纹落叶病后紧接着会出现严重的花叶病。然而，慢性阶段的症状偶尔也会非常轻微，例如患环斑病的烟草植株，开始表现为急性坏死病，然后就很少或者不表现出症状。病毒存在于这样的植株中，但数量比急性阶段少。这三个阶段的顺序通常就是这样的，但绝非全都如此，同一种病毒在不同的宿主中可能表现为不同的顺序。例如，马铃薯病毒Y，在一种宿主中只表现为局部病变，在第二种宿主中是局部病变后表现出两种全身性症状，在第三种宿主中不表现出局部病变而仅仅出现一种全身性症状。

　　除了改变植株的外部特征，病毒也能使植株内部产生变化。这些内部变化中，有的只是对正常结构或组织的修饰，例如叶绿体的减少或者韧皮部的坏死，但最典型的是涉及新的类型的细胞内包涵体的产生。包涵体并非发现于所有病毒性疾病中，

virus diseases, but their formation appears to be specific to viruses, for similar bodies have not been found either in healthy plants or in those suffering from other kinds of disease. Different viruses give rise to different kinds of inclusion body, and produce them in varying numbers and in different tissues. The most general type is a vacuolar, amoeboid-like body found in the cytoplasm, but crystalline and fibrous inclusions also occur in infections with a number of different viruses. At least two viruses give rise to crystalline inclusions in the nuclei. The precise nature of these bodies is still uncertain; but we know that they contain virus, and their production can in part be simulated *in vitro*. It seems most likely that they are insoluble complexes produced by the viruses combining with some metabolic product of the diseased plants.

Symptomatology without proof of transmissibility is insufficient to assign a particular disease to the virus group, for similar kinds of symptoms can be caused by toxins, deficiencies of mineral nutrients and aberrant genes. With hosts that are easily grafted, transmission by grafting is usually the first method tried; for once organic union is established, all viruses that cause systemic symptoms readily pass from infected scions into healthy stocks. Indeed, grafting is the only method of transmission known for many virus diseases, and it has almost become the critical test of a plant virus disease.

Infection occurs only through wounds, but wounds that permit one virus to enter may not permit another. Many viruses are readily transmitted by rubbing healthy leaves with sap from diseased plants, but others are not; some of both these types are transmitted by insects. Several different explanations can be offered for the failure of inoculation to transmit viruses that are readily transmitted by insects. First, some viruses may be able to establish themselves only in deep-seated tissues, such as the phloem, which are not penetrated by ordinary inoculation methods. Secondly, conditions in the expressed sap of some hosts may be such that the viruses are rapidly destroyed or rendered non-infective. Thirdly, the virus content of sap from some diseased plants may be below that required for infection. Thus, although failure to transmit by inoculation is often used as a specific character of a virus, clearly it may equally well be a reflexion of some property of the host.

Insects do not seem to act simply as mechanical carriers of viruses, for no insect vectors are known for the two viruses most easily transmitted by inoculation; and there appear to be specific relationships between insects and the viruses they transmit. Individual viruses are usually transmitted by only a few related species of insect and not by others, though these may have similar feeding habits and be vectors of other viruses. Vectors are usually insects with sucking mouth-parts; the most important are aphides, leaf-hoppers, white-fly and thrips. Two main types of behaviour in the insect have been distinguished. Vectors of one type of virus can infect healthy plants immediately after feeding for a short time on a diseased plant, and these usually cease to be infective within a few hour. After feeding on diseased plants, vectors of the other type cannot infect healthy plants for some time, which varies from minutes to days with different viruses, and such vectors remain infective for long periods, often for their whole lives. Some workers believe that viruses of the

但是它们的形成似乎是病毒特有的，因为在健康植株或者那些患其他疾病的植株中还从来没有发现过类似的小体。不同的病毒产生不同类型的包涵体，以不同的数目产生于不同的组织中。最常见的包涵体类型是一种发现于细胞质内的与变形虫类似的空泡，但多种不同的病毒感染后也会产生晶体状和纤维状的包涵体。至少有两种已知的病毒可以导致细胞核中产生晶体状包涵体。这些小体的确切本质仍然不确定，但我们知道它们包含有病毒，在体外条件下可以部分模拟这些小体的产生过程。看上去最有可能的是，包涵体是由病毒与受感染植株的一些代谢产物形成的不溶性复合物。

那些没有证据可以确认其可遗传性的症状还不足以将一种特定的疾病归入病毒类中，因为相似的症状也可能由毒素、矿质营养素的缺乏或基因缺陷引起。对于容易嫁接的宿主植株，人们通常首先会尝试用嫁接传染的方法。一旦宿主与接穗之间建立了有机联系，引起全身性症状的所有病毒就很容易从受感染的接穗转移到健康的宿主植物中。实际上，嫁接是许多病毒性疾病已知的唯一传播方式，它几乎已经成为植物病毒性疾病的决定性检测手段。

病毒只能通过伤口造成感染，但允许一种病毒侵入的伤口不一定会允许另一种病毒侵入。通过取自受感染植株的汁液来涂抹健康叶片这种方式就可以使许多病毒得以传播，但另外一些病毒却不行。这两种类型的病毒中都有一些可以通过昆虫传播。对于通过昆虫很容易传播却不能通过接种传播的现象，我们可以提供几种不同的解释。第一，有些病毒只能在像韧皮部这样的深层组织中存活，而普通的接种方法并不能渗透到这么深的部位。第二，一些宿主挤压汁的条件可能使病毒在其中很快被破坏或丧失感染性。第三，来自受感染植株的树汁中的病毒含量可能低于成功感染所需的量。因此，虽然接种传播的失败经常被视为病毒特异性的表征，但很明显的是，它也完全可能只是宿主植株的某些特性的反映。

昆虫似乎并不仅仅是病毒的被动型携带者，因为对于两种很容易通过接种方式传播的病毒，我们到目前还未发现任何昆虫媒介，因此在昆虫和它们所传播的病毒之间似乎存在专一性关联。特定的病毒通常只能通过几种亲缘关系接近的昆虫来传播，而不能通过其他可能有着相似取食习性并且也可以作为其他病毒媒介的昆虫来传播。病毒传播者通常都是那些具有刺吸式口器的昆虫，最重要的代表包括蚜虫、叶蝉、飞虱和牧草虫等。在昆虫中已经发现了两种主要的行为方式。一类病毒的传播昆虫在摄食受感染植株后的很短一段时间内就能够马上侵染健康植株，并且它们的感染性通常在几小时后就会消失。另一类病毒的传播昆虫在摄食受感染植株后有一段时间是不能感染健康植株的，针对不同的病毒而言，这段时间可以从几分钟到几天不等，但这种携带者能在较长时期间内保持感染性，经常可以保持一生。一些

second type multiply in the insects. There is no obvious reason why they should not, and the theory would explain some of the now puzzling features of the behaviour of these viruses; but there is no conclusive evidence that insects ever contain more virus than they acquire while feeding on infected plants. Studies on the virus causing dwarf disease of rice supplies the best circumstantial evidence for multiplication. This virus is unique in being the only one known to pass from infective adults through eggs to their progeny. Progeny up to the seventh generation have once been found to be infective and from on infected egg the progeny have infected more than 1,000 plants. This is regarded by some workers as "overwhelming" evidence for multiplication, as they consider that the quantity of virus in the original eggs could not have been enough to give all the infections. But is this so? If the virus multiplied in the insects to anything like the extent it does in plants, then there would be no reason why the progeny should not continue to be infective indefinitely, and infect as many plants as they feed on. We know nothing of the size of this virus, but if it is of the same order as other plant viruses the sizes of which are approximately known, then 1,000 particles would weigh less than 10^{-14} gm., and many times this quantity could surely be contained in a leaf-hopper's egg without difficulty.

Transmission of some viruses has been achieved by linking diseased and healthy plants with the parasite dodder (*Cuscuta* sp.). This novel method of transmission promises to be valuable in extending the host ranges of some viruses to plants more favourable for study than those in which the viruses occur naturally. One of the greatest differences between individual viruses lies in the numbers of different plants they can attack. Some are known to infect hundreds of plant species, belonging to many different families and orders; others have been transmitted to only a few closely related species. This difference may be apparent rather than real, for viruses transmissible only by grafting or by insects will normally have host ranges restricted to plants which can be intergrafted or which can act as food plants for the insect vector.

For more than forty years, work on plant viruses was largely concerned with symptoms, transmission and host ranges. It showed that viruses could multiply and alter, and produced few results conflicting with the generally accepted conclusion that they were small organisms, essentially similar to bacteria. There were opposers of this, usually from among those studying tobacco mosaic virus, but they could offer nothing definite to support their alternative views. The intensive study during the last ten years of the viruses *in vitro* has led to results that necessitate considerable modification of the earlier views. They do not, however, justify the sweeping conclusions implied by such facile phrases as "lifeless molecules", which are increasingly applied to viruses.

What has been achieved is the successful application of the techniques of protein chemistry to the purification of a dozen or so viruses. This has shown us that the particles of these viruses are not organized cellularly like organisms, and that in many ways they resemble constituent parts of organisms rather than whole organisms. They can be obtained in forms chemically much simpler than bacteria, free from diffusible components, and with a much greater regularity of internal structure than is usual with

研究人员认为第二类病毒会在昆虫体内增殖。没有明显的证据表明为什么病毒不能在昆虫体内增殖。此外，这个理论也可以用来解释目前这些病毒行为的很令人费解的一些特征；但并没有确切的证据表明昆虫体内的病毒含量比它摄食受感染植株时所获得的更多。针对引起稻谷矮化病的病毒开展的实验研究为这样的增殖理论提供了最好的旁证。这种病毒很独特，它是人们知道的唯一一种能从具有感染性的成虫通过其卵细胞而传递给后代的病毒，甚至到第七代的昆虫都仍有传染性。在一次实验中，一个被感染的卵最后竟然感染了 1,000 多株植物！这被一些研究人员看作是增殖理论"无可辩驳"的证据，因为他们认为最初的卵里病毒的数量是不足以感染这么多植株的。确实如此吗？如果病毒在昆虫里增殖的程度与病毒在植株中增殖的程度是一样的话，那便无法解释为什么昆虫后代不继续具有无穷的感染性进而感染它们摄食的所有植株。我们目前对这种病毒的大小还一无所知，但是如果它的大小与我们大约知道大小的其他植物病毒处于同一数量级，那么 1,000 个病毒颗粒的重量应该低于 10^{-14} 克，一个叶蝉的卵可以轻易装下比这一数量多许多倍的病毒。

一些病毒的传播是通过寄生植物菟丝子（菟丝子属）将受感染植株与健康植株连接在一起而实现的。这种全新的传播方式在将一些病毒的宿主范围扩展到比自然发生的病毒感染的植株更适于开展研究的植株方面很有价值。不同病毒之间最大的差异之一在于侵染的植株种类范围不同。我们知道，有一些病毒可以感染上百种属于不同科和不同目的植物，而另外一些只能感染少数几种紧密相关的物种。这种差异可能仅仅是表面的，而非真实存在的，因为对于只依靠嫁接或者昆虫传播的病毒，它们正常的宿主范围仅局限于能进行相互嫁接的植株或能被昆虫携带者当作食物的植株。

四十多年来，对植物病毒的研究大多关注的是症状、传播和宿主范围。这些研究的结果表明，病毒能够增殖和变异，几乎没有结果与病毒是小的有机体且与细菌基本类似这一被人们普遍接受的结论相冲突。也有人反对这一观点，他们通常都是那些烟草花叶病毒的研究者，但他们不能提供明确的证据来支持他们的不同看法。近十年来对病毒进行的比较集中的体外研究结果表明需要对早期的观点做相当的修正。然而，这样的观察结果也并没有对"无生命的分子"这类草率术语所隐含的全新结论提供支持，尽管这种术语越来越多地被应用到病毒上。

人们已经成功地将蛋白质化学技术应用于对大约十几种病毒的纯化工作。这提示我们，这些病毒颗粒并非像生物有机体那样是由细胞组织构成的，并且它们在许多方面类似于有机体的组成部分而非整个有机体。研究人员得到的病毒的化学形式比细菌简单得多，不包含可扩散的成分，与生物有机体通常的情形相比其内部结构更加规则。目前纯化得到的病毒都与核蛋白具有相同的化学形式。它们都含有核

organisms. The viruses so far purified have all been obtained in the same chemical form, as nucleoproteins. They all contain nucleic acid of the ribose type, but the proportion of nucleic acid to protein varies with the individual viruses. It is far too early to conclude that all plant viruses are essentially nucleoproteins; but we can say that it will be a major discovery if one is found to be anything else, for those already purified cover a diversity of types, some known to be insect-transmitted and others not. They range from potato virus Y, which denatures and loses infectivity within a few days, to tobacco mosaic virus, which remains stable for years. Stability as a native protein, however, is not always the same thing as stability as a virus; the infectivity of preparations of any of these viruses can be destroyed by some treatments that have no appreciable effects on the physical, chemical and serological properties.

The shape of the particle is responsible for some of the most striking differences between the properties of preparations of different viruses. Solutions of purified tobacco mosaic virus, and of potato viruses X and Y, show phenomena characteristic of greatly elongated particles; they are anomalous in all their physical properties and are polydisperse. No true crystals have been prepared from these, but dilute solutions show anisotropy of flow strongly, and concentrated solutions are liquid crystalline. X-ray studies of solutions of tobacco mosaic virus have demonstrated a regularity of structure previously unsuspected in fluids, for the particles are arranged equidistant from one another so that the available space is filled uniformly. When mixed with their antisera, these rod-shaped virus particles precipitate almost immediately, giving bulky, fluffy precipitates resembling those produced by bacterial flagellar antigens.

Solutions of bushy stunt and tobacco necrosis viruses behave very differently and show none of the anomalous properties characteristic of elongated particles. By suitable treatments they can be induced to crystallize in forms characteristic of the individual virus. When mixed with their antisera, they precipitate more slowly than the rod-shaped viruses and, as might be expected with spherical particles, pack more closely to give dense, granular precipitates resembling those produced by somatic antigens.

What is the relationship between these isolated nucleoproteins, which in laboratory work behave much like preparations of other proteins, and the viruses as they occur in the plant? There is enough evidence now to show that these proteins are the viruses in the sense that they can initiate infection. Nevertheless, it would be premature to assume that, while active in the host plant, the viruses are chemically so simple as analysis of the purified preparations suggests. During the course of isolation, many materials are discarded as impurities; most of these are certainly constituents of the normal host, but some may well be specific products of virus activity. Any such are clearly not essential for infectivity; but if the virus were organized cellularly, they would be retained within a cell wall and would be accepted as integral parts of the virus, which would immediately look a much more complex body than does our naked protein particle.

糖型的核酸，只是核酸与蛋白质的比例随病毒种类的不同而不同。所有的植物病毒基本上都是核蛋白这样的说法还言之过早。但是，如果发现由其他物质组成的病毒的话，那肯定将是一个重大发现，因为已经被纯化的那些病毒涵盖了多种类型，已知其中一部分是靠昆虫传播的，另外一些却并非如此。它们涵盖了从马铃薯病毒 Y——在几天之内就会变性并失去感染性的一种病毒，到烟草花叶病毒——多年之后仍旧可以保持其感染性稳定不变的一种病毒。然而，天然蛋白质的稳定性和病毒的稳定性并不完全相同。这些病毒制备物的感染性可能会被某些对其物理、化学、血清学特性没有明显影响的处理过程破坏。

病毒颗粒的形态不同是造成不同病毒制备物特性之间具有惊人差异的原因。纯化出的烟草花叶病毒、马铃薯病毒 X 和 Y 的溶液都表现出了高度伸长颗粒的特征，它们的所有物理特性都反常，并处于多分散性的不均一状态。从这些溶液中人们没有得到过真正的晶体，但是它们的稀释溶液表现出很强的流动各向异性，而浓缩溶液是液晶态的。对烟草花叶病毒溶液的 X 射线研究揭示了一种先前未知的在液体中的规则结构，因为颗粒之间的排列是等距离的以至于那些可被利用的空间都被均一地填充了。当与它们的抗血清混合后，这些棒状病毒颗粒几乎立刻就会形成大块的蓬松沉淀，这类似于由细菌鞭毛抗原产生的沉淀。

浓密矮化病毒和烟草坏死病毒溶液的表现与上述情况极其不同，并不显示出任何伸长颗粒那样的特征性异常行为。经过适当的处理，它们能被诱导形成晶体，形态因病毒而异。当与它们的抗血清混合后，这些病毒沉淀的速度比那些棒状病毒慢。正如人们对球状颗粒所期望的那样，它们排列得更加密集，产生出粒状沉淀物，类似于菌体抗原产生的沉淀。

这些分离到的在实验室研究中行为非常类似于其他蛋白质制备物的核蛋白与植物中出现的病毒之间具有什么关系呢？就它们能够引发感染来说，现在已经有足够的证据表明，这些蛋白质就是病毒。然而，虽然对宿主植物有感染活性，但是现在就假定病毒在化学组成上就如我们对纯化的制备样品进行分析得到的结果所暗示的那么简单的话肯定还为时尚早。在分离过程中，许多物质都被当作杂质而除掉了，毫无疑问，这其中的大部分都是正常宿主的组成成分，但有一部分很可能就是植物中因为病毒的感染而产生的特异产物。无疑，这些杂质中的任何组分都不是病毒感染特性所必需的；但如果病毒是在细胞内组装而成的话，这些特异性杂质就会被保留在细胞壁以内，并成为病毒整体的一部分，这样一来，病毒颗粒立刻就变得比我们得到的裸露的蛋白质颗粒更加复杂了。

In the absence of specific tests for any product of virus activity, we have no positive evidence for their occurrence in plants, but evidence from various sources suggests that purification may be altering the viruses. Purified preparations of tobacco mosaic virus, for example, contain particles about 15 mμ wide but varying in length from less than 100 mμ to more than 1,000 mμ. There is nothing to show that the greatly elongated particles occur in the plant, and much to suggest that they are produced by the linear aggregation of small particles during the course of preparation. By taking suitable precautions, solutions of tobacco mosaic virus can be made that show little or no anisotropy of flow and behave serologically more like somatic antigens; but these are unstable and readily change into anisotropic solutions with serological behaviour characteristic of flagellar antigens. This change seems to be connected with the removal of other material from the small nucleoprotein particles, which then join together end-to-end. The change in size and shape may explain the failure to produce true crystals of this virus *in vitro*, though they occur abundantly in infected plants.

We know also that the purified virus readily combines with other proteins such as trypsin and ribonuclease, and that these can be removed again without affecting infectivity. May not similar combinations occur within the host, and be responsible for converting this nucleoprotein into a functioning system capable of multiplication and of the activities of which the results are so obvious?

In addition to the changes produced by purification, there is other evidence that virus does occur in the plant in forms with different properties from those of the purified nucleoproteins. Until recently, all laboratory work on plant viruses was done with the sap that is expressed from macerated infected leaves. This was thought to contain all the virus in the plant, for washing the fibrous residues gives little extra virus. However, these residues actually contain as much virus as does the sap; but normally this is insoluble, probably because it is combined with other substances, and special treatments are needed to get it into solution. It is possible that this insoluble virus is the biologically active system, whereas that free in the sap may be merely excess virus functioning as a mobile source of infection for other cells. We know so little about the multiplication of viruses, and of their activities within the host, that at present we must suspend judgment. But it is probably safest to regard the nucleoproteins as the chemical minima—equivalent to reproductive organs or embryonic viruses—which develop into working entities only when placed in an environment containing the materials or enzyme systems they lack in their purified state.

(**155**, 156-158; 1945)

F. C. Bawden: Rothamsted Experimental Station.

在对病毒感染导致的产物缺乏特异检测方法的情况下，它们在植物中是否的确存在，我们对此还缺乏肯定性的证据。但是源自各方面的证据都表明，纯化过程可能会改变病毒结构。例如，烟草花叶病毒的纯化制备物中就含有宽度在 15 纳米，长度从小于 100 纳米到大于 1,000 纳米不等的颗粒。没有证据表明这些极其伸长的颗粒是在植物中产生的，多方面证据暗示它们是在样品制备过程中由小颗粒通过线性聚集而成。通过采取适当的预防措施，我们能制备出很少出现甚至不出现流动各向异性的烟草花叶病毒溶液，其血清学行为更加类似于菌体抗原，但这样的溶液并不稳定，很容易转变成血清学行为具有鞭毛抗原特征的各向异性溶液。这种变化似乎与从小的核蛋白质颗粒中清除其他物质的过程有关，小的核蛋白质颗粒就是在这一过程中首尾相连的。这种大小和形态的变化也许可以解释为什么这种病毒在体外未能形成真正的晶体，尽管这样的晶体在受感染的植株中大量出现。

我们也知道纯化出的病毒很容易与胰岛素、核糖核酸酶这样的其他蛋白质结合，并且这些蛋白质也可以再次被去除而不影响病毒的感染性。在宿主植物中难道不会发生类似的结合现象而使得这种病毒核蛋白转化为研究结果明显表明的那样能够增殖并进行感染的功能系统吗？

除了纯化过程带来的改变之外，还有其他证据表明病毒的确能以某些特性有异于纯化核蛋白那样的形式存在于宿主植株中。直到最近，与植物病毒有关的所有实验室研究都是利用从被浸泡的受感染植株的叶子中得到的榨汁而开展的。人们认为这样的汁液中包含了植株中的所有病毒，因为洗涤剩下的纤维性残渣很少能得到更多的病毒。然而，这些残渣中实际上包含着和汁液中一样多的病毒，但通常这些病毒处于不溶状态，可能是因为这些病毒结合了其他物质，所以需要经过特殊的处理才能使它们进入溶液中。很可能这种不溶性病毒才是具有生物学活性的系统，而那些存在于汁液中的自由病毒可能仅仅是作为其他细胞的一种移动性感染源而发挥作用的额外病毒。我们对病毒在宿主内的增殖和感染机制知道得如此之少，以至于目前我们只能暂时不予评判。但是，将核蛋白看作是病毒的最基本化学结构——相当于生殖器官或胚胎病毒——也许是最稳妥的，只有把这些基本的化学结构放到它们处于纯化状态时所缺乏的某些物质或酶系统的环境中后，它们才能成为一个能够发挥其功能的完整实体。

（韩玲俐 翻译；昌增益 审稿）

Action of Penicillin on the Rate of Fall in Numbers of Bacteria *in vivo*

A. B. MacGregor and D. A. Long

Editor's Note

By 1945, penicillin's antibacterial activity was well known, but the drug was thought to have its effects by stopping growing cells from dividing. Alexander B. MacGregor and David A. Long show in this paper that the biggest drop in bacterial number happens within 15 minutes of penicillin being given, too quickly for the "bacteriostatic" theory to hold. They suggest that penicillin may sometimes kill bacteria.

DURING work on the use of penicillin pastilles in oral infections, of which a preliminary report has been published[1], numerous experiments have been undertaken in order to determine the total and differential fall in numbers of different species of bacteria in the mouth and the rate of this fall, under the influence of penicillin. This rate of fall is of particular interest, and as it appears that certain deductions on the mode of action of penicillin can be drawn from the experiments, it is considered that it is worth directing attention to them in a separate publication. The technique of determining the rate of fall was as follows:

0.1 c.c. of saliva was added to a measured quantity of normal saline. 1/50 c.c. of this mixture was then inoculated on to a blood agar plate. This was incubated at 37°C. for twenty-four hours, when the number of colonies was counted. From this figure the approximate number of bacteria per c.c. of saliva was calculated.

Immediately the first specimen of saliva had been obtained, a 500-unit penicillin pastille was placed in the buccal sulcus between the cheek and the teeth, and allowed to dissolve without sucking. A fresh pastille was inserted every thirty minutes. At fifteen-minute intervals further specimens were taken, and the number of bacteria later estimated in the manner described.

In these experiments saliva diluted with normal saline was used as the inoculum; it was therefore possible that the penicillin present in the saliva and transferred to the plate might be sufficient to inhibit growth: to guard against this action penicillinase was added to the medium.

The results of these experiments are shown in graph *A*, which represents the mean of three, though the findings have been constant in a far larger series of experiments using pastilles of different strengths.

954

在体内青霉素对于细菌数量减少速率的作用

麦格雷戈，朗

编者按

在 1945 年以前，青霉素的抗菌活性已是众所周知，不过普遍认为这种药物是通过阻止增殖期细菌的分裂而实现抑菌效果的。亚历山大·麦格雷戈和戴维·朗在这篇文章中指出，细菌数量在给药之后的 15 分钟之内发生最大幅度的下降，这个过程太快了，难以用"抑制细菌繁殖"的理论来解释。他们认为青霉素在一些情况下会杀死细菌。

在从事将青霉素锭剂用于口腔感染治疗的研究期间（初步报告已发表 [1]），已有大量实验被用来确定在青霉素作用下口腔中细菌总量的减少和不同菌种的减少量，以及减少的速率。此减少速率受到格外关注，并且似乎有可能从相关实验中对青霉素作用模式作出推断，因此我们认为有必要就这些实验单独发表一篇文章。测定细菌量减少速率的方法如下：

先向一定量的生理盐水中加入 0.1 毫升唾液，接着将 1/50 毫升此混合溶液接种到一块血琼脂平板上。在 37℃ 下培育 24 小时后进行菌落计数。根据这个数值可以估算出每毫升唾液中的细菌总数。

得到第一份唾液样品之后，立即将 500 单位的青霉素锭剂置入颊齿之间的口腔沟槽内，使其在不被吸入的前提下溶解。接着每隔 30 分钟置入新的锭剂。每隔 15 分钟采集一次样品，然后用上述方法估算细菌总数。

在上述实验中，使用经生理盐水稀释过的唾液作为接种物，因此存在于唾液中并被转移到血琼脂平板上的青霉素有可能就足以抑制细菌的生长。为排除这种情况我们向培养基中加入了青霉素酶。

曲线 A 显示了这些实验的结果，它代表了 3 次重复实验的平均值。不过，在用不同强度的青霉素锭剂进行的大量实验中结果一直保持恒定。

It will be seen from this graph that the maximum fall in the total number of organisms occurred within the first fifteen minutes after the application of the penicillin.

Increased salivation due to the presence of a pastille in the mouth could have been a factor in this rapid fall, and in order to exclude this possibility the experiments were repeated using pastilles made of base alone, without penicillin. Pastilles of this type were maintained in the mouth for one and a half hours, and estimations on the total number of organisms in the saliva carried out as in the previous experiments.

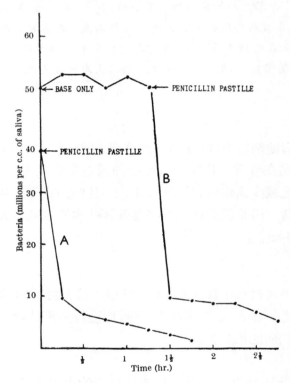

At one and a half hours, pastilles of the same base, but containing 500 units of penicillin each, were inserted and maintained for an equal period of time. The results expressed in graph *B* show that the pastille base alone produced no reduction in the total number of organisms, but substitution of the pastilles containing penicillin caused a fall in numbers comparable with the results shown in graph *A*. The possibility of the mechanical effect of salivation causing a reduction in numbers of organisms could therefore be excluded.

Consideration of the results shows that the most rapid fall in the total number of bacteria occurred in the first fifteen minutes after application of the penicillin. This rapidity of action is difficult to explain on the current hypothesis that penicillin is bacteriostatic, and would suggest that *in vivo*, when conditions of temperature, etc., are favourable, it may have a true bactericidal action.

(**155**, 201-202; 1945)

从图中可以看出，在使用青霉素后的最初 15 分钟内细菌总数出现最大幅度的减少。

口腔内存在锭剂导致的唾液分泌增多也可能造成细菌数量的快速下降。为了排除这种可能性，我们又用只含基质而不含青霉素的锭剂重复了这一实验。将这种不含青霉素的锭剂在口腔内放置一个半小时，用前面实验所采用的方法估计唾液中细菌的总数。

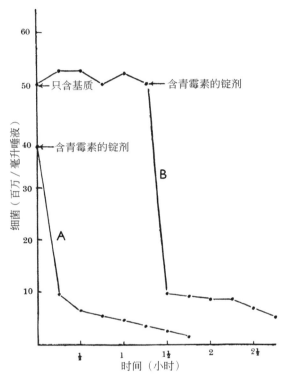

一个半小时之后，将既含有同样基质又含有 500 单位青霉素的锭剂置入口腔内，持续同样长的时间。结果如曲线 B 所示，只含基质的锭剂没有导致细菌总数的减少，而含青霉素的锭剂则导致了细菌总数的减少，并且这种减少程度与曲线 A 中的类似。由此可以排除唾液增多造成细菌数量减少的可能性。

以上结果显示细菌总数最大幅度的下降出现在使用青霉素后的最初 15 分钟内。这种作用的速度之快很难用现有的假说(即青霉素是抑菌剂)加以解释。这提示我们，当体内温度等条件都合适时，青霉素可能有直接的杀菌作用。

（王耀杨 翻译；金侠 审稿）

Alexander B. MacGregor and David A. Long: Hill End Hospital and Clinic, (St. Bartholomew's), St. Albans, Herts, Jan. 11.

Reference:

1. MacGregor and Long, *Brit. Med. J.*, ii, 686 (1944).

Biphasic Action of Penicillin and Other Sulphonamide Similarity

W. S. Miller *et al.*

Editor's Note

Here W. Sloan Miller, C. A. Green and H. Kitchen from the Royal Naval Medical School sum up the current state of knowledge about penicillin by comparing similarities between the antibiotic and antibacterial sulphonamide drugs. Both are selective and temperature-sensitive, and show two contrasting behaviours: stimulating growth at low concentrations and slowing it at high ones. They add that like sulphonamides, penicillin can also kill bacteria, a suggestion posited by MacGregor and Long in the previous paper. The authors also note, rather ominously, that "organisms can be trained to resist either penicillin or sulphonamides to a surprising degree."

SUBSTANCES generally acknowledged as being toxic to cells may have an opposite effect in higher dilution. This biphasic action—inhibition in high concentrations and stimulation in low concentrations—has been observed with a wide variety of substances, including narcotics, cyanide, pyrithiamine[1] and sulphonamides[2]. There is ample evidence that low concentrations of the last group stimulate bacterial growth; and it would appear that the period of active proliferation, which frequently precedes bacteriostasis by sulphonamides in higher concentrations, is a manifestation of the same phenomenon. We here report what appears to be an expression of the same effect occurring with penicillin.

The growth of sensitive bacteria in broth is quantitatively inhibited by suitably graded dilutions of penicillin, and the degree of inhibition can be measured turbidimetrically[3]. With the Oxford H staphylococcus (No. 6571 N.C.T.C.) as test organism, and measuring turbidity on the logarithmic scale of a Spekker photoelectric absorptiometer, we have obtained turbidity-penicillin concentration curves generally sigmoid in shape, with broth penicillin concentrations from 0.05 Oxford units per ml. to nil. Frequently, however, we have observed that tubes containing 0.005 U./ml., and sometimes 0.01 U./ml., have shown significantly more turbidity than those containing no penicillin. This effect appeared inconsistently when the incubation temperature was 37°C. At that temperature it has been noted after 4-24 hours of incubation, with a staphylococcal inoculum of between one and ten million per ml. broth, and with different samples of commercial sodium penicillin assaying from 84-820 units per mgm. It occurred in nutrient broth containing "Marmite" and 0.1 percent glucose, and in 10 percent horse serum broth without the addition of sugar. In a preliminary investigation of this phenomenon we have been unable to define the exact conditions necessary for its occurrence at 37°C., but the amount of bacterial inoculum and duration of subsequent incubation are certainly concerned; whereas the *p*H of the medium, age of inoculum, the order of mixing and initial temperatures of the various reagents in the test, within certain limits, are not critical.

青霉素与磺胺的类似性：两相行为及其他

米勒等

编者按

来自英国皇家海军医务学校的斯隆·米勒、格林和基钦在这篇文章中通过比较青霉素与磺胺类抗生素的相似之处，总结了目前对于青霉素的认识水平。它们都具有选择性和温度敏感性，而且都表现出了两种相反的作用：低浓度时促进细菌生长，而高浓度时抑制细菌生长。他们还认为青霉素和磺胺类药物一样也可以杀死细菌，这一观点由麦格雷戈和朗在之前的文章中提出。很不妙的是，作者们也注意到"有机体对青霉素以及磺胺类药物可产生惊人的耐药性"。

通常认为对细胞有毒性的物质在高度稀释状态下可能会有相反的效果。这种两相行为——高浓度时有抑制作用而低浓度时有促进作用——已经在很多种物质中被观测到，包括麻醉剂、氰化物、吡啶硫胺[1]和磺胺类药物[2]。已有充分的证据表明，上文提到的最后一组物质在低浓度情况下能促进细菌增殖；而且，在高浓度磺胺类药物抑菌现象出现之前，经常出现的活性增殖期可能也是上述同一现象的表现形式之一。在这里，我们将阐述青霉素在此类效应中的表现。

适度逐级稀释的青霉素对肉汤中敏感细菌的增殖具有可量化的抑制作用，抑制作用的程度可以用比浊滴定法来测定[3]。以牛津 H 葡萄球菌（No. 6571，N.C.T.C.）为待测有机体，把用斯佩克光电吸收计测定的浊度用对数的形式表示出来，我们可以得到基本上是 S 形的浊度 – 青霉素浓度曲线，其中，肉汤中青霉素浓度的范围为零到每毫升 0.05 牛津单位。但是，我们经常观测到含有浓度为 0.005 单位 / 毫升甚至 0.01 单位 / 毫升青霉素的试管比那些不含青霉素的试管呈现出明显更大的浊度。这种现象在 37℃ 的培育温度下时不时地出现。在 37℃ 的温度下，将浓度为每毫升 100 万 ~ 1,000 万个葡萄球菌菌种的肉汤培养 4~24 小时，并用浓度变化范围为 84~820 单位 / 毫克的不同商业青霉素钠盐进行实验分析，我们都观察到了上述现象。同时，这种现象在含马麦脱酸酵母和 0.1% 葡萄糖的营养肉汤以及含 10% 马血清但不添加糖类的肉汤中都会出现。在对这种现象的初步研究中，我们还无法确定在 37℃ 下出现该现象的准确条件，但是初始的菌种数量和随后的培养时间肯定是重要因素；在一定范围内，培养基的 pH 值、菌种的新老程度、测试中使用的各种试剂混合的顺序以及它们各自的初始温度都不是很关键。

We have been able to study this phenomenon more easily by incubation at temperatures below 37°C. It may be consistently reproduced by overnight (16 hr.) incubation at 24°C. of 20 ml. amounts of nutrient broth containing "Marmite" and dextrose (0.1 percent), with an inoculum of approximately 5,000,000 cocci per ml., from a 24-hour broth culture. Under these conditions a well-marked growth-stimulating effect has been repeatedly obtained with penicillin concentrations in the broth of about 0.01 Oxford units per ml., as shown in the accompanying graph from an actual test. The addition of *p*-amino-benzoic acid (5 mgm. per 100 ml.) to the medium makes no qualitative difference to the result, nor does the addition of 10 percent horse serum.

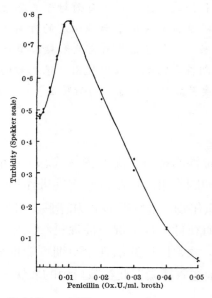

Turbidity-penicillin concentration curve.

Staphylococcal broth after 16 hr. incubation at 24°C. The concentrations lower than 0.01 U./ml. are 0.008, 0.006, 0.004, 0.002 and 0.001 U./ml. respectively. Test in duplicate.

The increased turbidity is not due to mere enlargement or distortion of the individual cocci[4]. The organisms from tubes at the peak of the curve (containing growth-stimulating dilutions of penicillin) are morphologically indistinguishable from those containing no penicillin. In fact, plate counts have provided unequivocal evidence that there may be twice as many viable bacteria in the penicillin growth stimulated cultures as in controls containing no penicillin. That this observation is caused by impurities seems unlikely in view of consistent reproducibility of the effect with pure crystalline penicillin; significant increases in turbidity over penicillinless controls can be obtained with as little as 0.0006 micrograms per ml.

Apart from recording the participation of penicillin in a rather general biological phenomenon, the object of this communication is to direct attention to the accumulating empirical evidence of the similarity penicillin and sulphonamide action. So far as we are aware, the only commonly held conception of the mode of action of penicillin is that it

在低于 37℃ 的温度下进行培养，研究这一现象就容易得多。取 20 毫升含有马麦脱酸酵母和右旋葡萄糖（0.1%）且经过 24 小时肉汤培养后的每毫升约 5,000,000 个球菌菌种的营养肉汤，在 24℃ 下经过一夜（16 小时）的培养，就可以重复观察到这一现象。在上述条件下，我们可以在青霉素浓度为每毫升约 0.01 牛津单位的肉汤中重复获得明显增强的促进增殖的效应，附图显示的是一次实际实验的结果。在培养基中添加对氨基苯甲酸（浓度为 5 毫克每 100 毫升）或添加 10% 的马血清对于结果都没有太大的影响。

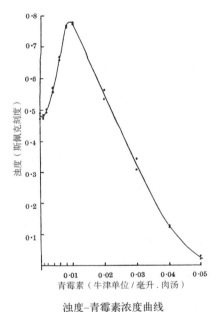

浊度-青霉素浓度曲线

葡萄球菌肉汤在24℃下培养16个小时。低于0.01单位/毫升的浓度值分别是0.008、0.006、0.004、0.002和0.001单位/毫升。检测进行两次。

浊度的增加并不仅仅是由于单个球菌的增大和变形[4]。位于曲线峰值处的试管中的有机体（含促进增殖的青霉素稀释液）与不含青霉素的试管中的有机体在形态上没有区别。事实上，平板计数结果已提供了明确的证据，在有青霉素促进增殖的培养液中可存活的细菌数量可以是不含青霉素的对照组中的两倍。由于使用纯的结晶青霉素进行了多次实验都得到了同一现象，所以这一现象看来不太可能是由杂质造成的；在青霉素浓度低到每毫升 0.0006 微克的对照组中也能看到浊度的明显上升。

除了报道青霉素也存在这种相当普遍的生物学现象以外，本文的目的还在于希望将大家的注意力引向越来越多的关于青霉素与磺胺类药物存在相似行为的经验证据上。就我们所知，关于青霉素作用模式的唯一共识是，它通过阻止正在生长的细胞的分裂而起到抑制细菌的作用。这是在加德纳的观察基础上得出的，加德纳观察

acts bacteriostatically by preventing division of growing cells. This is based on Gardner's observation that bacteria subjected to concentrations of penicillin too small to inhibit growth completely undergo distortion and enlargement[4]. Analogous morphological changes are frequently associated with sulphonamide action. It has been further proposed that penicillin acts only on dividing bacteria[5], and that this action is bactericidal[6]. One of the final conclusions reached by Henry, in a very comprehensive review of the mode of action of sulphonamides, is that they achieve their effect by stopping cell division[7]. In general, the antibacterial action of both penicillin and sulphonamides, *in vitro* and *in vivo*, appears to be primarily "bacteriostatic". Under certain experimental conditions, however, penicillin[6,8], like sulphonamides, may exert a "bactericidal" effect. Confusion is caused by drawing too fine a distinction between these terms.

The fundamental antibacterial action of penicillin and sulphonamides is inhibition of cell multiplication. Sulphonamides inhibit the growth of almost every variety of cell besides bacteria, although in widely varying concentration; there is as yet little evidence that penicillin will have such a general effect, but Cornman has reported survival of normal cells in penicillin solutions lethal to malignant cells[9]. Sulphonamide action is usually biphasic; our observations suggest that this may be true of penicillin. Primary bacterial proliferation preceding bacteriostasis, as occurs with sulphonamides, has recently been noted with penicillin and *Leptospira icterohoemorrhagioe*[10]. (As mentioned previously, this may well be another aspect of the biphasic phenomenon.) Penicillin growth-inhibition, in conformity with that of sulphonamides, appears to obey the law of mass action, in that (*a*) the inhibition is reversible, by removing the bacteria from contact with penicillin or destroying the penicillin with penicillinase, and (*b*) the inhibition is directly related to the penicillin concentration[3]. Both penicillin[6,8] and sulphonamide activity are directly related to the temperature. In the presence of a constant amount of sulphonamide, antibacterial activity is inversely related to the number of organisms present; this is a phenomenon which awaits satisfactory explanation; and the explanation is also required in respect of penicillin[6]. A feature of sulphonamide activity is that it varies from one bacterial species to another, from strain to strain, and even perhaps from organism to organism. Penicillin exemplifies this selectivity *par excellence*. Antibacterial effect is greatly influenced by the sulphonamide chemical structure, and scientific progress with penicillin must be seriously impeded until its structure is made known. By analogy, however, there is every reason to expect that substances chemically related to penicillin will have different bacterial "spectra". Chemical information is also lacking for a comparison of the effect of *p*H changes on penicillin action; at present this factor appears more important to sulphonamide action. Organisms can be trained to resist either penicillin or sulphonamides to a surprising degree, and with almost equal ease. Penicillin shares with sulphonamides synergism of antibacterial effect by antibodies and cellular defence mechanisms.

The commonly accepted theory of sulphonamide action, that of Woods and Fildes, casts *p*-amino-benzoic acid in an essential role[11]. Since this substance plays no similar part in penicillin action, some fundamental difference in mode of action might be presumed.

到当青霉素浓度小到完全不能抑制细菌生长时，细菌发生了变形和增大 [4]。类似的形态方面的变化经常被认为与磺胺类药物的作用有关。有人进一步提出，青霉素只对分裂中的细菌起作用 [5]，并且这种作用是杀菌作用 [6]。亨利在一篇关于磺胺类药物作用模式的非常全面的评述中给出的最终结论之一是，磺胺类药物通过终止细胞分裂而起作用 [7]。一般来说，青霉素和磺胺类药物无论是在体外还是在体内，抗菌作用看来主要都是"抑制性的"。不过，在某些特定的实验条件下，与磺胺类药物相似，青霉素 [6,8] 可以产生"杀菌性的"效果。对这些术语的意思区分得太细会造成困惑。

青霉素和磺胺类药物的基础抗菌作用是抑制细胞的增殖。除了细菌之外，磺胺类药物能抑制几乎所有类型细胞的增殖，当然对不同细胞起作用的浓度不同，变化范围很大；目前几乎没有证据表明青霉素也有如此普遍的效果，但是康曼已经报道了在对恶性肿瘤细胞有破坏作用的青霉素溶液中正常细胞能够正常存活 [9]。磺胺类药物的作用通常是两相的；我们的观测结果表明青霉素的作用可能也是两相的。如同在磺胺类药物中所发生的那样，最近我们注意到在青霉素和出血性黄疸钩端螺旋体体系中也发生了细菌抑制前的初期细菌增殖 [10]。（如同之前曾提到的那样，这很可能是两相现象的另一个方面。）青霉素抑制细菌增殖的作用与磺胺类药物的作用是一致的，似乎也遵循质量作用定律，具体表现在：(a) 在消除细菌与青霉素的接触或用青霉素酶破坏青霉素之后，抑制作用也会被消除。(b) 青霉素对细菌的抑制作用与青霉素浓度有直接的关系 [3]。无论是青霉素 [6,8] 还是磺胺类药物，其活性都与温度直接相关。在有恒定量的磺胺类药物存在时，抗菌活性与有机体的数量存在负相关的关系；这一现象仍有待人们作出合理的解释；对青霉素的研究也同样需要对这种现象给出合理解释 [6]。磺胺类药物活性的一个特征是：其对不同菌种、不同菌株甚至不同个体的活性都有所不同。青霉素为这一**超乎寻常的**选择性提供了例子。由于磺胺类药物的化学结构极大地影响了其抗菌效应，所以在搞清楚青霉素的结构之前，青霉素的科学应用进展必将遭遇巨大的阻碍。不过，通过类比，我们有足够的理由期待与青霉素具有化学相关性的物质会有不同的细菌"谱"。在比较不同 pH 值对青霉素作用的影响时还缺乏足够的化学信息；目前看来，pH 值对于磺胺类药物的作用更为重要。有机体对青霉素以及磺胺类药物可产生惊人的耐药性，不同有机体产生这种耐药性的难易程度相当。青霉素与磺胺类药物都具有通过抗体和细胞防御机制发挥抗菌效应的协同作用。

关于磺胺类药物的作用机制，被普遍接受的理论是由伍兹和法尔兹提出的，这个理论认为对氨基苯甲酸具有关键性的作用 [11]。既然对氨基苯甲酸这种物质在青霉

But Henry's conclusions throw considerable doubt on the Woods-Fildes explanation, and reconcile this apparent anomaly in sulphonamide-penicillin similarity[7]. There appears to be general agreement that sulphonamide bacteriostasis is achieved by direct inhibition of one or more enzymes. The profound biological activity shown by penicillin in trace concentrations would appear to be eminently explicable in terms of enzymic phenomena. It is not our purpose, however, to speculate on the mode of action of penicillin; but to suggest, on the basis of empirical observations available now, that it is not likely to be fundamentally unique. The differences that do exist between sulphonamides and penicillin, and which place the latter in its preeminent therapeutic position, appear to be differences of degree so far as mode of action is concerned.

Much of the technical work on which our observations are based was performed by laboratory assistants in the Royal Navy, to whom we are indebted. The crystalline penicillin was generously given by I. C. (P.), Ltd.

Addendum. Additional information has become available since this communication was written. It is now clear that at least three chemically different varieties of penicillin have already been identified and that their relative efficiencies for various bacteria are probably different[12]. The effect of pH on penicillin activity[13] is, in fact, in striking conformity with what has been reported for sulphonamides. The direct relationship of temperature to penicillin activity has been amplified[13,14]. Todd[15] has demonstrated the frequency with which primary multiplication occurs in cultures subjected to the influence of penicillin, and noted that Fleming originally reported this phenomenon in 1929.

(**155**, 210-211; 1945)

W. Sloan Miller, C. A. Green and H. Kitchen: Royal Naval Medical School.

References:

1. Woolley, D. W., and White, A. G. C., *J. Expt. Med.*, **78**, 489 (1943).

2. Finklestone-Sayliss *et al.*, *Lancet*, ii, 792 (1937). Green, H. N., *Brit. J. Expt. Path.*, **21**, 38 (1940). Green, H. N., and Bielschowsky, F., *Brit. J. Expt. Path.*, **23**, 1 (1942). Lamanna, C., *Science*, **95**, 304 (1942). Lamanna, C., and Shapiro, I. M., *J. Bact.*, **45**, 385 (1943). Colebrook *et al.*, *Lancet*, ii, 1323 (1936). McIntosh, J., and Whitby, E. H., *Lancet* (i), 431 (1939).

3. Foster, J. W., *J. Biol. Chem.*, **144**, 285 (1942). Foster, J. W., and Wilkers, B. L., *J. Bact.*, **46**, 377 (1943). Foster, J. W., and Woodruff, H. B., *J. Bact.*, **46**, 187 (1943). Joslyn, D. A., *Science*, **99**, 21 (1944). Lee *et al.*, *J. Biol. Chem.*, **152**, 485 (1944). McMahan, J. R., *J. Biol. Chem.*, **153**, 249 (1944).

4. Gardner, A. D., *Nature*, **146**, 837 (1940).

5. Miller, C. P., and Foster, A. Z., *Proc. Soc. Expt. Biol. N.Y.*, **56**, 205 (1944). Hobby, G. L., and Dawson, M. H., *Proc. Soc. Expt. Biol. N.Y.*, 181 (1944).

6. Bigger, J. W., *Lancet*, ii, 497 (1944).

7. Henry, R. J., *Bact. Rev.*, 7, 175 (1943).

8. Garrod, L. P., *Lancet*, ii, 673 (1944).

9. Cornman, I., *Science*, **99**, 247 (1944).

10. Alston, J. M., and Broom, J. C., *Brit. Med. J.*, **2**, 718 (1944).

11. Woods, D. D., and Fildes, P., *Chem. and Ind.*, **59**, 133 (1940).

12. See *Nature*, **154**, 725 (1944).

13. Garrod, *Brit. Med. J.*, i, 107 (1945).

14. Eagle and Musselman, *J. Exp. Med.*, **80**, 493 (1944).

15. *Lancet*, i, 74 (1945).

素作用机制中起的作用完全不同，我们就可以认为青霉素的作用模式与磺胺类药物存在某些根本的差异。但是亨利的结论对伍兹和法尔兹的解释提出了相当强的质疑，从而消除了磺胺类药物与青霉素类似性中的这个明显差异[7]。看来一般性的共识是磺胺类药物的抑菌作用是通过直接抑制一种或多种酶来实现的。酶现象似乎可以很好地解释痕量浓度的青霉素表现出的奇妙的生物学活性。然而，我们的目的并不是要推测出青霉素的作用模式，而是在目前已有的经验观测的基础上提出这种作用模式从本质上看并不是单一的。就作用模式而言，磺胺类药物与青霉素之间的差异只是作用程度上的差异，这种差异使青霉素在治疗中显得非常优秀。

我们对皇家海军的实验室助理表示感谢，因为我们的观察所依赖的大量技术工作都是由他完成的。帝国化学（制药）有限公司慷慨地为我们提供了结晶青霉素。

附录：在写完这篇通讯之后我们又得到了一些新的信息。现在明确的是，至少已经鉴定出 3 种化学性质不同的青霉素变体，而且它们对于不同细菌的相对作用效果可能也是很不一样的[12]。事实上，pH 值对于青霉素活性的影响[13]与之前报道的 pH 值对磺胺类药物的影响具有惊人的一致性。温度对青霉素活性产生的直接影响被夸大了[13,14]。托德[15]展示了受青霉素影响的培养中初始增殖发生的频率，并且注意到弗莱明最早于 1929 年报道了这种现象。

（王耀杨 翻译；莫韫 审稿）

Causality or Indeterminism?

H. T. H. Piaggio

Editor's Note

John von Neumann had recently claimed to prove that no theory could go beyond the current quantum theory in giving a causal account of quantum physics. Thus while some physicists, such as Einstein, suspected that quantum theory might only be an approximate theory, statistical in character because it left out details of some deeper level of physical reality, von Neumann claimed that this was impossible. Henry Piaggio here reviews the arguments for and against this claim, concluding that while the balance of evidence seemed to weigh against the possibility of deterministic laws, they could not be ruled out. Many years later, von Neumann's argument would be dismantled by John Bell, who helped revitalize interest in deterministic quantum theories.

A short article published in *Nature* of July 22, 1944[1], entitled "Collapse of Determinism", contained a brief statement of von Neumann's claim to have demonstrated that the results of the quantum theory cannot be obtained by averaging any exact causal laws. If one may judge from the number of communications referring to this point which have been submitted to the Editors, many regard this claim with suspicion and desire a more detailed discussion of the grounds on which it is based. Mr. W. W. Barkas[2] suggested that the existence of statistical regularity when large numbers of events are considered is incompatible with indeterminism, and that if the final result of the behaviour of a million photons were fixed, the behaviour of the first 999,000 must influence the other 1,000. Prof. (now Sir Edmund) Whittaker[2] replied that it might be profitable to consider the behaviour of tossed coins. He asked, in particular, whether the statistical regularity for this case, calculated by the ordinary theory of probability, involves the assumption of "crypto-determinism" (that is, real determinism hidden by lack of detailed information) or merely the assumption of symmetry. This reply produced further letters, too numerous for the Editors to publish in full, and I have been asked to give a connected account of the points raised. I shall start with the experimental evidence concerning coin-tossing, and contrast it with the theoretical discussion. After this I shall touch upon similar considerations for the kinetic theory of gases. Finally, and most important, I shall give some details of von Neumann's supposed disproof of causality, and give the arguments for and against it.

Buffon, the French naturalist, tossed a coin until he obtained 2,048 heads. The results were quoted by De Morgan[3], who gave also an account of three similar experiments by his own pupils or correspondents. The arrangement by which the last toss ended with a head gave a small advantage to heads, but too small to make any significant difference. Much more extensive experiments, on somewhat different lines, were carried out by W. S. Jevons[4], who took "a handful of ten coins, usually shillings", and tossed the ten together. He made two series of 1,024 such tossings of ten coins, so that in each series 10,240 coins were tossed.

因果律还是非决定论？

编者按

约翰·冯·诺伊曼最近宣称，他将证明在对量子物理给出的因果解释方面没有任何一个理论能够超过当今的量子理论。虽然一些物理学家，例如爱因斯坦，认为量子理论也许仅仅是一个近似理论，具有统计特征，因为它忽视了物理现实中某些更深层次的细节，但冯·诺伊曼却不这样认为。在这篇文章中，亨利·皮亚焦对这两种不同的观点进行了评论，最后得出结论：虽然证据不利于决定论，但也不能将其完全排除。许多年以后，约翰·贝尔又推翻了冯·诺伊曼的观点，这使得人们开始再次关注决定论的量子理论。

发表在 1944 年 7 月 22 日《自然》上的一篇题为《决定论的崩溃》的短文 [1]，简单地描述了冯·诺伊曼的观点，即不能通过对一些精确的因果规律取平均来得到量子理论的结果。如果仅从编辑部收到的关注这一观点的信函的数量来看，我们发现很多人都对这一观点表示怀疑，并且希望能就这一观点建立的基础进行更详细的讨论。巴卡斯 [2] 先生认为，当考虑大量的事件时，统计规律与非决定论是不相符的，他还提到，如果 100 万个光子的最终行为结果是确定的，那么，前 999,000 个光子的行为必定会影响另外 1,000 个光子的行为。惠特克 [2] 教授（现在是埃德蒙爵士）对此的回应是：我们也许可以分析一下抛掷硬币的行为。他特别问道，对于抛掷硬币来说，根据一般的概率理论计算出来的统计规律是涉及了"隐秘决定论"（即由于缺乏详细信息而隐藏了真正的决定论）的假设，还是仅与对称性假设有关。这一回应又引发了很多评论文章，因其数量太多致使编辑部很难将其全部发表，而且我也被要求针对这些观点给出有关的解释。我将从抛掷硬币的实验结果开始谈起，并将它与理论值进行比较。之后，我也将对气体的动力学理论作相似的分析。最后，也是最为重要的，我将详细解释冯·诺伊曼对于因果律的假设反驳，并且给出支持和反对它的理由。

法国博物学家布丰不停地抛掷一枚硬币，直到他得到 2,048 次正面朝上为止。德·摩尔根 [3] 引证了这一结果，并介绍了由他的学生或相关人员完成的 3 个与之相似的实验。这种规定以正面朝上为结束的抛掷实验让正面朝上的结果略占优势，但是，这个优势太小以至于可以忽略不计。杰文斯 [4] 以稍为不同的方式进行了更为广泛的实验，他以"10 个硬币（通常是面额为 1 先令的硬币）作为一组"，并一起抛掷。他做了两个系列的实验，各含 1,024 次这种 10 个一组的抛掷，因此每个系列中

The results of these six experiments were as follows:

No. of heads	2,048	2,048	2,048	2,048	5,222	5,131
No. of tails	1,992	2,044	2,020	2,069	5,018	5,109
Total	4,040	4,092	4,068	4,117	10,240	10,240
Excess of heads over mean	28	2	14	−10.5	102	11
Proportion of heads	0.5069	0.5005	0.5034	0.4974	0.5100	0.5011
Excess over mean	0.0069	0.0005	0.0034	−0.0026	0.0100	0.0011

If we examine these results, we see that it is easy to misinterpret the meaning of "statistical regularity". It is certainly not true, as some correspondents seemed to think, that the numbers of heads and tails are bound to be equal. In fact, the divergence from the mean actually increased from a maximum of 28 in the first four experiments, each based on roughly 4,096 tosses, to a maximum of 102 in the last pair, each based on 10,240 tosses. This is quite in accordance with theory, which, assuming that the probability of a head in one toss is 0.5, deduces that for a large number n of tosses, it is as likely as not that the divergence from the expected mean $n/2$ will exceed $0.3372\sqrt{n}$, but it is almost certain (99.73 percent probability) that it will be less than $1.5\sqrt{n}$. For $n = 4,096$ the "as-likely-as-not divergence" is, to the nearest integer, 22, and the "scarcely-ever divergence" is 96. For $n = 10,240$, the corresponding numbers are 34 and 152. Thus the actual divergences, though larger and more one-sided than some might have expected, are quite compatible with the theory. But the phrase "statistical regularity" really refers to the *proportion* of heads, which, according to theory, should be very nearly 0.5, with an "as-likely-as-not divergence" of $0.3372\sqrt{n}$ and a "scarcely-ever divergence" of $1.5/\sqrt{n}$. Both these divergences diminish indefinitely as n increases. We may also estimate the theoretical divergence of the proportion by its root-mean-square or "standard deviation". This has the value $0.5/\sqrt{n}$, a result which we shall contrast later with Heisenberg's Principle of Uncertainty.

We now come to an important criticism of the theory of probability on which the above calculations are based. As pointed out by Lieut.-Colonel E. Gold[5], there is an assumption of symmetry, not only in the two faces of the coin, but also in the actions of the hand that tosses the coin. When the hand was replaced by a machine, such as that devised by J. Horzelski[6], the absence of this symmetry was manifest. By a certain adjustment of the pressure actuating a lever, he obtained 98 heads out of 100 tosses. He then slightly altered the pressure, keeping the head, as before, initially upwards on the machine, and obtained only one head in the next 100 tosses. In this case the tossing mechanism is not a hidden parameter, but is visible and definite, whereas in the usual tossing it is indefinite and, so far as we can manage it, symmetrically distributed. It is possible that the excess of heads in Jevons's experiments was due to some slight lack of symmetry in his tossing conditions. Whether this was so or not, it appears obvious that *the description of reality given by the theory of probability in coin-tossing is not complete.*

It is therefore erroneous to suppose that the properties of a perfectly normal distribution must necessarily correspond exactly with physical reality, however useful they may be in

都抛掷了 10,240 个硬币。上述 6 个实验的统计结果如下：

正面朝上次数	2,048	2,048	2,048	2,048	5,222	5,131
反面朝上次数	1,992	2,044	2,020	2,069	5,018	5,109
总次数	4,040	4,092	4,068	4,117	10,240	10,240
正面朝上次数超过平均数的量	28	2	14	−10.5	102	11
正面朝上的比例	0.5069	0.5005	0.5034	0.4974	0.5100	0.5011
正面朝上的比例超过 50% 的量	0.0069	0.0005	0.0034	−0.0026	0.0100	0.0011

如果我们查看这些统计数字，就很容易曲解"统计规律"的含义。有些人认为，正面朝上和反面朝上的次数一定会是相等的，这显然是不正确的。实际上，前 4 个实验都抛掷了约 4,096 次，正面朝上的的次数超过平均数的最大值为 28，而最后 2 个实验各抛掷了 10,240 次，其最大值为 102，因此，偏离平均数的差值实际上是在增加的。这一点同理论吻合得非常好，理论认为，在一次抛掷硬币的过程中，正面朝上的概率为 0.5，据此推断，如果抛掷 n（一个很大的数字）次硬币，那么偏离预期平均值 $n/2$ 的差值很可能会超过 $0.3372\sqrt{n}$，但是几乎可以肯定（99.73% 的可能性）该值会小于 $1.5\sqrt{n}$。当 $n = 4,096$ 时，"很可能的偏差"最接近整数 22，而"几乎不可能出现的偏差"是 96。当 $n = 10,240$ 时，相应的值为 34 和 152。因此，尽管实际的偏差要比一些人预期的大且不均衡，但与这个理论还是非常一致的。但是，根据理论，"统计规律"这个短语真正的意义指的是正面朝上出现的**比例**应该非常接近 0.5，其"很可能的偏差"为 $0.3372\sqrt{n}$，"几乎不可能出现的偏差"为 $1.5/\sqrt{n}$。随着 n 的增加，这两个偏差都会无限地减少。我们也可以根据这个比例的均方根或"标准偏差"来估算其理论偏差。得到的值为 $0.5/\sqrt{n}$，稍后我们会将这一结果与海森堡的测不准原理进行比较。

现在我们来讨论一下上面计算所依据的概率理论的一个重要的不妥之处。正如陆军中校戈尔德[5]指出的，对称性的假设不仅存在于硬币本身的正反两面，而且还存在于抛掷硬币时手的动作。当用机器取代手时，比如霍莱斯基[6]设计的机器，实验结果就出现了明显的不对称性。通过对驱动杠杆的压力进行适当调节，在抛掷 100 次硬币后，他得到了 98 次正面朝上的结果。接着，他轻微地改变了压力，初始时硬币在机器上同样保持正面朝上，但在接下来的 100 次抛掷中，只得到了一次正面朝上的结果。在这种情况下，抛掷机制不是一个隐藏的参数，而是可见并且确定的参数，而在一般的抛掷情况下，这个参数是不确定的，而且在我们所能控制的范围内，它就是对称分布的。在杰文斯的实验中，正面朝上的情况太多很可能是因为抛掷情况缺乏对称性。不管情况是否如此，很明显，**在抛掷硬币的实验中，概率理论给出的事实描述是不完善的。**

因此，认为完美正态分布的性质必定严格符合物理现实是错误的，不过通常情况下这些性质可以为事实提供一个很好的近似。我们不能仅仅通过宣称抛掷细节搅

giving a good approximation to the facts. We cannot disprove the existence of the details of the projection merely by claiming that they upset the purity of the normal distribution. It is rather the very purity of that distribution which goes beyond the physical facts, and so is not a complete description of reality. Similar considerations apply to the kinetic theory of gases, but in this case the symmetry assumed in the theory[7] is a much closer approximation to the actual facts. But it is only an approximation, and here, as elsewhere in classical physics, pure statistical aggregates do not exist.

This brings us to the question whether such aggregates exist in non-classical physics, in particular in quantum mechanics. We shall examine von Neumann's arguments, using for this purpose not only his well-known treatise "Mathematische Grundlagen der Quantenmechanik" (1932), but also the shorter account, in English, that he gave in Warsaw[8] in 1937, and the discussion that ensued. The starting point is an analysis of the qualitative laws obeyed by the mathematical "hypermaximal projective" operators which correspond to the physical quantities occurring in quantum mechanics. Everything is said to be based on six laws, of which two seem more important than the rest. One is the principle of superposition, extended to quantities not necessarily simultaneously measurable. The other may be called the principle of exact functional correspondence; for example, if an operator represents a physical quantity, then the square of the operator represents the square of the quantity.

In my opinion, however, the emphasis on these simple laws conceals the fact that other conditions of greater importance are imposed by the definition of "hypermaximal projective" operators. This definition implies some characteristic results of quantum mechanics, and the simple laws are merely the final requirements. Von Neumann shows that aggregates are of two kinds, "pure" and "mixed". The essential property of a pure aggregate is that it cannot be regarded as a mixture of two other non-identical aggregates. The qualitative laws of quantum mechanics show that the aggregates concerned must be pure, whereas all aggregates based upon causal laws, such as tossed coins or gas particles, must be mixed. Hence, he concludes, causality is incompatible with quantum mechanics, and the process of averaging causal laws, as applied in the kinetic theory of gases, cannot possibly be extended to quantum mechanics. There is no need, he says, to go more deeply into the details of a supposed system which is governed by further conditions ("hidden parameters") in addition to the wave functions. These hidden parameters would upset the qualitative laws of quantum mechanics. He admits that quantum mechanics in its present form is certainly defective, and, in spite of its great success in explaining physical phenomena, may possibly, in the long run, turn out to be false. But this is true of every theory; we can never say that it is proved by experiment, but only that it is the best summing up of experiment at present known.

Von Neumann therefore concludes that there is at present no reason and no excuse for supposing the existence of causality in quantum mechanics. This conclusion is described by Whittaker[9] as not only novel and unexpected, but also almost incredible, yet he endorses it with the exultant declaration "the bonds of necessity have been broken; for

乱了正态分布的纯正性，从而否认这些细节的存在。事实上，正是因为分布太过纯正，超出了物理的现实，因此，它才不是对现实的完整描述。同样的道理也适用于气体的动力学理论，但在这种情况下，该理论中[7]的对称性假设更接近于实际的事实。但仅仅只是接近而已，就像在经典物理学的其他地方一样，在这里纯粹的统计集合是不存在的。

这使我们遇到这样一个问题，即这样的集合是否也存在于非经典物理学中，特别是量子力学之中呢？为了得到解答，我们将查证冯·诺伊曼的观点，其中不仅涉及到他的著作《量子力学的数学基础》（1932 年），还涉及到他于 1937 年在华沙[8]用英文写的简短解释和对此所作的进一步的讨论。其起始点是对数学的"超大投影"算符所遵循的定性法则的分析，该算符与量子力学中出现的物理量相对应。一切都基于六条法则，其中有两条似乎尤为重要。一条是叠加原理，它适用于不必同时测量的物理量。另一条是严格的函数对应性原理；比如说，如果一个算符代表一个物理量，那么算符的平方就代表这个物理量的平方。

然而在我看来，过分注重这些简单的法则使我们忽视了通过"超大投影"算符的定义所带来的其他一些更为重要的条件。这个定义暗含了量子力学的一些特定结果，并且这些简单的法则仅仅是最后的必要条件。冯·诺伊曼认为集合分为"纯集合"和"混合集合"两种。纯集合的主要性质是它不能被表示为两个不同集合的混合。量子力学的定性法则表明与其有关的集合必然是纯集合，而如抛掷硬币或气体粒子等所有服从因果论的集合都必然是混合的。因此他得出结论：因果论与量子力学是不兼容的，并且在气体动力学理论中用到的平均因果论的方法不能应用于量子力学。他认为，对于一个受波函数控制以外还受其他条件（"隐参量"）控制的设定系统，没有必要去深究细节。这些隐参量将会打乱量子力学的定性法则。他承认当时的量子力学的确是有缺陷的，尽管它在解释物理现象方面取得了巨大的成功，但以后仍然有可能被证明是错误的。不过，每一个理论都是这样的；我们永远不可能声称用实验证明了它，只能说目前这是对实验的最好总结。

因此，冯·诺伊曼得出结论：目前在量子力学中没有任何理由能够推测出因果律的存在。惠特克[9]认为这个结论不仅是新奇且出人意料的，而且几乎是令人难以置信的，他还用兴奋的语言对其表示认同，"必然性的联系已被打破；对于某几类现

certain classes of phenomena, crypto-determinism is definitely disproved".

Other comments have been more sceptical. At the Warsaw conference, the president, C. Bialobrzeski, after hearing von Neumann, admitted the validity of the argument that it was impossible to fit causality into the framework of quantum mechanics, but expressed a doubt as to the logical coherence of that framework. In his opinion it is deficient because it does not take account of irreversible changes, and also because, in certain conditions of measurement, the indeterminism of the final state disappears, and the assumptions of discontinuity and indeterminism do not correspond to reality. He thought it necessary to introduce a new postulate concerning measurement. At a later meeting of the same conference a letter from Heisenberg said that the quantum theory, in its present form, could not yet give a logically coherent account of nuclear physics or of cosmic rays.

Many critics are suspicious of purely abstract arguments which make no reference to experiment. Of course, such experiments as those of Davisson and Germer on electron diffraction and of Condon and Gurney on radioactivity, though excellent as illustrations of the Uncertainty Principle, yet have no value in deciding whether this uncertainty is due only to lack of detailed knowledge, or to true indeterminism. On a somewhat different plane is the argument of Whittaker[9], who, though a supporter of von Neumann, illustrates his argument by a reference to the passage of plane-polarized light passing through a Nicol prism, and shows that the phenomena cannot be explained by causal laws governing any hidden parameters attributed to the photons. However, H. Pelzer[10] gives two models in which hidden parameters, attributed at least partly to the Nicol prism, can exist and obey causal laws. From this he infers that the arguments of Whittaker and von Neumann are incomplete, even though he agrees with their conclusion that quantum phenomena are truly indeterminate.

My own criticism of von Neumann is founded upon a paper by A. Einstein, B. Podolsky and N. Rosen[11]. By considering the problem of making predictions concerning a system on the basis of measurements made on another system which had previously interacted with it, they conclude that *the description of reality as given by a wave function is not complete*. As a wave function is a mathematical way of representing a probability distribution, this conclusion is almost exactly the same as that which I enunciated concerning coin-tossing. I therefore, with great diffidence, offer the opinion that the existence of causality has *not* been disproved. It is true that Einstein's opinion has been rejected by N. Bohr[12], but there are other grounds for supporting it. In fact, the postulate of quantum mechanics that electrons cannot be distinguished from one another appears, at least to me, not to be a statement that Nature is incomprehensible, but merely that quantum mechanics is incomplete. However, I do not wish to insist that there is no difference between coin-tossing and quantum mechanics. One striking difference is that in coin-tossing the standard deviation of the proportion of heads depends only upon the number of tosses, and can be diminished indefinitely; but in quantum mechanics the Principle of Uncertainty gives for the product of the standard deviations of the momentum and displacement a minimum value, namely, $h/4\pi$. The occurrence of Planck's constant in this result seems to show

象，隐秘决定论将完全被推翻"。

其他评论则对此持有更多的怀疑。在华沙会议上，会议主席比亚洛布尔泽斯基在听取了冯·诺伊曼的演讲后，承认现在确实不可能将因果律纳入到量子力学的理论框架中，但他对这一理论框架的逻辑连贯性提出了质疑。他认为，由于没有考虑到不可逆变化，也由于在一定的测量条件下终态的不确定性消失了，而且不连续性和不确定性的假想与现实并不相符，所以这是有缺陷的。他认为有必要根据测量提出一个新的假定。在会议后期的一个会上，海森堡在一封来信中说，当前的量子理论还无法为核物理学或宇宙射线给出一个逻辑一致的解释。

许多评论家都质疑这些没有实验作为依托的完全抽象的理论观点。当然，尽管像戴维孙和革末在电子衍射方面的实验以及康登和格尼在放射性方面的实验都对测不准原理进行了完美的阐释，但是人们依旧无法说明这个不确定性究竟只是因为缺乏具体知识还是确实无法确定。惠特克 [9] 从一个稍微不同的角度阐述了自己的观点，惠特克是冯·诺伊曼的支持者，但是他通过引用一篇平面偏振光通过尼科尔棱镜的文章来表明，这种现象不能用控制着由光子引起的一些隐参量的因果律来解释。但是佩尔泽 [10] 给出了两个模型，其中的隐参量能够存在并遵循因果律，而这些隐参量至少部分来源于尼科尔棱镜。从这点他得出推断：惠特克和冯·诺伊曼的观点是不完整的，尽管他也认同他们关于量子现象确实不可确定的结论。

我对冯·诺伊曼的批判基于一篇由爱因斯坦、波多尔斯基和罗森 [11] 共同撰写的论文。他们基于对曾经与该系统发生过相互作用的另一系统的测量来考虑对该系统进行预测的问题，他们得出的结论是：**仅仅用波函数来描述现实世界是不完整的**。因为波函数只是描述概率分布的一种数学方法，这个结论和我对于抛掷硬币实验所得的结论几乎完全一样。因此我非常不自信地提出：因果律的存在还**没有**完全被否认。爱因斯坦的观点确实已经被玻尔 [12] 推翻，但还是存在一些其他依据来支持它。事实上，量子力学中关于电子与电子间无法区分的假设出现了，至少对我来说，这并不表明大自然是不可理解的，它仅仅说明量子力学是不完整的。但我并非想说量子力学与抛掷硬币没有任何区别。两者之间一个很明显的不同是在抛掷硬币中正面朝上的比例的标准偏差仅取决于抛掷的次数，并且可以无限减小；但是在量子力学中测不准原理给出了动量与位移的标准偏差的乘积的最小值，即 $h/4\pi$。这个结果中普朗克常数的出现似乎说明有一些新的东西尚待挖掘。我觉得如果冯·诺伊曼的结论

that there is something essentially new. I should find it easier to accept von Neumann's conclusions if his arguments, instead of being purely qualitative, contained this constant. Perhaps it is really concealed somewhere in the background, like a hidden parameter!

To conclude, I will quote the opinion expressed by Bertrand Russell[13] in 1936, that at present there is no decisive reason in favour of complete determinism (causality) in physics, but that there is no reason against it, and that it is theoretically impossible that there should be any such reason. But Russell does not mention von Neumann's arguments. My own conclusion is that the balance of the present evidence is rather against complete causality, but that the question is still unsettled.

(**155**, 289-290; 1945)

H. T. H. Piggio: University College, Nottingham.

References:
1. *Nature*, **154**, 122 (1944).
2. *Nature*, **154**, 676 (1944).
3. "Budget of Paradoxes", 170 (1872).
4. "Principles of Science", 238 (1874); or 2nd ed., 208 (1877).
5. *Nature*, **155**, 111 (1945).
6. *Nature*, **155**, 111 (1945).
7. Preston, "Theory of Heat", 4th ed., 782 (1929).
8. "New Theories in Physics", 30-45.
9. *Proc. Phys. Soc.*, **55**, 459 (1943).
10. *Proc. Phys. Soc.*, **53**, 195 (1944).
11. *Phys. Rev.*, **47**, 777 (1935).
12. *Phys. Rev.*, **48**, 696 (1935).
13. *Proc. Univ. of Durham Phil. Soc.*, **9**, 228 (1936).

中也包含这个常数，而不仅仅是一些完全定性的分析的话，我们将更容易接受他的结论。当然，也许在其背景理论中也存在像隐参量一样的某个常数！

综上所述，我将引用伯特兰·罗素[13]在 1936 年表述的观点：目前尚没有强有力的理由支持物理学中的完全决定论（因果律），但也没有任何理由反对它，并且理论上也不会存在这种理由。但是罗素没有提到冯·诺伊曼的观点。我的结论是现在的证据不利于完全的因果律，但是这个问题依旧没有被彻底解决。

（刘霞 翻译；赵见高 审稿）

Mode of Action of Penicillin

G. Lapage

Editor's Note

Here Geoffrey Lapage summarises the ongoing debate about how penicillin works. We now know that penicillin blocks cell wall synthesis, killing bacteria by making them burst. Alexander Fleming's colleague Edgar W. Todd veered towards this conclusion in a 1945 paper demonstrating the ability of penicillin to lyse bacteria, but he also thought the antibiotic could kill without lysis. Irish bacteriologist Joseph Bigger doubted the ability of penicillin to kill non-dividing bacteria, suggesting the drug be given intermittently to increase efficacy. Others came much closer to the truth, suggesting that penicillin is bacteriostatic, bactericidal and bacteriolytic in that order. Lapage notes that certain bacteria can be made much more resistant to penicillin, and notes that a unified theory of resistance is still lacking.

IN an article on penicillin treatment in *Nature* (677, Nov. 25, 1944) reference was made to the work of Lieut.-Colonel J. W. Bigger (*Lancet*, 497, Oct. 14, 1944), who concluded that penicillin actually kills *Staphylococcus pyogenes*. He suggested that it kills them at the time of division and has no effect upon individual cocci which are not dividing. These, therefore, persist in broth cultures, which penicillin frequently fails to sterilize, and are the explanation of that failure. Bigger proposed to give penicillin intermittently, in the hope that these "persisters" would begin dividing in the intervals of the penicillin doses and so would be killed by the next dose. Bigger refers to the work of C. D. Gardner (*Nature*, **146**, 837; 1940), who found that, in weak concentrations of penicillin, cocci swelled to three times their normal size without division, and bacilli showed similar changes.

E. W. Todd (*Lancet*, 74, Jan. 20, 1945) also refers to this and other work in his report on his experiments on the bacteriolytic action of penicillin. Working with Pneumococcus Types I, II and III and with *Streptococcus viridans*, haemolytic streptococci, staphylococci and *Clostridium welchii*, he found that all the strains of these organisms which he used were lysed by penicillin, but that such organisms as *Bact. coli* and *Pseudomonas pyocyanea*, which resist penicillin, were not lysed by it. But penicillin, he concluded, can kill organisms without lysis. When lysis occurs, its rate depends on the actual or potential rate of multiplication of the organisms. Their multiplication, as G. L. Hobby, K. Meyer and E. Chaffee (*Proc. Soc. Expt. Biol., N.Y.*, **50**, 281; 1942) also found, is essential for the action of penicillin. "It would appear that bacteriostasis, bactericidal action and bacteriolysis may be different stages of a single process proceeding in that order." The most rapid lysis occurs with organisms at the maximal rate of multiplication. This may be the real reason why penicillin is so effective, that is, because young actively multiplying cultures are more susceptible to bacteriolysis, so that organisms in the phase which enables them most readily to invade the human body are also then most susceptible to lysis.

青霉素的作用机制

拉帕吉

编者按

杰弗里·拉帕吉在这篇文章中对尚有争议的青霉素的作用机制进行了综述。我们现在知道青霉素阻断细胞壁的合成，使细菌胀裂而死。亚历山大·弗莱明的同事埃德加·托德在 1945 年的一篇描述青霉素对细菌的溶解能力的文章中得出这一结论，但他同时认为这种抗生素可以不通过溶解作用而杀死细菌。爱尔兰的细菌学家约瑟夫·比格对于青霉素杀死不分裂的细菌的能力颇为质疑，他建议通过间歇性给药来提高药效。另一些人的观点则更接近事实，他们认为青霉素依次具有抑制细菌增殖、杀菌和溶菌的性能。拉帕吉注意到有些细菌会对青霉素产生较强的耐药性，他还指出目前仍缺乏一个关于耐药性的统一理论。

《自然》（第 677 页，1944 年 11 月 25 日）中一篇关于青霉素治疗的文章引用了比格中校的工作（《柳叶刀》，第 497 页，1944 年 10 月 14 日），他的结论是青霉素直接杀死化脓葡萄球菌。不过，他认为青霉素杀死了处于分裂期的球菌，而对不分裂的个体则没有影响。因此，这些球菌继续存活于肉汤培养基中，青霉素无法将其清除，从而导致青霉素失效。于是，比格提出间歇性地加入青霉素，希望这些"顽固者"能在加药间歇期开始分裂从而被下一剂青霉素杀死。比格引用了加德纳的工作（《自然》，第 146 卷，第 837 页，1940 年），后者发现在低浓度的青霉素中，球菌膨胀到正常体积的三倍而不分裂，杆菌也表现出类似的变化。

托德（《柳叶刀》，第 74 页，1945 年 1 月 20 日）在关于青霉素溶菌作用实验的报道中也引用了这一研究和其他研究结果。在用 I 型、II 型和 III 型肺炎双球菌、绿色链球菌、溶血链球菌、葡萄球菌和韦氏梭菌进行的研究中，他发现所用的这些菌株都被青霉素溶解了，然而像大肠杆菌和绿脓杆菌等对青霉素具有抗性的细菌则不被溶解。但是他认为青霉素不通过溶菌作用也能杀死细菌。当溶菌发生时，其速率取决于细菌增殖的实际速率或潜在速率。霍比、迈耶和查菲（《实验生物学会会刊》，纽约，第 50 卷，第 281 页，1942 年）同样也发现细菌的增殖对青霉素是否有效起关键作用。"看来抑菌、杀菌和溶菌可能是同一过程中依次进行的不同阶段。"最快的溶菌速度出现在增殖速率最大的细菌中。这也许就是青霉素如此有效的真正原因，也就是说，培养时间不长的增殖活跃的细菌更易受到溶菌作用影响，虽然这时细菌最容易侵入人体，但是同时也最容易被溶解。

These conclusions may be compared with those of Prof. L. P. Garrod (*Brit. Med. J.*, 108, Jan 27, 1945), who agrees that penicillin actually kills susceptible bacteria. He quotes the further opinion of L. A. Rautz and W. M. M. Kirby (*J. Immunol.*, **48**, 335; 1944) that penicillin is actually bactericidal. Garrod gives, however, only qualified support to Bigger's hypothesis that penicillin is bactericidal only to organisms when they are about to divide, which was, he says, also put forward by G. L. Hobby and M. H. Dawson (*Proc. Soc. Expt. Biol., N.Y.*, **56**, 178; 1944) and by C. P. Miller and A. Z. Foster (*ibid.*, **56**, 205). Against this hypothesis, Garrod maintains, are (1) his experiments on the effects of temperature; like other disinfectants, penicillin is more active at higher temperatures, but is even more active at 42°C., when bacterial growth ceases, than at 37°C.; incidentally, Garrod finds that its action is impaired by increase of the acidity between pH 7.0 and 5.0; (2) the fact that bacteria from both old and very young cultures are almost uniformly susceptible. Garrod therefore thinks that there is no conclusive evidence in support of Bigger's proposal to give penicillin intermittently, and claims that clinical experience supports his view. Penicillin treatment fails because the organisms are inaccessible inside necrotic areas or in undetected abscesses.

Further important conclusions drawn by Garrod are that nothing is to be gained by using higher concentrations of penicillin (cf. Sir A. Fleming, *Lancet*, 621, Nov. 11, 1944; see also *Nature*, **155**, 341, March 17, 1945), especially in local treatment. The idea that higher doses will be more effective does not apply to penicillin. The reverse is truer. A concentration of 1 unit per c.c. is not only just as effective as one of 1,000 units, but is often more effective. The only good reason for using stronger solutions in local treatment is to ensure that the concentration does not fall below the minimum fully effective level of about 0.1 unit per c.c. Garrod further emphasizes the importance of the purity of the penicillin which is being used experimentally. He found that all commercial penicillins tested were less active in higher than in low concentrations. Presumably impurities were responsible for this, and they cause serious obstacles to the study of the action of penicillin. It will be necessary to find out whether penicillin is a single substance of unvarying composition and uniform action.

Discussing these results in a valuable leading article, the *British Medical Journal* (123, Jan. 27, 1945) directs attention to the enormous variation in the susceptibility of various bacteria to penicillin. Some species classed as totally resistant are affected by higher concentrations of penicillin; for example, the typhoid bacillus and the salmonellas. H. F. Helmholz and C. Sung (*Amer. J. Dis. Children*, **68**, 236; 1944) have found that some resistant bacteria in the urine are affected by high concentrations, for example, *Proteus* and some strains of *B. coli*. Only *Bact. aerogenes* and *Pseudomonas pyocyanea* remained unaffected. The treatment of some infections of the urinary tract with penicillin might thus be effective. E. W. Todd, G. S. Turner and L. G. W. Drew (*Brit. Med. J.*, 111, Jan. 27, 1945) have found that *Staphylococcus* strain Oxford H. can be trained by growth in increasing quantities of penicillin to become 3,000 times more resistant to penicillin than it originally was. Similar results were obtained

上述结论可以与加罗德教授（《英国医学杂志》，第 108 页，1945 年 1 月 27 日）的结论相比较，加罗德教授也认为青霉素确实可以杀死敏感细菌。他进一步引述了劳兹和柯比的看法（《免疫学杂志》，第 48 卷，第 335 页，1944 年），即青霉素实际上是杀菌的。不过，加罗德对于比格提出的青霉素只对即将分裂的细菌才有杀菌作用的假说只给予了部分肯定；他提到霍比和道森（《实验生物学会会刊》，纽约，第 56 卷，第 178 页，1944 年）以及米勒和福斯特（同前，第 56 卷，第 205 页）也提出过类似的观点。加罗德提出的反对观点包括：（1）他关于温度影响的实验，与其他杀菌剂相似，青霉素在较高温度时活性更强，在 42℃时格外地强，而细菌的增殖在超过 37℃时就停止了；另外，加罗德发现在 pH 7.0 到 5.0 之间时青霉素的作用随着酸性增加而减弱；（2）无论是在久置的还是全新的培养基中，细菌对药物的敏感程度基本一致。加罗德由此认为，并没有决定性的证据支持比格关于间断性施用青霉素的提议，并宣称临床经验支持他的看法。青霉素治疗失败是因为那些细菌处于青霉素无法接触到的坏死区域内部或者未检测到的脓肿之中。

加罗德得出的更为重要的结论是，使用高浓度的青霉素不会有什么效果（对比弗莱明爵士的文章，《柳叶刀》，第 621 页，1944 年 11 月 11 日；另见《自然》，第 155 卷，第 341 页，1945 年 3 月 17 日），尤其是在治疗局部感染时。剂量越大效果越好的观念并不适用于青霉素。事实恰好相反。每毫升 1 个单位的青霉素不仅可以与 1,000 个单位的药效一样，而且常常更为有效。在局部治疗中使用较浓药液的唯一恰当的理由是为了保证药物浓度不会减少到约每毫升 0.1 个单位的最小有效剂量之下。加罗德进一步强调了实验用青霉素纯度的重要性。他发现所有被检测的商品青霉素在高浓度时都比低浓度时活性更差。估计这是由杂质造成的，而杂质严重阻碍了对青霉素作用的研究。有必要确定青霉素是否是一种组成不变、作用一致的单一物质。

在《英国医学杂志》中，一篇重要的前沿文章对上述结果进行了讨论（第 123 页，1945 年 1 月 27 日），并引导大家关注各种细菌对青霉素敏感性的巨大差异。某些被列为具有完全耐药性的细菌会受到较高浓度青霉素的影响，例如伤寒杆菌和沙门氏菌。赫姆霍尔兹和宋（《美国儿童疾病杂志》，第 68 卷，第 236 页，1944 年）发现尿液中的某些耐药性细菌也受高浓度青霉素影响，例如变形杆菌属和大肠杆菌的某些菌株，只有产气杆菌和绿脓杆菌仍然不受影响。因此用青霉素治疗某些尿道感染可能是有效的。托德、特纳和德鲁（《英国医学杂志》，第 111 页，1945 年 1 月 27 日）发现葡萄球菌类的牛津 H 菌株可以通过在浓度逐渐增大的青霉素中培养而达到比最初大 3,000 倍的耐药性。对另一种葡萄球菌菌株的培养也得到了类似结果。不

with another strain of *Staphylococcus*. Unlike other organisms which become "drug-fast", however, *Staphylococcus* lost this property rapidly in media not containing penicillin. The authors refer to work which showed, on the other hand, that pneumococcus type III, made resistant to penicillin, either by culture in media containing penicillin (G. Rake *et al.*, *J. Immunol.*, **48**, 271; 1944) or by passage through mice treated with penicillin (L. H. Schmidt and C. L. Sesler, *Proc. Soc. Expt. Biol.*, *N.Y.*, **52**, 353; 1943), retained its resistance. The nature of these phenomena of resistance requires further investigation. Although some organisms can produce a penicillinase which destroys penicillin (see, for example, the penicillinase produced by *B. subtilis* reported by E. S. Duthie, *Brit. J. Expt. Path.*, **25**, 96; 1944), resistance to penicillin apparently does not always depend on the production by the resistant organism of penicillinase. W. M. Kirby (*Science*, 452, June 2, 1944) has extracted a substance which is not penicillinase from *Staphylococcus* resistant to penicillin.

(**155**, 403-404; 1945)

过，与产生"耐药性"的细菌不同，葡萄球菌在不含青霉素的培养基中迅速失去耐药性。作者也引用了与此相反的另外一些研究结果：无论是通过在含青霉素的培养基中进行病菌培养（雷克等人，《免疫学杂志》，第 48 卷，第 271 页，1994 年）还是借助用青霉素治疗过的老鼠进行病菌传代（施密特和塞斯勒，《实验生物学会会刊》，纽约，第 52 卷，第 353 页，1943 年），抗青霉素的 III 型肺炎双球菌的耐药性保持不变。这些耐药性现象的机制还有待于进一步研究。尽管某些细菌能够产生破坏青霉素的酶（例如，达西报道了枯草杆菌产生的青霉素酶，《英国实验病理学杂志》，第 25 卷，第 96 页，1944 年），不过青霉素耐药性显然并不总是取决于耐药菌能否产生青霉素酶。柯比（《科学》，第 452 页，1944 年 6 月 2 日）已经从有青霉素抗性的葡萄球菌中提取出了一种并非青霉素酶的物质。

（王耀杨 翻译；金侠 审稿）

Natural History of Granite

A. Holmes

Editor's Note

Geologists argued throughout the nineteenth century whether granite, a very common rock, is igneous or metamorphic—that is, the primary result of the crystallization of molten magma, or a chemically altered form of either igneous or sedimentary rocks under the action of permeating fluids. Here British geologist Arthur Holmes reviews the history of the debate, drawing particularly on a survey presented two years earlier to the British Geologists' Association by H. Read. The consensus, according to Holmes and Read, is that, while granites show some diversity of mineral composition, they are mostly the result of a single (yet complex) process of "granitization" that adds some material to, and removes some from, igneous basalts. That view remains supported today.

FOR a century and a half the origin of granite (including granodiorite) has remained one of the most intractable and controversial of the problems geologists have tried to solve. Fouqué and Levy's comment in 1882, that "it excites the most lively discussion", is as true today as ever before; and indeed might be regarded in some countries as a mild understatement of the passions that are aroused by apparent conflicts of evidence and very real conflicts of opinion. Hutton clearly established the status of granite as a crystalline plutonic rock, but the French geologists and Lyell and his followers soon realized that not all granites are necessarily of igneous origin. Some occurrences were seen to have no sharp contact against the aureole of metamorphic rocks, but to merge into the surrounding schists through a transitional zone of gneisses and felspathized schists so gradually that at no point could it be said that the rock ceased to be metamorphic and became igneous. These granites consequently came to be regarded, not as representing the cause of metamorphism, but as being the extreme products of its action.

Discussion thus became focused on the question whether a given mass of granite had crystallized from an intrusive magma which mechanically displaced the pre-existing rocks, or whether the granite had been made out of the pre-existing rocks by some process of ultra-metamorphism which was thought to culminate locally in actual fusion. The extreme magmatists have since come to admit that magma may react with the invaded rocks and assimilate the products; while adherents of the metamorphic view have realized that chemical changes are essential for the formation of granite, and that the pre-existing rocks must therefore have been permeated by granite magma or its derivatives (including the *ichor* of Sederholm and the hydrothermal solutions favoured in America), or by more tenuous migrating materials of unspecified origin, referred to as mineralizing agents or emanations. Between these limits of interpretation, many grades of opinion have been held, especially as regards the origin of granite magmas. Those who insist that all granites are igneous accept granite magma as having been available, either in its own right or, more

花岗岩的自然史

霍姆斯

编者按

整个 19 世纪地质学家们一直在争论常见的花岗岩到底是火成的还是变质的，也就是说它究竟是岩浆结晶的主要产物，还是其他的火成岩或沉积岩在液体侵入的情况下发生化学成分改变的结果。英国地质学家阿瑟·霍姆斯在这篇文章中主要借鉴了里德于两年前在英国地质学家协会上的调查报告，对这场争论的历史进行了回顾。霍姆斯和里德一致认为，尽管花岗岩的矿物成分有一定的差异，但它们大都是通过一个单一(但很复杂)的"花岗岩化"过程而形成的，火成玄武岩在此过程中被加入了一些成分，同时也被移去了一些成分。这个观点今天看来仍是正确的。

    一个半世纪以来，地质学家们都在尝试解决一些极为棘手且饱受争议的问题，而花岗岩（包括花岗闪长岩）的起源问题便是其中之一。福凯和利维在 1882 年对此作了以下评论——"它激起了最热烈的讨论"，这个评语不论是在过去还是现在都是正确的；其实，由于证据的明显不同和观点的完全差异，这种争论在有些国家被淡化了。赫顿明确指出，花岗岩是一种结晶的火成岩，但是法国地质学家们和赖尔以及赖尔的拥护者很快认识到并不是所有花岗岩的形成都必须是火成的。有些花岗岩与变质岩的接触带之间并不存在一个截然边界，而是通过片麻岩与长石化片岩的过渡区融入到周围的片岩之中。它们之间的边界是逐渐过渡的，并没有明确的一点可以显示此处的岩石已经变为火成岩而不再是变质岩。因此，这些花岗岩最终被认为不是造成变质作用的原因，而是变质作用的最终产物。

    讨论因此集中到这样一个问题上，即一定量的花岗岩究竟是由侵入到先成岩石中的岩浆结晶而成，还是由先成岩石通过某种超变质作用发生局部融熔而成。极端岩浆论者坚持认为岩浆可能与被侵入的岩石相互作用并发生了同化；而变质论的支持者则认为化学变化是花岗岩形成的关键，因此先成岩石肯定已被花岗岩浆或其衍生物（包括塞德霍尔姆的**岩汁**和美洲人所认为的热水溶液）所渗透，或被来源不确定的更细微的迁移物质（后者被看作是矿化剂或析出物）所渗透。介乎于上述两种解释之间仍存在许多不同层次的见解，特别是关于花岗岩浆的起源。坚持认为花岗岩全是火成的人相信，肯定存在花岗岩浆，它可能是一种特有的岩浆，或按照最近的说法，花岗岩浆可能是由残余玄武质岩浆部分结晶而形成。那些认为花岗岩主要

recently, as a residual magma thought to have been derived by fractional crystallization from an antecedent basaltic magma. Those who regard granites as having been largely formed from the pre-existing rocks recognize that they passed through a stage when part of the material was mobile or fluid. The partially fluid mash has been styled *migma* by Reinhard, to distinguish it from a mash consisting of incompletely crystallized magma. Moreover, magma may be generated from migma either by the attainment of complete fluidity or, at any stage, by the squeezing out of the fluid portion.

It is unfortunately not generally realized that the battle between rival camps has been repeated more than once, with varying fortunes at different times and in different countries. Most of the older English-speaking petrologists of today were brought up, like myself, in the faith that granite, being by definition an igneous rock, must have crystallized from a magma; and many of us have had to rediscover for ourselves that the plutonic characters of granite are not in themselves a guarantee of igneous origin: a fact, long overlooked, to which Scheerer had already specifically directed attention so early as 1847. Still worse, we were left in ignorance of the stimulating ideas of the French school, or with the impression that they were old-fashioned and unworthy of serious consideration. Looking back, it is obvious that a carefully balanced historical introduction would have dispersed the fog of dogma and prejudice in which we were unconsciously groping. But no one had undertaken the arduous task of preparing such a survey, and in its absence enlightenment was slow and largely dependent on the luck of one's personal experience in the field. Iddings[1], it is true, had published a historical review of the origin of igneous rocks in 1892, but this dealt mainly with volcanic rocks and their magmas, and neither the problems associated with granite nor the achievements of the French school were as much as mentioned. Now, half a century later, full amends have been made to the masters of the past in two illuminating presidential addresses delivered by Prof. H. H. Read[2] to the Geologists' Association, the keynote being Hutton's remark: "I have been particularly anxious about this subject of granite". Fortunately, our historian has a background of field experience that ensures sympathetic and competent judgments. Inevitably he holds up the mirror to himself as well as to others, but only to reveal himself as a good-humoured guide who neither claims authority nor acknowledges any, save only in the rocks themselves.

One of the "high lights" of the story is the record of the great contributions made by the French, a record which anticipates in the most remarkable way the more detailed developments of recent years. In 1824 we find Ami Boué describing what would now be called granitization, and suggesting that the passage through crystalline schists of heat and gaseous exudations from the earth's interior was responsible for the growth of veins and disseminated crystals, and eventually for "a kind of igneous liquefaction". In 1837-38 Fournet distinguishes metamorphic rocks due to simple recrystallization from others in which partial melting has occurred, combined on occasion with inward and outward migrations of material. In 1841 Deville introduces the idea of mineralizing agents—gases which carry mineral matter and so chemically transform (as we should now say, by metasomatism) the rock substances through which they diffuse. In 1844 Virlet d'Aoust uses the term *imbibition* to express the idea that igneous materials have soaked into

是由先成岩石而形成的人则承认，花岗岩经历了一个部分物质呈流体或液体状态的阶段。这种半液态的浆状物被赖因哈德命名为**混合岩浆**，以便与由没有完全结晶的岩浆构成的浆状物区别开来。另外，岩浆可以由混合岩浆产生，要么完全从液体产生，要么在某个阶段从液体部分挤出。

　　令人遗憾的是，人们没有普遍认识到对立阵营之间的争论已经发生了不止一次，而随着国家和时间的不同占优势的论点也不相同。今天大多数讲英语的老一辈岩石学家，例如我从小就被告知，被定义为火成岩的花岗岩肯定是由岩浆结晶形成的；我们中的许多人现在不得不重新调整自己的认识，花岗岩的侵入特征本身并不能保证它一定是火成的，舍雷尔早在1847年就已经提醒公众关注这一被长期忽略的事实。更糟糕的是我们一直忽视法兰西学派的这些新颖的观点，或者认为它们是过时的，并不值得认真对待。回首过去，有一点很明显，仔细权衡过的历史介绍将有助于我们祛除教条和偏见的迷雾，而我们没有觉察到我们一直在这样的迷雾中苦苦摸索。然而，没有人愿意承担对历史进行考察的艰巨任务，因此领悟的过程就会比较缓慢，且在很大程度上依赖于个人在野外工作中的运气。虽然伊丁斯[1]在1892年确实已经发表过一篇关于火成岩起源的历史性回顾文章，但他主要论述了火山岩及其岩浆，并没怎么提及与花岗岩有关的问题以及法兰西学派的成就。在半个世纪之后的今天，里德[2]教授为地质学家协会作了两次很有启发性的演讲，他对前辈学者的论点进行了充分修正，演讲的主题是赫顿的一句话："我一直特别关注花岗岩问题。"幸运的是，我们的历史学家有野外工作经验，这可以确保他们能做出令人满意的正确评价。里德教授无疑会如实反映自己和他人的想法，他只把自己当成是一个随和的指导者，从不自称权威也不承认权威，他只看重岩石本身。

　　这个演讲的一个"亮点"是指出了法国人的巨大贡献，法国人用最卓越的方式预见了近几年的发展趋势。我们发现阿米·布韦在1824年曾经描述过现在称之为花岗岩化的过程，他认为来自地球内部的热和气体缓慢渗透结晶片岩的过程是脉体和扩散晶体生长的原因，并最终导致"火成液化"。在1837~1838年期间，福内特将由简单再结晶而形成的变质岩与其他一些部分熔融并伴有物质向内和向外迁移的岩石区别开来。德维尔在1841年引入了矿化剂的概念——矿化剂是携带矿物质的气体，它能使所侵入的岩石体发生化学成分转变（我们现在应该称之为交代作用）。1844年，维莱特·道斯特用术语**吸浸作用**来表述火成物质渗入到变质沉积岩中并将其转变成为花岗岩的观点。在不久之后的1847年，他又把这个过程称为**花岗岩化**。同年，福

metamorphosed sedimentary rocks and transformed them into granite. Shortly afterwards, in 1847, he speaks of the process as *granitification*. In the same year, Fournet notes that, in certain metamorphosed sediments, far more felspar has developed than could possibly be accounted for by simple recrystallization, and so provides evidence that introduction of material must have taken place. In 1869 Delesse submits the hypothesis that granitized plutonic rocks may become so mobile that they can be squeezed towards the surface, to form intrusive granites at high levels in the crust, where they may have lost all the characters from which their true origin could be determined.

Before considering one of the major turning points in the history of petrogenesis which was now approaching, it is of interest to see what was happening in the British Isles during the rise of the French school. Following Lyell's suggestion, "metamorphic" granites had been widely claimed in Scotland and Ireland, but more stress was given to heat and fusion, partial or complete, than to change of composition and fluxing by introduced materials. In 1862 Scott and Haughton advocated a twofold origin for the granitic rocks of Donegal, of which they recognized both metamorphic and intrusive varieties. In 1871 Green[3] described the vestiges of bedding that visibly remain in the granite of the Errigal district; and suggested that in places these ghost-like structures had been destroyed by fusion, and that the fused material, in virtue of its superior mobility, had behaved intrusively. The objection that in order to convert sedimentary rocks into granite certain missing substances would have to be restored was apparently not realized. A few years later this difficulty was independently faced by Clifton Ward (1876) on lines that the French work should already have made familiar. Discussing the origin of the granites of the Lake District, he writes: "Although a simple melting down might never produce granite, yet a moist fusion, accompanied by elementary substances, brought upwards from still greater depths, might effect a great transformation". Ward's suggestion was stillborn, and the old ideas lingered on in Ireland until adverse criticism from Callaway[4] and Bonney, whose sympathies were with Rosenbusch, finally banished "metamorphic" granite from the pages of the memoirs of the Irish Survey.

The critical year appears to have been 1877, when Rosenbusch[5] published his classic work on the contact metamorphism of the slates around the granite of Barr-Andlau (Vosges) and showed by a series of chemical analyses that there was no significant change of composition in the altered rocks as they were traced towards the margin of the granite. Having found in this example no evidence of transfer of material into the country rocks, Rosenbusch afterwards denied the very possibility of such permeation, and claimed that the gneisses and felspathized schists which elsewhere appeared to demand introduction of granite-making substances were themselves merely granites that had suffered dynamic metamorphism during orogenic movements. Like Werner, Rosenbusch attracted from abroad many students who afterwards achieved fame, and so great was his authority—outside France—that his doctrines dominated petrological opinion for two generations.

The French, however, did not allow their case to go by default. Barrois (Rostrenon, 1884), Michel Levy (Flammanville, 1893), and Lacroix (Pyrenees, 1898-1900) found large, well-

内特在一些变质沉积物中发现大量的长石，大量长石的出现不可能简单地用重结晶来解释，因此证明肯定发生过物质的加入。德莱斯在 1869 年提出一个假设，花岗岩化的深成岩石也许具有很强的流动性，以至于它们可能被挤向地表，从而在地壳浅层形成侵入花岗岩。这些岩石可能已经失去了可以确定它们真实起源的全部特征。

接下来我们要讨论岩石成因学历史上的一个主要转折点，但在此之前有必要关注一下在法兰西学派兴起时不列颠群岛上发生了什么。根据赖尔的看法，那时"变质"花岗岩已经在苏格兰和爱尔兰得到了广泛的承认，但是他们主要强调热的作用以及部分或全部熔融，而较少关注成分的变化和外来物质的加入。1862 年，斯科特和霍顿提出多尼戈尔地区的花岗岩具有双重成因，因为他们在其中识别出变质和侵入两种成因类型。1871 年格林 [3] 描述了留存在埃里格尔山区花岗岩中明显的层理痕迹；他认为这些神秘的结构在许多地区已经被熔融所破坏，而熔融物由于具有很强流动性已表现出侵入性。当时显然并没有意识到这样一个困难，即为了把沉积岩转变成花岗岩，就必须要恢复一些消失了的物质。几年之后，克利夫顿·沃德（1876 年）也独自碰到了这个困难，他的思路是此前法兰西学派应该已经熟知了的。在讨论湖区的花岗岩成因时，他写道："虽然单一的熔化过程可能产生不了花岗岩，但是伴随来自更深处原始物质的湿熔融作用可能会导致巨大变化。"然而沃德的提议没被接受，直到卡拉韦 [4] 和邦尼提出反对意见，旧的观点才逐渐在爱尔兰消失，他们支持罗森布施的观点，并最终将"变质"花岗岩从爱尔兰地质调查局的论文集中剔除。

1877 年是个重要年份，罗森布施 [5] 在那一年发表了关于巴尔－昂德洛（孚日省）山区花岗岩周围板岩的接触变质作用的经典著作，通过一系列化学分析，他发现花岗岩附近的那些已发生变化的岩石在成分上并没有发生明显的改变。在这个实例中，没有发现物质向围岩转移的迹象，因此罗森布施最终否定了物质渗入的可能性，他认为那些在别处需要花岗质物质侵入的片麻岩和长石片岩，在这里其本身就是在造山运动中经受了动力学变质的花岗岩。和维尔纳一样，罗森布施从国外招纳了很多学生，这些人后来也都成了名，罗森布施在法国以外的地区有着很高的威望，以至于他的学说在岩石学界影响了两代人。

然而法国人并没有默然接受这一观点。巴鲁瓦（1884 年于罗斯特勒南）、米歇尔·利维（1893 年于弗拉芒维尔）和拉克鲁瓦（1898~1900 年于比利牛斯）在花岗岩

shaped crystals of orthoclase, identical with those of the adjoining porphyritic granite, not only in the sedimentary schists outside the granite, but also in enclaves of similar material occurring within the granite. Neither the felspars nor the granites show any sign of dynamic metamorphism, and the structures are entirely different from those of, say, the Mont Blanc granite, which has demonstrably been sheared. The crucial nature of the evidence provided by the "big felspars" has long been realized, since no one has seriously doubted that they must all have shared a common origin. Either they grew in solid rock or they crystallized from a magma: identical felspars could not be assumed to have originated in two entirely different physicochemical environments. Those who believed that they could form only by crystallization from a magma resorted to various expedients to avoid the disturbing implications of their presence in contact zones and enclaves. Rosenbusch stubbornly maintained his earlier interpretation, to the justifiable astonishment of Lacroix. Actually, the possibility of transfer of silicate-making materials was never widely admitted until the publication of Goldschmidt's proof (1921) that influx of silica and soda had accompanied the contact metamorphism of pelitic rocks in the Stavanger area. Before this convincing demonstration, and even afterwards, Cole[6] (1915) and Thomas and Campbell Smith (1932), among others, took refuge in the unmanageable hypothesis that the big felspars had somehow been bodily introduced from an assumed magmatic source. A fatal objection to this awkward idea is that the felspars are to be found in obviously sedimentary contacts and enclaves, among which, as Read points out, there are examples where "delicate bedding displayed often in three dimensions, is not disturbed in the least". Innumerable exposures show that the felspars cannot have been introduced mechanically. Harker ignored or minimized the evidence, and many other petrologists preferred to remain silent on the matter, presumably because they had nothing to say about what could not be understood. Nevertheless, a definite and far-reaching conclusion can be drawn in all cases where it can be established—as it generally can—that the felspars did not grow as "porphyritic" crystals of post-granite formation. To quote Read: "Where the xenoliths [enclaves] containing the felspars are sedimentary, then what encloses the xenoliths and similar felspars is also sedimentary—the porphyritic granites are produced from the sediments by an intensification of the felspathization process"; and, he pertinently adds, no one can *demonstrate* a magmatic origin for the porphyritic granite which contains the "xenoliths".

Meanwhile, as a result of several comparative studies of felspathization and granitization, the French geologists became convinced that these processes increase in intensity downwards until the contact zones of the higher crustal levels merge into regions where the rocks have been quietly made over into granite without significant disturbance of the pre-existing strata. Both Michel Levy and Lacroix thought of the active agent as granite magma, but Lacroix makes it clear that the magma must have been chemically and physically very different from merely molten granite, since it generates granite only after incorporating the schists that were there before the granite. Termier (1904 and 1910) developed this conception to its logical conclusion by pointing out that the active magma envisaged by Lacroix could itself be accounted for in terms of pre-existing rocks and highly energized emanations. He speaks of the latter as *colonnes filtrantes*, which rise

外侧的沉积性片岩中以及花岗岩内部由相似物质组成的包体中都发现了形状很好的正长石大晶体，这些正长石晶体与邻近的斑状花岗岩中的正长石晶体完全一样。无论是长石还是花岗岩都没有表现出任何动力变质的迹象，其结构完全不同于那些发生过明显构造剪切作用的花岗岩，如勃朗峰花岗岩。"大长石"提供的证据的重要意义很早就已被认识到，因为没有人对它们具有相同的成因表示过严重的怀疑。不论长石生长在固体岩石中，还是由岩浆结晶而成：相同的长石不可能在两种完全不同的物理化学环境中形成。那些认为大长石只可能从岩浆中结晶而成的人尽量避免讨论出现在接触带和包体中的大长石的意义。罗森布施顽固地坚持他以前的解释，这令拉克鲁瓦感到惊讶，但也能够理解。1921 年，戈耳什密特发表了一项研究成果，即认为斯塔万格地区泥质岩在接触变质过程中伴随着二氧化硅和碳酸钠的加入，直到此时，人们才开始广泛接受形成硅酸盐的物质发生迁移的可能性。在这个具有说服力的研究成果发表之前，甚至之后，以科尔 [6]（1915 年）、托马斯及坎贝尔·史密斯（1932 年）为代表的一些人提出了一个臆想，认为大长石可能是由一个假设的岩浆源整体加入进来的。这个糟糕论点有一个致命缺陷，对于那些出现在明显的沉积边界处以及包体中的长石，如里德所指出，其中有些在"三维空间上表现出的一些细微层理完全没有被扰乱"，而上述论点无法对此进行解释。无数岩石露头显示长石不可能被机械地挤入。哈克忽视或低估了这些证据，而其他岩石学家对此也宁可保持沉默，也许是因为对于难以理解的事物他们也没有什么意见可说。然而，像在大多数情况下一样，根据所有能够利用的证据应该可以得出一个明确而有影响的结论，即长石不会在花岗岩形成以后生长成"斑"晶。引用里德的话说："如果含有长石的捕虏体（包体）是沉积岩，那么包围捕虏体与类似长石的岩石也是沉积性的——斑状花岗岩是由强烈长石化的沉积物形成的。"他还恰当地补充说，没人能够**证明**包含"捕虏岩"的斑状花岗岩为岩浆成因。

与此同时，在比较了几个长石化和花岗岩化过程之后，法国地质学家们开始相信这些过程的强度自上而下逐渐增加，它们向地壳深部过渡到另一区域，在那里岩石平静地转化为花岗岩，对先存的地层没有明显的扰动。米歇尔·利维和拉克鲁瓦两人都认为花岗岩浆为活动营力，而拉克鲁瓦进一步明确指出，这种岩浆在物理和化学性质上与单一的熔融花岗岩有很大的差别，因为它是与早期片岩融合后才产生的花岗岩。泰尔米埃（1904 年和 1910 年）发展了这一概念并得出一个合理的结论，他认为拉克鲁瓦所说的活动岩浆本身就可以用先成岩石和强烈的析出物来解释。泰尔米埃将后者称为**残余岩浆**，这种岩浆来自地槽的深部，在上升过程中经过能量的

from the depths into, say, geosynclinal strata, adding energy and exchanging new elements for old as they ascend and spread out. Where the intensity is greatest the rocks are granitized and locally transformed into magma, while the displaced elements are driven forward with the other migrating materials in an advancing and slowly declining wave of metamorphism. Part of the magma generated in depth may invade the superstructure, forming granite intrusions with contacts of various kinds, including those of Rosenbusch's Barr-Andlau type. For Termier, regional metamorphism and intrusions (at all levels) "are but two effects of the same cause". Although Termier's impressive synthesis was too imaginative to command serious attention, it nevertheless foreshadowed much of the progress that has since been made in this complex field of research. In particular, we find in it a revival of Fournet's early hint of what has recently come to be known as the advance of the "migmatite front".

The term *migmatite* was proposed by Sederholm for rocks which suggest by their appearance that they originated "by the mixture of older rocks and a later erupted granite magma". Along the shores of southern Finland and its fringing archipelagoes, the wave-swept rock surfaces display spectacular examples of all the phenomena associated with granitization. By means of a series of lavishly illustrated memoirs (1907-34), as well as by conducting several international excursions, Sederholm made these challenging exposures so generally familiar that the baleful influence of the Rosenbusch school was at last effectively countered. Sederholm did not maintain his first conviction that what had injected and permeated the older rocks was a primary granite magma, but he seems never to have abandoned altogether the idea—although he wavered at times—that such magma was the ultimate source of the invading materials. He envisaged an ultra-metamorphic process referred to as *anatexis*, involving injection, solution, refusion, assimilation and differentiation, whereby new magma was formed. The newly born magma, having the original granite magma and the country rocks as its parents, became available in its turn for further migmatization. Later, he ascribed less importance to granite magma, whether primary or secondary, and more to what he called *ichor*, a derivative magmatic solution highly charged with water and other volatiles, and thereby endowed with great penetrative power. The primary granite magma thus became only a grandparent of the second generation of ichor. The weakness of this conception lies in the implication that relatively small quantities of ichor, though derived by magmatic differentiation, had nevertheless sufficient energy and chemical activity to promote anatexis on a regional scale and so to make more magma and more ichor out of large quantities of country rock. Evidently if the immigrating materials are to be capable of effecting granitization or anatexis on the scale observed, they must differ fundamentally in properties and origin from the late-stage exudations of a granite magma as ordinarily conceived. For this reason the neutral term *emanations*, which is free from genetic implications, is now coming increasingly into favour.

Wegmann, now Argand's successor at Neuchâtel, has greatly clarified our ideas by the results of his long and detailed field studies in Finland (1931, in collaboration with Kranck) and Greenland (1935 and 1938). Wegmann is especially interested in the mechanism of *stoffwanderung*, the migration of atoms involved in migmatization and granitization, and

补充和新旧物质的交换，然后喷涌而出。在强度最大的地方，岩石就会发生花岗岩化，并局部转化为岩浆，而被置换的成分与其他迁移物质一起向前推移，但变质程度在向前移动的过程中逐渐减弱。深层形成的部分岩浆可侵入到上部构造中，形成具有多种接触类型的花岗岩侵入体，其中包括罗森布施所称的巴尔－昂德洛型。泰尔米埃认为，区域变质作用和侵入体（在所有层次上）"仅仅是同一原因造成的两种结果"。尽管泰尔米埃引人注目的假说因想象的成分过多而未被认真对待，但这一学说后来对这一复杂的研究领域所取得的许多成果都有指导意义。特别是我们在其中看到了福内特早期论点的复兴，该论点最近被称为"混合岩前缘"的扩展。

塞德霍尔姆提出**混合岩**这一术语是为了说明那些从表面上看来是"由早期岩石和后来喷发的花岗岩浆混合而成"的岩石。在芬兰南部海岸及其边缘的群岛，波浪洗刷过的岩石表面表现出与花岗岩化有关的所有壮观的景象。通过在一系列附有优美插图的论文集（1907~1934年）以及多次国际野外考察，塞德霍尔姆使这些具有挑战性的结论广为人知，并使罗森布施学派的有害影响最终遭到了有力的反击。塞德霍尔姆并未坚持自己最初的观点，即认为注入和渗入到先期岩石中的是原始花岗岩浆，尽管他的观点有时会摇摆不定，但他似乎从未完全放弃把这种岩浆看作是侵入物质最终源头的想法。他把一种超变质作用称为**深熔作用**，该过程包括注入、分解、再熔化、同化、分异，最后形成新的岩浆。以原始花岗岩浆和围岩为母体，这种新生岩浆的存在可导致进一步混合岩化的发生。他随后认为花岗岩浆无论是原始的还是次生的皆不重要，他更强调一种被称为**岩汁**的派生岩浆流体，该流体富含水和其他挥发性物质，所以具有很强的渗透力。因此初始花岗岩浆仅仅是第二代岩汁的母体的母体。这一设想的弱点在于，产生于岩浆分异作用但相对较少的岩汁为何具有足够的能量和化学活性去引发区域性的深熔作用，并从大量的围岩中生成更多的岩浆和岩汁。显然，如果迁移物质能够在可观察到的尺度上对花岗岩化或深熔作用产生影响，那么它们必然在性质和成因上与普通意义上的后期溢出花岗岩浆有本质的区别。由于这个原因，没有成因内涵的中性术语**析出物**现在越来越流行了。

韦格曼现在是阿尔冈在瑞士纳沙泰尔地区的接班人，他在芬兰（1931年，与克兰克合作）和格陵兰（1935年和1938年）长期而详细的野外研究结果极好地阐明了我们的观点。韦格曼对**物质迁移**机制特别感兴趣，即混合岩化和花岗岩化过程中

has made familiar the concept of an advancing migmatite front. He is also a pioneer in the attempt to unravel the complex relationships between orogenic movements and atomic migrations. He draws a graphic distinction between:

(a) migration of elements through a framework of earlier rocks which remains stationary and so retains its former structures, despite extensive exchange of materials and recrystallization; and

(b) migration through a framework which is itself deformed by movements during or after the migmatization; in this case relative movement between the more mobile migmatized parts and the more rigid parts of the framework leads inevitably to intrusive contacts; and when, as must often have happened, the final crystallization of such mobile masses outlasts the movements, the ancestral structures are obliterated, except perhaps for a few schlieren and enclaves, and the eventual result is a more or less massive granite.

The leading exponent of the subject in Sweden is Backlund, whose views have developed along essentially similar lines. He has particularly discussed the transformations of rocks such as limestone, quartzite and metabasite and has shown how selective and progressive metasomatism dispels the chemical difficulties that seemed insuperable to Callaway and Bonney and, more recently, to Harker and Niggli; the granitizing materials that are retained and fixed vary with the composition of the rocks that are being granitized. He has also stressed the important fact that granitization has been a normal accompaniment of orogenesis throughout geological time. Read gives an admirable account of these recent Fennoscandian developments, including a summary of the spirited debate between Backlund and von Eckermann (1937-38) on the genesis of the rapakivi granites.

The geochemical relationships involved in granitization can be briefly summarized in the formula: granite = pre-existing rock *plus* added material (A) introduced by and abstracted from the incoming emanations (A+x), *minus* displaced material (B) driven forward with the outgoing emanations (B+x). When successive stages of the transformation of pre-existing rock into granite can be seen in the field, it is possible (provided that there has been no significant volume change) to determine A and B. The most notable work along these lines has been that of Doris L. Reynolds[7]. In the course of her investigation of the Newry complex, she has proved by chemical analyses of carefully correlated specimens that the minimum introductions (A) required for the granitization of the country rocks were sodium, calcium and silicon; while, after several intermediate exchanges that are traced in detail, the displaced materials (B) eventually carried forward consisted of aluminium, iron, magnesium, potassium, hydrogen, titanium, phosphorus and manganese. The latter, together with some remaining sodium, calcium and silicon, became fixed in adjacent bands of hornfels which were thereby basified and transformed into rocks chemically equivalent to certain varieties of quartz-diorite. From these results and other relevant evidence, Dr. Reynolds concludes:

原子的迁移，他还使混合岩前缘扩展的概念广为人知。在解释造山运动与原子迁移之间的复杂关系方面，他也是位先驱者。他对二者做了生动的区分，如下：

(a) 元素是通过早期岩石框架发生迁移的，虽然经历了强烈的物质交换和再结晶过程，岩石框架却仍保持静止并维持先前的结构不变；

(b) 元素迁移所通过的岩石框架是在混合岩化期间或之后发生的变形；在这种情况下，流动性较强的混合岩化部分和比较坚硬的框架之间的相对运动必然会导致侵入式接触；像经常发生的那样，当流动体最终结晶的时间长于这种运动时，岩石最初的结构将荡然无存，但可能有少数异离体和包体会残留下来，而最终产生的或许就是一个块状花岗岩。

在瑞典，这个论点的主要倡导者是巴克隆德，他的理论基本是沿着类似的思路发展的。他专门论述了一些岩石的转换过程，例如灰岩、石英岩和变基性岩，他还解释了有选择性的渐进式交代变质作用是如何解决了化学方面的难题，而这些难题对于卡拉韦和邦尼，以及今天的哈克和尼格利来说是无法逾越的；保留和固定下来的花岗岩化物质因发生花岗岩化的岩石成分不同而有所变化。他也强调了这样一个重要的事实，即在地质历史中，造山运动一般都伴随有花岗岩化。里德非常清晰地描述了芬诺斯坎迪亚地区最近的研究进展，其中还简要介绍了巴克隆德与冯·埃克曼（1937~1938 年）在环斑花岗岩成因问题上的激烈争论。

花岗岩化过程中涉及的地球化学关系可以用以下公式来简要说明：花岗岩 = 先成岩石 + 加入物质 (A)（来自于向内的渗入物质 ($A+x$)）– 被置换物质 (B)（来自于向外的析出物 ($B+x$)）。如果可以在野外识别出先成岩石向花岗岩转变的连续阶段，那么就有可能（假设没有发生过明显的体积变化）确定出 A 和 B 的成分。多丽丝·雷诺兹 [7] 沿循这一思路做出的研究成果最为突出。她在考察北爱尔兰的纽里杂岩时，对详细挑选的样品进行了化学分析，结果证明围岩发生花岗岩化需要的加入物质 (A) 中至少应含有元素钠、钙和硅；然而在经过了几个被详细示踪的中间变化后，证明被最终置换出的物质 (B) 中含有元素铝、铁、镁、钾、氢、钛、磷和锰。物质 (B) 与一些残留的钠、钙、硅一起，在邻近的角岩条带中存留下来，这些角岩进一步通过基性化作用转变为化学成分与某些石英闪长岩相似的岩石。根据以上结果和其他一些相关证据，雷诺兹博士得出以下结论：

(a) that the introduced material ($A+x$) cannot have been an ordinary magma, since x has left no recognizable traces in the rocks;

(b) that the basic material migrating from a region of granitization, besides enriching the surrounding aureole in biotite and other minerals, was probably also responsible for the "igneous-looking" basic and ultrabasic rocks that overlie the granitic rocks of many plutonic complexes; and

(c) that before a given mass of country rock was actually granitized, it passed through a preliminary stage of basification.

From the nature of the case, little can be said about the ultimate source of the granite-making emanations. The granophyric contact zones and rheomorphic veins locally associated with dolerite sills and dykes in non-orogenic regions[8] indicate that at least some basaltic magmas have been capable of providing a limited supply. In depth, basaltic magma may be a potential source of considerable importance. In orogenic regions, however, attempts to relate the emanations to the supposed magmas of associated basic rocks are weakened by the possibility, in some cases confirmed, that such rocks have themselves originated as complementary by-products of the granitization process. The major processions of emanations may conceivably be liberated from abyssal magmas by differentiation, or squeezed out of the intensely sheared roots of growing mountain ranges; or they may have a source of some quite unsuspected kind. But our ignorance of the source of orogenic emanations in no way militates against the evidence of their passage through the rocks. The origin of basaltic magma remains equally uncertain, despite many optimistic suggestions to the contrary. Read quotes with approval Kennedy's recognition (1938) of two contrasted expressions of magmatic activity, distinguished respectively as:

(a) *volcanic* associations, derived from a parental basaltic magma which originates by the remelting of the earth's basaltic layer; and

(b) *plutonic* associations, derived from a parental granodioritic magma which originates where tectonic thickening of the crust brings the "granite" layer within the range of melting; the ascent of such magma is preceded by an advancing wave of granitization and migmatization.

Since 1938, more precise estimates have been made of the heat generated in rocks by radioactivity, and of the crustal heat flow that escapes at the surface in Britain, South Africa and eastern North America. The results imply that in these non-volcanic regions the normal granitic and basaltic layers fall short of the temperatures required for magma formation by several hundreds of degrees[9]. In the light of the evidence now available, we can do no more than speculate as to how basaltic magma comes into existence. Where the granitic layer is greatly thickened in the roots of mountain ranges, the temperature at the base might eventually rise to the point required to start selective fusion, but many millions

（a）被加入的物质（$A+x$）不可能是一种原始岩浆，因为 x 在岩石中没有留下可辨认的痕迹。

（b）从花岗岩区迁移出的基性物质不仅使其周边接触变质带中的黑云母和其他矿物变得富集,还有可能导致了"外表类似火成岩"的基性和超基性岩石的形成，它们就位于有许多深成杂岩体的花岗岩之上。

（c）在一定量的围岩开始发生花岗岩化以前，它已经经历了一个基性岩化的初级阶段。

从这个过程本身判断不出形成花岗岩的析出物到底来源于哪里。在非造山区[8]局部与粗玄武岩岩床和岩脉相关的花斑状接触带和流变脉体说明，至少有一些玄武岩浆可以成为部分析出物的来源。玄武岩浆也许是深部重要的潜在源区。然而在造山带地区，岩浆的析出物与相伴基性岩的岩浆似乎就没有什么关系了，因为一些实例证实，基性岩本身就是花岗岩化的副产品。可以设想，大部分析出物可能是在深部岩浆的分异过程中被释放的，或者是在生长山脉的根部发生强烈剪切时被挤出的；或者另有其他未知的来源。虽然我们对造山带的析出物的来源缺乏了解，但不能因此否定析出物在岩石中发生迁移的事实。玄武岩浆的起源同样不能确定，尽管许多乐观的意见并不这么认为。里德赞同肯尼迪（1938 年）关于岩浆活动的两种不同表达方式，它们分别为：

（a）**火山岩**组合：来源于由于地球玄武岩层再熔化而形成的玄武岩浆；

（b）**深成岩**组合：来源于花岗闪长岩浆，这种岩浆形成的温度范围与地壳构造增厚而导致"花岗岩"层处于融化时的温度范围相同；这种岩浆在上升之前先发生了花岗岩化和混合岩化作用。

自1938年以来,人们更加精确地估算了放射性在岩石中产生的热量,以及英国、南非和北美东部地表的热流。结果说明，在非火山活动区，一般花岗岩和玄武岩层达不到形成岩浆所需的温度，实际上还差几百度[9]。根据现在已知的证据，我们只能对玄武岩浆的成因进行推测。在山脉根部花岗岩岩层很厚的地方，底部的温度可能最终会上升到发生选择性熔融的起始点，但这个过程可能需要几百万年，即使这样，仍需要潜在热源作为补充。因而，上述过程不能解释我们观察到的下

of years would be required, and even then latent heat would have to be supplied. The suggested process therefore fails to account for the observed fact that granitic rocks began to be formed (at levels well within the range of subsequent denudation) *while* the orogenic movements were actively in progress. Thus the whole problem of magma generation, apart from the possibilities associated with the emanation hypothesis, is still as baffling as ever.

There remains for consideration the all-important space problem: How have large masses (batholiths) of granitic rocks come to occupy their present positions, and what has happened to the rocks that were previously there? The bodily intrusion of gigantic volumes of magma appears to be mechanically impossible; and, as Read puts it: "The only solution is to suggest that in fact no large bodies of granitic magma were in existence. The large granite masses result from replacement, they are granitization products. Many of the small granites may of course also be of the same origin, but some of them may result from the consolidation of migma and some from the consolidation of magma. Thus, though there may be granites and granites, most of them are of one kind and all of them may likely be of one connected origin." With this conclusion I am in full agreement.

(**155**, 412-415; 1945)

References:

1. Iddings, J. P., *Bull. Phil. Soc. Washington*, **12**, 91 (1892).

2. Read, H. H., "Meditations on Granite: Part I", *Proc. Geol. Assoc.*, **54**, 64 (1943); Part II, *ibid.*, **55**, 45 (1944)

3. Green, A. H., *Geol. Mag.*, **8**, 428, 553 (1871).

4. Callaway, C., *Quart. J. Geol. Soc.*, **41**, 221 (1885).

5. Rosenbusch, H., *Abh. Geol. Spezialkarte Elsass-Lothr.*, **1**, 80 (1877).

6. Cole, G. A. J., *Quart. J. Geol. Soc.*, **71**, 184 (1915).

7. Reynolds, D. L., *Proc. Roy. Irish Acad.*, **48** B, 231 (1943); *Quart. J. Geol. Soc.,* **99**, 205 (1943).

8. Reynolds, D. L., *Quart. J. Geol. Soc.*, **97**, 1 (1941). Walker, F., and Poldervaart, A., *Trans. Roy. Soc. S. Africa.*, **29**, 285 (1942).

9. Holmes, A., "Principles of Physical Geology", 480-483 (Edinburgh, 1944).

References already given by Read (see ref. 2) have not been repeated; the above are additional.

列事实，即为什么花岗岩（在后期剥露的不同层位范围内）在造山运动很活跃时就开始形成了。对于岩浆的成因问题，我们只知道其可能与析出物有关，除此之外，仍一无所知。

下面要考虑的是至关重要的空间占位问题：大的花岗岩体（岩基）是如何占据它现有的位置的，原来在那的岩石到哪里去了？巨量岩浆的整体侵入在力学上似乎是不可能实现的。正如里德所指出："唯一的解释是事实上根本就不存在大的花岗岩浆体。大的花岗岩体是通过置换作用生成的，是花岗岩化的产物。许多小的花岗岩可能具有同样成因，但有些也许是混合岩浆凝固的结果，还有一些也许是岩浆凝固的结果。因此，虽然可能存在不同花岗岩，但其中大多数都属于同一类型，很可能有一个相关的起源。"我完全同意这个结论。

（孙惠南 翻译；孟庆任 审稿）

Rubbers and Their Characteristics: Real and Ideal*

L. R. G. Treloar

Editor's Note

By 1945, the properties of rubbers had earned their place as a subject of technological significance. Japanese annexation of the supply of rubber latex from Malaysia forced the Allied war effort to rely on "synthetic rubber" or polyisoprene, as well as other synthetic polymers such as neoprene. Leslie Treloar here describes the latest understanding of the mechanical behaviour of these rubbers, in particular the theory of their elasticity proposed in 1932. This stated that the rubberiness has an origin not in intermolecular forces between the polymer chains but in an entropic driving force that collapses the chains into relatively compact bundles. Treloar also mentions the recent introduction of a copolymer of styrene and butadiene, a hard rubber used in tyres.

Chemical Structure of Rubbers

NATURAL rubber, extracted from latex by coagulation with acid, and afterwards washed and rolled, appears on the market as crepe or smoked sheet. Raw rubber, as these materials are called, is essentially a hydrocarbon $(C_5H_8)_n$ having the chemical structure shown in Fig. 1. It is a polymer of isoprene, the isoprene units being joined together in the form of a long chain. The actual length of the molecular chain, or *molecular weight*, of rubber has been the subject of much discussion, estimates obtained by different methods having ranged from about 1,000 to about 500,000; and it is only within the last few years that the question has been settled. The reliable measurements of Dr. G. Gee show that the mean molecular weight of a typical raw rubber is about 350,000, corresponding to a chain of about five thousand isoprene units.

This long-chain molecular structure accounts for the very high viscosity of rubber solutions in ordinary solvents like benzene. We imagine that the resistance to flow is due largely to the mutual interferences and loose entanglements between these very long molecules. However, raw rubber is ultimately completely soluble, and we conclude, therefore, that the molecules are not in any way chemically joined together.

It is otherwise with vulcanized rubber, which swells considerably in solvents (to five or ten times its original size), as if it were trying to dissolve, and yet does not go into solution at all. In this case it is reasonable to suppose that the vulcanization (that is, chemical combination with sulphur) has led to a cross-linking of the molecules (see below).

Fig. 1 is intended to show the diversity of chemical composition of materials which, under

---

* Royal Institution discourse delivered on December 15.

橡胶及其特性：现实的和理想的[*]

特雷洛尔

编者按

到 1945 年时，橡胶的性质使之成为了具有重要意义的技术性课题。日本对于马来西亚胶乳供应的控制迫使同盟国部队不得不依赖"合成橡胶"或聚异戊二烯以及其他一些如氯丁橡胶等的合成高分子。本文中，莱斯利·特雷洛尔描述了对于这些橡胶的力学行为的最新见解，尤其是在 1932 年提出的橡胶弹性理论。这一理论认为橡胶的特性并非来源于分子链间的分子间作用力，而是源于一种熵作用力，这种力使高分子链团聚成相对紧密的分子链束。特雷洛尔也提到了新近被用于轮胎的一种硬质橡胶，即苯乙烯和丁二烯的共聚物。

橡胶的化学结构

天然橡胶是用酸将橡胶树胶乳凝聚后经过清洗和辊轧而得到的，以绉胶片或者烟胶片的形式投入市场。这种物质被称为生胶，其本质是一种碳氢化合物（分子式为 $(C_5H_8)_n$），化学结构如图 1 所示。作为一种异戊二烯聚合物，其异戊二烯单元以长链的形式连接起来。橡胶分子链的实际长度，或者说**分子量**，一直是一个热议的主题，而利用不同方法得到的分子量估算值从 1,000 上下到 500,000 上下不等，直到最近几年这个问题才算尘埃落定。来自吉博士的可靠的测量结果表明，一种典型生胶的平均分子量大约为 350,000，相当于一条含有大约 5,000 个异戊二烯单元的链。

由于橡胶具有这种长链的分子结构，因此当它溶于诸如苯等常见溶剂时，其溶液具有极高的黏度。我们猜想流动阻力主要来自于这些极长分子之间的相互阻碍和松散缠绕。然而由于生胶从根本上是完全可溶的，因此我们断言这些分子并没有以任何化学方式连接在一起。

硫化橡胶则有所不同，它在溶剂中会发生相当程度的膨胀（达到初始尺寸的 5~10 倍），好像它试图溶解于溶液而又无法实现。在这种情况下，合理的看法是硫化过程（即通过硫进行化学结合）导致分子之间发生交联（见下面描述）。

图 1 试图说明那些在某些特定条件下呈现出类似橡胶的弹性的物质所具有的化

---

[*] 12 月 15 日在皇家研究院发表的演说。

certain conditions, show rubber-like elasticity. Whereas most practical rubbers are built up on a chain of carbon atoms, this is by no means an essential feature, as the examples of gelatin and elastic sulphur show. The important and invariable feature of all rubbers is the pattern of their molecular structure; there is no highly elastic material, so far as I am aware, which is not built up of very long chain-like molecules.

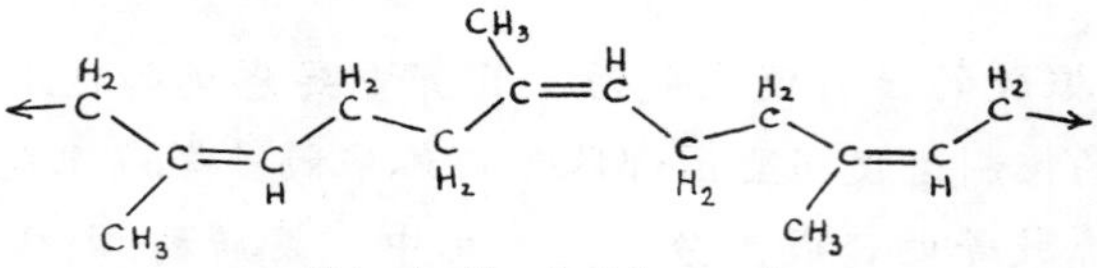

Natural rubber (polyisoprene).

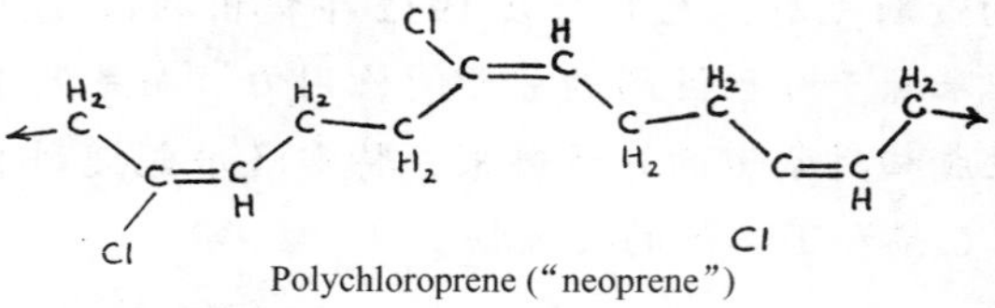

Polychloroprene ("neoprene")

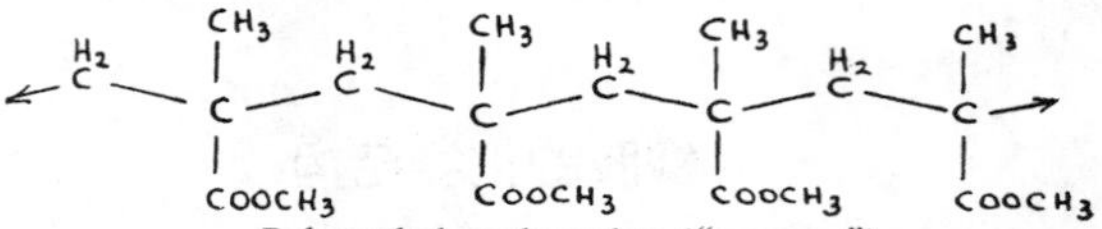

Polymethyl methacrylate ("perspex")

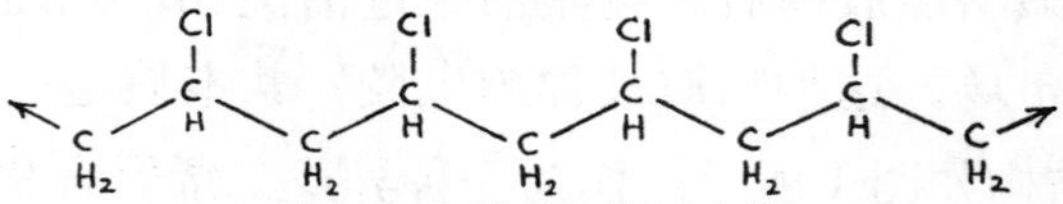

Polyvinyl chloride ("welvic")

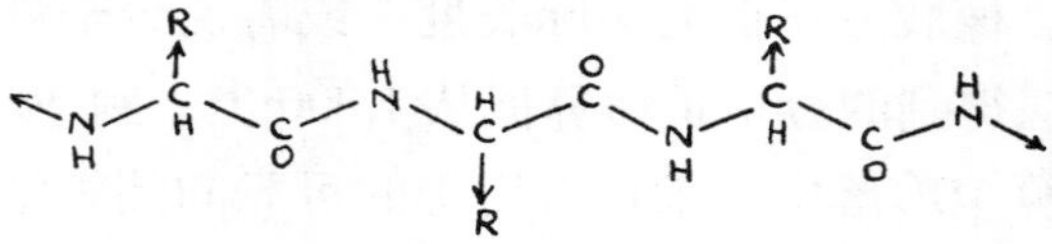

Protein (gelatin)

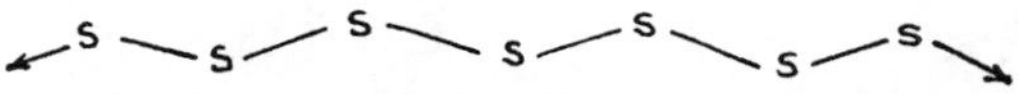

Elastic sulphur.

Fig. 1

Origin of the Elasticity

Until about twelve years ago, none of the theories of the elasticity of rubber which had been proposed could be regarded as even approximately satisfactory. Attempts to interpret long-range elasticity on the basis of interatomic forces were manifestly inadequate, and it was not until Meyer, v. Susich and Valko introduced the conception of a *dynamic*, in contrast to a *static*, basis for the phenomenon that the mystery was solved. The theory developed rapidly through the work of Guth and Mark and of Kuhn, and is now generally accepted as representing the correct method of approach.

To understand the kinetic point of view we must first examine the form of a long-chain molecule, considered as an isolated unit. For this purpose it is usual to consider the

学组成的多样性。尽管大多数实际应用的橡胶是由碳原子链构成的，但正如明胶和弹性硫所显示的那样，这决不是一个本质特征。所有橡胶都具有的重要且不变的特征是其分子结构的构象；据我所知，所有具有高度弹性的材料都是由极长的链状分子构成的。

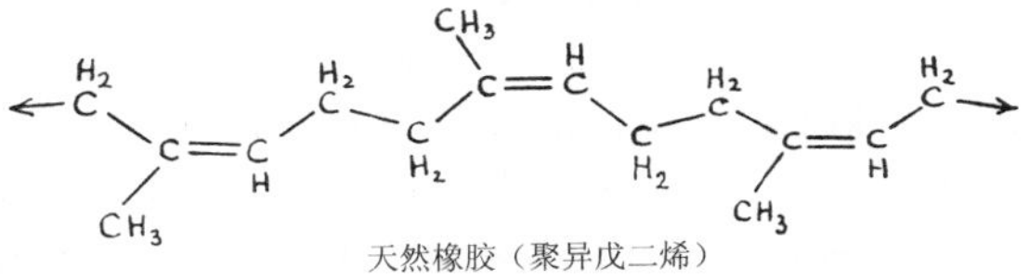

天然橡胶（聚异戊二烯）

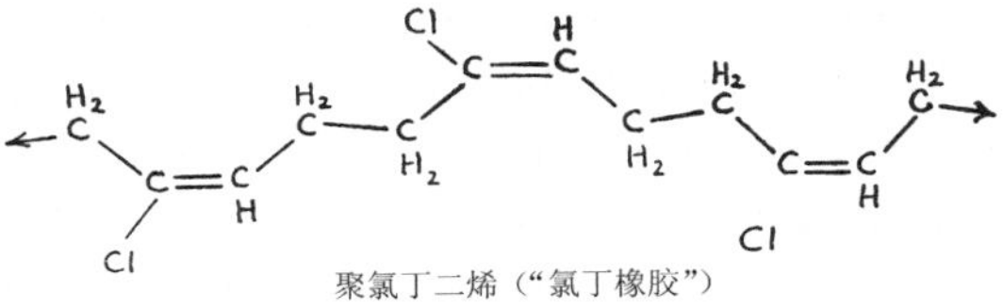

聚氯丁二烯（“氯丁橡胶”）

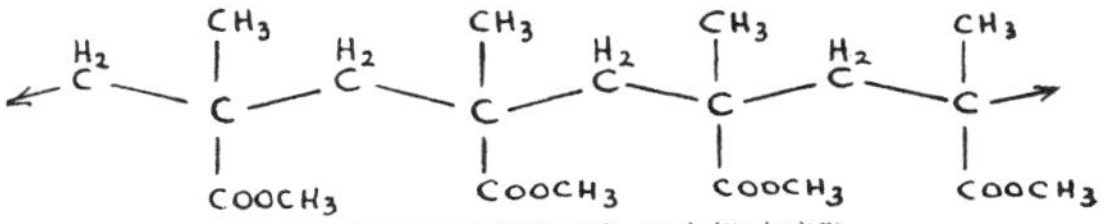

聚甲基丙烯酸甲酯（“有机玻璃”）

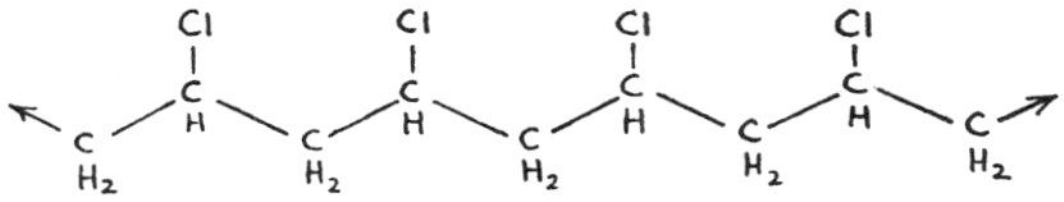

聚氯乙烯（“威尔维”）

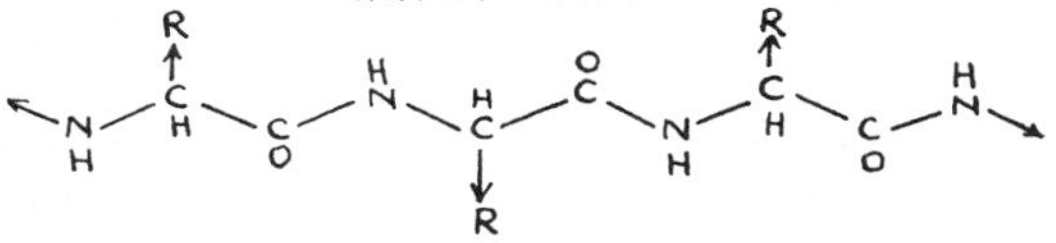

蛋白质（明胶）

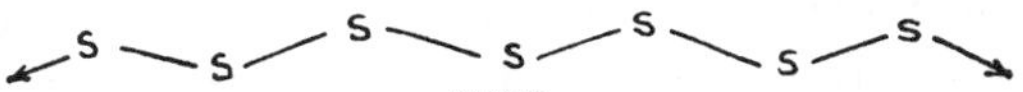

弹性硫

图 1

弹性的由来

直到大约 12 年前，已提出的任何一种橡胶弹性理论都不能令人基本满意。在原子间作用力的基础上对长程弹性进行解释的尝试明显是不充分的，直到后来，迈耶、苏西克和瓦尔科在解释这种现象的基本原则中引入了一种**动态**的概念（相对于**静态**而言），其中的奥秘才最终被解开。后来在古思和马克以及库恩的研究工作基础上这一理论得到了快速的发展，现在已经成为人们普遍认可的正确的研究方法。

要理解这种动态观点，我们必须首先把长链分子看作一个独立的个体来考察它

simplest possible chain structure, namely, the paraffin molecule. The assumption is made that the carbon atoms of the chain are in a state of continual thermal vibration, so that they may take up any relative positions consistent with the maintenance of a fixed bond-length and a fixed angle between bonds $(109\frac{1}{2}°)$. According to this assumption, each C–C bond may be regarded as rotating freely about the preceding bond as axis. There is chemical evidence that such rotation does take place. In consequence of this random rotation about bonds, the chain will not be a uniform zigzag in one plane, as in Fig. 2a, but will assume a randomly kinked form in three dimensions, as indicated in Fig. 2b. The distance between the ends of the chain in this form is likely to be very much less than the outstretched length of the molecule in Fig. 2a, and the statistical treatment of the problem enables the probability of any given end-to-end distance to be calculated. The function representing this probability turns out to be the ordinary Gaussian error function, which is represented in Fig. 3. The normal state of the free molecule may be identified with the maximum of this curve; that is, it is the most probable state, and the corresponding length is found to be proportional to the square root of the number of "links" in the chain.

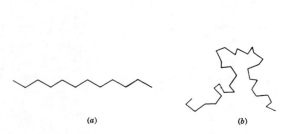

(a)   (b)

Fig. 2. Paraffin chains: (a) planar zig-zag;
(b) randomly kinked.

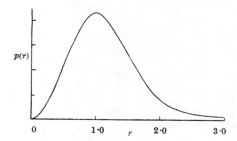

Fig. 3. Function representing the probability
$p(r)$ that a molecule has the length r.

We see, then, that if the molecule is forcibly extended, and then released, the random thermal motion will rapidly restore it to a length not very different from the statistically most probable length. The molecule, therefore, exhibits elasticity. Moreover, its elastic extensibility is proportional to the square root of the number of chain links, or the molecular weight. This theory, therefore, explains in a natural manner why long-range extensibility is found only in association with chain-like molecules of very great length.

The thermodynamic development of the kinetic theory leads to some rather striking conclusions. Two of the more important of these are:

(a) In rubber held at constant extension, the tension is proportional to the absolute temperature.

(b) The extension of rubber takes place without change in its internal energy; hence there is an evolution of heat equal to the work done on the rubber by the stretching force.

的形态。为此我们通常会考虑最简单的且可获得的链结构分子，即石蜡分子。假定链中的碳原子处于持续的热振动状态，因此在保持固定键长和固定键角（109.5°）的前提下，它们可以处于任何一种相对位置。根据这一假定，可以认为每一个 C–C 键都能以前一个键为轴自由旋转。有化学证据表明，这样的旋转确实存在。但是作为键的随机旋转的结果，链不会形成如图 2a 所示的规则的锯齿形平面结构，而是形成一种如图 2b 所示的三维随机曲折的形态。在这种形态中，链端之间的距离可能会远远小于图 2a 中处于伸展状态的分子链的链端距离，利用统计学的处理方法就可以计算出任一给定的两链端之间的距离的概率。代表这一概率分布的函数就是通常的高斯误差函数，如图 3 所示。由该曲线的最大值可以确定自由分子的平均状态；也就是说，它是可能性最高的状态，而相应的长度与链中"链节"数目的平方根成正比。

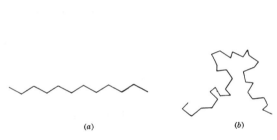

图 2. 石蜡链：(a) 平面折线；(b) 随机曲折。

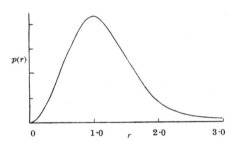

图 3. 表示某分子具有长度 r 的概率 $p(r)$ 的函数。

于是我们看到，如果分子受力伸展，接着将其释放，那么随机热运动将会使它快速恢复到某一长度，而这一长度与统计学上概率最大的长度相差无几。分子也由此而表现出弹性。此外，它的弹性延伸度正比于链节数目的平方根，或者说分子量的平方根。于是，这种理论以一种自然的方式解释了为什么只有具有极大长度的链状分子才具有较大的延伸度。

这种动态理论的热力学发展导致了一些惊人的结论。其中较为重要的两条是：

(a) 长度固定的橡胶其张力与绝对温度成正比；

(b) 橡胶的伸展不会引起内能的变化；这意味着，拉伸力对橡胶所做的功转化成了等量的热能。

In these two respects the behaviour of rubbers is closely analogous to that of a gas. The agreement with experiment which is found provides very strong evidence in favour of the theory.

The Ideal Rubber

Thus far our attention has been focused on the individual molecule. We have yet to consider in more detail how the elastic properties of the molecule are to be conveyed to the material in bulk. When we consider this problem, we see that in order to be able to take up a variety of statistical forms in the way required by the theory, the molecular chains must have a freedom of movement comparable with that in a liquid. On the other hand, for the rubber to maintain a permanent shape, and to resist applied stresses, the molecules must somehow be fixed in their *average* positions relatively to one another. To meet these two rather contradictory requirements it is necessary to think of the molecules as linked together by a relatively small number of unbreakable bonds. These will be present in sufficient numbers to produce a complete three-dimensional network throughout the material, but owing to the great length of the chains they need not seriously impede the freedom of motion of the segments of molecules between such points of junction.

We are thus led to postulate three necessary conditions for the occurrence of rubber-like elasticity, namely:
 (1) The presence of long-chain molecules, with freely rotating links.
 (2) Weak secondary forces around these molecules.
 (3) A few points of cross-linkage, resulting in a loose 3-dimensional network.

The ideal rubber may be thought of as a permanent network of long-chain molecules held together by unbreakable bonds, but otherwise completely free to move. The stress-strain properties of such an ideal network have been worked out by a number of authors. The most satisfactory development in this direction is due to Wall (1942), who obtained the following equations for the case of a simple elongation (or uni-directional compression) and simple shear respectively:

For elongation,

$$F_\alpha = NkT \left(\alpha - \frac{1}{\alpha^2} \right),$$

where F_α is stretching force, referred to original section of 1 cm.^{2}, N is number of "molecules", a "molecule" being the length of chain between its points of junction to the network, k is Boltzmann's constant, T is absolute temperature, and α is the ratio of stretched to unstretched length.

For simple shear,

$$F_\sigma = NkT\sigma$$

where F_σ is shear stress and σ is amount of shear.

从这两个方面来看，橡胶的行为与气体极为相似。与该理论相吻合的实验结果为这一理论提供了强有力的证据支持。

理想的橡胶

到现在为止我们的注意力一直集中于单个的分子。我们还需对此进行更为详细的研究，即分子的这种弹性性质是如何转化到整个材料中的。在考虑这一问题时，我们注意到，若想获得统计理论得出的各种分子形态，分子链必须具有近似于其在液体中的运动自由度。另一方面，为了使橡胶保持恒定形状，并且能够抵抗外加应力，在某种程度上分子必须固定在其相对于彼此的**平均**位置上。若要满足这两个相当矛盾的需求，就必须设想分子是通过相对少量的不能断裂的化学键连接在一起。这些键的数目应当足以产生贯穿整个材料的三维网络，但是由于链很长，它们并不会严重妨碍上述连接点之间的分子链段的自由运动。

于是，我们可以假定出现与橡胶类似的弹性所需的三个必要条件为：
（1）存在长链分子，链内的连接处可自由旋转；
（2）分子间存在弱的次级相互作用力；
（3）存在少量能产生一个松散的三维网络的交联点。

可以将理想的橡胶设想为长链分子通过牢固的键维系在一起的永久性网络，但同时又可以完全自由地运动。这样一种理想网络的应力－应变性质已经由多位学者计算出来。在这一研究方向上，最令人满意的进展应归功于沃尔（1942 年），他得到了分别对应于简单拉伸（或者单向压缩）和简单剪切两种情况下的方程：

对于拉伸来说，

$$F_\alpha = NkT\left(\alpha - \frac{1}{\alpha^2}\right)$$

其中 F_α 是拉力，对应于初始截面 1 cm²，N 是"分子"的数目，一个"分子"是指网络中交联点之间的链长度，k 是玻尔兹曼常数，T 是绝对温度，而 α 则是拉伸长度与未拉伸长度之比。

对于简单剪切来说，

$$F_\sigma = NkT\sigma$$

其中 F_σ 是剪切应力，而 σ 则是剪切量。

There are a number of particularly interesting features of these equations. first, the stress-strain curve for elongation is non-linear, that is, Hooke's Law does not apply, while for shear the relation is linear. Secondly, the only molecular property which enters into these equations is N, the number of chain elements in the network. This quantity is simply related to the "molecular weight" of the chain. The precise constitution of the molecule or the number of freely rotating links which it contains is of no significance in this connexion. The third point, which is related to this, is that one physical constant only is sufficient to define the elastic properties of a highly elastic material.

I have extended the elastic network theory to the case of a deformation of any type, and shown experimentally that the resultant equations give a reasonably satisfactory account of the properties of well-vulcanized rubber under a number of different types of deformation, except under very high strains, when the underlying assumptions of the theory are no longer applicable.

Application to Real Materials

Having now defined the conditions under which rubber-like behaviour is to be expected, let us inquire to what extent real materials satisfy these conditions, and the way in which the non-fulfilment of these conditions leads to departures from the simple behaviour of the ideal rubber.

The first point of difference is that in practice rubber-like properties appear only within a certain range of temperature. At low temperatures rubbers are transformed to a glass-hard condition. Below the transition temperature the molecular chains become immobile, the thermal energy no longer being sufficient to overcome the secondary forces between the molecules. For a material like natural rubber, these secondary forces are relatively weak, and the transition temperature is very low ($-70°$C.). If the intermolecular forces are comparatively strong, the transition temperature is very much higher. This is exemplified by polymethylmethacrylate (Fig. 1), which is a glass at normal temperatures (being extensively used for its non-splintering property), but becomes highly elastic above about $70°$C.

Rubber-like properties may also be lost at *high* temperatures, where, in the case of polymers which are not cross-linked, the molecules become sufficiently mobile to slide bodily past one another, the rubber thus becoming a viscous liquid. The longer the molecules, the higher the temperature at which this effect becomes noticeable.

This plastic property of rubber and the "thermoplastics" is made use of in the processes of moulding, extrusion, etc. In the case of rubber the final form is "fixed" by vulcanization—that is, combination with sulphur—which leads to a chemical cross-linking of the molecules.

上述方程中包含很多特别而有趣的特征。第一，拉伸的应力－应变曲线是非线性的，也就是说胡克定律在这里不适用，而剪切的应力－应变曲线则是线性的。第二，分子性质中唯一被纳入上述方程的是 N，即网络中链单元的数目。这个值与链的"分子量"具有简单的关系。也就是说分子的具体构造或者其中所包含的可以自由旋转的连接点的数目在上述关系中无足轻重。与此相关的第三点是，仅依据一个物理常数就足以描述一种高弹性物质的弹性特性。

我已将这种弹性网络理论拓展到任意类型形变的情况，而且实验结果表明，对于充分硫化的橡胶在多种不同形变时所具有的性质，得到的方程给出了一个相当令人满意的说明，除了在极高应变时，那时该理论的基本假设已不再适用。

应用于现实材料

现在我们已经确定了可以预期产生类橡胶行为的条件，接着我们将探寻现实材料在何种程度上会满足上述条件，以及不满足这些条件时，材料将会以何种方式背离理想橡胶所具有的这种简单行为。

第一个不同是，类橡胶性质实际上只出现在特定温度范围之内。在低温时，橡胶转变为玻璃态。在低于玻璃化转变温度时，分子链变得不可运动，热能不再足以克服分子之间的次级作用力。对于像天然橡胶那样的物质来说，这种次级作用力是相当弱的，其玻璃化转变温度非常低（−70℃）。如果分子间作用力比较强，那么玻璃化转变温度就会非常高。聚甲基丙烯酸甲酯很好地证明了这一点（图 1），它在室温下是一种玻璃（因其具有不会碎裂的性质而得到广泛应用），但在高于 70℃ 左右时就会变得极富弹性。

在**高**温下类橡胶性质也可能会消失。对于未交联的聚合物而言，分子具有足够的运动能力而彼此滑过，橡胶因此而变成一种黏性液体。分子链越长，表现出这种效应所需的温度就越高。

橡胶的这种塑性性能和"热塑性"可以用在模压和挤出等加工工艺成型中。对于橡胶来说，其最终形态是通过硫化（即与硫的结合）产生分子的化学交联而得以"固定"。

Crystallization

So far I have omitted one very important phenomenon which profoundly affects the mechanical behaviour of rubber, namely, crystallization. If raw rubber is held at temperatures below 0°C. for several days, it becomes comparatively hard and inelastic, and at the same time loses its transparency. This state is not to be confused with the glassy state, which occur on quickly cooling to very much lower temperatures. The X-ray diffraction pattern of normal "amorphous" rubber is like that of a liquid, there being only a single broad halo present. The same pattern is given in the glass-hard state. But the slowly frozen rubber shows a number of well-defined rings, which are to be interpreted as due to the presence of crystallites oriented at random, as in a powder.

Owing to the enormous length of the molecules, there are significant differences between the process of crystallization in rubber and in an ordinary low-molecular liquid. The crystallites are separated by regions of "amorphous" or disordered molecules (crystallization is never complete), and, furthermore, a single molecule may pass alternately through several crystalline and amorphous regions. Thus the crystallites are bound together by amorphous rubber. This intimate binding of amorphous and crystalline components leads to a certain indefiniteness in the melting point of the crystalline phase, but at the same time imparts a degree of flexibility or toughness which is normally absent from crystalline bodies. The peculiar advantages of this type of molecular structure are made use of in polyethylene, which is chemically the same as paraffin wax, but has a much higher molecular weight. It is flexible, yet sufficiently hard for use as a cable-insulating material, and since the crystals hold the structure together vulcanization is unnecessary. The exceptionally valuable dielectric properties of the pure hydrocarbon are thus unimpaired.

Crystallization occurs not only in unstretched rubber at low temperatures, but also in stretched rubber at ordinary temperatures. By stretching, the molecules are brought into an approximately parallel arrangement, which greatly facilitates the crystallization process.

In stretched crystalline rubber the crystals all have one axis pointing in a fixed direction. Viewed by X-rays, this kind of arrangement gives rise to a series of spots arranged in a characteristic pattern. This pattern bears a rather strong resemblance to the X-ray pattern of natural fibres (cotton, wool, etc.), and in fact, stretched crystalline rubber behaves mechanically like a fibrous material, as Hock showed in 1924. If stretched crystalline rubber is frozen in liquid air and hammered, it splits along the fibre axis, just like a piece of wood. Also, it is very easily torn along the direction of the grain, but is, of course, exceedingly tough in other directions.

The rubber crystal is birefringent, hence stretched rubber is highly doubly refracting. If a piece of vulcanized rubber is stretched between crossed "Polaroid" plates, a succession of brilliant interference colours is developed as the extension increases; on retraction, the effect disappears. If the same is done with unvulcanized rubber, the effect does not disappear entirely on removal of the tension; in this case the crystals are more permanent. The method may be employed for the quantitative study of crystallization in stretched rubber. Fig. 4 shows the birefringence of raw rubber as a function of the elongation.

结　晶

到目前为止，我一直忽略了一种极为重要的现象，它极大地影响着橡胶的力学行为，这就是结晶。如果将生胶在低于 0℃ 的温度下保持几天，它就会变得相当坚硬而且没有弹性，同时还会失去透明性。对于玻璃态来说，这种情况不难理解，当材料被快速冷却到很低的温度时，就会出现玻璃态。常见"无定形"橡胶的 X 射线衍射图案与液体类似，其中只出现简单的宽晕环。玻璃态的橡胶给出了同样的图案。但是缓慢冷却的橡胶则呈现出大量界限分明的环，它们可以被解释为由随机取向的微晶所致，就像粉末的图像那样。

由于橡胶分子非常大，因此其结晶过程与普通小分子液体的结晶过程存在显著差异。微晶被"无定形"区域或无序分子（结晶过程总是不完全的）所分隔，而且单个分子还可能会交替穿过若干个结晶区域和无定形区域。于是这些微晶通过无定形橡胶分子被连接在一起。这种无定形与结晶成分的紧密连接导致了结晶相的熔点的某种不确定性，但是同时赋予橡胶一定程度的柔韧性或韧性，这种性质是通常情况下的结晶态物质所不具备的。这种类型的分子结构所具有的特定优势被应用于聚乙烯中，聚乙烯的化学组成与固体石蜡相同，但具有高得多的分子量。聚乙烯柔韧又足够坚硬，可以用作电缆绝缘材料；而且由于晶体将所有分子连接在一起，硫化过程就不必要了。因此纯烃类物质极具价值的电介质性质被保留了下来。

结晶不仅仅发生在处于低温下的未经拉伸的橡胶中，它也发生在常温下的经过拉伸的橡胶中。通过拉伸，分子处于近似平行的排列方式，这就极大地促进了结晶过程。

在拉伸的结晶态橡胶中，所有晶体都具有一个指向固定方向的晶轴。通过 X 射线来看，这种排列方式表现为排列成一种特征图案的一系列点。这种图案与天然纤维（棉、毛等）的 X 射线图案具有很大的相似性，实际上这正如霍克在 1924 年所指出的那样，拉伸的结晶态橡胶的力学行为类似于纤维材料。如果将拉伸的结晶态橡胶在液态空气中冷却并进行敲打，它会沿着纤维轴破碎，就像一片木头一样。而且，它很容易沿着纹理的方向破裂，但在其他方向上仍极为结实。

橡胶晶体具有双折射性质，因此拉伸的橡胶也具有很强的双重折射性。如果将一片硫化橡胶在交叉的"宝丽来"（译者注：即偏振片）薄板之间拉伸，随着伸展的增加，会产生一系列鲜艳的彩色干涉；收缩时，这种效应消失。如果用未经硫化的橡胶进行同样的实验，则移除张力时该效应不会完全消失；在这种情况下，晶体会更持久。这种方法可以用于对拉伸橡胶中结晶的定量研究。图 4 表明生胶的双折射性质是伸长率的函数。

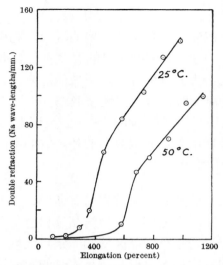

Fig. 4. Double refraction in raw rubber. Each point refers to a fresh
piece of sheet held at the appropriate extension for one hour.

The Synthetic Rubber GR–S

Before concluding, I should like to devote a few words to the consideration of the general purpose synthetic rubber GR–S now being produced in considerable quantities. This rubber, like the German "Buna", is formed by polymerizing together butadiene and styrene. The chains are thus lacking in regularity (Fig. 5), since these two components occur in a random order, with the result that crystallization is not possible. This probably accounts for the much lower tensile strength of GR–S vulcanizates which do not contain a reinforcing agent like carbon black, compared with similar natural rubber vulcanizates. Moreover, there would appear to be a possibility of the formation of branched chains (Fig. 5b) leading to a cross-linked structure. It is suggested that this effect may account not only for the comparative difficulty encountered in milling it to a suitable softness, but also for its most unfortunate lack of self-adhesion. Self-adhesion involves a mutual diffusion at the surface of contact; any branching or cross-linking of the chains will considerably reduce such diffusion.

butadiene   styrene

(a) Straight chain.   (b) Branched chain.

Fig. 5. Possible chain forms for synthetic rubber GR–S (butadiene-styrene polymer)

(**155**, 441-444; 1945)

L. R. G. Treloar: British Rubber Producers' Research Association.

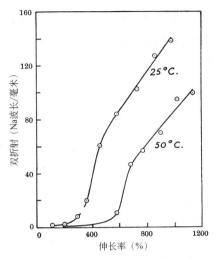

图 4. 生胶的双折射。每个点对应于在适当拉伸条件下保持一个小时
的一个新的层片。

合成橡胶 GR–S

在作出结论之前，我想用少许篇幅来谈谈对目前正大量生产的通用合成橡胶GR–S 的看法。就像德国的"布纳橡胶"一样,这种橡胶由丁二烯和苯乙烯聚合而成。因为这两种单体是以随机顺序出现的，所以由此形成的链缺少规整度（图 5），所带来的结果是不可能结晶。这或许可以用来解释，为什么相比于类似的天然橡胶硫化物而言，不包含诸如炭黑等增强剂的 GR–S 硫化橡胶具有低得多的拉伸强度。此外还存在一种可能，即支化链的结构（图 5b）导致了交联结构的形成。有人认为，这种效应可能不仅解释了在将它塑炼成适当软度时所遇到的巨大困难，还解释它那颇为令人惋惜的自黏性的缺失。自黏性涉及到接触表面的相互扩散；链的任何支化或交联都会在很大程度上削弱这种扩散。

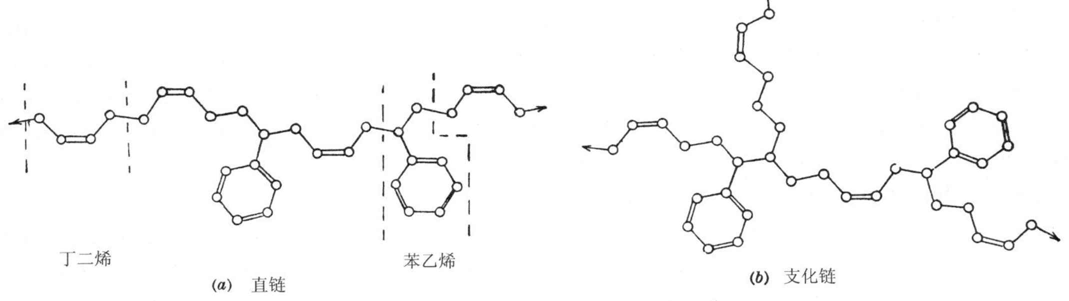

丁二烯   苯乙烯

(a) 直链   (b) 支化链

图 5. 合成橡胶 GR–S 可能具有的链形态（丁二烯 – 苯乙烯聚合物）

（王耀杨 翻译；栗付平 审稿）

Penicillin Treatment of Venereal Disease and Spirochaetal Infections

G. Lapage

Editor's Notes

Penicillin was widely used to treat infections during the Second World War, and here Geoffrey Lapage summarises the antibiotic's use to treat gonorrhoea and syphilis. United States Army medical men had already noted that penicillin yielded immediate effects in syphilis, outperforming arsenical treatments. But whilst subsequent papers backed this up, the twice-daily repeated injections were seen as a problem. In the United States, where around 200,000 mega units of penicillin were produced, many syphilis trials were ongoing. So Lapage suggests that "we are justified in expending a large proportion of even the limited British supplies of penicillin on the study of its effects on syphilis." He also notes that penicillin is effective against other syphilis-like bacteria, as well as gonorrhoea.

THE remarkably successful treatment of gonorrhoea with penicillin was recorded in an earlier note on penicillin treatment (*Nature*, 677, Nov. 25, 1944). In that note also the opinion of United States Army medical men that the immediate effects of penicillin in the treatment of syphilis are better than those of arsenical preparations was recorded. Leading articles in the *Lancet* (853, Dec. 30, 1944) and the *British Medical Journal* (821, Dec. 23, 1944) discuss the whole question of penicillin treatment of human syphilis, with references to the relevant literature.

In the United States the first experiments on this problem were done on rabbits infected with syphilis, and J. F. Mahoney, R. C. Arnold and A. Harris (*Ven. Dis. Inform.*, **24**, 355; 1943) were apparently the first to record penicillin treatment of human syphilis. In Britain, E. M. Lourie and H. O. J. Collier (*Ann. Trop. Med. and Parasitol.*, **37**, 200; 1943) showed that penicillin will cure infections of mice with *Treponema recurrentis* and *Spirillum minus*. In co-operation with A. O. F. Ross and R. B. Wilson (*Lancet*, 845, Dec. 30, 1944) they report on the treatment of five cases of human syphilis with penicillin. All these cases had well-marked secondary lesions, and the immediate response "could not have been bettered by any known form of treatment". The spirochaetes and lesions disappeared at least as rapidly as they do under treatment with arsenicals and bismuth. But all these cases were in the secondary stage of the disease, and later observations upon them showed that only one of the five cases was apparently cured. It was therefore doubtful whether penicillin was as beneficial as arsenicals and bismuth would have been. These authors concluded that penicillin will not become suitable for routine civilian practice until frequently repeated day- and night-injections can be avoided.

青霉素治疗性病和螺旋体感染

拉帕吉

编者按

第二次世界大战期间，青霉素被广泛用于治疗感染性疾病，杰弗里·拉帕吉对使用青霉素治疗淋病和梅毒进行了总结。美国军医已经注意到青霉素对梅毒的即时疗效比砷剂更好。虽然后续的文章支持这种观点，但每天两次重复注射被视为一个问题。在美国，大约已生产出 200,000 百万单位的青霉素，许多治疗梅毒的实验正在进行之中。因此拉帕吉认为"我们也应扩大研究青霉素对梅毒的影响，即使它会消耗英国有限青霉素产量的大部分。"他还注意到青霉素对其他类似梅毒的致病菌及淋病也是有效的。

关于青霉素疗法的一篇早期文章（《自然》，第 677 页，1944 年 11 月 25 日）中就记录了用青霉素成功治疗淋病的实例，其中也记录了美国军医的观点，他们认为青霉素对梅毒的即时疗效好于砷剂。在参考相关文献的基础上，《柳叶刀》（第 853 页，1944 年 12 月 30 日）和《英国医学杂志》（第 821 页，1944 年 12 月 23 日）上的重要文章讨论了青霉素治疗人类梅毒的全部问题。

在美国，针对这个问题实施的首例实验是利用感染了梅毒的兔子完成的。显然，马奥尼、阿诺德和哈里斯（《性病学通报》，第 24 卷，第 355 页，1943 年）是最早记录青霉素治疗人类梅毒的人。在英国,劳里和科利尔（《热带医学与寄生虫学纪事》，第 37 卷，第 200 页，1943 年）发现青霉素能够治愈感染了回归热密螺旋体和鼠咬热螺旋体的小鼠。在与罗斯和威尔逊的合作研究中（《柳叶刀》，第 845 页，1944 年 12 月 30 日），他们报道了 5 例用青霉素治疗人类梅毒的病例。所有这些病例都存在明显的二期损伤，而且其即时疗效是"其他任何已知的治疗方法不能超越的"。螺旋体和病变部位消失的速度至少和用砷剂以及铋剂治疗的一样快。但是所有这些病例都处于该病的二期阶段，随后的观察发现 5 例中只有一例是明显治愈的。因此，有人质疑青霉素是否和砷剂以及铋剂一样有效。这些作者最后得出的结论是，除非能够避免日夜频繁重复注射的缺点，否则青霉素将不适合普通常规使用。

The problem of dosage in the treatment of syphilis is discussed by both the *British Medical Journal* and the *Lancet* (*loc. cit.*). In the United States, where so much more penicillin is available, extensive trials of it for the treatment of syphilis have been going on at thirty-one centres, and the *Lancet* discusses the reports on these and the supply of penicillin, stating that, by April 1944, the tentative production programme of the United States and Canada was, according to R. D. Coghill (*Chem. Engineer. News*, **22**, 588; 1944), of the order of 200,000 mega units (1 mega unit is 1 million Oxford units). There will be general agreement that we are justified in expending a large proportion of even the limited British supplies of penicillin on the study of its effects on syphilis. Arsenical treatment is more toxic and is not infallible; it involves supervision of the patient for a year or longer, and J. Marshall (*Nature*, **153**, 187; 1944) has pointed out that less than half the patients get enough of such treatment to ensure a cure-rate of 80 percent, because they default. One danger of future penicillin treatment is emphasized by both the *Lancet* and the *British Medical Journal* (*loc. cit.*). A patient may have both gonorrhoea and syphilis at the same time. The gonococcus is more susceptible to penicillin than the spirochaete of syphilis. Treatment with doses of penicillin which are sufficient to cure the gonorrhoea may therefore suppress the early signs of the syphilis, without being sufficient to cure this disease, especially if the syphilis is at an early stage when the only sign of it may be a hidden chancre. The diagnosis of syphilis may therefore be only made later when the secondary signs appear. F. L. Lydon and W. R. S. Cowe (*Brit. Med. J.*, 110, Jan. 27, 1945) also discuss this subject, adding the point that battle casualties treated with penicillin for gonorrhoea, for which it is, they agree, the drug of choice, may by incubating syphilis as well, which would thus escape detection. They think that routine blood-tests should be enforced by law upon the whole population. Similar cases of coincident infections with these two venereal diseases are discussed by F. A. Ellis (*J. Amer. Med. Assoc.*, **126**, 80; 1944) and by C. R. Wise and D. M. Spillsbury (*Brit. J. Surg.*, **32**, 214; 1944).

Penicillin seems to be very effective also against other spirochaetes and their relatives. Brigadier G. M. Findlay, Major K. R. Hill and A. Macpherson (*Nature*, 795, Dec. 23, 1944) report some success in the treatment with penicillin of yaws, due to *Spirochoeta pertenue* and of tropical ulcers infected with spirochaetes, fusiform bacilli and other organisms. Ulcers have caused, during 1944, the loss of 30,000 men-days among West African troops. A. B. MacGregor and D. A. Long (*Brit. Med. J.*, 686, Nov. 25, 1944) report the rapid disappearance of *Treponema vincenti*, the cause of Vincent's gingivitis, under treatment with penicillin incorporated in pastilles. J. M. Alston and J. C. Broom (*Brit. Med. J.*, 718, Dec. 2, 1944) report on their experiments on its action on nine strains of *Leptospira icterohoemorrhagioe*, the cause of Weil's disease (six strains were human, two were from rats and one from a dog) and on one strain of *L. canicola*, the cause of another form of leptospiral infection of man and dogs. Penicillin killed all these strains in cultures and also inhibited their multiplication. It also cured infections of guinea pigs with leptospira virulent to them, provided that it was given early enough (eighteen hours after infection). It did not prevent the development in the guinea pigs of serum antibodies or resistance to re-infection. It was not toxic to the guinea pigs as others have reported it to be. In the same issue of the *British Medical Journal* (p. 720), V. Lloyd Hart reports upon the treatment of

《英国医学杂志》和《柳叶刀》（文献同前）都对治疗梅毒时青霉素的剂量问题进行了讨论。在美国，由于有大量的青霉素可供使用，关于其治疗梅毒的大量实验正在 31 个中心开展。《柳叶刀》讨论了这些研究报告以及青霉素的供给问题，并指出：依据科格希尔的文章（《化学化工新闻》，第 22 卷，第 588 页，1944 年），截止到 1944 年 4 月，美国和加拿大的总产量预期可达到 200,000 百万单位（1 个百万单位就是 100 万个牛津单位）。在此将达成一致共识，即使我们在研究青霉素对梅毒的影响时消耗了英国有限供给的大部分青霉素，那也是有意义的。砷剂治疗具有较强的毒性而且并非总是有效；另外，它需要对患者进行一年或者更长时间的随访，而且马歇尔（《自然》，第 153 卷，第 187 页，1944 年）指出只有不到一半的患者能够得到充分治疗以确保 80% 的治愈率，因为他们不能坚持。《英国医学杂志》和《柳叶刀》（文献同前）都强调了将来青霉素疗法的一个风险。患者可能同时患有淋病和梅毒。淋病球菌较之梅毒螺旋体对青霉素更敏感。用足以治愈淋病的青霉素剂量治疗时可能因此抑制了梅毒的早期表现，而不足以治愈该病，尤其如果梅毒正处于早期阶段，此时它唯一的表现可能是一个隐性硬下疳。因此，只有在二期症状出现后才能作出梅毒的诊断。莱登和科维（《英国医学杂志》，第 110 页，1945 年 1 月 27 日）也讨论了这个问题并进行了补充，他们一致认为，用青霉素治疗患淋病的战伤人员时该首选药物可能使梅毒潜伏而无法被检测到。他们认为应该有法律强制性地对整个人群进行血常规检验。埃利斯（《美国医学会志》，第 126 卷，第 80 页，1944 年）和怀斯、斯皮尔斯伯利（《英国外科学杂志》，第 32 卷，第 214 页，1944 年）也对同时感染这两种性病的类似病例进行了讨论。

青霉素对其他螺旋体及其亲缘微生物似乎也十分有效。芬德利准将、希尔少校和麦克弗森（《自然》，第 795 页，1944 年 12 月 23 日）报道了成功地用青霉素治疗由细弱螺旋体感染引起的雅司病以及由螺旋体、梭状杆菌及其他生物感染引起的热带溃疡。1944 年，溃疡引起西非军队丧失 30,000 人工作日。麦格雷戈和朗（《英国医学杂志》，第 686 页，1944 年 11 月 25 日）报道了用整合到锭剂中的青霉素进行治疗可以使引起奋森氏牙龈炎的奋森氏密螺旋体快速消失。奥尔斯顿和布鲁姆（《英国医学杂志》，第 718 页，1944 年 12 月 2 日）报道了青霉素对 9 个品系的黄疸出血型钩端螺旋体的效果的实验，这种钩端螺旋体可引起威尔氏病（6 个品系来自人类，2 个来自大鼠，1 个来自狗）。此外还对 1 个种系的犬钩端螺旋体展开实验，其可引起人类和狗另一种钩端螺旋体病。青霉素杀死了培养基中的所有这些品系，并抑制了它们的增殖。如果用药足够早的话（感染后的 18 小时内），它也能治愈感染了恶性钩端螺旋体的豚鼠。它并不阻止豚鼠血清抗体以及对再次感染的抵抗力的形成。就像之前报道的其他动物一样，它对豚鼠没有毒性。在同一期的《英国医学杂志》

one Italian male suffering from Weil's disease. The results suggest that even the very small doses, given at relatively long intervals, had some curative effect; but Hart also emphasizes the need for early administration. It is, however, difficult to diagnose Weil's disease in its early stages. The same necessity for early administration is emphasized by Brig. E. Bulmer (*Brit. Med. J.*, 113, Jan. 27, 1945) in his summary of the treatment by various medical officers of sixteen cases of the same disease in Normandy. It is thought that Weil's disease is spread by infected rats, which pass the spirochaetes in their urine. The spirochaetes can live for a time in stagnant water, wells and sewers, so that men infect themselves by drinking and bathing. Up to December 1944, cases had been notified between mid-July and the end of September, and only from Normandy. It is, Bulmer thinks, surprising that cases have not occurred in the Low Countries, where there is "plenty of water". There was great difficulty in assessing the results of the penicillin treatment. The liver and kidneys are rapidly damaged by the spirochaete, so that penicillin should ideally be given before the diagnosis can be made. Inadequate doses of penicillin appeared, however, to shorten the duration of the fever and to cause dramatic improvement, especially when high doses were given. It did not appear to influence the damage done to the liver and kidney. In the same issue of the *British Medical Journal* (p. 119), A. E. Carragher reports on the treatment of one other case, a soldier invalided from France. After only six injections of penicillin the *Leptospira* disappeared from the blood and there was rapid clinical improvement.

Among other organisms of the spirochaete type are *Streptobacillus moniliformis* and *Spirillum minus*, the causative organisms of the two rat-bite fevers. The reasons for the conclusions that two organisms are concerned in the etiology of this disease have been discussed (*Lancet*, 540, Oct. 21, 1944), together with the effect of penicillin on them. F. R. Heilman and W. E. Herrell (*Proc. Staff Meeting, Mayo Clinic*, 19, 257; 1944) and H. Eagle and H. J. Magnuson (*Pub. Health Rep. Wash.*, 59, 583; 1944) have confirmed the results obtained by Lourie and Collier mentioned above. Heilman and Herrell found that penicillin cured mouse infections with *Sp. minus* and *Strept. moniliformis*, so that both forms of rat-bite fever may prove susceptible to it. The former responds dramatically to organic arsenicals, but the latter resists arsenic, sulphonamides and gold treatment. F. F. Kane (*Lancet*, 548, Oct. 21, 1944) reports on the infection of an Ulster boy with *Strept. moniliformis* as the result of a rat-bite, which was successfully treated with penicillin after gold treatment had failed. Eagle and Magnuson obtained cures with penicillin of infections of rats and mice with *Spirochoeta recurrentis* (=*Treponema novyi*), so that it is possible that penicillin may prove better than arsenic for the treatment of relapsing fever of man, which is caused by this organism.

(**155**, 459-461; 1945)

（第 720 页）中，劳埃德·哈特报道了对一位患有威尔氏病的意大利男性患者的治疗。结果显示即使是非常小的剂量，给药间隔期相对较长，也有一些治疗效果；但是哈特同样强调了早期治疗的必要性。然而，在早期阶段很难诊断出威尔氏病。布尔默（《英国医学杂志》，第 113 页，1945 年 1 月 27 日）在总结诺曼底多个医疗官员治疗 16 个相同病例的经验中也强调了早期治疗的必要性。人们认为威尔氏病是由感染的老鼠传播的，它们从尿液中排出螺旋体。这些螺旋体能够在静水、水井和下水道中生存一段时间，人类在饮用这些水或者在这些水中洗澡时受到感染。直到 1944 年 12 月，报告的病例发生在 7 月中旬和 9 月底，而且只来自于诺曼底。布尔默认为没有在低地国家发现病例是很奇怪的，因为这些国家有"大量的水"。评价青霉素治疗的结果是非常困难的。螺旋体能快速损伤肝脏和肾脏，因此，较为理想的情况是，青霉素应该在给出诊断前使用。即使不足量的青霉素看起来也能够缩短发烧持续的时间，并具有显著的疗效，大剂量使用时效果更加明显。但它似乎不能影响肝脏和肾脏已经发生的损伤。在同一期《英国医学杂志》（第 119 页）中，卡拉格报道了对另一个病例的治疗——一名法国伤兵。在仅仅注射 6 次青霉素后，其血液中的钩端螺旋体就消失了，临床症状也获得了快速的改善。

螺旋体家族的其他生物包括念珠状链杆菌和小螺旋菌，分别是两种鼠咬热的病原体。判定这两种生物是这些疾病的病原体的理由以及青霉素对它们的效果都已经被讨论过了（《柳叶刀》，第 540 页，1944 年 10 月 21 日）。海尔曼和赫里尔（《梅奥诊所记录》，第 19 卷，第 257 页，1944 年）以及伊格尔和马格努森（《公共卫生报告》，第 59 卷，第 583 页，1944 年）已经证实了劳里和科利尔在前面提及的结果。海尔曼和赫里尔发现青霉素能够治愈感染了小螺旋菌和念珠状链杆菌的小鼠，因此这两种形式的鼠咬热都对青霉素敏感。前者对有机砷剂的治疗反应十分显著，但是后者可以耐受砷剂、磺胺类药物和金制剂。凯恩（《柳叶刀》，第 548 页，1994 年 10 月 21 日）报道了一位被鼠咬后感染念珠状链杆菌的北爱尔兰男孩在金制剂治疗失败后用青霉素成功地治愈。伊格尔和马格努森用青霉素治愈了感染回归热螺旋体的大鼠和小鼠，这证明青霉素在治疗人类由于感染该病菌而引起的回归热时很可能比砷剂更加有效。

（毛晨晖 翻译；金侠 审稿）

Comments on Chromosome Structure

I. Manton

Editor's Note

British cytologist Irene Manton wrote these comments on chromosome structure after an "appreciative perusal" of Erwin Schrödinger's *What is Life?*, a book that speculated on how genetic storage might work. Although the structure of DNA was yet to be deciphered, Schrödinger mused on the size of genes, and Manton says what Schrödinger "really wishes to discuss is the fundamental molecular unit of chromosome structure." At the time there were two extreme views: chromosome threads were either single- or many-stranded. Manton says the single-strand theory fits well with the proposed helical structure of chromosomes. And she uses Schrödinger's calculations to help estimate that a chromosome could harbour between "300 and 12,000 duplicate versions of the genetical material."

WHEN a great physicist takes the trouble to explain in simple language some of his matured thoughts on topics of general interest outside his own subject, it is an event for which one cannot be too grateful. The following remarks have been aroused by the appreciative perusal of Prof. E. Schroedinger's delightful little book "What is Life?"[1].

Without attempting to summarize the whole of Prof. Schroedinger's argument, it is valuable to notice the great stress which is laid on the existence of two very different methods of obtaining orderly behaviour of matter in Nature. In the inanimate world "order from disorder" is said to be the rule; the behaviour of matter in bulk being in most cases the expression of a statistical average of the behaviour of vast numbers of particles (atoms, molecules or the like) which, individually, may be doing the most diverse things under the sole compulsion of a tendency towards increased randomness. In biological systems, on the other hand, "order from order" is met with. In such a system the most complex sequence of events may be determined and set in motion by the pattern of arrangement in space of a comparatively minute number of individual particles occupying relatively fixed positions with regard to one another. The paramount importance of the pattern of atomic arrangement in the particular case of the genetical material carried by the chromosomes is, in Prof. Schroedinger's view, the most interesting discovery of our time.

Few biologists will probably wish to dispute this in general terms. Cytological comment is, however, aroused by the details of its presentation from the circumstance that Prof. Schroedinger, at various points, is thinking in terms of certain assumptions regarding chromosome structure which are by no means universally held. It may therefore be of interest to inquire what change of view, if any, will be entailed if these assumptions are altered.

关于染色体结构的评论

曼顿

编者按

英国细胞学家艾琳·曼顿在阅读了埃尔温·薛定谔的《生命是什么》这本"令人欣喜的小册子"之后写下了对于染色体结构的评论，这本书着力于解释遗传信息是如何工作的。尽管当时并不知道 DNA 的结构，薛定谔假想了基因的大小，而曼顿认为薛定谔"真正想讨论的是染色体结构的最基本分子单元"。当时有两种极端的观点：染色体要么是单链的要么是多链的。曼顿认为单链的理论与假设的染色体的螺旋结构更为相符。她进一步用薛定谔的计算方法估算出一个染色体能够储存"300~12,000个副本的遗传物质"。

当一位伟大的物理学家费神地去关注他本专业领域以外的大众话题，并用简单的语言发表自己成熟的观点时，人们对此应该无限感激。以下是我怀着感激的心情拜读了薛定谔教授所著的《生命是什么？》[1]这本令人欣喜的小册子后作的一些评论。

我并不打算总结薛定谔教授的全部观点，我只关注他着重强调的一个观点：在自然界中，不同的物质获得有序行为的方法有两种。在无生命的世界中，物质遵循从无序到有序的规则；在大多数情况下，大量物质的行为可以用数量巨大的粒子（如原子、分子或者其他相似物）行为的统计平均值来描述，而每个粒子可能都是在增加随机性的单向强迫力下做不同的运动。相反在生物系统中，物质遵循从有序到有序的规则；在这个系统里，单个粒子在空间中相对于其他粒子有固定的位置，其中一些数量不多的粒子会按照在空间排列的模式进行运动，从而产生一系列非常复杂的行为。以薛定谔教授的观点，在染色体所携带的遗传物质这个特例中，原子的排列模式是极其重要的，这是我们这个时代里最有意思的发现。

很少有生物学家愿意用简单的词语来讨论这个问题。薛定谔教授从不同的方面考虑了这种有关染色体结构的假说，虽然这种假说还没有被普遍认可。在此情形下，有关这种假说的细节引发了细胞学家们的讨论。令人感兴趣的是，如果这些假说发生变化，那么会使观点变成什么样呢（如果会有变化的话）。

Prof. Schroedinger is much impressed by the singleness of the "code script" in inheritance, by code script meaning the sum of hereditary material carried by a haploid nucleus (in genetical parlance this would be referred to as a genome). That only one chromosome set or genome is actually necessary for development is clearly shown by the existence of haploid organisms, for example, many of the lower plants, or cases of parthenogenesis in both plants and animals; it is therefore quite legitimate to ignore diploidy and polyploidy. Difficulties, however, appear at once if "singleness" is interpreted literally in a molecular sense, and that this is Prof. Schroedinger's interpretation seems clear from his very interesting discussion of the size of a gene.

It might perhaps be questioned whether the "size of a gene" is a desirable or legitimate use of words. In its original sense a "gene" meant nothing more than the physical basis of an externally visible mutation, and if a mutation can be caused, as Prof. Schroedinger suggests, by a change of atomic arrangement, of the nature of a quantum jump, occurring within a molecule, then a gene, strictly speaking, is the changed part of that molecule and nothing else. It is an unfortunate biological practice which Prof. Schroedinger cannot be personally blamed for following, that the word is now often used in so many extended senses that it has little precise meaning left. In discussing the maximum size of a "gene" from genetical data, the word denotes either the smallest piece of a chromosome which can have a genetically detectable effect, or the shortest distance between two mutations which can be separated by crossing-over; a numerical estimate of either of these by existing genetical or cytological methods may be expected to yield purely subjective values expressing present crudities of technique. In discussing the minimum size of a "gene" as deduced from induction of mutations by ionizing radiations, the word is apparently equated with the range of influence of the minimum degree of ionization required to induce a mutation. The thing that Prof. Schroedinger really wishes to discuss is the fundamental molecular unit of chromosome structure, which is not necessarily identical with any of these concepts. The use of the word gene for this also may seem particularly unfortunate to a cytologist because some idea of structural discontinuity is almost inevitably implied. Mutations are discontinuous and arranged in linear sequence along a chromosome. Whether the fundamental genetical material in which the mutations occur is or is not also discontinuous (like beads on a string) is quite another question and one which neither cytology nor genetics can yet determine. This linguistic difficulty would perhaps best be met if the word gene were deleted from the vocabulary; one of the most pregnant of Prof. Schroedinger's sentences could then be paraphrased as—"We believe a mutation to be of the nature of a quantum jump and the fundamental unit of chromosome structure—or perhaps the whole chromosome fibre—to be an aperiodic solid".

At this point the sense in which the "whole chromosome fibre" can be regarded as a unit becomes of importance. There are at present two extreme views as to this, both supported by some positive evidence. According to the one which Prof. Schroedinger is using, the

遗传学上代码指令的单一性给薛定谔教授留下了很深刻的印象。代码指令是指单倍体细胞核中遗传物质的总和（按遗传学的说法应该是指基因组）。事实上，对于生物发育来说只有一套染色体组或者基因组是必要的。单倍体生物的存在，例如许多低等植物，以及一些动植物的单性繁殖，就能证明这一点。因此我们可以完全忽略对二倍体和多倍体的研究。然而，如果"单一性"这个名词在分子意义上仅仅是字面意思（很明显，这是薛定谔教授从基因大小的有趣讨论中得出的名词），那就会出现很多困惑。

使用"基因的大小"这种表述是否可取或是否合理，是值得怀疑的。"基因"的本来意义仅仅是一种外在可见突变的物质基础，而按照薛定谔教授的观点，突变的产生源自于原子排列的改变，本质为量子的跃迁。突变首先发生在一个分子内，接着是基因，严格地说，基因仅仅是指分子中发生了变化的那部分而已。令人遗憾的是，在生物学上，"基因"这个词现在经常被广泛应用到许多延伸的领域，已经不存在确切的定义了，所以这并不能单单怪罪薛定谔教授一人。在讨论"基因"的最大值（从遗传学资料中分析）时，"基因"所代表的含义是最小的染色体片段（这个片段在遗传学上可以产生可见的效果）或者两个突变位点之间最短的距离（这两个突变能够被杂交实验所分离）。通过现有遗传学或者细胞学方法对上述任一数值进行估算，由于目前技术粗糙，只能得到纯粹主观的数值。在讨论"基因"的最小值时（从离子辐射诱导突变的推断中分析），很明显，"基因"等同于引起突变所需的最小的离子辐射范围。其实薛定谔教授真正想讨论的是染色体结构的最基本分子单元，与上述的这些概念并不相符。基因这个词汇被如此滥用对于细胞学家来说是非常不幸的，因为这些解释几乎不可避免地暗示了一些基因结构不连续性的观点：突变不连续地分布在一条染色体的线性序列中。那些发生突变的基本遗传物质是否同样具有不连续性呢（就像一条串起的珠链），这是一个新的问题，而且这个问题也不是现在的遗传学和细胞学所能解决的。如果把"基因"这个词从词汇里删去，那么这语言上的困难就很容易解决了。如果这样的话，薛定谔教授最富有深意的一句话将会被解释成："我们认为突变的本质是量子跃迁，染色体结构的基本单元或者说整个染色体纤维是一个非周期性的实心体。"

在这一点上，"整个染色体纤维"被视为一个单元变得尤为重要。目前对于这样的描述有两种极端的观点，这两种观点都有一些正面证据来支持。按照其中的一种

whole chromosome thread is a single structure at all times, except for a limited period during prophase when it is doubled in preparation for a nuclear division. The strongest piece of evidence in support of this is the differential behaviour of certain nuclear stages to irradiation by X-rays at dosages sufficient to cause gross chromosome fracture. Assuming that the statements in the literature are correct (for example, Riley 1936[2]) the position appears to be that in some organisms such as *Tradescantia*[3], irradiation at prophase can cause fracture of half-chromosomes (chromatid breaks) but at other stages only breakage of whole chromosomes. In interpreting this as meaning that the chromosome thread is single at all stages other than prophase it is not always realized that this singleness could be conferred by spiral structure and is not necessarily based on singleness of the genetical material.

The spiral structure of chromosomes (or perhaps more correctly the helical structure, since the geometrical figure involved would, in mathematics, be termed a helix) is probably not as widely known to scientific workers in general as its importance deserves and it is still far from being fully understood even by cytologists. That the apparent diameter of a fully developed chromosome is that of a helical coil has been known since 1880[4] for meiotic chromosomes, though owing to technical difficulty the basic facts for mitotic chromosomes have only recently been elucidated. Examples of the structure, as revealed by special treatment or in rare instances spontaneously, are shown in Figs. 1-4 for the different sorts of division in the fern *Osmunda*. Fig. 1 shows an unpaired chromosome at the first meiotic division, with four large coils. At this stage all cytologists are agreed that the genetical material is double in preparation for the second meiotic division and that in a paired chromosome genetical crossing-over between chromatids (half-chromosomes) has taken place; both chromatids, however, share a common spiral path. At the second meiotic division, Fig. 2, the two chromatids diverge so widely that they are only in contact at the region known as the centromere (marked *c* in the figure). A new spiral, differing in diameter and in number of coils from that at the previous division, affects each chromatid. At a somatic division, Fig. 3, the number of coils is increased still further but the two chromatids lie close together. It is, however, certain that the spiral in each has been independently formed for, in the case figured, direction of coiling was determined in corresponding parts of the sister chromatids and found to be opposite[5]. There must therefore be two separate spirals during prophase and it is possibly this which is detected by the X-ray breakages. At anaphase one of the two spirals passes to each pole, and that the helical coil at anaphase is indeed single seems to follow from the unusually clear case of Fig. 4. This differs from the preceding in that it had been subjected to X-rays some hours previously and many types of fusion and fracture are displayed. The unusual clarity of the undoubtedly single spiral in certain of the chromosomes is perhaps also an after-effect of the irradiation, but it accords very fully with the other evidence.

观点（薛定谔教授所采用的），整个染色体纤维自始至终都保持着一个单一结构，细胞有丝分裂前期的一小段时间除外，因为在这个时候，染色体丝为核分裂作准备而复制翻倍。支持这个观点的最强有力的证据是，在细胞核的不同阶段用剂量足以使所有染色体破裂的 X 射线照射后会发生不同的情况。假定文献（例如，赖利，1936 年 [2]）中的这种观点是正确的，那么同样的情况一定会出现在一些生物中，比如紫露草 [3]。在有丝分裂前期 X 射线辐射可以导致半数染色体破裂(染色单体破裂)，而在有丝分裂的其他时期就会导致整个染色体的破裂。对于在任何时期(除前期以外)染色体都是单一结构这样的解释，他们并没有意识到这种单一结构可以被赋予螺旋结构的形式，而且这种单一结构也不必一定要建立在遗传物质的单一结构上。

染色体的螺旋结构（称作螺旋体结构也许更确切，因为在数学上这种几何形状应当被定义为螺旋体）可能还不像它值得重视的程度那样，为一般的科学工作者所知。即便是对于细胞学家而言，对它的了解也是远远不够的。自 1880 年 [4] 开始对减数分裂染色体进行研究以来，由于技术上的困难，关于有丝分裂染色体的一些基础证据和事实直到最近才被阐明，但我们已经知道了完全形成螺旋状卷曲的整个染色体的表观尺寸。图 1~4 展示的是蕨类植物薇菜处于不同分裂时期的染色体结构的一些例子，包括经过特殊处理或者在自然条件下自发形成的很少见的一些结构。图 1 显示的是减数第一次分裂中尚未配对的染色体，可以看到 4 个巨大的卷曲。所有的细胞学家都一致认为，在这个阶段遗传物质处于双倍的状态，为减数第二次分裂作准备；与此同时，配对的染色单体（半染色体）之间会发生遗传物质的交叉互换，这两条配对的染色单体共享同一个螺旋轨道。在减数第二次分裂中，如图 2 所示，两条染色单体彼此分开，通过我们称之为着丝点的区域相互连接（在图中标记为 c）。一条在直径和螺旋圈数上都与先前分裂产生的螺旋不同的新螺旋影响了每一条染色单体。在体细胞分裂中，如图 3 所示，螺旋圈数仍然在进一步增加，但是两条染色单体却相互靠近。然而，可以肯定的是每一条染色单体的螺旋都是独立形成的，在这个图例中，螺旋盘绕的方向是由两条姐妹染色单体对应的部分决定的，并且两者盘绕方向相反 [5]。因此，在细胞分裂前期，必然可以通过 X 射线的破损作用检测到两条分离的螺旋。在细胞分裂后期，两条螺旋分别分到两极，我们可以见到相当清晰的单个螺旋卷曲，如图 4 所示。这与先前实验的区别在于，样品处理前经过了数小时 X 射线的照射，产生了多种类型的融合和破裂。在图 4 中，某些染色体中的单个螺旋显得非常清楚，也许这是射线照射后的效应，但它与其他的证据完全符合。

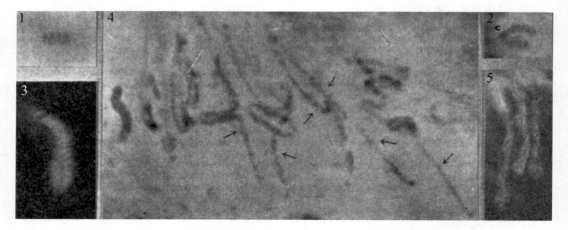

Fig. 1. Unpaired chromosome of *Osmunda* at the first meiotic division after ammonia treatment for spiral structure. Acetocarmine preparation photographed in clove oil by visual light. (×2,000.)

Fig. 2. Split chromosome at the second meiotic division in *Osmunda* after ammonia treatment for spiral structure, the two chromatids are attached only at the centromere (*c*). Acetocarmine preparation, ultra-violet photograph. (×2,000.)

Fig. 3. Split chromosome at metaphase of the third spore division in *Osmunda* showing spiral structure without special treatment. Acetocarmine preparation, ultra-violet photograph (×4,000) negative print (the positive of this and others in Manton and Smiles, 1943[5]).

Fig. 4. Anaphase of the first spore division in *Osmunda* fixed 30 hours after irradiation of the uninucleate spore with X-rays at 2,500 r. showing fractures, fusions and abnormally clear spiral structure. Acetocarmine preparation, visual light photograph. (×1,000.)

Fig. 5. Anaphase of the third spore division in *Todea* after ammonia treatment, showing lateral separation of component strands. Acetocarmine preparation, ultra-violet photograph (×4,000), negative print (the positive of this and other chromosomes in Manton, 1945[6]).

The other extreme view of chromosome structure, which is becoming increasingly accepted in the U.S.S.R. and the U.S.A. and (before the War) in Japan, though in Great Britain it has been somewhat opposed, is that a chromosome is fundamentally many-stranded at all stages. If the physical basis of unitary behaviour of chromosome or chromatid can in part at least be interpreted in terms of helical structure rather than molecular structure then perhaps the chief objection to this view has been removed. An example of the type of observational evidence on which the view is based is contained in Fig. 5[6]. The specimen here is at a later stage of anaphase than that of Fig. 4 and had not been subjected to X-rays. Instead it had been given the normal pretreatment with ammoniated alcohol which is generally necessary to make the spiral appear. The plant concerned is, however, not *Osmunda* but the closely related fern *Todea*, and the pretreatment and method of mounting acting together have in this case produced a remarkable lateral separation of longitudinally running strands. No less than four strands per chromosome are unmistakably present, most clearly countable, in the original print, in the leftmost chromosome. With the detection of quarter-chromosomes the limit of optical resolution has been reached, even with light of short wave-length; but it is by no means impossible that further subdivision would be found to be present if resolution could be extended.

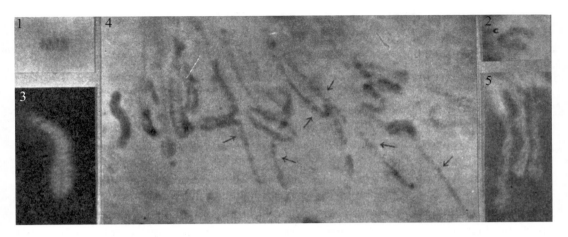

图 1. 薇菜减数第一次分裂中尚未配对的染色体。螺旋结构经过氨处理。在丁香油中加入醋酸洋红染色，可见光成像。（×2,000）

图 2. 薇菜减数第二次分裂中已经分开的染色体。螺旋结构经过氨处理。两条染色单体通过着丝点相互连接（c）。醋酸洋红染色，紫外光成像。（×2,000）

图 3. 薇菜孢子第三次分裂中期已经分开的染色体，出现了螺旋结构。没有经过特殊处理。醋酸洋红染色，紫外光成像（×4,000）负影像。（此实验的正影像和其他一些情况，在 1943 年曼顿和斯迈尔的文章中有介绍[5]。）

图 4. 薇菜孢子第一次分裂后期。用 2,500 r 的 X 射线照射单核孢子 30 小时，出现了破裂、融合和异常清晰的螺旋结构。醋酸洋红染色，可见光成像。（×1,000）

图 5. 块茎蕨中孢子第三次分裂后期。经过氨处理。显示了染色纤维组分的横向分离。醋酸洋红染色，紫外光成像（×4,000），负影像。（此实验的正影像和其他一些染色体的情况，在 1945 年曼顿的文章中有介绍[6]。）

　　关于染色体纤维的另外一种极端观点认为，染色体纤维在所有阶段都是多线状结构。苏联、美国以及日本（在战争爆发之前）的科学家正逐渐接受这种观点，尽管在英国还有略微的反对之声。如果染色体或者染色单体整体行为的物质基础可以（至少部分可以）被解释为螺旋结构而不是分子结构，那么针对这种观点的最主要的异议就不攻自破了。这种观点所依据的一个观察例证显示在图 5 中[6]。相对于图 4 而言，这个实验样品处于细胞分裂后期更靠后的一个阶段，没有经受过 X 射线的照射。相反，它采用氨化的乙醇进行正常的预处理过程，通常来讲这个过程对螺旋的解聚是必需的。实验所研究的植物不是薇菜，而是与之相近的蕨类植物块茎蕨。在这个例子中，样品经过预处理和固定后，在纵向排列的染色体上出现了显著的侧面横向分离。在每条染色体上至少存在 4 个条束，在最初发表的影像中最左边的那条染色体上，大部分条束都清楚可辨。我们能观察到四分染色体的存在，这已经达到了光学分辨率的极限，即使采用短波长的光也是如此；但是这绝不意味着进一步的细分是不可能的，只要分辨能力进一步提高，就一定会发现更进一步的细分。

It is not easy to determine the diameter of an object near the limit of visibility, but the fact that quarter-chromosomes are visible at all suggests that their thickness is likely to be of the same order as the wave-length of the light used (275 μμ). In round numbers and for the sake of argument this may be put as approximately 3,000 A. Now if Prof. Schroedinger's figures for the "size of a gene" be utilized, some simple arithmetic will provide a rough estimate of the possible limits of many-strandedness assuming this to exist. The higher limit for the "size of a gene" is given as 300 A. and there would therefore be room in a quarter chromosome of *Todea* for some 75 threads of this width. The lower limit of size is given as "ten atomic distances cubed" which, for a protein molecule, might perhaps be put as of the order of 50 A. cubed. There is room in a quarter chromosome of *Todea* for nearly three thousand threads of diameter 50 A. The real unit of chromosome structure is likely to lie in between these two extremes and it is probable that allowance must also be made for some empty spaces between the strands. Nevertheless the figures, rough as they are, indicate at least the possibility that in a whole chromosome, not one but between 300 and 12,000 duplicate versions of the genetical material may be present.

This is not quite the same as the unique phenomenon visualized by Prof. Schroedinger, though it is no doubt sufficiently close to it still to come under the general heading of "order from order" rather than "order from disorder". The importance attributed to atomic arrangement in the "aperiodic solid" of the unit fibre is almost certainly correct, and this property is shared by many other protoplasmic structures besides the chromosomes, notably by enzymes. If the view of chromosome structure put forward above be correct, however, a chromosome may be found to owe some of its peculiar powers not to the aperiodic fibre as such but to the fact that bundles of these are co-ordinated together in a manner recalling, though not necessarily exactly resembling, the periodic crystals. The "whole chromosome fibre" may in fact have to be visualized as an aperiodic solid in its longitudinal dimension but as periodic in its transverse dimension.

The recognition of an element of periodic structure in one dimension of the genetical material would perhaps be a minor emendation in the general philosophic view of a chromosome. The issues raised are, however, of immediate importance in cytology, and I trust that Prof. Schroedinger will forgive me if I have used his very interesting little book as an occasion for directing attention to them.

(**155**, 471-473; 1945)

I. Manton: University of Manchester.

References:

1. Schroedinger, E., "What is Life? The Physical Aspects of the Living Cell" (Cambridge, 1944).

2. Riley, H. P., *Cytologia*, 7, 139 (1936).

3. Catcheside, D. G., *Biol. Rev.*, **20**, 14 (1945) (a recent summary received since the above was written differs somewhat).

4. Baranetzky, J., *Bot. Zeit.*, **38**, 241 (1880).

5. Manton, I., and Smiles, J., *Ann. Bot.*, New Series, 7, 195 (1943).

6. Manton, I., *Amer. J.* Bot., in the press (1945).

　　在接近分辨率极限的情况下测定物体的直径是很困难的，但是能够观测到四分染色体，这从根本上说明它们的厚度可能和使用的光的波长（275 皮米）处于同一个数量级。为了便于讨论，以整数表示的染色体大小应该接近 3,000 Å。如果借用薛定谔教授对基因大小的描述，那也许用一些简单的算术就可以对这些多线状染色体结构的可能极限（假定是存在的）作一粗略的估计。如果基因大小的最高限是 300 Å，那么块茎蕨四分染色体大概可以容纳 75 条直径为 300 Å 的染色丝。如果基因大小的最低限为 10 倍原子间距的立方，比如对于一个蛋白分子来说大约就是 50 Å 的立方，那么块茎蕨四分染色体可以容纳大约 3,000 多条直径为 50 Å 的染色丝。染色体结构的真实大小很可能就介于这两个极限之间，而且很可能在线状结构之间留有一些空隙。尽管这些数据很粗略，但至少我们看到一种可能，就是在整个染色体中含有不止一个，而是 300~12,000 个副本的遗传物质。

　　尽管这些结果与薛定谔教授揭示的独特现象有些不同，但毫无疑问的是，把这种现象归入"从有序到有序"更为贴切，而非"从无序到有序"。在纤维单元"非周期性实心体"中原子的排列很重要，这种说法在某种程度上来说是正确的，许多原生质结构（除染色体外）都有这种性质，特别是酶。如果上述有关染色体结构的观点是正确的话，那么，染色体的一些特殊能力并不归功于非周期性纤维而归功于非周期性纤维束，这些纤维束在某种形式上相互协调，让人联想到周期性晶体，尽管两者并不完全相似。实际上"整个染色体纤维"也许在纵向维度上可以被看作是一个非周期性的实心体，但在横向维度上可以被看作是周期性的。

　　在遗传物质这样一个维度上探讨周期性结构的要素是对现有的染色体哲学观点的一点修正。这些争论在细胞学上是非常重要的。我相信薛定谔教授会原谅我引用他有趣的小册子作为引导这些争论的引子。

（刘振明 翻译；刘京国 审稿）

Artificial Protein Fibres: Their Conception and Preparation

W. T. Astbury

Editor's Note

This review of the molecular structure of protein fibres by William Astbury begins with an observation commonly heard today of how apparently academic work can prove invaluable to applied science and industry. The study of natural fibrous proteins such as keratin using X-ray crystallography, which Astbury helped pioneer, suggested that it should be possible to make fibrous proteins from non-fibrous ones. Now industry was producing such artificial fibres for textiles from proteins in nuts, milk and beans. This involved "denaturing" the globular form of such proteins and aligning the strands into the parallel "β-sheet" form which, as demonstrated by silk, can be very strong. Such studies involve issues of protein folding and structural versatility that are still hot topics today.

A principal aim of science in relation to industry is to elucidate for the industrialist the nature of his working materials. All fundamental research into the structure and properties of things is therefore of potential value to industry; but this is a platitude to the man of science. To the nonscientific majority, however, it is not yet so obvious, and it is still regrettably necessary to make play with the more spectacular discoveries in order to attract proper support for research.

A recent development that has captured the imagination of the public is the discovery how to make artificial protein fibres from nuts, beans, milk, and other not visibly fibrous protein sources, and the official announcement during December 1944 by Imperial Chemical Industries, Ltd., of the successful production of "Ardil" from the protein of peanuts suggests an occasion for briefly re-telling the story, but this time more from the fundamental point of view than has been possible in the popular accounts that have appeared. I have no intention here of labouring the theme of what industry owes to science, or vice versa, or of emphasizing again that the great industries of the future must draw their sustenance from unremitting research; but I would certainly like to stress the case of the artificial protein fibres as being a most impressive example of the indivisibility of science. The discovery of the underlying principles was of purely academic origin, an outcome of X-ray and related studies of the molecular structure of biological tissues—studies that were neither supported by nor consciously dedicated to industry; the basic experiments were compounded of physics, chemistry, and biology, and were carried out in a university. Thereafter the development to commercial satisfaction was the work of industrial chemists and technologists.

It is not claimed, of course, that artificial protein fibres had never been produced

人造蛋白纤维：概念与制备

阿斯特伯里

编者按

威廉·阿斯特伯里在这篇关于蛋白纤维的分子结构的综述中，开篇便提出如今被广泛认可的学术研究对应用科学和工业具有非常显著的无法估量的作用。以阿斯特伯里为先驱，应用 X 射线晶体学对诸如角蛋白等天然纤维状蛋白质进行的研究表明，利用非纤维状蛋白质制备纤维状蛋白质应该是可能的。现在，工业上已经在利用来自坚果、牛奶以及豆类中的蛋白质生产这种人造纤维用于纺织了。这需要将蛋白质的球形结构"变性"，变成像丝绸中平行的"β 片层"一样非常强韧的线状结构。这类研究包括蛋白质折叠以及结构的多功能性等问题，这些在今天仍然是热点问题。

与工业有关的科学的一个主要目标就是为工业家阐明其工作原料的性质，因此对于物质的结构与性质的所有基础性研究对工业都具有潜在的价值；这对科学界人士而言可谓老生常谈。然而，对非科学界的大多数人而言显然不是这样的，并且令人遗憾的是，我们仍然必须要对那些重大发现加以强调才能吸引适当的研究支持。

最近有一项进展引起了公众的想象，这项进展便是发现了如何利用坚果、豆类、牛奶和其他一些看起来并非显然由纤维状蛋白质构成的物质来生产人造蛋白质纤维，并且帝国化学工业公司于 1944 年 12 月正式宣布成功地用花生蛋白生产出了"阿笛尔"纤维，这为我们简要地重新回顾人造蛋白纤维的产生历程提供了一个契机，不过这一次更多的是从基础研究的视角而非那些可能在通俗记述中已出现的方面进行回顾。我并非想要在这里细数工业受惠于科学之处或相反的看法，也不想再次强调未来的伟大工业必定从坚持不懈的研究中获得助力；但是我肯定乐于强调的是，人造蛋白纤维这个案例是一个最能给人留下科学具有不可或缺性这一深刻印象的实例。其基础性原理的发现有着纯粹的学术渊源，它正是 X 射线技术以及生物组织的分子结构的相关研究的结果——这些研究既未得到工业的支持也不曾有意识地致力于工业；基础性实验融合了物理学、化学和生物学等学科，并且在一所大学中实施。此后不断满足商业需求的发展就是工业化学家和技术专家的工作了。

当然，这并不是说以前从未生产过人造蛋白纤维——事实上，比如酪蛋白纤维

previously—indeed, it happens that the casein fibre, "Lanital", for example, was launched in Italy at almost the same time as the quite independent fundamental investigations about to be described were pointing the way to the general solution of the problem—but it is clear that in the absence of any structural picture of the protein molecule, and especially of the relation between the fibrous and the non-fibrous proteins, all such ventures were necessarily along empirical lines. The difference now is that what industry there was has been re-born as an inseparable part of protein science, with all the potentialities for advancement that this profoundest of molecular studies has to offer. It is in fact a logical *prediction* from the X-ray interpretation of protein denaturation that it should be possible to make fibrous from non-fibrous proteins: we can see now both what has to be done and the reason for it.

Since the beginning of the century, chemists have been increasingly convinced that all proteins are polypeptide chain systems, alone or in combination with various prosthetic groups; but there seemed to be a distinction between the fibrous and non-fibrous kinds in that the molecules of the latter are massive, rounded bodies that often aggregate to build orthodox, visible crystals; hence the name "corpuscular" proteins. With the growth of the concept of fibres as "molecular yarns" constructed from long chain-molecules, a concept to which many techniques have contributed but which first became "real" under the methods of X-ray analysis, there ceased to be any formal difficulty with regard to the protein fibres, as was demonstrated by Meyer and Mark when, in 1928, they interpreted the diffraction pattern given by natural silk (fibroin[1]); but the problem of the arrangement inside the corpuscular proteins remained, for sometimes the X-ray photographs showed sharp reflexions—characteristic to be sure of regular crystal lattices but not to be carried much beyond that on account of the large number of atomic parameters involved—but more often they showed simply two diffuse rings of spacing about $9\frac{1}{2}$ A. and $4\frac{1}{2}$ A., respectively. The first requirement was to explain these two rings, and this was done[2] on the basis of the X-ray data given by the *elastic* fibrous protein, keratin. Keratin did not fit in with the idea of extended polypeptide chains that had been found to suffice for fibroin; only the stretched form (β-keratin) could be interpreted on such a view, but the normal, unstretched form (α-keratin) demanded the postulate of a regularly folded configuration besides. The reversible intramolecular transformation between α- and β-keratin, corresponding to the transition between two distinct types of diffraction pattern, was recognized as providing the explanation of the well-known long-range elasticity of mammalian hairs and other keratinous tissues[3].

Among other things, then, the X-ray study of keratin brought out the two main points from which in due course the theory of artificial protein fibres followed naturally. The α-form revealed for the first time the existence of polypeptide chains that are normally in a folded state, while the β-form gave the average dimensions per amino-acid residue (and therewith an estimate of the order of density of proteins and the mass per unit area of protein monolayers[2,4]), and so bridged the gap to analytical chemistry and laid the foundations of a structural stoichiometry[5]. Thus was evolved the concept of the "polypeptide grid", and the two rings so common in protein diffraction patterns were

"拉尼塔"就是在意大利生产出来的，几乎在同一时间，就有人报道生产人造蛋白纤维这一问题的一般解决方法的独立的基础性研究——但是很明显，在对蛋白质分子的任何结构图像特别是对纤维状蛋白质与非纤维状蛋白质之间的关系一无所知的情况下，所有这些尝试必然是走经验路线。现在的不同之处在于，现代工业作为蛋白质科学不可分割的一部分而复兴，具有了最深刻的分子研究所赋予的发展潜能。事实上，根据蛋白质变性的 X 射线解释所作出的**预测**——可以利用非纤维状蛋白质制造纤维状蛋白质是符合逻辑的：现在我们既知道什么是必须要做的也知道这样做的理由。

自本世纪以来，化学家已经逐步确信所有的蛋白质都是独立的或与各种辅基相结合的多肽链体系；但是纤维状蛋白质和非纤维状蛋白质之间还存在着差别，后者的分子较大且为球形，经常聚集形成普遍的、可见的晶体，因此被称为"颗粒"蛋白。随着纤维就是由长链分子构成的"分子纱"这一概念的发展（很多技术都对此概念的发展有所贡献，而 X 射线分析方法首先使此概念成为"真的"），关于蛋白纤维不再存在任何结构上的困难，如同迈耶和马克在 1928 年解释天然丝（蚕丝蛋白 [1]）的衍射图案时所阐明的那样；但是颗粒蛋白内部的排列问题仍然存在，因为有时 X 射线照片显示出明显的衍射——这固然是正方晶格的特征，但由于涉及大量的原子参量而进展不大——但是更经常的是它们仅仅呈现出两个间距分别约为 $9\frac{1}{2}$ 埃和 $4\frac{1}{2}$ 埃的散射环。首先要做的是解释这两个环，以角蛋白这种**弹性**纤维蛋白给出的 X 射线数据为基础已经做到了这一点 [2]。角蛋白与之前发现的适用于蚕丝蛋白的伸展多肽链的想法并不符合；从这个角度只能解释其拉伸的结构（β–角蛋白），要解释正常的未拉伸结构（α–角蛋白）还需要假定一个有规则的折叠结构。α–角蛋白与 β–角蛋白之间可逆的分子内转换对应着两种不同类型的衍射图案的转换，这被认为可以解释哺乳动物毛发和其他角蛋白组织的显而易见的较大幅度的弹性 [3]。

此外，角蛋白的 X 射线研究给出了两个要点，它们适时而自然地引出了随后产生的人造蛋白纤维理论。α–结构第一次表明了在正常状态下处于折叠形式的多肽链的存在，而 β–结构给出了每个氨基酸残基的平均尺度（从而可以估计蛋白质密度以及单层蛋白质单位面积质量的数量级 [2,4]），因而弥补了分析化学的不足并为结构化学计量学奠定了基础 [5]。由此发展出了"多肽网"的概念，并且认为蛋白质衍射图案中非常常见的两个环起源于相邻多肽链之间的两种主要连接模式，即侧链之间

identified as arising from the two principal modes of linkage between neighbouring polypeptide chains, namely, that between the side-chains and that between the backbones[2]. The corresponding spacings are now always referred to as the "side-chain" and "backbone" spacings.

The next advance came from an X-ray comparison of a number of protein preparations before and after wetting[6]. It was found that not only did the inner ring show the greater spacing variation from protein to protein, but also it generally showed a spacing increase on wetting. Both these properties would be expected if, as had been inferred from keratin, the reflexion represented the lateral separation of the main chains in the direction of the side-chains, and the evidence was in fact accepted as establishing the inference.

In the same investigation, among the preparations examined were egg and serum albumins that had been denatured (and coagulated) by heat. The obvious change brought about by this treatment was seen to be a marked sharpening of the backbone reflexion, and, less obvious, the appearance of at least one other outer ring of spacing about 3.6 A. (see Figs. 1a and 1b). In short, it became clear—what has been demonstrated since on many other protein preparations—that *the denaturation and aggregation of a corpuscular protein leads ultimately to a diffraction pattern like that given by disoriented β-keratin*. When keratin is stretched from the α- to the β-form, the side-chain reflexion remains and a strong backbone reflexion arises by the process of flattening the polypeptide grids—pulling out the folds, that is, that lie in planes transverse to the side-chains. This is a mechanical operation, but it appeared now that a similar sort of change could be brought about in the structure of the corpuscular proteins by thermal agitation, for example. (Later, it was shown[7] that the muscle protein, myosin, belongs to the same molecular family as keratin, and myosin can give either an oriented β-photograph by stretching or a disoriented β-photograph by heating.) In some way, therefore, the arrangement inside the corpuscular proteins was a generalization of the α-keratin idea; the situation was like α-keratin only more so. The polypeptide chains were there, but presumably they were folded and grouped in specific configurations from which in most cases they could be liberated fairly easily to produce a variety of nonspecific configurations. Subsequent aggregation (at least as regards the more organized regions that are responsible for the regular diffraction pattern) involved a building of "crystallites"—sometimes more perfect, sometimes less perfect, but at any rate of the type of the aggregates of polypeptide grids that constitute the crystallites of β-keratin. (Denaturation of a corpuscular protein as here described is the thoroughgoing irreversible phenomenon as it is usually understood in Great Britain. Reversible loss of solubility and specificity is sometimes described as "reversible denaturation", but such changes are conceivable without disorganization of the molecule as a whole. Sometimes, too, no clear distinction is recognized between denaturation and the aggregation of proteins that are already in an extended configuration[8]. Myosin "denatured" by simple drying is still in the folded α-form, but there is disorganization of the folds if it is heated.)

和骨架之间的连接模式 [2]。现在经常将其对应的间距称为"侧链"间距和"骨架"间距。

下一步进展来自于对大量蛋白质制剂在浸湿前后进行的 X 射线比较 [6]。结果发现里面的环不仅随蛋白质的不同表现出较大的间距变化，而且在湿润条件下它通常表现出间距的增加。如果像已经从角蛋白推论得到的那样，衍射体现了主链在侧链方向上的横向间距，并且如果能够接受事实证据建立推论，那么上述这些性质就是可以预期的。

在同样的研究中，接受检验的制剂是已通过热变性（并且凝固）的卵清蛋白和血清蛋白。这种处理导致的显著变化是主链衍射明显锐化，另外不那么显著的则是出现了至少一个间隔约 3.6 埃的靠外的环（见图 1*a* 和图 1*b*）。简而言之，情况逐渐清晰——许多其他的蛋白质制剂已经证明——**颗粒蛋白的变性和聚集最终导致类似于无定向 β–角蛋白的衍射图案。**当角蛋白从 α–结构拉伸变成 β–结构时，侧链衍射维持不变，而一个强的主链衍射则由于多肽网拉平——将位于侧链横截平面内的折叠打开——而出现。这是一种机械作用，不过现在看来，可以通过诸如热搅动等方法使颗粒蛋白的结构发生这种类似的改变。（后面将会指出 [7]，肌肉中的蛋白——肌球蛋白与角蛋白属于同一分子家族，并且肌球蛋白既能通过拉伸而呈现定向的 β–照片也能通过加热而呈现无定向的 β–照片。）因此，在某种意义上，颗粒蛋白内部的排列是对 α–角蛋白情况的概括；从某种程度上来说，情况类似于角蛋白那样。根据推测，多肽是折叠的并且按特定构型形成肽基，这样在大多数情况下它们可以很容易地得到释放并产生多种非特异性结构。随后的聚合（至少对更有组织的区域而言这是产生规则衍射图案的原因）涉及到"微晶"的构造——有时是完美的，有时则不那么完美，但无论如何都是构成 β–角蛋白微晶的多肽网的某种类型的聚合。（此处描述的颗粒蛋白的变性是完全不可逆的现象，就像在英国通常所理解的那样。在溶解性和特异性方面的可逆损失有时被称为"可逆变性"，但这类变化是在作为整体的分子没有解体的前提下发生的。有时候还不能清晰地分辨出蛋白质的变性和已经处于伸展构型的蛋白质的聚合 [8]。由简单的干燥引起"变性"的肌球蛋白仍具有折叠的 α–结构，但如果将它加热便会破坏折叠结构。）

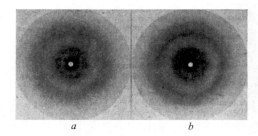

Fig. 1. X-ray powder photographs of (*a*) dried egg white, and (*b*) dried boiled egg white.

It followed at once from this line of argument that if, after unfolding the polypeptide chains, they could be drawn parallel, or approximately parallel, then artificial *fibres* would result; and the test would be the production of an *oriented* β-photograph. Decisive orientation effects were first obtained with denatured preparations of the seed globulins, edestin (from hemp seed) and excelsin (from Brazil nuts), and also with "poached" egg white[9]; while the first actual fibres were spun from strong urea solutions[9]. When edestin, for example, is dissolved in strong aqueous urea, the solution in time becomes very viscous, and elastic fibres may be produced either by drawing out the viscous mass or by squirting it through a capillary tube into water or dilute salt solution. (This sort of observation is not new, but it seems that X-rays first clearly exposed the reason for the rise in viscosity—the unfolding of round molecules to give polypeptide chains in extended configurations.) In general, though, such fibres have to be stretched farther in order to reveal definite orientation effects in the X-ray photographs. As a matter of interest, some of the early diffraction patterns are reproduced in Fig. 2. They illustrate the first demonstration by X-rays of the transformation of an originally crystalline protein into an elastic fibrous structure.

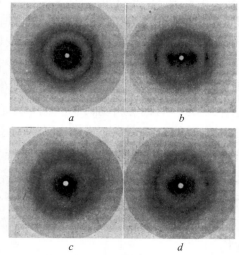

Fig. 2. (*a*) Disoriented β-keratin; (*b*) oriented β-keratin; (*c*) disoriented denatured edestin; (*d*) oriented (stretched) denatured edestin.

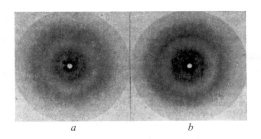

图 1. X 射线粉末照片。(a) 干燥的卵清蛋白，(b) 干燥的煮熟的卵清蛋白。

从这段论述中我们可以立刻得出，多肽链在打开折叠之后可能被拉伸成平行或近似于平行的状态，接着便会产生人造**纤维**；检测依据就是一张**定向** β–照片的产生。决定性的定向效应最初通过种球蛋白、麻仁球蛋白（来自大麻种子）和巴西果蛋白（来自巴西坚果）的变性制剂以及从"煮熟的"卵清蛋白获得[9]，而最早实际出现的纤维从浓的尿素溶液中获得[9]。例如，当把麻仁球蛋白溶解于浓的尿素溶液中时，溶液会立刻变得非常黏稠，通过拉出黏性物质或者通过一根毛细管将其喷入水或稀释的盐溶液中便可以产生弹性纤维。（这种现象并非是全新的，但似乎是 X 射线最先明确地揭示出其黏性增加的原因——球形分子中的折叠打开，形成伸展构型的多肽链。）不过一般地说，这种纤维还需进一步拉伸以便在 X 射线照片中呈现出明确的定向效应。根据其重要性，图 2 再现了一些早期的衍射图像。这些衍射图像是首次通过 X 射线方法证明从初始的结晶蛋白到弹性纤维构象转变的例证。

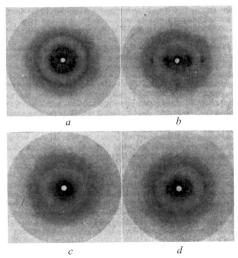

图 2. (a) 无定向 β–角蛋白；(b) 定向 β–角蛋白；(c) 无定向变性麻仁球蛋白；(d) 定向（拉伸的）变性麻仁球蛋白。

Experiments on continuous fibre production from urea solutions were then conducted in Prof. A. C. Chibnall's laboratory at the Imperial College of Science and Technology, London; but later, though considerable further advances were made, it was felt better to return to the more fundamental side of protein research. Thereafter, as indicated above, the production of "Ardil" (see Fig. 3) and its development to commercial satisfaction was the work of chemists of Imperial Chemical Industries, Ltd.[10]. "Ardil" is produced from the peanut globulin, arachin, and the original urea process has now been replaced by extraction and "maturing" with dilute alkali; also, striking new after-treatments have been evolved for improving the tensile properties of the fibres and their resistance to dyeing and finishing processes. Actually, the present stage of development was reached by the beginning of the War, but since then further work has been held up.

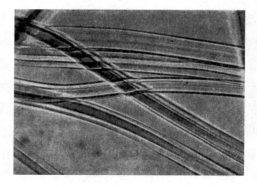

Fig. 3. Ardil fibres.

"Ardil" is a cream-coloured, crimped, elastic fibre that is soft and warm: it is a kind of artificial wool without surface scales. It greatly enhances the felting of wool, however, and dyes like wool, but it is not attacked by moths. Its elasticity arises from the circumstance that the unfolding of the original corpuscular molecules is imperfect, vestigial folds remaining that are an irregular counterpart of the regular α-folds to which the elasticity of keratin is due. As now produced, "Ardil" shows no orientation in its diffraction pattern, but an oriented β-pattern begins to appear on stretching. Fabrics have been made purely of "Ardil", but its best use is likely to be in combination with wool and other fibres. A by-product of its manufacture is, of course, arachis oil, of which peanuts contain 48-50 percent; furthermore, after the oil and protein have been extracted, the residue can be used for cattle food.

During the last few years a number of important papers have been published in America on the preparation of artificial protein fibres with the aid of detergents[11]. Products such as "Nacconol NRSF" (which is essentially dodecyl benzene sodium sulphonate) are found to act as excellent unfolding agents for the corpuscular proteins, and with the technique described it is possible to make fibres much stronger than anything reported previously. Using egg albumin, for example, the complex formed by mixing equal portions of 3 percent solutions of recrystallized egg albumin and detergent is first precipitated with saturated magnesium sulphate, the resulting "dough" is drawn out into fibres, which are

接着，伦敦帝国理工学院奇布诺尔教授的实验室进行了用尿素溶液持续生产纤维的实验研究；尽管已经取得了相当程度的进展，但后来他们还是觉得返回到蛋白质研究中更基础的方面比较好。从那以后，如同上面已指出的，"阿笛尔"的生产（见图3）及其针对商业需求的发展成为帝国化学工业公司化学家们的工作[10]。"阿笛尔"是由花生的球蛋白——花生球蛋白来生产的，并且最初的尿素工艺现在已经被稀碱抽提和"成熟"取代，而且还发展出令人惊奇的新的后期处理方法来改善纤维的拉伸性能以及它们对染色和修整工序的抗性。实际上，目前的发展水平在大战之初便已达到，但是从那以后进一步的研究便搁置起来。

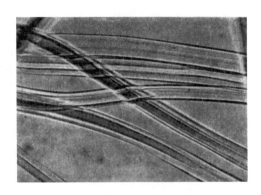

图 3. 阿笛尔纤维

"阿笛尔"是一种淡黄色的、有皱褶的弹性纤维，柔软而温暖：它是一种没有表面覆盖层的人造织物。这大大改善了织物的触感，尽管它能像羊毛一样被染色，却不会受到蛀虫的侵害。它的弹性来源于最初的颗粒状分子的不彻底伸展，保留下来的不完全折叠正是使得角蛋白具有弹性的规则 α–折叠的不规则对应物。现在生产出的"阿笛尔"在其衍射图案中不显示方向，但是在拉伸时开始呈现出定向的 β–图案。织物是完全由"阿笛尔"制成的，但其最佳用法可能是与毛线和其他纤维制品结合。当然，该产品的副产物是花生油——占花生的 48%~50%；此外，在提取出油和蛋白质之后，残余物可以用来作为家畜饲料。

最近几年，美国发表了大量关于借助去污剂制备人造蛋白纤维的重要论文[11]。已发现诸如"烷基芳基磺酸钠"（实质上就是十二烷基苯磺酸钠）等产品可以充当出色的颗粒蛋白展开剂，用前文描述的技术就有可能制造出比之前报道的任何纤维都更强的纤维。例如，以卵清蛋白为原料，将 3% 的重结晶卵清蛋白溶液与去污剂等量混合形成复合物，首先用饱和硫酸镁使其沉淀，将生成的"生面团"拉伸成纤维，接着将其用水洗涤，并用 60∶40 的丙酮－水溶液抽提，最后在流通蒸汽中将纤维拉

washed with water and extracted with 60:40 acetone-water solution, and then finally the fibres are stretched by about 400 percent in live steam. Before the stretching in steam, the orientation in the X-ray diffraction pattern is of the "crossed" type first observed with stretched films of poached egg white[9], that was interpreted as corresponding to chain-bundles broader than they are long; but after the stretching it is as in β-keratin with the chain-bundles lying along the direction of stretching. (The effect illustrated in Palmer and Galvin's paper[12] is slight and was at first thought not to be there; but it is now agreed that before stretching in steam there is no real discrepancy with the "poached egg effect". Private communication.) The oriented β-pattern given by these stretched egg albumin fibres is very good indeed: it is shown in Fig. 4, which is a reproduction of a photograph kindly sent me by Dr. Palmer. Egg albumin is one of the most typical and most studied of all the crystalline corpuscular proteins, and here in the end it is made to yield one of the best β-fibre photographs! The wheel has now come full circle.

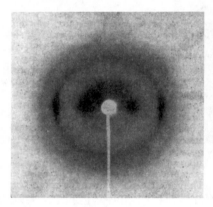

Fig. 4. Fibre pattern (β-keratin type) given by egg albumin fibres prepared by Lundgren
and photographed by Palmer and Galvin.

Lundgren and O'Connell report that artificial fibres from egg albumin (and from chicken-feather keratin, which also responds to the technique just described) have been prepared with breaking strengths of more than 70×10^3 lb. per sq. in.: to appreciate what this means, it may be noted that in the same table they quote 72-100 for nylon, 46-74 for natural silk, and 17-25 for wool. Incidentally, lest it should seem somewhat indecent these days to talk about using egg white for making fibres, it should be added that the same authors point out that there are available annually in the United States more than 26,000,000 lb. of inedible technical egg white (much of which goes to waste) and more than 170,000,000 lb. of chicken feathers.

(**155**, 501-503; 1945)

W. T. Astbury: F.R.S., Textile Physics Laboratory, University of Leeds.

References:
1. Meyer, K. H., and Mark, H., *Ber.*, **61**, 1932 (1928).

长约 400%。在蒸汽中进行拉伸之前，X 衍射图案中的定向属于"交叉"类型，这种类型首先是在拉伸的熟蛋白薄膜中观察到的 [9]，这可以解释为对应的链束比其长度宽；但是在拉伸之后，图案与 β–角蛋白相似，其链束方向位于拉伸方向上。（帕尔默和高尔文的论文 [12] 中描述的效应是微弱的，最初认为它不存在；但是现在我们同意，在蒸汽中进行拉伸之前，该效应与"煮熟的鸡蛋效应"没有实质性的差别。私人交流。）由上述卵清蛋白纤维所给出的定向 β–图案实际上是很好的：图 4 显示了该图案，这是帕尔默博士友情赠送给我的一张照片的副本。卵清蛋白是所有结晶颗粒蛋白中最典型的、被研究得最多的一种，而这里终于用它得到了一张最好的 β–纤维照片！这样就圆满了。

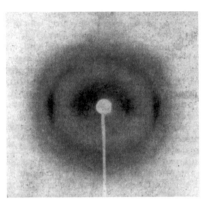

图 4. 由伦德格伦制备、帕尔默和高尔文照相的卵清蛋白纤维的纤维图案（β–角蛋白型）。

伦德格伦和奥康奈尔指出，现在已经能够由卵清蛋白来制备人造纤维了（还可以用鸡毛角蛋白，也适用于刚才描述的那种技术），其断裂强度超过 70×10^3 磅 / 平方英寸：要理解其中的含义，可以参考他们在同一个表格中提供的数据：尼龙为 72~100，天然丝为 46~74，羊毛为 17~25。顺便提一下，为了避免大家认为这些天来谈论的用卵清蛋白制造纤维这件事似乎有些不妥当，应当补充的是，这些作者指出，在美国每年都会有超过 26,000,000 磅的不可食用的用于工业技术的卵清蛋白（其中的大部分都被浪费了）和超过 170,000,000 磅的鸡毛。

（王耀杨 翻译；刘京国 审稿）

2. Astbury, W. T., *Trans. Faraday Soc.*, **29**, 193, 217 (1933).

3. For references see, for example, Astbury, W. T., *Nature*, **137**, 803 (1936).

4. See also Astbury, W. T., Bell, F. O., Gorter, E., and van Ormondt, J., *Nature*, **142**, 33 (1938).

5. Astbury, W. T., "Advances in Enzymology", **3**, 63 (1943).

6. Astbury, W. T., and Lomax, R., *J. Chem. Soc.*, 846 (1935).

7. Astbury, W. T., and Dickinson, S., *Nature*, **135**, 95 (1935); *Proc. Roy. Soc.*, B, **129**, 307 (1940).

8. See, for example, Coleman, D., and Howitt, F. O., *Nature*, **155**, 78 (1945).

9. Astbury, W. T., Dickinson, S., and Bailey, K., *Biochem. J.*, **29**, 2351(1935).

10. Traill, D., *Chem. and Ind.*, Feb. 24, 1945, p. 58.

11. Lundgren, H. P., *J. Amer. Chem. Soc.*, **63**, 2854 (1941); Lundgren, H. P., Elam, D. W., and O'Connell, R. A., *J. Biol. Chem.*, **149**, 183 (1943); Palmer, K. J., and Galvin, J. A., *J. Amer. Chem.* Soc., **65**, 2187 (1943); Palmer, K. J., *J. Phys. Chem.*, **48**, 12 (1944); Lundgren, H. P., and O'Connell, R. A., *Ind. Eng. Chem.*, **36**, 370 (1944).

12. Palmer, K. J., and Galvin, J. A., *J. Amer, Chem. Soc.*, **65**, 2187 (1943).

Appendix: Index by Subject
附录：学科分类目录

Physics
物理学

Chemistry
化学

Biology
生物学

Astronomy
天文学

Geoscience
地球科学

Engineering & Technology
工程技术

Others
其他